R.P. CRANSTON   ONDE

SESSION 1965-66

ADVANCED LEVEL
PHYSICS

BOOKS BY M. NELKON

Published by Heinemann
LIGHT AND SOUND
A MODERN ELECTRICITY
MECHANICS AND PROPERTIES OF MATTER
GRADED EXERCISES IN PHYSICS
TEST PAPERS IN PHYSICS
EXERCISES IN PRACTICAL PHYSICS
ADVANCED LEVEL PRACTICAL PHYSICS
(with J. Ogborn)
AN INTRODUCTION TO THE MATHEMATICS OF PHYSICS
(with J. H. Avery)
ELEMENTARY PHYSICS, Books I and II *(with A. F. Abbott)*
NOTES ON ORDINARY LEVEL PHYSICS
REVISION NOTES IN PHYSICS
Book I. Heat, Light, Sound
Book II. Magnetism, Electricity, Mechanics & Properties of Matter
SOLUTIONS TO ORDINARY LEVEL PHYSICS QUESTIONS
SOLUTIONS TO ADVANCED LEVEL PHYSICS QUESTIONS
GENERAL SCIENCE PHYSICS
SCHOLARSHIP PHYSICS

Published by Arnold
ELECTRICITY AND MAGNETISM
PHYSICS AND RADIO

Published by Blackie
PRINCIPLES OF TECHNICAL ELECTRICITY
HEAT

Published by Chatto & Windus
PRINCIPLES OF PHYSICS

BOOKS BY P. PARKER

Published by Heinemann
INTERMEDIATE HEAT
ELECTRICITY AND MAGNETISM

Published by Arnold
ELECTRONICS

ADVANCED LEVEL
PHYSICS

by

M. NELKON
M.SC. (LOND.), A.INST.P., A.K.C.
Head of the Science Department, William Ellis School, London

and

P. PARKER
M.SC., F.INST.P., A.M.I.E.E.
Late Senior Lecturer in Physics,
Northampton College of Advanced Technology, London

HEINEMANN EDUCATIONAL
BOOKS LTD · LONDON

Heinemann Educational Books Ltd
LONDON   MELBOURNE   TORONTO
SINGAPORE   CAPE TOWN   AUCKLAND
IBADAN   HONG KONG

FIRST PUBLISHED AS ONE VOLUME 1958
REPRINTED 1959, 1960, 1961, 1962

SECOND EDITION 1964
REPRINTED WITH ADDITIONS 1965

PUBLISHED BY
HEINEMANN EDUCATIONAL BOOKS LTD
48 CHARLES STREET, MAYFAIR, LONDON, W.1
PRINTED AND BOUND IN GREAT BRITAIN
BY JARROLD AND SONS LTD, NORWICH

CONTENTS

PART ONE: MECHANICS AND PROPERTIES OF MATTER

PART TWO: HEAT

PART THREE: LIGHT AND SOUND

CONTENTS

PART FOUR: ELECTRICITY AND MAGNETISM

LIST OF PLATES

PREFACE

This text-book is designed for Advanced Level students of Physics, and covers Mechanics and Properties of Matter, Heat, Light, and Sound. Magnetism and Electricity to that standard. It is based on the experience gained over many years of teaching and lecturing to a wide variety of students in schools and polytechnics.

In the treatment, an Ordinary Level knowledge of the subject is assumed. We have aimed at presenting the physical aspect of topics as much as possible, and then at providing the mathematical arguments and formulae necessary for a thorough understanding. Historical details have also been given to provide a balanced perspective of the subject. As a help to the student, numerous worked examples from past examination papers have been included in the text.

It is possible here to mention only a few points borne in mind by the authors. In Mechanics and Properties of Matter, the theory of dimensions has been utilized where the mathematics is difficult, as in the subject of viscosity, and the "excess pressure" formula has been extensively used in the treatment of surface tension. In Heat, the kinetic theory of gases has been fully discussed, and the experiments of Joule and Andrews have been presented in detail. The constant value of $\mu \sin i$ has been emphasized in refraction at plane surfaces in Light, there is a full treatment of the angular magnification of optical instruments, details are given of the numerous methods of determining optical constants of mirrors and lenses, and there is a qualitative account of interference, diffraction and polarization. In Sound, the physical principles of stationary waves, and their applications to pipes and strings, have been given prominence. Finally, in Electricity the electron and ion have been used extensively to provide explanations of phenomena in electrostatics, magnetism, electrolysis and atomic physics; the concept of e.m.f. has been linked at the outset with energy; and there are full accounts of measurements and instruments. In response to the general feeling amongst experienced physics teachers, the electromagnetism sections have utilized traditional units, and a brief account of the M.K.S. units has been provided in an Appendix.

We acknowledge our gratitude to the following for their kindness in reading sections of the work before the complete volume was compiled: Mr. J. H. Avery, Stockport Grammar School; Dr. J. Duffey, formerly of Watford Technical College; Mr. J. Newton, Northampton College of Advanced Technology, London; Mr. A. W. K. Ingram, Lawrence Sheriff School, Rugby; Mr. O. C. Gay, College of Technology, Hull; Mr. T. N. Littledale, Gunnersbury Grammar School; Mr. C. R. Ensor, Downside School, Bath; Mr. L. S. Powell, Garnett College, London;

Dr. D. W. Stops, Northampton College of Advanced Technology, London; and Professor H. T. Flint, London University. We are also indebted to the following Examining Boards for permission to reprint questions set in past Advanced-level examinations:

Matriculation and School Examinations, London University   (*L.*)
Northern Universities Joint Matriculation Board   (*N.*)
Cambridge Local Examinations Syndicate   (*C.*)
Oxford and Cambridge Joint Board   (*O. & C.*)
Welsh Joint Education Committee   (*W.*)

SECOND EDITION

In this edition I have added an introduction to Atomic Structure, which covers a new Advanced level syllabus on this topic. I am particularly indebted to Mr. J. Yarwood, M.Sc., F.Inst.P., head of the physics and mathematics department, Regent Street Polytechnic, London, for reading this section and for valuable advice, and to Dr. L. Pincherle, Bedford College, London University, for his kind assistance in parts of the text. An account of the triode as an oscillator and the Michelson-Morley experiment, and recent examination questions, have also been added.

I am also indebted to Mr. G. Ullyott, Charterhouse School, for his helpful comments on dynamics.

NOTE TO 1965 REPRINT

In this reprint a section on X-rays has been added to Chapter XLV.

PUBLISHER'S NOTE

All four parts are available as separate volumes with the following titles:

Mechanics and Properties of Matter by M. Nelkon, with additional Scholarship level matter.
Intermediate Heat by P. Parker.
Light and Sound by M. Nelkon, with additional Scholarship level matter.
Electricity and Magnetism by P. Parker, with additional Scholarship level matter.

PART ONE

MECHANICS AND PROPERTIES OF MATTER

MECHANICS

CHAPTER I

DYNAMICS

1. Motion in a Straight Line. Velocity.

The "velocity" of a moving object is defined as "the distance moved in a constant direction in unit time". If a car travels steadily in a constant direction and covers a distance s in a time t, then its velocity $= s/t$. If the car does not travel steadily, then s/t is its average velocity, and

$$\text{the distance, } s, = \text{average velocity} \times t.$$

Velocity can be expressed in "centimetres per second" or "kilometres per hours"; or in "ft. per sec." or "miles per hour". By calculation, 60 m.p.h. = 88 ft. per sec. It should be noted here that "velocity" is a quantity which has direction as well as magnitude (p. 6).

If an object moving in a straight line travels equal distances in equal times, no matter how small these distances may be, the object is said to be moving with *uniform* velocity. The velocity of a falling stone increases continuously, and so is a *non-uniform* velocity.

Suppose an object moving with a non-uniform velocity has travelled a distance s in a time t. If δs is the further small distance travelled in a small time δt, the velocity, v, over the small distance $= \delta s/\delta t$. Thus, in the limit, the velocity v at the time t is given by

$$v = \frac{ds}{dt},$$

using the calculus notation.

When a stone is released from a height it falls a distance s in feet given by the equation $s = 16t^2$, where t is the time of fall (p. 3). Thus, by differentiation, the velocity of the stone is given by

$$v = \frac{ds}{dt} = 2 \times 16t = 32t.$$

Hence at the end of 2 secs., when $t = 2$, the velocity is 64 ft. per sec.

2. Acceleration.

The *acceleration* of a moving object at an instant is defined as the *rate of change of its velocity* (i.e., the velocity change per sec.) at that

1

instant. In the case of a train accelerating steadily from 30 m.p.h. (44 ft. per sec.) to 45 m.p.h. (66 ft. per sec.) in 10 secs., the acceleration

$$= (45 - 30) \text{ m.p.h.}/10 \text{ secs.} = 1\cdot5 \text{ m.p.h. per sec.},$$

or

$$(66 - 44) \text{ ft. per sec.}/10 \text{ sec.} = 2\cdot2 \text{ ft. per sec. per sec.}$$

Since the time element (second) is repeated twice in the latter case, the acceleration is usually given as $2\cdot2$ ft. per sec.[2] Another unit of acceleration is "cm. per sec.[2]" In terms of the calculus, the acceleration f of a moving object is given by

$$f = \frac{dv}{dt},$$

where dv/dt is the velocity change per sec.

If the velocity changes by equal amounts in equal times, no matter how small the time-intervals may be, the acceleration is said to be *uniform*. Suppose that the velocity of an object moving in a straight line with uniform acceleration f increases from a value u to a value v in a time t. Then, from the definition of acceleration,

$$f = \frac{v - u}{t},$$

from which $\qquad\qquad \mathbf{v = u + ft} \qquad . \qquad . \qquad . \qquad . \qquad (1).$

3. Distance Travelled with Uniform Acceleration. Equations of Motion.

Suppose an object with a velocity u accelerates with a uniform acceleration f for a time t and attains a velocity v. The distance s travelled by the object in the time t is given by

$$s = \text{average velocity} \times t$$
$$= \tfrac{1}{2}(u + v) \times t$$

But $\qquad\qquad v = u + ft$

$$\therefore s = \tfrac{1}{2}(u + u + ft)t$$

$$\therefore \mathbf{s = ut + \tfrac{1}{2}ft^2} \qquad . \qquad . \qquad . \qquad . \qquad (2).$$

If we eliminate t by substituting $t = (v - u)/f$ from (1) in (2), we obtain, on simplifying,

$$\mathbf{v^2 = u^2 + 2fs} \qquad . \qquad . \qquad . \qquad . \qquad (3).$$

Equations (1), (2), (3) are the equations of motion of an object moving in a straight line with uniform acceleration. When an object undergoes a uniform *retardation*, for example when brakes are applied to a car, f has a *negative* value.

EXAMPLES

1. A car moving with a velocity of 30 m.p.h. accelerates uniformly at the rate of 2 yd. per sec.^{2}. Calculate the distance travelled from the place where acceleration began to that where the velocity reaches 45 m.p.h., and the time taken to cover this distance.

(i) 30 m.p.h. = 44 ft. per sec., 45 m.p.h. = 66 ft. per sec., acceleration $f = 6$ ft. per sec.^{2}

Using

$$. \ v^2 = u^2 + 2fs,$$
$$\therefore 66^2 = 44^2 + 2 \times 6 \times s$$
$$\therefore s = \frac{66^2 - 44^2}{2 \times 6} = 201\tfrac{2}{3} \text{ ft.}$$

(ii) Using

$$v = u + ft.$$
$$\therefore 66 = 44 + 6t$$
$$\therefore t = \frac{66 - 44}{6} = 3\tfrac{2}{3} \text{ secs.}$$

2. A train travelling at 60 m.p.h. undergoes a uniform retardation of 4 ft. per sec.^{2} when brakes are applied. Find the time taken to come to rest and the distance travelled from the place where the brakes were applied.

(i) 60 m.p.h. = 88 ft. per sec., and $f = -4$ ft. per sec.^{2}, $v = 0$.

Using

$$v = u + ft.$$
$$\therefore 0 = 88 - 4t$$
$$\therefore t = 22 \text{ secs.}$$

(ii) The distance, $s, = ut + \tfrac{1}{2}ft^2$
$$= 88 \times 22 - \tfrac{1}{2} \times 4 \times 22^2 = 968 \text{ ft.}$$

4. Motion Under Gravity.

When an object falls to the ground under the action of gravity experiment shows that the object has a constant or uniform acceleration of about 32 ft. per sec.^{2}, or 980 cm. per sec.^{2}, while it is falling (see p. 43). The numerical value of this acceleration is usually denoted by the symbol g. Suppose that an object is dropped from a height of 100 ft. above the ground. Then the initial velocity $u = 0$, and the acceleration $f = g = 32$, in this case. Substituting in $s = ut + \tfrac{1}{2}ft^2$, the distance s fallen is calculated from

$$s = \tfrac{1}{2}gt^2 = 16t^2.$$

When the object reaches the ground, $s = 100$ ft.

$$\therefore 100 = 16t^2, \text{ or } t = \frac{10}{4} = 2\tfrac{1}{2} \text{ secs.}$$

Thus the object takes $2\tfrac{1}{2}$ secs. to reach the ground.

If a cricket-ball is thrown vertically upwards, it slows down owing to the attraction of the earth. The ball is thus retarded, and the magnitude of the retardation is 32 ft. per sec.², or g. Mathematically, a retardation can be regarded as a negative acceleration in the direction along which the object is moving; and hence $f = -32$ ft. per sec.² in this case.

Suppose the ball was thrown straight up with an initial velocity, u, of 80 ft. per sec. The time taken to reach the top of its motion can be obtained from the equation $v = u + ft$. The velocity, v, at the top is zero; and since $u = 80$ and $f = -32$ numerically, we have

$$0 = 80 - 32t.$$

$$\therefore t = \frac{80}{32} = 2\tfrac{1}{2} \text{ secs.}$$

The highest distance reached is thus given by

$$s = ut + \tfrac{1}{2}ft^2$$
$$= 80 \times 2\tfrac{1}{2} - 16 \times 2\tfrac{1}{2}^2 = 100 \text{ ft.}$$

5. Distance-Time Curve.

When the distance s of a moving car from some fixed point is plotted against the time t, a *distance-time ($s - t$) curve* of the motion is obtained. The velocity of the car at any instant is given by the change in distance per second at that instant; i.e., by the *gradient* to the curve at the instant considered. If the distance-time curve is a straight line CD,

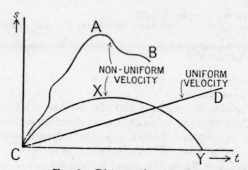

FIG. 1.   Distance-time curves.

the gradient is constant at all points; it therefore follows that the car is moving with a *uniform* velocity, Fig. 1. If the distance-time curve is a curve CAB, the gradient varies at different points. The car then moves with non-uniform velocity, and we can deduce that the velocity is zero at the instant corresponding to A, since the gradient at A to the curve CAB is zero.

When a ball is thrown upwards, the height s reached at any instant t is given by $s = ut - \frac{1}{2}gt^2 = ut - 16t^2$, where u is the initial velocity. The graph of s against t is represented by the parabolic curve CXY in Fig.1; the gradient at X is zero, showing that the velocity of the ball at its maximum height is zero.

6. Velocity-Time Curves.

When the velocity of a moving train is plotted against the time, a "velocity-time curve" is obtained. Useful information can be deduced from this curve, as we shall see shortly. If the velocity is uniform, the velocity-time graph is a straight line parallel to the time-axis, as shown by line (1) in Fig. 2. If the train accelerates uniformly from rest, the velocity-time graph is a straight line, line (2), inclined to the time-axis.

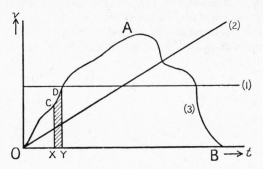

FIG. 2. Velocity-time curves.

If the acceleration is not uniform, the velocity-time graph is curved In Fig. 2, the velocity-time graph OAB represents the velocity of a train starting from rest which reaches a maximum velocity at A, and then comes to rest at the time corresponding to B; the acceleration and retardation are both not uniform in this case.

Since acceleration is the change of velocity per second, i.e., the rate of change of the velocity, *the acceleration of the train at any instant is given by the gradient to the velocity-time graph* at that instant. At the peak point A of the curve OAB the gradient is zero, i.e., the acceleration is then zero. At any point between A, B the gradient to the curve is negative, i.e., the train undergoes a retardation.

7. Area Between Velocity-Time Graph and Time-Axis.

Consider again the velocity-time graph OAB, and suppose the velocity increases in a very small time-interval XY from a value represented by

XC to a value represented by YD, Fig. 2. Since the small distance travelled = average velocity × time XY, the distance travelled is represented by the *area* between the curve CD and the time-axis, shown shaded in Fig. 2. By considering every small time-interval between OB in the same way, it follows that *the total distance travelled by the train in the time OB is given by the area between the velocity-time graph and the time-axis.* This result applies to any velocity-time graph, whatever its shape. In calculus notation, the distance s travelled from an instant t_1 to an instant t_2 is given by

$$s = \int_{t_1}^{t_2} v \, . \, dt.$$

8. Vector and Scalar Quantities.

Cambridge is 50 miles from London in a direction 20° E. of N. We can therefore represent the distance between the cities in magnitude and direction by a straight line LC 2·5 cm. long 20° E. of N., where 1 cm. represents 20 miles, Fig. 3 (i). Similarly, we can represent the

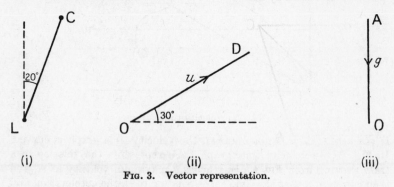

(i)   (ii)   (iii)

Fig. 3.   Vector representation.

velocity u of a ball initially thrown at an angle of 30° to the horizontal by a straight line OD drawn to scale in the direction of the velocity u, the arrow on the line showing the direction, Fig. 3 (ii). The acceleration due to gravity, g, is always represented by a straight line OA to scale drawn vertically downwards, since this is the direction of the acceleration, Fig. 3 (iii).

A physical quantity which can be represented in magnitude and direction by a straight line is known as a *vector* quantity; acceleration and velocity are examples of vector quantities. The tension in a rope can be represented in magnitude and direction by a straight line, and thus "force" is a vector quantity. The mass of an object, its volume, and its temperature have magnitude but no direction, and they are known as *scalar* quantities

9. Resultant. Components.

If a boy is running along the deck of a ship in a direction OA, and the ship is moving in a different direction OB, the boy will move relatively to the sea along a direction OC, between OA and OB, Fig. 4 (i). Now in one second the boat moves from O to B, where OB represents the velocity of the boat in magnitude and direction, and the boy moves from O to A in the same time, where OA represents the velocity of the boy in magnitude and direction. Thus in one second the net effect relative to the sea is that the boy moves from O to C. It can now be seen that if lines OA, OB are drawn to represent in magnitude and direction the respective velocities of the boy and the ship, the magnitude and direction of the **resultant** velocity of the boy is represented by the diagonal OC of the completed parallelogram having OA, OB as two of its sides; OACB is known as a *parallelogram of velocities*. Conversely, a velocity represented completely by OC can be regarded as having an "effective part", or *component* represented by OA, and another component represented by OB.

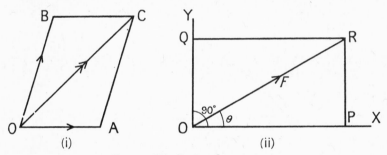

Fig. 4.   Resultant and component.

In practice, we often require to find the component of a vector quantity in a certain direction. Suppose OR represents the vector F, and OX is the direction, Fig. 4 (ii). If we complete the parallelogram OQRP by drawing a perpendicular RP from R to OX, and a perpendicular RQ from R to OY, where OY is perpendicular to OX, we can see that OP, OQ represent the components of F along OX, OY respectively. Now the component OQ has no effect in a perpendicular direction; consequently OP represents the total effect of F along the direction OX. OP is called the "resolved component" in this direction. If θ is the angle ROX, then, since triangle OPR has a right angle at P,

$$OP = OR \cos \theta = F \cos \theta \qquad . \qquad . \qquad . \qquad (4).$$

The component of the acceleration g due to gravity in a direction inclined at 60° to it is thus given by $g \cos 60°$, or $32 \cos 60°$ ft. per sec.^{2}, which is 16 ft. per sec.^{2}.

10. Projectiles.

Suppose a cricket-ball is thrown with a velocity u in a direction making an angle a with the horizontal, Fig. 5. The component of the velocity in a horizontal direction is $u \cos a$. The component in a vertical direction $= u \cos (90° - a) = u \sin a$. Now the acceleration in a vertical direction $= -g$. Thus, from $v = u + ft$ and $s = ut + \frac{1}{2}ft^2$ respectively, the vertical velocity v at the end of a time t is given by

$$v = u \sin a - gt \quad . \quad . \quad . \quad \text{(i).}$$

and the vertical distance s at the end of the time is given by

$$s = u \sin a \,.\, t - \tfrac{1}{2}gt^2 \quad . \quad . \quad . \quad \text{(ii).}$$

The graph of s vs . t is thus a parabola OAB, as shown in Fig. 5. The horizontal component, $u \cos a$, remains constant in magnitude, since there is no component of gravity in a horizontal direction.

The vertical velocity of the ball at the *maximum* height A is zero.

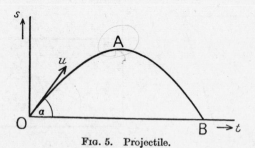

FIG. 5. Projectile.

Now
$$v = u + ft \text{ (p. 2).}$$

$$\therefore 0 = u \sin a - gt,$$

where t is the time to reach A.

$$\therefore t = \frac{u \sin a}{g} \quad . \quad . \quad . \quad . \quad \text{(iii).}$$

When the ball reaches the ground again at a time corresponding to OB, the vertical distance s travelled is zero. Thus, from (ii),

$$0 = u \sin a \,.\, t - \tfrac{1}{2}gt^2.$$

$$\therefore t = \frac{2u \sin a}{g}$$

∴ horizontal distance travelled = range of ball

= horizontal velocity × time

$$= u \cos a \times \frac{2u \sin a}{g}$$

$$= \frac{u^2}{g} \sin 2a \quad . \quad . \quad . \quad . \quad \text{(iv)}.$$

Since the maximum magnitude of sin $2a$ is 1, the angle $2a = 90°$ for a maximum range. Thus, for a given velocity of throw, a ball should be thrown at an angle of 45° to the horizontal to achieve a maximum range.

11. Addition of Vectors.

Suppose a ship is travelling due east at 30 m.p.h. and a boy runs across the deck in a north-west direction at 6 m.p.h., Fig. 6 (i). We can find the velocity and direction of the boy relative to the sea by adding the two velocities. Since velocity is a vector quantity, we draw a line OA to represent 30 m.p.h. in magnitude and direction, and then, from

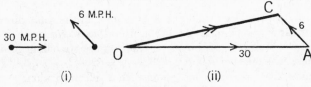

Fig. 6.   Addition of vectors.

the end of A, draw a line AC to represent 6 m.p.h. in magnitude and direction, Fig. 6 (ii). The sum, or resultant, of the velocities is now represented by the line OC in magnitude and direction, because a distance moved in one second by the ship (represented by OA) together with a distance moved in one second by the boy (represented by AC) is equivalent to a movement of the boy from O to C relative to the sea.

12. Subtraction of Vectors.

The sum of two vectors X, Y is thus represented by one side of a triangle whose other two sides are drawn to represent X, Y in magnitude and direction. By adopting a similar method we can *subtract* two vectors, P, Q say, a process required in finding relative velocity for example (p. 10), Fig. 7 (i). The subtraction can be represented by $\vec{P} - \vec{Q}$, the arrows above the letters indicating that P and Q are vector quantities and not scalar quantities. Now

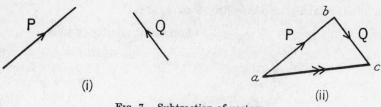

Fig. 7. Subtraction of vectors.

$$\overrightarrow{P} - \overrightarrow{Q} = \overrightarrow{P} + (- \overrightarrow{Q}).$$

In words, the difference between the vectors $\overrightarrow{P}$, $\overrightarrow{Q}$ is the *sum* of the vectors $\overrightarrow{P}$ and ($- \overrightarrow{Q}$). Now ($- \overrightarrow{Q}$) is a vector drawn exactly equal and opposite to the vector $\overrightarrow{Q}$. We therefore draw ab to represent $\overrightarrow{P}$ completely, and then draw bc to represent ($- \overrightarrow{Q}$) completely, Fig. 7 (ii). Then $\overrightarrow{P} + (- \overrightarrow{Q}) =$ the vector represented by $ac = \overrightarrow{P} - \overrightarrow{Q}$.

13. Relative Velocity and Relative Acceleration.

If a car A travelling at 30 m.p.h. is moving in the same direction as another car B travelling at 32 m.p.h., the *relative velocity* of B to A = 32 – 30 = 2 m.p.h. If, however, the cars are travelling in opposite directions, the relative velocity of B to A = 32 – (– 30) = 62 m.p.h.

Suppose that a car X is travelling with a velocity v along a road 30° east of north, and a car Y is travelling with a velocity u along a road

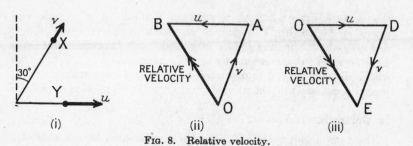

Fig. 8. Relative velocity.

due east, Fig. 8 (i). Since "velocity" has direction as well as magnitude, i.e., "velocity" is a vector quantity (p. 6), we cannot subtract u and v numerically to find the relative velocity. We must adopt a method which takes into account the direction as well as the magnitude of the velocities, i.e., a vector subtraction is required.

The velocity of X relative to $Y = \vec{v} - \vec{u} = \vec{v} + (-\vec{u})$. Suppose OA represents the velocity, v, of X in magnitude and direction, Fig. 8 (ii). Since Y is travelling due east, a velocity AB numerically equal to u but in the due *west* direction represents the vector $(-\vec{u})$. The vector sum of OA and AB is OB from p. 9, which therefore represents in magnitude and direction the velocity of X relative to Y. By drawing an accurate diagram of the two velocities, OB can be found.

The velocity of Y relative to $X = \vec{u} - \vec{v} = \vec{u} + (-\vec{v})$, and can be found by a similar method. In this case, OD represents the velocity, u, of Y in magnitude and direction, while DE represents the vector $\left(-\vec{v}\right)$, which it is drawn numerically equal to v but in the *opposite* direction, Fig. 8 (iii). The vector sum of OD and DE is OE, which therefore represents the velocity of Y relative to X in magnitude and direction.

When two objects P, Q are each accelerating, the acceleration of P relative to Q = acceleration of P – acceleration of Q. Since "acceleration" is a vector quantity, the relative acceleration must be found by vector subtraction, as for the case of relative velocity.

EXAMPLE

Explain the difference between a scalar and a vector quantity.

What is meant by the relative velocity of one body with respect to another? Two ships are 10 sea-miles apart on a line running S. to N. The one farther north is steaming W. at 20 knots. The other is steaming N. at 20 knots. What is their distance of closest approach and how long do they take to reach it? (*C.*)

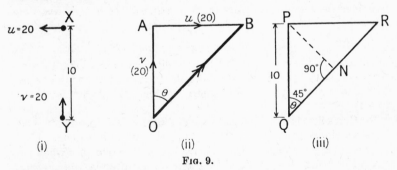

Fⁱᵍ. 9.

First part. See text.

Second part. Suppose the two ships are at X, Y, moving with velocities u, v respectively, each 20 knots, Fig. 9 (i). The velocity of Y relative to $X = \vec{v} - \vec{u} = \vec{v} + (-\vec{u})$. We therefore draw OA to represent $\vec{v}$ (20) and add to it AB, which represents $(-\overrightarrow{u})$, Fig. 9 (ii). The relative velocity is then represented by OB.

Since OAB is a right-angled triangle,

$$OB = \sqrt{OA^2 + AB^2} = \sqrt{20^2 + 20^2} = 28 \cdot 28 \text{ knots} \qquad . \qquad \text{(i).}$$

Also, $\tan \theta = \dfrac{AB}{OA} = \dfrac{20}{20} = 1$, i.e., $\theta = 45°$ $\qquad . \qquad . \qquad .$ (ii).

Thus the ship Y will move along a direction QR relative to the ship X, where QR is at 45° to PQ, the north-south direction, Fig. 9 (iii). If PQ = 10 sea miles, the distance of closest approach is PN, where PN is the perpendicular from P to QR.

$$\therefore PN = PQ \sin 45° = 10 \sin 45° = 7 \cdot 07 \text{ sea-miles.}$$

The distance QN $= 10 \cos 45° = 7 \cdot 07$ sea-miles. Since, from (i), the relative velocity is $28 \cdot 28$ knots, it follows that

$$\text{time to reach N} = \frac{7 \cdot 07}{28 \cdot 28} = \tfrac{1}{4} \text{ hour.}$$

LAWS OF MOTION. ENERGY AND MOMENTUM

14. Newton's Laws of Motion.

In 1686 Sir Isaac Newton published a work called *Principia*, in which he expounded the Laws of Mechanics. He formulated in the book three "laws of motion" which paved the way for the later development of machines in motion:

Law I. *Every body continues in its state of rest or uniform motion in a straight line, unless impressed forces act on it.*

Law II. *The change of momentum per unit time is proportional to the impressed force, and takes place in the direction of the straight line along which the force acts.*

Law III. *Action and reaction are always equal and opposite.*

These laws cannot be proved in a formal way; we believe they are true because all the theoretical results obtained by assuming them agree with the experimental observations, as for example in astronomy (p. 51).

Newton's first law expresses the idea of **inertia**. The inertia of a body is its reluctance to start moving, and its reluctance to stop once it has begun moving. Thus an object at rest begins to move only when it is pushed or pulled, i.e., when a *force* acts on it; an object moving in a straight line with constant velocity changes its direction or moves faster only if a new force acts on it. Passengers in a bus or car appear to be jerked forward when the vehicle stops suddenly, as they continue in their state of motion until brought to rest by friction or collision.

15. Mass. Momentum. Force.

Observation shows that a given force produces a greater acceleration in a light object A than in a heavy object B. We say that the *mass* of A is less than the mass of B. The mass of an object is constant all over the world; it is measured in pounds in this country, and in grams in the scientific (c.g.s.) system.

When an object X is moving it is said to have an amount of *momentum* given, by definition, by

$$momentum = mass\ of\ X \times velocity \qquad (5).$$

Thus an object of mass 200 lb. moving with a velocity of 30 ft. per sec. has a momentum of 6,000 units. If another object collides with X its velocity alters, and thus the momentum of X alters. The *force* of the collision, from Newton's Law II, is proportional to the change of momentum per second. Thus if P is the magnitude of a force acting on a constant mass m,

$$P \propto m \times \text{change of velocity per second}$$

$$\therefore P \propto mf,$$

where f is the *acceleration* produced by the force, by definition of f.

$$\therefore P = kmf \qquad . \qquad . \qquad . \qquad . \qquad . \qquad (i).$$

where k is a constant.

The **poundal** is a unit of force which is defined as the force acting on a mass of 1 lb. which gives it an acceleration of 1 ft. per sec.^{2}. Substituting $P = 1$ poundal, $m = 1$ lb., and $f = 1$ ft. per sec.^{2} in (i), we obtain $k = 1$; thus

$$\mathbf{P = mf,} \qquad . \qquad . \qquad . \qquad . \qquad . \qquad (6)$$

a standard equation in Dynamics.

The **dyne** is the unit of force in the centimetre-gram-second system; it is defined as the force acting on a mass of 1 gram which gives it an acceleration of 1 cm. per sec.^{2}. The equation $P = mf$ also applies when m is in grams, f is in cm. per sec.^{2}, and P is in dynes.

16. Weight. Relation between poundal and lb. wt., dyne and gm. wt.

The *weight* of an object is defined as the *force* acting on it due to gravity; the weight of an object can hence be measured by attaching it to a spring-balance and noting the extension, as the latter is proportional to the force acting on it (p. 137).

Suppose the weight of an object of mass m is denoted by W. If the object is released so that it falls to the ground, its acceleration is g.

Now $P = mf$. Consequently the force acting on it, i.e., its weight, is given by

$$W = mg \qquad . \qquad . \qquad . \qquad (7).$$

If the mass m is 1 lb., then, since $g = 32$ ft. per sec.^{2}, the weight $W = 1 \times 32 = 32$ poundals. We call the force due to gravity on a mass of 1 lb. a *pound-weight* (*lb. wt.*), and hence it follows that

1 lb. wt. = 32 poundals.

At this stage the reader should note carefully the difference between the "pound" and the "pound-weight"; the former is a *mass* and is therefore constant all over the earth, whereas the pound-weight is a *force* whose magnitude depends on the value of g. The acceleration due to gravity, g, depends on the distance of the place considered from the centre of the earth; it is slightly greater at the poles than at the equator, since the earth is not perfectly spherical (see p. 43). It therefore follows that the weight of an object differs in different parts of the world.

The weight of a mass of 1 gram is called a *gram-weight* (*gm. wt.*). From $P = mf$, it follows that

1 gm. wt. = 1 × 980 = 980 dynes,

since $g = 980$ cm. per sec.^{2} (approx.). The relations between 1 gm. wt. and 1 dyne, and between 1 lb. wt. and 1 poundal, are used extensively in later sections, and should be memorised by the reader.

17. Verification of P = mf. Fletcher's Trolley.

The relation between the force P and the acceleration f can be investigated with the aid of *Fletcher's trolley*, Fig. 10. This consists of a heavy trolley H, with holes in the side in which various masses can

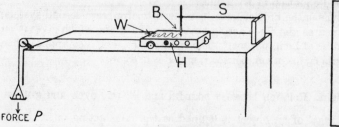

Fig. 10. Fletcher's trolley.

be inserted. The trolley is connected to a scale pan by a light string passing over a grooved wheel, and the force acting on the trolley is varied by placing different weights on the scale-pan. The total mass moved is that of the trolley plus the scale-pan and masses on it; but as the latter is negligible compared with the mass of the trolley, the mass moved is practically constant and equal to the mass of the trolley.

The time of movement of the trolley is measured by means of a springy strip of metal S fixed to one end, with an inked pen B attached to the other end. S is drawn back and released so that it vibrates, the trolley is then allowed to accelerate from rest, and the pen B marks a wavy trace W on a sheet of paper on the trolley as a result of the vibrations of S. The time to make one complete wave is constant and equal to the period of vibration of the spring, which is sometimes marked on the spring.

In order to verify that the acceleration of an object is proportional to the force acting on it, a weight is placed on the scale-pan and a wavy trace is obtained when the trolley is released from rest. Now the acceleration f is given by $s = ut + \frac{1}{2}ft^2 = \frac{1}{2}ft^2$, since $u = 0$. Hence $f = 2s/t^2$. The distance s moved by the trolley at the end of the fourth trace, for example, is measured, and the corresponding time t is 4 units, where one unit is the period of vibration of the spring. Thus f is known. The experiment is now repeated with different weights in the scale-pan, i.e., P is varied, and the corresponding acceleration f is measured. *Experiment shows that P/f is a constant*; and hence $P \propto f$ for a given mass. By placing different masses in the holes of the trolley the mass m can be varied; and if the force P is kept constant and the acceleration f is measured each time, experiment shows that $f \propto 1/m$.

18. Action and Reaction are Equal and Opposite.

When a brick is resting on the ground, the brick exerts a downward force on the ground and the ground exerts an upward force on the brick. The downward force may be termed the "action" on the ground, and is equal to the weight of the brick. The upward force is called the *reaction* at the ground, and from Newton's third law (p. 12), the reaction is equal to the weight of the brick. Similarly, when a cricket-ball is hit by a bat, the force on the bat at the instant of collision is equal and opposite to the force on the ball at that instant.

Newton's third law applies to all branches of Physics. Thus if a magnet attracts a piece of iron with a force of 100 dynes, the iron attracts the magnet with a force of 100 dynes acting in the opposite direction. If an electric current in a wire produces a force of 10 dynes on a magnet near it, the wire is subjected to a force of 10 dynes in the opposite direction.

EXAMPLES

1. An object of mass 200 gm. is attached to the hook of a spring-balance, and the latter is suspended vertically from the roof of a lift. What is the reading on the spring-balance when the lift is (i) ascending with an accelera-tion of 20 cm. per sec.² (ii) descending with an acceleration of 10 cm. per sec.² (iii) ascending with a uniform velocity of 15 cm. per sec.

Suppose T is the tension (force) in the spring-balance in dynes.

(i) The object is acted upon two forces: (*a*) The tension T dynes in the spring-balance, which acts upwards, (*b*) its weight, 200×980 dynes, which acts downwards. Since the object moves upwards, T is greater than 200×980 dynes, and hence the net force, P, acting on the object $= (T - 200 \times 980)$ dynes.

But $$P = mf,$$

where f is the acceleration.

$$\therefore T - 200 \times 980 = 200 \times 20$$

$$\therefore T = 200 \times 20 + 200 \times 980 \text{ dynes}$$

$$\therefore T = \frac{200 \times 20 + 200 \times 980}{980} \text{ gm. wt.}$$

$$= 204 \text{ gm. wt.}$$

Thus 204 gm. wt. is the reading on the spring-balance.

(ii) Since the lift is descending, the weight is greater than the tension T_1 in the spring. Hence the net force $P = (200 \times 980 - T_1)$ dynes.

But $$P = mf$$

$$\therefore 200 \times 980 - T_1 = 200 \times 10$$

$$\therefore T_1 = 200 \times 980 - 200 \times 10 \text{ dynes}$$

$$\therefore T_1 = \frac{200 \times 980 - 20) \times 10}{980} \text{ gm .wt.}$$

$$= 198 \text{ gm. wt.}$$

Thus 198 gm. wt. is the reading on the spring-balance.

(iii) If the velocity is uniform, the net force $P = 0$. Thus the tension is now equal to the weight, and hence

$$\text{reading on spring-balance} = 200 \text{ gm. wt.}$$

2. An object of mass 10 lb. rests on a smooth table, and is attached by an inextensible string passing over a grooved wheel to a 20 lb. object hanging over the table. Assuming friction is negligible, calculate the acceleration of the objects when they are allowed to move.

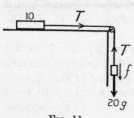

FIG. 11.

Suppose T is the tension in poundals in the string, Fig. 11. The acceleration f of the two objects is the same since they are connected together. For the object of mass 20 lb., the net force acting downwards $= (20g - T)$ poundals, where $g = 32$, since the weight $= 20$ lb. wt. $= 20g$ poundals. From $P = mf$, we have

$$20g - T = 20f \quad \cdot \quad \cdot \quad \cdot \quad \cdot \quad \cdot \quad \cdot \quad \text{(i).}$$

The force T is the only force acting on the object in a horizontal direction.

$$\therefore T = 10f \quad . \quad . \quad . \quad . \quad . \quad . \quad \text{(ii)}.$$

Adding (i) and (ii) to eliminate T,

$$\therefore 20g = 30f.$$

$$\therefore f = \frac{20g}{30} = \frac{20 \times 32}{30} = 21\tfrac{1}{3} \text{ ft. per sec.}^2$$

3. A hose ejects 80 c.c. of water per second through a hole 2 mm. in diameter. Find the backward force on the person holding the hose.

The area of the hole $= \pi r^2 = \pi \times (0\cdot1)^2$ sq. cm.

$$\therefore \text{ velocity, } v, \text{ of water } = \frac{80}{\pi \times (0\cdot1)^2} \quad \text{cm. per sec.}$$

If the initial velocity of water is zero, the change of momentum per second produced

$$= mv = 80 \times \frac{80}{\pi \times (0\cdot1)^2}$$

But force is defined as the "change of momentum per second" (p. 12).

$$\therefore \text{ force on water } = 80 \times \frac{80}{\pi \times (0\cdot1)^2} = 20\cdot4 \times 10^4 \text{ dynes.}$$

$$\therefore \text{ backward force on person } = 20\cdot4 \times 10^4 \text{ dynes.}$$

19. Work.

When an engine pulls a train with a constant force of 50 units through a distance of 20 units, the engine is said by definition to do an amount of *work* equal to 50 × 20 or 1,000 units, the product of the force and the distance. Thus if W is the amount of work,

$$W = force \times distance \quad . \quad . \quad . \quad (8).$$

Since the unit of a force is a "poundal" or a "lb. wt.", the work done is expressed in *ft. poundals* or *ft. lb. wt.* (the latter is often written as "ft. lb." but "ft. lb. wt." is intended). Suppose a force of 640 poundals pulls an object 20 ft. in its direction. The work done is then 640 × 20 or 12,800 ft. poundals. Since 640 poundals = 640/32 lb. wt. (p. 14) = 20 lb. wt., the work done is also given by 20 × 20 or 400 ft. lb. wt.

The c.g.s. unit of work is the **erg**, which is defined as the work done when a force of 1 dyne moves a distance 1 centimetre in its direction. If a force of 5 gm. wt. pulls an object 10 cm. in its direction, then, since 1 gm. wt. = 980 dynes,

$$\text{work done} = 5 \times 980 \times 10 = 49,000 \text{ ergs.}$$

In practice the erg is so small (it is approximately equal to the work done in raising a milligram one centimetre) that a larger unit is adopted.

This is the **joule**, named after the famous scientist J. P. JOULE. By definition,

$$1 \; joule = 10 \; million \; ergs = 10^7 \; ergs.$$

Before leaving the topic of "work", the reader should note carefully that we have assumed the force to move an object in its own direction. Suppose, however, that a force P pulls an object a distance s along a line OA acting at an angle θ to it, Fig. 12. The component of P along

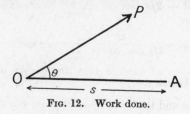

FIG. 12. Work done.

OA is $P \cos \theta$ (p. 7), and this is the effective part of P pulling along the direction OA. The component of P along a direction perpendicular to OA has no effect along OA. Consequently

$$\text{work done} = P \cos \theta \times s.$$

In general, the work done by a force is equal to the product of the force and the displacement of its point of application in the direction of the force.

20. Power.

When an engine does work quickly, it is said to be operating at a high *power*; if it does work slowly it is said to be operating at a low power. "Power" is defined as the *work done per second*, i.e.,

$$\text{power} = \frac{\text{work done}}{\text{time taken}} \qquad . \qquad . \qquad (9).$$

The c.g.s. unit of power is thus "erg per sec.", or "joule per sec." The **watt** is defined as **one joule per second** rate of working, or 10^7 *ergs per second*. The f.p.s. unit of power is "ft. lb. wt. per sec.", and by definition

$$1 \text{ horse power (h.p.)} = 550 \text{ ft. lb. wt. per sec.}$$

By changing the units, it can be shown that

$$1 \text{ h.p.} = 746 \text{ watts.}$$

21. Kinetic Energy.

An object is said to possess *energy* if it can do work. When an object possesses energy because it is moving, the energy is said to be *kinetic*,

DYNAMICS 19

e.g., a flying stone can disrupt a window. Suppose that an object of mass m is moving with a velocity u, and is gradually brought to rest in a distance s by a constant force P acting against it. The kinetic energy originally possessed by the object is equal to the work done against P, and hence

$$\text{kinetic energy} = P \times s.$$

But $P = mf$, where f is the retardation of the object. Hence $P \times s = mfs$. From $v^2 = u^2 + 2fs$ (see p. 2), we have, since $v = 0$ and f is negative in this case,

$$0 = u^2 - 2fs, \text{ i.e., } fs = \frac{u^2}{2}.$$

$$\therefore \textit{kinetic energy} = mfs = \tfrac{1}{2}mu^2 \quad . \quad . \quad . \quad (10).$$

When m is in grams and the velocity u is in cm. per sec., then $\tfrac{1}{2}mu^2$ is in *ergs*; when m is in pounds and u is in ft. per sec., then $\tfrac{1}{2}mu^2$ is in *ft. poundals*.

A car of 15 cwt. moving with a velocity of 30 m.p.h. has thus an amount W of kinetic energy given by

$$W = \tfrac{1}{2}mu^2 = \tfrac{1}{2} \times 15 \times 112 \times 44^2 \text{ ft. poundals,}$$

since 15 cwt. $= 15 \times 112$ lb. and 30 m.p.h. $= 44$ ft. per sec.

$$\therefore W = 1626240 \text{ ft. poundals.}$$

$$= \frac{1626240}{32} \text{ ft. lb. wt.} = 50,820 \text{ ft. lb. wt.}$$

A bullet of 40 grams moving with a velocity of 300 cm. per sec. has an amount W of kinetic energy given by

$$W = \tfrac{1}{2}mu^2 = \tfrac{1}{2} \times 40 \times 300^2 = 1,800,00 \text{ ergs,}$$

$$= \frac{1,800,000}{10^7} \text{ joules} = 0{\cdot}18 \text{ joules.}$$

22. Potential Energy.

A weight held stationary above the ground has energy, because, when released, it can raise another object attached to it by a rope passing over a pulley, for example. A coiled spring also has energy, which is released gradually as the spring uncoils. The energy of the weight or spring is called *potential energy*, because it arises from the position or arrangement of the body, and not from its motion.

If the mass of an object is m, and the object is held stationary at a height h above the ground, the energy released when the object falls to the ground

$$= \text{force} \times \text{distance}$$

$$= \text{weight of object} \times h.$$

When m is in grams, its weight is m gm. wt. or mg dynes, where $g = 980$ numerically. In this case, at a height of h cm.,

$$potential\ energy = mgh\ ergs \qquad . \qquad . \qquad . \qquad \text{(11A)}.$$

If m is in $lb.$, its weight is m lb. wt.; and hence, if h is in feet,

$$\text{potential energy} = mh \text{ ft. lb. wt.} \qquad . \qquad . \qquad \text{(11B)}.$$

Thus if an object of mass 4 kilograms is 2 metres above the ground, its potential energy, W, $= 4000 \times 980 \times 200 = 784{,}000{,}000$ ergs. If an object of mass 50 lb. is 12 ft. above the ground, its potential energy $= 50 \times 12 = 600$ ft. lb. wt.

23. Conservation of Energy.

One of the fundamental principles in Science is the Principle of the Conservation of Energy, which states that the total energy in a given system is constant although energy may change from one form to another. As a simple illustration of the principle in Mechanics, consider an object of mass m held at O at a height h above the ground, Fig. 13.

FIG. 13.
Conservation of energy.

The energy of the stationary object $=$ the potential energy at O. Suppose the object is released and falls to a point A at a height x above the ground. The velocity, v, at A is given by

$$v^2 = u^2 + 2fs = 0 + 2g(h - x) = 2g(h - x).$$

$$\therefore \text{kinetic energy at A} = \tfrac{1}{2}mv^2 = \tfrac{1}{2}m \times 2g(h - x) = mg(h - x).$$

Also, potential energy at A $= mgx.$

$$\therefore \text{total energy at A} \quad = \text{potential energy} + \text{kinetic energy}$$

$$= mgx \qquad\qquad + mg(h - x)$$

$$= mgh.$$

But the energy at O $= mgh$. Consequently the energy is conserved.

When the object just reaches the ground at B the whole of its energy is kinetic and equal to $\tfrac{1}{2}mv_1^2$, where v_1 is the velocity at B.

But

$$v_1^2 = u^2 + 2fs = 0 + 2gh = 2gh,$$

$$\therefore \text{kinetic energy at B} = \tfrac{1}{2}mv_1^2 = mgh = \text{energy at A or O}.$$

The resistance of the air has been omitted from these calculations. If the resistance is taken into account, some work is done against it as the object falls and some mechanical energy is therefore lost; the energy reappears, however, as *heat*.

24. Mass.

Newton said that the "mass" of an object was the "quantity of matter" in it, which is a very vague definition of "mass". In 1905, however, EINSTEIN proved from his Theory of Relativity that the energy W released from an object when its mass decreases by an amount m is given by

$$W = mc^2 \ , \qquad . \quad . \quad . \quad . \qquad \text{(i)}$$

where c is the numerical value of the velocity of light. When m is in grams and c is in cm. per sec., then W is in ergs. Experiments in Radioactivity on objects emitting radiation showed that Einstein's law was true. Now, from (i), $m = W/c^2$. Einstein therefore declared that *the mass of an object is a measure of the total energy obtainable from its atoms.* Thus, since $c = 3 \times 10^{10}$ in cm. per sec., an object can be said to have a mass of 1 gram if 9×10^{20} ergs of energy can be obtained from all its atoms.

Before Einstein proved that the mass of an object was a measure of the energy of its atoms, two recognised laws of science were:

(1) *The Principle of the Conservation of Mass* (the total mass of a given system of objects is constant even though collisions or other actions took place between them);

(2) *The Principle of the Conservation of Energy* (the total energy of a given system is constant). From Einstein's relation, however, the two laws can be combined into one, namely, the Principle of the Conservation of Energy.

On p. 88 we shall see that the masses of objects can be compared by a common balance. Thus if we define a mass of 1 pound as the mass of a certain piece of platinum, we can measure the masses of objects as so many "pounds".

The summary on page 22 may assist the reader; it refers to the units of some of the quantities encountered, and their relations.

25. Conservation of Linear Momentum.

Newton defined the force acting on an object as the rate of change of its momentum, the momentum being the product of its mass and velocity (p. 12). Momentum is thus a vector quantity. Suppose that the mass of an object is m, its initial velocity is u, and its final velocity due to a force P acting on it for a time t is v. Then

Quantity	c.g.s. Unit	f.p.s. Unit	Relations
Force	Dyne or gm. wt.	Poundal or lb. wt.	980 dynes = 1 gm. wt. 32 poundals = 1 lb. wt.
Mass	Gram	Pound (lb.)	
Energy	Ergs or joules	Ft. lb. wt.	10^7 ergs = 1 joule
Power	Watt	Ft. lb. wt./sec. or horse-power	1 watt = 1 joule/sec. 1 h.p. = 550 ft. lb. wt. per sec. = 746 watts.

$$\text{change of momentum} = mv - mu,$$

and hence
$$P = \frac{mv - mu}{t}$$

$$\therefore Pt = mv - mu = momentum\ change \qquad . \qquad . \qquad (13).$$

The quantity Pt (force × time) is known as the *impulse* of the force on the object, and from (13) it follows that the units of momentum are the same as those of Pt, i.e., *dyne-sec.* or *poundal-sec.*

Suppose that a moving object A, of mass m_1 and velocity u_1, collides with another object B, of mass m_2 and velocity u_2, moving in the same direction, Fig. 14. By Newton's law of action and reaction, the force P

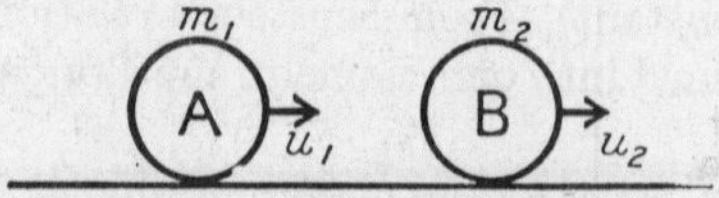

FIG. 14.   Collision of bodies.

exerted by A on B is equal and opposite to that exerted by B on A. Moreover, the time t during which the force acted on B is equal to the time during which the force of reaction acted on A. Thus the magnitude of the impulse, Pt, on B is equal and opposite to the magnitude of the impulse on A. Now from equation (13), the impulse is equal to the change of momentum. It therefore follows that the change in the total momentum of the two objects is *zero*, i.e., the total momentum of the two objects is constant although a collision had occurred. Thus if A moves with a reduced velocity v_1 after collision, and B then moves with an increased velocity v_2,

$$m_1u_1 + m_2u_2 = m_1v_1 + m_2v_2.$$

The *principle of the conservation of momentum* states that, *if no external forces act on a system of colliding objects, the total momentum of the objects remains constant.*

Example. Suppose that the sphere A has a mass of 15 lb., the sphere B has a mass of 10 lb., and that their respective velocities prior to collision are 6 ft. per sec. and 4 ft. per sec. in the same direction. Their total momentum in this direction

$$= 15 \times 6 + 10 \times 4 = 130 \text{ poundal-sec.}$$

If the two spheres are inelastic, they collide and move with a common velocity u. The new total momentum in the same direction as before $= 15u + 10u = 25u$. From the principle of the conservation of momentum, it follows that

$$25u = 130$$
$$\therefore u = \frac{130}{25} = 5 \cdot 2 \text{ ft. per sec.}$$

26. Verification of Principle of Conservation of Momentum.

The Principle of the Conservation of Momentum can be verified by HICKS' ballistic balance, Fig. 15. Two masses A, B are placed on light wooden blocks or scale pans, each suspended by four strings, and the

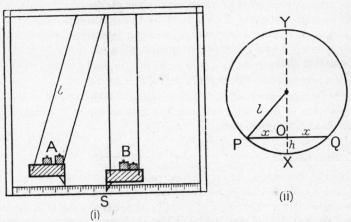

FIG. 15.   Ballistic balance.

horizontal displacement of each mass is measured on the scale S with the aid of a pointer attached to each block. The mass A is first displaced as shown in Fig. 15 (i), and collides with B after it is released. The horizontal displacements of A and B before and after collision are then noted.

Suppose A is initially at P on the arc of a circle of radius l, Fig. 15 (ii). Its velocity is then zero. When it collides with B it passes through its lowest position X with a velocity u given by $mgh = \frac{1}{2}mu^2$, by the principle of conservation of energy, where h is the vertical distance, OX, traversed by A, Fig. 15 (ii). Thus

$$u^2 = 2gh.$$

Now XO . OY = PO . OQ, from the geometry of the circle, where XY is a diameter. Suppose $2l$ is the diameter, and x is the horizontal distance PO.

$$\therefore h(2l - h) = x . x = x^2$$

$$\therefore h = \frac{x^2}{2l},$$

if h is small compared with l, which is true in practice.

$$\therefore u^2 = 2gh = 2g \times \frac{x^2}{2l} = \frac{gx^2}{—}.$$

$$\therefore u \propto x,$$

since g, l are constants. *Thus the velocity of A as it collides with B is proportional to the horizontal displacement of A.* It can be shown by a similar treatment that the velocities of A and B after the collision are also proportional to their respective horizontal displacements, which may be read on the scale S. From a table of measurements of the masses m_1, m_2 of A, B, the velocity u of A just before it collides with B, and the velocities u_1, v_1 of A, B respectively after collision, it can be verified by calculation that

$$m_1u = m_1u_1 + m_2v_1.$$

The total momentum of A, B before collision is thus equal to the total momentum of A, B after collision, the momentum of B being initially zero since B was stationary.

27. Dimensions.

By the *dimensions* of a physical quantity we mean the way it is related to the fundamental quantities mass, length, and time; these are usually denoted by [M], [L], and [T] respectively. An area, length $\times$ breadth, has dimensions [L] $\times$ [L] or [L]^2; a volume has dimensions [L]^3; density, which is mass/volume, has dimensions [M]/[L]^3 or [M] [L]$^{-3}$; specific gravity has no dimensions, since it is the ratio of similar quantities, in this case two weights (p. 95); an angle has no dimensions, since it is the ratio of two lengths.

The following are the dimensions of some quantities in Mechanics:

Velocity. Since velocity $= \dfrac{\text{distance,}}{\text{time}}$ its dimensions are $\dfrac{[L]}{[T]}$ or [L] [T]$^{-1}$.

Acceleration. The dimensions are those of velocity/time, i.e., $\dfrac{[L]}{[T]^2}$ or $[L] [T]^{-2}$.

Force. Since force $=$ mass $\times$ acceleration, its dimensions are $[M] [L] [T]^{-2}$.

Work or Energy. Since work $=$ force $\times$ distance, its dimensions are $[M] [L]^2 [T]^{-2}$.

28. Application of Dimensions.

Simple pendulum. If a small mass is suspended from a long thread so as to form a simple pendulum, we may reasonably suppose that the period, T, of the oscillations depends only on the mass m, the length l of the thread, and the acceleration, g, due to gravity at the place concerned. Suppose then that

$$T = km^x l^y g^z \qquad \text{. . . . .} \qquad \text{(i)}$$

where x, y, z, k are unknown numbers. The dimensions of g are $[L] [T]^{-2}$ from above. Now the dimensions of both sides of (i) must be the same.

$$\therefore [T] = [M]^x [L]^y [L]^z [T]^{-2z}$$

Equating the indices of M, L, T on both sides, we have

$$x = 0,$$
$$y + z = 0,$$
and $$- 2z = 1.$$
$$\therefore z = - \tfrac{1}{2}, y = \tfrac{1}{2}, x = 0.$$

Thus, from (i), the period T is given by

$$\mathrm{T} = kl^{\frac{1}{2}}g^{-\frac{1}{2}},$$

or $$\mathrm{T} = k \sqrt{\dfrac{l}{g}}.$$

We cannot find the magnitude of k by the method of dimensions, since it is a number. A complete mathematical investigation shows that $k = 2\pi$ in this case, and hence $T = 2\pi \sqrt{l/g}$. (See also p. 42.)

29. Velocity of Transverse Wave in a String.

As another illustration of the use of dimensions, consider a wave set up in a stretched string by plucking it. The velocity, V, of the wave depends on the tension, F, in the string, its length l, and its mass m, and we can therefore suppose that

$$V = kF^x l^y m^z, \qquad . \qquad . \qquad . \qquad . \qquad . \qquad \text{(i)}$$

where x, y, z are numbers we hope to find by dimensions and k is a constant.

The dimensions of velocity, V, are $[L][T]^{-1}$, the dimensions of tension, F, are $[M][L][T]^{-2}$, the dimension of length, l, is $[L]$, and the dimension of mass, m, is $[M]$. From (i), it follows that

$$[L][T]^{-1} = [M]^x [L]^x [T]^{-2x} \times [L]^y \times [M]^z.$$

Equating power of $[M]$, $[L]$, and $[T]$ on both sides,

$$\therefore \; 0 = x + z \; , \qquad . \qquad . \qquad . \qquad . \qquad . \qquad . \qquad \text{(i)}$$

$$1 = x + y \; , \qquad . \qquad . \qquad . \qquad . \qquad . \qquad . \qquad \text{(ii)}$$

and

$$- 1 = - 2x \qquad . \qquad . \qquad . \qquad . \qquad . \qquad \text{(iii)}$$

$$\therefore \; x = \tfrac{1}{2}, z = -\tfrac{1}{2}, y = \tfrac{1}{2}.$$

$$\therefore \; V = k \, . \, F^{\frac{1}{2}} \, l^{\frac{1}{2}} \, m^{-\frac{1}{2}},$$

$$\text{or } V = k\sqrt{\frac{Fl}{m}} = k\sqrt{\frac{F}{m/l}} = k\sqrt{\frac{\text{Tension}}{\text{mass per unit length}}}$$

A complete mathematical investigation shows that $k = 1$.

The method of dimensions can thus be used to find the relation between quantities when the mathematics is too difficult. It has been extensively used in hydrodynamics, for example. See also pp. 160, 165.

EXAMPLES

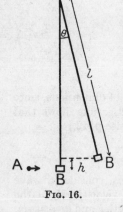

FIG. 16.

1. What is understood by (a) the principle of the *conservation of energy;* (b) the principle of the *conservation of momentum*?

A bullet of mass 20 gm., travelling horizontally at 100 metres per sec., embeds itself in the centre of a block of wood of mass 1 kgm. which is suspended by light vertical strings 1 metre in length. Calculate the maximum inclination of the strings to the vertical.

Describe in detail how the experiment might be carried out and used to determine the velocity of the bullet just before the impact of the block. (*N.*)

First part. See text.

Second part. Suppose A is the bullet, B is the block suspended from a point O, and θ is the maximum inclination to the vertical, Fig. 16. If v cm. per sec. is the common velocity of block and bullet when the latter is brought to rest relative to the block, then, from the principle of the conservation of momentum,

$$(1000 + 20) v = 20 \times 10,000$$

$$\therefore v = \frac{10{,}000}{51} \text{ cm. per sec.}$$

The vertical height h risen by block and bullet is given by

$$v^2 = 2gh.$$

But

$$h = l - l \cos \theta = l(1 - \cos \theta)$$

$$\therefore v^2 = 2gl(1 - \cos \theta)$$

$$\therefore \left(\frac{10{,}000}{51}\right)^2 = 2 \times 980 \times 100 \, (1 - \cos \theta)$$

$$\therefore 1 - \cos \theta = \left(\frac{10{,}000}{51}\right)^2 \times \frac{1}{2 \times 980 \times 100} = 0 \cdot 1962$$

$$\therefore \cos \theta = 0 \cdot 8038$$

$$\therefore \theta = 36 \cdot 5°$$

The velocity, v, of the bullet can be determined by means of the apparatus described on p. 23, applying the conservation of momentum principle.

Thus $mv = (m + M)V$, where m is the mass of the bullet, M is the mass of the block, and V is the common velocity. Then $v = (m + M)V/m$. The quantities m and M can be found by weighing, and V is calculated from the displacement h of the block.

2. State and explain what is meant by the law of conservation of momentum and describe an experiment to illustrate it.

A wooden pendulum bob is moving east with a velocity of 2m./sec. and is hit by a bullet travelling north-west with a velocity of 100 m./sec. If the mass of the pendulum bob is 1 kg. and that of the bullet 100 gm., and if the bullet remains embedded in the bob, find the velocity after impact. (*C*.)

First part. For the law and the experiment, see text.

Second part. Suppose A is the pendulum bob moving eastward, B is the bullet moving north-west, and u is the velocity after impact in metres/sec. in a direction $\theta°$ N. of W., Fig. 17. Applying the conservation of momentum in a west direction,

$$\therefore (1000 + 100)u \cos \theta = 100 \times 100 \cos 45° - 1000 \times 2$$

$$\therefore 1100u \cos \theta = 5070 \quad . \quad . \quad . \quad . \quad \text{(i)}$$

Applying the conservation of momentum in a north direction,

$$\therefore (1000 + 100)u \sin \theta = 100 \times 100 \sin 45°$$

$$\therefore 1100u \sin \theta = 7070 \quad . \quad . \quad . \quad . \quad . \quad \text{(ii)}$$

Fig. 17.

Squaring (i) and (ii), and then adding,

$$\therefore 1100^2 u^2 \, (\cos{}^2\theta + \sin{}^2\theta) = 5070^2 + 7070^2$$

$$\therefore 1100^2 u^2 = 5070^2 + 7070^2$$

$$\therefore u = \sqrt{\frac{5070^2 + 7070^2}{1100^2}} = 7\cdot9 \text{ metres/sec.}$$

Also, dividing (ii) by (i),

$$\therefore \tan \theta = \frac{7070}{5070} = 1\cdot394$$

$$\therefore \theta = 54° \, 21'$$

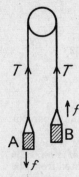

3. Derive the principle of the conservation of momentum from two of Newton's laws of motion. Two buckets, each of mass 15 lb., joined by a weightless string which passes over a frictionless pulley. If a 2-lb. lump of putty falls from a height of 4 ft. into one of the buckets, find (a) the velocity of the system immediately after the impact, (b) its subsequent acceleration. (L.)

First part. Newton's law of action and reaction, and his law relating to force, are used in deriving the principle of the conservation of momentum. See text.

Second part. (a) The velocity v of the putty as it falls into the bucket A is given by

$$v^2 = u^2 + 2fs = 0 + 2 \times 32 \times 4. \quad \text{(Fig. 18.)}$$

Fig. 18. $\therefore v = \sqrt{2 \times 32 \times 4} = 16 \text{ ft./sec.}$

Suppose v is the velocity of the system immediately after the impact. Then, from the conservation of momentum,

$$2 \times 16 = (2 + 15 + 15)v.$$

$$\therefore v = 1 \text{ ft. per sec.}$$

(b) Let $f =$ the subsequent acceleration, and $T =$ the tension in poundals in the string. The net force downwards on the bucket A $= (17g - T)$ poundals, where g is numerically 32. Hence, from $P = mf$,

$$17g - T = 17f \quad . \qquad . \qquad . \qquad . \qquad . \quad \text{(i)}$$

The net force upwards on the bucket B $= (T - 15g)$ pounds.

$$\therefore T - 15g = 15f \quad . \qquad . \qquad . \qquad . \qquad . \quad \text{(ii)}$$

Adding (i) and (ii) to eliminate T,

$$\therefore 17g - 15g = 32f.$$

$$\therefore f = \frac{2g}{32} = \frac{2 \times 32}{32} = 2 \text{ ft. per sec.}^2$$

EXERCISES I

(Assume g = 32 ft. per sec.² or 980 cm. per sec.²)

1. A car moving with a velocity of 30 m.p.h. accelerates uniformly at 2 ft./sec.² until it reaches a velocity of 45 m.p.h. Calculate (i) the time taken, (ii) the distance travelled during the acceleration, (iii) the velocity attained 100 yds. from the place where the acceleration began.

2. A ball of mass 4 oz. is thrown vertically upwards with an initial speed of 60 m.p.h. Calculate (i) the time taken to return to the thrower, (ii) the maximum height reached, (iii) the kinetic and potential energies of the ball when half-way up.

3. The velocity of a ship A relative to a ship B is 10 m.p.h. in a direction N. 45° E. If the velocity of B is 20 m.p.h. in a direction N. 60° W., find the actual velocity of A in magnitude and direction.

4. Calculate the energy of (i) a 50 lb. object held stationary 10 ft. above the ground, (ii) a 2 kilogram object moving with a velocity of 10 metres/sec., (iii) a 10 kilogram object held stationary 5 metres above the ground, (iv) a 20 lb. object moving with a velocity of 30 m.p.h.

5. A 4 lb. ball moving with a velocity of 10 ft. per sec. collides with a 16 lb. ball moving with a velocity of 4 ft. per sec. (i) in the same direction, (ii) in the opposite direction. Calculate the velocity of the balls in each case if they coalesce on impact, and the loss of energy resulting from the impact. State the principle used to calculate the velocity.

6. A ship X moves due north at 30 m.p.h.; a ship Y moves N. 60° W. at 20 m.p.h. Find the velocity of Y relative to X in magnitude and direction. If Y is 10 miles due east of X at this instant, find the closest distance of approach of the two ships.

7. Two buckets of mass 6 lb. are each attached to one end of a long inextensible string passing over a fixed pulley. If a 2 lb. mass of putty is dropped from a height of 4 ft. into one bucket, calculate (i) the initial velocity of the system, (ii) the acceleration of the system, (iii) the loss of energy of the 2 lb. mass due to the impact.

8. State the principle of the conservation of momentum, and describe a collision experiment to illustrate it.

For driving a pile, a heavy weight, the "monkey", is allowed to fall from a height on to the top of the pile. If the monkey weighs 500 lb. wt. and falls through 4 ft. on to a pile of weight 1,000 lb. wt., and there is no recoil, what will be the initial velocity of the pile? How much heat is produced at the impact? (Assume 1,400 ft. lb. wt. ≐ 1 lb. deg. C.) (*L.*)

9. Describe *either* Atwood's machine *or* Fletcher's trolley and experiments made with the one you describe to verify that the acceleration of a body is proportional to the force acting on it. (*L.*)

10A. State Newton's Laws of Motion. How can masses be compared by means of a ballistic balance?

A garden syringe ejects 10 c.c. of water a second through an orifice 1 mm. in diameter. Calculate the backwards thrust on the operator's hands. (*O. & C.*)

10B. Show that a body travelling in a straight line, initially moving with a velocity u and acceleration f, traverses a distance S in time t given by the expression

$$S = ut + \tfrac{1}{2}ft^2.$$

How would you test this relation experimentally for a body starting from rest and moving under a constant acceleration?

A body falls freely from the top of a cliff, and during the last second it falls 11/36 of the whole height. What is the height (in feet) of the cliff? (*C.*)

11. Distinguished between *mass* and *weight*. A body of mass 10 lbs. is transferred to the surface of the moon. Calculate (*a*) its weight, (*b*) the force required to give it an acceleration of 5 ft. per sec.^{2}, (*c*) the force required to keep it in uniform motion on a horizontal plane with a coefficient of friction 0·5. Assume that the gravitational acceleration on the moon is 6 ft. per sec.^{2}

A mass of 10 lbs. and specific gravity 2·5 is suspended, completely immersed in water, from a spring balance attached to the roof of a lift. What will be the reading of the balance (*a*) if the lift is moving up with an acceleration of 8 ft. per sec.^{2}, (*b*) if the lift is falling freely under gravity? (*O. & C.*)

12. What do you understand by the *conservation of energy*? Illustrate your answer by reference to the energy changes occurring (*a*) in a body whilst falling to and on reaching the ground, (*b*) in an X-ray tube.

The constant force resisting the motion of a car, of mass 1,500 kgm., is equal to one-fifteenth of its weight. If, when travelling at 48 km. per hour, the car is brought to rest in a distance of 50 metres by applying the brakes, find the additional retarding force due to the brakes (assumed constant) and the heat developed in the brakes. (*N.*)

13. Explain what is meant by the relative velocity of one moving object with respect to another.

A ship A is moving eastward with a speed of 15 knots and another ship B, at a given instant 10 nautical miles east of A, is moving southwards with a speed of 20 knots. How long after this instant will the ships be nearest to each other, how far apart will they be then, and in what direction will B be sighted from A? (*C.*)

14. State Newton's Second Law of Motion. Deduce from the law a definition of the unit of force.

A shot of mass 1 lb. strikes a fixed block of wood of mass 11 lb. with a given velocity and penetrates a distance of 6 inches. If the block had been free to move and the shot travelled along a line passing through the centre of mass of the block, how far would the shot have penetrated? (*W.*)

15. Explain what is meant by the principle of conservation of energy for a system of particles not acted upon by any external forces. What modifications are introduced when external forces are operative?

A bobsleigh is travelling at 30 m.p.h. when it starts ascending an incline of 1 in 100. If it comes to rest after travelling 500 ft. up the slope, calculate the proportion of the energy lost in friction and deduce the coefficient of friction between the runners and the snow. (*O. & C.*)

16. A bullet of mass 25 gm. and travelling horizontally at a speed of 200 metres sec.$^{-1}$ imbeds itself in a wooden block of mass 5 kgm. suspended

by cords 3 metres long. How far will the block swing from its position of
rest before beginning to return? Describe a suitable method of suspending
the block for this experiment and explain briefly the principles used in the
solution of the problem. (*L.*)

17. State Newton's Laws of Motion and deduce from them the relation
between the distance travelled and the time for the case of a body acted
upon by a constant force. Explain the units in which the various quantities
are measured.

A fire engine pumps water at such a rate that the velocity of the water
leaving the nozzle is 50 ft./sec. If the jet be directed perpendicularly on to a
wall and the rebound of the water be neglected, calculate the pressure on
the wall (1 cu. ft. water weighs 62·35 lb.). (*O. & C.*)

18. A point *A* moves with constant velocity *u* to the north, while a
point *B* moves with velocity *v* to the east. Explain how you would determine the velocity of *A* relative to *B*.

A road running north-south intersects a road running east-west. A car
travelling towards the crossing from the west at 20 m.p.h. is 200 yds. from
the crossing, when a second car, travelling at 30 m.p.h. towards the crossing
from the north, is 400 yds. from the crossing. What is the velocity of the
first car relative to the second, and what is the least distance that will
separate them? Where are the cars at the moment of closest approach?
(*W.*)

19. Derive an expression for the kinetic energy of a moving body.

A vehicle of mass 2 tons travelling at 30 m.p.h. on a horizontal surface is
brought to rest in a distance of 40 ft. by the action of its brakes. Calculate
the average retarding force. What horse-power must the engine develop
in order to take the vehicle up an incline of 1 in 10 at a constant speed of
30 m.p.h. if the frictional resistance is equal to 50 lb. wt.? (*L.*)

20. Define velocity and acceleration. A body is projected from a point
above level ground with a velocity of 64 ft. sec.$^{-1}$ at an angle of 60° above
the horizontal and takes 4 secs. to reach the ground. Calculate (*a*) the
height of the point of projection above the ground, (*b*) the horizontal
distance between the point of projection and the point at which the body
strikes the ground, (*c*) the maximum height reached by the body. (*L.*)

CHAPTER II

CIRCULAR MOTION

SIMPLE HARMONIC MOTION

1. Angular Velocity.

In the previous chapter we discussed the motion of an object moving in a straight line. There are numerous cases of objects moving in a *curve* about some fixed point. The earth and the moon revolve continuously round the sun, for example, and the rim of the balance-wheel of a watch moves to-and-fro in a circular path about the fixed axis of the wheel. In this chapter we shall study the motion of an object moving in a circle with a *uniform speed* round a fixed point O as centre, Fig. 19.

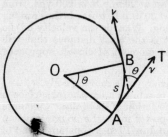

FIG. 19.   Circular motion.

If the object moves from A to B so that the radius OA moves through an angle θ, its *angular velocity*, ω, about O is defined as the *change of the angle per second*. Thus if t is the time taken by the object to move from A to B,

$$\omega = \frac{\theta}{t} \qquad . \qquad . \qquad . \qquad . \qquad . \qquad (14).$$

Angular velocity is usually expressed in "radians per second". From (14),

$$\theta = \omega t \qquad . \qquad . \qquad . \qquad . \qquad . \qquad (15).$$

which is analogous to the formula "distance = uniform velocity $\times$ time" for motion in a straight line. It will be noted that the time T to describe the circle once, known as the *period* of the motion, is given by

$$T = \frac{2\pi}{\omega}, \qquad . \qquad . \qquad . \qquad (16)$$

since 2π radians $= 360°$ by definition.

If s is the length of the arc AB, then $s/r = \theta$, by definition of an angle in radians.

32

$$\therefore \quad s = r\theta.$$

Dividing by t, the time taken to move from A to B,

$$\therefore \quad \frac{s}{t} = r\frac{\theta}{t}.$$

But $s/t =$ the *velocity*, v, of the rotating object, and θ/t is the angular velocity.

$$\therefore \quad v = r\omega \qquad . \qquad . \qquad . \qquad . \qquad (17).$$

2. Acceleration of Rotating Object.

When an object is whirled round in a circle at the end of a string, the force (tension) in the rope makes the object move in its path continuously. As we shall now see, the object has a constant *acceleration* towards the centre of the circle.

Suppose the object is at A at some instant; it is then moving with a velocity v along the tangent AT, Fig. 19. If the object moves to B in a small interval of time, the change in velocity along AT

$$= v \cos \theta - v = 0,$$

since θ is so small that $\cos \theta$ is practically equal to $\cos 0°$ or 1. There is, consequently, no acceleration along the tangent.

If we resolve the velocity v at B in a direction parallel to the radius OA, then

$$\text{change in velocity towards centre} = v \sin \theta.$$

$$\therefore \text{ acceleration towards centre} = \frac{v \sin \theta}{t},$$

where t is the time. But $\sin \theta = \theta$ in radians when θ is very small.

$$\therefore \text{ acceleration} = \frac{v\theta}{t} = v\omega,$$

since $\theta/t = \omega$. But $v = r\omega$.

$$\therefore \text{ acceleration} = \omega^2 r, \text{ or } \frac{v^2}{r} \qquad . \qquad . \qquad . \qquad . \qquad (18).$$

Thus the rotating object has a constant acceleration *towards the centre* equal to $\omega^2 r$ or v^2/r.

3. Central Forces.

When a stone of mass m at the end of a string is swung round in a horizontal circle of radius r with constant speed v, the force mv^2/r

towards the centre is provided by the tension in the string. This is known as the *centripetal force*. By Newton's law of action and reaction, a force of magnitude mv^2/r acts away from the centre on the support. It is known as the *centrifugal force*.

If some water is placed in a bucket attached to the end of a string, the bucket can be whirled in a vertical plane without any water falling out. When the bucket is vertically above the point of support, the weight mg of the water is now less than the required force mv^2/r towards the centre and so the water stays in. The reaction of the bucket base on the water provides the rest of the force. If $mg > mv^2/r$, part of the weight provides the force mv^2/r. The rest of the weight causes the water to accelerate downward and hence to leave the bucket.

Cream is separated from milk by rotating the mixture in a vessel. In this case the centrifugal force acting on the milk is greater than that on the cream at the same place, since the cream is less dense, and hence the milk moves away from the centre to the rim.

4. Motion of Bicycle Rider Round Circular Track.

When a person on a bicycle rides round a circular track, a frictional force F towards the centre is exerted at the ground, Fig. 20. If we now

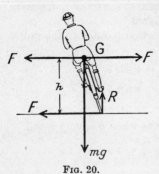

imagine two equal and opposite forces F at the centre of gravity G of the bicycle and rider, each parallel to the force F at the ground, we can see there is a force F at G towards the centre, which has a magnitude mv^2/r poundals, where m is the mass of bicycle and rider. There is also a *couple* (p. 81), tending to overturn the bicycle outwards, which has a moment $F \times h$, where h is the height of G above the ground. If the rider leans inwards towards the centre of the track, the normal reaction R at the ground is equal to mg poundals, since there is no

Fig. 20.

Bicycle rider on circular track.

motion vertically, and consequently there is now a restoring couple on the bicycle.

5. Motion of Car (or Train) Round Circular Track.

Suppose a car (or train) is moving with a velocity v round a horizontal circular track of radius r, and let R_1, R_2 be the respective normal reactions at the wheels A, B, and F_1, F_2 the corresponding frictional forces, Fig. 21. If we imagine two equal and opposite forces $(F_1 + F_2)$, at G, the centre of gravity of the car (or train), we have

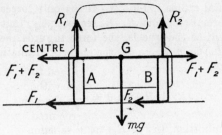

FIG. 21. Car on circular track.

$$F_1 + F_2 = \frac{mv^2}{r}, \qquad \cdots \qquad \text{(i)}$$

and
$$R_1 + R_2 = mg. \qquad \cdots \qquad \text{(ii)}$$

Also, taking moments about G,

$$(F_1 + F_2)h + R_1a - R_2a = 0 \qquad \cdots \qquad \text{(iii)},$$

where $2a$ is the distance between the wheels, assuming G is mid-way between the wheels, and h is the height of G above the ground. From these three equations, we find

$$R_2 = \tfrac{1}{2}m\left(g + \frac{v^2h}{ra}\right)$$

and
$$R_1 = \tfrac{1}{2}m\left(g - \frac{v^2h}{ra}\right).$$

R_2 never vanishes since it always has a positive value. But if $v^2 = arg/h$, $R_1 = 0$, and the car is about to overturn outwards. R_1 will be positive if $v^2 < arg/h$.

6. Motion of Car (or Train) Round Banked Track.

Suppose a ear (or train) is moving round a banked track in a circular

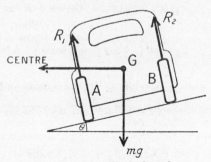

FIG. 22. Car on banked track.

path of horizontal radius r, Fig. 22. If the only forces at the wheels A, B are the normal reactions R_1, R_2 respectively, that is, there is no side-slip or strain at the wheels, the force towards the centre of the track is $(R_1 + R_2) \sin \theta$, where θ is the angle of inclination of the plane to the horizontal.

$$\therefore (R_1 + R_2) \sin \theta = \frac{mv^2}{r} \qquad . \qquad . \qquad . \qquad \text{(i)}$$

For vertical equilibrium, $(R_1 + R_2) \cos \theta = mg$ . . . (ii)

Dividing (i) by (ii), $\qquad \therefore \tan \theta = \dfrac{v^2}{rg}$ . . . (iii).

Thus for a given velocity v and radius r, the angle of inclination of the track for no side-slip must be $\tan^{-1}(v^2/rg)$. As the speed v increases, the angle θ increases, from (iii). A racing-track is made saucer-shaped because at higher speeds the cars can move towards a part of the track which is steeper and sufficient to prevent side-slip. The outer rail of a curved railway track is raised above the inner rail so that the force towards the centre is largely provided by the component of the reaction at the wheels. It is desirable to bank a road at corners for the same reason as a racing track is banked.

7. Thrust at Ground.

Suppose now that the car (or train) is moving at such a speed that the frictional forces at A, B are F_1, F_2 respectively, each acting towards the centre of the track (not shown in Fig. 22).

Resolving horizontally,

$$\therefore (R_1 + R_2) \sin \theta + (F_1 + F_2) \cos \theta = \frac{mv^2}{r} \qquad . \qquad . \qquad \text{(i)}$$

Resolving vertically,

$$\therefore (R_1 + R_2) \cos \theta - (F_1 + F_2) \sin \theta = mg \qquad . \qquad . \qquad \text{(ii)}$$

Solving, we find

$$F_1 + F_2 = m \left(\frac{v^2}{r} \cos \theta - g \sin \theta \right) \qquad . \qquad . \qquad . \qquad \text{(iii).}$$

If $\dfrac{v^2}{r} \cos \theta > g \sin \theta$, then $(F_1 + F_2)$ is positive; and in this case both the thrusts on the wheels at the ground are towards the centre of the track.

If $\dfrac{v^2}{r} \cos \theta < g \sin \theta$, then $(F_1 + F_2)$ is negative. In this case the forces $F_1 + F_2$ act outwards away from the centre of the track.

For stability, we have, by moments about G,

$$(F_1 + F_2)h + R_1 a - R_2 a = 0$$

$$\therefore (F_1 + F_2)\frac{h}{a} = R_2 - R_1$$

From (iii), $\quad \therefore \frac{mh}{a}\left(\frac{v^2}{r}\cos\theta - g\sin\theta\right) = R_2 - R_1 \quad . \quad . \quad$ (iv).

The reactions R_1, R_2 can be calculated by finding $(R_1 + R_2)$ from equations (i), (ii), and combining the result with equation (iv). This is left as an exercise to the student.

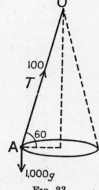

FIG. 23.

EXAMPLE

Explain the action of a centrifuge when used to hasten the deposition of a sediment from a liquid.

A pendulum bob of mass 1 kilogramme is attached to a string 1 metre long and made to revolve in a horizontal circle of radius 60 cm. Find the period of the motion and the tension of the string. (*C.*)

First part. See text, p. 34.

Second part. Suppose A is the bob, and OA is the string, Fig. 23. If T is the tension, and θ is the angle of inclination of OA to the horizontal, then, for motion in the circle,

$$T\cos\theta = \frac{mv^2}{r} = \frac{mv^2}{60} \quad . \quad . \quad . \quad$$ (i).

Since the bob A does not move in a vertical direction, then

$$T\sin\theta = mg \quad . \quad . \quad . \quad . \quad$$ (ii).

Now $\cos\theta = 60/100 = 3/5$; hence $\sin\theta = 4/5$.
From (ii),

$$\therefore T = \frac{mg}{\sin\theta} = \frac{1,000g}{4/5} = 1,250 \text{ gm. wt.}$$

From (i), $\qquad v = \sqrt{\dfrac{60\,T\cos\theta}{m}}$

$$= \sqrt{\frac{60 \times 1,250 \times 980 \times 3}{5 \times 1,000}} = 210 \text{ cm./sec.}$$

$$\therefore \text{ angular velocity, } \omega = \frac{v}{r} = \frac{210}{60} = \frac{7}{2} \text{ radians/sec.}$$

$$\therefore \text{ period, } T, = \frac{2\pi}{\omega} = \frac{2\pi}{7/2} = \frac{4\pi}{7} \text{ sec.}$$

$$\therefore T = 1 \cdot 8 \text{ sec.}$$

SIMPLE HARMONIC MOTION

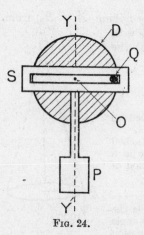

FIG. 24.

When the bob of a pendulum moves to-and-fro through a small angle, the bob is said to be moving with *simple harmonic motion*. The prongs of a sounding tuning fork, and the layers of air near it, are moving with simple harmonic motion, and light waves can be considered due to simple harmonic variations.

We can gain some insight into the analysis of simple harmonic motion by considering a mechanism sometimes used for actuating a pump-plunger P, Fig. 24. The slotted cage S is driven up and down by the pin Q, which rotates with the disc D about the axle O. Consequently the to-and-fro or simple harmonic motion of P is the *projection* of the circular motion of Q on the vertical line YY'.

8. Formulæ in Simple Harmonic Motion.

Consider an object moving round a circle of radius r and centre Z with a uniform angular velocity ω, Fig. 25. If CZF is a fixed diameter, the *foot* of the perpendicular from the moving object to this diameter moves

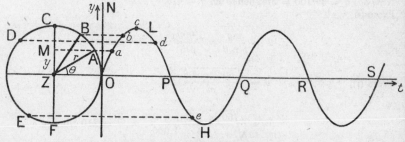

FIG. 25. Simple harmonic motion.

from Z to C, back to Z and across to F, and then returns to Z, while the object moves once round the circle from O in an anti-clockwise direction. The to-and-fro motion along CZF of the foot of the perpendicular is defined as *simple harmonic motion.*

Suppose the object moving round the circle is at A at some instant, where angle OZA $= \theta$, and suppose the foot of the perpendicular from A to CZ is M. The acceleration of the object at A is $\omega^2 r$, and this acceleration is directed along the radius AZ (see p. 33). Hence the acceleration of M towards Z

$$= \omega^2 r \cos \text{AZC} = \omega^2 r \sin \theta.$$

But $r \sin \theta = \text{MZ} = y$ say.

$$\therefore \text{ acceleration of M towards Z} = \omega^2 y.$$

Now ω^2 is a constant.

$$\therefore \textit{acceleration of M towards Z} \propto \textit{distance of M from Z.}$$

It we wish to express mathematically that the acceleration is always directed towards Z, we must say

$$\text{acceleration towards Z} = -\omega^2 y \qquad . \qquad . \qquad . \quad (19).$$

The minus indicates, of course, that the object begins to retard as it passes the centre, Z, of its motion. If the minus were omitted from equation (19) the latter would imply that the acceleration increases as y increases, and the object would then never return to its original position.

We can now form a definition of simple harmonic motion. If a particle is vibrating to-and-fro in such a way that its acceleration is directed towards a fixed point at any instant and is proportional to its distance from that point, the particle is moving with simple harmonic motion.

9. Period, Amplitude.   Sine Curve.

The time taken for the foot of the perpendicular to move from C to F and back to C is known as the *period* (T) of the simple harmonic motion. In this time, the object moving round the circle goes exactly once round the circle from C; and since ω is the angular velocity and 2π radians (360°) is the angle described, the period T is given by

$$T = \frac{2\pi}{\omega} \qquad . \qquad . \qquad . \qquad . \qquad . \qquad . \quad (20).$$

The distance ZC, or ZF, is the maximum distance from Z of the foot of the perpendicular, and is known as the *amplitude* of the motion. It is equal to r, the radius of the circle.

We have now to consider the variation with time, t, of the distance, y, from Z of the foot of the perpendicular. The distance $y = ZM = r \sin \theta$. But $\theta = \omega t$, where ω is the angular velocity,

$$\therefore y = r \sin \omega t \qquad . \qquad . \qquad . \qquad . \qquad (21).$$

The graph of y v.t is shown in Fig. 25, where ON represents the y-axis and OS the t-axis; since the angular velocity of the object moving round the circle is constant, θ is proportional to the time t. Thus as the foot of the perpendicular along CZF moves from Z to C and back to Z, the graph OLP is traced out; as the foot moves from Z to F and returns to Z, the graph PHQ is traced out. The graph is a *sine curve*. The complete set of values of y from O to Q is known as a **cycle**.

10. Velocity during S.H.M.

Suppose the object moving round the circle is at A at some instant, Fig. 25. The velocity of the object is $r\omega$, where r is the radius of the circle, and it is directed along the tangent at A. Consequently the velocity parallel to the diameter FC at this instant $= r\omega \cos \theta$, by resolving.

$$\therefore \text{ velocity, } v, \text{ of M along FC} = r\omega \cos \theta.$$

But
$$y = r \sin \theta$$

$$\therefore \cos \theta = \sqrt{1 - \sin^2 \theta} = \sqrt{1 - y^2/r^2} = \frac{1}{r} \sqrt{r^2 - y^2}$$

$$\therefore v = \omega \sqrt{r^2 - y^2} \qquad . \qquad . \qquad . \qquad . \qquad (22)$$

This is the expression for the velocity of an object moving with simple harmonic motion. The maximum velocity, v_m, corresponds to $y = 0$, and hence

$$v_m = \omega r.$$

Summarising our results for simple harmonic motion:

(1) If the acceleration of an object $= -\omega^2 y$, where y is the distance or displacement of the object from a fixed point, the motion is simple harmonic motion.

(2) The period, T, of the motion $= 2\pi/\omega$, where T is the time to make a complete to-and-fro movement.

(3) The amplitude, r, of the motion is the maximum distance on either side of the fixed point of the vibrating object.

(4) The velocity at any instant, v, $= \omega \sqrt{r^2 - y^2}$; the maximum velocity $= \omega r$.

EXAMPLE

What is *simple harmonic motion*? Show how it is related to the uniform motion of a particle with velocity v in a circle of radius a.

A steel strip, clamped at one end, vibrates with a frequency of 20 cycles per sec. and an amplitude of 5 mm. at the free end. Find (a) the velocity of the end when passing through the zero position, (b) the acceleration at the maximum displacement. (*L*.)

First part. For definition of simple harmonic motion, see p. 39. The foot of the perpendicular from the particle to the diameter moves with simple harmonic motion as the particle proceeds round the circle. See p. 39.

Second part. Suppose $y = r \sin \omega t$ represents the vibration of the strip where r is the amplitude.

(a) The velocity, v, $= \omega \sqrt{r^2 - y^2}$ (p. 40). When the end of the strip passes through the zero position $y = 0$; and the maximum speed, v_m, is given by

$$v_m = \omega r.$$

Now $\omega = 2\pi f = 2\pi \times 20$, and $r = 0.5$ cm.

$$\therefore v_m = 2\pi \times 20 \times 0.5 = 62.8 \text{ cm./sec.}$$

(b) The acceleration $= - \omega^2 y = - \omega^2 r$ at the maximum displacement.

$$\therefore \text{acceleration} = (2\pi \times 20)^2 \times 0.5$$

$$= 7{,}894 \text{ cm./sec.}^2$$

11. Simple Pendulum.

We shall now study some cases of simple harmonic motion. Consider a *simple pendulum*, which consists of a small mass m attached to the end of a length l of wire, Fig. 26. If the other end of the wire is attached to a fixed point P and the mass is displaced slightly, it oscillates to-and-fro along the arc of a circle of centre P. We shall now show that the motion of the mass about its original position O is simple harmonic motion.

Suppose that the vibrating mass is at B at some instant, where $OB = y$ and angle $OPB = \theta$. At B, the force pulling the mass towards O is directed along the tangent at B, and is equal to $mg \sin \theta$. The tension, T, in the wire has no component in this direction, since PB is perpendicular to the tangent at B. Thus, since force $=$ mass $\times$ acceleration (p. 13),

$$- mg \sin \theta = mf,$$

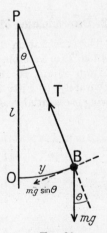

FIG. 26.
Simple pendulum.

where f is the acceleration along the arc OB; the minus indicates that the force is towards O, while the displacement, y, is measured along the arc from O in the opposite direction. *When θ is small, sin θ = θ in radians; also θ = y/l.* Hence,

$$- mg\theta = - mg\frac{y}{l} = mf$$

$$\therefore f = -\frac{g}{l}y = -\omega^2 y,$$

where $\omega^2 = g/l$. Since the acceleration is proportional to the distance y from a fixed point, the motion of the vibrating mass is simple harmonic motion (p. 40). Further, from p. 40, the period $T = 2\pi/\omega$.

$$\therefore \mathbf{T} = \frac{2\pi}{\sqrt{g/l}} = 2\pi\sqrt{\frac{l}{g}} \qquad . \qquad . \qquad . \qquad (23).$$

At a given place on the earth, where g is constant, the formula shows that the period T depends only on the length, l, of the pendulum. Moreover, the period remains constant even when the amplitude of the vibrations diminish owing to the resistance of the air. This result was first obtained by Galileo, who noticed a swinging lantern one day, and timed the oscillations by his pulse (there were no clocks in his day). He found that the period remained constant although the swings gradually diminished in amplitude.

12. Determination of g by Simple Pendulum.

The acceleration due to gravity, g, can be found by measuring the period, T, of a simple pendulum corresponding to a few different lengths, l, from 80 cm. to 180 cm. for example. To perform the experiment accurately: (i) Fifty oscillations should be timed, (ii) a small angle of swing is essential, less than 10°, (iii) a small sphere should be tied to the

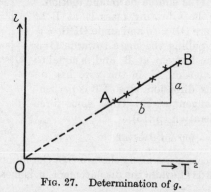

FIG. 27. Determination of g.

end of a thread to act as the mass, and its radius added to the length of the thread to determine l.

A graph of l against T^2 is now plotted, and a straight line AB, which should pass through the origin, is then drawn to lie evenly between the points, Fig. 27.

Now
$$T = 2\pi \sqrt{\frac{l}{g}},$$

$$\therefore T^2 = \frac{4\pi^2 l}{g}$$

$$\therefore \quad g = 4\pi^2 \times \frac{l}{T^2} \quad . \quad . \quad . \quad . \quad (24)$$

The gradient a/b of the line AB is the magnitude of l/T^2; and by substituting in (24), g can then be calculated.

13. Magnitudes of g.

The first determination of g was by the simple pendulum method. The magnitude of g, which is determined nowadays by much more accurate methods, varies all over the globe, according to the longitude and latitude, and altitude, of the place concerned. Some of the values obtained are shown below:

PLACE	g (CM. PER SEC.^{2})
National Physical Laboratory, London	981·181
Cavendish Laboratory, Cambridge	981·266
Greenwich Observatory	981·188
Washington	980·080
Paris Observatory	980·943
Cape Town Observatory	979·659
Melbourne	979·987
Potsdam	981·274
Ottawa	980·607
Calcutta	978·816

14. Proportionality of Weight and Mass.

The simple pendulum experiment can be used to show that the weight W of an object is directly proportional to its mass m. Consider again a vibrating object B of mass m. See Fig. 26, p. 41. Then, since force = mass × acceleration, and W is the weight acting vertically,

$$- W \sin \theta = mf.$$

But sin $\theta = \theta$ in radians when the angle is small; and $\theta = y/l$, where $y = OB$.

$$\therefore - W\frac{y}{l} = mf$$

$$\therefore f = - \frac{W}{ml}y = - \omega^2 y,$$

where $\omega^2 = W/ml$.

$$\therefore \text{period of motion}, \ T, \ = 2\pi\sqrt{\frac{ml}{W}}$$

$$\therefore \frac{T^2}{4\pi^2 l} = \frac{m}{W} \qquad . \qquad . \qquad . \qquad . \qquad (i)$$

Now experiment with varying lengths, l, of the simple pendulum reveals that the square of the period, T^2, is directly proportional to l, or $T^2/l = $ constant. See Fig. 27. Hence, from (i),

$$\frac{m}{W} = \text{constant}$$

$$\therefore W \propto m.$$

$$\therefore \text{weight of object} \propto \text{mass of object.}$$

15. Simple Pendulum Suspended from Inaccessible Point.

Suppose a simple pendulum is suspended from an inaccessible point, for example from the ceiling of a very tall room, the string reaching almost to the floor. If h is the height of the room and T_1 is the period, then

$$T_1 = 2\pi\sqrt{\frac{h}{g}} \qquad . \qquad . \qquad . \qquad (i)$$

To find the acceleration due to gravity, suppose a measured length a of the thread is cut off and the new period T_2 is measured. Then

$$T_2 = 2\pi\sqrt{\frac{h - a}{g}} \qquad . \qquad . \qquad . \qquad (ii).$$

From (i),
$$g\frac{T_1{}^2}{4\pi^2} = h,$$

and from (ii)
$$g\frac{T_2{}^2}{4\pi^2} = h - a.$$

Subtracting, $\therefore \dfrac{g}{4\pi^2}(T_1{}^2 - T_2{}^2) = a$

$$\therefore g = \frac{4\pi^2 a}{T_1{}^2 - T_2{}^2}.$$

Thus g can be calculated from measurements of a, T_1, and T_2. The height of the room is then given by $gT_1{}^2/4\pi^2$ from (i).

16. The Spiral Spring or Elastic Thread.

When a weight is suspended from the end of a spring or an elastic thread, experiment shows that the extension of the spring, i.e., the increase in length, is proportional to the weight, provided that the elastic limit of the spring is not exceeded (see p. 137). Generally, then, *the tension (force)*, T, *in a spring is proportional to the extension x produced*, i.e., $T = kx$, where k is a constant of the spring.

Consider a spring or an elastic thread PA of length l suspended from a fixed point P, Fig. 28. When a mass m is placed on it, the spring stretches to O by a length a given by

$$mg = ka, \qquad \cdots \qquad \text{(i)}$$

since the tension in the spring is then mg. If the mass is pulled down a little and then released, it vibrates up-and-down above and below O. Suppose at an instant that B is at a distance x below O. The tension T of the spring at B is then equal to $k(a + x)$, and hence the force towards $O = k(a + x) - mg$. Since force = mass $\times$ acceleration,

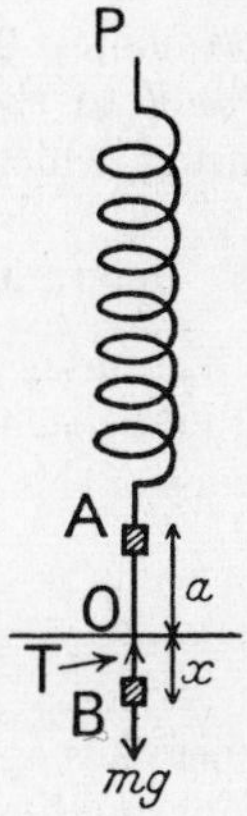

FIG. 28.
Spiral Spring

$$\therefore -[k(a + x) - mg] = mf;$$

the minus indicates that the net force is upward at this instant, whereas the displacement x is measured from O in the opposite direction at the same instant. From this equation,

$$-ka - kx + mg = mf.$$

But, from (i), $mg = ka$

$$\therefore -kx = mf$$

$$\therefore f = -\frac{k}{m}x$$

$$\therefore f = -\omega^2 x,$$

where $\omega^2 = k/m$. Thus the motion is simple harmonic about O, and the period T is given by

$$T = \frac{2\pi}{\omega} = 2\pi\sqrt{\frac{m}{k}} \quad \cdot \quad \cdot \quad \cdot \quad (25).$$

Also, since $mg = ka$, it follows that $m/k = a/g$.

$$\therefore T = 2\pi\sqrt{\frac{a}{g}} \quad \cdot \quad \cdot \quad \cdot \quad (26).$$

From (25), it follows that $T^2 = 4\pi^2 m/k$. Consequently a graph of T^2 v. m should be a straight line passing through the origin. In practice, when the load m is varied and the corresponding period T is measured, a straight line graph is obtained when T^2 is plotted against m, thus verifying indirectly that the motion of the load was simple harmonic. The graph does not pass through the origin, however, owing to the mass and the movement of the various parts of the spring, which has not been taken into account in the foregoing theory.

17. Determination of g by Spiral Spring.

The mass s of a vibrating spring should also be taken into account, in addition to the mass m suspended at the end. Theory beyond the scope of this book then shows that the period of vibration, T, is given by

$$T = 2\pi\sqrt{\frac{m + \lambda s}{k}} \quad \cdot \quad \cdot \quad \cdot \quad (i)$$

where λ is approximately $1/3$ and k is the elastic constant of the spring. Squaring (i) and re-arranging,

$$\therefore \frac{k}{4\pi^2} T^2 = m + \lambda s \quad \cdot \quad \cdot \quad \cdot \quad (ii)$$

Thus, since λ, k, s are constants, a graph of T^2 vs. m should be a straight line when m is varied and T observed. A straight line graph verifies indirectly that the motion of the mass at the end of the spring is simple harmonic. Further, the magnitude of $k/4\pi^2$ can be found from the slope of the line, and hence k can be calculated.

If a mass M is placed on the end of the spring, producing a steady extension a less than the elastic limit, then $Mg = ka$.

$$\therefore g = \frac{a}{M} \times k \quad \cdot \quad \cdot \quad \cdot \quad (iii)$$

By attaching different masses to the spring, and measuring the corresponding extension, the magnitude of a/M can be found by plotting a v. M and measuring the slope of the line. This is called the "static" experiment on the spring. From the magnitude of k obtained in the "dynamic" experiment when the period was determined for different loads, the value of g can be found by substituting the magnitudes of a/M and k in (iii).

18. Oscillations of a Liquid in a U-Tube.

If the liquid on one side of a U-tube T is depressed by blowing gently down that side, the levels of the liquid will oscillate for a short time about their respective initial positions O, C, before finally coming to rest, Fig. 29.

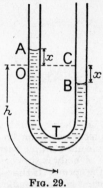

The period of oscillation can be found by supposing that the level of the liquid on the left side of T is at A at some instant, at a height x above its original (undisturbed) position O. The level B of the liquid on the other side is then at a depth x below its original position C, and hence the excess pressure on the whole liquid, as shown on p. 102,

FIG. 29.
Oscillation of liquid.

$$= \text{excess height} \times \text{density of liquid} \times g$$

$$= 2x\rho g.$$

Now pressure = force per unit area.
∴ force on liquid = pressure × area of cross-section of the tube

$$= 2x\rho g \times a,$$

where a is the cross-sectional area of the tube.

This force causes the liquid to accelerate. The mass of liquid in the U-tube = volume × density = $2ha\rho$, where $2h$ is the total length of the liquid in T. Now the acceleration, f, towards O or C is given by

$$\text{force} = \text{mass} \times f,$$

and hence

$$- 2x\rho ga = 2ha\rho f.$$

The minus indicates that the force towards O is opposite to the displacement measured from O at that instant.

$$\therefore f = - \frac{g}{h}x$$

$$= - \omega^2 x,$$

where $\omega^2 = \dfrac{g}{h}$. The motion of the liquid about O (or C) is thus simple harmonic, and the period T is given by

$$T = \frac{2\pi}{\omega} = 2\pi\sqrt{\frac{h}{g}} \qquad . \qquad . \qquad (27).$$

EXAMPLES

1. Define *simple harmonic motion* and state the relation between displacement from its mean position and the restoring force when a body executes simple harmonic motion.

A body is supported by a spiral spring and causes a stretch of 1·5 cm. in the spring. If the mass is now set in vertical oscillation of small amplitude, what is the periodic time of the oscillation? (*L.*)

First part. Simple harmonic motion is the motion of an object whose acceleration is proportional to its distance from a fixed point and is always directed towards that point. The relation is: Restoring force $= -k \times$ distance from fixed point, where k is a constant.

Second part. Let m be the mass of the body in grams. Then

$$mg = k \times 1\cdot5, \qquad . \qquad . \qquad . \qquad . \qquad . \qquad (i)$$

where k is a constant of the spring. Suppose the vibrating body is x cm. below its original position at some instant and is moving downwards. Then, since the extension is $(x + 1\cdot5)$ cm., the net downward force

$$= mg - k\,(x + 1\cdot5)$$
$$= mg - k \times 1\cdot5 - k\,x$$
$$= -k\,x,$$

from (i).   Now mass $\times$ acceleration $=$ force.

$$\therefore m \times \text{acceleration} = -k\,x$$

$$\therefore \text{acceleration} = -\frac{k}{m}\,x$$

But, from (i),
$$\frac{k}{m} = \frac{g}{1\cdot5}$$

$$\therefore \text{acceleration} = -\frac{g}{1\cdot5}\,x = -\omega^2 x,$$

where $\omega^2 = g/1\cdot5$.

$$\therefore \text{period } T = \frac{2\pi}{\omega} = 2\pi\sqrt{\frac{1\cdot5}{g}} = 2\pi\sqrt{\frac{1\cdot5}{980}}$$
$$= 0\cdot25 \text{ sec.}$$

2. The bob of a long pendulum is suspended by string from a point on the ceiling of a room, and observations of the period, T, with the height, l, of the bob above the floor are taken when the length of the pendulum is shortened by cutting off string. Explain how the height of the room, and the acceleration g due to gravity, can be determined from a suitable graph between T and l.

Suppose h is the height of the room. The length of the pendulum is then $(h - l)$, and hence

$$T = 2\pi \sqrt{\frac{h - l}{g}}.$$

Squaring, $$\therefore T^2 = \frac{4\pi^2}{g}h - \frac{4\pi^2 l}{g} \qquad . \qquad . \qquad . \qquad \text{(i)}$$

Since h and g are constants, it follows from (i) that *a straight line graph is obtained when T^2 is plotted against l*, Fig. 30. From (i), the slope, m, of the

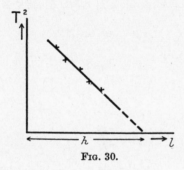

Fig. 30.

T^2 v. l graph is given numerically by $4\pi^2/g$. Thus

$$g = \frac{4\pi^2}{m},$$

and hence g can be calculated.

From (i), when T^2 is zero,

$$\frac{4\pi^2}{g}h - \frac{4\pi^2}{g}l = 0.$$

$$\therefore \ l = h \text{ in this case.}$$

The height h of the room is thus given by the intercept on the l-axis when the straight line graph is produced to intersect it (Fig. 30).

3. Define simple harmonic motion and show from your definition that the bob of a simple pendulum oscillates in simple harmonic motion provided its amplitude of vibration is small. Obtain an expression for the period.

A small bob of mass 50 gm. oscillates as a simple pendulum, with amplitude 5 cm. and period 2 sec. Find the velocity of the bob and the tension in the supporting thread, when the velocity of the bob is a maximum. (*W.*)

First part. See text.

Second part. The velocity, v, of the bob is a maximum when it passes through its original position. With the usual notation (see p. 40), the maximum velocity v_m is given by

$$v_m = \omega r,$$

where r is the amplitude of 5 cm. Since $T = 2\pi/\omega$,

$$\therefore \quad \omega = \frac{2\pi}{T} = \frac{2\pi}{2} = \pi \quad \cdot \quad \cdot \quad \cdot \quad \cdot \quad \cdot \quad \text{(i)}$$

$$\therefore v_m = \omega a = \pi \times 5 = 15 \cdot 7 \text{ cm. per sec.}$$

Suppose P is the tension in dynes in the thread. The net force towards the centre of the circle along which the bob moves is then given by $(P - mg)$, or $(P - 50g)$. The acceleration towards the centre of the circle, which is the point of suspension, is $v_m{}^2/l$, where l is the length of the pendulum.

$$\therefore P - 50g = \frac{50v_m{}^2}{l}$$

$$\therefore P = 50g + \frac{50v_m{}^2}{l}$$

Now
$$T = 2\pi\sqrt{\frac{l}{g}}$$

$$\therefore l = \frac{gT^2}{4\pi^2} = \frac{g \times 4}{4\pi^2} = \frac{g}{\pi^2}$$

$$\therefore P = 50g + \frac{50(5\pi)^2\pi^2}{g}, \text{ from above.}$$

$$= 50g + \frac{1250\pi^4}{g}$$

$$= 50 \cdot 13g \text{ dynes.}$$

$$\therefore P = 50 \cdot 13 \text{ gm. wt.}$$

GRAVITATION

19. Kepler's Laws.

The motion of the planets in the heavens had excited the interest of the earliest scientists, and Babylonian and Greek astronomers were able to predict their movements fairly accurately. It was considered for some time that the earth was the centre of the universe, but about 1542 COPERNICUS suggested that the planets revolved round the sun as centre. A great advance was made by KEPLER about 1609. He had studied for many years the records of observations on the planets made by TYCHO BRAHE, and he enunciated three laws known by his name. These state:

(1) The planets describe ellipses about the sun as one focus.

(2) The line joining the sun and the planet sweeps out equal areas in equal times.

(3) The squares of the periods of revolution of the planets are proportional to the cubes of their mean distances from the sun.

The third law was announced by Kepler in 1619.

20. Newton's Law of Gravitation.

About 1666, at the early age of 24, NEWTON discovered a universal law known as the *law of gravitation*.

He was led to this discovery by considering the motion of a planet moving in a circle round the sun as centre. The force acting on the planet of mass m is $mr\omega^2$, where r is the radius of the circle and ω is the angular velocity of the motion (p. 33). Since $\omega = 2\pi/T$, where T is the period of the motion,

$$\text{force on planet} = mr\left(\frac{2\pi}{T}\right)^2 = \frac{4\pi^2 mr}{T^2}.$$

This is equal to the force of attraction of the sun on the planet. *Assuming an inverse-square law*, then

$$\text{force on planet} = \frac{k}{r^2},$$

where k is a constant.

$$\therefore \frac{k}{r^2} = \frac{4\pi^2 mr}{T^2}$$

$$\therefore T^2 = \frac{4\pi^2 m}{k} r^3$$

$$\therefore T^2 \propto r^3,$$

since m, k, π are constants.

Now Kepler had announced that the squares of the periods of revolution of the planets are proportional to the cubes of their mean distances from the sun (see above). Newton thus suspected that *the force between the sun and the planet was inversely proportional to the square of the distance between them*. The great scientist now proceeded to test the inverse-square law by applying it to the case of the moon's motion round the earth. The moon has a period of revolution, T, about the earth of approximately 27·3 days, and the force on it $= mR\omega^2$, where R is the radius of the moon's orbit and m is its mass.

$$\therefore \text{force} = mR\left(\frac{2\pi}{T}\right)^2 = \frac{4\pi^2 mR}{T^2}.$$

If the planet were at the earth's surface, the force of attraction on it due to the earth would be mg, where g is the acceleration due to gravity. Assuming that the force of attraction varies as the inverse square of the distance between the earth and the moon,

$$\therefore \frac{4\pi^2 mR}{T^2} : mg = \frac{1}{R^2} : \frac{1}{r^2},$$

where r is the radius of the earth.

$$\therefore \frac{4\pi^2 R}{T^2 g} = \frac{r^2}{R^2},$$

$$\therefore g = \frac{4\pi^2 R^3}{r^2 T^2} \qquad . \qquad . \qquad . \qquad (28)$$

Newton substituted the then known values of R, r, and T, but was disappointed to find that the answer for g was not near to the observed value, 32 ft. per sec.[2] Some years later, he heard of a new estimate of the radius of the moon's orbit, and on substituting its value he found that the result for g was close to 32 ft. per sec.[2] Newton saw that a universal law could be formulated for the attraction between any two particles of matter. His *law of gravitation* states: *The force of attraction between two given masses is inversely proportional to the square of their distance apart.*

21. Gravitational Constant, G, and its Determination.

From Newton's law, it follows that the force of attraction, F, between two masses m, M at a distance r apart is given by $F \propto \dfrac{mM}{r^2}$.

$$\therefore F = G\frac{mM}{r^2}, \qquad . \qquad . \qquad . \qquad (29)$$

where G is a universal constant known as the *gravitational constant*.

G can be defined as numerically equal to the force in dynes between two masses of 1 gram placed 1 cm. apart, and its dimensions are given by $[G] = [F][r^2]/[mM] = [MLT^{-2} \times L^2]/[M^2] = [M^{-1}L^3T^{-2}]$.

A celebrated experiment to measure G was carried out by C. V. Boys in 1895, using a method similar to one of the earliest determinations of G by Cavendish in 1798. Two identical balls, a, b, of gold, 0·2 in. in diameter, were suspended by a long and a short fine quartz fibre respectively from the ends, C, D, of a highly-polished bar CD, Fig. 31. Two large identical lead spheres, A, B, $4\frac{1}{2}$ ins. in diameter, were brought into position near a, b respectively, and as a result of the

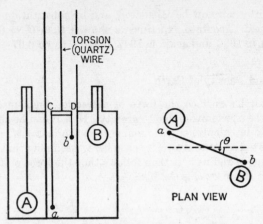

Fig. 31. Boys' experiment (*not to scale*).

attraction between the masses, two equal but opposite forces acted on CD. The bar was thus deflected, and the angle of deflection, θ, was measured by a lamp and scale method by light reflected from CD. The high sensitivity of the quartz fibres enabled the small deflection to be measured accurately, and the small size of the apparatus allowed it to be screened considerably from air convection currents.

22. Calculation for G.

Suppose d is the distance between a, A, or b, B, when the deflection is θ. Then if m, M are the respective masses of a, A,

$$\text{couple on } CD = G\frac{mM}{d^2} \times CD.$$

But   couple $= c\theta$,

where c is the couple in the torsion wire per unit radian of twist.

$$\therefore G\frac{mM}{d^2} \times CD = c\theta$$

$$\therefore G = \frac{c\theta d^2}{mM \times CD} \quad . \quad . \quad . \quad . \quad (i)$$

The constant c was determined by allowing CD to oscillate through a small angle and then observing its period of oscillation, T, which was of the order of 3 minutes. If I is the known moment of inertia of the system about the torsion wire, then (see p. 71),

$$T = 2\pi\sqrt{\frac{I}{c}}.$$

The constant c can now be calculated, and by substitution in (i), G can be determined. Accurate experiments showed that $G = 6\cdot66 \times 10^{-8}$ c.g.s. HEYL in 1930, and again in 1942, found G to be $6\cdot67 \times 10^{-8}$ c.g.s.

23. Mass and Density of Earth.

At the earth's surface the force of attraction on a mass m is mg, where g is the acceleration due to gravity. Now it can be shown that it is legitimate in calculations to assume that the mass, M, of the earth is concentrated at its centre, if it is a sphere. Assuming that the earth is spherical and of radius r, it then follows that the force of attraction of the earth on the mass m is GmM/r^2.

$$\therefore G\frac{mM}{r^2} = mg.$$

$$\therefore g = \frac{GM}{r^2}.$$

$$\therefore M = \frac{gr^2}{G}.$$

Thus if g, r, and G are known, the mass of the earth can be calculated; its magnitude is about $5\cdot3 \times 10^{27}$ grams.

The volume of a sphere is $4\pi r^3/3$, where r is its radius. Thus the density, ρ, of the earth is approximately given by

$$\rho = \frac{M}{V} = \frac{gr^2}{4\pi r^3 G/3} = \frac{3g}{4\pi rG}.$$

By substituting known values of g, G, and r, the density of the earth is found to be about $5\cdot5$ gm. per c.c.

It is now believed that gravitational force travels with the speed of light. Thus if the gravitational force between the sun and earth were suddenly to disappear by the vanishing of the sun, it would take about 7 minutes for the effect to be experienced on the earth, which would then fly off along a tangent to its original curved path.

EXAMPLE

Derive an expression for the acceleration of a particle moving along a circular path with uniform speed. Show how this expression, combined with the law of gravitation, leads to the relationship $\omega^2 R^3 = gr^2$, where ω is the mean angular velocity of the moon round the earth, R is the mean radius of the moon's orbit, and r is the radius of the earth. Given that $R = 60r$, and that the period of the moon's rotation around the earth is $27\frac{1}{2}$ days, find R. (C.)

First part. The acceleration $= \omega^2 r$, where r is the radius of the circle, and this is proved on p. 33.

Second part. Suppose M is the mass of the earth, m is the mass of the moon. Then, equating the force towards the centre (earth) to the gravitational pull on the moon, we have

$$G \frac{Mm}{R^2} = mR\omega^2$$

$$\therefore \omega^2 R^3 = GM \qquad . \qquad . \qquad . \qquad . \qquad . \qquad \text{(i)}$$

Now if an object of mass m_1 is situated on the earth's surface, its weight $= m_1 g =$ gravitational pull due to the earth's attraction.

$$\therefore \quad m_1 g = G\frac{Mm_1}{r^2}$$

$$\therefore \quad gr^2 = GM \qquad . \qquad . \qquad . \qquad . \qquad . \qquad \text{(ii)}$$

From (i) and (ii), $\quad \therefore \omega^2 R^3 = gr^2 \qquad . \qquad . \qquad . \qquad . \qquad \text{(iii)}.$

Third part. Since $\omega = \dfrac{2\pi}{T} = \dfrac{2\pi}{27\frac{1}{2} \times 24 \times 3600}$ radians per sec.,

$$\text{and } r = \frac{R}{60},$$

then, substituting in (iii),

$$\frac{4\pi^2}{(27\frac{1}{2} \times 24 \times 3600)^2} \times R^3 = 32 \times \frac{R^2}{60^2}$$

$$\therefore R = \frac{32 \times (27\frac{1}{2} \times 24 \times 3600)^2}{4\pi^2 \times 60^2}\text{feet}$$

$$= \frac{32 \times (27\frac{1}{2} \times 24 \times 3600)^2}{4\pi^2 \times 60^2 \times 5280}\text{miles}$$

$$= 240,000 \text{ miles}$$

EXERCISES II

(Assume $g = 32$ ft. per sec.^{2} or 980 cm. per sec.^{2})

Circular Motion; G

1. An object of mass 4 lb. moves round a circle of radius 6 ft. with a constant speed of 30 ft./sec. Calculate (i) the angular velocity, (ii) the force towards the centre.

2. An object of mass 10 lb. is whirled round a horizontal circle of radius 4 ft. by a revolving string inclined to the vertical. If the uniform speed of the object is 20 ft. per sec., calculate (i) the tension in the string in lb. wt., (ii) the angle of inclination of the string to the horizontal.

3. A racing-car of 15 cwt. moves round a banked track at a constant speed of 90 m.p.h. Assuming the total reaction at the wheels is normal to the track, and the horizontal radius of the track is 200 ft., calculate the angle of inclination of the track to the horizontal and the reaction at the wheels.

4. An object of mass 8 lb. is whirled round in a vertical circle of radius 4 ft. with a constant velocity of 20 ft. per sec. Calculate the maximum and minimum tensions in the string.

5. Calculate the force of attraction between two small objects of mass 5 and 8 kilograms respectively which are 10 cm. apart. ($G = 6\cdot7 \times 10^{-8}$ c.g.s.)

6. If the acceleration due to gravity is 980 cm. per sec.^{2} and the radius of the earth is $6\cdot4 \times 10^8$ cm., calculate a value for the mass of the earth. ($G = 6\cdot7 \times 10^{-8}$ c.g.s.) Give the theory.

7. Assuming that the mean density of the earth is 5·5 gm. per c.c., that the constant of gravitation is $6\cdot7 \times 10^{-8}$ c.g.s., and that the radius of the earth is $6\cdot4 \times 10^8$ cm., find a value for the acceleration due to gravity at the earth's surface. Derive the formula used.

8. Derive from first principles an expression for the acceleration of a particle describing a circular path with constant speed. Explain why it is desirable to bank the road at corners, and calculate the optimum angle of bank for a curve of radius r to be traversed at a speed v.
A train is travelling round a circular arc of radius 500 ft. which is not banked. The gauge of the railway is 4 ft. 9 in. and the height of the centre of gravity is 3 ft. 6 in. above the track. If there is no pressure on the inner rail, what is the speed of the train? (*O. & C.*)

9. A single pendulum hangs from the roof of a vehicle. During the motion of the vehicle in a horizontal circle of radius 160 ft. the pendulum hangs at an angle of 20° with the vertical. Show in a diagram the forces acting on the pendulum bob, and calculate the speed of the vehicle. Show that the free surface of a liquid contained in a vessel placed in the vehicle would be perpendicular to the pendulum. (*W.*)

10. Show that a body moving in a circle of radius r with speed v has an acceleration of v^2/r towards the centre of the circle. Describe a simple experiment which demonstrates this relation.

Either: Give examples where such an acceleration is made to serve a useful purpose and point out instances in ordinary life where its existence needs to be taken into account.

Or: Solve the following problem: Calculate the angle to the horizontal at which a curved railway track of radius of curvature 880 yd. needs to be "banked" so that the reaction on the track may be normal to the track when a train is travelling along it at 60 m.p.h. (*C.*)

11. Give an account of the torsion balance method of measuring Newton's constant of gravitation, G. Two pieces of apparatus A and B for measuring G by the torsion balance are made of similar materials, and are constructed so that the linear dimensions of all parts of A, except the torsion wires, are n times as great as the corresponding parts of B. The torsion wires are so chosen that the two suspended systems have equal periods. Compare the deflexions of the torsion bars of A and B.

Assuming that the moon describes a circular orbit of radius R about the earth in 27 days, and that Titan describes a circular orbit of radius $3.2R$ about Saturn in 16 days, compare the masses of Saturn and the earth. (O. & C.)

12. Assuming that the planets are moving in circular orbits, apply Kepler's laws to show that the acceleration of a planet is inversely proportional to the square of its distance from the sun. Explain the significance of this and show clearly how it leads to Newton's law of universal gravitation.

Obtain the value of g from the motion of the moon, assuming that its period of rotation round the earth is 27 days 8 hours and that the radius of its orbit is 60.1 times the radius of the earth. (Radius of earth = 6.36×10^6 metres.) (N.)

13. Explain what is meant by the *gravitation constant* (G), and describe an accurate laboratory method of measuring it. Give an outline of the theory of your method.

Assuming that the earth is a sphere of radius 6,370 kilometres and that $G = 6.66 \times 10^{-8}$ c.g.s. units, calculate the mean density of the earth. (O. & C.)

Simple Harmonic Motion

14. An object moving with simple harmonic motion has an amplitude of 2 inches and a frequency of 20 cycles per sec. Calculate (i) the period of oscillation, (ii) the acceleration at the middle and end of an oscillation, (iii) the velocities at the corresponding instants.

15. Calculate the length in centimetres of a simple pendulum which has a period of 2 seconds. If the amplitude of swing is 2 inches, calculate the velocity and acceleration of the bob (i) at the end of a swing, (ii) at the middle, (iii) 1 inch from the centre of oscillation.

16. Define *simple harmonic motion.* An elastic string is extended 1 inch when a small weight is attached at the lower end. If the weight is pulled down $\frac{1}{4}$ inch and then released, show that it moves with simple harmonic motion, and find the period.

17. A uniform wooden rod floats upright in water with a length of 2 ft. immersed. If the rod is depressed slightly and then released, prove that its motion is simple harmonic and calculate the period.

18. A simple pendulum, has a period of 4.2 sec. When the pendulum is shortened by 1 metre, the period is 3.7 sec. From these measurements, calculate the acceleration due to gravity and the original length of the pendulum.

19. What is *simple harmonic motion*? Show how it is related to the uniform motion of a particle with velocity v in a circle of radius r.

A steel strip, clamped at one end, vibrates with a frequency of 50 cycles per sec. and an amplitude of 8 mm. at the free end. Find (a) the velocity of the end when passing through the zero position, (b) the acceleration at the maximum displacement.

20. Define *simple harmonic motion.* A point P describes a circular path about a centre O with uniform angular velocity. Show that Q, the foot of the perpendicular drawn from P to a fixed diameter of the circle, executes a simple harmonic motion of period

$$T = 2\pi \sqrt{\frac{\text{Displacement of Q from O}}{\text{Acceleration of Q towards O}}}.$$

Hence, or otherwise, deduce an expression for the period of oscillation of a simple pendulum.

The point of suspension of a simple pendulum of original length l is fixed. The length of the pendulum is now adjusted so that the period of oscillation is (a) increased by 25%, (b) decreased by 25%. Find the corresponding changes in the height of the bob above the floor. (L.)

21. Explain what is meant by simple harmonic motion. Deduce an expression for the periodic time of the vertical oscillations of a mass suspended by a helical spring, the extension of which is proportional to the load. The mass of the spring may be neglected.

Describe in some detail how such an arrangement might be used to obtain an estimate of the acceleration due to gravity. (N.)

22. Define simple harmonic motion, and write down expressions for the velocity and the acceleration of a particle moving in simple harmonic motion of period T and amplitude a, when the displacement of the particle from the centre of the oscillation is x.

A body of mass 200 gm. is placed on a horizontal platform which oscillates vertically in simple harmonic motion of period 2 sec. and amplitude 5 cm. Find the maximum and minimum values of the force exerted by the body on the platform. What is the value of this force when the platform is moving through its central position? (W.)

23. What is meant by simple harmonic motion? Obtain an expression for the kinetic energy of a body of mass m, which is performing S.H.M. of amplitude a and period $2\pi/\omega$, when its displacement from the origin is x.

Describe an experiment, or experiments, to verify that a mass oscillating at the end of a helical spring moves with simple harmonic motion. (C.)

24. State the dynamical condition under which a particle will describe simple harmonic motion. Show that it is approximately fulfilled in the case of the bob of a simple pendulum, and derive, from first principles, an expression for the period of the pendulum.

Explain how it can be demonstrated from observations on simple pendulums, that the weight of a body at a given place is proportional to its mass. (O. & C.)

25. Define simple harmonic motion. Show that a heavy body supported by a light spiral spring executes simple harmonic motion when displaced vertically from its equilibrium position by an amount which does not exceed a certain value and then released. How would you determine experimentally the maximum amplitude for simple harmonic motion?

A spiral spring gives a displacement of 5 cm. for a load of 500 gm. Find the maximum displacement produced when a mass of 80 gm. is dropped from a height of 10 cm. on to a light pan attached to the spring. (N.)

26. Show that when a simple pendulum is slightly displaced from its position of equilibrium and then allowed to swing freely, it performs simple harmonic oscillations and determine their period.

The period of a simple pendulum is increased by 1/100 sec. when the length is increased by 1 cm. Find the original length of the pendulum. (*L.*)

27. Derive an expression for the period of oscillation of a body moving with simple harmonic motion in terms of its acceleration and displacement at any instant.

A weight, hanging from a fixed point by a light elastic string, is given a small vertical displacement and then released. If the extension of the string when the weight hangs at rest is *b*, find the period of the vertical oscillations of the weight. If *b* = 1·5 ins., what is the greatest velocity of the weight during an oscillation of amplitude 0·5 in.? (*W.*)

28. A test-tube of weight 6 gm. and external diameter 2 cm. is floated vertically in water by placing 10 gm. of mercury at the bottom of the tube. The tube is depressed by a small amount and then released. Find the time of oscillation. (*O. & C.*)

29. Define simple harmonic motion, and show that the total energy (kinetic and potential) of a particle executing simple harmonic motion is proportional (*a*) to the square of the amplitude, (*b*) to the square of the frequency.

The total energy of a particle executing a simple harmonic motion of period 2π sec. is 10,240 ergs. $\pi/4$ sec. after the particle passes the mid-point of the swing its displacement is $8\sqrt{2}$ cm. Calculate the amplitude of the motion and the mass of the particle. (*O. & C.*)

CHAPTER III

MOMENTS OF INERTIA

So far in this book we have considered the equations of motion and other dynamical formulæ associated with a particle. In practice, however, an object is made of millions of particles, each at different places, and we need now to consider formulæ for moving objects.

1. Moment of Inertia, I.

Suppose a rigid object is rotating about a fixed axis O, and a particle A of the object makes an angle θ with a fixed line OY in space at some instant, Fig. 32. The angular velocity, $d\theta/dt$ or ω, of every particle about O is the same, since we are dealing with a rigid body, and the velocity v_1 of A at this instant is given by $r_1\omega$, where $r_1 =$ OA. Thus the kinetic energy of A $= \frac{1}{2}m_1v_1^2 = \frac{1}{2}m_1r_1^2\omega^2$. Similarly, the kinetic energy of another particle of the body $= \frac{1}{2}m_2r_2^2\omega^2$, where r_2 is its distance from O and m_2 is its mass. In this way we see that the kinetic energy, K.E., of the whole object is given by

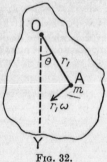

Fig. 32.
Rotating body.

$$\text{K.E.} = \frac{1}{2}m_1r_1^2\omega^2 + \frac{1}{2}m_2r_2^2\omega^2 + \frac{1}{2}m_3r_3^2\omega^2 + \ldots$$
$$= \frac{1}{2}\omega^2(m_1r_1^2 + m_2r_2^2 + m_3r_3^2 + \ldots)$$
$$= \frac{1}{2}\omega^2(\Sigma mr^2),$$

where Σmr^2 represents the sum of the magnitudes of "mr^2" for all the particles of the object. We shall see shortly how the quantity Σmr^2 can be calculated for a particular object. The magnitude of Σmr^2 is known as the *moment of inertia* of the object about the axis concerned, and we shall denote it by the symbol I. Thus

$$\text{Kinetic energy, K.E.,} = \frac{1}{2}I\omega^2. \qquad . \qquad . \qquad (30)$$

The kinetic energy of a particle of mass m moving with a velocity v is $\frac{1}{2}mv^2$. It will thus be noted that the formula for the kinetic energy of a rotating object is similar to that of a moving particle, the mass m being replaced by the moment of inertia I and the velocity v being replaced by the angular velocity ω.

2. Moment of Forces on a Rigid Body.

The force acting on the particle A in Fig. 32 $= m_1 \times$ acceleration $=$
$m_1 \times \dfrac{d}{dt} (r_1\omega) = m_1 \times r_1\dfrac{d\omega}{dt} = m_1 r_1\dfrac{d^2\theta}{dt^2}$, since $\omega = \dfrac{d\theta}{dt}$. The moment of
this force about the axis O $=$ force $\times$ perpendicular distance from
O $= m_1 r_1\dfrac{d^2\theta}{dt^2} \times r_1$, since the force acts perpendicularly to the line OA.

$$\therefore \text{moment} = m_1 r_1{}^2\frac{d^2\theta}{dt^2}.$$

$\therefore$ total moment of all forces on body about O

$$= m_1 r_1{}^2\frac{d^2\theta}{dt^2} + m_2 r_2{}^2\frac{d^2\theta}{dt^2} + m_3 r_3{}^2\frac{d^2\theta}{dt^2} + \ldots$$

$$= (\Sigma m r^2) \times \frac{d^2\theta}{dt^2},$$

since the angular acceleration, $d^2\theta/dt^2$, about OY is the same for all
particles.

$$\therefore \text{total moment about O} = I\frac{d^2\theta}{dt^2}, \qquad \ldots \quad (31)$$

where $I = \Sigma m r^2 =$ moment of inertia about O.

3. Angular Momentum.

The momentum of the particle A about O in Fig. 32 $=$ mass $\times$
velocity $= m_1 \times r_1\omega$. Consequently the *moment* of *the momentum*
about O, which is called the *angular momentum* about O,

$$= m_1 r_1\omega \times r_1 = m_1 r_1{}^2\omega.$$

$\therefore$ total angular momentum $= \Sigma m r^2\omega = \omega\Sigma m r^2$

$$= I\omega,$$

where I is the moment of inertia of the body about O.

Angular momentum is analogous to "linear momentum" in the
dynamics of a moving particle. Further, the conservation of angular
momentum, which corresponds to the conservation of linear momentum,
states that the angular momentum about an axis of a given rotating
body or system of bodies is constant if no external forces act. Thus
when a high diver jumps from a diving board, his moment of inertia
can be decreased by curling his body more, in which case his angular

velocity is increased, and he may then be able to turn somersaults. Similarly, a dancer on skates can spin faster by folding her arms.

We can now see that the formulæ for the kinetic energy of a rotating object, its angular momentum about an axis, and the moment about the axis of the forces acting on it all contain the moment of inertia, I. Before proceeding further, therefore, we shall calculate the moment of inertia of several objects about a particular axis.

4. Moment of Inertia of Uniform Rod.

(1) *About axis through middle.* The moment of inertia of a small element δx about an axis PQ through its centre O perpendicular to the length $= \left(\dfrac{\delta x}{l} M \right) x^2$, where l is the length of the rod, M is its mass, and x is the distance of the small element from O, Fig. 33.

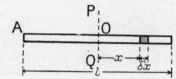

Fig. 33.   Moment of inertia of uniform rod.

$$\therefore \text{ moment of inertia, } I, = 2 \int_0^{l/2} \left(\frac{dx}{l} M \right) x^2$$

$$= \frac{2M}{l} \int_0^{l/2} x^2 dx = \frac{Ml^2}{12} \quad . \quad . \quad (32)$$

Thus if the mass of the rod is 60 gm. and its length is 20 cm., the moment of inertia $I = 60 \times 20^2/12 = 2000$ gm. cm.^{2}

(2) *About the axis through one end, A.* In this case, measuring distances x from A instead of O,

$$\text{moment of inertia, } I, = \int_0^l \left(\frac{dx}{l} M \right) \times x^2 = \frac{Ml^2}{3} \quad . \quad . \quad (33)$$

5. Moment of Inertia of Ring.

Every element of the ring is the same distance from the centre. Hence the moment of inertia about an axis through the centre perpendicular to the plane of the ring $= Ma^2$, where M is the mass of the ring and a is its radius.

6. Moment of Inertia of Circular Disc.

Consider the moment of inertia of a circular disc about an axis through its centre perpendicular to its plane, Fig. 34. If we take a small ring of the disc enclosed between radii x and $x + \delta x$, its mass $= \dfrac{2\pi x\, \delta x}{\pi a^2} M$, where a is the radius of the disc and M is its mass. Each element of the ring is distant x from the centre, and hence the moment of inertia of the ring about the axis through O $=$

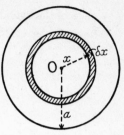

FIG. 34. Moment of inertia of circular disc.

$$\left(\frac{2\pi x\, \delta x}{\pi a^2} M \right) \times x^2$$

$\therefore$ moment of inertia of whole disc $= \displaystyle\int_o^a \frac{2\pi x\, dx}{\pi a^2} M \times x^2$

$$= \frac{Ma^2}{2} \qquad . \qquad . \qquad (34)$$

Thus if the disc weighs 60 gm. and has a radius of 10 cm., its moment of inertia $= 60 \times 10^2/2 = 3000$ gm. cm.^{2}.

7. Moment of Inertia of Cylinder.

If a cylinder is *solid*, its moment of inertia about the axis of symmetry is the sum of the moments of inertia of discs into which we may imagine the cylinder cut. The moment of inertia of each disc $= \frac{1}{2}$ mass $\times a^2$, where a is the radius; and hence, if M is the mass of the cylinder,

$$\text{moment of inertia of solid cylinder} = \tfrac{1}{2}Ma^2 \qquad . \qquad . \qquad (i)$$

If a cylinder is *hollow*, its moment of inertia about the axis of symmetry is the sum of the moments of inertia of the curved surface and that of the two ends, assuming the cylinder is closed at both ends. Suppose a is the radius, h is the height of the cylinder, and σ is the mass per unit area of the surface. Then

$$\text{mass of curved surface} = 2\pi ah\sigma,$$

and $\qquad$ moment of inertia about axis $= \text{mass} \times a^2 = 2\pi a^3 h\sigma,$

since we can imagine the surface cut into rings.

The moment of inertia of one end of the cylinder $= \text{mass} \times a^2/2 = \pi a^2\sigma \times a^2/2 = \pi a^4\sigma/2$. Hence the moment of inertia of both ends $= \pi a^4\sigma$.

$\therefore$ moment inertia of cylinder, I, $= 2\pi a^3 h\sigma + \pi a^4\sigma$.

The mass of the cylinder, M, $= 2\pi a h\sigma + 2\pi a^2\sigma$

$$\therefore I = \frac{2\pi a^3 h\sigma + \pi a^4\sigma}{2\pi a h\sigma + 2\pi a^2\sigma}\ M.$$

$$= \frac{2a^2 h + a^3}{2h + 2a}\ M.$$

$$= \tfrac{1}{2}Ma^2 + \frac{a^2 h}{2h + 2a}\ M \quad . \quad . \quad . \quad . \quad \text{(ii)}$$

If a hollow and a solid cylinder have the same mass M and the same radius and height, it can be seen from (i) and (ii) that the moment of inertia of the hollow cylinder is greater than that of the solid cylinder about the axis of symmetry. This is because the mass is distributed on the average at a greater distance from the axis in the former case.

8. Moment of Inertia of Sphere.

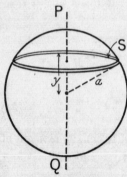

FIG. 35. Moment of inertia of sphere.

The moment of inertia of a sphere about an axis PQ through its centre can be found by cutting thin discs such as S perpendicular to the axis, Fig. 35. The volume of the disc, of thickness δy and distance y from the centre,

$$= \pi r^2\delta y = \pi(a^2 - y^2)\delta y.$$

$$\therefore \text{mass } M' \text{ of disc} = \frac{\pi(a^2 - y^2)\delta y}{4\pi a^3/3}\ M$$

$$= \frac{3M}{4a^3}\ (a^2 - y^2)\ \delta y,$$

where M is the mass of the sphere and a is its radius, since the volume of the sphere $= 4\pi a^3/3$. Now the moment of inertia of the disc about PQ

$$= M' \times \frac{\text{radius}^2}{2}$$

$$= \frac{3M}{4a^3}\ (a^2 - y^2)\ \delta y \times \frac{(a^2 - y^2)}{2}$$

$$\therefore \text{moment of inertia of sphere} = \frac{3M}{8a^3}\int_{-a}^{+a}(a^2 - y^2)^2 dy$$

$$= \frac{3M}{8a^3} \int_{a}^{+a} (a^4 - 2a^2y^2 + y^4)\,dy$$

$$= \frac{2}{5} Ma^2 \quad . \quad . \quad . \quad . \quad (35)$$

Thus if the sphere weighs 10 lb. and has a radius of 2 ft., the moment

of inertia $= \frac{2}{5} \times 10 \times 2^2 = 16$ lb. ft.^{2}.

9. Radius of Gyration.

The moment of inertia of an object about an axis, Σmr^2, is sometimes written as Mk^2, where M is the mass of the object and k is a quantity called the *radius of gyration* about the axis. For example, the moment of inertia of a rod about an axis through one end $= Ml^2/3$ (p. 62) $= M(l/\sqrt{3})^2$. Thus the radius of gyration, k, $= l/\sqrt{3} = 0.58l$. The moment of inertia of a sphere about its centre

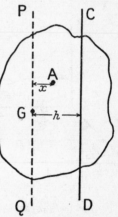

$= \frac{2}{5}Ma^2 = M \times \left(\sqrt{\frac{2}{5}}a\right)^2$. Thus the radius of

gyration, k, $= \sqrt{\frac{2}{5}}a = 0.63a$ in this case.

10. Relation Between Moment of Inertia About C.G. and Parallel Axis.

Suppose I is the moment of inertia of a body about an axis CD and I_G is the moment of inertia about a parallel axis PQ through the centre of gravity, G, distant h from the axis CD, Fig. 36. If A is a particle of mass m whose

Fig. 36. Moment of inertia and parallel axis.

distance from PQ is x, its moment of inertia about CD $= m(h - x)^2$.

$$\therefore I = \Sigma m(h - x)^2 = \Sigma mh^2 + \Sigma mx^2 - \Sigma 2mhx.$$

Now $\Sigma mh^2 = h^2 \times \Sigma m = Mh^2$, where M is the total mass of the object, and $\Sigma mx^2 = I_G$, the moment of inertia through the centre of gravity. Also, $\Sigma 2mhx = 2h\Sigma mx = 0$, since Σmx, the sum of the moments about the centre of gravity, is zero; this follows because the moment of the resultant (the weight) about G is zero.

$$\therefore I = I_G + Mh^2 \quad . \quad . \quad . \quad . \quad . \quad (36)$$

From this result, it follows that the moment of inertia, I, of a disc of radius a and mass M about an axis through a point on its circumference $= I_G + Ma^2$, since $h = a =$ radius of disc in this case. But $I_G =$ moment of inertia about the centre $= Ma^2/2$ (p. 63).

$$\therefore \text{ moment of inertia, } I, = \frac{Ma^2}{2} + Ma^2 = \frac{3Ma^2}{2}.$$

Similarly the moment of inertia of a sphere of radius a and mass M about an axis through a point on its circumference $= I_G + Ma^2 = 2Ma^2/5 + Ma^2 = 7Ma^2/5$, since I_G, the moment of inertia about an axis through its centre, is $2Ma^2/5$.

11. Relation Between Moments of Inertia about Perpendicular Axes.

Suppose OX, OY are any two perpendicular axes and OZ is an axis perpendicular to OX and OY, Fig. 37 (i). The moment of inertia, I, of

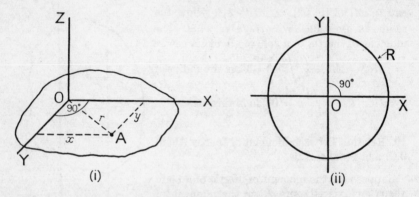

(i)   (ii)

FIG. 37. Moments of inertia and perpendicular axes.

a body about the axis $OZ = \Sigma mr^2$, where r is the distance of a particle A from OZ and m is its mass. But $r^2 = x^2 + y^2$, where x, y are the distances of A from the axis OY, OX respectively.

$$\therefore I = \Sigma m(x^2 + y^2) = \Sigma mx^2 + \Sigma my^2.$$

$$\therefore I = I_y + I_x, \qquad \cdot \quad \cdot \quad \cdot \quad \cdot \quad \cdot \quad \cdot \quad (37)$$

where I_y, I_x are the moments of inertia about OY, OX respectively.

As a simple application, consider a ring R and two perpendicular axes OX, OY in its plane, Fig. 37 (ii). Then from the above result,

$$I_y + I_x = I = \text{moment of inertia through O perpendicular to ring.}$$

$$\therefore I_y + I_x = Ma^2.$$

But $I_y = I_x$, by symmetry.

$$\therefore I_x + I_x = Ma^2,$$

$$\therefore I_x = \frac{Ma^2}{2}.$$

This is the moment of inertia of the ring about any diameter in its plane.

In the same way, the moment of inertia, I, of a disc about a diameter in its plane is given by

$$I + I = \frac{Ma^2}{2},$$

since the moments of inertia, I, about the two perpendicular diameters are the same and $Ma^2/2$ is the moment of inertia of the disc about an axis perpendicular to its plane.

$$\therefore 2I = \frac{Ma^2}{2}$$

$$\therefore I = \frac{Ma^2}{4}.$$

12. Kinetic Energy of a Rolling Object.

When an object such as a cylinder or ball rolls on a plane, the object is rotating as well as moving bodily along the plane; therefore it has rotational energy as well as translational energy.

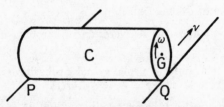

FIG. 38.   Rolling object.

Consider a cylinder C rolling along a plane without slipping, Fig. 38. At any instant the line of contact, PQ, with the plane is at rest, and we can consider the whole of the cylinder to be rotating about this axis. Hence the energy of the cylinder $= \frac{1}{2}I_1\omega^2$, where I_1 is the moment of inertia about PQ and ω is the angular velocity.

But if I is the moment of inertia about a parallel axis through the centre of gravity of the cylinder, M is the mass of the cylinder and a its radius, then

$$I_1 = I + Ma^2,$$

from the result on p. 65.

$$\therefore \text{ energy of cylinder } = \tfrac{1}{2}(I + Ma^2)\omega^2$$
$$= \tfrac{1}{2}I\omega^2 + \tfrac{1}{2}Ma^2\omega^2$$
$$\therefore \text{Energy} = \tfrac{1}{2}I\omega^2 + \tfrac{1}{2}Mv^2 \qquad . \qquad . \qquad (38)$$

since, by considering the distance rolled and the angle then turned, $v = a\omega = $ velocity of centre of gravity. This energy formula is true for any moving object.

As an application of the energy formula, suppose a *ring* rolls along a plane. The moment of inertia about the centre of gravity, its centre, $= Ma^2$ (p. 62); also, the angular velocity, ω, about its centre $= v/a$, where v is the velocity of the centre of gravity.

$$\therefore \text{ kinetic energy of ring } = \tfrac{1}{2}Mv^2 + \tfrac{1}{2}I\omega^2$$

$$= \tfrac{1}{2}Mv^2 + \tfrac{1}{2}Ma^2 \times \left(\frac{v}{a}\right)^2 = Mv^2.$$

By similar reasoning, the kinetic energy of a sphere rolling down a plane

$$= \tfrac{1}{2}Mv^2 + \tfrac{1}{2}I\omega^2$$

$$= \tfrac{1}{2}Mv^2 + \tfrac{1}{2} \times \frac{2}{5}Ma^2 \times \left(\frac{v}{a}\right)^2 = \frac{7}{10}\,Mv^2,$$

since $I = 2Ma^2/5$ (p. 64).

13. Acceleration of Rolling Object.

We can now deduce the acceleration of a rolling object down an inclined plane.

As an illustration, suppose a solid cylinder rolls down a plane. Then
$$\text{kinetic energy} = \tfrac{1}{2}Mv^2 + \tfrac{1}{2}I\omega^2.$$

But moment of inertia, I, about an axis through the centre of gravity parallel to the plane $= \tfrac{1}{2}Ma^2$, and $\omega = v/a$, where a is the radius.

$$\therefore \quad \text{kinetic energy} = \tfrac{1}{2}Mv^2 + \tfrac{1}{4}Mv^2 = \tfrac{3}{4}Mv^2.$$

If the cylinder rolls from *rest* through a distance s, the loss of potential energy $= Mgs \sin \alpha$, where α is the inclination of the plane to the horizontal.

$$\therefore \tfrac{3}{4}Mv^2 = Mgs \sin \alpha$$

$$\therefore v^2 = \frac{4g}{3} s \sin \alpha$$

But
$$v^2 = 2fs.$$

$$\therefore 2fs = \frac{4g}{3} s \sin \alpha$$

$$\therefore f = \frac{2g}{3} \sin \alpha \qquad . \quad . \quad . \qquad \text{(i)}$$

The acceleration if *sliding*, and no rolling, took place down the plane is $g \sin \alpha$. The cylinder has thus a smaller acceleration when rolling.

The time t taken to move through a distance s from rest is given by $s = \frac{1}{2} f t^2$. Thus, from (i),

$$s = \tfrac{1}{3} g t^2 \sin \alpha,$$

$$\text{or} \quad t = \sqrt{\frac{3s}{g \sin \alpha}}.$$

If the cylinder is *hollow*, instead of solid as assumed, the moment of inertia about an axis through the centre of gravity parallel to the plane is greater than that for a solid cylinder, assuming the same mass and dimensions (p. 64). The time taken for a hollow cylinder to roll a given distance from rest on the plane is then greater than that taken by the solid cylinder, from reasoning similar to that above; and thus if no other means were available, a time test on an inclined plane will distinguish between a solid and a hollow cylinder of the same dimensions and mass. If a torsion wire is available, however, the cylinders can be suspended in turn, and the period of torsional oscillations determined. The cylinder of larger moment of inertia, the hollow cylinder, will have a greater period, as explained on p. 71.

14. Period of Oscillation of Rigid Body.

On p. 61 we showed that the moment of the forces acting on rotating objects $= I d\omega/dt = I d^2\theta/dt^2$, where I is the moment of inertia about the axis concerned and $d^2\theta/dt^2$ is the angular acceleration about the axis. Consider a rigid body oscillating about a fixed axis O, Fig. 39. The moment of the weight mg (the only external force) about O is $mgh \sin \theta$, or $mgh\theta$ if θ is small, where h is the distance of the centre of gravity from O.

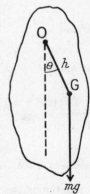

Fig. 39. Oscillation of rigid body.

$$\therefore I\frac{d^2\theta}{dt^2} = - mgh\,\theta,$$

the minus indicating that the moment due to the weight always *opposes* the growth of the angle θ.

$$\therefore \frac{d^2\theta}{dt^2} = \frac{- mgh}{I}\,\theta = - \omega^2\theta,$$

where $\omega^2 = mgh/I$.

$\therefore$ the motion is simple harmonic motion (p. 40),

and   period, $T, = \dfrac{2\pi}{\omega} = \dfrac{2\pi}{\sqrt{mgh/I}} = 2\pi\sqrt{\dfrac{I}{mgh}}$ . . . (39)

If $I = mk_1{}^2$, where k_1 is the radius of gyration about O,

$$T = 2\pi\sqrt{\frac{mk_1{}^2}{mgh}} = \sqrt{\frac{k_1{}^2}{gh}} \quad . \quad . \quad . \quad . \quad (40)$$

15. Compound Pendulum. Since $I = I_G + mh^2 = mk^2 + mh^2$, where I_G is the moment of inertia about the centre of gravity, h is the distance of the axis O from the centre of gravity, and k is the radius of gyration about the centre of gravity, then, from (39),

$$T = 2\pi\sqrt{\frac{I}{mgh}} = 2\pi\sqrt{\frac{mk^2 + mh^2}{mgh}}.$$

$$\therefore T = 2\pi\sqrt{\frac{k^2 + h^2}{gh}}.$$

Hence $T = 2\pi\sqrt{\dfrac{l}{g}}$,

where $l = \dfrac{k^2 + h^2}{h}$ . . . . (i).

Thus $(k^2 + h^2)/h$ is the length, l, of the *equivalent simple pendulum*.

From (i), $h^2 - hl + k^2 = 0$.

$$\therefore h_1 + h_2 = l, \text{ and } h_1 h_2 = k^2,$$

where h_1 and h_2 are the roots of the equation.

By timing the period of vibration, T, of a long rod about a series of axes at varying distances h on either side of the centre of gravity, and then plotting a graph of T vs . h, two different values of h giving the same period can be obtained, Fig. 40. Suppose h_1, h_2 are the two values. Then, from the result just obtained, $h_1 + h_2 = l$, the length of the equivalent simple pendulum. Thus, since $T = 2\pi \sqrt{l/g}$,

$$g = \frac{4\pi^2 l}{T^2} = \frac{4\pi^2(h_1 + h_2)}{T^2}.$$

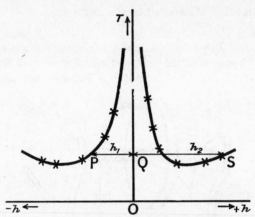

FIG. 40. Compound pendulum graph.

In Fig. 40, $PQ + QS = h_1 + h_2 = i$.

The compound pendulum can provide a very accurate determination of "g". For details of the experiment the reader should consult a text-book of practical physics, such as *Advanced Practical Physics for Students* by Worsnop and Flint (Methuen). See also p. 186.

16. Measurement of Moment of Inertia of Plate.

The moment of inertia of a circular disc or other plate about an axis perpendicular to its plane, for example, can be measured by means of torsional oscillations. The plate is suspended horizontally from a vertical torsion wire, and the period T_1 of torsional oscillations is measured. Then, from (39),

$$T_1 = 2\pi \sqrt{\frac{I_1}{c}}, \qquad \text{.} \qquad \text{.} \qquad \text{.} \qquad \text{(i)}$$

where I_1 is the moment of inertia and c is the constant (opposing couple per unit radian) of the wire (p. 146). A ring or annulus of *known* moment of inertia I_2 is now placed on the plate concentric with the axis, and the new period T_2 is observed. Then

$$T_2 = 2\pi \sqrt{\frac{I_1 + I_2}{c}} \qquad \text{.} \qquad \text{.} \qquad \text{.} \qquad \text{(ii).}$$

By squaring (i) and (ii), and then eliminating c, we obtain

$$I_1 = \frac{T_1{}^2}{T_2{}^2 - T_1{}^2} \cdot I_2.$$

Thus knowing T_1, T_2, and I_2, the moment of inertia I_1 can be calculated.

17. Measurement of Moment of Inertia of Flywheel.

The moment of inertia of a flywheel W about a horizontal axle A can be determined by tying one end of some string to a pin on the axle, winding the string round the axle, and attaching a mass M to the other end of the string, Fig. 41. The length of string is such that M reaches

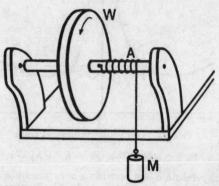

FIG. 41. Moment of inertia of fly-wheel.

the floor, when released, at the same instant as the string is completely unwound from the axle.

M is released, and the number of revolutions, n, made by the wheel W up to the occasion when M strikes the ground is noted. The further number of revolutions n_1 made by W until it comes finally to rest, and the time t taken, are also observed by means of a chalk-mark on W.

Now the loss in potential energy of M = gain in kinetic energy of M + gain in kinetic energy of flywheel + work done against friction.

$$\therefore Mgh = \tfrac{1}{2}Mr^2\omega^2 + \tfrac{1}{2}I\omega^2 + nf, \qquad . \qquad . \qquad . \qquad \text{(i)}$$

where h is the distance M has fallen, r is the radius of the axle, ω is the angular velocity, I is the moment of inertia, and f is the energy per turn expended against friction. Since the energy of rotation of the flywheel when the mass M reaches the ground = work done against friction in n_1 revolutions,

$$\tfrac{1}{2}I\omega^2 = n_1 f.$$

$$\therefore f = \tfrac{1}{2}\frac{I\omega^2}{n_1}.$$

Substituting for f in (i),

$$\therefore Mgh = \tfrac{1}{2}Mr^2\omega^2 + \tfrac{1}{2}I\omega^2\left(1 + \frac{n}{n_1}\right) \qquad . \qquad . \qquad \text{(ii)}$$

Since the angular velocity of the wheel when M reaches the ground is ω, and the final angular velocity of the wheel is zero after a time t, the average angular velocity $= \omega/2 = 2\pi n_1/t$. Thus $\omega = 4\pi n_1/t$. Knowing ω and the magnitude of the other quantities in (ii), the moment of inertia I of the flywheel can be calculated.

EXAMPLES

1. A solid cylinder (i) slides down, (ii) rolls down a smooth plane inclined at 30° to the horizontal without slipping. Compare the accelerations down the plane in each case if the cylinder starts from rest.

(i) When the cylinder slides down the plane, its acceleration down the plane, f, $= g \sin 30° = 32 \sin 30° = 16$ ft. per sec.²

(ii) When the cylinder rolls down the plane, its gain of kinetic energy

$$= \tfrac{1}{2}I\omega^2 + \tfrac{1}{2}Mv^2 \text{ (p. 68)}$$

$$= \tfrac{1}{2}(\tfrac{1}{2}Ma^2)\left(\frac{v}{a}\right)^2 + \tfrac{1}{2}Mv^2,$$

since I = moment of inertia about centre of gravity $= Ma^2/2$ and $\omega = v/a$.

$$\therefore \text{ gain of kinetic energy } = \tfrac{3}{4}Mv^2.$$

But loss of potential energy $= Mgs \sin 30°$, where s is the distance travelled along the plane.

$$\therefore \tfrac{3}{4}Mv^2 = Mgs \sin 30°.$$

$$\therefore v^2 = \frac{4g}{3}s \sin 30°.$$

But $\qquad\qquad v^2 = 2fs,$

where f is the acceleration, since the initial velocity is zero.

$$\therefore 2fs = \frac{4g}{3}s \sin 30°$$

$$\therefore f = \frac{2g}{3}\sin 30° = \frac{2 \times 32}{3}\sin 30°$$

$$= 10\tfrac{2}{3} \text{ ft. per sec.}^2$$

$\therefore$ ratio of accelerations $= 16 : 10\tfrac{2}{3} = 3 : 2.$

2. Calculate the period of oscillation of (i) a uniform rod 12 ft. long about one end, (ii) a hoop of radius 2 ft. about an axis through its circumference perpendicular to its plane. What is the length of the equivalent simple pendulum in each case?

(i) The period of oscillation of the rod, T, $= 2\pi\sqrt{\dfrac{I}{mgh}}$ (p. 70).

But $I = ml^2/3$, where l is the length of the rod (p. 62), and $h =$ distance of centre of gravity from axis $= l/2$.

$$\therefore T = 2\pi\sqrt{\frac{ml^2/3}{mgl/2}} = 2\pi\sqrt{\frac{2\,l}{3\,g}} \qquad \cdot \quad \cdot \quad \cdot \quad \cdot \qquad \text{(i)}$$

$$= 2\pi\sqrt{\frac{2}{3} \times \frac{12}{32}} = 3 \cdot 14 \text{ sec.}$$

The simple pendulum period, $T = 2\pi\sqrt{\dfrac{\text{length.}}{g}}$ From (i) it follows that

length of equivalent simple pendulum $= \dfrac{2}{3}l = \dfrac{2}{3} \times 12 = 8$ ft.

(ii) The moment of inertia, I, of the hoop about an axis through its circumference $= I_G + Mh^2 = Ma^2 + Ma^2$, since $I_G = Ma^2$ and $h = a$ (see p. 65).

$$\therefore I = 2Ma^2$$

$$\therefore \text{period, } T, = 2\pi\sqrt{\frac{I}{Mgh}} = 2\pi\sqrt{\frac{2Ma^2}{Mga}}.$$

$$= 2\pi\sqrt{\frac{2a}{g}} = 2\pi\sqrt{\frac{2 \times 2}{32}} = 2 \cdot 2 \text{ sec.}$$

Since period, T, of simple pendulum $= 2\pi\sqrt{\dfrac{\text{length}}{g}}$,

length of equivalent simple pendulum $= 2a = 4$ ft.

3. Define the moment of inertia of a body about a given axis. Describe how the moment of inertia of a fly-wheel can be determined experimentally.

A horizontal disc rotating freely about a vertical axis makes 100 r.p.m. A small piece of wax of mass 10 gm. falls vertically on to the disc and adheres to it at a distance of 9 cm. from the axis. If the number of revolutions per minute is thereby reduced to 90, calculate the moment of inertia of the disc. (*N.*)

First part. See text.

Second part. Let $I =$ moment of inertia of disc. Then if ω_1, ω_2 are the initial and final angular velocities,
the respective angular momentum about the axis $= I\omega_1$, $I\omega_2$ (p. 61). The angular momentum of the wax about the axis $= mr\omega_2 \times r = mr^2\omega_2$,

where $r = 9$ cm., $m = 10$ gm. Since the angular momentum is constant,

$$\therefore I\omega_1 = I\omega_2 + mr^2\omega_2$$

$$\therefore I(\omega_1 - \omega_2) = mr^2\omega_2$$

$$\therefore I = mr^2\left(\frac{\omega_2}{\omega_1 - \omega_2}\right)$$

$$= 10 \times 9^2 \times \left(\frac{90}{100 - 90}\right), \text{ from above,}$$

$$= 7,290 \text{ gm. cm}^2.$$

EXERCISES III

1. A uniform rod has a mass of 60 gm. and a length a 20 cm. Calculate the moment of inertia about an axis perpendicular to its length (i) through its centre, (ii) through one end. Prove the formulæ used.

2. What is the *Theorem of Parallel Axes?* A uniform disc has a mass of 4 lb. and a radius of 6 ft. Calculate the moment of inertia about an axis perpendicular to its plane (i) through its centre, (ii) through a point of its circumference.

3. What is the *Theorem of Perpendicular Axes?* A ring has a radius of 20 cm. and a mass of 100 gm. Calculate the moment of inertia about an axis (i) perpendicular to its plane through its centre, (ii) perpendicular to its plane passing through a point on its circumference, (iii) in its plane passing through the centre.

4. What is the formula for the kinetic energy of (i) a particle, (ii) a rigid body rotating about an axis through its centre of gravity, (iii) a rigid body rotating about an axis through any point? Calculate the kinetic energy of a disc of mass 5 lb. and radius 2 ft. rolling along a plane with a uniform velocity of 10 ft. per sec.

5. A sphere rolls down a plane inclined at 30° to the horizontal. Find the acceleration and velocity of the sphere after it has moved 16 ft. from rest along the plane, assuming the moment of inertia of a sphere about a diameter is $2Ma^2/5$, where M is the mass and a is the radius.

6. A uniform rod of length 9 ft. is suspended at one end so that it can move about an axis perpendicular to its length, and is held inclined at 60° to the vertical and then released. Calculate the angular velocity of the rod when (i) it is inclined at 30° to the vertical, (ii) reaches the vertical.

7. Define the *moment of inertia* of a rigid object about an axis.
A ring of radius 6 ft. oscillates about an axis on its circumference which is perpendicular to the plane of the ring. Calculate the period of oscillation. Give an explanation of any formula used.

8 Derive an expression for the moment of inertia of a uniform circular disc of mass M, radius r, about a central axis perpendicular to its plane. How would you determine this moment of inertia experimentally?

A circular disc of mass 800 gm., radius 10 cm., is suspended by a wire through its centre perpendicular to its plane and makes 50 torsional oscillations in 59·8 sec. When an annulus is placed symmetrically on the disc, the system makes 50 oscillations in 66·4 sec. Calculate the moment of inertia of the annulus about the axis of rotation. (*N*.)

9. What is meant by "moment of inertia"? Explain the importance of this concept in dealing with problems concerning rotating bodies.
Describe, with practical details, how you would determine whether a given cylindrical body were hollow or not without damaging it. (*C*.)

10. Define *moment of inertia*, and find an expression for the kinetic energy of a rigid body rotating about a fixed axis.
A sphere, starting from rest, rolls (without slipping) down a rough plane inclined to the horizontal at an angle of 30°, and it is found to travel a distance of 1,350 cm. in the first 3 secs. of its motion. Assuming that *F*, the frictional resistance to the motion, is independent of the speed, calculate the ratio of *F* to the *weight* of the sphere. (For a sphere of mass *m* and radius *r*, the moment of inertia about a diameter is $\frac{2}{5}mr^2$.) (*O*. & *C*.)

11. Obtain an expression for the moment of inertia of a uniform circular cylinder of mass M and radius *a* about its axis. If such a cylinder is set in rotation about its axis with angular velocity ω, find its kinetic energy.
A uniform circular disc of mass 500 gm. and radius 50 cm. can rotate in its own plane about a fixed horizontal axis passing through a point on its circumference. If the disc is pulled aside until its centre of gravity is on the same horizontal level as the axis and then released, find the linear velocity of the centre of gravity as it passes through its equilibrium position. (*W*.)

12. A flat plate of irregular shape is pierced by a number of small holes, distributed at random, through which a knitting needle can pass easily. Describe how, using the plate and the needle, you would find the acceleration due to gravity and give the theory of the method.
A thin uniform rod swings as a pendulum about a horizontal axis at one end, the periodic time being 1·65 sec. If the mass of the rod is 125 gm., what is (*a*) its length, (*b*) its moment of inertia about the horizontal axis? (*N*.)

13. Explain the meaning of the term *moment of inertia*. Describe in detail how you would find experimentally the moment of inertia of a bicycle wheel about the central line of its hub.
A uniform cylinder 20 cm. long, suspended by a steel wire attached to its mid-point so that its long axis is horizontal, is found to oscillate with a period of 2 secs. when the wire is twisted and released. When a small thin disc, of mass 10 gm., is attached to each end the period is found to be 2·3 secs. Calculate the moment of inertia of the cylinder about the axis of oscillation. (*N*.)

14. Obtain an expression for the period of small oscillations of a compound pendulum. A circular hoop oscillates in its own plane about a horizontal axis normal to its plane and passing through its circumference. A simple pendulum of length 100 cm. swings with the same period as the hoop. Find the radius of the hoop. (*W*.)

CHAPTER IV

STATICS

1. Statics

1. Statics is a subject which concerns the *equilibrium* of forces, such as the forces which act on a bridge. In Fig. 42 (i), for example, the joint O of a light bridge is in equilibrium under the action of the two forces P, Q acting in the girders meeting at O and the reaction S of the masonry at O.

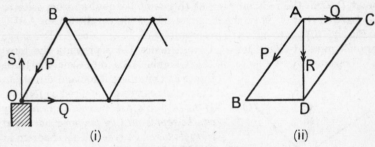

Fig. 42. Equilibrium of forces.

2. Parallelogram of Forces.

A force is a vector quantity, i.e., it can be represented in magnitude and direction by a straight line (see p. 6). If AB, AC represent the forces P, Q respectively at the joint O, their *resultant*, R, is represented in magnitude and direction by the diagonal AD of the parallelogram ABDC which has AB, AC as two of its adjacent sides, Fig. 42 (ii). This is known as the *parallelogram of forces*, and is exactly analogous to the parallelogram of velocities discussed on p. 7.

By trigonometry for triangle ABD, we have

$$AD^2 = BA^2 + BD^2 - 2BA \cdot BD \cos ABD.$$

$$\therefore R^2 = P^2 + Q^2 + 2PQ \cos \theta,$$

where θ = angle BAC, the angle between the forces P, Q, = 180° − angle ABD. This formula enables R to be calculated when P, Q and the angle between them are known. The angle BAD, or a, between the resultant R and the force P can then be calculated from the relation

77

$$\frac{R}{\sin \theta} = \frac{Q}{\sin \alpha},$$

applying the sine rule to triangle ABD and noting that angle ABD = $180° - \theta$.

Resolved component. On p. 7 we saw that the effective part, or resolved component, of a vector quantity X in a direction θ inclined to it is given by $X \cos \theta$. Thus the resolved component of a force P in a direction making an angle of 30° with it is $P \cos 30°$; in a perpendicular direction to the latter the resolved component is $P \cos 60°$, or $P \sin 30°$. In Fig. 42 (i), the downward component of the force P on the joint of O is given by $P \cos$ BOS.

3. Forces in Equilibrium. Triangle of Forces.

Since the joint O is in equilibrium, Fig. 42 (i), the resultant of the forces P, Q in the rods meeting at this joint is equal and opposite to the reaction S at O. Now the diagonal AD of the parallelogram ABDC in Fig. 42 (ii) represents the resultant R of P, Q since ABDC is the parallelogram of forces for P, Q; and hence DA represents the force S. Consequently the sides of the triangle ABD represent the three forces at O in magnitude and direction:

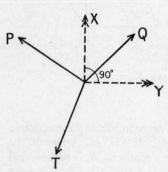

FIG. 43. Resolution of forces.

This result can be generalised as follows. *If three forces are in equilibrium, they can be represented by the three sides of a triangle taken in order.* This theorem in Statics is known as the *triangle of forces*. In Fig. 42 (ii), AB, BD, DA, in this order, represent P, Q, S respectively in Fig. 42 (i).

We can derive another relation between forces in equilibrium. Suppose X, Y are the respective algebraic sums of the resolved components in two perpendicular directions of three forces P, Q, T in equilibrium, Fig. 43. Then, since X, Y can each be represented by the sides of a *rectangle* drawn to scale, their resultant R is given by

$$R^2 = X^2 + Y^2 \qquad . \qquad . \qquad . \qquad . \qquad \text{(i)}$$

Now if the forces are in equilibrium, R is zero. It then follows from (i) that X must be zero and Y must be zero. Thus *if forces are in equilibrium the algebraic sum of their resolved components in any two perpendicular directions is respectively zero.* This result applies to any number of forces in equilibrium (p. 83).

4. Moments.

When the steering-wheel of a car is turned, the applied force is said to exert a *moment*, or turning-effect, about the axle attached to the wheel. The magnitude of the moment of a force P about a point O is defined as *the product of the force P and the perpendicular distance OA from O to the line of action of P*, Fig. 44 (i). Thus

$$\text{moment} = P \times AO.$$

The magnitude of the moment is expressed in dyne cm. when P is in dynes and AO is in cm.; or in lb. wt. ft. if P is in lb. wt. and AO is in feet. We shall say that an anticlockwise moment is positive in sign, and that a clockwise moment is negative in sign.

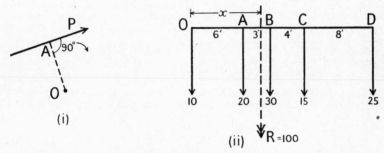

Fig. 44. Moments of forces.

5. Parallel Forces.

If a bridge carries loads of 10, 20, 30, 15, and 25 cwt. at O, A, B, C, D respectively, the resultant R of the weights, which are parallel forces, is equal to their sum, Fig. 44 (ii). Thus

resultant, $R, = 10 + 20 + 30 + 15 + 25 = 100$ cwt.

Experiment and theory show that *the moment of the resultant of a number of forces about any point is equal to the algebraic sum of the moments of the individual forces about the same point.* This result enables us to find where the resultant R acts. Taking moments about O for all the forces in Fig. 44 (ii), we have

$$(20 \times 6) + (30 \times 9) + (15 \times 13) + (25 \times 21),$$

because the distances between the forces are 6 ft., 3 ft., 4 ft., 8 ft., as shown. If x ft. is the distance of the line of action of R from O, the moment of R about $O = R \times x = 100 \times x$.

$$\therefore 100 \, x = (20 \times 6) + (30 \times 9) + (15 \times 13) + (25 \times 21),$$

from which $\qquad\qquad x = 11 \cdot 1$ ft.

The resultant of a number of forces *in equilibrium* is zero; and the moment of the resultant about any point is hence zero. It therefore follows that the algebraic sum of the moments of all the forces about any point is zero when those forces are in equilibrium.

6. Equilibrium of Three Coplanar Forces Acting on Rigid Body.

If any object is in equilibrium under the action of *three* forces, the resultant of two of the forces must be equal and opposite to the third force. Thus the line of action of the third force must pass through the point of intersection of the lines of action of the other two forces.

As an example of calculating unknown forces in this case, suppose that a 12 ft. ladder of 20 lb. wt. is placed at an angle of 60° to the horizontal, with one end B leaning against a smooth wall and the other end A on the ground, Fig. 45. The force R at B on the ladder is called the *reaction* of the wall, and if the latter is smooth, R acts perpendicularly to the wall. Assuming the weight, W, of the ladder acts at its mid-point G, the forces W and R meet at O, as shown. Consequently the frictional force F at A passes through O.

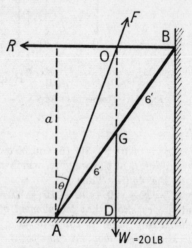

FIG. 45.　Equilibrium of ladder.

The *triangle of forces* can be used to find the unknown forces R, F. Since DA is parallel to R, AO is parallel to F, and OD is parallel to W, the triangle of forces is represented by AOD. By means of a scale drawing R and F can be found, since

$$\frac{W(20)}{\text{OD}} = \frac{F}{\text{AO}} = \frac{R}{\text{DA}}.$$

A quicker method is achieved by taking moments about A for all the forces. The algebraic sum of the moments is zero about any point since the object is in equilibrium, and hence

$$R \cdot a - W \cdot AD = 0,$$

where a is the perpendicular from A to R. (F has zero moment about A.)
But $a = 12 \sin 60°$, and AD $= 6 \cos 60°$.

$$\therefore R \times 12 \sin 60° - 20 \times 6 \cos 60° = 0.$$

$$\therefore R = 10 \frac{\cos 60°}{\sin 60°} = 5 \cdot 77 \text{ lb.}$$

Suppose θ is the angle F makes with the vertical.

Resolving the forces vertically, $F \cos \theta = W = 20$ lb.

Resolving horizontally, $F \sin \theta = R = 5 \cdot 77$ lb.

$$\therefore F^2 \cos^2\theta + F^2 \sin^2\theta = F^2 = 20^2 + 5 \cdot 77^2.$$

$$\therefore F = \sqrt{20^2 + 5 \cdot 77^2} = 20 \cdot 8 \text{ lb.}$$

7. Couples and their Moments.

There are many examples in practice where two forces, acting
together, exert a moment or turning-effect on some object. As a very
simple case, suppose two strings are tied to a wheel at X, Y, and *two
equal and opposite forces*, P, are exerted tangentially to the wheel,
Fig. 46 (i). If the wheel is pivoted at its centre, O, it begins to rotate
about O in an anticlockwise direction.

Two equal and opposite forces whose lines of action do not coincide
are said to constitute a *couple* in Mechanics. The two forces always
have a turning-effect, or moment, which is defined by

moment = one force × perpendicular distance between forces . (42)

Since XY is perpendicular to each of the forces P in Fig. 46 (i), the

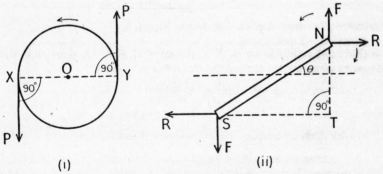

Fig. 46. Moments of couples.

moment of the couple acting on the wheel $= P \times XY = P \times$ diameter
of wheel. Thus if $P = 10$ lb. wt. and the diameter is 6 ft., the moment
of the couple $= 60$ lb. wt. ft.

In Magnetism, we meet cases in which a magnet is kept in equilibrium by two couples acting on it, Fig. 46 (ii) represents a magnet NS in equilibrium under the action of a couple due to the forces F and an opposing couple due to the forces R. The former couple has a clockwise moment $= F \times$ ST: the latter couple has an anticlockwise moment $= R \times$ NT. Since the magnet does not move, the moments are equal

$$\therefore F \times \text{ST} = R \times \text{NT}$$

$$\therefore F = R \times \frac{\text{NT}}{\text{ST}} = R \tan \theta,$$

where θ is the angle NST.

8. Work Done by a Couple.

Suppose two equal and opposite forces F act tangentially to a wheel W, and rotate it through an angle θ while the forces keep tangentially to the wheel, Fig. 47. The moment of the couple is then constant. The

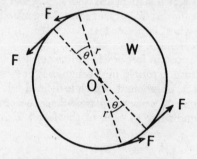

Fig. 47. Work done by couple.

work done by each force $= F \times$ distance $= F \times r\theta$, since $r\theta$ is the distance moved by a point on the rim if θ is in radians.

$\therefore$ total work done by couple $= Fr\theta + Fr\theta = 2Fr\theta.$

But moment of couple $\qquad = F \times 2r = 2Fr$

$\therefore$ work done by couple $\qquad =$ moment of couple $\times \theta$. . . . (43)

Although we have chosen a simple case, the result for the work done by a couple is always given by *moment* $\times$ *angle of rotation*. In the formula, it should be carefully noted that θ is in radians. Thus suppose $F = 100$ gm. wt. $= 100 \times 980$ dynes, $r = 4$ cm., and the wheel makes 5 revolutions while the moment of the couple is kept constant. Then

$$\text{angle of rotation} = 2\pi \times 5 \text{ radians},$$

and moment of couple $= (100 \times 980) \times (2 \times 4)$ cm. **dyne.**

$\therefore$ work done $= (100 \times 980) \times 2 \times 4 \times 2\pi \times 5 =$
$$2.46 \times 10^7 \text{ ergs.}$$

9. Equilibrium of any Number of Coplanar Forces.

On p. 80 we showed how unknown forces could be calculated when an object is in equilibrium under the action of three forces. If an object is in equilibrium under any number of coplanar forces their resultant in any direction is zero. Consequently the algebraic sum of the resolved components of all the forces in any two perpendicular directions is respectively zero (see p. 78). But this cannot be the only condition satisfied by the forces, because they might reduce to two equal and opposite forces whose lines of action do not coincide. In this case the algebraic sum of the resolved components is zero, but the forces are not in equilibrium because they reduce to a couple. We must therefore stipulate in addition that the algebraic sum of the moments of the forces about any point must be zero, in which case there cannot be a couple. Summarizing, the necessary conditions of equilibrium of any number of coplanar forces are:

(1) The algebraic sum of the resolved components of all the forces in any two perpendicular directions must be respectively zero.

(2) The algebraic sum of the moments of the forces about any point must be zero.

10. Equilibrium of Parallel Forces.

If an object such as a bridge is in equilibrium under the action of any number of parallel forces, it follows that:

(1) the sum of the forces in one direction = the sum of the forces in the opposite direction:

(2) the algebraic sum of the moments of all the forces about any point is zero.

As a simple example of the equilibrium of parallel forces, suppose a

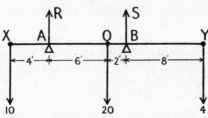

Fig. 48. Equilibrium of parallel forces.

light beam XY rests on supports A,B, and has loads of 10, 20, and 4 lb. concentrated at X, O, Y respectively, Fig. 48. Let R, S be the reactions at A,B respectively. Then, for equilibrium in a vertical direction,

$$R + S = 10 + 20 + 4 = 34 \text{ lb. wt.} \qquad . \qquad . \qquad \text{(i)}$$

To find R, we take moments about a suitable point such as B, in which case the moment of S is zero. Then, for the remaining four forces,

$$+ 10 \cdot 12 + 20 \cdot 2 - R \cdot 8 - 4 \cdot 8 = 0,$$

from which $R = 16$ lb. wt. From (i), it follows that $S = 34 - 16 = 18$ lb. wt.

11. Centre of Gravity.

Every particle is attracted towards the centre of the earth by the force of gravity, and the *centre of gravity* of a body is the point where the *resultant* force of attraction acts. In the simple case of a ruler, the centre of gravity is the point of support when the ruler is balanced. A similar method can be used to find roughly the centre of gravity of a flat plate. A more accurate method consists of suspending the object in turn from two points on it, so that it hangs freely in each case, and finding the point of intersection of a plumb-line, suspended in turn from each point of suspension. This experiment is described in elementary books.

An object can be considered to consist of many small particles. The forces on the particles due to the attraction of the earth are all parallel since they act vertically, and hence their resultant is the sum of all the forces. The resultant is the *weight* of the whole object, of course. In the case of a rod of uniform cross-sectional area, the weight of a particle A at one end, and that of a corresponding particle A′ at the other end, have a resultant which acts at the mid-point O of the rod, Fig. 49,

RESULTANT

Fig. 49. Centre of gravity of uniform rod.

Similarly, the resultant of the weight of a particle B, and that of a corresponding particle at B′, have a resultant acting at O. In this way, i.e., by symmetry, it follows that the resultant of the weights of all the particles of the rod acts at O, and hence the centre gravity of a uniform rod is at its mid-point.

The *centre of mass* of an object is the point where the total mass acts. Except for enormous objects, the centre of mass is situated at the same place as the centre of gravity.

12. Positions of Centre of Gravity.

The following are the positions of the centre of gravity (C.G.) of some objects:

(1) *Circular disc.* The C.G. is at the centre.

(2) *Circular wire.* The C.G. is at its centre of the circle.

(3) *Triangular lamina or plate.* The C.G. is at the point of inter-

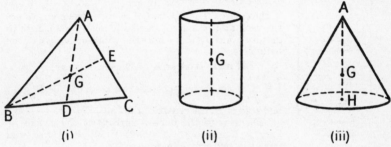

(i)   (ii)   (iii)

Fig. 50.   Centre of gravity of objects.

section of the medians, which are the lines joining the points of the triangle such as A, B to the mid-points of the opposite sides, D, E, Fig. 50 (i). It can be shown that $AG = \frac{2}{3} AD$, where $BD = DC$ and G is the centre of gravity, and hence the C.G. is two-thirds of the way along the median from a point of the triangle.

(4) *Parallelogram, rectangle, or square lamina.* The C.G. is at the point of intersection of the diagonals.

(5) *Curved surface of a hollow cylinder.* The C.G. is at the mid-point of the axis of the cylinder, Fig. 50 (ii).

(6) *Solid cylinder.* The C.G. is at the mid-point of the axis of the cylinder.

(7) *Right solid cone.* The C.G. is three-quarters of the way along the axis from the apex, i.e., $AG = \frac{3}{4}AH$, Fig. 50 (iii).

13. Centre of Gravity of Combined Objects.

The position of the centre of gravity of *combined objects* can be found by applying the law of moments for parallel forces, since the weights are parallel forces. This law states:

The moment of the resultant (total) weight about any point = the algebraic sum of the moments, in the same direction, of the separate weights about the same point (see p. 79).

The following example illustrates how this principle is applied:

EXAMPLE

What is meant by (a) the centre of mass of a body, (b) the centre of gravity of a body?

A cylindrical can is made of a material weighing 10 gm./sq. cm. and has no lid. The diameter of the can is 25 cm. and its height 50 cm. Find the position of the centre of mass when the can is half full of water. (C.)

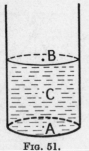

Fig. 51.

First part. The "centre of mass" is the point where the resultant mass of the body acts; the "centre of gravity" is the point where the resultant *weight* of the body acts.

Second part. The area of the base $= \pi r^2 = \pi \times \left(\frac{25}{2}\right)^2$ sq. cm.; hence the mass is $\pi \times (25/2)^2 \times 10$ gm., and acts at A, the centre of the base, Fig. 51.

The mass of the curved surface of the centre $= 2\pi rh \times 10$ gm. $= 2\pi \times (25/2) \times 50 \times 10$ gm., and acts at B, half-way along the axis.

The mass of water $= \pi r^2 h$ gm. $= \pi \times (25/2)^2 \times 25$ gm., and acts at C, the mid-point of AB.

Thus the resultant mass in grams

$$= \frac{\pi \times 625 \times 10}{4} + \frac{2\pi \times 25 \times 50 \times 10}{2} + \frac{\pi \times 625 \times 25}{4}$$

$$= \pi \times 625 \times 28\tfrac{3}{4}$$

Taking moments about A,

$$\therefore \pi \times 625 \times 28\tfrac{3}{4} \times x = (\pi \times 12500) \times AB + \left(\pi \times \frac{625 \times 25}{4}\right) \times AC$$

where x is the distance of the centre of mass from A.

$$\therefore 28\tfrac{3}{4} x = 20 \times 25 + \frac{25}{4} \times 12\tfrac{1}{2}$$

$$\therefore \quad x = 20 \cdot 1$$

∴ centre of mass is 20·1 cm. from the base.

14. Machines.

A *machine* is an instrument which enables a force W to be applied at a certain point by the application of another force P at a different point. A pulley system, for example, enables a heavy load, W, to be raised by a smaller force or effort, P.

The *mechanical advantage* (M.A.) of a machine is defined by the ratio

$$\text{M.A.} = \frac{\text{load } (W)}{\text{effort } (P)} \quad . \quad . \quad . \quad . \quad . \quad (44)$$

The *velocity ratio* (V.R.) of the machine is defined by the ratio

$$\text{V.R.} = \frac{\text{distance per sec. moved by effort } (x)}{\text{distance per sec. moved by load } (y)} \quad . \quad (45)$$

On account of friction, for example, the energy, or work, obtained from a machine is always less than the energy, or work, supplied to it. The *efficiency*, η, of the machine is defined by

$$\eta = \frac{\text{work or energy obtained}}{\text{work or energy supplied}} \quad . \quad . \quad . \quad (46)$$

$$= \frac{\text{work done on load, } W \times y}{\text{work done by effort, } P \times x},$$

since work = force × distance. But W/P = mechanical advantage (M.A.), and x/y = velocity ratio (V.R.).

$$\therefore \eta = \frac{\text{M.A.}}{\text{V.R.}}$$

In practice, therefore, the mechanical advantage is less than the velocity ratio, which is independent of friction. If the machine were perfect, i.e., if no energy were lost, the two quantities would be equal.

15. Levers.

A *lever* is a machine in which a load, W, is attached to one point of a rod, which is capable of rotating about another point known as the *fulcrum*. The effort, P, is applied at another point of the rod. In the **first class** of levers, the load W and the effort P are on opposite sides of the fulcrum O, and P is further from the fulcrum than W., Fig. 52 (i).

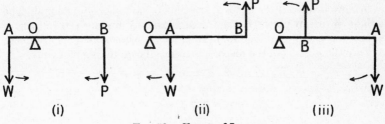

(i)   (ii)   (iii)

Fig. 52.   Classes of Levers.

Taking moments about O, we have $W \cdot OA = P \cdot OB$, or $W/P = OB/OA$. The mechanical advantage is thus equal to the ratio of the "arms" of the lever. Examples of this class of lever are the crowbar, pincers, and pliers.

In the **second class** of levers the load W and the effort P are on the same side of the fulcrum, O, with W nearer to O than P, Fig. 52 (ii). By taking moments about O, the mechanical advantage, $W/P = OB/OA$. Examples of this class of levers are the wheelbarrow, the nut-cracker, and the oar. In the **third class** of levers the load W and the effort P are on the same side of the fulcrum, O, but the load is further away from the fulcrum than the effort, Fig. 52 (iii). Examples of this class of levers are the coal-tongs and the human arm. By taking moments about O, the mechanical advantage, W/P , $= OB/OA$, which is less than unity, unlike the other two classes of levers.

16. Common Balance.

The common balance is basically a lever of the first class whose two arms are equal, Fig. 53. The fulcrum, about which the beam and pointer tilt, is an agate wedge resting on an agate plate; agate wedges, B, at the ends of the beam, support the scale-pans. The centre of gravity of the

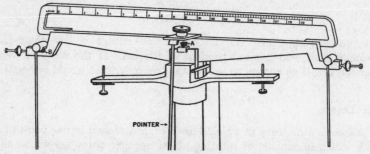

FIG. 53.   Top of Common Balance; beam tilted by small load.

beam and pointer is vertically below the fulcrum, to make the arrangement stable. The weight placed on the two scale-pans are equal when there is a "balance".

On rare occasions the arms of the balance are slightly unequal. The weight W of an object is then determined by finding the respective weights W_1, W_2 required to balance it on each scale-pan. Suppose a, b are the lengths of the respective arms. Then, taking moments,

$$\therefore W_1 \cdot a = W \cdot b, \text{ and } W \cdot a = W_2 \cdot b.$$

$$\therefore \frac{W}{W_1} = \frac{a}{b} = \frac{W_2}{W}$$

$$\therefore W^2 = W_1 W_2$$

$$\therefore \; W = \sqrt{W_1 W_2}$$

Thus W can be found from the two weights W_1, W_2.

17. Sensitivity of a Balance.

A balance is said to be very *sensitive* if a small difference in weights on the scale-pans causes a large deflection of the beam. To investigate the factors which affect the sensitivity of a balance, suppose a weight W_1 is placed on the left scale-pan and a slightly smaller weight W_2 is

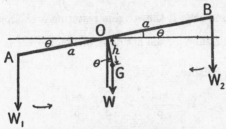

FIG. 54.   Sensitivity of balance.

placed on the right scale-pan, Fig. 54. The beam AOB will then be inclined at some angle θ to the horizontal, where O is the fulcrum.

The weight W of the beam and pointer acts at G, at a distance h below O. Suppose AO = OB = a. Then, taking moments about O,

$$W_1 a \cos \theta = Wh \sin \theta + W_2 a \cos \theta$$

$$\therefore (W_1 - W_2) a \cos \theta = Wh \sin \theta$$

$$\therefore \tan \theta = \frac{(W_1 - W_2)a}{Wh}$$

Thus for a given value of $(W_1 - W_2)$, the difference of the weights on the scale-pans, θ will increase when a increases and W, h both decrease. In theory, then, a sensitive balance must be light and have long arms, and the centre of gravity of its beam and pointer must be very close to the fulcrum. Now a light beam will not be rigid. Further, a beam with long arms will take a long time to settle down when it is deflected. A compromise must therefore be made between the requirements of sensitivity and those of design.

If the knife-edges of the scale-pan and of the beam are in the same plane, the balance has the same sensitivity over a considerable range of loads, because the two scale-pans and the weights on them rise and fall respectively by the same amount. When the knife-edge of the beam is below the knife-edges of the two scale-pans, the sensitivity increases with the load; the reverse is the case if the knife-edge of the beam is above those of the scale-pans.

18. Buoyancy Correction in Weighing.

In very accurate weighing, a correction must be made for the buoyancy of the air. Suppose the body weighed has a density ρ and a mass m. From Archimedes principle (p. 97), the upthrust due to the air of density σ is equal to the weight of air displaced by the body, and hence the net downward force $= \left(m - \dfrac{m}{\rho} . \sigma \right)g$, since the volume of the body is m/ρ. Similarly, if the weights restoring a balance have a total mass m_1 and a density ρ_1, the net downward force $= \left(m_1 - \dfrac{m_1}{\rho_1} . \sigma \right)g$.

Since there is a balance,

$$m - \frac{m\sigma}{\rho} = m_1 - \frac{m_1\sigma}{\rho_1}$$

$$\therefore m = m_1 \frac{\left(1 - \dfrac{\sigma}{\rho_1} \right)}{1 - \dfrac{\sigma}{\rho}}$$

Thus knowing the density of air, σ, and the densities ρ, ρ_1, the true mass m can be found in terms of m_1. The pressure and temperature of air, which may vary from day to day, affects the magnitude of its density σ, from the gas laws; the humidity of the air is also taken into account in very accurate weighing, as the density of moist air differs from that of dry air.

EXAMPLES

1 What is meant by (a) the *mechanical advantage*, (b) the *velocity ratio*, (c) the *efficiency* of a machine? A forearm is held horizontally, with the upper part of the arm vertical, and a 500 gm. weight is held in the hand so that its centre of gravity is 30 cm. from the elbow joint. Assuming that the lower and upper ends of the biceps muscles are attached at points 5 cm. and 12 cm. from the elbow joint, and that the lever system is perfectly efficient, find (i) the tension in the muscle, (ii) the velocity ratio of the system. (Neglect the weight of the forearm itself.) (*L*.)

First part. See text.

Second part. Suppose O is the elbow joint, C is the 500 gm. wt., A is the point of attachment of the lower end of the bicep muscle, and B is that of the upper end, Fig. 55. If T is the tension in the muscle AB, then, taking moments about O,

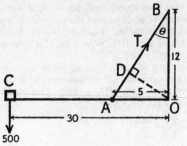

Fig. 55.

$$T \times OD = 500 \times OC.$$

But $OD = 12 \sin \theta = 12 \times \dfrac{5}{13}$ cm., since $AB = \sqrt{12^2 + 5^2} = 13$, and $OC = 30$ cm.

$$\therefore T \times 12 \times \frac{5}{13} = 500 \times 30$$

$$\therefore T = \frac{500 \times 30 \times 13}{12 \times 5} = 3250 \text{ gm. wt.}$$

The velocity ratio of the system is equal to the mechanical advantage if the lever system is perfectly efficient (p. 87). Thus velocity ratio = mechanical advantage $= \dfrac{3250}{500} = 6 \cdot 5$.

2. State the conditions of equilibrium of a rigid body under coplanar forces. How would you illustrate one of the conditions stated? A trap-door is hinged at one end and held in a horizontal position by a cord of length 4 ft. attached to the mid-point of the opposite edge, and fixed to a point 3 ft. vertically above the mid-point of the hinge. Find the tension in the cord and the reaction at the hinge if the weight of the trap-door is 20 lb. (*C.*)

First part. See text.

Second part. Suppose AB is the trap-door section, AC is the cord attached to C, and B is the section of the hinge, Fig. 56. Since there are

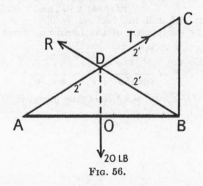

Fig. 56.

3 forces acting on the trap-door, and its weight acts vertically at O, it follows that the reaction R at B passes through D, the point of intersection of the weight and T, the tension. Further, since AO = OB, AD = DC. Hence D is the centre of the circle which can be drawn round the triangle ACB, and thus DB = DC = 2 ft.

One method of finding R and T is to note that triangle CBD is the triangle of forces for the system. CB represents the 20 lb. wt., DC represents T, and BD represents R. Now CD = DB. Hence $T = R$. Further, as BC = 3 ft. and DC = 2 ft., we have

$$\frac{T}{2} = \frac{20}{3}$$

$$\therefore T = \frac{40}{3} = 13\tfrac{1}{3} \text{ lb. wt.} = R.$$

An alternative method is to take moments about B to eliminate R, and then to take moments about A to eliminate T. This is left as an exercise to the student.

3. State what is meant by *scalar* and *vector* quantities, giving examples of each.

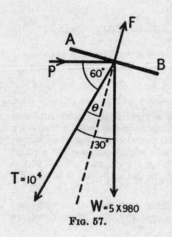

Explain how a flat kite can be flown in a wind that is blowing horizontally. The line makes an angle of 30° with the vertical and is under a tension of 10^4 dynes; the mass of the kite is 5 gm. What angle will the plane of the kite make with the vertical, and what force will the wind exert on it? (*O. & C.*)

First part. See text.

Second part. When the kite AB is inclined to the horizontal, the wind blowing horizontally exerts an upward force F normal to AB, Fig. 57. For equilibrium of the kite, F must be equal and opposite to the resultant of the tension T, 10,000 dynes, and the weight W, 5 × 980 or 4900 dynes. By drawing the parallelogram of forces for the resultant of T and W, F and the angle θ between F and T can be found. θ is nearly 10°, and F is about 14800 dynes.

Fig. 57.

The angle between AB and the vertical = 60° + θ = 70° (approx.). Also, since F is the component of the horizontal force P of the wind,

$$P \cos (60° + \theta) = F.$$

$$\therefore P = \frac{F}{\cos (60° + \theta)} = \frac{14,800}{\cos 70°}$$

$$= 43,300 \text{ dynes (approx.)}$$

EXERCISES IV

1. A flat plate is cut in the shape of a square of side 2 ins., with an equilateral triangle of side 2 ins. adjacent to the square. Calculate the distance of the centre of gravity from the apex of the triangle.

2. The foot of a uniform ladder is on a rough horizontal ground, and the top rests against a smooth vertical wall. The weight of the ladder is 40 lb., and a boy weighing 80 lb. stands on the ladder one-quarter of its length from the bottom. If the inclination of the ladder to the horizontal is 30°, find the reaction at the wall and the total force at the ground.

3. A rectangular plate ABCD has two forces of 10 lb. wt. acting along AB and DC in opposite directions. If AB = 3 ft., BC = 5 ft., what is the moment of the couple acting on the plate? What forces acting along BC and AD respectively are required to keep the plate in equilibrium?

4. A hollow metal cylinder 2 ft. tall has a base of diameter 14 ins. and is filled with water to a height of (i) 1 ft., (ii) 6 ins. Calculate the distance of the centre of gravity in feet from the base in each case if the cylinder has no top. (Metal weighs 3 lb. per sq. ft. of surface; density of water = 62·5 lb. per cu. ft. Assume $\pi = 22/7$.)

5. A trap-door 4 ft. by 4 ft. is kept horizontal by a string attached to the mid-point of the side opposite to that containing the hinge. The other end of the string is tied to a point 3 ft. vertically above the hinge. If the trap-door weight is 5 lb., calculate the tension in the string and the reaction at the hinge.

6. Two smooth inclined planes are arranged with their lower edges in contact; the angles of inclination of the plane to the horizontal are 30°, 60° respectively, and the surfaces of the planes are perpendicular to each other. If a uniform rod rests in the principal section of the planes with one end on each plane, find the angle of inclination of the rod to the horizontal.

7. Describe and give the theory of an accurate beam balance. Point out the factors which influence the sensitivity of the balance. Why is it necessary, in very accurate weighing, to take into account the pressure, temperature, and humidity of the atmosphere? (O. & C.)

8. Summarise the various conditions which are being satisfied when a body remains in equilibrium under the action of three non-parallel forces.

A wireless aerial attached to the top of a mast 20 ft. high exerts a horizontal force upon it of 60 lb. wt. The mast is supported by a stay-wire running to the ground from a point 6 ft. below the top of the mast, and inclined at 60° to the horizontal. Assuming that the action of the ground on the mast can be regarded as a single force, draw a diagram of the forces acting on the mast, and determine by measurement or by calculation the force in the stay-wire. (C.)

9. A rigid body is in equilibrium under the action of three forces, one of which is its weight; state the conditions which the system of forces must satisfy. Would your statement require modification if the forces were more than three in number?

A rod AB of mass 30 lb. and 10 ft. long has its centroid at a point distant 4 ft. from A. The rod is hinged at A so as to be rotatable about A in a vertical plane, but is maintained in an inclined position by a thin horizontal cord attached at B and secured at a point C which is 6 ft. directly above the hinge at A. CB is 8 ft. Find graphically, or otherwise, the reaction at the hinge and the tension in the cord. (*W*.),

10. Give an account of the essential features of a good physical balance. Describe how, using a balance with slightly unequal arms, (*a*) the true mass of a body, (*b*) the ratio of the arms, may be determined. (*L*.)

11. Three forces in one plane act on a rigid body. What are the conditions for equilibrium?

The plane of a kite of mass 12 lb. is inclined to the horizon at 60°. The resultant thrust of the air on the kite acts at a point 10 ins. above its centre of gravity, and the string is attached at a point 12 in. above the centre of gravity. Find the thrust of the air on the kite, and the tension in the string. (*C*.)

12. Describe a good type of physical beam balance and point out the conditions which such a balance should fulfil. On what does the sensitivity of the balance depend? How would you determine the sensitivity experimentally?

A body is weighed first in the left- and then in the right-hand pan of a balance, the respective weights being 9·842 gm. and 9·833 gm. Find the true weight of the body and the ratio of the lengths of the arms of the balance. (*N*.)

13. The beam of a balance weighs 150 gm. and its moment of inertia is 5,000 gm. cm.² Each arm of the balance is 10 cm. long. When set swinging the beam makes one complete oscillation in 6 sec. How far is the centre of gravity of the beam below its point of support, and through what angle would the beam be deflected by a weight of 1 milligram placed in one of the scale pans? (*C*.)

CHAPTER V

HYDROSTATICS

1. Density.

The *density* of a substance is defined as its *mass per unit volume*. Thus

$$\text{density, } \rho, = \frac{\text{mass of substance}}{\text{volume of substance}} \qquad \cdots \qquad (47)$$

The density of steel is 8·5 grams per c.c.; the density of aluminium is 2·7 gm. per c.c.; the density of water at 4° C. is 1 gram per c.c. or about 62½ lb. per cubic foot.

Substances which float on water have a density less than 1 gram per c.c. (p. 97). For example, ice has a density of about 0·9 gm. per c.c.; cork has a density of about 0·25 gm. per c.c. Steel, of density 8·5 gm. per c.c., will float on mercury, whose density is about 13·6 gm. per c.c. at 0° C.

2. Specific Gravity.

The specific gravity, *s*, of a substance is defined by the relation

$$s = \frac{W}{w}, \qquad \cdots \qquad (48)$$

where *W* is the weight of the substance and *w* is the weight of *an equal volume of water*. Since "specific gravity" is the ratio of two weights, specific gravity is simply a number; it has no units, unlike density. The specific gravity of steel is 8·5; the specific gravity of mercury is 13·6 at 0° C.

If we consider 1 c.c. of the substance, then *W* in (48) is the *density* of the substance, by definition. As *w* is then the density of water, the specific gravity of a substance can be defined as "its density relative to that of water". The density of water is 1 gram per c.c. Since the specific gravity of mercury is 13·6, the density of mercury is 13·6 gm. per c.c. The density of mercury is also 13·6 × 62½ or 850 lbs. per cu. ft., since the density of water is 62½ lb. per cu. ft.

3. Determination of Density and Specific Gravity of Liquid.

The density, or specific gravity of a liquid can be measured accurately

FIG. 58. Specific
gravity bottle.

by means of a *specific gravity bottle*, which has a tight-fitting glass stopper with a fine hole in it, Fig. 58. The bottle can thus always be filled to a high degree of accuracy with the same volume of liquid, the excess being wiped off. Since 1 gram of water has a volume of 1 c.c., the volume of the bottle is numerically equal to the mass in grams of water, m say, filling it completely. If the bottle is dried, and m_1 grams is the mass of an unknown liquid filling the bottle, then

$$\text{density of liquid, } \rho, = \frac{m_1}{m} \text{ grams per c.c.}$$

The specific gravity of the liquid is also given by the ratio m_1/m, since we have compared the weights of equal volumes of liquid and water.

4. Density of Crystals Soluble in Water.

The density of crystals of copper sulphate, hypo, or other substances soluble in water can be found by using oil and making the following measurements:

(1). Weight of specific gravity bottle empty (m_0).

(2). Wt. of bottle + some crystals . . . (m_1).

(3). Wt. of bottle + crystals + oil filling remainder of bottle (m_2)

(4). Wt. of bottle + oil filling whole bottle (m_3).

The oil used is one in which the crystals are not soluble, for example, paraffin oil can be used for copper sulphate or hypo crystals. From these measurements,

$$\text{weight of crystals} = m_1 - m_0,$$

$$\text{and volume of crystals} = [(m_3 - m_0) - (m_2 - m_1)]/\rho,$$

where ρ is the density of the oil.

$$\therefore \text{density of crystals} = \frac{m_1 - m_0}{[(m_3 - m_0) - (m_2 - m_1)]/\rho}$$

$$= \frac{(m_1 - m_0)\rho}{(m_3 - m_0) - (m_2 - m_1)}.$$

The density ρ of the oil can be found from a preliminary experiment with a specific gravity bottle, and hence the density of the crystals can be calculated.

5. Density of Sand.

The density of sand or other particles insoluble in water can be found from the following measurements, using a specific gravity bottle:

(1) Weight of specific gravity bottle empty (m_0).

(2) Weight of bottle + some sand (m_1).

(3) Weight of bottle + sand + water filling remainder of bottle (m_2)

(4) Weight of bottle + water filling whole bottle (m_3).

Thus weight of sand $= m_1 - m_0$,

and volume of sand $= (m_3 - m_0) - (m_2 - m_1)$

$$\therefore \text{density of sand} = \frac{m_1 - m_0}{(m_3 - m_0) - (m_2 - m_1)}.$$

6. Archimedes Principle.

An object immersed in a liquid experiences a resultant upward force owing to the pressure of liquid on it. This upward force is called the *upthrust* of the liquid on the object, and ARCHIMEDES was the first person to give the law concerning its magnitude. He stated that *the upthrust is equal to the weight of liquid displaced by the object*, and this is known as *Archimedes' Principle*. Thus if an iron cube of volume 400 c.c. is totally immersed in water of density 1 gm. per c.c., the upthrust on the cube $= 400 \times 1 = 400$ gm. wt. If the same cube is totally immersed in oil of density 0·8 gm. per c.c., the upthrust on it $= 400 \times 0·8 = 320$ gm wt.

As we shall now see, Archimedes' Principle can be used to measure the density, or specific gravity, of solids and liquids.

7. Determination of Density (or Specific Gravity) by Archimedes Principle. Density of Solid.

The density or specific gravity of a solid such as brass or iron can be determined by (1) weighing it in air, m_0 gm. say, (2) weighing it when it is totally immersed in water, m_1 gm. say. Then

upthrust $= m_0 - m_1 =$ wt. of water displaced.

$$\therefore \text{specific gravity of solid} = \frac{m_0}{m_0 - m_1},$$

and density of solid, $\rho, = \dfrac{m_0}{m_0 - m_1}$ gm. per c.c.

8. Density of Copper Sulphate.

If a solid dissolves in water, such as a copper sulphate crystal for example, its density can be found by totally immersing it in a liquid in which it is insoluble. Copper sulphate can be weighed in paraffin oil, for example. Suppose the apparent weight is m_1, and the weight in air is m_0. Then

$$m_0 - m_1 = \text{upthrust in liquid} = V\rho,$$

where V is the volume of the solid and ρ is the density of the liquid.

$$\therefore V = \frac{m_0 - m_1}{\rho}$$

$$\therefore \text{density of solid} = \frac{\text{mass}}{\text{volume}} = \frac{m_0}{V} = \frac{m_0}{m_0 - m_1} \cdot \rho.$$

The density, ρ, of the liquid can be found by means of a specific gravity bottle, for example. Thus knowing m_0 and m_1, the density of the solid can be calculated.

9. Density of Cork.

If a solid floats in water, cork for example, its density can be found by attaching a brass weight or "sinker" to it so that both solids become totally immersed in water. The apparent weight (m_1) of the sinker and cork together is then obtained. Suppose m_2 is the weight of the sinker in air, m_3 is the weight of the sinker alone in water, and m_0 is the weight of the cork in air.

Then $m_2 - m_3 = \text{upthrust on sinker in water.}$

$$\therefore m_0 + m_2 - m_1 - (m_2 - m_3) = \text{upthrust on cork in water}$$

$$= m_0 - m_1 + m_3$$

$$\therefore \text{density of cork} = \frac{m_0}{m_0 - m_1 + m_3}.$$

10. Density of Liquid.

The density or specific gravity of a *liquid* can be found by weighing a solid in air (m_0), then weighing it totally immersed in the liquid (m_1), and then when it is totally immersed in water (m_2).

Now $m_0 - m_2 = \text{upthrust in water} = \text{weight of water displaced,}$

and $m_0 - m_1 = \text{upthrust in liquid} = \text{weight of liquid displaced.}$

$$\therefore \frac{m_0 - m_1}{m_0 - m_2} = \text{specific gravity of liquid,}$$

or $\quad \dfrac{m_0 - m_1}{m_0 - m_2} = \text{density of liquid in grams per c.c.}$

11. The Simple (Constant Weight) Hydrometer.

A *hydrometer* is an instrument used for measuring the specific gravity or density of a liquid. Hydrometers are used for testing the specific gravities of milk, spirits, and acid in accumulators.

A simple hydrometer can be made by attaching a piece of lead to the bottom, C, of a length of wood D of uniform cross-sectional area, Fig. 59. The wood then floats upright in a liquid, and if h is the length DC of wood immersed,

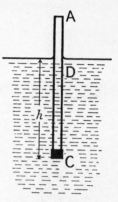

upthrust on wood = weight of liquid displaced

$$= ha\rho,$$

where a is the cross-sectional area and ρ is the density of the liquid. But if the wood floats, the upthrust is equal to its weight, w.

$$\therefore ha\rho = w.$$

$$\therefore \rho = \frac{w}{ah}$$

$$\therefore \rho \propto \frac{1}{h}.$$

If the depth h immersed in water of density 1 gram per c.c. is noted, the length of the wood can be labelled with density values, since $\rho \propto 1/h$. The wood then acts as a simple hydrometer.

12. Practical Hydrometer.

In practice a hydrometer has a narrow stem, BL, of uniform cross-sectional area, a wide bulb below the stem, and lead shot or other heavy substances at the bottom M, Fig. 60. Suppose y is the length of stem *not* immersed when the hydrometer floats in a liquid of density ρ. Then if a is the cross-sectional area of the stem, and V is the volume of the whole hydrometer, the volume of liquid displaced $= V - ay$. By Archimedes principle, it follows that

$$(V - ay) \rho = w,$$

where w is the weight of the hydrometer.

$$\therefore V - ay = \frac{w}{\rho}$$

$$\therefore y = \frac{1}{a}\left(V - \frac{w}{\rho}\right) = \frac{V}{a} - \frac{w}{a} \cdot \frac{1}{\rho}.$$

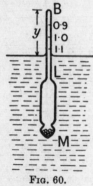

FIG. 60.
Hydrometer.

Since w/a and V/a are constants for a given hydrometer, the relation between y and $1/\rho$ is a linear one. To calibrate the stem in terms of density, ρ, the hydrometer is immersed in two liquids of known density, the corresponding distances y are observed, and the values of y are then plotted against $1/\rho$. The two points thus obtained are joined. From this straight line graph, the values of $1/\rho$ corresponding to a particular value of y can be read off, and thus the stem can be calibrated in terms of density.

In general a hydrometer is not as accurate as a specific gravity bottle for determining the density of a liquid, owing to the downward pull on the hydrometer due to the surface tension of the liquid in which it is placed.

13. Nicholson's (Constant Volume) Hydrometer.

NICHOLSON designed a hydrometer which had a hollow metal cylindrical body X, a "basket" B, a thin upper stem M, and a scale-pan S above M. When the hydrometer is placed in a liquid, weights are placed in the pan S,

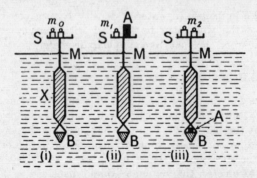

FIG. 61.   Nicholson's hydrometer.

or taken from it, until the instrument sinks to a fixed mark on M. *The volume of the hydrometer immersed is thus kept constant each time.*

The weight m_0 required to sink the hydrometer in water to the fixed mark is first found, Fig. 61 (i). An object A whose density is required is placed on S, and the reduced weight m_1 to restore the hydrometer level is obtained, Fig. 61 (ii). Then $m_0 - m_1$ = the weight of A. The object A is then placed in the basket B, and the new weight m_2 on S to restore the level is noted, Fig. 61 (iii). Then $m_2 - m_1$ = the upthrust on A in water = the weight of water displaced by A.

$$\therefore \text{ specific gravity of A} = \frac{m_0 - m_1}{m_2 - m_1}.$$

If the object A floats in water, it can be tied to B and the procedure repeated.

The density or specific gravity of a *liquid* can easily be found by the Nicholson hydrometer. Suppose m_3, m_4 are the respective weights on the scale-pan S required to sink the hydrometer to the fixed mark when it is placed first in water and then in the liquid. Then, if m is the weight of the hydrometer,

upthrust on hydrometer in liquid = $m + m_4$,

and   upthrust on hydrometer in water = $m + m_3$.

From Archimedes principle, the upthrust in each case is equal to the weight of liquid displaced. Thus, since the volumes of the liquids are the same in each case,

$$\text{specific gravity of liquid} = \frac{m + m_4}{m + m_3}.$$

It should be noted that Nicholson's hydrometer is a constant volume hydrometer, whereas the common hydrometer (p. 100) is a constant weight hydrometer. The surface tension of the liquid reduces the accuracy of the hydrometer.

14. Pressure in a Liquid.

The *pressure* at a place in a liquid is defined as the *force per unit area* there. Observation shows that the pressure increases with the depth, h, below the liquid surface and with its density ρ, and acts in all directions at a given place in the liquid.

To obtain a formula for the pressure, p, suppose that a horizontal plate X of area A is placed at a depth h below the liquid surface, Fig. 62. By drawing vertical lines from points on the perimeter of X, we can see that the force on X due to the liquid is equal to the weight of liquid of height h and uniform cross-section A. Since the volume of this liquid is Ah, the mass of the liquid = $Ah \times \rho$.

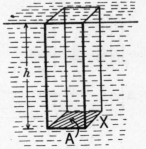

FIG. 62. Pressure in liquid.

$$\therefore \text{ weight} = Ah\rho g \text{ dynes,}$$

where g is 980, h is in cm., A is in sq. cm., and ρ is in grams per c.c.

$$\therefore \text{ pressure, } p, \text{ on } X = \frac{\text{force}}{\text{area}} = \frac{Ah\rho g}{A}$$

$$\therefore \mathbf{p = h\rho g} \qquad . \qquad . \qquad . \qquad . \quad (49)$$

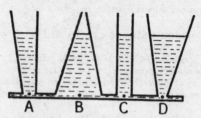

FIG. 63. Pressure constant at same horizontal level.

When h, ρ, g have the units already mentioned, the pressure p is in dynes per sq. cm. Thus suppose the atmospheric pressure corresponds to a column of mercury 76 cm. high (called *one atmosphere*). Since the density of mercury, ρ, is 13·6 grams per c.c., the atmospheric pressure $p = 76 \times 13·6 \times 980 = 1·01 \times 10^6$ dynes per sq. cm.

The student is advised to commit the expression for pressure, $p = h\rho g$, to memory; it is required in many branches of Physics. From the formula, it follows that *the pressure in a liquid is the same at all points on the same horizontal level in it.* Experiment also gives the same result. Thus a liquid filling the vessel shown in Fig. 63 rises to the same height in each section if ABCD is horizontal. The cross-sectional area of B is greater than that of D; but the force on B is the sum of the weight of water above it together with the (downward) reaction of the sides of the vessel, whereas the force on D is the weight of water above it *minus* the (upward) reaction of the sides of the vessel. It will thus be noted that the pressure in a vessel is independent of the cross-sectional area of the vessel.

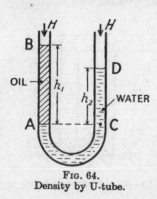

FIG. 64.
Density by U-tube.

15. Measurement of Density of Liquid.

U-tube method. Suppose a U-tube is partly filled with water, and oil is then poured into the left side of the tube. The oil will then reach some level B at a height h_1 above the surface of separation, A, of the water and oil, while the water on the right side of the tube will then reach some level D at a height h_2 above the level of A, Fig. 64.

Since the pressure in the water at A is equal to the pressure at C on the same horizontal level, it follows that

$$H + h_1\rho_1 g = H + h_2\rho_2 g,$$

where H is the atmospheric pressure, and ρ_1, ρ_2 are the respective densities of oil and water. Simplifying,

$$h_1\rho_1 = h_2\rho_2$$

$$\therefore \quad \rho_1 = \rho_2 \times \frac{h_2}{h_1}.$$

Since $\rho_2 = 1$ gram per c.c., and h_2, h_1 are known, the density ρ_1 of the oil can be calculated. Mercury can be used as the liquid originally in the U-tube, for liquids much denser than water.

Hare's apparatus. The densities of dilute and concentrated copper sulphate solution, for example, cannot be compared by the U-tube method, as the two liquids would mix. HARE used two vertical connected tubes to compare the densities of liquids, and placed them in beakers B, C respectively which contained the two liquids. By means of a tap at A, some of the liquids were drawn up the two tubes, as shown in Fig. 65.

Suppose h_1, h_2 are then the respective heights of the two liquids above the surface of the liquids in each beaker; ρ_1, ρ_2 are the respective densities; p, H are the respective

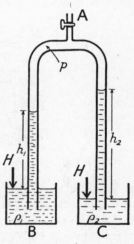

FIG. 65. Density by Hare's apparatus.

pressures of the air above the liquid in the tube and the atmospheric pressure.

Then

$$H = p + h_1\rho_1 g = p + h_2\rho_2 g.$$

$$\therefore \quad h_1\rho_1 g = h_2\rho_2 g$$

$$\therefore \quad \frac{\rho_1}{\rho_2} = \frac{h_2}{h_1}.$$

The densities are thus inversely proportional to the heights in the tubes. Hare's apparatus can also be used to find the actual densities of liquids such as oil, in which case the beaker B is filled with the oil and the beaker C is filled with water, of known density 1.

16. Atmospheric Pressure.

The pressure of the atmosphere was first measured by Galileo, who observed the height of a water column in a tube placed in a deep well. About 1640 TORRICELLI thought of the idea of using mercury instead of water, to obtain a much shorter column. He completely filled a glass tube about a metre long with mercury, and then inverted it in a vessel D containing the liquid, taking care that no air entered the tube. He observed that the mercury in the tube fell to a level A about 76 cm. (or 30 in.) above the level of the mercury in D, Fig. 66. Since there was

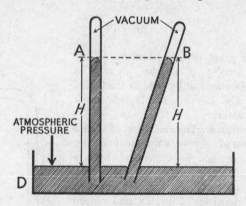

FIG. 66. Simple barometer.

no air originally in the tube, there must be a vacuum above the mercury at A, and it is called a *Torricellian vacuum*. This was the first occasion in the history of science that a vacuum had been created.

If the tube in Fig. 66 is inclined to the vertical, the mercury ascends the tube to a level B at the same vertical height H above the level of the mercury in D as A.

The pressure on the surface of the mercury in D is atmospheric pressure; and since the pressure is transmitted through the liquid, the atmospheric pressure supports the column of mercury in the tube. Suppose A is at a height H above the level of the mercury in D. Now the pressure, p, at the bottom of a column of liquid of height H cm. and density ρ gm. per c.c. is given by $p = H\rho g$ dynes per sq. cm., where g is 980 (p. 102). Thus if H is 76 cm.,

$$p = H\rho g = 76 \times 13 \cdot 6 \times 980 = 1 \cdot 012 \times 10^6 \text{ dynes per sq. cm.,}$$

since the density of mercury is 13·6 gm. per c.c. The pressure at the bottom of a column of mercury 76 cm. high is known as *standard pressure* or *one atmosphere*, and *standard temperature and pressure* (*S.T.P.* or *N.T.P.*) is 0° C. and 76 cm. pressure.

A *bar* is the name given to a pressure of one million (10^6) dynes per sq. cm., and is thus very nearly equal to one atmosphere.

17. Fortin's Barometer.

A *barometer* is an instrument for measuring the pressure of the atmosphere, which is required in weather-forecasting, for example. The most accurate form of barometer is due to FORTIN, and like the simple arrangement already described, it consists basically of a barometer tube containing mercury, with a vacuum at the top, Fig. 67. One end of the tube dips into a pool of mercury contained in a washleather bag B. A brass scale graduated in centimetres (C) or inches (I) is fixed at the top of the barometer. The zero of the scale correspondings to the tip of an ivory tooth P, and hence, before the level of the top of the mercury is read from the scales, the screw S is adjusted until the level of the mercury in B just reaches the tip of P. A vernier scale V can be moved by a screw D until the bottom of it just reaches the top of the mercury in the tube, and the reading of the height of the mercury is taken from C and V or from I and V. Torricelli was the first person to observe the variation of the barometric height as the weather changed.

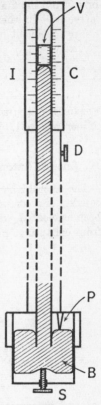

FIG. 67.
Fortin's barometer.

18. "Correction" to the Barometric Height.

For comparison purposes, the pressure read on a barometer is often "reduced" or "corrected" to the magnitude the pressure would have at 0° C. and at sea-level, latitude 45°. Suppose the "reduced" pressure is H_o cm. of mercury, and the observed pressure is H_t cm. of mercury, corresponding to a temperature of $t°$ C. Then, since pressure $= h\rho g$ (p. 102),

$$H_o \rho_o g = H_t \rho_t g',$$

where g is the acceleration due to gravity at sea-level, latitude 45°, and g' is the acceleration at the latitude of the place where the barometer was read.

$$\therefore H_o = H_t \times \frac{\rho_t}{\rho_o} \times \frac{g'}{g}.$$

The magnitude of g'/g can be obtained from standard tables. The ratio ρ_t/ρ_o of the densities $= 1/(1 + \gamma t)$, where γ is the absolute coefficient of cubical expansion of mercury. Further, the observed height, H_t, on the brass scale requires correction for the expansion of brass from the temperature at which it was correctly calibrated. If the latter is $0°$ C., then the corrected height is $H_t(1 + at)$, where a is the linear coefficient of brass. Thus, finally, the "corrected" height H_o is given by

$$H_o = H_t \cdot \frac{1 + at}{1 + \gamma t} \cdot \frac{g'}{g}.$$

For further accuracy, a correction must be made for the surface tension of mercury (p. 115).

19. Aneroid Barometer.

The aneroid barometer is one which does not use any liquid. It consists of a corrugated metal box B from which nearly all the air has been evacuated, with a spring S attached to the top to prevent the box from collapsing, Fig. 68. When the atmospheric pressure varies, the

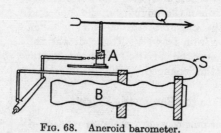

Fig. 68. Aneroid barometer.

top and bottom of the box move in or out. The slight movement is magnified by a system of jointed levers, which pull a chain wound round a spindle A. A pointer Q then rotates over a scale (not shown), which is calibrated in centimetres of mercury by noting the corresponding pressure from a Fortin barometer.

The pressure of the atmosphere decreases approximately by one centimetre of mercury for every 1,000 ft. ascended. The aneroid barometer is therefore used as an *altimeter* (height-measurer) in aeroplanes, and it is also used for the same purpose by mountain climbers.

20. Pressure of a Gas.

The pressure of a gas can be measured by connecting it to a U-tube, M, containing water or mercury, Fig. 69. The liquid in the two sides

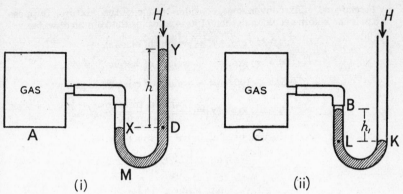

FIG. 69. Measurement of pressure.

of the *manometer*, as M is called, then registers a difference in levels.
Suppose the level, Y, in the open side of M is higher than the level, X,
in the other side, Fig. 69 (i). Then the pressure at X, p, = the pressure
at the same level, D, on the other side.

$$\therefore p = H + h\rho g,$$

where H is the atmospheric pressure, h is the difference in levels of the
liquid, and ρ is the density of the liquid. If the level, K, of the liquid
in the open side of the manometer is lower than the level, B, of the other
side, the pressure at K = the pressure at L = $p + h_1\rho g$, where p is
the pressure of the gas and h_1 is the difference in levels of the liquid,
Fig. 69 (ii). But the pressure at K = the atmospheric pressure = H.

$$\therefore \quad p + h_1\rho g = H$$

$$\therefore \quad p = H - h_1\rho g.$$

The pressure of the gas is thus *less* than the atmospheric pressure in
this case.

EXAMPLES

1. Describe a hydrometer suitable for the determination of the specific
gravity of spirits. How would you test the graduation of a hydrometer?

A mixture of alcohol (s.g. 0·84) and water has a specific gravity of 0·90.
What is the proportion of the constituents (a) by weight, (b) by volume
(neglecting any change of volume which occurs on mixing)? (C.)

First part. See text. The graduation would be tested by placing the
hydrometer in turn in water and other liquids whose specific gravities are
found accurately by the specific gravity bottle method.

Second part. For convenience, consider 100 c.c. of the mixture. Suppose x c.c. is the volume of alcohol; then $(100 - x)$ c.c. is the volume of water.

$$\therefore 0{\cdot}84x \text{ gm. wt.} = \text{weight of alcohol,}$$

$$(100 - x) \text{ gm. wt.} = \text{weight of water.}$$

$$\therefore 0{\cdot}84x + 100 - x = \text{weight of mixture in gm. wt.}$$

$$\text{Now specific gravity} = \frac{\text{weight of mixture}}{100 \text{ gm. wt.}},$$

since 100 gm. wt. is the weight of an equal volume of water.

$$\therefore \quad 0{\cdot}90 = \frac{0{\cdot}84x + 100 - x}{100}$$

$$\therefore \quad 90 = 100 - 0{\cdot}16x$$

$$\therefore 0{\cdot}16x = 10$$

$$\therefore \quad x = \frac{10}{0{\cdot}16} = 62{\cdot}5 = \text{volume of alcohol in c.c}$$

$$\therefore \quad 100 - 62{\cdot}5 = 37{\cdot}5 = \text{volume of water in c.c.}$$

(b) $\quad \therefore$ proportion of constituents by volume $= 62{\cdot}5 : 37{\cdot}5 = 5 : 3$.

(a) Weight of alcohol in 100 c.c. of mixture

$$= 62{\cdot}5 \times 0{\cdot}84 = 52{\cdot}5 \text{ gm. wt.}$$

Also, weight of water in 100 c.c. of mixture $= 37{\cdot}5$ gm. wt.

$\therefore$ proportion by weight $= 52{\cdot}5 : 37{\cdot}5 = 7 : 5$.

2. A hydrometer consists of a bulb of volume V and a uniform stem of volume v per cm. of its length. It floats upright in water so that the bulb is just completely immersed. Explain for what density range this hydrometer may be used and how you would determine the density of such liquids. Describe the graph which would be obtained by plotting the reciprocal of the density against the length of the stem immersed.

A hydrometer such as that described sinks to the mark 3 on the stem, which is graduated in cm., when it is placed in a liquid of density 0·95 gm./c.c. If the volume per cm. of the stem is 0·1 c.c., find the volume of the bulb. (*L.*)

First part. (i) When the hydrometer is placed in liquids less dense than water, it sinks more than in water (p. 99). Consequently the hydrometer can be used for liquids whose density is less than 1. The density of the liquids can be determined by using a specific gravity bottle. (ii) The graph obtained is a straight line (see p. 100).

Second part. Let $V = $ volume of bulb in c.c.
Then upthrust in water $= V \times 1 = $ wt. of hydrometer.
In the liquid of density 0·95 gm./c.c., the volume immersed $= (V + 3 \times 0{\cdot}1)$

$$\therefore \text{upthrust} = (V + 0{\cdot}3)\,0{\cdot}95 = \text{wt. of hydrometer.}$$

$$\therefore \quad V \times 1 = (V + 0{\cdot}3)\,0{\cdot}95$$

$$\therefore \quad 0{\cdot}05V = 0{\cdot}3 \times 0{\cdot}95$$

$$\therefore \quad V = 5{\cdot}7 \text{ c.c.}$$

3. State the principle of Archimedes. A body of mass 100 gm. and of specific gravity 2·00 is suspended by a thread so as to be completely immersed in a liquid of specific gravity 0·92. Find the tension in the thread. If the thread is cut, what will be the initial acceleration of the body? Why will this acceleration not be maintained as the body falls in the liquid? (*W.*)

First part. See text.

Second part. The volume of the body $= \dfrac{100}{2\cdot00} = 50$ c.c.

$$\therefore \text{ upthrust on body } = \text{weight of liquid displaced.}$$
$$= 50 \times 0\cdot92 = 46 \text{ gm. wt.}$$
$$\therefore \text{ tension in thread } = 100 - 46 = 54 \text{ gm. wt.}$$

The net downward force on the body $=$ weight $-$ upthrust $= 54$ gm. wt.
$$= 54 \times 980 \text{ dynes}$$

$$\therefore \text{ initial acceleration } f \text{ if thread cut} = \frac{54 \times 980}{100},$$

since $f = P/m$.

$$\therefore f = 529\cdot2 \text{ cm. per sec.}^2$$

This acceleration is not maintained as the body falls through the liquid, owing to the friction or viscosity of the liquid. The frictional force diminishes the acceleration, and a constant (terminal) velocity is reached (p. 165).

EXERCISES V

1. An alloy of mass 588 gm. and volume 100 c.c. is made of iron of specific gravity 8·0 and aluminium of specific gravity 2·7. Calculate the proportion (i) by volume, (ii) by weight of the constituents of the alloy.

2. A string supports a solid iron object of mass 180 grams totally immersed in a liquid of density 0·8 gm. per c.c. Calculate the tension in the string if the density of iron is 8·0 gm. per c.c.

3. Describe how you would measure (i) the density of sand, (ii) the density of copper sulphate crystals. Give imaginary measurements, and calculate the result, for each case.

4. A hydrometer floats in water with 6·0 cm. of its graduated stem unimmersed, and in oil of specific gravity 0·8 with 4·0 cm. of the stem unimmersed. What is the length of stem unimmersed when the hydrometer is placed in a liquid of specific gravity 0·9?

5. State *Archimedes' Principle*. Describe how you would measure the density of cork, giving numerical values in illustration and calculating the result.

6. An alloy of mass 170 gm. has an apparent weight of 95 gm. in a liquid of density 1·5 gm. per c.c. If the two constituents of the alloy have specific gravities of 4·0 and 3·0 respectively, calculate the proportion by volume of the constituents in the alloy.

7. Distinguish between *mass* and *weight*. Define *density*.

Describe and explain how you would proceed to find an accurate value for the density of gold, the specimen available being a wedding ring of pure gold.

What will be the reading of (a) a mercury barometer, (b) a water barometer, when the atmospheric pressure is 10^6 dyne cm.$^{-2}$? The density of mercury may be taken as 13·6 gm. cm.$^{-3}$ and the pressure of saturated water vapour at room temperature as 1·3 cm. of mercury. (*L.*)

8. Describe an accurate form of barometer and illustrate your description with a sketch. Indicate how a vernier may be used to obtain an accurate reading. Explain the corrections which have to be applied to the reading observed to make it suitable for meteorological purposes. (*N.*)

9. State the principle of Archimedes, and discuss its application to the determination of specific gravities by means of a common hydrometer. Why is this method essentially less accurate than the specific gravity bottle?

A common hydrometer is graduated to read specific gravities from 0·8 to 1·0. In order to extend its range a small weight is attached to the stem, above the liquid, so that the instrument reads 0·8 when floating in water. What will be the specific gravity of the liquid corresponding to the graduation 1·0? (*O. & C.*)

10. State Archimedes' principle. A measuring jar containing 200 c.c. of water at 0° C. A lump of ice at 0° C. is added, which brings the level of the water up to 240 c.c. mark. Deduce the mass of the lump of ice. If the ice is allowed to melt, the contents of the jar being maintained at 0° C., deduce the final level of the water surface. (You may assume that the density of water at 0° C. is 1 gm./cm.^{3})

Brass "weights" of density 8·4 gm./cm.^{3} are employed in the determination of the weight of a given quantity of water. Show that, if the air buoyancy correction is applied, a correction of about 0·1 per cent. will be necessary to obtain the true weight from the recorded weight. (Density of air = 0·00125 gm./cm.^{3}) (*W.*)

11. Describe two methods by which you could measure the density of ice. Calculate the mass of lead which must be attached to 90 gm. of wax in order that the whole may float totally immersed in a solution of density 1·04 gm. per c.c. The densities of lead and wax respectively are 11·3 and 0·86 gm. per c.c. (*L.*)

12. A variable immersion hydrometer has a range from 1·00 to 1·02 gm./cm.^{3} marked on its stem, which is of uniform cross-section. The distance between these extreme markings is 30 cm. Find the distance between the 1·02 mark and the 1·01 mark on the hydrometer stem. (*W.*)

13. Describe some form of barometer used for the accurate measurement of atmospheric pressure, and point out the corrections to be applied to the observation.

Obtain an expression for the correction to be applied to the reading of a mercurial barometer when the reading is made at a temperature other than 0° C. (*L.*)

14. Define *hydrostatic pressure* at a point, and state the units in which it may be measured. Obtain an expression for the pressure at a point h cm. below the surface of the sea, if d_1 is the density of sea-water, P_0 is the height of the mercury barometer, and d_2 is the density of mercury, all in c.g.s. units.

A hollow metal ball, with a small hole at the bottom and an eyelet at the top, is lowered into a fresh-water lake by means of a wire attached to the eyelet. Find the tension at the upper end of the wire when the ball has been lowered 50 metres, given that ball and 50 metres of wire together weigh 780 gm. and have a common density of 7·8 gm./cm.³, volume of hollow interior of ball is 500 cm.³, atmospheric pressure is 760 mm. of mercury of density 13·6 gm./cm.³, and temperature everywhere is 18° C. Show that the tension might be used to indicate the temperature of the water at 50 metres depth, and calculate the amount by which the tension would alter per deg. C. in the neighbourhood of 18° C. (*W.*)

15. State Archimedes principle, and describe how you would verify it experimentally.

A hydrometer of mass 50 gm. floats in water with a mark X on its stem level with the water. If a mass of 5 gm. is placed on top of the hydrometer, it sinks again to the mark X when placed in brine. Calculate the specific gravity of the brine.

16. State the principle of Archimedes and use it to derive an expression for the resultant force experienced by a body of weight W and density σ when it is totally immersed in a fluid of density ρ.

A solid weighs 237·5 gm. in air and 12·5 gm. when totally immersed in a liquid of specific gravity 0·9. Calculate (*a*) the specific gravity of the solid, (*b*) the specific gravity of a liquid in which the solid would float with one-fifth of its volume exposed above the liquid surface. (*L.*)

CHAPTER VI

SURFACE TENSION

It is a well-known fact that some insects, for example a water-carrier, are able to walk across a water surface; that a drop of water may remain suspended for some time from a tap before falling, as if the water particles were held together in a bag; that mercury gathers into small droplets when spilt; and that a dry steel needle S may be made, with care, to float on water, Fig. 70 (i). These observations suggest that *the surface of a liquid acts like an elastic skin covering the liquid.*

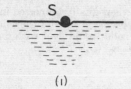   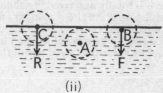

(i)   (ii)

FIG. 70.   Needle on water.   Molecular explanation of surface tension.

1. The Force on Molecules in the Liquid Surface.

We can understand why the surface of a liquid acts like a skin if we consider firstly molecules such as A in the interior of the liquid, Fig. 70 (ii). All the molecules which have an appreciable attraction on A are those contained in a sphere of centre A which has a very small but finite radius, known as the *sphere of molecular activity*. This is represented by an exaggerated dotted circle round A in Fig. 70 (ii). Since there are as many molecules attracting A in one direction as attract it in the opposite direction, the resultant force on A in *any* direction is zero. Now consider a molecule B of the liquid very close to the surface. If the sphere of molecular activity is drawn round it, part of the sphere will be in the air above the liquid, as shown. The horizontal attractive forces on B in any direction will still cancel out; but there is now a resultant force F on B acting towards the interior of the liquid, because there are more liquid molecules in the hemisphere below B than above B. If we draw the sphere of molecular activity round a molecule C in the surface, half the sphere is in air and half is in liquid; with the result that the force R on C is inwards towards the liquid. (It must be emphasised here that B is very close to the surface, and that Fig. 70 (ii) is exaggerated for clarity.)

112

2. The Shape of Liquids.

The inward forces on the molecules in the liquid surface will tend to make the molecules move towards the interior. As a result, the liquid surface tends to contract and become as small as possible, which implies that (i) the surface acts like a skin covering the liquid, (ii) the *area of the surface is a minimum* for a given volume of liquid. Now a *sphere* is that shape which has a minimum surface area for a given volume. We can therefore expect that liquids assume a spherical shape when care is taken to neutralise forces, such as gravity, other than those just discussed. PLATEAU placed a drop of oil in a mixture of alcohol and water of the same density, in which case the weight of oil was exactly balanced by the upthrust of the mixture and the effect of gravity on the drop was neutralised. He then observed that the drop was a perfect sphere.

Observations also show that a small drop of mercury is spherical; that a rain-drop falling through air is spherical; and that a soap-bubble is spherical. Lead shot is made by pouring a fine stream of molten lead from a tall tower, when the stream breaks up into small spherical drops owing to surface tension forces.

3. Surface Tension.

Since the surface of a liquid acts like an elastic skin, the surface is in a state of tension. As a very rough analogy we can think of a blown-up football bladder, whose surface is in a condition of tension. Any line in the surface is then acted on by two equal and opposite forces, and if the bladder is cut with a knife the rubber draws away from the incision under the action of the two forces.

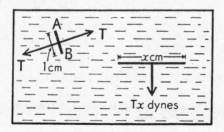

FIG. 71. Surface tension forces.

The surface tension, T, of a liquid is defined *as numerically equal to the force in the surface acting at right angles to one side of a line AB one centimetre long drawn in the surface*, Fig. 71. The unit of T is thus *dynes per cm.* or *dyne cm.*[-1]

The magnitude of T depends on the temperature of the liquid and on the medium on the other side of the surface. For water at 20° C. in contact with air, $T = 72·6$ dynes per cm. (dyne cm.$^{-1}$). For mercury at 20° C. in contact with air, $T = 465$ dynes per cm. The surface tension of a water-oil (olive-oil) boundary is 20·6 dynes per cm., and for a mercury-water boundary it is 427 dynes per cm.

4. Dimensions of Surface Tension.

Since surface tension is a "force per unit length", the dimensions of

$$\text{surface tension} = \frac{\text{dimensions of force}}{\text{dimension of length}}$$

$$= \frac{[M]\,[L]\,[T]^{-2}}{[L]} \text{ (p. 25)}.$$

$$= [M]\,[T]^{-2}$$

5. Phenomena Concerning Surface Tension.

The effect of surface tension forces in a soap film can be demonstrated by placing a thread B carefully on a soap film formed in a metal ring A, Fig. 72 (i). If the film enclosed by the thread is pierced, the thread

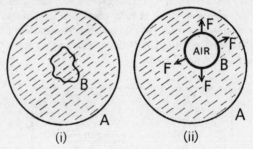

Fig. 72. Demonstration of surface tension.

is pulled out into a circle by the surface tension forces F at the junction of the air and soap-film, Fig. 72 (ii).

Another demonstration of surface tension forces can be made by sprinkling light dust or lycopoduim powder over the surface of water contained in a dish. If the middle of the water is touched with the end of a glass rod which had previously been dipped into soap solution, the powder is carried away to the sides by the water. The explanation lies in the fact that the surface tension of water is greater than that of a soap-film (p. 121). The resultant force at the place where the rod touched the water is hence *away from* the rod, and thus the powder moves away from the centre towards the sides of the vessel.

A toy duck moves by itself across the surface of water when it has a small bag of camphor attached to its base. The camphor lowers the surface tension of the water in contact with it, and the duck is urged across the water by the resultant force on it.

6. Capillarity.

When a capillary tube is immersed in water, and then placed vertically with one end in the liquid, observation shows that the water rises in the tube to a height above the surface. The narrower the tube, the greater is the height to which the water rises, Fig. 73 (i). See also

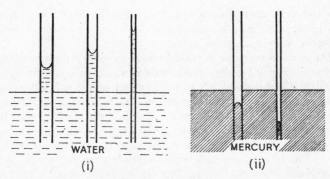

(i)   (ii)

Fɪɢ. 73.   Capillarity.

p. 125. This phenomenon is known as *capillarity*, and it occurs when blotting-paper is used to dry ink. The liquid rises up the pores of the paper when it is pressed on the ink.

When a capillary tube is placed inside mercury, however, the liquid is depressed *below* the outside level, Fig. 73 (ii). The depression increases as the diameter of the capillary tube decreases. See also p. 126.

7. Angle of Contact.

In the case of water in a glass capillary tube, observation of the meniscus shows that it is hemispherical if the glass is clean, that is, the glass surface is tangential to the meniscus where the water touches it. In other cases where liquids rise in a capillary tube, the tangent BN to the liquid surface where it touches the glass may make an acute angle θ with the glass, Fig. 74 (i). The angle θ is known as the *angle of contact* between the liquid and the glass, and is always measured *through the liquid*. The angle of contact between two given surfaces varies largely with their freshness and cleanliness. The angle of contact between

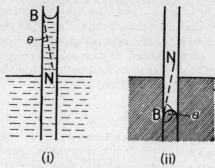

FIG. 74. Angle of contact.

water and very clean glass is zero, but when the glass is not clean the angle of contact may be about 8°. The angle of contact between alcohol and very clean glass is zero.

When a capillary tube is placed inside mercury, observation shows that the surface of the depressed liquid in the tube is convex upwards. Fig. 74 (ii). The tangent BN to the mercury at the point B where the liquid touches the glass thus makes an obtuse angle, θ, with the glass when measured through the liquid. We shall see later (p. 124) that a liquid will rise in a capillary tube if the angle of contact is acute, and that a liquid will be depressed in the tube if the angle of contact is obtuse. For the same reason, water spreads over, or "wets", a clean glass surface when spilt on it, Fig. 75 (i), whereas mercury gathers

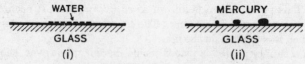

FIG. 75. Water and mercury on clean glass.

itself into small pools or globules when spilt on glass, and does not "wet' glass, Fig. 75 (ii).

The difference in behaviour of water and mercury on clean glass can be explained in terms of the attraction between the molecules of these substances. It appears that the force of *cohesion* between two modecules of water is less than the force of *adhesion* between a molecule of water and a molecule of glass; and thus water spreads over glass. On the other hand, the force of cohesion between two molecules of mercury is greater than the force of adhesion between a molecule of mercury and a molecule of glass; and thus mercury gathers in pools when spilt on glass.

8. The Angle of Contact of Mercury with Glass

can be measured by placing mercury in an inverted flask, and connecting a movable column M of mercury to it, Fig. 76. When M is moved vertically, the mercury surface in the flask appears horizontal right up to the edges of the glass at some position AB. In this case the tangent DAC to the flask at A is also a tangent to the liquid where the latter meets the glass. Thus angle BAC is the angle of contact between mercury and glass. By measuring the diameter of AB, and knowing the radius AO of the sphere, the angle AOB subtended at the centre, O, can be calculated by simple trigonometry.

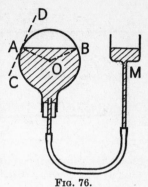

FIG. 76.
Angle of contact of mercury.

Angle DAB is half the angle AOB, by geometry; and hence the supplementary angle BAC, the angle of contact, is easily obtained. For a freshly-formed mercury drop in contact with a clean glass plate, the angle of contact is 137°.

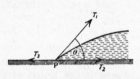

FIG. 77. Angle of contact.

Spreading and Wetting. We have already seen that the surface boundary between a liquid and air has a surface tension (p. 112). By analogous reasoning, it follows that the surface boundary between a solid and air, or between a solid and liquid, has a surface tension.

Consider a drop of liquid in equilibrium on a solid P, with an angle of contact θ, Fig. 77. Suppose T_1, T_2, T_3 denote the respective surface-tensions of the air-liquid, liquid-solid, and air-solid boundaries. If we consider the horizontal forces on a line 1 cm. long through P into the paper, we must have, for equilibrium,

$$T_1 \cos \theta + T_2 = T_3.$$

$$\therefore \cos \theta = \frac{T_3 - T_2}{T_1}.$$

If T_3 is greater than T_2, $\cos \theta$ is positive and θ is less than 90°. In this case (an acute angle of contact), "wetting" of the surface takes place. If T_3 is less than T_2, $\cos \theta$ is negative and θ must be an obtuse angle; in this case there is no "wetting". "Wetting" is the result of a relatively high degree of attraction between the molecules of the solid and liquid concerned.

9. Surface Tension and Surface Energy.

We come now to a relation between the surface energy of a liquid and its surface tension T. Consider a film of liquid stretched across a horizontal frame ABCD, Fig. 78. If T is the surface tension of the liquid in dynes per centimetre, the force on the rod BC due to surface tension

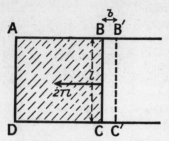

FIG. 78. Surface energy.

forces $= 2T \times l$ dynes, where BC is l cm. long, since there are two surfaces to the film.

Suppose the rod is now moved a distance b cm. from BC to B'C' against the surface tension forces, so that the surface area of the film increases. The temperature of the film then usually decreases, in which case the surface tension alters (p. 129). If the surface area increases under *isothermal* (constant temperature) conditions, however, the surface tension is consant; and we can then say that, if T is the surface tension at that temperature,

work done in enlarging surface area = force $\times$ distance

$$= 2Tl \times b = T \times 2lb.$$

But $2lb$ is the total increase in surface area of the film.

$\therefore$ work done per sq. cm. in enlarging area $= T$.

Thus the surface tension, T, can be defined as *the work done in increasing the surface area of a liquid by one square centimetre under isothermal conditions*, which is also called the *free surface energy*. (See also p. 200.)

It is a well-known principle in Mechanics that an object is in stable equilibrium when its potential energy is a minimum. From our discussion, this implies that a given volume of liquid, under surface tension forces, will assume a minimum surface area, which is the shape of a sphere (see p. 113).

EXAMPLES

1. (i) Calculate the work done against surface tension forces in blowing a soap bubble of 1 cm. diameter if the surface tension of soap solution is 25 dynes per cm. (ii) Find the work required to break up a drop of water of radius 0·5 cm. into drops of water each of radii 1 mm. (Surface tension of water = 70 dynes per cm.)

(i) The original surface area of the bubble is zero, and the final surface area $= 2 \times 4\pi r^2$ (two surfaces of bubble) $= 2 \times 4\pi \times 0\cdot5^2 = 2\pi$ sq. cm.

$\therefore$ work done $= T \times$ increase in surface area in sq. cm.

$$= 25 \times 2\pi = 157 \text{ ergs.}$$

(ii) Since volume of a drop $= \frac{4}{3}\pi r^3$,

$$\text{number of drops formed} = \frac{\frac{4}{3}\pi \times 0\cdot5^3}{\frac{4}{3}\pi \times 0\cdot1^3} = 125.$$

∴ final total surface area of drops

$$= 125 \times 4\pi r^2 = 125 \times 4\pi \times 0.1^2$$
$$= 5\pi \text{ sq. cm.}$$

But original surface area of drop $= 4\pi \times 0.5^2 = \pi$ sq. cm.

∴ work done $= T \times$ change in surface area

$$= 70 \times (5\pi - \pi) = 879 \text{ ergs.}$$

2. A soap bubble in a vacuum has a radius of 3 cm. and another soap bubble in the vacuum has a radius of 6 cm. If the two bubbles coalesce under isothermal conditions, calculate the radius of the bubble formed.

Since the bubbles coalesce under isothermal conditions, the surface tension T is constant. Suppose R is the radius in cm. of the bubble formed.

Then   work done $= T \times$ surface area $= T \times 8\pi R^2$.

But   original work done $= T \times 8\pi . 3^2 + T \times 8\pi . 6^2$.

$$\therefore T \times 8\pi R^2 = T \times 8\pi . 3^2 + T . 8\pi . 6^2.$$

$$\therefore R^2 = 3^2 + 6^2$$

$$\therefore R = \sqrt{3^2 + 6^2} = 6.7 \text{ cm.}$$

10. Measurement of Surface Tension by Capillary Tube Method.

Theory. Suppose T is the magnitude of the surface tension of a liquid such as water, which rises up a clean glass capillary tube and has an angle of contact zero. Fig. 79 shows a section of the meniscus M at B, which is a hemisphere. Since the glass AB is a tangent to the

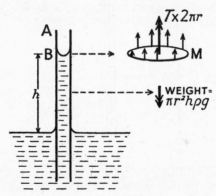

FIG. 79. Theory of capillary tube method.

liquid, the surface tension forces, which act along the boundary of the liquid with the air, act vertically downwards on the glass. By the law of action and reaction, the glass exerts an equal force in an upward direction on the liquid. Now surface tension, T, is the force per unit length acting in the surface of the liquid, and the length of liquid in contact with the glass is $2\pi r$, where r is the radius of the capillary tube.

$$\therefore 2\pi r \times T = \text{upward force on liquid.}$$

This force supports the weight of a column of height h above the outside level of liquid. The volume of the liquid $= \pi r^2 h$, and thus the mass, m, of the liquid column $=$ volume $\times$ density $= \pi r^2 h \rho$, where ρ is the density. The *weight* of the liquid $= mg = \pi r^2 h \rho g$ dynes, where r and h are in centimetres, ρ is in grams per c.c., and $g = 980$ numerically.

$$\therefore \quad 2\pi r T = \pi r^2 h \rho g$$

$$\therefore \quad T = \frac{rh\rho g}{2} \qquad . \qquad . \qquad . \qquad . \qquad . \qquad (50)$$

In deriving this formula for T it should be noted that we have (i) assumed the glass to be a tangent to the liquid surface meeting it, (ii) neglected the weight of the small amount of liquid above the bottom of the meniscus at B, Fig. 79.

Experiment. In the experiment, the capillary tube C is supported in a beaker Y, and a pin P, bent at right angles at two places, is attached to C by a rubber band, Fig. 80. P is adjusted until its point just touches

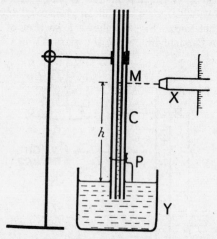

Fig. 80.   Surface tension by capillary tube method.

the horizontal level of the liquid in the beaker. A travelling microscope is now focussed on to the meniscus M in C, and then it is focussed on to the point of P, the beaker being removed for this observation. In this way the height h of M above the level in the beaker is determined. The radius of the capillary at M can be found by cutting the tube at this place and measuring the diameter by the travelling microscope; or by measuring the length, l cm., and mass, m grams, of a mercury thread drawn into the tube, and calculating the radius, r cm., from the relation $r = \sqrt{m/\pi l \rho}$, where ρ is the density of mercury, 13·6 gm. per c.c. The surface tension T is then calculated from the formula $T = rh\rho g/2$. Its magnitude for water at 15° C. is 73·3 dynes per cm.; for alcohol at 20° C. it is 23·0 dynes per cm.; for paraffin oil at 25° C. it is 26·4 dynes per cm.

11. Measurement of Surface Tension by Microscope Slide.

Besides the capillary tube method, the surface tension of water can be measured by weighing a microscope slide in air, and then lowering it until it just meets the surface of water, Fig. 81. The surface tension

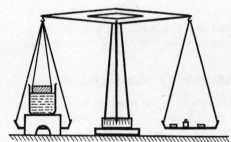

FIG. 81.   Surface tension by microscope slide method.

force acts vertically downward round the boundary of the slide, and pulls the slide down. Thus the apparent increase, m grams, in the weight is equal to $T(2a + 2b)$ where a, b are the length and thickness of the slide in cm., since, by definition, T is the force per unit length acting in the liquid surface.

$$\therefore T(2a + 2b) = mg,$$

where g is 980.

$$\therefore T = \frac{mg}{2a + 2b},$$

Thus T can be calculated in dynes per cm.

12. The Surface Tension of a Soap Solution can be found by a similar method. A soap-film is formed in a three-sided metal frame ABCD, and the apparent weight is found, Fig. 82. When the film is broken by piercing it, the decrease in the apparent weight, m grams, is equal to the surface tension force acting downwards when the film existed. This is equal to $2Tb$, where $b = $ BC cm., since the film has *two* sides.

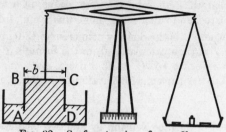

FIG. 82. Surface tension of soap film.

$$\therefore 2Tb = mg$$

$$\therefore T = \frac{mg}{2b}.$$

It will be noted that the surface tension forces on the sides AB, CD of the frame act horizontally, and their resultant is zero.

13. Pressure Difference in a Bubble or Curved Liquid Surface.

As we shall see presently, the magnitude of the curvature of a liquid, or of a bubble formed in a liquid, is related to the surface tension of the liquid.

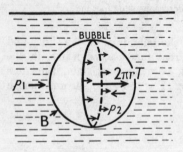

FIG. 83.
Excess pressure in a bubble.

Consider a bubble formed inside a liquid, Fig. 83. If we consider the equilibrium of *one half*, B, of the bubble, we can see that the surface tension force on B plus the force on B due to the external pressure $p_1 =$ the force on B due to the internal pressure p_2 inside the bubble. The force on B due to the pressure p_1 is given by $\pi r^2 \times p_1$, since πr^2 is the area of the circular face of B and pressure is "force per unit area"; the force on B due to the pressure p_2 is given similarly by $\pi r^2 \times p_2$. The surface tension force acts round the *circumference* of the bubble, which has a length $2\pi r$; thus the force is $2\pi rT$. It follows that

$$2\pi rT + \pi r^2 p_1 = \pi r^2 p_2$$

Simplifying, $$\therefore 2T = r(p_2 - p_1),$$

or $$p_2 - p_1 = \frac{2T}{r}.$$

Now $(p_2 - p_1)$ is the excess pressure, p, in the bubble over the outside pressure.

$$\therefore \; excess \; pressure, \, p, = \frac{2T}{r} \qquad . \qquad . \qquad . \qquad . \qquad (51)$$

Although we considered a bubble, the same formula for the excess pressure holds for any curved liquid surface or meniscus, where r is its radius of curvature and T is its surface tension, provided the angle of contact is zero. If the angle of contact is θ, the formula is modified by replacing T by $T \cos \theta$. Thus, in general,

$$excess \; pressure, \, p, = \frac{2T \cos \theta}{r} \qquad . \qquad . \qquad . \qquad (52)$$

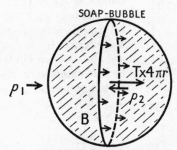

Fig. 84.   Excess pressure in a soap bubble.

14. Excess Pressure in Soap Bubble.

A soap bubble has two liquid surfaces in contact with air, one inside the bubble and the other outside the bubble. The force on one half, B, of the bubble due to surface tension forces is thus $T \times 2\pi r \times 2$, i.e., $T \times 4\pi r$, Fig. 84. For the equilibrium of B, it follows that

$$4\pi r T + \pi r^2 p_1 = \pi r^2 p_2,$$

where p_2, p_1 are the pressures inside and outside the bubble respectively. Simplifying,

$$\therefore \; p_2 - p_1 = \frac{4T}{r}$$

$$\therefore \; excess \; pressure = \frac{4T}{r} \qquad . \qquad . \qquad . \qquad . \qquad (53)$$

The result for the excess pressure should now be compared with the result obtained for a bubble formed inside a liquid, equation (51).

Two soap-bubbles of unequal size can be blown on the ends of a tube, communication between them being prevented by a closed tap in the middle. If the tap is opened, the *smaller* bubble is observed to collapse gradually and the size of the larger bubble increases. This can be explained from our formula $p = 4T/r$, which shows that the pressure of air inside the smaller bubble is greater than that inside the larger bubble. Consequently air flows from the smaller to the larger bubble when communication is made between the bubbles, and the smaller bubble thus gradually collapses.

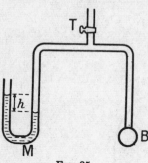

FIG. 85.
Surface tension of soap bubble.

15. Surface Tension of Soap-Bubble.

The surface tension of a soap solution can be measured by blowing a small soap-bubble at the end B of a tube connected to a manometer M, Fig. 85. The tap T is then closed, the diameter d of the bubble is measured by a travelling microscope, and the difference in levels h of the liquid in the manometer is observed with the same instrument. The excess pressure, p, in the bubble $= h\rho g$, where ρ is the density of the liquid in M.

$$\therefore h\rho g = \frac{4T}{r} = \frac{4T}{d/2}.$$

$$\therefore T = \frac{h\rho g d}{8}.$$

16. Rise or Fall of Liquids in Capillary Tubes.

From our knowledge of the angle of contact and the excess pressure on one side of a curved liquid surface, we can deduce that some liquids will rise in a capillary tube, whereas others will be depressed.

Suppose the tube A is placed in water, for example, Fig. 86 (i). At first the liquid surface becomes concave upwards in the tube, because the angle of contact with the glass is zero. Consequently the pressure on the air side, X, of the curved surface is greater than the pressure on the liquid side Y by $2T/r$, where T is the surface tension and r is the radius of curvature of the tube. But the pressure at X is atmospheric, H. Hence the pressure at Y must be less than atmospheric by $2T/r$. Fig. 86 (i) is therefore impossible because it shows the pressure at Y equal to the atmospheric pressure. Thus, as shown in Fig. 86 (ii), the liquid ascends the tube to a height h such that the pressure at N is less than at M by $2T/r$, Fig. 86 (ii). A similar argument shows that a liquid rises in a capillary tube when the angle of contact is acute.

The angle of contact between mercury and glass is obtuse (p. 116). Thus when a capillary tube is placed in mercury the liquid first curves downwards. The pressure inside the liquid just below the curved surface is now greater than the pressure on the other side, which is atmospheric, and the mercury therefore moves down the tube until the excess pressure $= 2T \cos \theta/r$, with the usual notation. A liquid thus falls in a capillary tube if the angle of contact is obtuse.

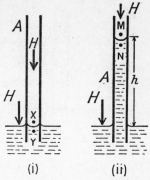

Fig. 86. Rise of liquid in capillary tube.

17. Capillary Rise and Fall by Pressure Method.

We shall now calculate the capillary rise of water by the excess pressure formula $p = 2T/r$, or $p = 2T \cos \theta/r$.

In the case of a capillary tube dipping into water, the angle of contact is practically zero, Fig. 87 (i). Thus if p_2 is the pressure of the atmosphere, and p_1 is the pressure in the liquid, we have

$$p_2 - p_1 = \frac{2T}{r}.$$

Now if H is the atmospheric pressure in dynes per sq. cm., h is the height of the liquid in the tube and ρ its density,

$$p_2 = H \text{ and } p_1 = H - h\rho g$$

$$\therefore \ H - (H - h\rho g) = \frac{2T}{r}$$

$$\therefore \ h\rho g = \frac{2T}{r}$$

$$\therefore \ h = \frac{2T}{r\rho g} \quad \cdot \quad \cdot \quad \cdot \quad \cdot \quad \text{(i)}$$

The formula shows that h increases as r decreases, i.e., the narrower the tube, the greater is the height to which the water rises (see Fig. 73 (i), p. 115).

If the height l of the tube above the water is less than the calculated value of h in the above formula, the water surface at the top of the tube now meets it at an acute angle of contact θ. Its radius is therefore $r/\cos \theta$, and $l\rho g = 2T/(r/\cos \theta)$, or

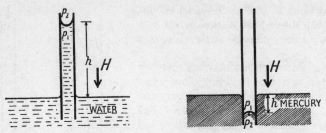

FIG. 87.   Rise and fall of liquids by excess pressure method.

$$l = \frac{2T \cos \theta}{r \rho g} \qquad . \qquad . \qquad . \qquad . \qquad \text{(ii)}$$

Dividing (ii) by (i), it follows that

$$\cos \theta = \frac{l}{h}.$$

18. With Mercury in Glass.

Suppose that the depression of the mercury inside a tube of radius r is h, Fig. 87 (ii). The pressure p_2 in the curved surface of the mercury is then greater than the (atmospheric) pressure p_1 outside the curved surface; and, from our general result,

$$p_2 - p_1 = \frac{2T \cos \theta}{r},$$

where θ is the supplement of the obtuse angle of contact of mercury with glass (about 137°) But $p_1 = H$ and $p_2 = H + h\rho g$, where H is the atmospheric pressure in dynes per sq. cm.

$$\therefore (H + h\rho g) - H = \frac{2T \cos \theta}{r}.$$

$$\therefore h\rho g = \frac{2T \cos \theta}{r}.$$

$$\therefore h = \frac{2T \cos \theta}{r \rho g} \qquad . \qquad . \qquad . \qquad \text{(54)}$$

The height of depression, h, thus increases as the radius r of the tube decreases. See Fig. 73 (ii), p. 115.

19. Effect of Surface Tension in Hare's Apparatus.

When we discussed the measurement of the specific gravity or density of a liquid by an inverted U-tube or Hare's apparatus, the effect of

surface tension was not considered. If the tubes are wide, the surface
tension effect can be neglected. If the tubes are narrow, we can take
surface tension into account in the following way.

With the notation on p. 103, and referring to Fig. 65,

$$p - p_1 = \frac{2T_1}{r_1},$$

where p_1 is the pressure in the liquid near the meniscus of the tube in
B, T_1 is the surface tension of the liquid, and r_1 is the radius of B. But,
from hydrostatics, $p_1 = H - h_1\rho_1 g$.

$$\therefore \ p - (H - h_1\rho_1 g) = \frac{2T_1}{r_1}$$

$$\therefore \ \ H - p = h_1\rho_1 g - \frac{2T_1}{r_1} \quad . \quad . \quad . \quad (i)$$

If T_2 is the surface tension of the liquid in C, and r_2 is the radius of
the tube in the liquid, then, by similar reasoning,

$$H - p = h_2\rho_2 g - \frac{2T_2}{r_2} \quad . \quad . \quad . \quad . \quad (ii)$$

From (i) and (ii),

$$\therefore \ h_2\rho_2 g - \frac{2T_2}{r_2} = h_1\rho_1 g - \frac{2T_1}{r_1}$$

Re-arranging,

$$\therefore \ h_2 = \frac{\rho_1}{\rho_2}h_1 - \frac{2}{\rho_2 g}\left(\frac{T_1}{r_1} - \frac{T_2}{r_2}\right)$$

Suppose the liquid in C is water, that is, $\rho_2 = 1$ gm. per c.c. Then

$$h_2 = \rho_1 h_1 - \frac{2}{g}\left(\frac{T_1}{r_1} - \frac{T_2}{r_2}\right),$$

which is an equation of the form $y = mx + c$, where c is a constant,
$h_2 = y$, $h_1 = x$, and $\rho_1 = m$. Thus by taking different values of h_2 and
h_1, and plotting h_2 against h_1, a straight-line graph is obtained whose
slope is equal to ρ_1, the density. In this way the effect of the surface
tension can be eliminated.

20. Variation of Surface Tension with Temperature. Jaeger's Method.

By forming a bubble inside a liquid, and measuring the excess
pressure, JAEGER was able to determine the variation of the surface

tension of a liquid with temperature. One form of the apparatus is shown in Fig. 88. A capillary or drawn-out tubing A is connected to a

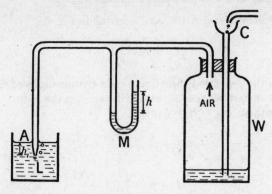

FIG. 88. Variation of surface tension with temperature.

vessel W containing a funnel C, so that air is driven slowly through A when water enters W through C. The capillary A is placed inside a beaker containing the liquid L, and a bubble forms slowly at the end of A when air is passed through at it a slow rate. *The bubble becomes unstable and breaks away from A when its radius is the same as that of A.* Thus as the bubble grows the pressure in it increases to a maximum, and then decreases as the bubble breaks away. The maximum pressure is observed from a manometer M containing a light oil of density ρ, and a series of observations are taken as several bubbles grow.

The maximum pressure inside the bubble $= H + h\rho g$ where h is the maximum difference in levels in the manometer M, and H is the atmospheric pressure. The pressure outside the bubble $= H + h_1\rho_1 g$, where h_1 is the depth of the orifice of A below the level of the liquid L, and ρ_1 is the latter's density.

$$\therefore \text{ excess pressure} = (H + h\rho g) - (H + h_1\rho_1 g) = h\rho g - h_1\rho_1 g$$

But   excess pressure $= \dfrac{2T}{r}$,

where r is the radius of the orifice of A (p. 123).

$$\therefore \frac{2T}{r} = h\rho g - h_1\rho_1 g$$

$$\therefore \ T = \frac{rg}{2}(h\rho - h_1\rho_1)$$

By adding warm liquid to the vessel containing L, the variation of the surface tension with temperature can be determined. Experiment shows that the surface tension of liquids, and water in particular, decreases with increasing temperature, as the table below indicates. Various formulæ relating the surface tension to temperature have been proposed, but none has been found to be completely satisfactory.

SURFACE TENSION OF WATER

TEMPERATURE ° C.	T (DYNES/CM.)
0	75·5
10	74·0
15	73·3
20	72·6
30	71·1
40	69·4
50	67·8
60	66·0
70	64·2

EXAMPLES

1. Define surface tension of a liquid and describe a method of finding this quantity for alcohol.

If water rises in a capillary tube 5·8 cm. above the free surface of the outer liquid, what will happen to the mercury level in the same tube when it is placed in a dish of mercury? Illustrate this by the aid of a diagram. Calculate the difference in level between the mercury surfaces inside the tube and outside. (S.T. of water = 75 dynes/cm. S.T. of mercury = 547 dynes per cm. Angle of contact of mercury with clean glass = 130°. Density of mercury = 13·6 gm./c.c.) (*L.*)

First part. "Surface tension" is defined in the text. The surface tension of alcohol can be found by measuring the rise in a capillary tube, p. 120.

Second part. The mercury is depressed a distance *h* below the outside level, and is convex upward, Fig. 89. Suppose *r* is the capillary tube radius. Then, since $T = rh\rho g/2$ for the case of the water (p. 120),

$$\frac{r \times 5·8 \times 1 \times 980}{2} = 75.$$

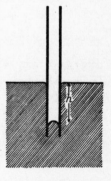

FIG. 89.

$$\therefore r = \frac{\cdot\ 150}{5\cdot8\ \times\ 980}.$$

In the case of the mercury, the equation which applies is

$$T \cos 50° = \frac{rh\rho g}{2},$$

since $180° - 130° = 50°$. See p. 126.

$$\therefore h = \frac{2T \cos 50°}{r\rho g}$$

$$= \frac{2\ \times\ 547 \cos 50°\ \times\ 5\cdot8\ \times\ 980}{13\cdot6\ \times\ 980\ \times\ 150},$$

substituting for r from above.

$$\therefore h = 2\cdot0\ \text{cm}.$$

2. Explain how to measure the surface tension of a soap film.

The diameters of the arms of a U-tube are respectively 1 cm. and 1 mm. A liquid of surface tension 70 dynes/cm. is poured into the tube which is placed vertically. Find the difference in levels in the two arms. The density may be taken as unity and the contact angle zero. (*L.*)

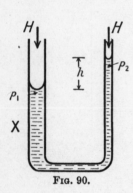

Fig. 90.

First part. The surface tension of a soap film can be measured by the "framework film" method, described on p. 121.

Second part. The liquid in the narrower tube reaches a greater height than that in the wider tube, Fig. 90. Suppose H is the atmospheric pressure and p_2 is the pressure in the liquid below the meniscus. Then, since excess pressure $= 2T/r$,

$$H - p_2 = \frac{2T}{r_2}, \qquad \cdot \quad \cdot \quad \cdot \quad \cdot \quad \text{(i)}$$

where $r_2 = \frac{1}{2}$ mm. $= 0\cdot05$ cm.

If p_1 is the pressure in the liquid below the meniscus in the wider tube, we have, similarly,

$$H - p_1 = \frac{2T}{r_1}, \qquad \cdot \quad \cdot \quad \cdot \quad \cdot \quad \text{(ii)}$$

where $r_1 = \frac{1}{2}$ cm. $= 0\cdot5$ cm.

Subtracting (ii) from (i),

$$\therefore p_1 - p_2 = \frac{2T}{r_2} - \frac{2T}{r_1}$$

But $\qquad\qquad p_1 - p_2 = h\rho g,$

where h is the difference in levels of the liquid.

$$\therefore h\rho g = \frac{2T}{r_2} - \frac{2T}{r_1}$$

$$\therefore h \times 1 \times 980 = \frac{2 \times 70}{0 \cdot 05} - \frac{2 \times 70}{0 \cdot 5}$$

$$\therefore h = 2 \cdot 6 \text{ cm.}$$

3. Define *surface tension* and derive an expression for the rise of a liquid in a vertical capillary tube whose lower end is immersed in the liquid. The lower ends of two vertical glass tubes, each 1 mm. internal diameter, are immersed in two beakers containing water and chloroform respectively, and the upper ends are joined by a T-piece. Air is withdrawn through the T-piece until the top of the water column is 20 cm. above the level in the beaker. Find the height of the chloroform column above the level in the beaker, assuming that the surface tensions of water and chloroform are 73 dyne cm.$^{-1}$ and 27 dyne cm.$^{-1}$ respectively, the specific gravity of chloroform is 1·5, and the angle of contact is zero for each liquid. (*L.*)

First part. See text.

Second part. Suppose h cm. is the height of the chloroform in cm., p is the pressure of the air inside the T-piece, H is the atmospheric pressure, Fig. 91.

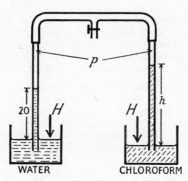

Fig. 91.

For the water, the pressure in the liquid on one side of the meniscus is $(H - 20g)$ if H is in dynes per sq. cm. Since the pressure of the air in the T-piece is p, the excess pressure $= p - (H - 20g) = p - H + 20g$.

$$\therefore p - H + 20g = \frac{2T}{r} = \frac{2 \times 73}{0 \cdot 05}, \qquad \cdot \qquad \cdot \qquad \cdot \qquad \text{(i)}$$

since $r = 0 \cdot 5$ mm. $= 0 \cdot 05$ cm.

By similar reasoning, the excess pressure for the chloroform meniscus $= p - (H - h\rho g) = p - H + h \times 1 \cdot 5g$, since $\rho = 1 \cdot 5$ for chloroform.

$$\therefore p - H + h \times 1 \cdot 5g = \frac{2T}{r} = \frac{2 \times 27}{0 \cdot 05} \qquad \cdot \qquad \cdot \qquad \cdot \qquad \text{(ii)}$$

From (i), $\qquad p - H = \dfrac{2 \times 73}{0 \cdot 05} - 20g.$

From (ii), $\qquad p - H = \dfrac{2 \times 27}{0 \cdot 05} - h \times 1 \cdot 5g.$

$$\therefore \frac{2 \times 73}{0 \cdot 05} - 20g = \frac{2 \times 27}{0 \cdot 05} - h \times 1 \cdot 5g$$

$$\therefore 1 \cdot 5 \, hg = \frac{54}{0 \cdot 05} - \frac{146}{0 \cdot 05} + 20g.$$

$$\therefore h = \frac{54}{0 \cdot 05 \times 980 \times 1 \cdot 5} - \frac{146}{0 \cdot 05 \times 980 \times 1 \cdot 5} + \frac{20}{1 \cdot 5}$$

$$= 12 \cdot 1 \text{ cm.}$$

EXERCISES VI

1. Define *surface tension*. A rectangular plate of dimensions 6 cm. by 4 cm. and thickness 2 mm. is placed with its largest face flat on the surface of water. Calculate the force due to surface tension on the plate. What is the downward force due to surface tension if the plate is placed vertical and its longest side just touches the water? (Surface tension of water = 70 dynes per cm.)

2. What are the *dimensions* of surface tension? A capillary tube of 0·4 mm. diameter is placed vertically inside (i) water of surface tension 65 dynes per cm. and zero angle of contact, (ii) a liquid of density 0·8 gm. per c.c. surface tension 50 dynes per cm. and angle of contact 30°. Calculate the height to which the liquid rises in the capillary in each case.

3. Define the *angle of contact*. What do you know about the angle of contact of a liquid which (i) wets glass, (ii) does not wet glass?

A capillary tube is immersed in water of surface tension 70 dynes per cm. and rises 6·2 cm. By what depth will mercury be depressed if the same capillary is immersed in it? (Surface tension of mercury = 540 dynes per cm.; angle of contact between mercury and glass = 140°; density of mercury = 13·6 gm. per c.c.)

4. (i) A soap-bubble has a diameter of 4 mm. Calculate the pressure inside it if the atmospheric pressure is 10^6 dynes per sq. cm. (Surface tension of soap solution = 28 dynes per cm.) (ii). Calculate the radius of a bubble formed in water if the pressure outside it is 10^6 dynes per sq. cm. and the pressure inside it is $1 \cdot 001 \times 10^6$ dynes per sq. cm. (Surface tension of water = 70 dynes per cm.)

5. Define *surface tension* of a liquid. State the units in which it is usually expressed and give its dimensions in mass, length, and time.

Derive an expression for the difference between the pressures inside and outside a spherical soap bubble. Describe a method of determining surface tension, based on the difference of pressure on the two sides of a curved liquid surface or film. (*L.*)

6. Explain briefly (*a*) the approximately spherical shape of a rain drop, (*b*) the movement of tiny particles of camphor on water, (*c*) the possibility of floating a needle on water, (*d*) why a column of water will remain in an open vertical capillary tube after the lower end has been dipped in water and withdrawn. (*N.*)

7. Explain what is meant by surface tension, and show how its existence is accounted for by molecular theory.

Find an expression for the excess pressure inside a soap-bubble of radius R and surface tension T. Hence find the work done by the pressure in increasing the radius of the bubble from a to b. Find also the increase in surface area of the bubble, and in the light of this discuss the significance of your result. (*C.*)

8. A clean glass capillary tube, of internal diameter 0·04 cm., is held vertically with its lower end below the surface of clean water in a beaker, and with 10 cm. of the tube above the surface. To what height will the water rise in the tube? What will happen if the tube is now depressed until only 5 cm. of its length is above the surface? The surface tension of water is 72 dynes per cm.

Describe, and give the theory of some method, other than that of the rise in a capillary tube, of measuring surface tension. (*O. & C.*)

9. Define *surface tension* and derive an expression for the pressure difference for equilibrium between the two sides of a spherical liquid surface.

Describe how you would determine the surface tension of soap solution by measurements made on *either* (*a*) a soap-bubble, *or* (*b*) a soap film.

Two bubbles of unequal size are blown on the two ends of a tube, communication between the bubbles being prevented by means of a closed tap in the tube. Describe and explain what happens when the tap is opened. (*N.*)

10. Describe the capillary tube method of measuring the surface tension of a liquid.

An inverted U-tube (Hare's apparatus) for measuring the specific gravity of a liquid was constructed of glass tubing of internal diameter about 2 mm. The following observations of the heights of balanced columns of water and another liquid were obtained:

Height of water (cm.)	2·8	4·2	5·4	6·9	8·5	9·8	11·6
Height of liquid (cm.)	2·0	3·8	5·3	7·0	9·1	10·7	13·0

Plot the above results, explain why the graph does not pass through the origin, and deduce from the graph an accurate value for the specific gravity of the liquid. (*N.*)

11. How does simple molecular theory account for surface tension? Illustrate your account by explaining the rise of water up a glass capillary.

A light wire frame in the form of a square of side 5 cm. hangs vertically in water with one side in the water-surface. What additional force is necessary to pull the frame clear of the water? Explain why, if the experiment is performed with soap-solution, as the force is increased a vertical film is formed, whereas with pure water no such effect occurs. (Surface tension of water is 74 dynes per cm.) (*O. & C.*)

12. Derive an expression for the excess pressure inside a spherical drop of liquid in terms of its radius and surface tension. Describe a method of finding the surface tension of a liquid in which this expression is utilized.

Would you expect the pressure inside (*a*) a soap-bubble, (*b*) a rubber balloon, to increase as the bubble or balloon is inflated? Give your reasons. (*O. & C.*)

13. What is meant by surface tension? Give **three** examples of simple demonstrations which demonstrate its existence.

The lower end of a vertical tube 2 mm. in diameter dips into soap-solution, and on the upper end is a soap-bubble 20 mm. in diameter. How much is the level of the liquid above that of the surrounding soap-solution?

[Surface tension of soap-solution 27 dynes per cm.; the density of soap-solution may be assumed to be 1.] (*C.*)

14. What is meant by the dimensions of a physical quantity? Explain, with examples, how the method of dimensions can be used to test the validity of an equation.

Find how the period of vibration of a drop of liquid depends upon the radius, the density, and the surface tension, assuming no other quantities involved. (*C.*)

15. Describe how you would measure the variation with temperature of surface tension of a liquid.

A capillary U-tube contains a liquid of surface tension 75 dyne cm.$^{-1}$ One limb of the tube has internal diameter 2 mm. and the other 0·4 mm., and the tube contains a liquid of density 1·2 gm. cm.$^{-3}$ which wets the glass. What is the difference of level of meniscus in the two limbs? (*L.*)

16. Deduce an expression for the excess pressure inside a spherical soap-bubble due to surface tension.

Calculate the work done against surface tension in blowing a bubble of 8 cm. diameter. If the bubble is blown on the end of a capillary tube and the air is then allowed to escape through this tube compare the times it will take for the bubble diameter to shrink by the same small amount (*a*) when the diameter is 8 cm., (*b*) when it has decreased to 4 cm. (Surface tension of soap-solution = 25 dynes per cm.) (*L.*)

17. Describe in detail the experiments you would make, using a capillary tube method, to find the surface tension of a liquid which wets glass.

A circular ring of thin wire of 2 cm. mean radius, suspended horizontally by a thread passing through the 5 cm. mark on a metre rule pivoted at its centre, is balanced by a 5 gm. weight suspended from the 70 cm. mark. A beaker of liquid is then arranged so that the ring is just attached to the liquid surface when the rule is horizontal. It is found necessary to move the 5 gm. to the 80 cm. mark in order to detach the ring from the liquid surface. Find the surface tension of the liquid. (*N.*)

18. Show, arguing from molecular theory, that the surface of a liquid must be in a state of tension. Define the quantity known as the *surface tension*, and state the units in which it is measured.

Describe in detail how you would determine the surface tension of water by observing the rise of water in a capillary tube. Emphasise the precautions which are necessary, and explain how the result is calculated.

How, if at all, does the result of this experiment depend on the material of the tube? (*W.*)

19. Give some explanation of each of the following observations: (*a*) A small drop of mercury resting on a table is nearly spherical, a larger drop is flattened. (*b*) Water gathers itself into drops on a dusty surface. (*c*) Small pieces of camphor move about on a clean water surface, but not on one contaminated with oil or grease. (*L.*)

20. Define *surface tension* and describe in detail a method, involving the use of a capillary tube, of determining the surface tension of alcohol.

The vertical limbs A and B of a Hare's apparatus consists of capillary tubing 0·5 mm. in diameter. Their lower ends dip into alcohol and water respectively and the liquids are sucked up the tubes so that the height of water in B is 20 cm. above the free surface. Find the height of the alcohol in A above the free surface. The surface tensions of water and alcohol are 73 and 22 dyne per cm. respectively and the specific gravity of alcohol is 0·80. Assume that the angle of contact of alcohol and glass is zero. (*L*.)

21. Derive an expression for the difference in pressure between the inside and outside of a spherical soap-bubble in terms of the surface tension *S* and radius *r*. Describe briefly any experiment, depending on this pressure difference, for the determination of surface tension.

Two soap-bubbles, of radii r_1 and r_2 are situated in a vacuum and coalesce under isothermal conditions. What is the radius of the resulting bubble? (*C*.)

22. Distinguish between *surface energy* and *surface tension*. Derive an expression for the excess pressure inside a spherical soap-bubble. A vertical U-tube contains liquid. One limb of this tube is open to the atmosphere while a soap film is formed across the end of the other limb, to which there is attached a side-tube so that, by blowing, the soap-film may be distended. Show that for different-sized bubbles the product of the radius of the bubble and the difference in height of the liquid levels in the U-tube is constant.

If the liquid in the U-tube is water and the above constant is 0·125 cm.^{2}, calculate a value for the surface tension of the soap solution. (*L*.)

23. Define *surface tension* of a liquid and deduce an expression for the difference in pressure on either side of spherical liquid surface. Using this formula, deduce the height of a liquid in a long glass capillary tube of internal radius 0·020 cm., held vertically in a vessel of the liquid with its lower end below the surface, the surface tension of the liquid being 27 dyne cm.$^{-1}$, its density 0·85 gm. cm.$^{-3}$, and its angle of contact with glass 26°.

Describe and explain what would happen if the part of the capillary tube above the free surface of the liquid around the tube were reduced to 2·5 cm. (*L*.)

24. Define *surface tension*. Derive an expression for the difference in pressure on opposite sides of a spherical interface between two fluids and use it to obtain an expression for the height to which water rises in a glass capillary tube.

A rectangular glass plate 0·50 mm. thick is hung from one arm of a balance in such a way that its lower edge, 6·00 cm. long, is horizontal, and the plate is counter-poised. A beaker containing alcohol is then raised from below the plate until the depth of immersion is such that the balance is once more counterpoised. Find the depth to which the plate is immersed, assuming that the alcohol wets the glass. [Take the density of alcohol as 0·800 gm. cm.$^{-3}$ and the surface tension of alcohol as 22·5 dyne cm.$^{-1}$.] (*L*.)

CHAPTER VII

ELASTICITY. MODULUS OF ELASTICITY

1. Elasticity.

A bridge, when used by traffic during the day, is subjected to loads of varying magnitude. Before a steel bridge is erected, therefore, samples of the steel are sent to a research laboratory, where they undergo tests to find out whether the steel can withstand the loads to which it is likely to be subjected.

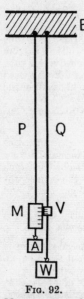

Fig. 92 illustrates a simple laboratory method of discovering useful information about the property of steel we are discussing. Two long thin steel wires, P, Q, are suspended beside each other from a rigid support B, such as a girder at the top of the ceiling. The wire P is kept taut by a weight A attached to its end and carries a scale M graduated in centimetres. The wire Q carries a vernier scale V which is alongside the scale M.

When a load W such as 1 kilogram is attached to the end of Q, the wire increases in length by an amount which can be read from the change in the reading on the vernier V. If the load is taken off and the reading on V returns to its original value, the wire is said to be **elastic** for loads from zero to 1 kilogram, a term adopted by analogy with an elastic thread. When the load W is increased to 2 kilograms the extension (increase in length) is obtained from V again; and if the reading on V returns to original value when the load is removed the wire is said to be elastic at least for loads from zero to 2 kilograms.

Fig. 92.
Measurement of Young's modulus.

2. Elastic Limit.

The extension of a thin wire such as Q for increasing loads may be found by experiment to be as follows:

W (kilograms)	0	1	2	3	4	5	6	7	8
Extension (mm.)	0	0·14	0·28	0·42	0·56	0·70	0·85	0·91	1·09

When the extension, e, is plotted against the load, W, a graph is

136

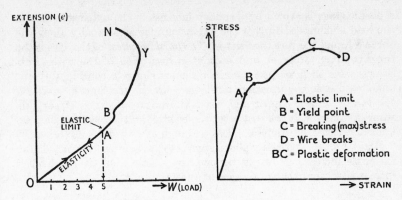

FIG. 93.   Graph of (i) extension v. load (*not to scale*) (ii) stress v. strain.

obtained which is a *straight line* OA, followed by a curve ABY rising slowly at first and then very sharply, Fig. 93. Up to 5 kilograms, then, the results in the table show that the extension increased by 0·14 mm. for every kilogram added to the wire. Further, the wire returned to its original length when the load was removed. For loads greater than 5 kilograms, however, the extension increases relatively more and more, and the wire now no longer returns to its original length when it is unloaded. The wire is thus permanently strained, and A corresponds to its *elastic limit*.

3. Hooke's Law.

From the straight line graph OA, we deduce that *the extension is proportional to the load or tension in the wire when the elastic limit is not exceeded*. This is known as *Hooke's law*, after ROBERT HOOKE, founder of the Royal Society, who discovered the relation in 1676.

The measurements also show that it would be dangerous to load the wire with weights greater than 5 kilograms, the elastic limit, because the wire then suffers a permanent strain. Similar experiments in the research laboratory enable scientists to find the maximum load in tons weight a steel bridge, for example, should carry for safety. Rubber samples are also subjected to similar experiments, to find the maximum safe tension in rubber belts used in machinery.

4. Yield Point.   Ductile and Brittle Substances.   Breaking Stress.

Careful experiments show that, for mild steel and iron for example, the molecules of the wire begin to "slide" across each other soon after the load exceeds the elastic limit, that is, the material becomes *plastic*. This is indicated by the slight "kink" at B beyond A in Fig. 93 (i), and it is called the *yield point* of the wire. The change from an elastic to a plastic stage is shown by a sudden increase in the extension, and as the load is increased further the extension increases rapidly along the curve YN and the wire then snaps. The *breaking stress* of the wire is the corresponding force per unit area of cross-section of the wire. Substances such as those just described, which elongate considerably and undergo plastic deformation until they break, are known as *ductile* substances. Lead, copper and wrought iron are ductile. Other substances, however, break just after the elastic limit is reached; they are known as *brittle* substances. Glass and high carbon steels are brittle.

Brass, bronze, and many alloys appear to have no yield point. These materials increase in length beyond the elastic limit as the load is increased without the appearance of a plastic stage.

5. Tensile Stress and Tensile Strain.   Young's Modulus.

We have now to consider the technical terms used in the subject of elasticity of wires. When a force or tension F is applied to the end of a wire of cross-sectional area A, Fig. 94,

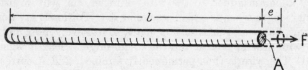

FIG. 94.   Tensile stress and strain.

$$\text{the } \textit{tensile stress} = \textit{force per unit area} = \frac{F}{A} \qquad . \qquad . \qquad (55)$$

If the extension of the wire is e, and its original length is l,

$$\text{the } \textit{tensile strain} = \textit{extension per unit length} = \frac{e}{l} \qquad . \qquad (56).$$

Thus if 2 kgm. is attached to the end of a wire of length 200 cm. of diameter 0·64 mm., and the extension is 0·60 mm., then, with tensile understood,

$$\text{stress} = \frac{\text{force}}{\text{area}} = \frac{2,000 \times 980 \text{ dynes}}{\pi \times (0·032)^2 \text{ sq. cm}}.$$

$$= \frac{2000 \times 980}{\pi \times (0·032)^2} \text{ dynes per sq. cm.,}$$

and $$\qquad \text{strain} = \frac{0·060}{200}.$$

It will be noted that "stress" has units such as "dynes per sq. cm."; "strain" has no units because it is the ratio of two lengths.

A *modulus of elasticity* of the wire, called **Young's modulus (E)**, is defined as the ratio

$$E = \frac{\text{stress}}{\text{strain}} \qquad \cdot \qquad \cdot \qquad \cdot \qquad \cdot \qquad \cdot \qquad (57)$$

Thus

$$E = \frac{F/A}{e/l}.$$

Using the above figures, $E = \dfrac{2000 \times 980/[\pi \times (0\cdot032)^2]}{0\cdot060/200}$

$$= \frac{2000 \times 200 \times 980}{\pi \times (0\cdot032)^2 \times 0\cdot060}$$

$$= 2\cdot0 \times 10^{12} \text{ dynes per sq. cm.}$$

It should be noted that Young's modulus, E, is calculated from the ratio stress: strain only when the wire is under "elastic" conditions, that is, the load does not then exceed the elastic limit (p. 137). Fig. 93 (ii) shows the general stress-strain diagram for a ductile material.

6. Dimensions of Young's Modulus.

As stated before, the "strain" of a wire has no dimensions of mass, length, or time, since, by definition, it is the ratio of two lengths. Now

$$\text{dimensions of stress} = \frac{\text{dimensions of force}}{\text{dimension of area}}$$

$$= \frac{[M] [L] [T]^{-2}}{[L]^2}$$

$$= [M] [L]^{-1} [T]^{-2}$$

$\therefore$ dimensions of Young's modulus, E,

$$= \frac{\text{dimensions of stress}}{\text{dimensions of strain}}$$

$$= [M] [L]^{-1} [T]^{-2}$$

7. Determination of Young's Modulus.

The magnitude of Young's modulus for a material in the form of a wire can be found with the apparatus illustrated in Fig. 92, p. 136, to which the reader should now refer. The following practical points should be specially noted:

(1) The use of two wires, P, Q, of the same material and length, eliminates the correction for (i) the yielding of the support when loads are added to Q, (ii) changes of temperature.

(2) Both wires should be free of kinks, otherwise the increase in length cannot be accurately measured. The wires are straightened by attaching weights to their ends, as shown in Fig. 92.

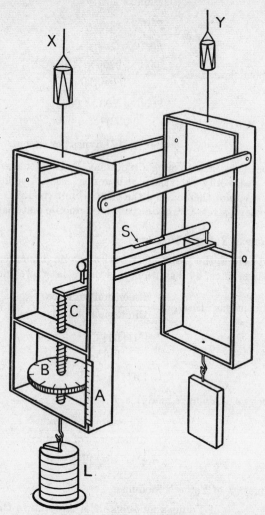

Fig. 95. Searle's apparatus for Young's modulus.

(3) A vernier scale is necessary to measure the extension of the wire since this is always small. The "original length" of the wire is measured from the top B *to the vernier V* by a ruler, since an error of 1 millimetre is negligible compared with an original length of several metres. For

very accurate work, the extension can be measured by an arrangement due to G. F. C. SEARLE. The two wires, X, Y, are attached to two frames connected by a spirit level S, one end of which rests on a screw C operated by a graduated wheel B, Fig. 95. The movement of B can be measured on a fixed scale A graduated in millimetres. The load is placed on L.

(4) The diameter of the wire must be found by a micrometer screw gauge at several places, and the average value then calculated. The area of cross-section, A, $= \pi r^2$, where r is the radius.

(5) The readings on the vernier are also taken when the load is gradually removed in steps of 1 kilogram; they should be very nearly the same as the readings on the vernier when the weights were added, showing that the elastic limit was not exceeded. Suppose the readings on V for loads, W, of 1 to 6 kilograms are a, b, c, d, e, f, as follows:

W (kg.)	1	2	3	4	5	6
Reading on V	a	b	c	d	e	f

The average extension for 3 kilograms is found by taking the average of $(d - a)$, $(e - b)$, and $(f - c)$. Young's modulus can then be calculated from the relation stress/strain, where the stress $= 3000 \times 980/\pi r^2$, and the strain $=$ average extension/original length of wire (p. 139).

8. Some Magnitudes of Young's Modulus are shown below:

	YOUNG'S MODULUS (dynes per sq. cm.)
Steel	19.5×10^{11}
Wrought iron	19×10^{11}
Cast iron	11.5×10^{11}
Copper	12.4×10^{11}
Brass	10×10^{11}
Silver	7.9×10^{11}
Ice	0.28×10^{11}
Oak	1.3×10^{11}

The breaking stress of cast-iron is about 10 tons per sq. in.; the breaking stress of mild steel (0.2% C.) is about 30 tons per sq. in.

At Royal Ordnance and other Ministry of Supply factories, tensile testing is carried out by placing a sample of the material in a machine known as an *extensometer*, which applies stresses of increasing value along the length of the sample and automatically measures the slight increase in length. When the elastic limit is reached, the pointer on the dial of the machine flickers, and soon after the yield point is reached the sample becomes thin at some point and then breaks. A graph showing the load *vs.* extension is recorded automatically by a moving pen while the sample is undergoing test.

9. Force in Bar Due to Contraction or Expansion.

When a bar is heated, and then prevented from contracting as it cools, a considerable force is exerted at the ends of the bar. We can derive a formula for the force if we consider a bar of Young's modulus E, a cross-sectional area A, a linear coefficient of expansion a, and a decrease in temperature of $t°$ C. Then, if the original length of the bar is l, the decrease in length e if the bar were free to contract $= alt$.

Now
$$E = \frac{F/A}{e/l}.$$

$$\therefore F = \frac{EAe}{l} = \frac{EAalt}{l}.$$

$$\therefore F = EAat.$$

As an illustration, suppose a steel rod of cross-sectional area 2·0 sq. cm. is heated to 100° C., and then prevented from contracting when it is cooled to 10° C. Since the linear coefficient of steel $= 0\cdot000012$ per ° C., and Young's modulus $= 2\cdot0 \times 10^{12}$ dynes per sq. cm.,

$$\therefore F = EA\,a\,t = 2\cdot0 \times 10^{12} \times 2\cdot0 \times 0\cdot000012 \times 90 \text{ dynes.}$$

$$\therefore F = 43\cdot2 \times 10^8 \text{ dynes}$$

$$= \frac{43\cdot2 \times 10^8}{980 \times 1000} = 4,400 \text{ kilogram wt.}$$

10. Energy Stored in a Wire.

Suppose that a wire has an original length l and is stretched by a length e when a force F is applied at one end. If the elastic limit is not exceeded, the extension is directly proportional to the applied load (p. 137). Consequently the force *in the wire* has increased in magnitude from zero to F, and hence the average force in the wire while stretching was $F/2$. Now

work done = force × distance.

$\therefore$ work = average force $\times$ extension

$$= \tfrac{1}{2}Fe \quad . \qquad . \qquad . \qquad . \qquad . \qquad 58(\text{i})$$

This is the amount of energy stored in the wire. The formula $\tfrac{1}{2}Fe$ gives the energy in ergs when F is in dynes and e is in centimetres.

Further, since $F = EAe/l$,

$$\text{energy} = \tfrac{1}{2}EA\,\frac{e^2}{l}.$$

From 58 (i), the energy per c.c. $= \tfrac{1}{2} Fe \div Al$, since Al is the volume of the wire. But F/A = stress, and e/l = strain.

$\therefore$ energy per c.c. $= \tfrac{1}{2}$ stress $\times$ strain   .   .   .   .   58 (ii)

Suppose that the wire has a load F_1 on it which produces an extension e_1, and that the load is increased to F_2, producing an extension e_2. If the elastic limit is not exceeded the graph of extension, e, against load,

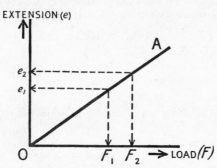

FIG. 96.   Energy in wire.

F, is a straight line OA, Fig. 96. Thus the extra energy, W, stored in the wire when the load is increased is given by

$$W = \text{average force} \times \text{extension}$$

$$= \tfrac{1}{2}(F_1 + F_2) \times (e_2 - e_1)$$

$$= \tfrac{1}{2}\left(\frac{EAe_1}{l} + \frac{EAe_2}{l}\right) \times (e_2 - e_1)$$

$$= \tfrac{1}{2}\frac{EA}{l}(e_1 + e_2)(e_2 - e_1)$$

$$= \tfrac{1}{2}\frac{EA}{l}(e_2{}^2 - e_1{}^2)$$

11. Bulk Modulus of Elasticity.

When a gas or a liquid is subjected to an increased pressure the substance contracts. A change in bulk thus occurs, and the *bulk strain* is defined by

$$\text{strain} = \frac{\text{change in volume}}{\text{original volume}}$$

The *stress* on the substance is the force per unit area, by definition. and the bulk modulus, k,

$$= \frac{\text{stress}}{\text{strain}}$$

$$= \frac{\text{force per unit area}}{\text{change in volume/original volume}}.$$

If the original volume of the substance is v, the change in volume may be denoted by $- \delta v$ when the pressure increases by a small amount δp; the minus indicates that the volume decreases. Thus

$$k = - \frac{\delta p}{\delta v / v}.$$

When δp and δv become very small, then, in the limit,

$$k = - v \frac{dp}{dv} \quad . \quad . \quad . \quad . \quad . \quad . \quad (59)$$

The bulk modulus of water is about 2×10^{10} dynes per sq. cm. for pressures in the range $1 - 25$ atmospheres; the bulk modulus of mercury is about 27×10^{10} dynes per sq. cm. The bulk modulus of gases depends on the pressure, as we shall now explain.

12. Bulk Modulus of a Gas.

If the pressure, p, and volume, v, of a gas change under conditions such that

$$pv = \text{constant},$$

which is Boyle's law, the changes are said to be *isothermal* ones. In this case, by differentiating the product pv with respect to v, we have

$$p + v \frac{dp}{dv} = 0.$$

$$\therefore p = - v \frac{dp}{dv}.$$

But the bulk modulus, k, of the gas is equal to $- v \dfrac{dp}{dv}$ by definition (see p. 144).

$$\therefore k = p \qquad . \qquad . \qquad . \qquad . \qquad . \qquad (60)$$

Thus the *isothermal bulk modulus is equal to the pressure.*

When the pressure, p, and volume, v, of a gas change under conditions such that

$$pv^\gamma = \text{constant},$$

where $\gamma = c_p/c_v =$ the ratio of the principal specific heats of the gas, the changes are said to be *adiabatic* ones. This equation is the one obeyed by local values of pressure and volume in air when a sound wave travels through it. Differentiating both sides with respect to v,

$$\therefore p \times \gamma v^{\gamma-1} + v^\gamma \dfrac{dp}{dv} = 0$$

$$\therefore \gamma p = - v \dfrac{dp}{dv}$$

$$\therefore \text{adiabatic bulk modulus} = \gamma p \qquad . \qquad . \qquad . \qquad . \qquad (61)$$

13. Velocity of Sound.

The velocity of sound waves through any material depends on (i) its density ρ, (ii) its modulus of elasticity, E. Thus if V is the velocity, we may say that

$$V = k \, E^x \rho^y \qquad . \qquad . \qquad . \qquad . \qquad (\text{i}),$$

where k is a constant and x, y are indices we cán find by the theory of dimensions (p. 25).

The units of velocity, V, are $[L] \, [T]^{-1}$; the units of density ρ are $[M] \, [L]^{-3}$; and the units of modulus of elasticity, E, are $[M] \, [L]^{-1} \, [T]^{-2}$ (see p. 139). Equating the dimensions on both sides of (i),

$$\therefore [L] \, [T]^{-1} = [M]^x \, [L]^{-x} \, [T]^{-2x} \times [M]^y \, [L]^{-3y}$$

Equating the indices of $[M]$, $[L]$, $[T]$ on both sides, we have

$$0 = x + y,$$

$$1 = - x - 3y,$$

$$- 1 = - 2x.$$

Solving, we find $x = \tfrac{1}{2}$, $y = - \tfrac{1}{2}$. Thus $V = kE^{\frac{1}{2}}\rho^{-\frac{1}{2}}$. A rigid investigation shows $k = 1$, and thus

$$V = E^{\frac{1}{2}}\rho^{-\frac{1}{2}} = \sqrt{\frac{E}{\rho}}.$$

In the case of a solid, E is Young's modulus. In the case of air and other gases, and of liquids, E is the bulk modulus. Laplace showed that the adiabatic bulk modulus must be used in the case of a gas, and since this is γp, the velocity of sound in a gas is given by the expression

$$V = \sqrt{\frac{\gamma p}{\rho}}.$$

14. Torsion Wire. Rigidity.

If a phosphor-bronze wire is fixed at one end and twisted through a small angle at the other end, the wire will unwind when left to itself and regain its initial appearance in a very short time. Phosphor-bronze has thus torsional elastic properties. Quartz fibre has a small torsion; it will twist to a considerable extent when a small force acts at one end. Silk thread is inelastic from this point of view.

When a phosphor-bronze wire or quartz fibre is twisted at one end through a small angle θ, the other end being fixed, *the material sets up an opposing couple whose magnitude is proportional to θ.* Thus

$$\text{opposing couple} = c\theta,$$

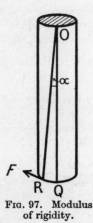

FIG. 97. Modulus of rigidity.

where c is a constant of the wire. If $\theta = 1$ radian, or 1 degree, the opposing couple $= c$. Thus c is the opposing couple per unit radian of twist (or per unit degree of twist), and it may therefore be expressed in "dyne cm. per radian (or per degree)". Phosphor-bronze wire is used in sensitive moving-coil electrical instruments to control the rotation of a coil of wire and the elastic constant, c, of the wire in one make of instrument is 200 dyne cm. per degree.

Suppose a wire of cross-sectional area A is fixed at one end O and twisted by applying a force F at the other end, Fig. 97. A line OQ on the wire is then displaced or sheared to the position $\overline{\text{OR}}$ through an angle a. The **modulus of rigidity**, n, of the wire is defined by the ratio "shearing stress/shearing strain", or

$$n = \frac{F/A}{a} \qquad \cdots \qquad (62)$$

The modulus of rigidity of quartz fibre is $3 \cdot 0 \times 10^{11}$ dynes per sq. cm.; for phosphor-bronze it is $4 \cdot 4 \times 10^{11}$ dynes per sq. cm.; for rubber it is $0 \cdot 00016 \times 10^{11}$ dynes per sq. cm. See also p. 192.

15. Poisson's Ratio.

When a rubber cord is extended its diameter usually decreases at the same time. *Poisson's ratio*, σ, is the name given to the ratio

$$\frac{\text{lateral contraction/original diameter}}{\text{longitudinal extension/original length}}, \quad \cdot \quad \cdot \quad \cdot \quad (63)$$

and is a constant for a given material. If the original length of a rubber strip is 100 cm. and it is stretched to 102 cm., the fractional longitudinal extension = 2/100. If the original diameter of the cord is 0·5 cm. and it decreases to 0·495 cm., the fractional lateral contraction = 0·005/0·5 = 1/100. Thus, from the definition of Poisson's ratio,

$$\sigma = \frac{1/100}{2/100} = \tfrac{1}{2}.$$

When the *volume* of a strip of material remains *constant* while an extension and a lateral contraction takes place, it can easily be shown that Poisson's ratio is 0·5 in this case. Thus suppose that the length of the strip is l and the radius is r.

Then   volume, $V, = \pi r^2 l$.

By differentiating both sides, noting that V is a constant and that we have a product of variables on the right side,

$$\therefore 0 = \pi r^2 \times \delta l + l \times 2\pi r \delta r$$

$$\therefore r \delta l = -2l \delta r$$

$$\therefore -\frac{\delta r/r}{\delta l/l} = \tfrac{1}{2}.$$

But $-\delta r/r$ is the lateral contraction in radius/original radius, and $\delta l/l$ is the longitudinal extension/original length.

$$\therefore \text{Poisson's ratio, } \sigma, = \tfrac{1}{2}.$$

Experiments show that σ is 0·48 for rubber, 0·29 for steel, 0·27 for iron, and 0·26 for copper. Thus the three metals increase in volume when stretched, whereas rubber remains almost unchanged in volume.

EXAMPLES

1. Define *stress, strain, Young's modulus.* Give a brief account of an experimental method for determining the value of Young's modulus for the material of a wire.

A weight of 20 kgm. hangs by a support 5 metres long compounded of two wires, respectively of brass and steel, each 5 metres long, joined at both ends. If the cross-sectional area of each wire is 0·01 sq. cm., by how much will the wires stretch when the weight is applied? [Young's modulus for steel = 20 × 10¹¹ c.g.s. units; for brass = 10 × 10¹¹ c.g.s. units.] (*C.*)

First part. See text.

Second part. The two wires stretch by the same amount, *e* cm. say.

Thus for the brass wire, from the formula $E = \dfrac{F/A}{e/l}$ (p. 138), we have

$$F = \frac{EAe}{l} = \frac{10 \times 10^{11} \times 0 \cdot 01 \times e}{500} , \qquad \text{(i)}$$

where *F* is the applied force and *l* = 5 metres = 500 cm. Similarly, for the steel wire,

$$F_1 = \frac{EAe}{l} = \frac{20 \times 10^{11} \times 0 \cdot 01 \times e}{500} , \qquad \text{(ii)}$$

where F_1 is the applied force on the steel wire. From (i) and (ii), it follows that

$$F_1 = 2F.$$

Also, $\qquad\qquad F + F_1 = 20 \text{ kgm. wt.}$

$$\therefore F + 2F = 20 \text{ kgm. wt., or } F = 6\tfrac{2}{3} \text{ kgm. wt.}$$

Substituting for *F* in dynes in (i),

$$\therefore 6\tfrac{2}{3} \times 1000 \times 980 = \frac{10 \times 10^{11} \times 0 \cdot 01 \times e}{500}.$$

$$\therefore e = \frac{20 \times 1000 \times 980 \times 500}{3 \times 10 \times 10^{11} \times 0 \cdot 01} = 0 \cdot 327 \text{ cm.}$$

2. Define *tensile stress, tensile strain, Young's modulus of elasticity.* Describe a method of measuring Young's modulus for a wire.

A mass of 10 kg. hangs from the lower end of a vertical steel wire whose upper end is fixed. Calculate the energy stored in the wire, the diameter of which is 1 mm. and the length 4 metres. (Young's modulus for steel = 2 × 10¹² dyne cm.⁻²) (*L.*)

First part. For definitions and method of measurement, see text.

Second part. The energy stored in the wire = average force in wire × extension = ½*Fe*.
With the usual notation,

$$\text{Young's modulus, } E = \frac{F/A}{e/l},$$

where *e* is the extension.

$$\therefore e = \frac{F \times l}{A \times E}$$

$$= \frac{10,000 \times 980 \times 400}{\pi(0 \cdot 05)^2 \times 2 \times 10^{12}} \text{ cm.,}$$

since *F* = 10,000 gm. wt. = 10,000 × 980 dynes.

$$\therefore \text{energy stored} = \tfrac{1}{2}Fe$$

$$= \frac{10{,}000^2 \times 980^2 \times 400}{2 \times \pi(0\cdot05)^2 \times 2 \times 10^{12}} \text{ ergs}$$

$$= 1\cdot22 \times 10^6 \text{ crgs.}$$

3. State Hooke's law, and describe in detail how it may be verified experimentally for copper wire. A copper wire, 200 cm. long and 1·22 mm. diameter, is fixed horizontally to two rigid supports 200 cm. long. Find the mass in grams of the load which, when suspended at the mid-point of the wire, produces a sag of 2 cm. at that point. Young's modulus for copper $= 12\cdot3 \times 10^{11}$ dyne cm.$^{-2}$ (*L.*)

First part. See text.

Second part. Suppose m is the mass in grams of the load at the mid-point O of the stretched wire AOC, Fig. 98. If T is the tension in the wire then, for vertical equilibrium,

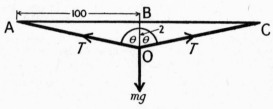

Fig. 98.   (Not to scale.)

$$2T \cos \theta = mg, \quad . \quad . \quad . \quad . \quad . \quad . \quad \text{(i)}$$

where $\theta =$ angle AOB. Now OB $= 2$ cm., AB $= 100$ cm. Thus

$$\text{AO} = \sqrt{100^2 + 2^2} = 100 \text{ cm.}$$

to a good approximation. Hence $\cos \theta = \text{OB}/\text{OA} = 2/100$. From (i),

$$\therefore 2T \times \frac{2}{100} = mg.$$

$$\therefore T = 25\,mg \quad . \quad . \quad . \quad . \quad . \quad \text{(ii)}$$

Now Young's Modulus, E, is given by

$$E = \frac{T/A}{e/l},$$

or $T = EAe/l.$

The extension $e = \text{AOC} - 200 = 2\text{AO} - 200$, and

$$\text{AO} = \sqrt{100^2 + 2^2} = 100 \left[1 + \left(\frac{2}{100} \right)^2 \right]^{\frac{1}{2}}.$$

$$= 100 \,[1 + 0\cdot0004\,]^{\frac{1}{2}} = 100 \,(1 + 0\cdot0002).$$

$$= 100\cdot02 \text{ cm.}$$

$$\therefore e = 200\cdot04 - 200 = 0\cdot04 \text{ cm.}$$

$$\therefore T = EA \times \frac{0\cdot04}{200}$$

$$= 12 \cdot 3 \times 10^{11} \times \pi (0 \cdot 061)^2 \times \frac{0 \cdot 04}{200} \text{ dynes},$$

since $r = 0 \cdot 061$ cm. From (ii), $T = 25 \times 980 \times m$.

$$\therefore m = \frac{12 \cdot 3 \times 10^{11} \times \pi (0 \cdot 061)^2 \times 0 \cdot 04}{25 \times 980 \times 200}.$$

$$= 117 \text{ gram wt.}$$

EXERCISES VII

1. Define *tensile stress, tensile strain, Young's modulus*. What are the units and dimensions of each?

A load of 2 kilograms is applied to the ends of a wire 4 metres long, and produces an extension of 0·24 mm. If the diameter of the wire is 2 mm., calculate the stress on the wire, its strain, and the value of Young's modulus.

2. What load in kilograms must be applied to a steel wire 6 metres long and diameter 1·6 mm. to produce an extension of 1 mm.? (Young's modulus for steel $= 2 \cdot 0 \times 10^{12}$ dynes per sq. cm.)

3. Find the extension produced in a copper wire of length 2 metres and diameter 3 mm. when a load of 3 kilograms is applied. (Young's modulus for copper $= 1 \cdot 1 \times 10^{12}$ dynes per cm.)

4. What is meant by (i) elastic limit, (ii) Hooke's law, (iii) yield point (iv) perfectly elastic? Draw sketches of stress *v.* strain to illustrate your answers.

5. Describe an experimental method for the determination of (*a*) Young's modulus, (*b*) the elastic limit, of a metal in the form of a thin wire.

A steel rod of mass 97·5 gm. and of length 50 cm. is heated to 200° C. and its ends securely clamped. Calculate the tension in the rod when its temperature is reduced to 0° C., explaining how the calculation is made. (Young's modulus for steel $= 2 \cdot 0 \times 10^{12}$ dyne cm.$^{-2}$; coefficient of linear expansion of steel $= 1 \cdot 1 \times 10^{-5}$ deg.$^{-1}$ C.; density of steel $= 7 \cdot 80$ gm. cm.$^{-3}$) (*L.*)

6. What do you understand by Hooke's law of elasticity? Describe how you would verify it in any particular case.

A wire of radius 0·2 mm. is extended by 0·1 per cent of its length when it supports a load of 1 kgm.; calculate Young's modulus for the material of the wire. (*L.*)

7. Explain in some detail how you would determine Young's modulus for a copper wire. Describe the behaviour of a copper wire as it is gradually loaded to just beyond the elastic limit and then gradually unloaded and reloaded to breaking point.

A steel rod of 1 in. diameter is heated to 200° C. and its ends are then fastened firmly to two rigid supports. Find, in tons wt., the tension in the rod when the temperature falls to 15° C. Assume that Young's modulus for steel is $1 \cdot 3 \times 10^4$ tons wt. per sq. in. and that the coefficient of linear expansion of steel is 12×10^{-6} per deg. C. (*N.*)

8. What is meant by saying that a substance is "elastic"?

A vertical brass rod of circular section is loaded by placing a 5 kilogramme weight on top of it. If its length is 50 cm., its radius of cross-section 1 cm., and the Young's modulus of the material $3 \cdot 5 \times 10^{11}$ dynes per sq. cm., find (a) the contraction of the rod, (b) the energy stored in it. (C.)

9. Give a short account of what happens when a copper wire is stretched under a gradually increasing load. What is meant by *modulus of elasticity, elastic limit, perfectly elastic*?

When a rubber cord is stretched the change in volume is very small compared with the change in shape. What will be the numerical value of Poisson's ratio for rubber, i.e., the ratio of the fractional decrease in diameter of the stretched cord to its fractional increase in length? (L.)

10. Describe an accurate method of determining Young's modulus for a wire. Detail the precautions necessary to avoid error, and estimate the accuracy attainable.

A steel tyre is heated and slipped on to a wheel of radius 40 cm. which it fits exactly at a temperature $t°$ C. What is the maximum value of t if the tyre is not to be stretched beyond its elastic limit when it has cooled to air temperature (17° C.)? What will then be the tension in the tyre, assuming it to be 4 cm. wide and 3 mm. thick? The value of Young's modulus for steel is 2×10^4 kg. per sq. mm., its coefficient of linear expansion is $1 \cdot 1 \times 10^{-5}$ per ° C., and its elastic limit occurs for a tension of 28 kg. per sq. mm. The wheel may be assumed to be at air temperature throughout, and to be incompressible. (O. & C.)

11. Define *elastic limit, Young's modulus*.

What geometrical changes occur in a uniform wire when it is stretched within the limits in which Hooke's law is obeyed? Derive an expression for the energy stored in unit volume of a wire when stretched in this way.

If Young's modulus for steel is $2 \cdot 0 \times 10^{12}$ dyne cm.$^{-2}$, calculate its value in ton-wt. in.$^{-2}$ (Assume 1 ft. = 30·5 cm., 1 kgm. = 2·20 lb.) (L.)

12. Define *Young's modulus*. How would you measure it for the material of a wire? A stretched wire, 35 cm. long between bridges, vibrates with a frequency of 500 cycles per sec. when struck. By how much will this part of the wire contract if the stretching force is removed? The density of steel is 7·9 gm. cm.$^{-3}$; Young's modulus for steel is 2×10^{12} dyne cm.$^{-2}$ (L.)

13. Define Young's modulus of elasticity. Describe an accurate method of determining it. The rubber cord of a catapult is pulled back until its original length has been doubled. Assuming that the cross-section of the cord is 2 mm. square, and that Young's modulus for rubber is 10^8 c.g.s. calculate the tension in the cord. If the two arms of the catapult are 6 cm. apart, and the unstretched length of the cord is 8 cm. what is the stretching force? (O. & C.)

14. Define *Young's modulus*. Calculate Young's modulus for rubber if a rubber tube 40 cm. long, whose external and internal diameters are 1·0 cm. and 0·40 cm. respectively, extends 0·60 mm. when stretched by a force of 5 kgm. wt. Indicate how the data given in the problem may be obtained. (L.)

15. Define *Young's modulus of elasticity* and *coefficient of linear expansion*. State units in which each may be expressed and describe an experimental determination of Young's modulus.

For steel, Young's modulus is $1 \cdot 8 \times 10^{12}$ and the coefficient of expansion

$1 \cdot 1 \times 10^{-5}$, the units being based on cm., gm., sec. and ° C. A steel wire 1 mm. in diameter is stretched between two supports when its temperature is 200° C. By how much will the force the wire exerts on the supports increase when it cools to 20° C., if they do not yield? Express the answer in terms of the weight of a kilogram. (L.)

16. Define *elastic limit* and *Young's modulus* and describe how you would find their values for a copper wire.

What stress would cause a wire to increase in length by one-tenth of one per cent if Young's modulus for the wire is 12×10^{11} dynes per sq. cm.? What load in kgm. wt. would produce this stress if the diameter of the wire is 0·56 mm.? (L.)

17. Define *Young's modulus*. How would you measure its value for a specimen of steel wire?

A copper wire of diameter 2 mm. is suspended vertically, a light load being attached to the lower end. If the temperature of the wire falls from 20° C. to 0° C., calculate in grams weight the additional load that must be added to prevent alteration in the length of wire. (Young's modulus for copper = $1 \cdot 1 \times 10^{12}$ c.g.s.; coefficient of linear expansion of copper = 0·000018 per ° C.) (L.)

18. State Hooke's law and describe, with the help of a rough graph, the behaviour of a copper wire which hangs vertically and is loaded with a gradually increasing load until it finally breaks. Describe the effect of gradually reducing the load to zero (a) before, (b) after the elastic limit has been reached.

A uniform steel wire of density 7·8 gm. per c.c. weighs 16 gm. and is 250 cm. long. It lengthens by 1·2 mm. when stretched by a force of 8 kg. weight. Calculate (a) the value of Young's modulus for the steel, (b) the energy stored in the wire. (N.)

19. You are provided with a length of elastic cord, a set of known masses, a stop clock and the usual facilities of a physical laboratory. Describe how you would use them to find a value for the acceleration due to gravity and give the theory of the method.

The ends of a light elastic cord of natural length 200 cm. and diameter 2 mm. are attached to two points 200 cm. apart in a horizontal plane. Find to the nearest gram the mass which, when suspended in equilibrium from the mid-point of the cord, produces a depression of 10 cm. at this point and calculate the energy which would then be stored in the strained cord. Young's modulus for the material of the cord is $5 \cdot 0 \times 10^{8}$ dynes cm.$^{-2}$ (N.)

CHAPTER VIII

FRICTION IN SOLIDS AND LIQUIDS

OSMOSIS, DIFFUSION

1. Static Friction.

When a person walks along a road, he or she is prevented from slipping by the force of friction at the ground. In the absence of friction, for example on an icy surface, the person's shoe would slip backwards when placed on the ground. The frictional force, however, always *opposes* the motion.

The frictional force between the surface of a table and a block of wood A can be investigated by attaching one end of a string to A and the other to a scale-pan S, Fig. 99. The string passes over a fixed

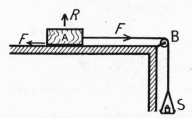

Fig. 99.   Measurement of coefficient of friction.

grooved wheel B. When small weights are added to S, the block does not move. The frictional force between the block and table is thus equal to the total weight on S together with the weight of S. When more weights are added, A does not move, showing that the frictional force has increased, but as the weight is increased further, A suddenly begins to slip. The frictional force now present between the surfaces is called the *limiting frictional force*, and we are said to have reached *limiting friction*. The limiting frictional force is the maximum frictional force between the surfaces.

2. Coefficient of Static Friction.

The normal reaction, R, of the table on A is equal to the weight of A. By placing various weights on A to alter the magnitude of R, we can

153

find how the limiting frictional force F varies with R by the experiment just described. The results show that, approximately,

$$\frac{\text{limiting frictional force } (F)}{\text{normal reaction } (R)} = \mu, \text{ a constant,}$$

and μ is known as the *coefficient of static friction* between the two surfaces. The magnitude of μ depends on the nature of the two surfaces; for example, it is about 0·2 to 0·5 for wood on wood, and about 0·2 to 0·6 for wood on metals. Experiment also shows that the limiting frictional force is the same if the block A in Fig. 99 is turned on one side so that its surface area of contact with the table decreases, and thus the limiting frictional force is independent of the area of contact when the normal reaction is the same.

The coefficient of static friction, μ, can also be found by placing the block A on the surface S, and then gently tilting S until A is on the point of slipping down the plane, Fig. 100. The static frictional force F

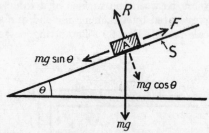

Fig. 100. Coefficient of friction by inclined plane.

is then equal to $mg \sin \theta$, where θ is the angle of inclination of the plane to the horizontal; the normal reaction R is equal to $mg \cos \theta$.

$$\therefore \mu = \frac{F}{R} = \frac{mg \sin \theta}{mg \cos \theta} = \tan \theta,$$

and hence μ can be found by measuring θ.

3. Kinetic Friction.   Coefficient of Kinetic (Dynamic) Friction.

When brakes are applied to a bicycle, a frictional force is exerted between the moving wheels and brake blocks. In contrast to the case of static friction, when one of the objects is just on the point of slipping, the frictional force between the moving wheel and brake blocks is called a *kinetic (or dynamic) frictional force*. Kinetic friction thus occurs between two surfaces which have relative motion.

The *coefficient of kinetic (dynamic) friction*, μ', between two surface is defined by the relation

$$\mu' = \frac{F'}{R},$$

where F' is the frictional force when the object moves with a uniform velocity and R is the normal reaction between the surfaces. The coefficient of kinetic friction between a block A and a table can be found by the apparatus shown in Fig. 99. Weights are added to the scale-pan, and each time A is given a slight push. At one stage A continues to move with a constant velocity, and the kinetic frictional force F' is then equal to the total weight in the scale-pan together with the latter's weight. On dividing F' by the weight of A, the coefficient can be calculated. Experiment shows that, when weights are placed on A to vary the normal reaction R, the magnitude of the ratio F'/R is approximately constant. Results also show that the cofficient of kinetic friction between two given surfaces is less than the coefficient of static friction between the same surfaces, and that the coefficient of kinetic friction between two given surfaces is approximately independent of their relative velocity.

4. Laws of Solid Friction.

Experimental results on solid friction are summarised in the *laws of friction*, which state:

(1) The frictional force between two surfaces opposes their relative motion.

(2) The frictional force is independent of the area of contact of the given surfaces when the normal reaction is constant.

(3) The limiting frictional force is proportional to the normal reaction for the case of static friction. The frictional force is proportional to the normal reaction for the case of kinetic (dynamic) friction, and is independent of the relative velocity of the surfaces.

These results are explained on p. 194.

5. Rope-Brake.

It is common knowledge that a rope wound several times round a cylindrical drum, for example, can sustain a powerful pull at one end by the application of a small force at the other end.

Suppose the rope is wound round a drum so that one end leaves it at X and the other end leaves it at Y, Fig. 101. If the tension T_1 at X is small and the tension T_2 at Y is large, the tension along the rope

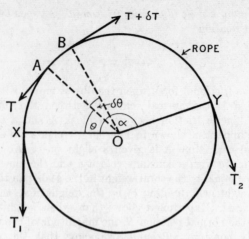

Fig. 101. The rope-brake.

increases gradually from X to Y. Suppose AB is a small element of the rope subtending an angle $\delta\theta$ at the centre O, T is the tension at A, and $T + \delta T$ is the tension at B. Then the normal pressure R on the drum due to AB, which passes through O,

$$= (T + \delta T) \sin\frac{\delta\theta}{2} + T \sin\frac{\delta\theta}{2}$$

$$= T\frac{\delta\theta}{2} + T\frac{\delta\theta}{2} = T\delta\theta,$$

since $\delta\theta$ and δT are both very small.

If the rope is just on the point of slipping, the frictional force $F = \mu R$, where μ is the coefficient of static friction.

$$\therefore F = \mu T \delta\theta.$$

But $$F = (T + \delta T) \cos \delta\theta - T = \delta T,$$

considering equilibrium along the tangent at A.

$$\therefore \delta T = \mu T \delta\theta$$

$$\therefore \int_{T_1}^{T_2}\frac{dT}{T} = \mu \int_0^\alpha d\theta,$$

where a is the angle XOY.

$$\therefore \log_e \frac{T_2}{T_1} = \mu a$$

$$\therefore T_2 = T_1 e^{\mu a}$$

As an illustration, suppose the pull at X is 20 lb. wt., the frictional coefficient between the rope and drum is 0·3, and the rope is wound three times round the drum, so that $a = 6\pi$ radians.

$$\therefore T_2 = 20e^{1·8\pi} = 5700 \text{ lb. wt.}$$

Thus a pull of 5700 lb. wt. could be sustained by a pull of 20 lb. wt.

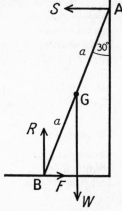

Fig. 102.

EXAMPLE

A uniform heavy ladder rests with its upper end against a smooth vertical wall. The bottom rests on rough horizontal ground, and is on the point of slipping when the ladder is 30° to the vertical. Calculate the coefficient of static friction between the bottom of the ladder and the ground.

Suppose F is the frictional force at the ground, R is the normal reaction there, S is the reaction at the wall acting perpendicular to the wall, W is the weight of the ladder acting at its mid-point G, and AB is the ladder of length $2a$, Fig. 102. Then, for vertical equilibrium,

$$R = W \qquad . \qquad . \qquad . \qquad . \qquad \text{(i)}.$$

For horizontal equilibrium, $F = S$.   .   .   .   .   . (ii).

Taking moments about B to find S in terms of W, we have

$$S \cdot 2a \cos 30° = W \cdot a \sin 30°.$$

$$\therefore S = \frac{W}{2} \tan 30°.$$

$$\therefore F = \frac{W}{2} \tan 30°, \text{ from (ii)}.$$

But coefficient of friction, μ, $= \dfrac{F}{R}.$

$$\therefore \mu = \frac{W}{2} \tan 30°/W = \tfrac{1}{2} \tan 30°.$$

$$\therefore \mu = 0·29.$$

VISCOSITY OF LIQUIDS

If we move through a pool of water we experience a resistance to our motion. This shows that there is a *frictional force* in liquids, and in this connection we refer to the **viscosity** of the liquid. If the frictional force is comparatively low, as in water, the viscosity of the liquid is low; if the frictional force is large, as in glue or glycerine, the viscosity of the liquid is high. We can compare roughly the viscosity of two liquids by filling two measuring cylinders with each of them, and allowing identical small steel ball-bearings to fall through each liquid. The sphere falls more slowly through the liquid of higher viscosity.

As we shall see later, the viscosity of a lubricating oil is one of the factors which decide whether it is suitable for use in an engine. The Ministry of Aircraft Production, for example, listed viscosity values to which lubricating oils for aero-engines must conform. The subject of viscosity has thus considerable practical importance.

6. Newton's Formula. Coefficient of Viscosity.

When water flows slowly and steadily through a pipe, the layer A of the liquid in contact with the pipe is practically stationary, but the central part C of the water is moving relatively fast, Fig. 103. At other

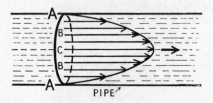

FIG. 103.   Velocity of layers of liquid in pipe.

layers between A and C, such as B, the water has a velocity less than at C, the magnitude of the velocities being represented by the length of the arrowed lines in Fig. 103. Now as in the case of two solid surfaces moving over each other, a frictional force is exerted between two liquid layers when they move over each other. Thus because the velocities of neighbouring layers are different, as shown in Fig. 103, a frictional force occurs between the various layers of a liquid when flowing through a pipe.

The basic formula for the frictional force, F, in a liquid was first suggested by NEWTON. He saw that the larger the *area* of the surface of liquid considered, the greater was the frictional force F. He also stated that F was directly proportional to the *velocity gradient* at the part of the liquid considered. If v_1, v_2 are the velocities of C, B respectively in Fig. 103, and h is their distance apart, the velocity gradient between the liquids is defined as $(v_1 - v_2)/h$. The velocity gradient can thus be expressed in (cm. per sec.)/cm., or as "sec.$^{-1}$"

Thus if A is the area of the liquid surface considered, the frictional force F on the surface is given by

$$F \propto A \times \text{velocity gradient},$$

or $$F = \eta A \times \text{velocity gradient}, \quad . \quad . \quad . \quad (64)$$

where η is a constant of the liquid known as the *coefficient of viscosity*. This expression for the frictional force in a liquid should be contrasted with the case of solid friction, in which the frictional force is independent of the area of contact and of the relative velocity between the solid surfaces concerned (p. 155).

7. Definition, Units, and Dimensions of Coefficient of Viscosity.

The magnitude of η is given by

$$\eta = \frac{F}{A \times \text{velocity gradient}} .$$

The unit of F is a dyne, the unit of A is a sq. cm., and the unit of velocity gradient is (1 cm. per sec.)/cm. Thus η may be defined as *the frictional force in dynes exerted on 1 square centimetre of a liquid when it is in a region of unit velocity gradient*.

From above, the unit of η is "dynes per sq. cm. per unit velocity gradient", or briefly "c.g.s. unit"; this unit is called a *poise*. The coefficient of viscosity of water at 10° C. is 0·013 poises, at 10° C. mercury has a coefficient of 0·016 poises, at 10° C. glycerine has a coefficient of 21·0 poises, and black treacle has a coefficient of 400 poises at 12·3° C. Since $F = \eta A \times$ velocity gradient, the frictional force over an area of 10 sq. cm. in water at 10° C. between two layers of water 0·1 cm. apart which move with a relative velocity of 2 cm. per sec. is given by

$$F = 0 \cdot 013 \times 10 \times \frac{2}{0 \cdot 1} = 2 \cdot 6 \text{ dynes.}$$

Dimensions. The dimensions of a force, F, ($=$ mass $\times$ acceleration $=$ mass $\times$ velocity change/time) are $[M] [L] [T]^{-2}$. See p. 25. The dimensions of an area, A, are $[L]^2$. The dimensions of velocity gradient

$$= \frac{\text{velocity change}}{\text{distance}} = \frac{[L]}{[T]} \div [L] = \frac{1}{[T]}$$

Now $$\eta = \frac{F}{A \times \text{velocity gradient}}$$

$$\therefore \text{ dimensions of } \eta = \frac{[M] [L] [T]^{-2}}{[L]^2 \times 1/[T]}$$

$$= [M] [L]^{-1} [T]^{-1}$$

8. Steady Flow of Liquid Through Pipe.   Poiseuille's Formula.

The steady flow of liquid through a pipe was first investigated thoroughly by POISEUILLE in 1844, who derived an expression for the volume of liquid issuing per second from the pipe. The proof of the formula is given on p. 162, but we can derive most of the formula by the *method of dimensions* (p. 25).

The volume of liquid issuing per second from the pipe depends on (i) the coefficient of viscosity, η, (ii) the radius, a, of the pipe, (iii) the *pressure gradient*, g, set up along the pipe. The pressure gradient $=$ p/l, where p is the pressure difference between the ends of the pipe and l is its length. Thus x, y, z being indices which require to be found, suppose

$$\text{volume per sec.} = k\eta^x a^y g^z \quad . \quad . \quad . \quad . \quad \text{(i)}$$

Now the dimensions of volume per sec. are $[L]^3/[T]$; the dimensions of η are $[M]/[L][T]$, see p. 159; the dimension of a is $[L]$; and the dimensions of g are

$$\frac{[\text{pressure}]}{[\text{length}]}, \text{ or } \frac{[\text{force}]}{[\text{area}][\text{length}]}, \text{ or } \frac{[M][L]}{[T^2][L]^2[L]}$$

Thus from (i), equating dimensions on both sides,

$$\frac{[L]^3}{[T]} = \frac{[M]^x}{[L]^x[T]^x}[L]^y\frac{[M]^z.}{[L]^{2z}[T]^{2z}}$$

Equating the respective indices of $[M]$, $[L]$, $[T]$ on both sides, we have

$$x + z = 0,$$

$$- x + y - 2z = 3$$

$$x + 2z = 1$$

Solving, we obtain $x = -1$, $z = 1$, $y = 4$. Hence, from (i),

$$\text{volume per sec.} = k\,\frac{a^4 g}{\eta} = k\frac{pa^4}{l\eta}.$$

We cannot obtain the numerical factor k from the method of dimensions. As shown on p. 162, the factor of $\pi/8$ enters into the formula, which is:

$$\textbf{Volume per second} = \frac{\pi pa^4}{8\eta l} \quad . \quad . \quad . \quad . \quad . \quad \text{(65)}$$

9. Turbulent Motion.

Poiseuille's formula holds as long as the velocity of each layer of the liquid is parallel to the axis of the pipe and the flow pattern has been

developed. As the pressure difference between the ends of the pipe is
increased, a critical velocity is reached at some stage, and the motion
of the liquid changes from an orderly to a *turbulent* one. Poiseuille's
formula does not apply to turbulent motion.

The onset of turbulence was first demonstrated by O. REYNOLDS in
1883, and was shown by placing a horizontal tube T, about 0·5 cm. in
diameter, at the bottom of a tank W of water, Fig. 104 (i). The flow of
water along T is controlled by a clip C on rubber tubing connected to T.
A drawn-out glass jet B, attached to a reservoir A containing coloured

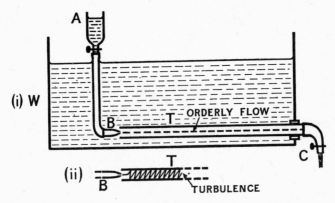

FIG. 104.   Demonstration of turbulent motion.

water, is placed at one end of T, and at low velocities of flow a thin
coloured stream of water is observed flowing along the middle of T. As
the rate of flow of the water along T is increased, a stage is reached
when the colouring in T begins to spread out and fill the whole of the
tube, Fig. 104 (ii). The critical velocity has now been exceeded, and
turbulence has begun.

10. Analogy with Ohm's Law.

For orderly flow along a pipe, Poiseuille's formula in equation (65)
states:

$$\text{Volume per second flowing} = \frac{\pi p a^4}{8 \eta l}$$

$$= \frac{p \times \pi a^2}{8 \pi \eta \times \dfrac{l}{\pi a^2}}.$$

Now $p \times \pi a^2 = $ excess pressure $\times$ area of cross-section of liquid =

excess force F on liquid, and $l/\pi a^2 = l/A$, where A is the area of cross-section.

$$\therefore \text{volume per second flowing} = \frac{F}{8\pi\eta \times \dfrac{l}{A}} \qquad . \qquad . \qquad . \qquad \text{(i)}$$

The volume of liquid per second is analogous to electric current (I) if we compare the case of electricity flowing along a conductor, and the excess force F is analogous to the potential difference (V) along the conductor. Also, the resistance R of the conductor $= \rho l/A$, where ρ is its resistivity, l is its length, and A is the cross-sectional area. Since, from Ohm's law, $I = V/R$, it follows from (i) that

$$8\pi\eta \text{ is analogous to } \rho, \text{ the resistivity};$$

that is, the coefficient of viscosity η is a measure of the "resistivity" of a liquid in orderly flow.

11. Proof of Poiseuille's Formula. Suppose a pipe of radius a has a liquid flowing steadily along it. Consider a cylinder of the liquid of radius r having the same axis as the pipe, where r is less than a. Then the force on this cylinder due to the excess pressure $p = p \times \pi r^2$. We can imagine the cylinder to be made up of cylindrical *shells*; the force on the cylinder due to viscosity is the algebraic sum of the viscous forces on these shells. The force on one shell is given by $\eta A dv/dr$, where dv/dr is the corresponding velocity gradient and A is the surface area of the shell. And although dv/dr changes as we proceed from the narrowest shell outwards, the forces on the neighbouring shells cancel each other out, by the law of action and reaction, leaving a net force of $\eta A dv/dr$, where dv/dr is the velocity gradient at the surface of the cylinder. The viscous force on the cylinder, and the force on it due to the excess pressure p, are together zero since there is no acceleration of the liquid, i.e., we have orderly flow.

$$\therefore \eta A \frac{dv}{dr} + \pi r^2 p = 0$$

$$\therefore \eta \cdot 2\pi r l \frac{dv}{dr} + \pi r^2 p = 0,$$

since $A = 2\pi r l$.

$$\therefore \frac{dv}{dr} = -\frac{pr}{2\eta l}$$

$$\therefore v = -\frac{p}{4\eta l} r^2 + c,$$

where c is a constant. Since $v = 0$ when $r = a$, at the surface of the tube, $c = pa^2/4\eta l$.

$$\therefore v = \frac{p}{4\eta l} (a^2 - r^2) \qquad . \qquad . \qquad . \qquad \text{(i)}$$

Consider a cylindrical shell of the liquid between radii r and $(r + \delta r)$.

The liquid in this shell has a velocity v given by the expression in (i), and the volume per second of liquid flowing along this shell = v × cross-sectional area of shell, since v is the distance travelled in one second, = $v \times 2\pi r \cdot \delta r$.

∴ total volume of liquid per second along tube

$$= \int_{o}^{a} v \cdot 2\pi r \cdot dr$$

$$= \int_{o} \frac{p}{4\eta l}\ (a^2 - r^2) \cdot 2\pi r \cdot dr$$

$$= \frac{\pi p a^4}{8\eta l}.$$

12. Determination of Viscosity by Poiseuille's Formula.

The viscosity of a liquid such as water can be measured by connecting one end of a capillary tube T to a constant pressure apparatus A, which provides a *steady* flow of liquid, Fig. 105. By means of a beaker B

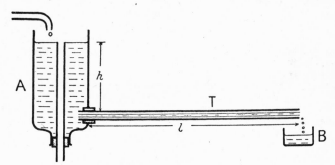

Fig. 105.   Viscosity by Poiseuille's method.

and a stop-clock, the volume of water per second flowing through the tube can be measured. The pressure difference between the ends of T is $h\rho g$ dynes per sq. cm., where h is the pressure head, ρ is the density of the liquid, and g is 980.

$$\therefore \text{ volume per second} = \frac{\pi p a^4}{8\eta l} = \frac{\pi h \rho g a^4}{8\eta l},$$

where l is the length of T and a is its radius. The radius of the tube can be measured by means of a mercury thread or by a microscope. The coefficient of viscosity η can then be calculated, since all the other quantities in the above equation are known.

13. Comparison of Viscosities. Ostwald Viscometer.

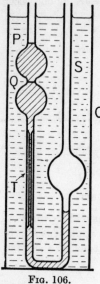

Fig. 106.
Ostwald viscometer.

An Ostwald viscometer, which contains a vertical capillary tube T, is widely used for comparing the viscosities of two liquids, Fig. 106. The liquid is introduced at S, drawn by suction above P, and the time t_1 taken for the liquid level to fall between the fixed marks P, Q is observed. The experiment is then repeated with the *same volume* of a second liquid, and the time t_2 for the liquid level to fall from P to Q is noted.

Suppose the liquids have respective densities ρ_1, ρ_2. Then, since the average head h of liquid forcing it through T is the same in each case, the pressure excess between the ends of T = $h\rho_1 g$, $h\rho_2 g$ respectively. If the volume between the marks P, Q is V, then, from Poiseuille's formula, we have

$$\frac{V}{t_1} = \frac{\pi (h\rho_1 g)a^4}{8\eta_1 l} \qquad \cdots \qquad \text{(i)},$$

where a is the radius of T, η_1 is the coefficient of viscosity of the liquid, and l is the length of T. Similarly, for the second liquid,

$$\frac{V}{t_2} = \frac{\pi (h\rho_2 g)a^4}{8\eta_2 l} \qquad \cdots \qquad \text{(ii)}$$

Dividing (ii) by (i),

$$\therefore \frac{t_1}{t_2} = \frac{\eta_1 \rho_2}{\eta_2 \rho_1}.$$

$$\therefore \frac{\eta_1}{\eta_2} = \frac{t_1}{t_2} \cdot \frac{\rho_1}{\rho_2} \qquad \cdots \qquad \text{(iii)}$$

Thus knowing t_1, t_2 and the densities ρ_1, ρ_2, the coefficients of viscosity can be compared. Further, if a pure liquid of a known viscosity is used, the viscometer can be used to measure the coefficient of viscosity of a liquid. Since the viscosity varies with temperature, the viscometer should be used in a cylinder C and surrounded by water at a constant temperature, Fig. 106. The arrangement can then also be used to investigate the variation of viscosity with temperature. In very accurate work a small correction is required in equation (iii). BARR, an authority on viscosity, estimates that nearly 90% of petroleum oil is tested by an Ostwald viscometer.

Experiment shows that the viscosity coefficient of a liquid diminishes as its temperature rises. The table shows some results for the viscosity coefficient of water at various temperatures.

TEMPERATURE ° C.	$\dot{\eta}$ (POISES)
0	0·179
10	0·013
15	0·011
30	0·008
50	0·006

14. Stokes' Law.   Terminal Velocity.

When a small object, such as a steel ball-bearing, is dropped into a viscous liquid like glycerine it accelerates at first, but its velocity soon reaches a steady value known as the *terminal velocity*. In this case the viscous force acting upwards, and the upthrust due to the liquid on the object, are together equal to its weight acting downwards, so that the resultant force on the object is zero. An object dropped from an aeroplane at first increases its speed, but soon reaches its terminal speed.

Suppose a sphere of radius a is dropped into a viscous liquid of coefficient of viscosity η, and its velocity at an instant is v. The frictional force, F, can be partly found by the method of dimensions. Thus suppose $F = ka^x\eta^yv^z$, where k is a constant. The dimensions of F are [M] [L] [T]$^{-2}$; the dimension of a is [L]; the dimensions of η are [M] [L]$^{-1}$ [T]$^{-1}$; and the dimensions of v are [L] [T]$^{-1}$.

$$\therefore \text{[M] [L] [T]}^{-2} = \text{[L]}^x \times \text{[M]}^y \text{[L]}^{-y} \text{[T]}^{-y} \times \text{[L]}^z \text{[T]}^{-z}.$$

Equating indices of [M], [L], [T] on both sides,

$$\therefore y = 1,$$
$$x - y + z = 1,$$
$$- y - z = - 2.$$

Hence $z = 1, x = 1, y = 1$. Consequently $F = k\eta av$. In 1850 STOKES showed mathematically that the constant k was 6π, and he arrived at the formula

$$F = 6\pi a\eta v \qquad . \qquad . \qquad . \qquad (66)$$

15. Comparison of Viscosities of Viscous Liquids.

Stokes' formula can be used to compare the coefficients of viscosity

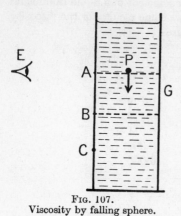

FIG. 107.
Viscosity by falling sphere.

of very viscous liquids such as glycerine or treacle. A tall glass vessel G is filled with the liquid, and a small ball-bearing P is dropped gently into the liquid so that it falls along the axis of G, Fig. 107. Towards the middle of the liquid P reaches its terminal velocity v_0, which is measured by timing its fall through a distance AB or BC.

The upthrust on P due to the liquid $= \frac{4}{3}\pi a^3 \sigma g$, where a is the radius of P and σ is the density of the liquid.

The weight of P is $\frac{4}{3}\pi a^3 \rho g$, where ρ is the density of the bearing's material. Since the resultant force is zero when the terminal velocity v_0 is reached,

$$\therefore \frac{4}{3}\pi a^3 \sigma g + 6\pi a \eta v_0 = \frac{4}{3}\pi a^3 \rho g$$

Solving for η,
$$\therefore \eta = \frac{2ga^2(\rho - \sigma)}{9v_0} \qquad . \qquad . \qquad \text{(i)}$$

When the experiment is repeated with a liquid of coefficient of viscosity η_1 and density σ_1, using the same ball-bearing, then

$$\eta_1 = \frac{2ga^2(\rho - \sigma_1)}{9v_1} \qquad . \qquad . \qquad \text{(ii)}$$

where v_1 is the new terminal velocity. Dividing (i) by (ii),

$$\therefore \frac{\eta}{\eta_1} = \frac{v_1(\rho - \sigma)}{v_0(\rho - \sigma_1)} \qquad . \qquad \text{(iii)}$$

Thus knowing v_1, v, ρ, σ_1, σ, the coefficients of viscosity can be compared. In very accurate work a correction to (iii) is required for the effect of the walls of the vessel containing the liquid.

16. Viscosity and Lubrication.

When two metal surfaces slide over each other, a considerable wear and tear of metal occurs. Lubricating oil separates the moving metal parts and reduces the frictional force considerably. Thus when a shaft rotates in a lubricated bearing, for example, a very thin film of oil exists between the metal surfaces; the layer of oil in contact with the stationary bearing is then at rest, the layer in contact with the moving shaft travels at the same speed, while intermediate layers have intermediate speeds. The force on the shaft, and the efficiency of the engine, will thus be affected by the *viscosity* of the oil, among other factors.

The viscosity of a lubricating oil must generally be low when it is cold, so that the engine can start easily. When the engine has been running for a time it becomes hot, and as the oil temperature then rises the viscosity of the oil diminishes (p. 165). If the oil viscosity is suitable at a low temperature, but decreases *rapidly* with temperature, the oil becomes unsuitable as the engine is running. Consequently a good lubricating oil is one whose viscosity decreases very slightly with temperature. It can now be seen that measurements of viscosity, and of the variation of viscosity with temperature, are essential in judging whether a lubricating oil is suitable for an engine. The variation of viscosity with pressure is also measured, as the oil is subjected to considerable pressure when the machine is moving.

Viscosity measurements are also used by chemists to find the molecular weight and shape of large organic molecules such as proteins and cellulose.

OSMOSIS

17. Semi-Permeable Membranes.

If a sugar solution contained inside an inverted funnel F by a parchment sheet P is placed in a vessel of pure water at the same temperature, the level of the liquid in F rises to some height h above the level of the water in the vessel, Fig. 108. The water has thus passed through the

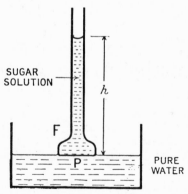

SUGAR SOLUTION

h

F

P

PURE WATER

FIG. 108. Osmosis.

parchment; but no sugar can be detected in the water in the vessel, so that the parchment only allows water molecules to pass through it and not sugar molecules. The parchment is called a *semi-permeable membrane* because it allows the solvent (water) to pass through it but not the solute (sugar). This phenomenon is known as **osmosis** after the greek word for "push", and the pressure $h\rho g$, where ρ is the density of the sugar solution, measures the **osmotic pressure** of the solution. The osmotic pressure may be defined as that pressure required to stop the passage of the solvent through a semi-permeable membrane into the solution.

Dried fruit swells when placed in water; this is an example of osmosis, the skin of the fruit acting as a semi-permeable membrane. For a similar reason, the skin of the fingers crinkle if they are placed in a strong soda solution. The cells of living plants and animals have semi-permeable membranes which allow water to pass through them; these membranes play an important part in maintaining the required concentration of salt solution in their systems, for example. The theory of osmosis is still not clearly understood.

18. Laws of Osmotic Pressure.

The first accurate investigations into osmotic pressure were carried out by PFEFFER about 1877. He placed a porous pot containing copper sulphate solution in potassium ferrocyanide solution, so that a strong semi-permeable membrane of copper ferrocyanide was formed in the pores of the pot. After filling the pot, P, with a known concentration of sugar solution he connected it to a uniform capillary tube containing nitrogen, sealed by a mercury column in a U-tube M, Fig. 109.

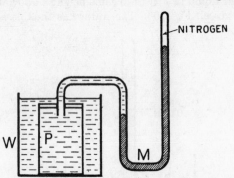

FIG. 109.   Measurement of osmotic pressure.

When the pot is placed in a vessel, W, of pure water at the same temperature, the nitrogen is compressed to a volume depending on the magnitude of the osmotic pressure. Having found the volume of nitrogen under atmospheric pressure, Pfeffer was easily able to calculate the osmotic pressure from Boyle's law. In this way he found that the osmotic pressure p increased as the concentration C increased. The following table shows some results obtained later for cane-sugar:

CONCENTRATION (C)	OSMOTIC PRESSURE (p)	VOLUME (V) OF GRAM-MOL.	PRODUCT pV
Gm./litre	Atm.	Litres	
2·02	0·134	169·3	22·7
10·0	0·66	34·2	22·6
20·0	1·32	17·1	22·6
45·0	2·97	7·60	22·6
93·75	6·18	3·65	22·5

19. Van't Hoff's Deductions.

VAN'T HOFF, in 1887, studied Pfeffer's results, and saw that *the osmotic pressure* (p) *is proportional to the concentration* (C) of the solute. From the above results, for example, $p/C = 0.066$ in each of the five cases. Now the concentration, C, $\propto 1/V$, where V is the volume of the solution. Hence, since p/C is a constant for the solution, it follows that

$$pV = \text{constant} \quad . \quad . \quad . \quad (67)$$

This result is similar to Boyle's law for gases. Van't Hoff, who first deduced the relation, then proposed the theory that the molecules of the solute (sugar for example) could be considered to move about in the solution and exert a pressure (osmotic pressure), just as the molecules of a gas exert a pressure.

Some years later, experiments were carried out on the variation of the osmotic pressure, p, with temperature for a given sugar concentration. For this purpose the solution in Fig. 109 was warmed to different temperatures, and the experiment described on p. 168 was carried out each time. Some results are shown below for the osmotic pressure variation with temperature of a solution containing 0·3 gram-molecule of sugar per litre of water:

OSMOTIC PRESSURE (p)	TEMPERATURE	$\dfrac{p}{\text{ABSOLUTE TEMP.}}$ (T)
Atm.		
7·085	0° C.	0·026
7·334	10° C.	0·026
7·605	20° C.	0·026
7·729	25° C.	0·026

Van't Hoff showed that, for dilute solutions,

$$p \propto T, \quad . \quad . \quad . \quad . \quad (68)$$

where T is the absolute temperature. This is exactly analogous to the law obeyed by the pressure of a given gas at constant volume when its temperature is altered.

20. Volume of Gram-Molecular Weight of Solute.

From the results given in the table on p. 169, 102·6 grams of cane-sugar in 1,000 c.c. of water at 10° C. has an osmotic pressure of 7·33 atmospheres. Now the gram-molecular weight of cane-sugar is 342 grams. Thus 1 gram-molecular weight of sugar in 1,000 c.c. of water at 10° C. has an osmotic pressure of 7·33 × 342/102·6 atmospheres. Hence the volume occupied by the gram-molecular weight at S.T.P. (0° C. and 1 atmosphere pressure)

$$= 1 \times \frac{7·33 \times 342}{102·6} \times \frac{273}{283} = 22·4 \text{ litres.}$$

But 22·4 litres is the volume occupied by 1 gram-molecular weight of any *gas* at S.T.P. *Thus the osmotic pressure of a dilute solution is equal to the pressure which the dissolved substance would exert if it were a gas,* and we can therefore apply all the gas laws to the dilute solution. The molecular weights of compounds of very high molecular weight, such as proteins or synthetic and natural rubber, have been determined by measuring the osmotic pressure of a solution of known concentration, and then calculating the weight which would exert a pressure of 1 atmosphere at 0° C. when the volume of the solution is 22·4 litres.

Experiments by Van't Hoff also showed that the osmotic pressures of dilute salt and mineral acid solutions were two or three times as great as that expected. This lent support to the *theory of dissociation* proposed by Arrhenius, which stated that acids and salts produce electrified particles (*ions*) in solution. Each molecule produces two or three ions, and thus the osmotic pressure is two or three times as great as that exerted if only molecules were present in the solution. Further discussion of Osmosis is outside the scope of this book, and the interested reader should refer to text-books such as Glasstone's *Physical Chemistry*.

DIFFUSION

21. Diffusion of Liquids.

If pure water is poured carefully on to a concentrated solution of copper sulphate in a beaker, a line of demarcation between the blue and the colourless liquids can be seen. When the beaker is left for a week the liquid becomes almost uniformly blue, showing that the copper sulphate molecules had intermingled with the water molecules. We say that the copper sulphate *diffused* into the water, and the phenomenon is known as *diffusion*. It is due to the mobility of the molecules of a liquid.

22. Graham's Experiments.

GRAHAM was one of the first to investigate the phenomenon of diffusion. In 1851 he placed a jar P containing a salt solution inside a wide beaker Q containing pure water, Fig. 110. The cover over P was than slid off, and after known intervals of time samples of the liquid in Q were drawn off by a pipette and analysed. In this way Graham found that (i) solutions of different salts diffuse at a different rate, (ii) salt solutions of different strengths diffuse at a rate proportional to their strength, (iii) the rate of diffusion of a solution increases with the temperature.

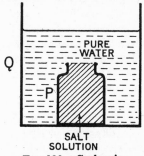

FIG. 110. Graham's experiment on diffusion.

Graham also found that substances could be divided into two classes. Albumen and gelatine solutions, for example, diffuse at a much slower rate than salt and acid solutions, and are known as **colloids**; salt and acid solutions are known as **crystalloids**.

23. Fick's Law of Diffusion.

In 1855 FICK proposed a law of diffusion, now generally accepted. This states:

The quantity per second (Q/sec.) of a solute flowing between two liquids is proportional to the area, the time, and the gradient of the concentration.

Thus
$$Q/\text{sec.} = kA \frac{c_1 - c_2}{x}, \qquad . \quad . \quad . \quad (69)$$

where A is the area in sq. cm., c_1, c_2 are the concentrations in gm. per c.c. at planes a distance x cm. apart, and k is a constant known as the *coefficient of diffusion*. Since the "concentration gradient" can be written as dc/dx, the quantity per second, Q/sec., $= kA\,dc/dx$ from (69). Fick was led to propose this law after a study of the work of Fourier on the conduction of heat some years before, in which it was stated that the quantity of heat per second flowing through a section of a conductor in the steady state was proportional to the area of the section and to the temperature gradient. On the molecular theory, however, we now recognise that conduction of heat is a transfer of energy of the molecules, whereas diffusion is a transfer of the mass of the molecules.

The determination of the coefficient of diffusion cannot be performed by drawing off samples of the liquid at different places, because this would disturb the concentration gradient. Lord Kelvin got over the difficulty by using floating balls of known density, and observing their positions. In this way it was possible to determine the concentration gradient and the quantity of solute flowing in the given time. The most accurate method, however, is an optical method, in which it is possible to measure the refractive index of the liquid while diffusion takes place, without disturbing the liquid. The concentration can be deduced from a knowledge of the refractive index by a previous calibration experiment. Modern technique utilises very thin layers of liquids so that the concentration gradient is high, and the concentration gradient and quantity of solute at points are determined by means of a photometric method.

24. Diffusion and Effusion of Gases.

A gas-jar of air, inverted over a jar of carbon dioxide, soon shows the presence of carbon dioxide, although the latter is heavier than air. Diffusion has thus taken place.

The term *effusion* refers to the passage of a gas through a hole whose diameter is less than the mean free path (average distance between successive collisions) of the molecules. Effusion can be studied by connecting a sealed pot P containing air to a manometer M containing oil, Fig. 111. When P is surrounded by a vessel Q containing carbon dioxide gas, the level of the oil on the left side of M rises, showing that the rate of effusion of air from P is greater than the rate of effusion of carbon dioxide into P. When P is surrounded by a vessel containing hydrogen, in place of carbon dioxide, the liquid level on the left of M falls, showing that the rate of effusion of hydrogen into P is greater than the rate of effusion of air out of P. By testing samples of the gases at various times Graham found that:

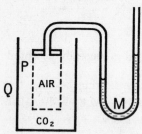

FIG. 111.   Effusion of gases.

The rate of effusion of a gas is inversely proportional to the square root of its density. This is known as *Graham's law.*

The relative densities of hydrogen and carbon dioxide are 1 : 22. Thus if a porous pot with hydrogen is placed in a vessel with carbon dioxide, the rates of effusion of the two gases initially are $\sqrt{22} : \sqrt{1}$; the hydrogen thus effuses into the carbon dioxide about 4·3 times as fast as the carbon dioxide effuses into the hydrogen. The concentration of hydrogen in the upper jar thus diminishes, whilst that in the lower jar increases. After a time there is a uniform concentration of the mixture of gases in both jars.

25. Separation of Gases by Effusion.

Graham saw that a mixture of gases could be separated by an effusion method. He surrounded a clay (porous) pipe P by a tube Q which was sealed, and then passed a mixture of air, carbon dioxide and oxygen through P, Fig. 112. As oxygen is the lighter gas it effuses faster

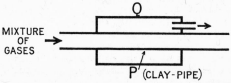

MIXTURE OF GASES

FIG. 112.   Separation of gases by effusion method.

through P into Q. In this way Graham obtained in Q air which had a relatively higher percentage of oxygen than ordinary air. This process of separating gases is known as **atmolysis**, and it was used by Ramsey in 1899 in his early attempt to isolate helium from the air. Having eliminated the oxygen from a sample of air, he passed the nitrogen and helium remaining along a porous pipe stem. Helium passed through the pipe at a rate of $\sqrt{28/4}$ or 2·6 times as fast as the nitrogen, and the process was repeated with the issuing gas, thus obtaining a mixture richer in helium than at the outset.

"Heavy hydrogen" or **deuterium** is an isotope of hydrogen which has a mass of two, and is present in hydrogen with the much more plentiful hydrogen of mass one. Urey first isolated heavy hydrogen in 1931, using an effusion method; the relative rates of effusion of the two isotopes are $\sqrt{2} : \sqrt{1}$, or 1·4 : 1, from Graham's law. The separation of isotopes by effusion is a slow process, but an electrolytic method is quicker. The mobility of heavy hydrogen ions in dilute acid solutions is less than those of mass one as the former are larger and heavier, and thus the concentration of heavy hydrogen in the solution increases as electrolysis takes place.

EXERCISES .VIII

Friction. Viscosity

1. Define *coefficient of sliding friction, coefficient of viscosity*. Contrast the laws of solid friction with those which govern the flow of liquids through tubes.

Sketch the apparatus you would employ to determine the coefficient of sliding friction between a wood block and a board and show how you would deduce the coefficient from a suitable graph. (*L.*)

2. A friction band is wrapped round a pulley (radius 10 cm.) attached to an electric motor. One end of the band supports a 2 kgm. weight, and the other is fastened to the hook of a spring dynamometer which is anchored to the floor. When the motor is running the band supports the weight in a stationary position and the dynamometer reads 200 gm. wt. If the motor makes 1,200 revolutions per minute what is its power output in watts? Give a diagram of the arrangement showing the direction of rotation. (*L.*)

3. Explain what is meant by the *dimensions* of a physical quantity in mass, length and time. Find the dimensions of *weight, velocity gradient, coefficient of viscosity*.

A small sphere of radius r, falling under gravity through a fluid of coefficient of viscosity η, ultimately attains a steady or terminal velocity v. Apply the method of dimensions to determine how v depends upon r, η, and w, where w is the effective weight of the sphere in the fluid, i.e., the difference between the true weight and the upward thrust due to the displaced fluid. (*O. & C.*)

4. Define *coefficient of viscosity*. For orderly flow of a given liquid through a capillary tube of length l, radius r, the volume of liquid issuing per sec. is proportional to pr^4/l where p is the pressure difference between the ends of the tube. How would you verify this relation experimentally for water at room temperature? How would you detect the onset of turbulence? (*N.*)

5. State the laws of friction between dry solid surfaces, and define *coefficient of friction*. Describe very briefly one method for finding this coefficient for two given surfaces, for example, a cardboard surface and the surface of a table.

A mass projected along the surface of a horizontal table, 3·2 ft. above floor-level, with an initial speed of 9 ft./sec., travels 4 ft. on the table surface and a further horizontal distance of 18 ins. beyond the edge of the table before striking the floor. At what inclination of the table would the same mass slide without acceleration? (*W.*)

6. Define *coefficient of viscosity*. What are its dimensions?

By the method of dimensions, deduce how the rate of flow of a viscous liquid through a narrow tube depends upon the viscosity, the radius of the tube, and the pressure difference per unit length. Explain how you would use your results to compare the coefficients of viscosity of glycerine and water. (*C.*)

7. Distinguish between *static* and *sliding* (kinetic) friction and define the *coefficient of sliding friction*.

How would you investigate the laws of sliding friction between wood and iron?

An iron block, of mass 10 lb., rests on a wooden plane inclined at 30° to the horizontal. It is found that the least force parallel to the plane which causes the block to slide *up* the plane is 10 lb. wt. Calculate the coefficient of sliding friction between wood and iron. (*N.*)

8. Explain the meaning of *terminal velocity* as applied to the motion of a small sphere falling through a viscous liquid. Describe an experiment to show how the terminal velocity of a ball-bearing falling under gravity in a viscous oil varies with the diameter.

An oil drop carrying a charge of 144×10^{-10} e.s.u. is balanced in air by an electric field of 5,000 volt cm.$^{-1}$ Determine (*a*) the radius of the drop, (*b*) the terminal velocity acquired after removal of the field. (Densities of the oil and of air are 0·9200 and 0·0013 gm. cm.$^{-3}$ respectively. 300 volt = 1 e.s.u. of potential. Viscosity of air, $1·824 \times 10^{-4}$ gm. cm.$^{-1}$ sec.$^{-1}$ (*N.*)

9. Give an account of the factors which determine the force of friction (i) between solids, (ii) in liquids.

A block weighing 12 kilograms is drawn along a horizontal surface by a steadily applied force of 4 kg. weight acting in the direction of motion. Find the kinetic energy acquired by the block at the end of 10 secs. and compare it with the total work done on the block in the same time. (Coefficient of friction = 0·28.) (*L.*)

10. Define *coefficient of viscosity*. Distinguish between orderly and turbulent flow of a liquid through a tube. Describe a method to determine for a given tube and liquid the pressure head at which the transition from orderly to turbulent flow occurs.

A horizontal capillary tube, 50 cm. long and 0·20 mm. internal radius, is inserted into the lower end of a tall cylindrical vessel of cross-sectional area 10 sq. cm. The vessel is filled with water which is allowed to flow out through the tube. Calculate the time taken for the level of the water in the vessel to fall from a height of 100 cm. to 50 cm. above the axis of the tube. Assume that the volume of water passing per sec. through a horizontal tube is $\pi a^4(p_1 - p_2)/8l\eta$, where a = tube radius, l = tube length, η = coefficient of viscosity of water, and $(p_1 - p_2)$ = difference in the pressures at the ends of the tube. Take the viscosity of water as 0·010 gm. cm.$^{-1}$ sec.$^{-1}$ and $\log_e 10 = 2·30$. (*N.*)

11. State the laws of sliding friction between solid surfaces and explain briefly how you would proceed to verify them.

Masses of 9 lb. and 12 lb. are connected by a tight cord and placed on a line of greatest slope of a rough plane which is slowly tilted. If the 9 lb. mass is the lower, find the inclination at which slipping will take place. The coefficient of friction between the plane and the 9 lb. mass is 1/3; between the plane and the 12 lb. mass, 1/2. (*W.*)

12. Define *coefficient of friction* and *coefficient of viscosity*.

Describe how you would (*a*) measure the coefficient of sliding friction between iron and wood, and (*b*) compare the viscosities of water and paraffin oil. (*L.*)

13. Define *coefficient of viscosity* and deduce its dimensions.

The annular space between an outer fixed cylinder of radius a_1 and an inner coaxial rotatable cylinder of radius a_2 is filled with a liquid of coefficient of viscosity η. If $a_1 - a_2$ is small compared with a_1, find the couple required to cause the inner cylinder to rotate with angular velocity ω

when immersed to a depth l. Explain how the effects of the ends of the cylinders can be eliminated in practice. (*C.*)

Osmosis. Diffusion.

14. What is meant by osmotic pressure? How does this pressure, in a dilute solution, depend on (*a*) the concentration of the solution used, and (*b*) the temperature of the solution?

Give a simple theoretical basis to account for all the phenomena you have described.

How would you measure the osmotic pressure of a solution? (*L.*)

15. Distinguish between *diffusion* and *osmosis*. What laws do you know concerning (*a*) the relative rates of diffusion of gases, and (*b*) the osmotic pressure of solutions? By whom were these laws discovered? Describe one experiment on gaseous diffusion and one on osmotic pressure. (*L.*)

16. Write an essay on osmosis and explain how the osmotic pressure of a dilute aqueous sugar solution may be measured. (*L.*)

17. What is meant by *osmosis* and by *osmotic pressure?* Describe how the osmotic pressure of a solution can be measured.

State the quantitative laws of osmotic pressure. (*L.*)

18. Write a brief account of the phenomenon of diffusion in liquids and in gases. (*L.*)

19. Calculate the osmotic pressure at 0° C. of a solution of sugar containing 10 gm. of sugar per litre, if the molecular weight of the sugar is 342 and the gram-molecular weight of a gas at S.T.P. occupies 22·4 litres.

20. An osmotic pressure of 35·4 cm. mercury is exerted by a sugar solution at 10° C. containing 8 gm. of sugar per litre. Calculate the concentration of sugar solution which has an osmotic pressure of 26·0 cm. mercury at 30° C.

21. State *Graham's law of effusion*. Describe an experiment (i) to demonstrate effusion, (ii) to verify Graham's law.

CHAPTER IX

SOME VERNIER AND SCREW INSTRUMENTS

1. The Vernier.

In order to measure lengths to a higher degree of accuracy than one millimetre, for example, VERNIER designed a scale V known as a *vernier*, which is placed alongside the millimetre scale, M, Fig. 113. The vernier scale has a length of 0·9 cm. and 10 divisions, and hence

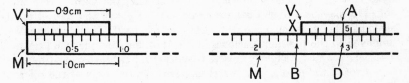

FIG. 113.   Vernier scale.

each division on the vernier is 0·09 cm. long. Thus each division on the vernier scale is (0·1 − 0·09) or 0·01 cm. less than each division on the millimetre scale.

When a vernier scale is used, we look along this scale, V, and the millimetre scale, M, and *we note the division on V which coincides with one of the divisions on M*. In Fig. 113, for example, the fifth division, A, on the vernier coincides with a division D on the scale M. From above, it follows that the division on the vernier on the immediate left of A is 0·01 cm. in front of the division on the left of D. Now we move five divisions from A on the vernier until the zero division of it, X, is reached; hence we conclude that X is 5 × 0·01 cm. in front of the division B on the millimetre scale M. The reading corresponding to X on the scale M is therefore 2·4 + 0·05, or 2·45 cm.

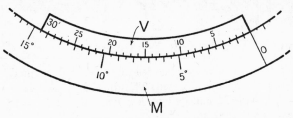

FIG. 114.   Circular vernier scale.

Circular vernier scales are used on instruments which measure angles, such as the spectrometer or the sextant. In Fig. 114, the main circular scale M is graduated from 0 − 360 degrees in half-degrees, and the circular vernier scale V occupies a length equivalent to 14·5° on M. Since the vernier is divided into 30 equal divisions, the difference between a division on M and a division on V

$$= \frac{1}{30}(15° - 14·5°) = \frac{1}{30} \times 0·5° = 1 \text{ minute of arc.}$$

The vernier thus enables the reading on M to be found to an accuracy of one minute.

2. Zero Error.

On occasions, the "zeros" of a vernier and the accompanying main scale may not originally coincide. For example, the vernier zero in Fig. 113 may be a little distance c say to the right of the zero of the straight main scale M before the instrument is used. If the vernier V is moved to the position X shown in Fig. 113, for example, the length 2·45 cm. recorded is slightly greater than the true distance moved by V. The error in the reading is c, which is called the *zero error* of the ruler. The zero error of an instrument must always be searched for and determined before the instrument is used.

3. Vernier Callipers.

Another instrument for measuring linear dimensions is the vernier callipers. This consists of a straight metal scale M graduated in millimetres (or inches), with a movable vernier scale V engraved on a metal B, Fig. 115. When the movable jaw on B is in contact with the

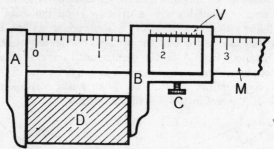

Fig. 115. Vernier callipers.

fixed jaw A of the instrument, the readings on A and V should be zero; if it is not, the "zero error" is noted. The object D is then placed between the jaws by moving B, and its length is read from the scales M and V, allowing for any "zero error"

4. The Micrometer Screw Gauge.

When a *screw* is rotated through one revolution its point advances through a distance known as the *pitch*, *p*, of the screw, which is the distance between corresponding points on consecutive threads of the screw, Fig. 116 (i).

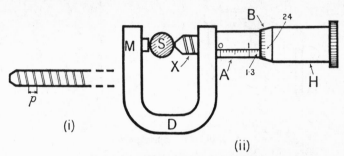

(i)

(ii)

FIG. 116.   Micrometer screw gauge.

The micrometer screw gauge is an instrument used for measuring the diameters of wires or ball-bearings, or the thickness of a thin plate, and consists of a screw X moving in a fixed curved metal frame D, Fig. 116 (ii). The screw moves inside a nut on which a linear scale A in millimetres is engraved, and it is operated by a head H which has a circular scale B engraved on it. When the screw X makes contact with the projection at M, the reading on A and on B should be zero; if not, the zero error is noted.

The pitch of the screw is found by turning the screw through one revolution and noting the advance of the screw from the scale A. Suppose the pitch is $\frac{1}{2}$ millimetre, and the number of divisions on B is 100. Then each division on B corresponds to a distance of $\frac{1}{200}$ or 0·005 mm. If the diameter of a ball-bearing S is required it is placed between the jaws of the gauge, and the screw is adjusted until it touches S gently. The readings on A and on B are then noted. Suppose the reading on A is 1·3 cm. and the reading on B corresponds to the 24th division and there is no zero error. Then

$$\text{diameter of S} = 1·3 + 24 \times 0·0005 = 1·312 \text{ cm.}$$

5. The Spherometer.

The spherometer is an instrument used for measuring the radii of curvature of surfaces, such as those of a lens or a curved mirror. It consists of a screw S which moves through a fixed nut by turning the head H, with three fixed legs A, B, C situated round S, Fig. 117 (i). The distances between the points of the legs are equal. A fixed vertical

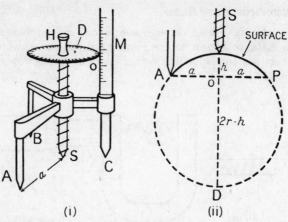

(i)   (ii)

FIG. 117. Spherometer.

scale M, graduated in millimetres, is attached to the instrument as shown, and a circular scale D, containing 50 divisions for example, moves along M as the screw is rotated by H. As with the micrometer screw gauge, the readings on the scale M and the circular scale D enable the distance moved by the screw to be calculated to three places of decimals.

The spherometer is first placed on a flat glass plate and the screw is moved until it just touches the plate. The readings on M and D are then noted. The spherometer is now placed with its three legs on the curved surface whose radius of curvature is required, and the screw is then turned until it just touches this surface, Fig. 117 (ii). Suppose h is the distance moved by the screw, a is the distance from S to any of the three legs A, B, C, and r is the radius of curvature; Fig. 117 (ii) represents a section of the surface taken through one leg A and the screw. Then, from the geometrical property of chords intersecting in a circle, we have, if S is the tip of the screw,

$$SO \cdot OD = AO \cdot OP.$$
$$\therefore h\,(2r - h) = a \cdot a = a^2,$$

since SD = diameter of circle = $2r$.

$$\therefore r = \frac{a^2 + h^2}{2h} = \frac{a^2}{2h} + \frac{h}{2}.$$

Thus by measuring h and a the radius of curvature r can be calculated. The spherometer can also be used to measure the radius of curvature of a concave surface, as well as a convex surface; in the former case h is the distance which the screw advances to make contact with the concave surface, having first placed the spherometer on a flat glass plate.

PART TWO
HEAT

HEAT

CHAPTER X

INTRODUCTION

TEMPERATURE

WE are interested in heat because it is the commonest form of energy, and because changes of temperature have great effects on our personal comfort, and on the properties of substances, such as water, which we use every day. *Temperature* is a scientific quantity which corresponds to primary sensations—hotness and coldness. These sensations are not reliable enough for scientific work, because they

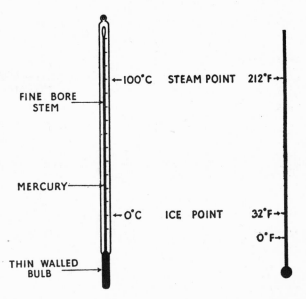

(a)   CENTIGRADE (CELSIUS)   *(b)* FAHRENHEIT

Fig. 118. Mercury-in-glass thermometer (left), and graduations.

depend on contrast—the air in a thick-walled barn or church feels cool on a summer's day, but warm on a winter's day, although a thermometer may show that it has a lower temperature in the winter. A thermometer, such as the familiar mercury-in-glass instrument (Fig. 118), is a device whose readings depend on hotness or coldness, and which we choose to consider more reliable than our senses. We are justified in considering it more reliable because different thermo-

meters of the same type agree with one another better than different
people do.

The temperature of a body, then, is its degree of hotness, as measured
on a thermometer. The thermometer was invented in Italy about
1630: it consisted of an open-ended tube, with a bulb full of water at
its lower end. The water rose in the tube when the bulb was warmed,
and fell when it was cooled.

As a liquid for use in thermometers, water soon gave way to linseed
oil or alcohol, and by about 1660 thermometer-makers had begun to
seal the top of the tube. Early thermometers had no definite scale,
like that of a modern thermometer; some of them were used for showing
the temperatures of greenhouses, and were mounted on wooden back-
boards, which were carved with grapes and peaches for example, to
indicate the correct temperatures for growing the different fruits.
The thermometer as we know it to-day, containing pure mercury and
graduated according to a universal scale, was developed by Fahrenheit
in 1724.

1. Temperature Scales.

When a mercury thermometer is to be graduated, it is placed first
in melting ice, and then in steam from boiling water (Fig. 119). The
temperature of the steam depends on the atmospheric pressure, as

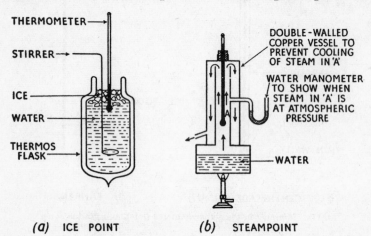

FIG. 119. Determination of fixed points.

we shall see in Chapter V; for calibrating thermometers, an atmospheric pressure of 76 cm. mercury is chosen. In both steam and ice,
when the level of the mercury has become steady, it is marked on the
glass: the level in ice is called the *lower fixed point*, or ice-point, and
the level in steam is called the *upper fixed point*, or steam-point. The

distance between the fixed points is called the *fundamental interval* of the thermometer. For scientific work, the fundamental interval is divided into 100 equal parts (Fig. 118 (a)). This division was first proposed by Celsius in 1742, and the graduations are called degrees Centigrade or, in modern nomenclature, degrees Celsius (°C.) ; the ice-point is 0° C. and the steam-point 100° C.

When a thermometer is intended for domestic or engineering use in England, its fundamental interval is divided into 180 equal parts. The ice-point is then called 32 degrees Fahrenheit (°F.), and the steam-point 212° F. (Fig. 118 (b)). These graduations arose because Fahrenheit took for his lower fixed point the lowest temperature he could reach: that of a mixture of ice and salt. He called it 0°. For his upper fixed point he took the temperature of the human body, which he called 96°. He then found that the temperature of melting ice was 32°, and of boiling water 212°; he was the first person to show definitely that liquids boiled at fixed temperatures, and was delighted by his discovery. A modern Fahrenheit thermometer, graduated with 32° for the ice-point and 212° for the steam-point, gives 98·4° F. for the average normal body temperature.

2. Types of Thermometer.

The *mercury-in-glass* thermometer depends on the change in volume of the mercury with hotness; it is cheap and simple, but is not reliable enough for accurate work (Chapter XVI). Other types of thermometer depend on the change, with hotness, of the pressure of a gas at constant volume or the electrical resistance of a metal (Fig. 120). Another type

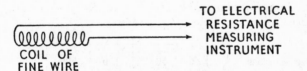

TO ELECTRICAL
RESISTANCE
MEASURING
INSTRUMENT

COIL OF
FINE WIRE

FIG. 120. A resistance thermometer; the wire is usually of platinum.

of thermometer depends on the electromotive force change with temperature of two metals joined together. Fig. 121 (a) shows two wires, one of copper and one of iron, soldered together at A. The ends of the wires are joined to a galvanometer G. When the junction A is heated, a current flows which deflects the galvanometer. The current usually increases with the temperature difference between the hot and cold ends of the wires. For temperature measurement two junctions are used, as in Fig. 121 (b) ; the second one, called the cold junction, is maintained at 0° C. by ice-water.

Each of these quantities—e.m.f., resistance, pressure—gives its own temperature scale, and the different scales agree only at the fixed

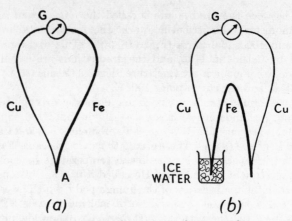

FIG. 121. Thermojunctions or thermocouples.

points, where their readings are *defined* as 0° C. and 100° C. (When we speak of a temperature *scale*, we refer to the quantity used to define it; the difference between °C. and °F. is only a difference in the *graduation* of a given scale.) If, for example, a given platinum wire has resistances R_0 and R_{100} at the ice- and steam-points respectively, then its fundamental interval is $R_{100} - R_0$. And if it has a resistance R at an unknown temperature, the value of that temperature, t_P, on the platinum resistance scale, is defined by

$$t_P = \frac{R - R_0}{R_{100} - R_0} \times 100 \ (^\circ\text{C.}).$$

The platinum-resistance scale differs appreciably from the mercury-in-glass scale, as the following table shows:

Mercury-in-glass	0	50	100	200	300	°C.
Platinum-resistance	0	50·25	100	197	291	°C.

We shall discuss temperature scales again later (p. 376); here we wish only to point out that they differ from one another, that no one of them is any more "true" than any other, and that our choice of which to adopt is arbitrary, though it may be decided by convenience.

3. Effects of Temperature.

Most bodies, when they are made hotter, become larger; their increase in size is called thermal expansion. Thermal expansion may be useful, as in a thermometer, or it may be a nuisance, as in bridges and railway lines. If the thermal expansion of a solid or liquid is

resisted, great forces are set up: that is why gaps are left between
railway lines, and why beer-bottles are never filled quite full. If the
thermal expansion of a gas is resisted, however, the forces set up are
not so great; the pressure of the gas increases, but not catastrophically.
The increase of pressure is, in fact, made use of in most forms of engine;
it is also made use of in accurate thermometry.

Besides causing a change in size or pressure, a change of temperature
may cause a change of
state—from solid to
liquid, liquid to gas, or
vice versa. If we heat
some crystals of lead
acetate in a crucible, and
measure their tempera-
ture, with a thermometer
reading to 300° C., we
find that the crystals
warm steadily up to
75° C. and then start to
melt. Their temperature
does not rise further until
they have all melted
(Fig. 122). After it has
melted, the lead acetate
warms up to 280° C.,

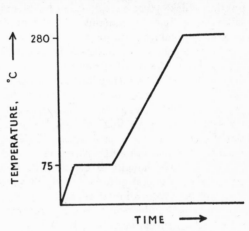

Fig. 122. Warming curve of lead acetate.

and then keeps a constant temperature until it has all boiled away.
We call 280° C. the boiling-point of lead acetate; likewise we call
75° C. the melting- (or freezing-) point of lead acetate.

QUANTITY OF HEAT

4. Heat and Temperature.

If we run hot water into a lukewarm bath, we make it hotter; if
we run cold water in, we make it cooler. The hot water, we say, gives
heat to the cooler bath-water; but the cold water takes heat from the
warmer bath-water. The quantity of heat which we can get from hot
water depends on both the mass of water and on its temperature: a
bucket-full at 180° F. will warm the bath more than a cup-full at
212° F. Roughly speaking, temperature is analogous to electrical
potential, and heat is analogous to quantity of electricity. We can
perceive temperature changes, and whenever the temperature of a
body rises, that body has gained heat. The converse is not always
true; when a body is melting or boiling, it is absorbing heat from the
flame beneath it, but its temperature is not rising.

5. Specific Heat and Latent Heat.

The heat which a body absorbs, in melting or boiling, it gives out again in freezing or condensing; such heat is called *latent*, or hidden, *heat*, because it does not show itself by a change in temperature. When a body absorbs heat without changing its state, its temperature rises, and the heat absorbed was first called " sensible heat."

The term " latent heat " was used by Black (1728–99); he and a Swede, Wilcke, discovered latent heats independently at about the same date—Black by hanging a bucket of ice in a warm room, Wilcke by pouring boiling water on to snow.

Also independently, Black and Wilcke studied what we now call *specific heats*; the name is due to Wilcke. In his experiments Wilcke dropped various hot bodies into cold water, and measured the temperature rises which they caused. In this way he showed that a given mass of glass, for example, gave out only one-fifth as much heat as an equal mass of water, in cooling through the same temperature range. He therefore said that the specific heat of glass was 0·2.

In the seventeenth and eighteenth centuries the nature of heat was disputed; some thought of heat as the motion of the particles of a body, others thought of it as a fluid, filling the body's pores. Measurements of heat were all relative, and no unit of the quantity of heat was defined. In the nineteenth century, however, the increasing technical importance of heat made a unit of it essential. The modern units of heat are:

(i) the *calorie* (cal.): this is the amount of heat required to warm 1 gm. of water through 1° C. (see also p. 11) ;

(ii) the *British Thermal Unit* (B.Th.U.): this is the amount of heat required to warm 1 lb. of water through 1° F.

6. Heat and Energy.

Steam-engines became common in the early part of the eighteenth century; but they were not thought of as heat-engines until the latter part of that century. Consequently the early engines were wasteful of fuel, squandering useful heat in warming and cooling the cylinder at every stroke of the piston. Watt reduced this waste of heat by his invention of the separate condenser in 1769. Trevithick, about 1800, devised an engine which was driven by steam which entered the cylinder at a pressure above atmospheric, and therefore at a temperature above 212° F. (p. 308). In this engine, the steam came out of the exhaust at a temperature no higher than in earlier engines, so that a greater fraction of the heat which it carried from the boiler was used in the engine.

The idea of heat as a form of energy was developed particularly by Benjamin Thompson (1753–1814); he was an American who, after adventures in Europe, became a Count of the Holy Roman Empire, and war minister of Bavaria. He is now generally known as Count Rumford. While supervising his arsenal, he noticed the great amount of heat which was liberated in the boring of cannon. The idea common at the time was that this heat was a fluid, pressed out of the chips of metal as they were bored out of the barrel. To measure the heat produced, Rumford used a blunt borer, and surrounded it and the end of the cannon with a wooden box, filled with water (Fig. 6). From the weight of water, and the rate at which its temperature rose, he concluded that the boring operation liberated heat at the same rate as "nine wax candles, burning with a clear flame". He showed that the amount of heat liberated was in no way connected with the mass of metal bored away, and concluded that it depended only on the work done against friction. It followed that **heat was a form of energy.**

Rumford published the results of his experiments in 1798. No similar experiments were made until 1840, when Joule began his study of heat and other forms of energy. Joule measured the work done, and the heat produced, when water was churned, in an apparatus which we shall describe later. He also measured the work done and heat produced when oil was churned, when air was compressed, when water was forced through fine tubes, and when cast iron bevel wheels were rotated one against the other. Always, within the limits of experimental error, he found that the heat liberated was proportional to the mechanical work done, and that the ratio of the two was the same in all types of experiment. His last experiments, made in 1878, showed that about 772 ft.-lb. of work were equivalent to one British thermal unit of heat. This ratio Joule called the *mechanical equivalent of heat*; nowadays we often call it *Joule's equivalent, J*. We also call the metric unit of work after Joule; in metric units

the mechanical equivalent of heat, J, is about 4·2 joules per calorie.

In other experiments, Joule measured the heat liberated by an electric current in flowing through a resistance; at the same time he measured the work done in driving the dynamo which generated the current. He obtained about the same ratio for work done to heat liberated as in his direct experiments. This work linked the ideas of heat, mechanical, and electrical energy; it has since led to the modern definitions of electrical units.

Joule also measured the heat produced by a current maintained by a battery, and related it to the amounts of the chemicals decomposed in the battery. In this way he linked the ideas of heat, electrical, and chemical energy.

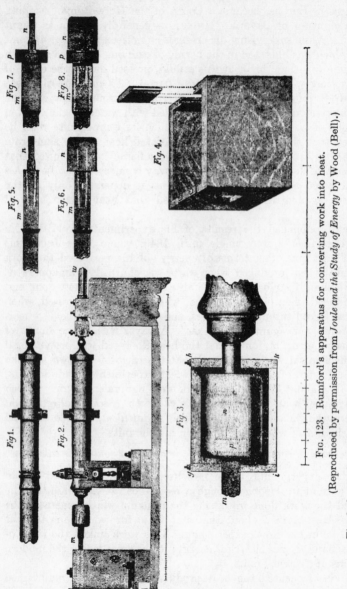

Fig. 123. Rumford's apparatus for converting work into heat.
(Reproduced by permission from *Joule and the Study of Energy* by Wood (Bell).)

Fig. 1 shows the cannon. Fig. 2 shows the complete apparatus; w is connected to machinery driven round by horses, m is joined to a blunt borer n in a cylinder shown enlarged in Fig. 3 and Fig. 4. Figs. 5, 6, 7, 8 show further details of m and n.

7. The Conservation of Energy.

As a result of all his experiments, Joule developed the idea that energy in any one form could be converted into any other. There might be a loss of useful energy in the process—for example, some of the heat from the furnace of a steam-engine is lost up the chimney, and some more down the exhaust—but no energy is destroyed. The work done by the engine can, with the help of Joule's equivalent, be expressed in heat units; if it is then added to the heat lost as described, and the heat developed as friction, it is equal to the heat provided by the fuel burnt. The idea underlying this statement is called the *Principle of the Conservation of Energy*. It implies that, if we start with a given amount of energy in any one form, we can convert it in turn into all other forms; we may not always be able to convert it completely, but if we keep an accurate balance-sheet we shall find that the total amount of energy, expressed in any one form—say heat or work—is always the same, and is equal to the original amount.

The conservation of energy applies to living organisms—plants and animals—as well as to inanimate systems. For example, we may put a man or a mouse into a box or a room, give him a treadmill to work, and feed him. His food is his fuel; if we burn a sample of it, we can measure its chemical energy, in heat units. And if we now add up the heat value of the work which the man does, and the heat which his body gives off, we find that their total is equal to the chemical energy of the food which the man eats. Because food is the source of man's energy, food values are commonly expressed in *large-calories*, which is the heat required to warm 1,000 gm. of water through 1° C. A man needs about 3,000 large-calories per day.

Muscles are unique in their capacity to turn chemical energy directly into mechanical energy. When a muscle is stimulated, complex phosphates in its tissues break down; in doing so, they cause the muscle fibres to swell and shorten. Thus, via the bones and joints, the muscle does external work. When the muscle is recovering after contraction, the phosphates are built up again by a series of reactions, involving the oxidation of sugars. The sugars and oxygen are brought to the muscle in the arterial blood; the waste products of the reactions, water and carbon dioxide, are carried away in the venous blood.[1] Recently physiologists have found evidence that muscles may also convert mechanical energy into chemical.[2] For example, when we walk downstairs, gravity does work on our leg-muscles; some of this appears as heat, but some, it now seems, is used in reversing the chemical actions of muscle activity.

All the energy by which we live comes from the sun. The sun's ultra-violet rays are absorbed in the green matter of plants, and

---

[1] DAVSON, *General Physiology*, Chap. XVII (Churchill, 1951).
[2] ABBOTT, AUBERT and HILL, *Jour. Physiology*, Vol. III (1950).

make them grow; the animals eat the plants, and we eat them—we are all vegetarians at one remove. The plants and trees of an earlier age decayed, were buried, and turned into coal. Even water-power comes from the sun—we would have no lakes if the sun did not evaporate the sea and provide the rainfall which fills the lakes. The relationship between all the principal forms of energy are summarized in Fig. 124.

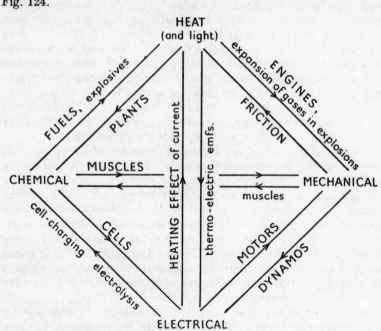

FIG. 124. Forms of energy, and their interconversions.

BIBLIOGRAPHY

ANDRADE, *Engines*. (Bell.)

HILL, *Living Machinery*. (Bell, 1939.)

RUHEMANN, *Power*. (Sigma Books, 1946.)

WOOD, *Joule and the Study of Energy*. (Bell, 1925.)

McKIE and HEATHCOTE, *The Discovery of Specific and Latent Heats*. (Arnold, 1935.)

HOGBEN, *Science for the Citizen*. (Allen and Unwin, 1938.)

MAGIE, *Source-Book in Physics*. (McGraw-Hill, 1935.)

PLEDGE, *Science since 1500*. (H.M.S.O., 1939.)

SINGER, *A Short History of Science*. (Oxford, 1941.)

DAMPIER, *A History of Science*. (Cambridge, 1942.)

JEANS, *The Growth of Physical Science*. (Cambridge, 1947.)

DARROW, *The Renaissance of Physics*. (Macmillan, 1937.)

BUCKLEY, *A History of Physics*. (Methuen.)

CHAPTER XI

CALORIMETRY

Calorimetry is the measurement of heat; here we shall be concerned with the measurement of specific heats, latent heats, and the mechanical equivalent of heat.

1. The Calorie.

In defining the calorie (p. 188), we implicitly assumed that the quantity of heat required to warm 1 gm. of water was the same between any two temperatures 1° C. apart. Experiment shows that this is, at least, very nearly true: if we take two equal masses of water, one at 100° C. and the other at 0° C., and mix them, then the temperature of the mixture is very nearly 50° C. The heat given out by a gramme in cooling from 100° C. to 50° C. is therefore very nearly equal to the heat required to warm a gramme from 0° C. to 50° C. For very accurate work, however, we define the calorie as the heat required to warm 1 gm. of water from 14·5° C. to 15·5° C. This quantity is called the *fifteen-degree calorie*.

Occasionally quantities of heat are expressed in "mean calories": if H calories are needed to warm 1 gm. of water from t_1° C. to t_2° C., then the quantity $\dfrac{H}{t_2 - t_1}$ is called the mean calorie over the range t_1 to t_2. Over the range 0° C. to 100° C., measurements give

1 mean calorie = 0·9995 fifteen-degree calorie.

2. Thermal Capacity, Specific Heat.

The *thermal capacity* of a body, such as a lump of metal, is the quantity of heat required to raise its temperature by 1°. It is expressed in "calories per °C." (or "British Thermal Units per °F."). The *specific heat* of a substance is the heat required to warm unit mass of it through 1°; it is the heat capacity of unit mass of the substance. Specific heats are expressed in *calories per gm. per °C.*, or *B.Th.U. per lb. per °F.* The specific heat of a given substance has the same value in English or metric units, because of the way in which the heat units are defined: each is the heat required to warm unit mass of water through 1°.

From the definition of specific heat, it follows that the thermal capacity of a body is equal to the product of its mass and its specific heat.

SPECIFIC HEATS

Substance	Sp. Ht.; Cal./gm./°C. (B.Th.U./lb./°F.)	Substance	Sp. Ht.: Cal./gm./°C. (B.Th.U./lb./°F.)
Aluminium	0·217	Ice . .	0·50
Brass .	0·092	Paraffin wax .	0·69
Copper .	0·093	Quartz . .	0·17
Iron .	0·113	Rubber . .	0·40
Lead .	0·031	Stone . .	0·2
Mercury .	0·033	Wood . .	0·4
Nickel .	0·109	Alcohol . .	0·6
Platinum .	0·032	Brine (25% by wt.)	0·79
Silver .	0·056	Carbon tetra-chloride	0·20
Solder .	0·043	Ether . .	0·56
Steel .	0·107	Glycerine .	0·58
Ebonite .	0·40	Paraffin oil .	0·5
Glass .	0·16	Turpentine .	0·42

MEASUREMENT OF SPECIFIC HEAT

3. Method of Mixtures.

The commonest way of measuring specific heats is the method of mixtures, which was used by Wilcke (p. 188). Fig. 125 shows how we may

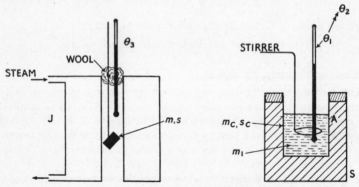

FIG. 125. Specific heat by mixtures.

apply it to a solid, such as a metal. We weigh the specimen (m gm.) and hang it on a thread in a steam jacket, J, fitted with a thermometer. The jacket is plugged with cotton wool to prevent loss of heat by convection. While the solid is warming, we weigh a thin-walled copper vessel A called a calorimeter (m_c gm.), then run about 50 cm.^{3} of water into it, and by subtraction find the mass m_1 of this water. We put the calorimeter into a draught-shield S, and take the temperature, θ_1, of the water in it. After we have given the specimen time to warm up— say half an hour—we read its temperature, θ_3; then we slide the calorimeter under the jacket, and drop the specimen into it. After stirring the mixture, we measure its final temperature, θ_2. If no heat leaves the calorimeter by radiation, conduction, or convection, after the hot specimen has been dropped into the calorimeter, we have:

heat lost by solid in cooling from θ_3 to θ_2 = heat gained by water and calorimeter in warming from θ_1 to θ_2.

(The heat gained by the thermometer and stirrer may be neglected if high accuracy is not required.

Therefore, if s is the specific heat of the solid, and s_c that of the calorimeter (which can be found from tables):

$$ms(\theta_3 - \theta_2) = m_1(\theta_2 - \theta_1) + m_c s_c(\theta_2 - \theta_1)$$
$$= (m_1 + m_c s_c)(\theta_2 - \theta_1),$$

whence $\qquad s = \dfrac{(m_1 + m_c s_c)(\theta_2 - \theta_1)}{m(\theta_3 - \theta_2)}.$ . . . . . (1)

4. Liquids.

The specific heat of a liquid can be found by putting some in a calorimeter and dropping a hot solid, of known specific heat s, into it. If m_l, s_l are the mass and specific heat of the liquid, then the product $m_l s_l$ replaces m in equation (1), from which s_l can be calculated.

5. Water Equivalent.

In equation (1), the quantity "$m_c s_c$" is called the *water equivalent* of the calorimeter, because it represents the mass of water which would increase in temperature by the same amount as the calorimeter if given the same amount of heat. A calorimeter of mass 90 gm. and specific heat 0·1 thus has a water equivalent of 90 × 0·1 or 9 gm. of water. If 60 gm. of water are placed in this calorimeter, and the temperature of the water increases by 8° C., then

heat gained by water and calorimeter = (60 + 9) × 8 = 552 cal.

"Water equivalent" is thus expressed in "grams of water", whereas "thermal capacity", though also calculated by mass × specific heat, is expressed in "calories per degree".

6. Heat Losses.

In a calorimetric experiment, some heat is always lost by leakage. Leakage of heat cannot be prevented, as leakage of electricity can, by insulation, because even the best insulator of heat still has appreciable conductivity (p. 338).

When convection is prevented, gases are the best thermal insulators. Hence calorimeters are often surrounded with a shield S, as in Fig. 125, and the heat loss due to conduction is made small by packing S with insulating material or by supporting the calorimeter on an insulating ring, or on threads. The loss by radiation is small at small excess temperatures over the surroundings. In some simple calorimetric experiments the final temperature of the mixture is reached quickly, so that the time for leakage is small. The total loss of heat is therefore negligible in laboratory experiments on the specific heats of metals, but not on the specific heats of bad conductors, such as rubber, which give up their heat slowly. When great accuracy is required, the loss of heat by leakage is always taken into account.

7. Newton's Law of Cooling.

Newton was the first person to investigate the heat lost by a body in air. He found that *the rate of loss of heat is proportional to the excess temperature over the surroundings.* This result, called *Newton's law of cooling*, is approximately true in still air only for a temperature excess

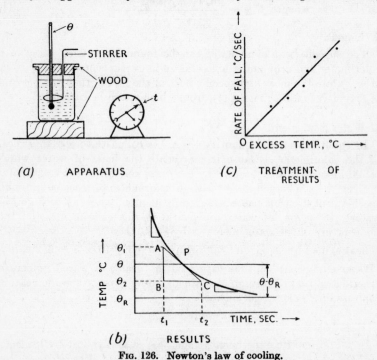

(a) APPARATUS

(c) TREATMENT OF RESULTS

(b) RESULTS

Fig. 126. Newton's law of cooling.

of about 20° C. or 30° C.; but it is true for all excess temperatures in conditions of forced convection of the air, i.e. in a draught. With natural convection Dulong and Petit found that the rate of loss of heat was proportional to $\theta^{5/4}$, where θ is the excess temperature, and this appears to be true for higher excess temperatures, such as from 50° C. to 300° C. At low excess temperatures, however, less than 1° C., G. T. P. Tarrant has pointed out that radiation, not convection, is the major contributing factor to the rate of cooling of an object (*School Science Review*, March, 1953).

To demonstrate Newton's law of cooling, we plot a temperature (θ)-time (t) cooling curve for hot water in a calorimeter placed in a draught (Fig. 126 (*a*)). If θ_R is the room temperature, then the excess temperature of the water is ($\theta - \theta_R$). At various temperatures, such as θ in Fig. 126 (*b*), we drew tangents such as APC to the curve. The slope of the tangent, in degrees per second, gives us the rate of fall of temperature, when the water is at the temperature θ:

$$\text{rate of fall} = \frac{\text{AB}}{\text{BC}} = \frac{\theta_1 - \theta_2}{t_2 - t_1}.$$

We then plot these rates against the excess temperature, $\theta - \theta_R$, as in Fig. 126 (*c*), and find a straight line passing through the origin. Since the heat lost per second by the water and calorimeter is proportional to the rate of fall of the temperature, Newton's law is thus verified.

8. Heat Loss and Temperature Fall.

Besides the excess temperature, the rate of heat loss depends on the exposed area of the calorimeter, and on the nature of its surface: a dull surface loses heat a little faster than a shiny one, because it is a better radiator (p. 349). This can be shown by doing a cooling experiment twice, with equal masses of water, but once with the calorimeter polished, and once after it has been blackened in a candle-flame. In general, for any body with a uniform surface at a uniform temperature θ, we may write, if Newton's law is true,

$$\text{heat lost/sec.} = \frac{dQ}{dt} = kS(\theta - \theta_R) \quad . \quad . \quad . \quad . \quad (2)$$

where S is the area of the body's surface, θ_R is the temperature of its surroundings, k is a constant depending on the nature of the surface, and Q denotes the heat lost from the body.

When a body loses heat Q, its temperature θ falls; if m is its mass, and s its specific heat, then its rate of fall of temperature, $d\theta/dt$, is given by

$$\frac{dQ}{dt} = -ms\frac{d\theta}{dt}.$$

Now the mass of a body is proportional to its volume. The rate of heat loss, however, is proportional to the surface area of the body. The

rate of fall of temperature is therefore proportional to the ratio of
surface to volume of the body. For bodies of similar shape, the ratio
of surface to volume is inversely proportional to any linear dimension.
If the bodies have surfaces of similar nature, therefore, the rate of fall
of temperature is inversely proportional to the linear dimension: a
small body cools faster than a large one. This is a fact of daily experience: a small coal which falls out of the fire can be picked up sooner
than a large one; a tiny baby should be more thoroughly wrapped up
than a grown man. In calorimetry by the method of mixtures, the
fact that a small body cools faster than a large one means that, the
larger the specimen, the less serious is the heat loss in transferring it
from its heating place to the calorimeter. It also means that the larger
the scale of the whole apparatus, the less serious are the errors due to
loss of heat from the calorimeter.

9. Correction for Heat Losses in Calorimetry.

Newton's law of cooling enables us to estimate the heat lost in an
experiment on the method of mixtures.

In doing the experiment, we take the temperature of the mixture
at half-minute intervals, and plot it against time, as in Fig. 127. The

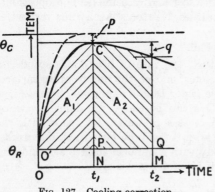

FIG. 127. Cooling correction.

broken line shows how we
would expect the tempera-
ture to rise if no heat were
lost; we have therefore to
estimate the difference, p,
between the plateau of this
imaginary curve, and the
crest of the experimental
curve, C. p is known as the
"cooling correction."

We start by drawing an
ordinate CN through the
crest, and another LM
through any convenient
point L further along the
curve; OM should be not less than twice ON—the greater it is, the
more accurate the correction. We next draw an abscissa O'PQ through
the room temperature, θ_R; and by counting the squares of the graph
paper, we measure the areas O'CP (A_1), PCLQ (A_2). Then, if q is the
fall in temperature from C to L:

$$\frac{p}{q} = \frac{\text{O'CP}}{\text{PCLQ}} = \frac{A_1}{A_2}, \qquad \cdots \qquad (3)$$

or
$$p = q\frac{A_1}{A_2}.$$

Before establishing this equation let us see how to use it. Suppose m_1, s, denote the mass and specific heat of the specimen; m denotes the mass of water; and W the water equivalent of the calorimeter. Then the heat which these lose to their surroundings is the heat which would have raised their temperature by p. Thus

$$\text{heat lost} = (m_1 s + m + W)p.$$

Let θ_1 denote the initial temperature of the specimen, θ_c the highest temperature of the mixture; and θ_2 the original temperature of the water and calorimeter. Then we have:

$$\text{heat given out} = \text{heat taken in} + \text{heat lost}.$$

$$\therefore \quad m_1 s(\theta_1 - \theta_c) = (m + W)(\theta_c - \theta_2) + (m_1 s + m + W)p,$$

from which $\quad m_1 s(\theta_1 - \overline{\theta_c + p}) = (m + W)(\overline{\theta_c + p} - \theta_2).$

To correct for the heat losses we must therefore add the correction p to the crest temperature θ_c, on each side of the heat balance equation. In equation (1), p. 195, p must be added to θ_2 in both numerator and denominator.

Theory of the Correction. To establish equation (3), we write down the expression for the heat lost per second from the calorimeter, assuming Newton's law of cooling:

$$\frac{dQ}{dt} = kS(\theta - \theta_R) \quad . \quad . \quad . \quad . \quad . \quad . \quad (4)$$

where k is a constant, and S the exposed area of the calorimeter. Between times $t = 0$ and $t = t_1$, the total heat lost is

$$Q_1 = \int_0^{t_1} kS(\theta - \theta_R)dt$$

$$= kS \int_0^{t_1} (\theta - \theta_R)dt$$

$$= kS \times \text{area O'CP} = kSA_1.$$

This is the heat, which, if it had not been lost, would have warmed the calorimeter and contents by p degrees. Therefore

$$(m_1 s + m + W)p = kSA_1 \quad . \quad . \quad . \quad . \quad . \quad (5)$$

Similarly the heat lost between t_1 and t_2 is given by $Q_2 = kSA_2$, and since this loss caused a fall in temperature of q, we have, by the argument above

$$(m_1 s + m + W)q = kSA_2 \quad . \quad . \quad . \quad . \quad (6)$$

On dividing equation (5) by equation (6), we find

$$\frac{p}{q} = \frac{A_1}{A_2},$$

or $$p = q\frac{A_1}{A_2}$$

10. Specific Heat of Liquid by Cooling.

Specific heats of liquids which react with water are often measured by the so-called *method of cooling*. The cooling curve of a calorimeter is plotted, first when it contains a known volume of hot water, and then when it contains an *equal* volume of hot liquid (Fig. 128). The

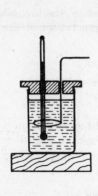
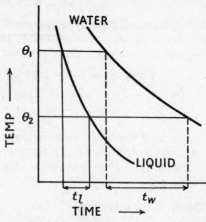

Fig. 128. Specific heat by cooling.

volumes are made equal so as to make the temperature distribution, over the surface of the calorimeter, the same in each experiment. From the curves, the respective times t_l and t_w are found which the calorimeter and contents take to cool from θ_1 to θ_2. Whatever the contents of the calorimeter, it gives off heat at a rate which depends only on its excess temperature, since the area and nature of its surface are constant. Therefore, at each temperature between θ_1 and θ_2, the calorimeter gives off heat at the same rate whatever its contents. Thus the average rate at which it loses heat, over the whole range, is the same with water and with liquid. Consequently

$$\frac{(m_1 s + W)(\theta_1 - \theta_2)}{t_l} = \frac{(m + W)(\theta_1 - \theta_2)}{t_w},$$

where m_1, s, are the mass and specific heat of the liquid, m is the mass of water, and W is the water equivalent of the calorimeter. Thus

$$\frac{m_1 s + W}{t_l} = \frac{m + W}{t_w},$$

from which s can be calculated.

MECHANICAL EQUIVALENT

11. Joule's Experiments.

About 1847 Joule measured the mechanical equivalent of heat by an apparatus of the form shown in Fig. 129. C is a copper cylinder, about a foot in diameter, containing water. The water is churned by paddles P, and prevented from whirling round *en masse* by baffles B.

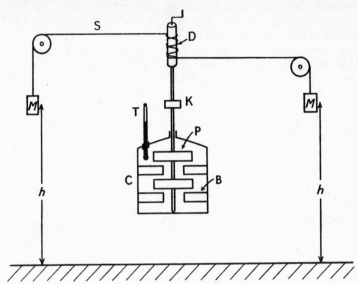

Fig. 129. Joule's apparatus for mechanical equivalent.

The paddles are connected by a coupling K to a drum D, which is rotated by strings S attached to lead weights M. A thermometer T shows the temperature of the water.

Joule would start an experiment by allowing the weights M to fall to the ground and turn the paddles. He would then break the coupling K, and re-wind the weights without disturbing the paddles. In this way he would make the weights fall twenty times or more, in a single experiment, and so increase the work done on the water and consequently the temperature rise.

Suppose n is the number of falls; then the work done on the water is $W' = 2nMgh$, where M is the mass of one weight, g is the acceleration of gravity, and h is the height of the fall. The heat gained by the cylinder and the water is $(m + W)\theta$, where m is the mass of water, W the water equivalent of the cylinder and paddles, and θ is their rise in temperature. The rise θ includes the correction for heat losses. The mechanical equivalent, J is given by

$$J = \frac{W'}{Q}$$
$$= \frac{2nMgh}{(m + W)\theta}. \qquad . \quad . \quad . \quad . \quad . \quad (7)$$

An experiment of this kind takes a long time—about half an hour—because a great deal of work, by everyday standards, must be done to produce a measurable amount of heat. The cooling correction is therefore relatively great; in a typical experiment the observed rise of temperature might be 0·5° F., and the cooling correction 0·1° F., whence $\theta = 0·5 + 0·1 = 0·6°$ F..

Many people refused to accept Joule's work at first, because of the very small temperature differences on which it rested. Nevertheless, Joule's final result (772 ft. lb./B.Th.U.) differs only by about one part in 400 from the value given by the best modern experiments. In calculating his final result, Joule made corrections for the kinetic energy of the weights as they struck the floor, the work done against friction in the pulleys and the bearings of the paddle wheel, and the energy stored by the stretching of the strings; he even estimated the energy in the hum which the strings emitted, but found it was negligible.

12. Joule's Large-scale Experiments.

In his last experiments, about 1878, Joule rotated the paddles with an engine, thereby eliminating many of the corrections just mentioned.

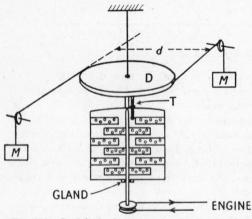

FIG. 130. Joule's final apparatus, also Rowland's.

He suspended the cylinder on a wire, and kept it in equilibrium by an opposing couple, applied by means of the wheel D (Fig. 130). This method was repeated in 1880 by Rowland, who had holes drilled in the paddles and baffles, to make their churning action more thorough. The moment, C, of the couple applied by the engine is equal and opposite to that of the couple applied by the masses M. Its value is therefore

$$C = Mgd,$$

where d is the diameter of the wheel. Now the work done by a couple is equal to the product of its moment and the angle θ in radians through which it turns. Hence if the paddles make n revolutions, the work done on the water, since $\theta = 2\pi n$, is

$$W' = 2\pi nC$$
$$= 2\pi nMgd.$$

The number of revolutions was measured on a revolution counter attached to the paddle spindle. If θ is the rise in temperature measured by T, corrected for cooling, the heat developed is

$$Q = (m + W)\theta,$$

in our previous notation.

$$\therefore J = \frac{W'}{Q} = \frac{2\pi n M g d}{(m + W)\theta}.$$

In terms of the 15° C. calorie, Rowland found J to be 4·188 joules per calorie; this is a little higher than the value accepted to-day (p. 205).

13. Laboratory Method.

Fig. 131 shows an apparatus for measuring J, devised by Callendar, which is suitable for a teaching laboratory. The brass drum D contains a little water, whose temperature is given by the bent thermometer T. The drum is rotated by hand, or by a motor, against the frictional force between the silk belt B and the drum. This force F, is the difference between the weight of the mass M, at one end of the belt, and the force f exerted by the spring balance S at the other end. Thus $\quad F = Mg - f.$

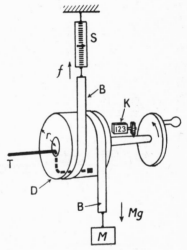

FIG. 131. Callendar's drum.

If r is the radius of the drum, the moment of F about its axis is Fr. This is therefore equal to the moment of the couple C exerted by the driving wheel : $\quad C = Fr.$

If the wheel makes n revolutions, shown by the counter K, the work done, $W' = C \times$ angle of rotation in radians

$$\therefore W' = 2\pi n C = 2\pi n F r = 2\pi n r (Mg - f).$$

If m, W, are the mass of water and water-equivalent of the drum, and θ is the rise in temperature, corrected for cooling, the heat produced is

$$Q = (m + W)\theta.$$

Thus

$$J = \frac{W'}{Q} = \frac{2\pi n r (Mg - f)}{(m + W)\theta}.$$

14. Continuous Flow Method (Callendar and Barnes').

In Joule's and Rowland's measurements of J, the greatest errors arose from the temperature measurements. Both workers used mercury-in-glass thermometers. Now the mass of mercury in the bulb of a thermometer has a heat capacity which cannot be neglected in an accurate experiment. Therefore, when the temperature outside it changes, an appreciable amount of heat must flow into it, to bring its temperature back to that of its surroundings. The flow of this heat takes time, and so makes the temperature of the mercury—and the reading of the thermometer—lag behind the temperature which is being measured.

In 1899, Callendar and Barnes devised a method of measuring J in which only steady temperatures have to be measured. In this way they eliminated errors due to lag. They also used platinum resistance thermometers, which are more accurate than mercury ones but take more time to read. In the measurement of steady temperatures, however, this is no drawback. As we shall see shortly *the water equivalent of the apparatus is not required*, which is a great advantage of the method.

Fig. 132 shows Callendar and Barnes' apparatus. Water from the constant-head tank K flows through the glass tube U, and can be

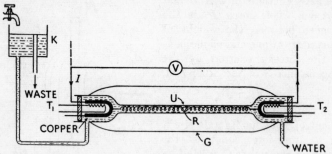

FIG. 132. Callendar and Barnes' apparatus (contracted several times in length relative to diameters).

collected as it flows out. It is heated by the spiral of resistance wire R, which carries a steady electric current I. Its temperature, as it enters and leaves, is measured by the thermometers T_1 and T_2. (In a simplified laboratory experiment, these may be mercury thermometers.) Surrounding the apparatus is a glass jacket G, which is evacuated, so that heat cannot escape from the water by conduction or convection.

When the apparatus is running, it settles down eventually to a steady state, in which the heat supplied by the current is all carried away by the water. *None is then taken in warming the apparatus, because every part of it is at a constant temperature.* The mass of water m, which flows out of the tube in t seconds, is then measured. If the water enters at a temperature θ_1 and leaves at θ_2, then:

heat gained by water = $Q = m(\theta_2 - \theta_1)$ calories.

The energy which liberates this heat is electrical, not mechanical.

To find it, the current I, and the potential difference across the wire V, are measured with a potentiometer. If I and V are in amperes and volts respectively, then, in t seconds:

electrical energy supplied to wire $= W = IVt$ joules.

$$\therefore J = \frac{W}{Q} = \frac{IVt}{m(\theta_2 - \theta_1)} \text{ joules per cal.}$$

To get the highest accuracy from this experiment, the small heat losses due to radiation, and conduction along the glass, must be allowed for. These are determined by the temperatures θ_1 and θ_2. For a given pair of values of θ_1 and θ_2, and constant-temperature surroundings (not shown), let the heat lost per second be h calories. Then, in t seconds,

heat supplied by heating coil $= m(\theta_2 - \theta_1) + ht$,

and therefore $\qquad IVt = J\{m(\theta_2 - \theta_1) + ht\}$ . . . . . (8)

To allow for the loss h, the rate of flow of water is changed, to about half or twice its previous value. The current and voltage are then adjusted to bring θ_2 back to its original value. The inflow temperature, θ_1, is fixed by the temperature of the water in the tank. If I', V', are the new values of I, V, and m' is the new mass of water flowing in the same t seconds, then:

$$I'V't = J\{m'(\theta_2 - \theta_1) + ht\} \quad . \quad . \quad . \quad . \quad (9)$$

On subtracting equation (9) from equation (8), we find

$$(IV - I'V')t = J(m - m')(\theta_2 - \theta_1),$$

whence $\qquad J = \dfrac{(IV - I'V')t}{(m - m')(\theta_2 - \theta_1)}$ joules per cal. . . . (10)

Callendar and Barnes found $J = 4\cdot182$ joules per 15° calorie. Later experiments, in which the water is churned by an electric motor, supplied with a measured amount of electrical power, give

$$J = 4\cdot1855 \text{ joules per 15° calorie.}$$

If we take $J = 4\cdot2$ joules per calorie, we make an error of about $1\cdot4$ parts in 400: about $0\cdot3$ per cent. This is less than the error in most laboratory experiments, and we may therefore take J to be $4\cdot2$ joules per calorie. We may also take its reciprocal—which is often useful—to be $1/J = 1/4\cdot2 = 0\cdot24$ calories per joule.

15. Variation of Specific Heat of Water.

Callendar and Barnes measured J over a wide range of temperatures, and found that it was not quite constant. Rowland had previously made the same observation and concluded that the specific heat of water varied slightly with the temperature. If we denote by s the mean specific heat of water between the temperatures θ_1 and θ_2 then equation (10) becomes

$$J = \frac{(IV - I'V')t}{(m - m')s(\theta_2 - \theta_1)}$$

or

$$s = \frac{(IV - I'V')t}{J(m - m')(\theta_2 - \theta_1)} \quad \cdot \quad \cdot \quad \cdot \quad \cdot \quad \cdot \quad (11)$$

When we define the 15° calorie, we arbitrarily make $s = 1$ in the neighbourhood of 15° C. Callendar and Barnes' measurements then give J in terms of this calorie, and equation (11) gives s at other temperatures. The following table shows some of the results.

SPECIFIC HEAT OF WATER

Temperature (°C.)	5	15	25	40	70	100
s (15° cal./gm./°C.)	1·0047	1·0000	0·9980	0·9973	1·0000	1·0057

16. Laboratory Electrical Method for J.

The simplest way to measure Joule's equivalent in the laboratory is by electrical heating, with the apparatus shown in Fig. 133. R is a

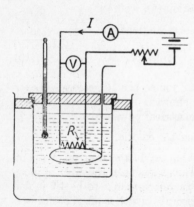

coil of resistance wire immersed in oil or glycerine (mass m, specific heat s), in a calorimeter of water equivalent W.

We pass a steady current I through the coil, and measure the potential difference V across it. Stirring continuously, we plot the temperature of the oil against the time. After a time t long enough to give several degrees rise, we switch off the current and plot the cooling curve. If θ is the corrected rise in temperature, we have

Fig. 133. Laboratory electrical method for J.

$$IVt = J(ms + W)\theta,$$

whence we can calculate J.

17. Electrical Method for Specific Heat.

Modern methods of measuring specific and latent heats generally use electrical heating. Nernst's method for the specific heat of a metal is illustrated in Fig. 134. The specimen S has a heating coil R of insulated platinum wire wound round the outside, and is covered with silver foil F to minimize heat loss by radiation. It is suspended by the leads to the coil in a glass vessel, which is then evacuated, to prevent losses by convection and conduction. The resistance of the coil is measured, and from it the temperature is calculated. A steady current I, at a known potential difference V, is then passed through the coil for t seconds. After the current has been switched off, the resistance of the coil is again measured, to find the rise in temperature of the specimen. Resistance measurements are made at intervals, and enable the cooling curve to be plotted. If m is the mass of the specimen, W the water equivalent of the coil and foil, and θ the corrected rise in temperature, then the specific heat s of the specimen is given by

$$IVt = J(ms + W)\theta.$$

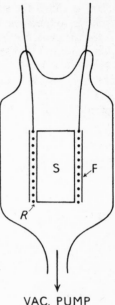

VAC. PUMP

Fig. 134. Nernst's calorimeter.

LATENT HEAT

18. Fusion.

The *latent heat of fusion* of a solid is the heat required to convert unit mass of it, at its melting-point, into liquid at the same temperature. It is expressed in calories per gramme, or British Thermal Units per lb.

MELTING-POINTS AND LATENT HEATS OF FUSION

Substance	M.P. °C.	L.H. cal./gm.	Substance	M.P. °C.	L.H. cal./gm.
Aluminium .	658	94	Acetic acid .	17·5	44
Antimony .	630	39	Beeswax . .	62	42
Bismuth .	271	14	Brass . .	900	—
Copper .	1,083	43	Naphthalene .	80	35
Gold . .	1,063	16	Paradichlorben-	53	—
Iron . .	1,530	49	zene (non-flam.)		
Lead . .	327	6	Ice . .	0	79·6
Mercury .	−38·9	3	Paraffin wax .	50–60	—
Nickel . .	1,452	65	Solder (soft) .	c. 180	12–20
Platinum .	1,773	27	Solder (hard) .	c. 900	—
Sulphur .	113–119	9	Steel . .	1,400	—
Silver .	960·8	26	Glass . .	300–400	—
Sodium .	97·5	27	Quartz (fused) .	1,700	—
Tin . .	232	14	Hypo . .	48·2	c. 40
Tungsten .	3,380	—			
Zinc . .	419	26			

Ice is one of the substances whose latent heat of fusion we are likely to have to measure. To do so, place warm water, at a temperature θ_1 a few degrees above room temperature, inside a calorimeter. Then add small lumps of ice, dried by blotting paper, until the temperature reaches a value θ_2 as much below room temperature as θ_1 was above. In this case a "cooling correction" is not necessary. Weigh the mixture, to find the mass m of ice which has been added. Then the latent heat L is given by:

$$\left.\begin{array}{l}\text{heat given by calori-}\\ \text{meter and water in}\\ \text{cooling}\end{array}\right\} = \left\{\begin{array}{l}\text{heat used in}\\ \text{melting ice}\end{array}\right\} + \left\{\begin{array}{l}\text{heat used in warming}\\ \text{melted ice from } 0^\circ\text{ C.}\\ \text{to } \theta_2\end{array}\right.$$

$$\therefore (m_1 + W)(\theta_1 - \theta_2) = mL + m(\theta_2 - 0),$$

where $m_1 =$ mass of water, $W =$ water equivalent of calorimeter, and $\theta_1 =$ initial temperature.

Hence
$$L = \frac{(m_1 + W)(\theta_1 - \theta_2)}{m} - \theta_2.$$

A modern electrical method, similar to Nernst's for specific heats, gives

$$L = 79 \cdot 6 \text{ cal./gm.},$$

and for all our purposes we may approximate this to 80 cal./gm.

19. Bunsen's Ice Calorimeter.

Bunsen's ice calorimeter is a device for measuring a quantity of heat by using it to melt ice.

When ice turns to water, it shrinks; the volume of 1 gm. of ice at 0° C. is $1 \cdot 0908$ cm.³, whereas that of 1 gm. of water at 0° C. is $1 \cdot 0001$ cm.³ (p. 300). Thus the melting of 1 gm. of ice causes a contraction of $0 \cdot 0907$ cm.³

In the Bunsen calorimeter, the contraction due to the melting is measured, and from it the mass of ice melted is calculated. The apparatus is shown in Fig. 135. It consists of a test-tube T fused into a wider tube S. The wider tube leads to a capillary C, and is filled with mercury from X to Y. The space above Y is filled with water from which all dissolved air has been boiled.

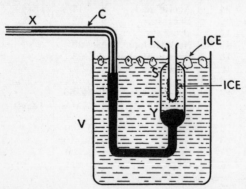

FIG. 135. Bunsen's ice calorimeter.

Except for the capillary, the whole apparatus is placed in ice-water in the vessel V, and, after some time, it all settles down to 0° C. A little ether is then poured into T, and air is blown through it via a thin tube; the ether evaporates and cools the tube T, so that ice forms on the outside of it. A pad of cotton wool is then dropped to the bottom of T and the apparatus is left for some more time, to allow the newly formed ice to settle down to 0° C.

When the apparatus is ready for use, the end of the mercury thread in C is observed by a travelling microscope. If the specific heat of a solid is to be measured, the specimen is weighed (m gm.) and left to come to room temperature θ. The solid is then gently dropped into the tube T. As it cools, it melts ice, and causes the mercury thread to run back along the capillary. When the thread has ceased to move, its end is again observed. If it has moved through l cm., and the cross-section of the capillary is a cm.^{2}, then the contraction is al cm.^{3} The mass of ice melted is therefore $al/0 \cdot 0907$ gm., and the heat absorbed is $80\ al/0 \cdot 0907$ calories. This heat is given out by m gm. of solid cooling from θ to 0° C.; the specific heat s of the solid is therefore given by

$$ ms\theta = \frac{80\ al}{0 \cdot 0907}. $$

In practice, the cross-section is not measured, and the instrument is calibrated by dropping into it a solid of known mass, m_1, and specific heat, s_1. If the room temperature is constant, then

$$ \frac{ms}{m_1 s_1} = \frac{l}{l_1}, $$

where l_1 is the displacement of the mercury in the calibration experiment.

20. Advantages of the Ice Calorimeter.

The advantages of the ice calorimeter are:

(i) no correction for water-equivalent: the specimen tube starts at 0° C. and finishes at 0° C.—all the heat from the specimen is used to melt ice, at constant temperature;

(ii) no heat losses from the apparatus—it is surrounded by a bath at the same temperature as itself, and therefore neither loses heat to the outside, nor gains any from it;

(iii) no loss of heat from the specimen before it enters the calorimeter—the specimen starts at room temperature, and therefore gives up no heat until it enters the specimen tube (contrast the method of mixtures, in which the specimen is heated to 100° C. or so): this is a great advantage when the specimen is small;

(iv) easy, and therefore accurate, thermometry—the only temperature to be measured is the room temperature, which is constant and can be determined at leisure.

An advantage sometimes asserted is that specimens can be added one after another, without having to re-set the apparatus. That is true, because each specimen comes to 0° C. in turn, and then behaves simply like part of the apparatus, taking no heat from any following specimen. But it does not mean that the calorimeter has the advantage of speed—the time taken to set it up would be enough for half a dozen measurements by the method of mixtures. A disadvantage of this calorimeter is that it never settles down completely—the mercury is always slowly creeping along the capillary, and the creep during an experiment must be estimated and allowed for.

The calorimeter was devised in 1871; it is rarely used nowadays, because electrical methods of calorimetry are more convenient and accurate. In 1947, however, it was used for measuring the specific heats of rare earths of which only small specimens were available.

21. Evaporation.

The *latent heat of evaporation* of a liquid is the heat required to convert unit mass of it, at its boiling-point, into vapour at the same temperature. It is expressed in calories per gramme, or B.Th.U. per lb.

BOILING-POINTS AND LATENT HEATS OF EVAPORATION

Substance	B.P. °C.	L.H. cal./gm.
Aluminium	1,800	—
Acetone	56·7	—
Alcohol (ethyl)	78·3	205
Alcohol (methyl) . . .	64·7	267
Benzene	80·2	93
Carbon disulphide . . .	46·2	83·8
Carbon tetrachloride (non-flam.) .	76·7	46
Ether	34·6	88·4
Glycerine	290	—
Turpentine	161	—
Mercury	357	65
Platinum	3,910	—
Sodium	877	—
Sulphur	444·6	—

To find the latent heat of evaporation of water, we pass steam into a calorimeter containing water (Fig. 136). On its way the steam passes through a vessel, T in the figure, which traps any water carried over by the steam and is called a steam-trap. The mass m of condensed steam is found by weighing. If θ_1 and θ_2 are the initial and final temperatures of the water, the latent heat L is given by:

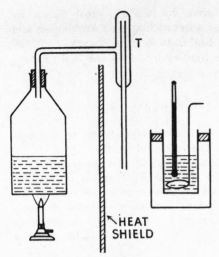

FIG. 136. Latent heat of evaporation of water.

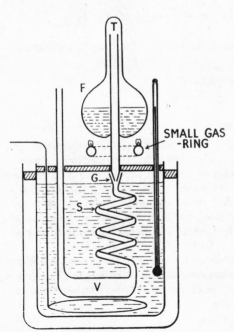

FIG. 137. Berthelot's apparatus for latent heat of evaporation.

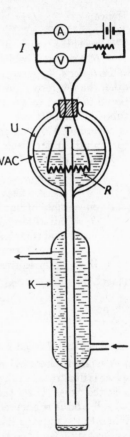

FIG. 138. Electrical method for latent heat of evaporation.

$$\left.\begin{array}{l}\text{heat given by steam}\\ \text{condensing}\end{array}\right\} + \left\{\begin{array}{l}\text{heat given by con-}\\ \text{densed water cooling}\\ \text{from } 100^\circ \text{ C. to } \theta_2\end{array}\right\} = \left\{\begin{array}{l}\text{heat taken by}\\ \text{calorimeter and}\\ \text{water}\end{array}\right.$$

$$mL \qquad + \qquad m(100 - \theta_2), \qquad = (m_1 + W)(\theta_2 - \theta_1)$$

where m_1 and W have their usual meanings.

Hence $\qquad L = \dfrac{(m_1 + W)(\theta_2 - \theta_1)}{m} - (100 - \theta_2).$

The accepted value of the latent heat of evaporation of water is $L = 539$ cal./gm., which may be approximated to 540 cal./gm.

Berthelot's Apparatus. An apparatus suitable for use with liquids other than water was devised by Berthelot in 1877 (Fig. 137, p. 211). The liquid is boiled in the flask F, and its vapour passes out through the tube T. This fits with a ground joint G into the glass spiral S, which is surrounded by water in a calorimeter. The vapour condenses in the spiral, and collects in the vessel V, where it can afterwards be weighed. Let

θ_b = boiling-point of liquid.
s = specific heat of liquid.
m = mass of liquid condensed.
θ_1 = initial temperature of water.
θ_2 = final temperature of water, *corrected for cooling.*
m_1 = mass of water.
W = water equivalent of calorimeter + glassware below joint.

Then $\qquad mL + ms(\theta_b - \theta_2) = (m_1 + W)(\theta_2 - \theta_1),$

whence $\qquad L = \dfrac{(m_1 + W)(\theta_2 - \theta_1)}{m} - s(\theta_b - \theta_2).$

22. Electrical Method for Latent Heat.

A modern electrical method for the latent heat of evaporation of water is illustrated in Fig. 138, p. 211. The liquid is heated in a vacuum-jacketed vessel U by the heating coil R. Its vapour passes down the tube T, and is condensed by cold water flowing through the jacket K. When the apparatus has reached its steady state, the liquid is at its boiling-point, and the heat supplied by the coil is used in evaporating the liquid, and in offsetting the losses. The liquid emerging from the condenser is then collected for a measured time, and weighed.

If I and V are the current through the coil, and the potential difference across it, the electrical energy supplied in t seconds is IVt. And if h is the heat lost from the vessel per second, and m the mass of liquid collected in t seconds, then

$$IVT/J = mL + ht \qquad . \quad . \quad . \quad . \quad (12)$$

The heat losses h are determined by the temperature of the vessel, which is fixed at the boiling-point of the liquid. Therefore they may be eliminated by a second experiment with a different rate of evaporation (cf. Callendar and Barnes, p. 204). If $I'V'$ are the new current and potential difference, and if m' grammes are evaporated in t seconds, then

$$I'V't/J = m'L + ht.$$

Hence by subtraction from equation (15)

$$L = \frac{(IV - I'V')t}{J(m - m')}.$$

EXAMPLES

1. Give an account of the experiments which lead us to believe that heat is a form of energy, and define the mechanical equivalent of heat.

The fly-wheel of an engine is 2 ft. in diameter and rotates at 1,500 r.p.m. A belt brake acts on the circumference. The belt supports a weight of 112 lb. on one side and a spring balance on the other side reads 12 lb. When the fly-wheel is immersed in 1,000 lb. of water the rate of rise of temperature was found to be 1·2° F. per min. Calculate a value for the mechanical equivalent of heat in these units (ft. lb. per B.Th.U.). (*O. & C.*)

First part (see p. 203). The mechanical equivalent of heat may be defined as the mechanical energy required to produce 1 unit of heat; or as the ratio W/Q, where W is the mechanical energy which produces an amount of heat Q.

Second part. The force, F, in the belt $= 112 - 12 = 100$ lb. wt.

The mechanical work done in one revolution

$$= F \times \text{distance} = F \times \text{circumference of wheel}.$$

∴ work done, W, per minute $= 100 \times 2\pi \times 1 \times 1,500$ ft. lb. wt.

But heat, Q, per min. $= 1,000 \times 1·2 = 1,200$ B.Th.U.

$$\therefore J = \frac{W}{Q} = \frac{100 \times 2\pi \times 1,500}{1,200}$$

$$= 785 \text{ ft. lb. wt. per B.Th.U.}$$

2. Describe very briefly *one* method of determining the mechanical equivalent of heat; comment fully on its merits and inherent errors.

In an experiment with a high-energy beam, hydrogen atoms each weighing $1·67 \times 10^{-24}$ gm. strike a target with a velocity of 2×10^9 cm. per sec. If 10^{15} atoms arrive each second, and the target is a lump of brass of 500 gm. thermally insulated, find how long it will take for the temperature of the brass to rise by 100° C. (Specific heat of brass $= 0·09$; $J = 4·2$ joules per cal.) (*O. & C.*)

First part. A non-electrical or an electrical method for J may be used (p. 203).

Second part. The kinetic energy of an atom $= \frac{1}{2}mv^2$ ergs, where m is the mass in gm. and v is the velocity in cm. per sec.

∴ energy brought to target in 1 sec. $= \frac{1}{2} \times 1·67 \times 10^{-24} \times (2 \times 10^9)^2 \times 10^{15}$ ergs.

But heat required for brass $=$ mass $\times$ specific heat $\times$ temp. rise

$$= 500 \times 0·09 \times 100 \text{ cal.}$$

$$= 500 \times 0·09 \times 100 \times 4·2 \text{ joules}$$

$$= 500 \times 0·09 \times 100 \times 4·2 \times 10^7 \text{ ergs}$$

since 1 joule $= 10^7$ ergs.

$$\therefore \text{ time in sec.} = \frac{500 \times 0.09 \times 100 \times 4.2 \times 10^7}{\frac{1}{2} \times 1.67 \times 10^{-24} \times (2 \times 10^9)^2 \times 10^{15}}$$

$$= 57 \text{ sec.}$$

3. Describe the continuous-flow calorimeter for the accurate determination of the specific heat of a liquid. What advantages does this method have over the method of mixtures?

An electric kettle with an 800-watt 250-volt immersion heater is connected to the 200-volt mains. How long will it take to raise 1,000 gm. of water to boiling-point if the water equivalent of the kettle is 100 gm. and the initial temperature of the water is 20° C.? (C.)

First part (see p. 203).

Second part. Since $P = V^2/R$, the resistance of the kettle element is given by

$$800 = \frac{250^2}{R}.$$

$$\therefore R = \frac{250^2}{800} = 78\frac{1}{8} \text{ ohms.}$$

Hence the power, P, on the 200-volt mains is given by

$$P = \frac{V^2}{R} = \frac{200^2}{78\frac{1}{8}} = 512 \text{ watts.}$$

$$\therefore \text{ power} = 512 \text{ joules per sec.} = \frac{512}{4.2} \text{ cal. per sec.}$$

Assuming the boiling-point of the water is 100° C., and t the time in sec.,

$$\therefore \frac{512}{4.2} \times t = (1,000 + 100)(100 - 20)$$

$$\therefore t = \frac{1,100 \times 80 \times 4.2}{512} = 722 \text{ sec.}$$

4. Describe the method of continuous flow for the determination of the specific heats of liquids. Discuss the advantages of the method.

Water flows at the rate of 150.0 gm. min.$^{-1}$ through a tube in which it is heated by an electric heater dissipating 25.2 watts. The temperature of the inflowing water is 15.2° C. and that of the outflowing water 17.4° C. These temperatures are unaltered when the rate of flow is increased to 231.8 gm. min.$^{-1}$ and the rate of dissipation of energy increased to 37.8 watts. Estimate (a) the value of the mechanical equivalent of heat, (b) the rate of loss of heat, in cal. min.$^{-1}$, from the tube. (L.)

First part. The advantages of the continuous flow method are: (i) The water equivalent of the tube is not required, (ii) the temperatures are steady, and can therefore be measured at leisure, (iii) the variation of the specific heat of the liquid with temperature can be accurately measured, (iv) the loss of heat can be eliminated easily. The method is described on p. 203.

Second part. Suppose J is the mechanical equivalent in *joules* per cal., and h is the heat lost per sec. Then, since 1 watt = 1 joule per sec.,

$$\frac{25.2}{J} = \frac{150.0}{60}(17.4 - 15.2) + h \quad \cdots \cdots \quad \text{(i)}$$

and

$$\frac{37.8}{J} = \frac{231.8}{60}(17.4 - 15.2) + h \quad \cdots \cdots \quad \text{(ii)}$$

Subtracting (i) from (ii) to eliminate h,

$$\therefore \frac{37 \cdot 8 - 25 \cdot 2}{J} = \left(\frac{231 \cdot 8 - 150 \cdot 0}{60}\right)(17 \cdot 4 - 15 \cdot 2)$$

$$\therefore J = \frac{12 \cdot 6 \times 60}{81 \cdot 8 \times 2 \cdot 2} = 4 \cdot 2 \text{ joules per cal.}$$

Substituting for J in (i), we find

$$h = 0 \cdot 5 \text{ cal. per sec.}$$

$$\therefore \text{ heat lost per min.} = 0 \cdot 5 \times 60 = 30 \text{ cal.}$$

5. Define *latent heat*. Describe the measurement of the latent heat of evaporation of water under school laboratory conditions.

A copper calorimeter of mass 70·5 gm. contains 100·0 gm. of water at 19·5° C. Naphthalene (M.P. 79·9° C.) is melted in a test tube, cooled to 80·0° C., and then poured into the calorimeter. If the highest temperature reached by the water after stirring is 28·7° C. and the final mass of the calorimeter and its contents is 188·3 gm. calculate the latent heat of fusion of naphthalene. (Specific heat of copper 0·1, of naphthalene 0·32.) (*L.*)

First part. The latent heat of a substance is the heat required to change 1 gm. of the solid at the melting-point to liquid at the same temperature (fusion), or the heat required to change 1 gm. of the liquid at the boiling-point to vapour at the same temperature (vaporization).

The measurement of the latent heat of evaporation of water requires the following, among other points: (i) use of a steam trap, (ii) a rise in temperature of the water in the calorimeter of about 10° C., (iii) a "correction" to 100° C. as the steam temperature, if the barometric pressure is not 76 cm. mercury, (iv) a cooling correction.

Second part. The mass of naphthalene $= 188 \cdot 3 - 170 \cdot 5 = 17 \cdot 8$ gm.

Heat lost by naphthalene = heat gained by water and calorimeter.

$$\therefore 17 \cdot 8L + 17 \cdot 8 \times 0 \cdot 32 \times (79 \cdot 9 - 28 \cdot 7) = (100 \cdot 0 + 70 \cdot 5 \times 0 \cdot 1)(28 \cdot 7 - 19 \cdot 5)$$

Solving, $\qquad \therefore L = 39 \cdot 0$ cal. per gm.

6. Give an account of a method, based on latent heat calorimetry, of determining the specific heat of a solid of which a small quantity only is available.

When a solid, of mass 5 gm. and specific heat 0·22 cal. gm.$^{-1}$ deg.$^{-1}$ C, is heated to 100° C. and then dropped into the inner tube of a Bunsen ice calorimeter, the meniscus in the capillary tube, bore 1·0 mm., is observed to move through 16 cm. Calculate the density of ice at 0° C. The latent heat of fusion of ice is 80 cal. per gm. (*L.*)

First part. See text.

Second part. Suppose ρ is the density of ice in gm. per cm.^{3}

$$\therefore \text{ change in volume when 1 gm. of ice melts} = \left(\frac{1}{\rho} - 1\right) \text{ cm.}^3$$

$$\text{Now number of gm. of ice melted} = \frac{5 \times 0 \cdot 22 \times (100 - 0)}{80} = \frac{11}{8}.$$

$$\therefore \text{ change in volume} = \frac{11}{8}\left(\frac{1}{\rho} - 1\right) \text{ cm.}^3$$

$$\text{But change in volume} = \pi \times (0 \cdot 05)^2 \times 16 \text{ c.c.}$$

$$\therefore \frac{11}{8}\left(\frac{1}{\rho} - 1\right) = \pi \times (0 \cdot 05^2) \times 16.$$

Solving, $\qquad \therefore \rho = 0 \cdot 91$ gm. per cm.^{3}

EXERCISES XI

Specific Heat: Latent Heat

1. A heating coil is embedded in a copper cylinder which also carries a thermocouple. The whole is thermally equivalent to 25 gm. of copper. The cylinder is suspended in liquid air until the thermocouple reading is constant. The cylinder is taken out and rapidly transferred into a beaker of water at 0° C. A coating of ice forms on the cylinder and when its temperature is again constant it is taken out of the water and suspended in a space maintained at 0° C. The heating coil is switched on at a steady energy dissipation of 24 watts. After 1 min. 5 sec. the whole of the ice has just melted. What is the temperature of the liquid air?

What assumptions were made in carrying out the calculations? (Mean specific heat of copper is 0·08 cal. gm.$^{-1}$ deg.$^{-1}$ C.) (L.)

2. Describe a continuous flow method of measuring the specific heat of a liquid. Explain the advantages of the method.

Use the following data to calculate the specific heat of the liquid flowing through a continuous flow calorimeter: *Experiment I*. Current 2·0 amp., applied p.d. 3·0 volts, rate of flow of liquid 30 gm./min., rise in temperature of liquid 2·7° C. *Experiment II*. Current 2·5 amp., applied p.d. 3·75 volts, rate of flow of liquid 48 gm./min., rise in temperature of liquid 2·7° C., $J = 4·2$ joules per cal. (L.)

3. Define *latent heat of evaporation*, and explain how the phenomenon is accounted for on the kinetic theory of matter.

If 5 gm. of ether are placed in the inner tube of a Bunsen ice calorimeter, and evaporated by connecting the tube to a vacuum pump, the mercury index is found to move a distance of 10 cm. Assuming that the density of ice is 0·91 gm. per c.c. and its latent heat of fusion 80 cal. per gm., what is the latent heat of evaporation of ether? The area of cross-section of the tube containing the mercury is 0·066 sq. cm. Give a sketch of the apparatus, and indicate by an arrow the direction of motion of the index. (O. & C.)

4. How would you find by experiment the latent heat of evaporation of alcohol?

A copper calorimeter of mass 150 gm. contains 250 gm. of alcohol at 25° C., and 20 gm. of steam at 100° C. are condensed in the alcohol. Assuming that no heat is lost to the surroundings, and neglecting heat effects resulting from mixing the steam and alcohol, find the amount of alcohol evaporated. The following data may be assumed: specific heat of copper = 0·1, specific heat of alcohol = 0·55, latent heat of evaporation of water = 540 cal./gm., latent heat of evaporation of alcohol = 260 cal./gm., boiling-point of alcohol = 78° C. (L.)

5. A cylinder of copper has an electric heating filament inside it, so that it may be heated by passing a current. After the temperature had been raised, the current was switched off and the copper allowed to cool. The following observations were made of the temperature at 20-sec. intervals: 86·0, 70·0, 60·0, 51·7, 44·5, 38·5° C.

The current was again switched on and adjusted to 3·5 amp. in order to keep the cylinder at a constant temperature of 53° C. If the specific heat of copper is 0·095 cal. per gm. per deg. C., and the mass of the cylinder 200 gm., what is the resistance of the heating filament? [Take the value of J as 4·2 joules per cal.] (L.)

6. Give a sketch of Bunsen's ice calorimeter explaining how you would use it to find the specific heat of a solid. If a solid of mass 3 gm., specific heat 0·095 cal. gm.$^{-1}$ deg. C.$^{-1}$ and temperature 105° C., is dropped into the ice calorimeter, find the travel of mercury produced in the capillary tube of diameter 1·6 mm., if the latent heat of melting of ice is 80 cal. gm.$^{-1}$ and the density of ice 0·917 gm. cm.$^{-3}$ (*L.*)

7. What are the particular advantages of the continuous-flow method in calorimetry? Describe in detail one application of the method.
How did work on the specific heat of water affect the definition of the calorie? (*L.*)

8. Describe the determination of the latent heat of fusion of ice by the method of mixtures and, in particular, show how allowance is made for heat interchange with the surroundings.
A calorimeter of water equivalent 20 gm. contains 980 gm. of water supercooled to −4° C. Taking the latent heat of fusion of ice at 0° C. as 80·0 cal. per gm., find the amount of ice formed when the water suddenly freezes. Calculate also the latent heat of fusion at −4° C. if the specific heat of ice is 0·5. (*N.*)

9. State Newton's law of cooling and specify the conditions under which it is valid. How would you verify the law experimentally?
A thermostatically controlled electric water heater has an external surface area of 8,000 sq. cm., the inner water container being insulated from the exterior case by a layer of cotton wool 4 cm. thick. To maintain the water at a temperature of 80° C. requires the consumption of 1 kilowatt-hour of electrical energy per day. Assuming that the thermal conductivity of the cotton wool is 0·0001 c.g.s. calculate the emissivity of the external surface. [$J = 4·2$ joules per cal. Room temperature may be taken as 20° C.] (*O. & C.*)

10. State Newton's law of cooling, and describe an experiment by which you would verify it. A calorimeter containing first 40 and then 100 gm. of water is heated and suspended in the same constant-temperature enclosure. It is found that the times taken to cool from 50° to 40° C. in the two cases are 15 and 33 minutes respectively. Calculate the water equivalent of the calorimeter. (*O. & C.*)

11. What is meant by the latent heat of vaporization of a substance? 2 gm. of iron wire at 15° C. are dropped into liquid oxygen maintained at its boiling-point in a thermos flask. The volume of oxygen driven off, measured at 16° C. and 80 cm. of mercury pressure, is 432 c.c. Find the latent heat of vaporization of oxygen. The specific heat of iron may be taken as 0·09, the boiling-point of oxygen as −184° C., and the density of oxygen at normal temperature and pressure 0·0014 gm. per c.c. (*O. & C.*)

12. Define latent heat of change of state. Describe how you would determine experimentally the latent heat of fusion of ice.
A calorimeter of weight 100 gm. and of specific heat 0·1, contains 50 gm. of ice and 50 gm. of water. Steam at 100° C. is passed through at a constant rate until the total weight is 210 gm. Determine the final temperature of the system and draw a rough graph showing the change of temperature with time. Heat losses may be neglected. [Latent heat of fusion of ice = 80 cal. per gm. Latent heat of vaporization of water = 540 cal. per gm.] (*C.*)

13. Draw a labelled diagram to illustrate an experiment for determining the latent heat of vaporization of water. Do *not* describe the experiment, but state how the result would be calculated from the experimental data.

Water in a vacuum flask is boiled steadily by passing an electric current through a coil of wire immersed in the water. When the potential difference across the coil is 5·25 volts and the current through it is 2·58 amp., 6·85 gm. of water evaporate in 20 min. When the potential difference and the current are maintained at 3·20 volts and 1·57 amp. respectively, 2·38 gm. of water evaporate in 20 min., all the other conditions being the same. Calculate the latent heat of vaporization of water in joules per gm. (*N.*)

Mechanical Equivalent of Heat

14. Give a detailed account of a non-electrical method for estimating the number of joules equivalent to 1 cal.

Obtain a value for the height in metres from which a hailstone at 0° C. and at rest must fall in order that when it strikes the ground one-fiftieth part of it shall melt. Neglect air resistance and assume the temperature of the surroundings to be everywhere 0° C. and that one-quarter of the energy possessed by the hailstone when it strikes the ground is converted into heat within the hailstone. (*L.*)

15. How does the constant flow technique in calorimetry compare with other methods? Illustrate your answer by considering methods for the determination of the mechanical equivalent of heat. (*L. Schol.*)

16. Explain the term *mechanical equivalent of heat* and describe an experiment to find its value when heat is generated by friction between two solid surfaces.

Oil at 15·6° C. enters a long glass tube containing an electrically heated platinum wire and leaves it at 17·4° C., the rate of flow being 25 c.c. per min. and the rate of supply of energy 1·34 watts. On changing the rate of flow to 15 c.c. per min. and the power to 0·76 watt the temperature again rises from 15·6° to 17·4° C. Calculate the mean specific heat of the oil between these temperatures. Assume that the density of the oil is 0·87 gm. per c.c. (*N.*)

17. What are the chief reasons for believing that heat is a form of energy? Explain the statement that $4·2 \times 10^7$ ergs are equivalent to 1 calorie, and describe an experiment involving the conversion of mechanical energy into heat by which it may be checked. Calculate the number of foot-pounds which are equivalent to the quantity of heat required to raise the temperature of 1 lb. of water 1° F. Assume that 1 ft. = 30·5 cm. and that the acceleration of gravity = 980 cm. sec.$^{-2}$ (*N.*)

18. Define the *mechanical equivalent of heat* and show how it may be measured experimentally. (Describe the continuous-flow method if possible.) (*L.*)

19. Give a brief account of the reasons which led to the abandonment of the caloric theory of heat and the adoption of the mechanical theory. Describe a non-electrical method of determining the mechanical equivalent of heat, suitable for use in a school laboratory.

What difference would exist between the temperature of the water above and below a fall 100 metres high if the whole of the gravitational energy lost was retained as heat in the water? (*L.*)

20. Give a critical account of the methods available for determining the mechanical equivalent of heat.

In the absence of bearing friction a winding engine would raise a cage weighing 1,000 kg. at 10 metres per sec., but this is reduced by friction to 9 metres per sec. How much oil, initially at 20° C., is required per sec. to keep the temperature of the bearings down to 70° C.? (Specific heat of oil = 0·5; g = 981 cm. per sec.²; J = 4·2 × 10⁷ ergs per cal.)   (O. & C.)

21. Describe a non-electrical method of measuring the mechanical equivalent of heat. Explain your calculation.

A roller-skater glides 50 times round the floor of a rink, keeping to a circle of average radius 78 ft., only one skate being on the floor at any one instant. If each skate, of mass 1 lb. and specific heat 0·1, is raised in temperature 20° F., calculate the average force applied by the skates in overcoming friction. Assume that 20 per cent. of the heat generated is received by the skates. (J = 780 ft. lb. per B.Th.U.) (N.)

CHAPTER XII

GASES

In this chapter we shall be concerned with the relationship between the temperature, pressure and volume of a gas. Unlike the case of a solid or liquid this can be expressed in very simple laws, called the Gas Laws, and reduced to a simple equation, called the Equation of State. We shall also deal in this chapter with the specific heats of gases.

THE GAS LAWS AND THE EQUATION OF STATE

1. Pressure and Volume : Boyle's Law.

In 1660 Robert Boyle—whose epitaph reads "Father of Chemistry, and Nephew of the Earl of Cork"—published the results of his experiments on the natural spring of air. In the vigorous language of the seventeenth century, he meant what we now tamely call the relationship between the pressure of air and its volume. Similar results were published in 1676 by Mariotte, who had not heard of Boyle's work. Boyle trapped air in the closed limb of a U-tube, with mercury (Fig. 139 (a)). He first adjusted the amount of mercury until its level was the same in each limb, so that the trapped air was at atmospheric

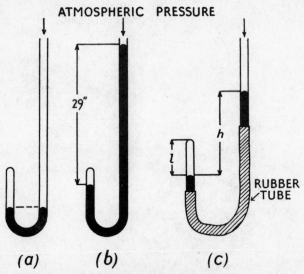

FIG. 139. Boyle's law apparatus.

220

pressure. He next poured in more mercury, until he had halved the volume of the trapped air (Fig. 139 (b)). Then "not without delight and satisfaction" he found that the mercury in the open limb stood 29 in. above the mercury in the closed limb. Since he knew that the height of the barometer was about 29 in. of mercury, he realized that to halve the volume of his air he had had to double the pressure on it.

We can repeat Boyle's experiment with the apparatus shown in Fig. 139 (c); its form makes the pouring of mercury unnecessary. We set the open limb of the tube at various heights above and below the closed limb and measure the difference in level, h, of the mercury. When the mercury in the open limb is below that in the closed, we reckon h as negative. At each value of h we measure the corresponding length l of the air column in the closed limb. To find the pressure of the air we add the difference in level h to the height of the barometer, H; their sum gives the pressure p of the air in the closed limb:

$$p = g\rho(H + h)$$

where g is the acceleration of gravity and ρ is the density of mercury.

If S is the area of cross-section of the closed limb, the volume of the trapped air is
$$V = lS.$$

To interpret our measurements we may either plot $H + h$, which is a measure of p against $1/l$ or tabulate the product $(H + h)l$. We find that the plot is a straight line, and therefore

$$(H + h) \propto \frac{1}{l} \quad . \quad . \quad . \quad . \quad . \quad . \quad (1)$$

Alternatively, we find
$$(H + h)l = \text{constant}, \quad . \quad . \quad . \quad . \quad . \quad (2)$$

which means the same as (1).

Since g, ρ, and S are constants, the relationships (1) and (2) give

$$p \propto \frac{1}{V}$$

or $$pV = \text{constant}.$$

A little later in this chapter we shall see that the pressure of a gas depends on its temperature as well as its volume. To express the results of the above experiments, therefore, we say that *the pressure of a given mass of gas, at constant temperature, is inversely proportional to its volume.* This is *Boyle's Law.*

2. Mixtures of Gases : Dalton's Law.

Fig. 140 shows an apparatus with which we can study the pressure of a mixture of gases. A is a bulb, of volume V_1, containing air at

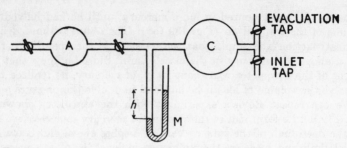

FIG. 140. Apparatus for demonstrating Dalton's law of partial pressures.

atmospheric pressure, p_1. C is another bulb, of volume V_2, containing carbon dioxide at a pressure p_2. The pressure p_2 is measured on the manometer M; in millimetres of mercury it is

$$p_2 = h + H,$$

where H is the height of the barometer. (In the same units, the air pressure, $p_1 = H$.)

When the bulbs are connected by opening the tap T, the gases mix, and reach the same pressure, p; this pressure is given by the new height of the manometer. Its value is found to be given by

$$p = p_1 \frac{V_1}{V_1 + V_2} + p_2 \frac{V_2}{V_1 + V_2}.$$

Now the quantity $pV_1/(V_1 + V_2)$ is the pressure which the air originally in A would have, if it expanded to occupy A and C; for, if we denote this pressure by p', then $p'(V_1 + V_2) = p_1V_1$. Similarly $p_2V_2/(V_1 + V_2)$ is the pressure which the carbon dioxide originally in C would have, if it expanded to occupy A and C. Thus the total pressure of the mixture is the sum of the pressures which the individual gases exert, when they have expanded to fill the vessel containing the mixture.

The pressure of an individual gas in a mixture is called its *partial pressure*: it is the pressure which would be observed if that gas alone occupied the volume of the mixture, and had the same temperature as the mixture. The experiment described shows that *the pressure of a mixture of gases is the sum of the partial pressures of its constituents*. This statement was first made by Dalton, in 1801, and is called *Dalton's Law of Partial Pressures*.

3. Volume and Temperature : Charles's Law.

Measurements of the change in volume of a gas with temperature, at constant pressure, were published by Charles in 1787 and by Gay-Lussac in 1802. Fig. 141 shows an apparatus which we may use for repeating their experiments. Air is trapped by mercury in the closed limb C of the tube AC; a scale engraved upon C enables us to measure the length of the air column, l. The tube is surrounded by a water-bath W, which we can heat by passing in steam. After making the temperature uniform by stirring, we level the mercury in the limbs A and C, by pouring mercury in at A, or running it off at B. The air in C is then always at atmospheric (constant) pressure. We measure the length l and plot it against the temperature, θ (Fig. 142).

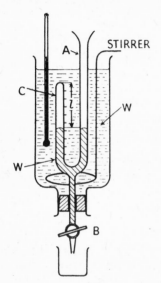

FIG. 141. Charles' law experiment.   FIG. 142. Results of experiment.

If S is the cross-section of the tube, the volume of the trapped air is

$$V = lS.$$

The cross-section S, and the distance between the divisions on which we read l, both increase with the temperature θ. But their increases are very small compared with the expansion of the gas, and therefore we may say that the volume of the gas is proportional to the scale-reading of l. The graph then shows that the volume of the gas, at constant pressure, increases uniformly with its temperature. A similar result is obtained with twice the mass of gas, as indicated in Fig. 142

4. Volume Coefficient.

We express the rate at which the volume of a gas increases with temperature by defining a quantity called its coefficient of expansion at constant pressure, α_p, or *volume coefficient*:

$$\alpha_p = \frac{\text{volume at } \theta° \text{ C.} - \text{volume at } 0° \text{ C.}}{\text{volume at } 0° \text{ C.}} \times \frac{1}{\theta}.$$

Thus, if V is the volume at $\theta°$ C., and V_0 the volume at $0°$ C., then

$$\alpha_p = \frac{V - V_0}{V_0\,\theta},$$

whence $\qquad V - V_0 = V_0\,\alpha_p\theta,$

or $\qquad V = V_0\,(1 + \alpha_p\theta).$

The coefficient α_p has the dimensions

$$\frac{[\text{volume}]}{[\text{volume}] \times [\text{temperature}]} = \frac{1}{[\text{temperature}]}.$$

Its value is about $\dfrac{1}{273}$ when the temperature is measured in °C., and we therefore say that

$$\alpha_p = \frac{1}{273} \text{ per °C., or } \frac{1}{273} \text{ °C.}^{-1}.$$

Charles, and Gay-Lussac, found that α_p had the same value, 1/273, for all gases. This observation is now called Charles's or Gay-Lussac's Law: *The volume of a given mass of any gas, at constant pressure, increases by* $\dfrac{1}{273}$ *of its value at* $0°\,C.$, *for every degree Centigrade rise in temperature.*

5. Absolute Temperature.

Charles's Law shows that, if we plot the volume V of a given mass of any gas at constant pressure against its temperature θ, we shall get a straight line graph A as shown in Fig. 143. If we produce this line back-

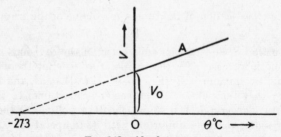

FIG. 143. Absolute zero.

wards, it will meet the temperature axis at $-273°$ C. This temperature is called the *absolute zero*. If a gas is cooled, it liquefies before it reaches $-273°$ C., and Charles's Law no longer holds; but that fact does not affect the form of the relationship between the volume and temperature at higher temperatures. We may express this relationship by writing

$$V \propto (273 + \theta).$$

The quantity $(273 + \theta)$ is called the *absolute temperature* of the gas, and is denoted by T. The idea of absolute temperature was developed by Lord Kelvin, and absolute temperatures are hence expressed in degrees Kelvin:

$$T^\circ \text{K.} = (273 + \theta)^\circ \text{C.}$$

From Charles's Law, we see that the volume of a given mass of gas at constant pressure is proportional to its absolute temperature, since

$$V \propto (273 + \theta) \propto T.$$

Thus if a given mass of gas has a volume V_1 at θ_1° C., and is heated at constant pressure to θ_2° C., its new volume is given by

$$\frac{V_1}{V_2} = \frac{273 + \theta_1}{273 + \theta_2} = \frac{T_1}{T_2}.$$

6. Pressure and Temperature.

The effect of temperature on the pressure of a gas, at constant volume, was investigated by Amontons in 1702. His work was forgotten, however, and was re-discovered only after the work of Gay-Lussac and Charles on the effect of temperature on volume.

An apparatus for measuring the pressure of a constant volume of gas at various known temperatures is shown in Fig. 144 (a). The bulb B

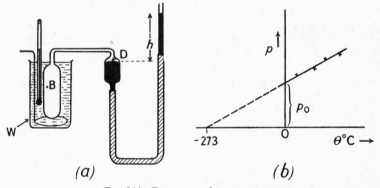

FIG. 144. Pressure and temperature.

contains air, which can be brought to any temperature θ by heating the water in the surrounding bath W. When the temperature is steady, the mercury in the closed limb of the tube is brought to a fixed level D, so that the volume of the air is fixed. The difference in level, h, of the mercury in the open and closed limbs is then added to the height of the barometer, H, to give the pressure p of the gas in cm. of mercury. If p, $(h + H)$, is plotted against the temperature, the plot is a straight line (Fig. 144 (b)).

The coefficient of pressure increase at constant volume, α_v, known as the *pressure coefficient*, is given by

$$\alpha_v = \frac{p - p_0}{p_0 \theta},$$

where p_0 is the pressure at $0°$ C. The coefficient α_v, which expresses the change of pressure with temperature, at constant volume, has practically the same value for all gases: $\dfrac{1}{273}$ per $°$C. It is thus numerically equal to the volume coefficient, α_p. We may therefore say that, at constant volume, the pressure of a given mass of gas is proportional to its absolute temperature T, since

$$p \propto (273 + \theta).$$

$$\therefore \frac{p_1}{p_2} = \frac{273 + \theta_1}{273 + \theta_2} = \frac{T_1}{T_2}.$$

7. Equality of Pressure and Volume Coefficients.

If a gas obeys Boyle's Law, its coefficient of pressure change at constant volume, α_v, and of volume change at constant pressure, α_p,

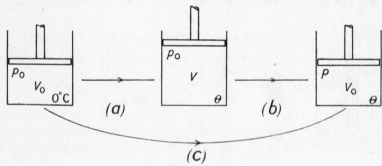

Fig. 145. Showing that $\alpha_v = \alpha_p$.

must be equal. For let us suppose that a given mass of gas is warmed at constant pressure, p_0, from $0°$ C. to $\theta°$ C. (Fig. 145 (a)). Its volume expands from V_0 to V, where

$$V = V_0(1 + \alpha_p\theta).$$

Now let us suppose that it is compressed, at constant temperature, until its volume returns to V_0 (Fig. 145 (b)). Then its pressure rises to p, where

$$pV_0 = p_0V$$
$$= p_0V_0(1 + \alpha_p\theta)$$

or $\qquad\qquad p = p_0(1 + \alpha_p\theta)$ . . . . (3)

The condition of the gas is now the same as if it had been warmed at constant volume from $0°$ C. to $\theta°$ C. (Fig. 145 (c)). Therefore

$$p = p_0(1 + \alpha_v\theta) ;$$

and, by equation (3), it follows that

$$\alpha_v = \alpha_p.$$

We shall see later that gases do not obey Boyle's law exactly, although at moderate pressures they do so very nearly. The difference between α_p and α_v provides a sensitive test for departures from Boyle's Law.

8. The Equation of State.

Fig. 146 illustrates the argument by which we may find the general relationship between pressure, volume and temperature of a given mass of gas. This relationship is called the *equation of state*.

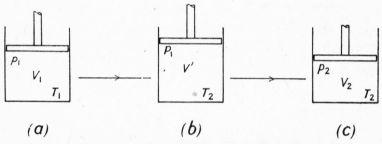

FIG. 146. Changing temperature and pressure of a gas.

At (a) we have the gas occupying a volume V_1 at a pressure p_1, and an absolute temperature T_1. We wish to calculate its volume V_2 at an absolute temperature T_2 and pressure p_2, as at (c). We proceed via (b), raising the temperature to T_2 while keeping the pressure constant at p_1. If V' is the volume of the gas at (b), then, by Charles's law:

$$\frac{V'}{V_1} = \frac{T_2}{T_1} \quad . \quad . \quad . \quad . \quad . \quad . \quad (4)$$

We proceed now to (c), by increasing the pressure to p_2, while keeping the temperature constant at T_2. By Boyle's law,

$$\frac{V_2}{V'} = \frac{p_1}{p_2} \quad . \quad . \quad . \quad . \quad . \quad (5)$$

Eliminating V' between equations (4) and (5), we find

$$\frac{V_2}{V_1} = \frac{T_2}{T_1} \cdot \frac{p_1}{p_2}$$

or

$$\frac{p_2 V_2}{T_2} = \frac{p_1 V_1}{T_1}.$$

In general therefore, $\qquad \dfrac{pV}{T} = R$ . . . . (6)

where R is a constant. This equation is often given in the form

$$pV = RT \qquad \text{. . . . .} \qquad (7)$$

Equation (7) is the *equation of state* for a perfect gas. The value of the constant R depends on the nature of the gas—air, hydrogen, etc.— and on the mass of the gas concerned. If we consider *unit mass* of a gas, we can denote its volume by V and write

$$pV = RT \qquad \text{. . . . . . .} \qquad (8)$$

R is called the gas-constant for unit mass of the gas. If ρ is the density of the gas, at absolute temperature T and pressure p, then

$$\rho = \frac{1}{V},$$

and equation (8) becomes $\qquad \dfrac{p}{\rho} = RT$ . . . . (9)

The volume V of an arbitrary mass M of the gas, at absolute temperature T and pressure p, is $V = MV$;

therefore, by (8), $\qquad\qquad pV = MRT;$ . . . . . . (10)

and, by (7), $\qquad\qquad\qquad R = MR.$

9. Magnitude of the Gas Constant.

To calculate the constant R for a gas, we need to know the density of the gas at a given temperature and pressure. Very often, in dealing with gases, we specify the pressure not in dynes per square centimetre, but simply in millimetres of mercury. We do so because we are concerned only with relative values. A pressure of 760 mm. of mercury, which is about the average pressure of the atmosphere, is sometimes called "standard" or "normal" pressure. A temperature of $0°$ C., or $273°$ K., is likewise called standard or normal temperature. The conditions $273°$ K. and 760 mm. pressure are together called standard temperature and pressure (s.t.p.) or normal temperature and pressure (n.t.p.). A pressure of 760 mm. mercury is given, in dynes per cm.², by

$$p = g\rho H$$
$$= 981 \times 13\!\cdot\!6 \times 76 = 1\!\cdot\!013 \times 10^6 \text{ dynes/cm.}^2,$$

where ρ is the density of mercury, $g =$ acceleration of gravity, $H = 76$ cm.

At s.t.p. the density of hydrogen is about $0\!\cdot\!09$ gm./litre, or $0\!\cdot\!00009$ gm./cm.³ The gas-constant for unit mass of hydrogen is therefore

$$R = \frac{p}{\rho T} = \frac{1\!\cdot\!013 \times 10^6}{0\!\cdot\!0009 \times 273}$$

$$= 4\!\cdot\!16 \times 10^7, \text{ in the appropriate units.}$$

We will now discuss the units in which R is expressed.

10. The Gas-constant Units : Work done in Expansion.

The gas-constant R for an *arbitrary mass* of gas is defined by the equation

$$pV = RT$$

or

$$R = \frac{pV}{T}.$$

Its unit is therefore that of

$$\frac{\text{pressure} \times \text{volume}}{\text{temperature}}.$$

The pressure may be given in dynes/cm.², mm. mercury, atmospheres, lb./in.², or any convenient unit. The volume may be in litres, cm.³, ft.³, or even pints if we wish. The temperature may be in °C. or °F. If we are given p, V, and T, and work out the value of R, we express it in the corresponding units. The constant per unit mass, R, has the unit of

$$\frac{\text{pressure} \times \text{volume}}{\text{temperature} \times \text{mass}}.$$

The value of it which we found above for hydrogen was in (dynes/cm.²) × cm.³, per °K., per gramme; for simplicity, we may say that it is in c.g.s. units, where the initials stand for centimetre, gramme, second.

Work Done. The product of pressure and volume has the dimensions of work. To see this, let us imagine some gas, at a pressure p, in a cylinder fitted with a piston (Fig. 147).

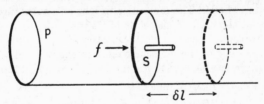

Fig. 147. Work done in expansion.

If the piston has an area S, the force on it is

$$f = pS.$$

If we allow the piston to move outwards a distance δl, the gas will expand, and its pressure will fall. But by making the distance very short, we can make the fall in pressure so small that we may consider the pressure constant. The force f is then constant, and the work done is

$$\delta W = f.\delta l = pS.\delta l.$$

The product $S.\delta l$ is the increase in volume, δV, of the gas, so that

$$\delta W = p.\delta V \quad . \quad . \quad . \quad . \quad . \quad (11)$$

The product of pressure and volume, in general, therefore represents work.
If the pressure p is in dynes/cm.^{2}, and the area S is in cm.^{2}, the force f
is in dynes.   And if the movement δl is in cm., the work $p \cdot \delta l$ is in dyne-
cm. or ergs.   The increase of volume, δV, is in cm.^{3} Thus the product
of pressure in dynes/cm.^{2}, and volume in cm.^{3}, represents work in ergs.

Consequently, if we express the pressure of a gas in dynes/cm.^{2},
and its volume in cm.^{3}, the gas-constant R, $= pV/T$, is in ergs per
degree.   The constant for 1 gm., R, is in ergs per degree per gramme.
The value of R for hydrogen, which we calculated on p. 228, is

$$R = 4 \cdot 16 \times 10^7 \text{ erg/}^\circ\text{K./gm.}$$

11. Avogadro's Hypothesis : Molecular Weight.

Amedeo Avogadro, with one simple-looking idea, illuminated
chemistry as Newton illuminated mechanics.   In 1811 he suggested
that chemically active gases, such as oxygen, existed not as single
atoms, but as pairs: he proposed to distinguish between an atom, O,
and a molecule, O_2.   Ampère proposed the same distinction, independ-
dently, in 1814.   Avogadro also put forward another idea, now called
Avogadro's hypothesis: that equal volumes of all gases, at the same
temperature and pressure, contained equal numbers of molecules.
The number of molecules in 1 cu. cm. of gas at s.t.p. is called Losch-
midt's number; it is $2 \cdot 69 \times 10^{19}$.

Avogadro's hypothesis became accepted in the middle of the nineteenth century.   Because molecules could not be observed, their
masses could not be measured directly; but they could be compared,
by chemical methods.   The molecular weight of a substance, μ, was at
first defined as the ratio of the mass of its molecule, m, to the mass of
a hydrogen atom.   Later, for the convenience of chemists, it was
defined as the ratio of the molecular mass to the mass of an imaginary
atom, this atom having 1/16th the mass of an oxygen atom:

$$\mu = \frac{\text{mass of molecule}}{1/16 \text{ mass of O-atom}} = \frac{m}{1/16 m_O} = \frac{16m}{m_O}.$$

On this scale, the mass of a hydrogen atom is $1 \cdot 008$ times the mass
of the imaginary atom.   And since the hydrogen molecule contains
two atoms, its molecular weight is

$$\mu_{H_2} = 2 \cdot 016.$$

The unit of molecular weight, $\dfrac{m_O}{16}$, is also the unit of atomic weight ;
its value is $1 \cdot 66 \times 10^{-24}$ gm.

12. Gramme-Molecular Weight : Universal Gas-constant.

The mass of a substance equal to its molecular weight—i.e. μ gm.—
is called a gramme-molecular weight of the substance (g.m.w.) or

simply a gramme-molecule. The number of molecules in a gramme-molecule, N, is given if m is the mass of a molecule, by

$$\mu = Nm,$$

whence
$$N = \frac{\mu}{m} = \frac{16m/m_O}{m}$$

$$= \frac{16}{m_O}.$$

The number of molecules per gramme-molecule is thus the same for all substances. It is called Avogadro's number, and is equal to $6\cdot02 \times 10^{23}$.

From Avogadro's hypothesis, it follows that the gramme-molecular weights of all gases, at the same temperature and pressure, occupy equal volumes. Experiment confirms this; at s.t.p. 1 gm.-molecule of any gas occupies $22\cdot4$ litres. Consequently, if we denote by V the volume of 1 gm.-molecule, then the ratio $\dfrac{pV}{T}$ is the same for all gases.

We call it the *gas constant per gramme-molecule*, R, and

$$R = \frac{pV}{T}.$$

At s.t.p. $V = 22\cdot4$ litres $= 22{,}400$ cm.^{3}

$p = 76$ cm. mercury $= 1\cdot013 \times 10^6$ dynes/cm.^{2} (p. 46)

$T = 273^\circ$ K.

$$\therefore R = \frac{1\cdot013 \times 10^6 \times 22{,}400}{273}$$

$= 8\cdot31 \times 10^7$ ergs/$^\circ$K./gm.-mol. $= 8\cdot31$ joules/$^\circ$K./gm.-mol.

The value of R is a universal constant. If μ gm. is the molecular weight of a gas, the constant for 1 gm. is

$$R = \frac{R}{\mu} \qquad . \quad . \quad . \quad . \quad . \quad . \quad (12)$$

KINETIC THEORY

The kinetic theory of matter, which regards all bodies as assemblies of particles in motion—either vibrating or flying about—is an old one. Lucretius described it in the first century A.D. and Gassendi and Hooke revived it in the seventeenth century. In 1738 D. Bernoulli applied it in detail to a gas, and from it deduced Boyle's law, which was already known from experiment. Another century passed, however, before the kinetic view of a gas was fully developed—mainly by Clausius (1822–88), Boltzmann (1844–1906), and Maxwell (1831–79).

In the kinetic theory of gases, we seek to explain the behaviour of gases by considering the motion of their molecules. In particular, we suppose that the pressure of a gas is due to the molecules bombarding the walls of its container. Whenever a molecule bounces off a wall, its momentum at right-angles to the wall is reversed; the force which it exerts on the wall is equal to the rate of change of its momentum. The average force exerted by the gas on the whole of its container is the average rate at which the momentum of its molecules is changed by collision with the walls.

To find the pressure of the gas we must find this force, and then divide it by the area of the walls. The following assumptions are made to simplify the calculation:

(*a*) The attraction between the molecules is negligible.

(*b*) The volume of the molecules is negligible compared with the volume occupied by the gas.

(*c*) The molecules are like perfectly elastic spheres.

(*d*) The duration of a collision is negligible compared with the time between collisions.

13. Calculation of the Pressure.

Fig. 148 shows part of the career of a molecule in a spherical vessel. We assume that its collisions with the walls are perfectly elastic.

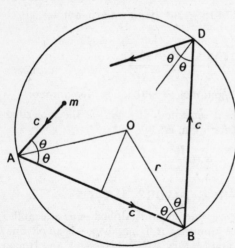

FIG. 148. Calculation of gas pressure.

Therefore, if it strikes the wall at A, making an angle θ with the radius OA, it bounces off at an equal angle θ. Also, since it loses no kinetic energy in the collision, its speed c does not change. We shall assume for the moment that the molecule does not collide with any other molecules. Then, from the geometry of the circle, we see that the molecule bounces for ever round the circle ABD, always striking the wall at the angle θ. At each collision, the molecule's momentum at right angles to the wall, $mc \cos \theta$, is reversed. Its momentum parallel to the wall is unchanged.

∴ change of momentum per collision = $2mc \cos \theta$.

The distance between collisions, AB, BD, is constant and equal to $2r \cos \theta$ where r is the radius of the sphere.

$$\therefore \text{ time between collisions} = \frac{2r \cos \theta}{c}.$$

$$\therefore \text{ change of momentum per second} = \frac{\text{change per collision}}{\text{time between collisions}}$$

$$= \frac{2mc \cos \theta}{\dfrac{2r \cos \theta}{c}}$$

$$= \frac{mc^2}{r}.$$

In fact, however, we cannot allow ourselves to assume that the molecules of a gas do not collide with one another. If, however, we assume that their collisions are perfectly elastic, both the kinetic energy and the momentum are conserved in them. The average momentum with which all the molecules strike the walls is then not changed by their collisions with one another; what one loses, another gains. The important effect of collisions between molecules is to distribute their individual speeds; on the average, the fast ones lose speed to the slow. We suppose, then, that different molecules have different speeds, and that the speeds of individual molecules vary with time, as they make collisions with one another; but we also suppose that the average speed of all the molecules is constant. These assumptions are justified by the fact that the kinetic theory leads to conclusions which agree with experiment.

We therefore say that the *average* change of momentum of a molecule per second in collision with the walls of a vessel is:

$$\text{average change of momentum per second} = \frac{m\overline{c^2}}{r}.$$

The symbol $\overline{c^2}$ denotes the average value of c^2—the average value of the squares of the speeds of the individual molecules. It is called the *mean-square speed* of the molecules. It is not equal to the square of their average speed, as we can easily see with an example. Let us suppose that the speeds of six molecules are, 1, 2, 3, 4, 5, 6 units. Their mean speed is

$$\bar{c} = \frac{1 + 2 + 3 + 4 + 5 + 6}{6} = \frac{21}{6} = 3 \cdot 5,$$

and its square is $\qquad (\bar{c})^2 = 3 \cdot 5^2 = 12 \cdot 25.$

Their mean square speed, however is

$$\overline{c^2} = \frac{1^2 + 2^2 + 3^2 + 4^2 + 5^2 + 6^2}{6} = \frac{91}{6} = 15 \cdot 2.$$

This differs by about 25 per cent. from the square of the mean speed.
If there are N molecules in the gas, then:

total change of momentum per second, at walls

$$= N \times \text{average momentum} = N\frac{m\overline{c^2}}{r}.$$

Thus the total force exerted by the gas on the walls, in terms of the
number of molecules per unit volume, n,

$$= f = \frac{4}{3}\pi r^3 n \; \frac{m\overline{c^2}}{r} = \frac{4\pi r^2 n m\overline{c^2}}{3}.$$

The force per unit area, or pressure, is therefore

$$p = \frac{f}{4\pi r^2} = \frac{1}{4\pi r^2} \frac{4\pi r^2 n m\overline{c^2}}{3}$$

or $\qquad\qquad p = \tfrac{1}{3} n m\overline{c^2}$ . . . . (13)

If n is in molecules per cm.^{3}, m in gm. and c in cm. per sec., the pressure
p is in dynes per cm.^{2}

14. Root-mean-square (R.M.S.) Speed.

In equation (13) the factor nm is the product of the molecules per
unit volume and the mass of one molecule. It is therefore the total
mass of the gas per unit volume: its density ρ. Thus the equation gives

$$p = \tfrac{1}{3}\rho\overline{c^2}$$ . . . . (14)

or $\qquad\qquad \dfrac{p}{\rho} = \tfrac{1}{3}\overline{c^2}$ . . . . (15)

If we substitute known values of p and ρ in equation (15), we can
find $\overline{c^2}$. For hydrogen at s.t.p.,

$$\rho = 0.09 \text{ gm./litre} = 0.09 \times 10^{-3} \text{ gm./cm.}^3$$

The pressure, in dynes per cm.^{2}, is $p = g\rho H$, where $g =$ acceleration
of gravity $= 981$ cm./sec.^{2}, $\rho =$ density of mercury $= 13.6$ gm./cm.^{3},
$H =$ barometer height $= 76$ cm.

$$\therefore \overline{c^2} = \frac{3p}{\rho} = \frac{3 \times 981 \times 13.6 \times 76}{9 \times 10^{-5}}$$

$$= 3.37 \times 10^{10} \text{ cm.}^2 \text{ sec.}^{-2}$$

The square root of $\overline{c^2}$ is called the *root-mean-square speed*; it is of the
same magnitude as the average speed, but not quite equal to it. Its
value is

$$\sqrt{\overline{c^2}} = \sqrt{3.37} \times 10^5 = 1.84 \times 10^5 \text{ cm./sec.}$$

$$= 1.84 \text{ km./sec.}$$

$$= 1.14 \text{ mile/sec.}$$

Molecular speeds were first calculated in this way by Joule in 1848; they turn out to have a magnitude which is high, but reasonable. The value is reasonable because it has the same order of magnitude as the speed of sound (1·30 km./sec. in hydrogen at 0° C.); the speed of sound is the speed with which the molecules of a gas pass on a disturbance from one to another, and this we may expect to be of the same magnitude as the speeds of their natural motion.

15. Introduction of the Temperature.

Let us consider a volume V of gas, containing N molecules. The number of molecules per unit volume is

$$n = \frac{N}{V},$$

and therefore the pressure of the gas, by equation (13) is

$$p = \tfrac{1}{3}nm\overline{c^2} = \tfrac{1}{3}\frac{N}{V}m\overline{c^2}$$

$$\therefore\ pV = \tfrac{1}{3}Nm\overline{c^2} \quad . \quad . \quad . \quad . \quad . \quad (16)$$

Equation (16) reminds us of the equation combining Boyle's and Charles's laws: $pV = RT.$

We can therefore make the kinetic theory consistent with the observed behaviour of a gas, if we write

$$\tfrac{1}{3}Nm\overline{c^2} = RT \quad . \quad . \quad . \quad . \quad . \quad . \quad (17)$$

Essentially, we are here assuming that the mean square speed of the molecules, $\overline{c^2}$, is proportional to the absolute temperature of the gas. This is a reasonable assumption, because we have learnt that heat is a form of energy; and the kinetic energy of a molecule, due to its random motion within its container, is proportional to the square of its speed. When we heat a gas, we expect to speed-up its molecules.

The kinetic energy of a molecule moving with a speed c is $\tfrac{1}{2}mc^2$; the average kinetic energy of the random motion of the molecule of a gas is therefore $\tfrac{1}{2}m\overline{c^2}$. To relate this to the temperature, we put equation (17) into the form

$$RT = \tfrac{1}{3}Nm\overline{c^2} = \tfrac{2}{3}N(\tfrac{1}{2}m\overline{c^2}),$$

whence $$\tfrac{1}{2}m\overline{c^2} = \tfrac{3}{2}\frac{R}{N}T \quad . \quad . \quad . \quad . \quad . \quad . \quad (18)$$

According to the kinetic theory, therefore, *the average kinetic energy of a molecule is proportional to the absolute temperature of the gas.*

The ratio R/N in equation (18) is a universal constant. To see that it is, we have only to consider a gramme-molecule. We have already seen that, for a gramme-molecule, the gas constant **R**, and number of molecules N, are universal constants. If our arbitrary mass of gas is x gramme-molecules, then $R = xR$, and $N = xN$; therefore

$$\frac{R}{N} = \frac{R}{N} = k.$$

The constant k, the gas constant per molecule, is also a universal constant, it is often called *Boltzmann's constant*. In terms of k equation (18) becomes

$$\tfrac{1}{2}m\overline{c^2} = \tfrac{3}{2}kT \quad . \quad . \quad . \quad . \quad . \quad . \quad (19)$$

Boltzmann's constant is usually given in ergs per degree, since it relates energy to temperature :

$$k = \frac{\tfrac{1}{2}m\overline{c^2}}{\tfrac{3}{2}T}.$$

Its value is $k = 1 \cdot 38 \times 10^{-16}$ erg/°K.

16. Diffusion : Graham's Law.

When a gas passes through a porous plug, a cotton-wool wad, for example, it is said to "diffuse." Diffusion differs from the flow of a gas through a wide tube, in that it is not a motion of the gas in bulk, but is a result of the motion of its individual molecules.

Fig. 149 shows an apparatus devised by Graham (1805–69) to compare the rates of diffusion of different gases. D is a glass tube, closed

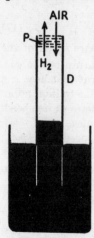

Fig. 149. Graham's apparatus for diffusion.

with a plug P of plaster of Paris. It is first filled with mercury, and inverted over mercury in a bowl. Hydrogen is then passed into it until the mercury levels are the same on each side ; the hydrogen is then at atmospheric pressure. The volume of hydrogen, V_H, is proportional to the length of the tube above the mercury. The apparatus is now left ; hydrogen diffuses out through P, and air diffuses in. Ultimately no hydrogen remains in the tube D. The tube is then adjusted until the level of mercury is again the same on each side, so that the air within it is at atmospheric pressure. The volume of air, V_A, is proportional to the new length of the tube above the mercury.

The volumes V_A and V_H are, respectively, the volumes of air and hydrogen which diffused through the plug in the same time. Therefore the rates of diffusion of the gases air and hydrogen are proportional to the volumes V_A and V_H :

$$\frac{\text{rate of diffusion of air}}{\text{rate of diffusion of hydrogen}} = \frac{V_A}{V_H}.$$

Graham found in his experiments that the volumes were inversely proportional to the square roots of the densities of the gases, ρ:

$$\frac{V_A}{V_H} = \sqrt{\frac{\rho_H}{\rho_A}}$$

thus $\qquad \dfrac{\text{rate of diffusion of air}}{\text{rate of diffusion of hydrogen}} = \sqrt{\dfrac{\rho_H}{\rho_A}}.$

In general: $\qquad$ rate of diffusion $\propto \dfrac{1}{\sqrt{\rho}};$

and in words: *the rate of diffusion of a gas is inversely proportional to the square root of its density.* This is *Graham's Law.*

Graham's law of diffusion is readily explained by the kinetic theory. At the same temperature T, the mean kinetic energies of the molecules of different gases are equal, since

$$\tfrac{1}{2}m\overline{c^2} = \tfrac{3}{2}kT$$

and k is a universal constant. Therefore, if the subscripts A and H denote air and hydrogen respectively,

$$\tfrac{1}{2}m_A\overline{c_A^2} = \tfrac{1}{2}m_H\overline{c_H^2},$$

whence $\qquad\qquad \dfrac{\overline{c_A^2}}{\overline{c_H^2}} = \dfrac{m_H}{m_A}.$

At a given temperature and pressure, the density of a gas, ρ, is proportional to the mass of its molecule, m, since equal volumes contain equal numbers of molecules:

Therefore $\qquad\qquad \dfrac{m_H}{m_A} = \dfrac{\rho_H}{\rho_A},$

whence $\qquad\qquad \dfrac{\overline{c_A^2}}{\overline{c_H^2}} = \dfrac{\rho_H}{\rho_A}.$

$$\therefore \quad \frac{\sqrt{\overline{c_A^2}}}{\sqrt{\overline{c_H^2}}} = \frac{\sqrt{\rho_H}}{\sqrt{\rho_A}} \quad \ldots \ldots \quad (20)$$

The average speed of the molecules of a gas is roughly equal to—and strictly proportional to—the square root of its mean square speed. Equation (20) therefore shows that the average molecular speeds are inversely proportional to the square roots of the densities of the gases. And so it explains why the rates of diffusion—which depend on the molecular speeds—are also inversely proportional to the square roots of the densities.

17. Thermal Agitations and Internal Energy.

The random motion of the molecules of a gas, whose kinetic energy depends upon the temperature, is often called the *thermal agitation* of the molecules. And the kinetic energy of the thermal agitation is called the *internal energy* of the gas. We must appreciate that this energy is quite independent of any motion of the gas in bulk: when a cylinder of oxygen is being carried by an express train, its kinetic energy as a whole is greater than when it is standing on the platform; but the random motion of the molecules within the cylinder is unchanged—and so is the temperature of the gas. The same is true of a liquid; in a water-churning experiment to measure the mechanical equivalent of heat, baffles must be used to prevent the water from acquiring any mass-motion—all the work done must be converted into random motion, if it is to appear as heat. Likewise, the internal energy of a solid is the kinetic energy of its atoms' vibrations about their mean positions: throwing a lump of metal through the air does not raise its temperature, but hitting it with a hammer does.

The internal energy of a gas depends on the number of atoms in its molecule. A gas whose molecules consist of single atoms is said to be monatomic: for example, chemically inert gases and metallic vapours,

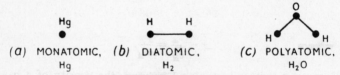

(a) MONATOMIC, (b) DIATOMIC, (c) POLYATOMIC,
    Hg H_2 H_2O

Fig. 150. Types of gas molecule.

Hg, Na, He, Ne, A. A gas with two atoms to the molecule is said to be diatomic: O_2, H_2, N_2, Cl_2, CO. And a gas with more than two atoms to the molecule is said to be polyatomic: H_2O, O_3, H_2S, CO_2, CH_4. The molecules of a monatomic gas we may regard as points, but those of a diatomic gas we must regard as " dumb-bells ", and those of a polyatomic gas as more complicated structures (Fig. 150). A molecule which extends appreciably in space—a diatomic or polyatomic molecule—has an appreciable moment of inertia. It may therefore have kinetic energy of rotation, as well as of translation. A monatomic molecule, however, must have a much smaller moment of inertia than a diatomic or polyatomic; its kinetic energy of rotation can therefore be neglected.

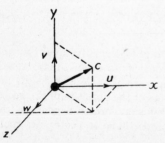

Fig. 151. Components of velocity.

Fig. 151 shows a monatomic molecule whose velocity c has been resolved into its components u, v, w along the x, y, z axes: $$c^2 = u^2 + v^2 + w^2.$$

The x, y, z axes are called the molecules' degrees of freedom: they are three directions such that the motion of the molecule along any one is independent of its motion along the others.

If we average the speed c, and the components u, v, w, over all the molecules in a gas, we have

$$\overline{c^2} = \overline{u^2} + \overline{v^2} + \overline{w^2}.$$

And since the molecules do not pile up in any corner of the vessel containing the gas, their average velocities in all directions must be the same. We may therefore write

$$\overline{u^2} = \overline{v^2} = \overline{w^2},$$

whence

$$\overline{c^2} = 3\overline{u^2} = 3\overline{v^2} = 3\overline{w^2},$$

or

$$\overline{u^2} = \overline{v^2} = \overline{w^2} = \tfrac{1}{3}\overline{c^2}.$$

The average kinetic energy of a molecule of the gas is given by equation (19):

$$\tfrac{1}{2}m\overline{c^2} = \tfrac{3}{2}kT.$$

Therefore the average kinetic energy of a monatomic molecule, in each degree of freedom, is

$$\tfrac{1}{2}m\overline{u^2} = \tfrac{1}{2}m\overline{v^2} = \tfrac{1}{2}m\overline{w^2} = \tfrac{1}{2}kT.$$

Thus the molecule has kinetic energy $\tfrac{1}{2}kT$ per degree of freedom.

18. Rotational Energy.

Let us now consider a diatomic or polyatomic gas. When two of its molecules collide, they will, in general, tend to rotate, as well as to deflect each other. In some collisions, energy will be transferred from the translations of the molecules to their rotations; in others, from the rotations to the translations. We may assume, then, that the internal energy of the gas is shared between the rotations and translations of its molecules.

To discuss the kinetic energy of rotation, we must first extend the idea of degrees of freedom to it. A diatomic molecule can have kinetic energy of rotation about any axis at right-angles to its own. Its motion about any such axis can be resolved into motions about two such axes at right-angles to each other (Fig. 152 (a)). Motions about these axes are

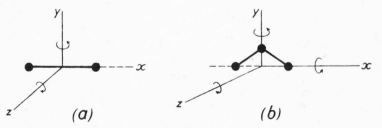

Fig. 152. Rotation of molecules.

independent of each other, and a diatomic molecule therefore has two degrees of rotational freedom. A polyatomic molecule, unless it happens to consist of molecules all in a straight line, has no axis about which its moment of inertia is negligible. It can therefore have kinetic energy of rotation about three mutually perpendicular axes (Fig. 152 (b)). It has three degrees of rotational freedom.

We have seen that the internal energy of a gas is shared between the translations and rotations of its molecules. Maxwell assumed that the average kinetic energy of a molecule, in each degree of freedom, *rotational as well as translational*, was $\frac{1}{2}kT$. This assumption is called the *principle of equipartition of energy*; experiment shows, as we shall find, that it is true at room temperature and above. At very low temperatures, when the gas is near liquefaction, it fails. At ordinary temperatures, then, we have:

average K.E. of monatomic molecule $= \frac{3}{2}kT$ (trans.);

average K.E. of diatomic molecule $= \frac{3}{2}kT$ (trans.) $+ \frac{2}{2}kT$ (rot.) $= \frac{5}{2}kT$;

average K.E. of polyatomic molecule $= \frac{3}{2}kT$ (trans.) $+ \frac{3}{2}kT$ (rot.) $= \frac{6}{2}kT$.

19. Internal Energy of any Gas.

From the average kinetic energy of its molecules, we can find the internal energy of a mass M of a gas. The number of molecules in this mass is, if m is the mass of one molecule.

$$N = \frac{M}{m}.$$

Its internal energy, U, is the total kinetic energy of its molecules' random motions; thus $\quad U = N \times$ average K.E. of molecule.

For a monatomic gas, therefore,

$$U = \frac{3}{2}NkT \text{ (monatomic).}$$

The constant k is the gas-constant per molecule; the product Nk is therefore the gas-constant R for the mass M of the gas. Thus

$$U = \frac{3}{2}RT \text{ (monatomic).}$$

In particular, if R is the gas-constant per gramme, the internal energy per gramme is

$$U = \frac{3}{2}RT \text{ (monatomic)} \quad . \quad . \quad . \quad . \quad . \quad (21)$$

Similarly, for a diatomic gas,

$$\left.\begin{aligned} U &= \frac{5}{2}NkT \\ &= \frac{5}{2}RT \\ U &= \frac{5}{2}RT \end{aligned}\right\} \text{diatomic} \quad . \quad . \quad . \quad . \quad . \quad (22)$$

And for a polyatomic gas,

$$\left.\begin{aligned} U &= \frac{6}{2}NkT \\ &= \frac{6}{2}RT \\ U &= \frac{6}{2}RT \end{aligned}\right\} \text{polyatomic} \quad . \quad . \quad . \quad . \quad . \quad (23)$$

20. Internal Energy and Volume.

In our simple account of the kinetic theory of gases, we have implicitly assumed that the molecules of a gas do not attract one another. If they did, any molecule approaching the boundary of the gas would be pulled towards the body of it, as is a molecule of water approaching the surface (See Chapter VI, *Surface Tension*, p. 112). The attractions of the molecules would thus reduce the pressure of the gas.

Since the molecules of a substance are presumably the same whether it is liquid or gas, the molecules of a gas must attract one another somewhat. But except for brief instants when they collide, the molecules of a gas are much further apart than those of a liquid. In 1 cubic centimetre of gas at s.t.p. there are 2.69×10^{19} molecules, and in 1 cubic centimetre of water there are 3.33×10^{22}; there are a thousand times as many molecules in the liquid, and so the molecules in the gas are ten times further apart. We may therefore expect that the mutual attraction of the molecules of a gas, for most purposes, can be neglected, as experiment, in fact, shows.

The experiment consists in allowing a gas to expand without doing external work; that is, to expand into a vacuum. Then, if the molecules attract one another, work is done against their attractions, as they move further apart. But if the molecular attractions are negligible, the work done is also negligible. If any work is done against the molecular attractions, it will be done at the expense of the molecular kinetic energies; as the molecules move apart, they will exert retarding forces on one another. Thus the internal energy of the gas, and therefore its temperature, will fall.

The expansion of a gas into a vacuum is called a "free expansion". If a gas does not cool when it makes a free expansion, then the mutual attractions of its molecules are negligible.

Joule's Experiments. Experiments on free expansion were made in 1807 by Gay-Lussac; they showed no fall in temperature. Joule repeated these experiments with a better vacuum in 1845; he got the same negative result, and the greater accuracy of his experiments made them more trustworthy. Joule used two forms of apparatus, as shown in Fig. 153 (a) and (b). Each consisted of a cylinder of air, R, at 22 atmospheres, connected by a stop-cock S to an evacuated cylinder E. In the apparatus (a) both cylinders stood in the same tin can C, which contains $16\frac{1}{2}$ lb. water. In (b) the cylinders stood in different cans, and the stop-cock in a third, also containing water. When the stop-cock was opened, gas expanded from R to E. With the apparatus (a) Joule found, after stirring the water, that its temperature was unchanged. The expanding gas had therefore neither liberated heat nor absorbed it. With the apparatus (b) Joule found that heat was absorbed from the water round R, and given to the water round S

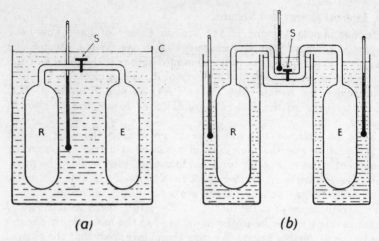

FIG. 153. Joule's experiment on internal energy

and E; the heat given out was equal to the heat taken in. The heat taken in represented the work done by the gas from R, expanding against the rising pressure of the gas in E and in the pipe beyond S. The heat given out represented the work done on the gas in E and S by the gas flowing in, against the rising pressure. The equality of the two showed that the total mass of gas neither gained nor lost energy in making its free expansion. Joule's experiments, therefore, showed that *the internal energy of a gas is independent of its volume.*

From Joule's results we may argue back to show that the mutual attractions of the molecules of the gas are negligible; in practice, however, it is the property of the bulk gas which is important—the fact that its internal energy does not depend on its volume.

Joule's experiments, though more reliable than Gay-Lussac's, were crude; with so much water, a small amount of heat would not produce a measurable temperature rise. Between 1852 and 1862, Joule worked with William Thomson, later Lord Kelvin, on more delicate experiments. They found that most gases, in expanding from high pressure to low, do lose a little of their internal energy. The loss represents work done against the molecular attractions, which are therefore not quite negligible.

If the internal energy of a gas is independent of its volume, it is determined only by the temperature of the gas. The simple expression for the pressure, $p = \frac{1}{3}\rho \overline{c^2}$, then holds; and the gas obeys Boyle's and Charles's laws. Its pressure coefficient, α_v, is equal to its volume coefficient, α_p. Such a gas is called an ideal, or perfect gas. All gases, when far from liquefaction, behave for most practical purposes as though they were perfect.

SPECIFIC HEATS

21. Specific Heats at Constant Volume and Constant Pressure.

When we warm a gas, we may let it expand or not, as we please. If we do not let it expand—if we warm it in a closed vessel—then it does no external work, and all the heat we give it goes to increase its internal energy. *The heat required to warm unit mass of a gas through one degree, when its volume is kept constant, is called the specific heat of the gas at constant volume.* It is denoted by c_V, and is generally expressed in calories per gramme per °C.

If we allow a gas to expand as we warm it, then it does external work. The heat we give the gas appears partly as an increase to its internal energy—and hence its temperature—and partly as the heat equivalent of the work done. The work done depends on the increase in volume of the gas, which in turn depends on the way in which we allow the gas to expand. We can get an important theoretical result by supposing that the pressure is constant, and defining the corresponding specific heat. *The specific heat of a gas at constant pressure is the heat required to warm unit mass of it by one degree, when its pressure is kept constant.* It is denoted by c_p, and is expressed in the same units as c_V.

22. Principal Specific Heats : their Difference.

Any number of specific heats can be defined for a gas, according to the mass and the conditions imposed upon its pressure and volume. For 1 gm. of a gas, the specific heats at constant pressure c_p, and at constant volume c_V, are called the *principal specific heats.*

Fig. 154 shows how we can find a relationship between the principal specific heats of a gas. We first consider 1 gm. of the gas warmed

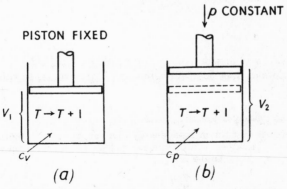

FIG. 154. Specific heats at constant volume and pressure.

through 1° C. at constant volume, (a). The heat required is c_V calories, and goes wholly to increase the internal energy.

We next consider 1 gm. warmed through 1° C. at constant pressure, (b). It expands from V_1 to V_2, and does an amount of external work given by
$$W = p(V_2 - V_1) \text{ (equation (11), p. 229).}$$

The work W is in ergs if p is in dynes/cm.², and the volumes in cm.³ The amount of heat required for this work is

$$Q = \frac{W}{J} = \frac{p(V_2 - V_1)}{J},$$

where J is the mechanical equivalent of heat, in ergs per calorie. The heat required to increase the internal energy of the gas depends only on the rise in temperature, since the internal energy does not change with the volume. This amount of heat is therefore the same as if the gas were warmed at constant volume, and is equal to c_V. The total amount of heat required to warm the gas at constant pressure is therefore

$$c_p = c_V + \frac{p(V_2 - V_1)}{J} \quad \ldots \ldots \ldots (24)$$

We can simplify the last term of this expression by using the equation of state for unit mass:
$$pV = RT,$$

where T is the absolute temperature of the gas, and R is the gas-constant for unit mass of it. If T_1 is the absolute temperature before warming, then

$$pV_1 = RT_1 \quad \ldots \ldots \ldots (25)$$

The absolute temperature after warming is $T_1 + 1$; therefore

$$pV_2 = R(T_1 + 1), \quad \ldots \ldots \ldots (26)$$

and on subtracting (25) from (26) we find

$$p(V_2 - V_1) = R.$$

Equation (24) now gives
$$c_p = c_V + \frac{R}{J},$$

or
$$c_p - c_V = \frac{R}{J} \quad \ldots \ldots \ldots (27)$$

Equation (27) was first derived by Robert Mayer in 1842. He used it, before Joule had done his water-churning experiments, to calculate a value for J.

23. Ratio of Principal Specific Heats.

We have seen that the internal energy of a gas, at a given temperature, depends on the number of atoms in its molecule. For a monatomic gas its value in ergs per gramme is

$$U = \frac{3}{2}RT \quad \ldots \ldots \ldots (21)$$

In calories per gramme, it is

$$\varepsilon = \frac{U}{J} = \frac{3}{2}\frac{R}{J} T.$$

The heat required to increase the internal energy of 1 gm. of a monatomic gas, when it is warmed through 1°, is therefore $\frac{3}{2}\frac{R}{J}$ calories. But this is the specific heat at constant volume, and so

$$c_V = \frac{3}{2}\frac{R}{J} \text{ cal./gm./°C.}$$

The specific heat of a monatomic gas at constant pressure is therefore

$$c_p = c_V + \frac{R}{J} = \frac{3}{2}\frac{R}{J} + \frac{R}{J}$$

$$= \frac{5}{2}\frac{R}{J} \text{ cal./gm./°C.}$$

Let us now divide c_p by c_V; their quotient is called the ratio of the principal specific heats, and is denoted by γ.

For a monatomic gas, its value is

$$\gamma = \frac{c_p}{c_V} = \frac{\dfrac{5}{2}\dfrac{R}{J}}{\dfrac{3}{2}\dfrac{R}{J}}$$

$$= \frac{5}{3} = 1\cdot667.$$

Similarly, for a diatomic molecule,

$$U = \frac{5}{2}RT \text{ ergs/gm.} \quad \cdot \quad \cdot \quad \cdot \quad \cdot \quad \cdot \quad \cdot \quad (22)$$

$$\varepsilon = \frac{5}{2}\frac{R}{J} T \text{ cal./gm.,}$$

whence

$$c_V = \frac{5}{2}\frac{R}{J} \text{ cal./gm./°C.}$$

and

$$c_p = c_V + \frac{R}{J} = \frac{7}{2}\frac{R}{J} \text{ cal./gm./°C.}$$

Hence

$$\gamma = \frac{c_p}{c_V} = \frac{7}{5} = 1\cdot400.$$

And for a polyatomic molecule,

$$U = \frac{6}{2}RT, \quad \cdot \quad \cdot \quad \cdot \quad \cdot \quad \cdot \quad \cdot \quad \cdot \quad (23)$$

$$c_V = \frac{6}{2}\frac{R}{J},$$

and

$$\gamma = \frac{c_p}{c_V} = \frac{8}{6} = 1\cdot333.$$

In general, if the molecules of a gas have f degrees of freedom, the average kinetic energy of a molecule is $f \times \frac{1}{2}kT$ (p. 239).

$$\therefore U = \frac{f}{2}RT,$$

$$c_V = \frac{f}{2}\frac{R}{J},$$

$$c_p = c_V + \frac{R}{J} = \left(\frac{f}{2} + 1\right)\frac{R}{J},$$

and

$$\gamma = \frac{c_p}{c_V} = \frac{\dfrac{f}{2} + 1}{\dfrac{f}{2}} = 1 + \frac{2}{f} \quad \cdots \cdots \quad (24)$$

The ratio of the principal specific heats of a gas thus gives us a measure of the number of atoms in its molecule, at least when that number is less than three. This ratio is fairly easy to measure, as we shall see later in this chapter. The poor agreement between the observed and theoretical values of γ for some of the polyatomic gases shows that, in its application to such gases, the theory is over-simple.

24. Measurement of c_V.

Fig. 155 shows an apparatus for measuring the specific heat of a gas at constant volume, called *Joly's differential steam calorimeter* (1886).

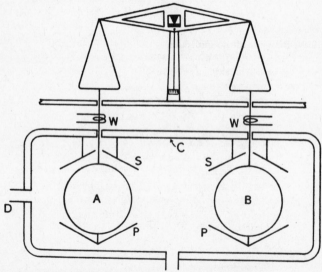

Fig. 155. Joly's differential steam calorimeter.

The calorimeter consists of two copper globes, A and B, as nearly identical as they can be made. They hang from the beam of a balance, and are surrounded by a chest C into which steam can be admitted at D. The sphere B is evacuated and A is filled with the gas whose specific heat is required. By filling A to a high pressure, the mass of gas can be made great enough to be accurately measurable on the balance. Let its value be M. Steam is now admitted to the chest, and condenses on both globes until they reach the temperature of the steam. This will generally be about 100° C., but we shall denote it by θ_1. The balance measures the excess steam condensed on A, over that condensed on B; let its mass be M_s. If the globes are identical, their heat capacities are equal, and the masses of steam required to warm the globes alone are equal. The excess steam condensed on A is then the mass required to warm the gas within it. Therefore if θ_R is the room temperature, and L the latent heat of evaporation of water, the specific heat c_V for the gas is given by

$$Mc_V(\theta_1 - \theta_R) = M_sL;$$

whence
$$c_V = \frac{M_sL}{M(\theta_1 - \theta_R)} \quad . \quad . \quad . \quad . \quad . \quad (25)$$

The calorimeter is called "differential" for the reason that it measures the difference in mass of the steam on the two globes. This is an important feature of it, because the heat capacities of the globes may be much greater than that of the gas. If a single globe were used, two measurements would have to be made, one with and one without the gas. The mass of steam condensed by the gas would then appear as the difference of two nearly equal masses, and could not be determined accurately. In practice the globes are not identical, and a control experiment with both evacuated is made to find the difference in mass of the steam condensed on them. This appears as a small correction to M_s in equation (25).

A small correction has also to be made to the result of the experiment, because the volume of the gas is not quite constant: the globe A expands when it is warmed.

The figure shows a few of the practical refinements of the apparatus. S, S are shields to prevent drops of moisture, condensed on the roof of the chest, from falling on to the globes. P, P are pans to catch any drops which, having condensed on A or B, might fall off. W, W are platinum wires heated by an electric current, which prevent drops forming in the holes through which the suspension wires pass out of the chest.

25. Measurement of c_p.

The method of mixtures was used to determine the specific heat of a gas at constant pressure by Regnault (1810–71). Regnault was one of the greatest experimenters of the nineteenth century—the reader who sees pictures of his apparatus in other books should remember that he worked before Bunsen had invented his famous burner—but his method for c_p is now outmoded. We shall describe here only a continuous flow method, similar to Callendar and Barnes' for the specific heat of water. It is due to Swann (1909).

Gas from a cylinder, A in Fig. 156, flows out through a needle valve N, which reduces its pressure to a little above atmospheric. If the pressure in the cylinder is high, it will fall slowly during an experiment, and the

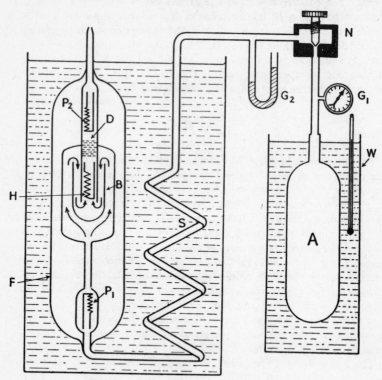

FIG. 156. Constant flow calorimeter for c_p.

pressure of the emerging gas will be almost constant. Manometers $G_1 G_2$ indicate the pressure of the gas in the cylinder, and of the gas emerging. The gas passes through a coiled tube S, in a water bath, which brings it to a uniform temperature. It then flows past a platinum resistance thermometer, P_1, which measures the temperature, θ_1 °C. From there it goes to a heating coil H, past a baffle B which enables it to receive any heat that escapes from the neighbourhood of the coil. Beyond the coil it passes through copper gauze D, which mixes the stream of gas and so brings it to a uniform temperature. This temperature, θ_2, is measured by the platinum resistance thermometer P_2. A vacuum jacket F makes the heat losses very small.

If M is the mass of gas flowing through the apparatus in t seconds, then the heat received by it is $Mc_p(\theta_2 - \theta_1)$. If the heat losses are negligible, the heat supplied by the coil in t seconds is IVt/J calories, where I is the current through it in amperes, V the potential difference across it in volts, and J the mechanical equivalent of heat in joules per calorie. Then

$$\frac{IVt}{J} = Mc_p(\theta_2 - \theta_1).$$

The mass of gas, M, is found from the fall of pressure in the cylinder. If v is the volume of the cylinder, and ρ_1 the density of the gas at the initial pressure p_1, then the mass initially in the cylinder is

$$M_1 = \rho_1 v.$$

And if, after t seconds, the pressure has fallen to p_2, and the density to ρ_2, the mass remaining in the cylinder is

$$M_2 = \rho_2.v$$

The mass of gas which has escaped in then

$$M = M_1 - M_2 = (\rho_1 - \rho_2)v.$$

The densities ρ_1 and ρ_2 can be readily calculated from the density ρ_0 at s.t.p.: if θ_3 is the temperature of the cylinder, and the pressures are measured in mm. mercury, then

$$\frac{p_1}{\rho_1(273 + \theta_3)} = \frac{p_2}{\rho_2(273 + \theta_3)} = \frac{760}{273\rho_0}.$$

The cylinder temperature θ_3 is kept constant by the water bath W.

CHANGES OF PRESSURE, VOLUME AND TEMPERATURE

In, for example, a steam engine or motor, gases expand and are compressed, cool and are heated, in ways more complicated than those which we have already described. We shall now consider some of these ways.

26. Isothermal Changes.

We have seen that the pressure p, and volume V of a given mass of gas are related by the equation

$$pV = RT \qquad . \qquad . \qquad . \qquad . \qquad . \qquad . \qquad (7)$$

where T is the absolute temperature of the gas, and R is a constant. If the temperature is constant the curve of pressure against volume is a rectangular hyperbola, $pV = $ constant,

representing Boyle's law. Such a curve is called an *isothermal* for the given mass of the given gas, at the temperature T. Fig. 157 shows a family of isothermals, for 1 gm. of air at different temperatures. When a gas expands, or is compressed, at *constant temperature*, its pressure and volume vary along the appropriate isothermal, and the gas is said to undergo an *isothermal compression or expansion*.

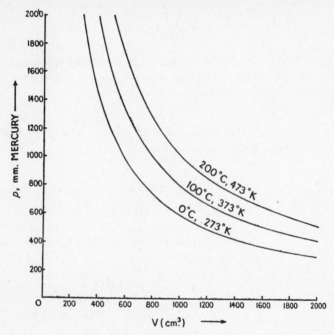

Fig. 157. Isothermals for 1 gm. air.

When a gas expands, it does work—for example, in driving a piston (Fig. 147, p. 229). The molecules of the gas bombard the piston, and if the piston moves they give up some of their kinetic energy to it; when a molecule bounces off a *moving* piston, it does so with a velocity less in magnitude than that with which it struck. The change in velocity is small, because the piston moves much more slowly than the molecule; but there are many molecules striking the piston at any instant, and their total loss of kinetic energy is equal to the work done in driving the piston forward.

The work done by a gas in expanding, therefore, is done at the expense of its internal energy. The temperature of the gas will consequently fall during expansion, unless heat is supplied to it. For an isothermal expansion, the gas must be held in a thin-walled, highly conducting vessel, surrounded by a constant temperature bath. And the expansion must take place slowly, so that heat can pass into the gas to maintain its temperature at every instant during the expansion.

27. External Work done in Expansion.

The heat taken in when a gas expands isothermally is the heat equivalent of the mechanical work done. If the volume of the gas increases by a small amount δV, at the pressure p, then the work done is

$$\delta W = p\delta V \text{ (equation (11), p. 229)}.$$

In an expansion from V_1 to V_2, therefore, the work done is

$$W = \int dW = \int_{V_1}^{V_2} pdV.$$

By the gas equation,

$$p = \frac{RT}{V},$$

whence

$$W = \int_{V_1}^{V_2} pdV = \int_{V_1}^{V_2} RT\frac{dV}{V}$$

or

$$W = RT \log_e\left(\frac{V_2}{V_1}\right).$$

The heat required is therefore

$$H = \frac{W}{J} = \frac{RT}{J} \log_e\left(\frac{V_2}{V_1}\right),$$

where J is the mechanical equivalent of heat.

Now let us consider an isothermal compression. When a gas is compressed, work is done on it by the compressing agent. To keep its temperature constant, therefore, heat must be withdrawn from the gas, to prevent the work done from increasing its internal energy. The gas must again be held in a thin well-conducting vessel, surrounded by a constant-temperature bath; and it must be compressed slowly.

The conditions for an isothermal compression or expansion of a gas are difficult to realize; heat cannot flow through the walls of the vessel unless there is at least a small difference of temperature across them, and therefore the temperature of the gas is bound to rise a little in compression, or to fall a little in expansion.

28. Adiabatic Changes.

Let us now consider a change of volume in which the conditions are at the opposite extreme from isothermal; no heat is allowed to enter or leave the gas.

An expansion or contraction in which *no heat* enters or leaves the gas is called an *adiabatic expansion or contraction.* In an adiabatic expansion, the external work is done wholly at the expense of the internal energy of the gas, and the gas therefore cools. In an adiabatic compression, all the work done on the gas by the compressing agent appears as an increase in its internal energy and therefore as a rise in its temperature.

The curve relating pressure and volume for a given mass of a given gas for adiabatic changes is called an "adiabatic". In Fig. 158, the heavy curve is an adiabatic for 1 gm. of air; it is steeper, at any point, than the isothermal through that point. The curve AB is the isothermal for the temperature $T_0 = 373$ °K., which cuts the adiabatic at the point $p_0 V_0$. If the gas is adiabatically compressed from V_0 to V_1, its

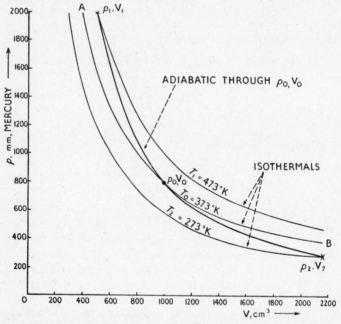

FIG. 158. Relationship between adiabatic and isothermals.

temperature rises to some value T_1. Its representative point p_1, V_1 now lies on the isothermal for T_1, since $p_1 V_1 = RT_1$. Similarly, if the gas is expanded adiabatically to V_2, it cools to T_2 and its representative point p_2, V_2 lies on the isothermal for T_2. Thus the adiabatic through any point—such as p_0, V_0—is steeper than the isothermal. We will find its equation shortly.

The condition for an adiabatic change is that no heat must enter or leave the gas. The gas must therefore be held in a thick-walled, badly conducting vessel; and the change of volume must take place rapidly, to give as little time as possible for heat to escape. However, in a rapid compression, for example, eddies may be formed, so that some of the work done appears as kinetic energy of the gas in bulk, instead of as random kinetic energy of its molecules. All the work done then does not go to increase the internal energy of the gas, and the tempera- ture rise is less than in a truly adiabatic compression. If the com- pression is made slowly, then more heat leaks out, since no vessel has perfectly insulating walls.

Perfectly adiabatic changes are therefore impossible; and so, we have seen, are perfectly isothermal ones. Any practical expansion or compression of a gas must lie between isothermal and adiabatic. It may lie anywhere between them, but if it approximates to isothermal, the curve representing it will always be a little steeper than the ideal (Fig. 159); if it approximates to adiabatic, the curve representing it will never be quite as steep as the ideal.

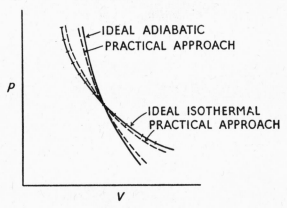

Fig. 159. Ideal and real p-V curves for a gas.

29. Equation of an Adiabatic.

Before considering adiabatic changes in particular, let us first consider a change of volume and temperature which takes place in an arbitrary manner. For simplicity, we consider unit mass of the gas, and we suppose that its volume expands from V to $V + \delta V$, and that an amount of heat δQ is supplied to it. In general, the internal energy of the gas will increase by an amount δU. And the gas will do an amount of external work equal to $p\delta V$, where p is its pressure. The mechanical equivalent of the heat supplied is equal to the increase in internal energy, plus the external work done:

$$J\delta Q = \delta U + p\delta V \quad . \quad . \quad . \quad . \quad (26)$$

The increase in internal energy represents a temperature rise, δT. We have seen already that the internal energy is independent of the volume, and is related to the temperature by the specific heat at constant volume, c_V (p. 243). Therefore

$$\delta U = Jc_V\delta T.$$

Equation (26) becomes $\quad J\delta Q = Jc_V\delta T + p\delta V,$

or $\qquad\qquad\qquad\qquad \delta Q = c_V\delta T + \dfrac{p\delta V}{J}$ . . . . . . (27)

Equation (27) is the fundamental equation for any change in the state of unit mass of a gas.

For an isothermal change, $\delta T = 0$, and $\delta Q = p\delta V/J$.

For an adiabatic change, $\delta Q = 0$ and therefore

$$c_V\delta T + \frac{p\delta V}{J} = 0 \qquad . \quad . \quad . \quad . \quad . \quad . \quad (28)$$

To eliminate δT we use the general equation, relating pressure, volume and temperature:
$$pV = RT,$$

where R is the gas constant for unit mass. Since both pressure and volume may change, when we differentiate this to find δT we must write
$$p\delta V + V\delta p = R\delta T,$$

whence $\qquad\qquad\qquad\qquad \delta T = \dfrac{p\delta V + V\delta p}{R}.$

Therefore, by equation (28),

$$c_V\frac{p\delta V + V\delta p}{R} + \frac{p\delta V}{J} = 0$$

or $\qquad\qquad\qquad c_V(p\delta V + V\delta p) + \dfrac{R}{J}p\delta V = 0.$

Now we have seen, on p. 62, that

$$\frac{R}{J} = c_p - c_V;$$

therefore $\qquad\qquad c_V(p\delta V + V\delta p) + (c_p - c_V)p\delta V = 0.$

Hence $\qquad\qquad\qquad c_V V\delta p + c_p p\delta V = 0$

or $\qquad\qquad\qquad V\delta p + \dfrac{c_p}{c_V}p\delta V = 0$

or $\qquad\qquad V\delta p + \gamma p\delta V = 0 \left(\text{where } \gamma = \dfrac{c_p}{c_V}\right).$

Therefore $\qquad\qquad\qquad \dfrac{\delta p}{p} + \gamma\dfrac{\delta V}{V} = 0.$

Integrating, we find $\qquad \displaystyle\int\dfrac{dp}{p} + \gamma\int\dfrac{dV}{V} = 0$

or $\qquad\qquad\qquad \log_e p + \gamma\log_e V = A,$

where A is a constant.

Therefore, $\qquad\qquad\qquad pV^\gamma = C,$

where C is also a constant. This is the equation of an adiabatic; the value of C can be found from the initial pressure and volume of the gas.

If we have a mass M of the gas, its volume at any temperature and pressure is
$$V = MV,$$

where V is the volume of unit mass at the same temperature and pressure. Therefore for any mass of gas, the equation of an adiabatic change is

$$pV^\gamma = \text{constant} \qquad . \quad . \quad . \quad . \quad . \quad . \quad (29)$$

30. Equation for Temperature Change in an Adiabatic.

If we wish to introduce the temperature, T, into equation (29), we use the general gas equation

$$pV = RT.$$

Thus
$$p = \frac{RT}{V}$$

and
$$pV^{\gamma} = \frac{RT}{V} \cdot V^{\gamma} = RTV^{\gamma-1}.$$

Thus equation (29) becomes

$$RTV^{\gamma-1} = \text{constant},$$

and since R is a constant for a given mass of gas, the equation for an adiabatic temperature change becomes

$$TV^{\gamma-1} = \text{constant}.$$

31. Measurement of γ.

In books on Sound, it is shown that sound waves are propagated through a gas by rapid compressions and rarefactions; these changes in pressure and volume are adiabatic. In consequence, the velocity of sound in a gas depends upon the ratio of the principal specific heats of the gas, γ; and the value of γ can be found from measurements of the velocity of sound in the gas. This is the most convenient way of measuring γ. (See p. 686).

A direct measurement of γ can be made by the method of Clément and Désormes (1819). A large vessel—such as a carboy—contains the gas, which in a teaching experiment is usually air (Fig. 160). The

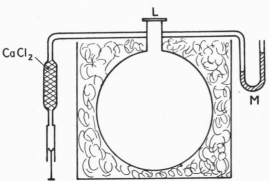

Fig. 160. Clément and Désormes experiment.

carboy is well lagged to minimize the exchange of heat with its surroundings. It is attached to a manometer M, and, via a drying-tube, to a bicycle pump. Its mouth has a large and well-fitting, flap-like, lid, L. Air is blown in until its pressure is a little above atmospheric, and time is allowed for the gas to settle down to room temperature. When it has done so the manometer reading becomes steady, and the pressure p_1 of the gas is recorded. The flap-valve is now sharply opened and closed. The gas makes an adiabatic expansion, and its pressure p_2 is immediately read. With the flap still closed, the gas is then left; it gradually returns to room temperature, absolute temperature T_1, at constant volume, and its pressure rises to p_3.

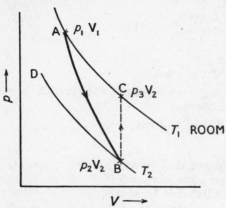

These changes are shown in Fig. 161. Since some gas escapes in the expansion, we must consider unit mass. Its state at the start of the experiment is represented by the point A on the isothermal for T_1, its volume being V_1. B represents the end of the adiabatic, when

FIG. 161. Theory of Clément and Désormes.

the gas has cooled to T_2, and expanded to V_2 per unit mass. DB is the isothermal for T_2. BC represents the return to room temperature. For the adiabatic AB, we have

$$p_1V_1{}^\gamma = p_2V_2{}^\gamma,$$

or

$$\frac{p_1}{p_2} = \left(\frac{V_2}{V_1}\right)^\gamma \qquad \cdots \cdots \quad (29)$$

After the gas has returned to room temperature, its representative point C lies on the same isothermal as A; therefore

$$p_3V_2 = p_1V_1,$$

or

$$\frac{p_1}{p_3} = \frac{V_2}{V_1}.$$

From equation (29), therefore,

$$\frac{p_1}{p_2} = \left(\frac{p_1}{p_3}\right)^\gamma$$

whence

$$\log_e p_1 - \log_e p_2 = \gamma(\log_e p_1 - \log_e p_3)$$

and

$$\gamma = \frac{\log_e p_1 - \log_e p_2}{\log_e p_1 - \log_e p_3}.$$

If h_1 is the difference in levels of M corresponding to the pressure p_1, and h_2 is the final difference in levels, corresponding to the pressure

p_3, it can be shown that, to a good approximation, the formula for γ reduces to

$$\gamma = \frac{h_1}{h_1 - h_2}.$$

A light oil is used in the manometer M.

VACUUM PUMPS AND GAUGES

32. The Filter Pump.

The simplest pump for evacuating a vessel is the filter pump, so-called because it is used for speeding-up filtration (Fig. 162). It consists of a nozzle N surrounded by a chamber C; water rushes from the nozzle and out of the chamber at the bottom. The layer of air around the jet is dragged along with it, and carried out of the chamber. The lowest pressure which this pump can produce is the saturation vapour-pressure of water, about 15 mm. mercury at 18° C. (Chapter XIV). It cannot produce what we would nowadays call a "good vacuum".

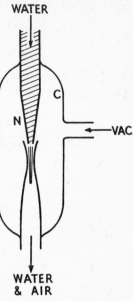

FIG. 162.   Filter pump.

33. The Piston Pump.

A piston-type air pump is similar to the common water pump, but more accurately made. Its plunger has a greased leather washer, W in Fig. 163, and its valves F_1 and F_2 are flaps of oiled silk.

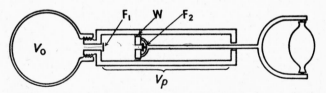

FIG. 163. Piston-type vacuum pump.

To develop a simple theory of the pump, we first assume that, when the piston is pushed right in, there is no space between it and the bottom of the barrel. We suppose that the pump is connected to a vessel of volume V_0, that the piston displaces a volume V_P, and that the pressure in the vessel is p_0 when the piston is right in, at the start of the evacuation. When the piston is pulled right out, the volume of the air originally in the vessel increases to $V_0 + V_P$. Since the action is slow, we may assume that the expansion is isothermal; the pressure p_1 after expansion is therefore given by

$$p_1(V_0 + V_P) = p_0 V_0,$$

whence

$$p_1 = \left(\frac{V_0}{V_0 + V_P}\right) p_0.$$

When the piston is pushed in again, the valve F_1 closes, and the air in the vessel remains at the pressure p_1. The second out-stroke then reduces the pressure to

$$p_2 = \left(\frac{V_0}{V_0 + V_P}\right) p_1 = \left(\frac{V_0}{V_0 + V_P}\right)^2 p_0.$$

Similarly, after n strokes, the pressure is reduced to

$$p_n = \left(\frac{V_0}{V_0 + V_P}\right)^n p_0.$$

According to this theory, the final pressure tends to zero as the number of strokes tends to infinity. In practice, however, a pump has a limiting pressure. This is due to the fact that the piston can never in practice be brought right down to the valve F_1, so that there is a residual volume, or dead-space, v, between the piston and the bottom of the barrel. Air can escape through the valve F_2 only when the pressure in the volume v is greater than atmospheric. And air can pass from the vessel through F_1 only when the pressure in the barrel is less than the pressure in the vessel. Thus the limiting pressure, p_∞, is the pressure which v cm.³ of gas, at atmospheric pressure, exert when expanded to V_P cm.³ That is to say

$$p_\infty V_P = p_{atmos.}\, v,$$

whence

$$p_\infty = \frac{v}{V_P}\, p_{atmos}$$

The ratio v/V_P may be about $1/1,000$, so that p_∞ is about 1 mm. mercury. Piston pumps of more elaborate designs can give better vacua than this, about 0·01 mm. mercury; they have all been made obsolete, however, by the rotary pump.

34. Rotary Pumps.

Fig. 164 illustrates one form of rotary vacuum pump. It consists of a rotor, R, which turns eccentrically in a casing, C, being a close fit at the ends and along the line A. The rotor carries two scraping blades B_1, B_2, separated by a strong spring. The vessel to be avacuated is connected to the inlet port I, and the outlet port O is fitted with a valve N. As the rotor turns, the volume V_1 increases, so that air expands from the vessel into the pump. When the blades are in the positions shown, the air in the space V_2 is being compressed; when its pressure rises to atmospheric, the valve N opens, and the air passes out through O. As the blade B_2 crosses the seat of the valve N, the valve closes because the air in V_3 is below atmospheric pressure. Thus atmospheric air cannot blow back into the pump. The lines of contact,

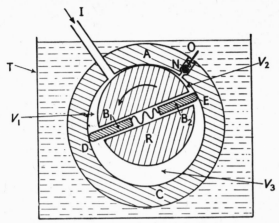

FIG. 164. Rotary vacuum pump.

A, D, E are made airtight by a film of oil. All the working parts of the pump are enclosed in a tank T containing oil. When the pump is at rest, the oil seeps back through the outlet valve and fills the working space; but the first revolutions of the pump sweep out the excess oil, and leave just the necessary film over the metal surfaces.

A single rotary pump will give an ultimate pressure of about 0·01 mm. mercury. Very often two pumps are housed in the same tank of oil, and driven off the same shaft; they are connected in cascade, and may give an ultimate pressure of less than 0·001 mm. mercury.

35. The MacLeod Gauge.

The MacLeod Gauge is a gauge used for measuring pressures below a few mm. mercury; these are pressures which cannot be measured accurately on a U-tube manometer. It consists of a bulb B, connected to a mercury reservoir M and terminated in a capillary tube T (Fig. 165 (a)); just below the bulb a branch-tube, P, leads to the vacuum system under test. It also carries a branch-tube, D, which is a capillary of the same bore as T. A millimetre scale, S, lies underneath T and D.

To measure the pressure in a vacuum system, the reservoir M is lowered until the mercury falls below the branch-point C. The air in B is then at the unknown pressure, p. The reservoir is now slowly raised. As soon as the mercury closes the branch at C, the air in B starts to be compressed. M is raised until the mercury in B just reaches the foot of the capillary T. The height h of the mercury in D, above that in B, is then measured. The purpose of having equal bores for T and D is to equalize surface tension effects in each.

If the pressure p is expressed in mm. mercury then the pressure of the air trapped in T is $p + h$. The volume of this air is the volume v

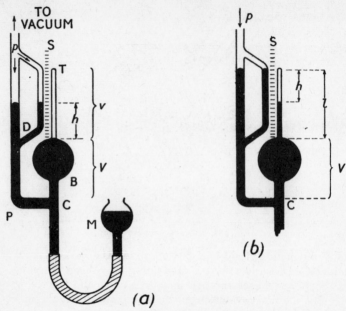

Fig. 165. MacLeod gauge.

of the capillary T. At the moment when the mercury passed the point C, this air had the pressure p, and the volume $V + v$, where V is the volume between C and the base of T. The compression is slow enough to be isothermal, so that

$$p(V + v) = (p + h)v.$$

Hence

$$pV = hv,$$

and

$$p = \frac{v}{V}h.$$

Another way of using the gauge is to raise the reservoir M until the mercury in D is level with the top of T (Fig. 165 (b)). Then if s is the cross-section of T, the volume of trapped air is hs. And if l is the whole length of T, its volume is ls. Therefore, as before,

$$p(V + ls) = (p + h)hs,$$

or

$$p(V + ls - hs) = h^2s,$$

whence

$$p = \frac{h^2s}{V + (l - h)s}.$$

The term $(l - h)s$ in the denominator is usually negligible compared with V, so that
$$p \simeq \frac{h^2 s}{V}.$$

Because p is proportional to h^2, the gauge can cover a wider range of pressures when it is used in this way, than when it is used in the way first described. But for the same reason it is less accurate. In practice the second way is generally chosen, and the scale S is calibrated to read the pressure p directly.

EXAMPLES

1. Assuming that the density of a gas is 1·775 gm. per litre at 27° C. and 10^6 dynes per sq. cm. pressure, and that its specific heat at constant pressure is 0·846 joules per gm. per deg. C., find the ratio of its specific heat at constant pressure to that at constant volume. Explain the theory underlying your calculation, and point out any significance to be attached to the result. (*L.*)

The gas constant per gramme of the gas is given by
$$R = \frac{pV}{T} = \frac{10^6 \times 1{,}000}{1 \cdot 775 \times 300} \text{ ergs per gm. per deg. C.,}$$

since $V = 1{,}000/1 \cdot 775$, $T = (273 + 27)$ °K.

$$\therefore R = \frac{10^6 \times 1{,}000}{10^7 \times 1 \cdot 775 \times 300} \text{ } joules \text{ per gm. per deg. C.}$$

Now * $c_p - c_v = R$

$$\therefore 0 \cdot 846 - c_v = \frac{10^6 \times 1{,}000}{10^7 \times 1 \cdot 775 \times 300} = 0 \cdot 188$$

$$\therefore c_v = 0 \cdot 846 - 0 \cdot 188 = 0 \cdot 658 \text{ joules per gm. per deg. C.}$$

$$\therefore \gamma = \frac{c_v}{c_p} = \frac{0 \cdot 846}{0 \cdot 658} = 1 \cdot 29.$$

This value for γ suggests that the gas is polyatomic (see p. 63).

* *Note.* Since c_p is expressed in joules per gm per. deg. C., and not in calories per gm. per. deg. C., we do not require here to use the value for the mechanical equivalent of heat J.

2. An ideal gas at 17° C. has a pressure of 76 cm. mercury, and is compressed (i) isothermally, (ii) adiabatically until its volume is halved. Calculate in each case the final pressure and temperature of the gas, assuming $c_p = 0 \cdot 42$, $c_v = 0 \cdot 30$ cal. per gm. per deg. C.

(i) Isothermally, $pV = $ constant.

$$\therefore p \times \frac{V}{2} = 76 \times V$$

$$\therefore p = 152 \text{ cm. mercury.}$$

The temperature is constant at 17° C.

(ii) Adiabatically, $pV^\gamma = $ constant, and $\gamma = 0 \cdot 42/0 \cdot 30 = 1 \cdot 40$.

$$\therefore p \times \left(\frac{V}{2}\right)^{1 \cdot 4} = 76 \times V^{1 \cdot 4}$$

$$\therefore p = 76 \times 2^{1 \cdot 4} = 201 \text{ cm. mercury.}$$

Since $TV^{\gamma-1} = \text{constant}$,

$$\therefore\ T \times \left(\frac{V}{2}\right)^{0 \cdot 4} = (273 + 17) \times V^{0 \cdot 4}$$

$$\therefore\ T = 290 \times 2^{0 \cdot 4} = 383\ °\text{K.}$$

$$\therefore\ \text{temperature} = 110°\ \text{C.}$$

3. State the laws of gases usually associated with the names of Boyle, Charles, Dalton and Graham. Two gas containers with volumes of 100 cm.³ and 1,000 cm.³ respectively are connected by a tube of negligible volume, and contain air at a pressure of 1,000 mm. mercury. If the temperature of both vessels is originally 0° C., how much air will pass through the connecting tube when the temperature of the smaller is raised to 100° C.? Give your answer in cm.³ measured at 0° C. and 760 mm. mercury. (*L.*)

First part. Boyle, Charles, Dalton, see above; Graham, see later.

Second part. The pressure is 1,000 mm. mercury when the temperature is 0 °C. (273 °K.). Let the density of air under these conditions be ρ_1. Let the volumes of the large and small vessels be V and V^1; then the mass of air in the two vessels is

$$M = (V + V^1)\rho_1 = (1,000 + 100)\rho_1 = 1,100\ \rho_1 \qquad . \quad . \quad \text{(i)}$$

When the smaller vessel is heated, the pressure throughout the system rises to p, say. Let ρ_2 be the density of the air in the smaller vessel; then, by equation (9), p. 228:

$$\frac{p}{\rho_2} = R \times 373;\ \frac{1,000}{\rho_1} = R \times 273 \quad . \quad . \quad . \quad . \quad \text{(ii)}$$

$$\therefore\ \frac{\rho_2}{\rho_1} = \frac{273}{373} \times \frac{p}{1,000}.$$

$$\therefore\ \rho_2 = \frac{273}{373} \times \frac{p}{1,000}\ \rho_1.$$

In the larger vessel, the temperature of the air does not change; therefore the density of the air in the larger vessel, ρ_3, is

$$\rho_3 = \frac{p}{1,000}\ \rho_1.$$

The total mass of air, which is unchanged, is therefore

$$M = V\rho_3 + V^1\rho_2 = 1,000\ \rho_3 + 100\ \rho_2$$

$$= 1,000\ \frac{p\rho_1}{1,000} + 100\ \frac{273}{373}\ \frac{p\rho_1}{1,000}$$

$$= 1 + \left(\frac{273}{3,730}\right)p\rho_1.$$

Hence, by equation (i),

$$1,100\ \rho_1 = \left(1 + \frac{273}{3,730}\right)p\rho_1,$$

and

$$p = \frac{3,730 \times 1,100}{4003} = 1,025\ \text{mm. mercury.}$$

The mass which flows out of the smaller vessel is

$$m = V^1(\rho_1 - \rho_2) = 100\ \rho_1\left(1 - \frac{\rho_2}{\rho_1}\right)$$

$$= 100\ \rho_1\left(1 - \frac{273}{373} \times \frac{p}{1,000}\right)$$

$$m = 100\ \rho_1\left(1 - \frac{273}{373} \times \frac{1,025}{1,000}\right) \quad \cdots \cdots \text{(iii)}$$

The volume of this mass, *at* $0°$ *C. and* 760 *mm. mercury,* is

$$V = \frac{m}{\rho_4},$$

where ρ_4 is the density of air at this temperature and pressure.

From the equation of state,

$$\frac{760}{\rho_4} = R \times 273;$$

therefore

$$\frac{\rho_1}{\rho_4} = \frac{1,000}{760},$$

or

$$\frac{1}{\rho_4} = \frac{100}{76\rho_1}.$$

Hence, by (iii), $\quad V = \dfrac{m}{\rho_4} = \dfrac{100 \times 100}{76}\left(1 - \dfrac{273}{373} \times \dfrac{1,025}{1,000}\right)$

$$= 33 \text{ cm.}^3$$

4. Distinguish between *isothermal* and *adiabatic* changes. Show that for an ideal gas the curves relating pressure and volume for an adiabatic change have a greater slope than those for an isothermal change, at the same pressure.

A quantity of oxygen is compressed isothermally until its pressure is doubled. It is then allowed to expand adiabatically until its original volume is restored. Find the final pressure in terms of the initial pressure. (The ratio of the principal specific heats of oxygen is to be taken at $1\cdot40$.) (*L.*)

First part. An isothermal change is one made at constant temperature; an adiabatic change is one made at constant heat, that is, no heat enters or leaves the system concerned.

For an isothermal change, $pV = \kappa$, or $p = \kappa/V$. By differentiation, the slope, $dp/dv, = -\kappa/V^2 = -pV/V^2 = -p/V$.

For an adiabatic change, $pV^\gamma = c$, or $p = c/V^\gamma$. By differentiation, we find the slope, $dp/dv, = -\gamma p/V$.

$$\therefore \text{ratio of adiabatic slope to isothermal slope} = \gamma.$$

Since γ is always greater than 1, the adiabatic slope is greater than the isothermal slope.

Second part. Let p_0, $V_0 =$ the original pressure and volume of the oxygen.

Since $pV =$ constant for an isothermal change,

$$\therefore \text{ new volume} = \frac{V_0}{2} \text{ when new pressure is } 2p_0.$$

Suppose the gas expands adiabatically to its volume V_0, when the pressure is p.

Then
$$p \times V_0^{1\cdot4} = 2p_0 \times \left(\frac{V_0}{2}\right)^{1\cdot4}$$

$$\therefore p = 2p_0 \times \left(\frac{1}{2}\right)^{1\cdot4} = 0\cdot8\,p_0.$$

5. Derive an expression for the difference between the principal specific heats of an ideal gas and discuss the significance of the ratio of these two specific heats for real gases.

Assuming that the ratio of the principal specific heats of hydrogen is 1·41 and that its density at s.t.p. is 0·0900 gm. litre⁻¹, find a value for its specific heat at constant volume in joules gm.⁻¹ deg.⁻¹ C.

What explanation can you suggest for the small difference between the principal specific heats of a solid? (Standard atmospheric pressure = 1·013 × 10⁶ dynes cm.⁻²) (*N.*)

First part. The expression required is $c_p - c_V = R/J$, discussed on p. 243.

The ratio, γ, of these two specific heats $= 1 + \dfrac{2}{n}$ on the kinetic theory of gases, where n is the number of degrees of freedom of the molecules. For a monatomic gas $n = 3$, so that $\gamma = 1\cdot66$; for a diatomic gas $n = 5$, so that $\gamma = 1\cdot4$; for triatomic gases γ is less than 1·4, e.g. 1·29. Thus γ gives a measure of the number of atoms in the molecule of the gas.

Second part. $c_p - c_V = R$, where R is in *joules* per gm. per deg. if c_p, c_V are in the same units. Since 0·09 gm. occupies 1,000 c.c., then, from $pV = RT$,

$$R = \frac{pV}{T} = \frac{(1\cdot013 \times 10^6) \times 1,000}{273 \times 0\cdot09} \ ergs \ \text{per gm. per deg.}$$

$$= \frac{1\cdot013 \times 10^6 \times 1,000}{273 \times 10^7 \times 0\cdot09} \ joules \ \text{per gm. per deg.}$$

$$= 4\cdot12 \ \text{joules per gm. per deg.}$$

$$\therefore c_p - c_V = 4\cdot12 \quad . \quad . \quad . \quad . \quad . \quad . \quad . \quad . \quad \textbf{(i)}$$

But
$$\frac{c_p}{c_V} = 1\cdot41 \quad . \quad . \quad . \quad . \quad . \quad . \quad . \quad . \quad . \quad \textbf{(ii)}$$

$$\therefore c_p = 1\cdot41\,c_V. \ \text{Substituting for } c_p \text{ in (i)},$$

$$\therefore 1\cdot41\,c_V - c_V = 4\cdot12 = 0\cdot41\,c_V.$$

$$\therefore c_V = \frac{4\cdot12}{0\cdot41} = 10\cdot5.$$

Third part. The difference in the specific heats of a solid is proportional to the external work done in expansion. But the expansion of a solid is small. Consequently the difference in specific heats of the solid is small.

EXERCISES XII

Gas Laws : Specific Heat of Gases.

1. State Boyle's law and Charles' law and show how they may be combined to give the equation of state of an ideal gas.

Two glass bulbs of equal volume are joined by a narrow tube and are filled with a gas at s.t.p. When one bulb is kept in melting ice and the other is placed in a hot bath, the new pressure is 87·76 cm. mercury. Calculate the temperature of the bath. (*L.*)

2. Define *specific heat* and *latent heat of evaporation*.

State the principle of the steam-calorimeter method of measuring specific heats, and describe how it may be employed in the accurate determination of the specific heat of (i) a gas at constant volume, and (ii) a solid. (*L.*)

3. Describe an experiment to determine the specific heat of a gas at constant volume.

The specific heat of hydrogen at constant pressure is 3·41 cal. gm.$^{-1}$ deg.$^{-1}$ C., and the ratio of the specific heat at constant pressure to that at constant volume is 1·41. Obtain a value for the mechanical equivalent of heat in ergs per calorie, deriving the expression used in the calculation. Assume that the density of hydrogen at s.t.p. is 0·09 gm. per litre. State and discuss any assumption made in the theoretical treatment. (*L.*)

4. State the laws obeyed by a perfect gas. Describe how the variation of pressure with temperature may be investigated experimentally, and how the observations lead to the conception of an absolute zero of temperature.

Two equal containers are joined by a connecting pipe, and are filled with dry air at 15° C. and atmospheric pressure. If one container is heated to 100° C., by how much will the pressure in the system rise? (*O. & C.*)

5. State the conditions under which the perfect gas obeys
(*a*) the relation $pv = RT$,
(*b*) the relation $pv^\gamma = $ constant.

100 c.c. of air at 0°C. and 760 mm. pressure are compressed adiabatically to 20 c.c. Find
(*a*) the new pressure,
(*b*) the new temperature,
(*c*) the work done in compression.
(Assume $\gamma = 1·4$.) (*C. Schol.*)

6. Define the two principal specific heats of a gas, and derive an expression for the difference between them in the case of a perfect gas. Describe in detail an accurate method of determining the specific heat of a gas at constant volume.

The specific heats of hydrogen at constant pressure and at constant volume are respectively 3·405 and 2·420 cal. per gm. The volume of 1 gm. of hydrogen at 273° K. and 10^6 dynes per sq. cm. is 11·2 litres. Calculate a value for the mechanical equivalent of heat. (*O. & C.*)

7. Boyle's law is expressed by the equation $pV = $ constant; upon what quantities does the constant depend? An expansible balloon filled with air floats on the surface of a lake with two-thirds of its volume submerged. How deep must it be sunk in the water so that it is just in equilibrium, neither sinking further, nor rising? It is assumed that the temperature of the water is constant and that the height of the water barometer is 30 ft. (*L.*)

8. State the laws connecting the pressure, volume, and temperature of gases. A barometer tube 90 cm. long contains some air above the mercury. The reading is 74·5 cm. when the true pressure is 76 cm. and the temperature 15° C. If the reading is observed to be 75·8 cm. on a day when the temperature is 5° C., what is the true pressure? (*O. & C.*)

9. Explain why a gas can have a range of specific heats. Under what conditions can the specific heat be zero?

A mass of 0·5 gm. of hydrogen at 0° C. is heated to 50° C. at constant pressure and is then cooled to 0° C. at constant volume. Compare the amount of heat absorbed with that which would have been absorbed if the change from the initial to the final state had been made isothermally.

Why is there a difference? (For hydrogen $c_p = 2\cdot4$ cal./gm./°C.; $R = 2\cdot0$ cal./°C./gm. mol.; $\log_e 10 = 2\cdot303$.) (*C. Schol.*)

10. Define what is meant by the specific heat of a gas at (*a*) constant volume, and (*b*) constant pressure. Why do they differ in value for the same gas? Describe an experiment for determining *one* of them.

Explain why air becomes hot when suddenly compressed, and why it cools on rapid expansion into a vacuum. (*C.*)

Kinetic Theory of Gases.

11. What is the kinetic theory of gases? Explain how it accounts for the temperature and pressure of a gas.

Show how the perfect-gas laws can be deduced from the kinetic theory, stating clearly the assumptions that have to be made about the properties of molecules.

Calculate the root mean square velocity of the hydrogen molecule at normal temperature and pressure. (Density of hydrogen at N.T.P. = 9×10^{-5} gm./c.c.; density of mercury = $13\cdot6$ gm./c.c.) (*C. Schol.*)

12. State the principal postulates for the elementary kinetic theory of gases. Give an account of important phenomena associated with real gases which are not accounted for by the elementary kinetic theory. Indicate how the theory may be modified to give a qualitative explanation of the properties of real gases. (*N. Schol.*)

13. Using the kinetic theory give qualitative explanations of the following phenomena: (*a*) the pressure exerted by a gas, (*b*) evaporation, (*c*) diffusion in gases.

Derive an expression for the mean square of the velocities of the molecules of a gas in terms of its density and pressure. Point out the bearing of the result on the diffusion of gases through partitions containing very fine pores. (*N.*)

14. Give a brief account of the simple kinetic theory of gases and show how it accounts for Boyle's law.

Explain what is meant by the universal gas constant, and show how it is related to the gas constant per gram of gas. Given that oxygen, molecular weight 32, has a density of $1\cdot429$ gm. litre^{-1} at s.t.p., obtain a value for the universal gas constant. (*L.*)

15. Give an account of the kinetic theory of matter referring in particular to (*a*) the distinction between solids, liquids and gases, (*b*) the differences between real gases and an ideal gas, (*c*) diffusion. (*N. Schol.*)

16. Use the kinetic theory to derive an expression for the pressure of a gas, pointing out any assumptions made.

Calculate the root mean square velocity of oxygen molecules at 17° C. and 745 mm. of mercury pressure if the density of oxygen at s.t.p. is $0\cdot00143$ gm. per c.c. and that of mercury is $13\cdot6$ gm. per c.c. (*N.*)

17. Without deriving any formulæ, use the kinetic theory of gases to explain (*a*) how a gas exerts a pressure, (*b*) why the temperature of a gas rises when the gas is compressed, (*c*) what happens when a quantity of liquid is introduced into a closed vessel. How are the differences in the behaviour of real and ideal gases explained by the kinetic theory? If there are $2\cdot7 \times 10^{19}$ molecules in a cubic centimetre of gas at 0° C. and 76 cm. of mercury pressure, what is the number per cubic centimetre (i) at 0° C. and 10^{-6} mm. pressure, (ii) at 39° C. and 10^{-6} mm. pressure? (*N.*)

18. Describe, with diagrams, the construction and mode of action of a pump that will reduce the pressure of the air in a vessel to $0\cdot001$ mm. of mercury. How are pressures of this order of magnitude measured? A piston pump of effective volume 200 c.c. is used to exhaust a vessel of volume 1 litre. How many complete strokes will be required to reduce the pressure of the air in the vessel to one-hundredth of its initial value? (Neglect the volume of the connecting tubes, etc., and assume that the temperature remains constant.) (*O. & C.*)

19. Explain, with the aid of suitable diagrams, the construction and principle of action of a bicycle pump and a tyre valve. The bottom of a bicycle pump was closed and the pump was lowered into deep water. The pump handle moved in so that, at the deepest point reached, the length of the enclosed air column was reduced to three-eighths of its former value. To what depth was the pump lowered into the water? Assume that the barometric pressure was 29·7 in. of mercury, and that the specific gravity of mercury is 13·6. (*N.*)

20. State the *fundamental* postulates on which the kinetic theory of gases is based, and show qualitatively how they account for the pressure exerted by a gas on the walls of the vessel containing it.

Show further, listing any additional assumptions which are necessary, that if ϱ is the density of a gas whose molecular weight is M, $\varrho = Mp/RT$, where p is the pressure, T is the absolute temperature, and R is the gas constant. (*O. & C.*)

21. Derive an expression for the pressure of an ideal gas in terms of the density and the root mean square velocity of the molecules. State clearly the assumptions made.

Given a short account of the experimental work on the deviation of gases from Boyle's law, illustrating your answer by means of suitable graphs. (*O. & C.*)

22. Explain the following in terms of the simple kinetic theory without mathematical treatment: (*a*) A gas fills any container in which it is placed and exerts a pressure on the walls of the container; (*b*) the pressure of a gas rises if its temperature is increased without the mass and volume being changed; (*c*) the temperature of a gas rises if it is compressed in a vessel from which heat cannot escape; (*d*) the pressure in an oxygen cylinder falls continuously as the gas is taken from it, while the pressure in a cylinder containing chlorine remains constant until very nearly all the chlorine has been used. The contents of the cylinder are kept at room temperature in both cases. (Critical temperature of chlorine = 146°C.) (*C.*)

CHAPTER XIII

THERMAL EXPANSION

In this chapter we shall discuss the thermal expansion of solids and liquids.

SOLIDS

1. Linear Expansion.

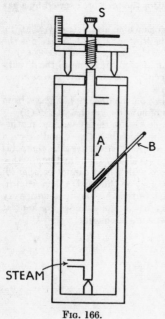

Fig. 166.

Most solids increase in length when they are warmed. Fig. 166 shows a simple apparatus with which we can measure the linear expansion of a metal tube A. We first measure the length of the tube, l_1, at room temperature, θ_1; then we screw the spherometer S against the end of the tube and take its reading, S_1. We next heat the tube by passing steam through it. At intervals we re-adjust the spherometer; when its reading becomes constant, the temperature of the rod is steady. We measure the temperature θ_2 on the thermometer B, and take the new reading of the spherometer, S_2. The expansion of the tube is

$$e = S_2 - S_1.$$

The increase in length, λ, of unit length of the material for one degree temperature rise is then given by

$$\lambda = \frac{\text{expansion}}{\text{original length} \times \text{temperature rise}} = \frac{e}{l_1(\theta_2 - \theta_1)}.$$

The quantity λ is called the *mean coefficient of linear expansion* of the metal, over the range θ_1 to θ_2. If this range is not too great—say less than $100°$ C.—the coefficient λ may, to a first approximation, be taken as constant.

The coefficient of linear expansion of a solid, like the pressure and volume coefficients of a gas, has the unit °C.$^{-1}$ (or °F.$^{-1}$); its dimensions are

$$[\lambda] = \frac{[\text{length}]}{[\text{length}] \times [\text{temp.}]} = [\text{temp.}]^{-1}.$$

MEAN COEFFICIENTS OF LINEAR EXPANSION
(Near room temperature)

Substance	λ, °C.$^{-1}$	Substance	λ, °C.$^{-1}$
	$\times 10^{-6}$		$\times 10^{-6}$
Copper . .	17	Bakelite . .	22
Iron . . .	12	Brick . . .	9·5
Brass . . .	19	Glass (soda) . .	8·5
Nickel . . .	13	Quartz (fused)	0·42
Platinum . .	9	(0–30° C.)	
Invar . . .	c. 0·1	Pine—across grain .	c. 0·34
(36% nickel-steel)		Pyrex . . .	3

From the definition of λ, we can estimate the new length of a rod, l_2, at a temperature θ_2 from the equation

$$l_2 = l_1\{1 + \lambda(\theta_2 - \theta_1)\}, \quad \ldots \ldots \quad (1)$$

where l_1 is the length of the rod at the temperature θ_1, and λ is the mean coefficient over a range which includes θ_2 and θ_1.

For accurate work, however, the length of a solid at a temperature θ must be represented by an equation of the form

$$l = l_0(1 + a\theta + b\theta^2 + c\theta^3 + \ldots), \quad \ldots \ldots \quad (2)$$

where l_0 is the length at 0° C., and a, b, c are constants. The constant a is of the same order of magnitude as the mean coefficient λ; the other constants are smaller.

When a solid is subjected to small changes of temperature, about a mean value θ, its coefficient of linear expansion λ_θ in the neighbourhood of θ may be defined by the equation

$$\lambda_\theta = \frac{1}{l}\frac{dl}{d\theta},$$

where l is the length of the bar at the temperature θ. The following table shows how the coefficient varies with temperature.

VALUES OF λ_θ FOR COPPER

θ	-87	0	100	400	600	°C.
λ_θ	14·1	16·1	16·9	19·3	20·9	$\times 10^{-6}$ °C.$^{-1}$

2. Accurate Measurement of Expansion.

An instrument for accurately measuring the length of a bar, at a controlled temperature, is called a *comparator* (Fig. 167). It consists of two microscopes, M_1, M_2, rigidly attached to steel or concrete pillars P_1, P_2. Between the pillars are rails R_1, R_2, carrying water-baths such as B. One of these baths contains the bar under test, X, which has scratches near its ends; the scratches are nominally a metre apart. Another water bath contains a substandard metre. The eye-pieces of the microscopes are fitted with cross-webs carried on micro-meter screws, m_1, m_2.

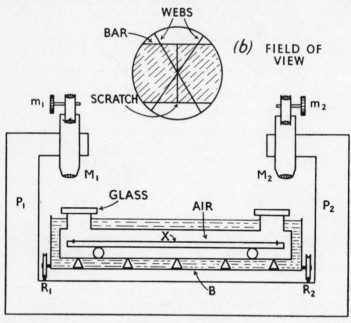

(a) GENERAL VIEW

FIG. 167. The comparator.

First the substandard metre is run under the microscopes, and the temperature of its bath is adjusted to that at which the bar was calibrated (usually about 18° C.).

When the temperature of the bar is steady, the eyepiece webs are adjusted to intersect the scratches on its ends (Fig. 167 (b)), and their micrometers are read. The distance between the cross-webs is then 1 metre.

The substandard is now removed, and the unknown bar put in its place; the temperature of the bar is brought to 0° C. by filling its bath with ice-water. When the temperature of the bar is steady, the eyepiece webs are re-adjusted to intersect the scratches on its ends, and their micrometers are read. If the right-hand web has been shifted x mm. to the right, and the left-hand y mm., also to the right, then the length of the bar at 0° C. is

$$l_0 = 1 \text{ metre} + (x - y) \text{ mm.}$$

The bath is now warmed to say 10° C., and the length of the bar again measured. In this way the length can be measured at small intervals of temperature, and the mean linear coefficient, or the coefficients a, b, c in equation (2), can be determined.

3. Expansion at High Temperatures.

Fig. 168 illustrates the principle of a method for measuring the expansion of a solid at high temperatures. A is a tube of fused silica, having a scale S engraved on the edge of an opening, H, in its side. B is the specimen, and C is a rod of fused silica with a second scale S' engraved on it.

The thermal expansion of fused silica is much less than that of most solids, over a given temperature range, and has been accurately measured by a method depending on optical interference. When the apparatus shown is placed in a high-temperature bath, the rod C rises by an amount equal to the difference in expansion of the specimen, and an equal length of fused silica. Its rise is measured by observing the displacement of the scale S' relative to S through a microscope.

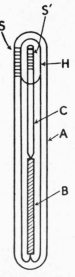

Fig. 168. Apparatus for measuring expansion at high temperatures.

4. Force set up when Expansion is Resisted.

Consider a metal rod between two supports P, which we suppose

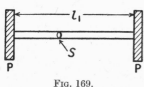

Fig. 169.

are immovable (Fig. 169). Let l_1 be the distance between the supports, and θ_1 the temperature at which the rod just fits between them. If the rod is heated to θ_2, it will try to expand to a greater length l_2, but will not be able to do so. The value of l_2 would be

$$l_2 = l_1\{ 1 + \lambda(\theta_2 - \theta_1)\},$$

and the expansion would be

$$e = l_2 - l_1 = l_1\lambda(\theta_2 - \theta_1),$$

where λ is the mean coefficient of linear expansion of the rod.

The force which opposes the expansion is the force which would compress a bar of natural length l_2 by the amount e. Its magnitude F

depends on the cross-section of the bar, S, and the Young's modulus of its material, E:

$$\frac{F}{S} = E\frac{e}{l_2}.$$

To a very good approximation we may replace l_2 by l_1, because their difference is small compared with either of them. Thus

$$\frac{F}{S} = E\frac{e}{l_1} = E\frac{\lambda l_1(\theta_2 - \theta_1)}{l_1}$$
$$= E\lambda(\theta_2 - \theta_1),$$
$$\therefore\ F = SE\lambda(\theta_2 - \theta_1).$$

For steel, $\lambda = 12 \times 10^{-6}$ per °C. and $E = 2 \times 10^{12}$ dynes per sq. cm. If the temperature difference, $\theta_2 - \theta_1$, is 100° C., then, for a cross-sectional area S of 4 sq. cm.,

$$F = 2 \times 10^{12} \times 12 \times 10^{-6} \times 4 \times 100 \text{ dynes}$$
$$= 96 \times 10^8 \text{ dynes.}$$

On converting to tons we find F is nearly 10 tons wt.

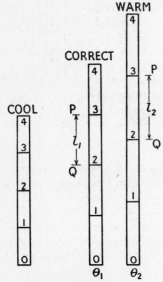

FIG. 170. Expansion of a measuring scale.

5. Expansion of a Measuring Scale.

A scale, such as a metre rule, expands with rise in temperature; its readings, therefore, are correct at one temperature, θ_1 say. When the temperature of the scale is greater than θ_1, the distance between any two of its divisions increases, and its reading is therefore too low (Fig. 170); when the scale is below θ_1, its reading is too high. Let us suppose that, at θ_1, the distance between any two points P, Q, on the scale is l_1 cm. At θ_2 it is

$$l_2 = l_1\{1 + \lambda(\theta_2 - \theta_1)\},$$

where λ is the mean coefficient of linear expansion of the material of this scale. According to the divisions on the scale, however, the distance between P and Q will still be only l_1 cm. Thus

$$\text{true distance at } \theta_2 = \text{scale value} \times \{1 + \lambda(\theta_2 - \theta_1)\} \quad . \quad . \quad (3)$$

6. Expansion of a Hole.

If a sheet of material with a hole in it is warmed, it expands, and the hole expands with it. In Fig. 171, A represents a hole in a plate, and A' represents a plug, of the same material, that fits the hole. If A and A' are at the same temperature, then A' will fit A, whatever the value of that temperature; for we can always imagine A' to have just been cut out, without loss of material. It follows that the

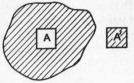

FIG. 171. Expansion of a hole.

expansion of the hole A, in every direction, is the same as the expansion of the *solid* plug A'.

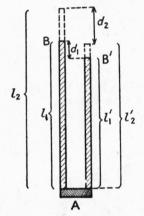

FIG. 172 (a). Differential expansion.

7. Differential Expansion.

The difference in the expansions of different materials is used in practical arrangements discussed shortly. Fig. 172 (a) shows two rods AB, AB', of different metals, rigidly connected at A. If l_1, l'_1, are their lengths at a temperature θ_1, their difference is

$$d_1 = BB' = l_1 - l'_1$$

If λ and λ' are the mean coefficients of linear expansion of the materials of the rods, then the lengths of the rods at θ_2 are

$$l_2 = l_1\{1 + \lambda(\theta_2 - \theta_1)\},$$
$$l'_2 = l'_1\{1 + \lambda'(\theta_2 - \theta_1)\}.$$

The distance between their ends is now

$$d_2 = l_2 - l'_2 = l_1 - l'_1 + (l_1\lambda - l'_1\lambda')(\theta_2 - \theta_1),$$

or $\qquad d_2 = d_1 + (l_1\lambda - l'_1\lambda')(\theta_2 - \theta_1)$ . . . . . . (4)

By a suitable choice of lengths and materials, the distance BB' can be made to vary with temperature in any one of the following ways:

(1) The bar AB' is made of invar, a nickel-steel whose coefficient of linear expansion is very small (p. 269). The point B' then does not move with changes of temperature. In equation (4) we neglect λ', and find: $\qquad d_2 = d_1 + l_1\lambda(\theta_2 - \theta_1).$

Thus the short distance BB' expands by the same amount as the long distance AB. Consequently, the relative expansion of BB' with temperature is much greater than that of a bar of length d_1.

(2) AB is made of invar, so that λ is negligible. The point

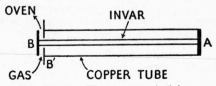

FIG. 172 (b). Thermostat principle.

B then does not move, and the distance BB' *shrinks* rapidly as the temperature rises. This principle is used in the thermostats used to maintain gas ovens at constant temperatures (Fig. 172 (b)).

(3) The lengths and materials are chosen so that

$$\frac{l_1}{l_1'} = \frac{\lambda'}{\lambda},$$

or

$$l_1\lambda = l_1'\lambda'.$$

Then, by equation (4), d_1 or BB' does not change with temperature. This principle is used in compensating clock pendula for temperature changes (p. 276).

8. Bimetal Strip.

Fig. 173 (a) shows two strips of different metals, welded together along AB, called a bimetal strip. The metal M_1 has a greater coefficient of linear expansion than the metal M_2. Therefore, when the strip is heated, M_1 will expand more than M_2, and the strip will curl with M_1 on the outside. The reverse is true when the strip is cooled, as M_1 then shrinks more than M_2 (see Fig. 173 (a)).

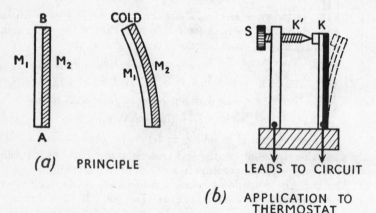

(a) PRINCIPLE

(b) APPLICATION TO THERMOSTAT

Fig. 173. Principle of gas thermostat.

Bi-metal strips are used in electrical thermostats for ovens, irons, laboratories, etc. The strip carries a contact, K in Fig. 173 (b), which presses against another contact K' on the end of an adjusting screw S. When the strip warms, it tends to curl away from K'; the temperature at which the contact is broken can be set by turning the screw. When the contacts open, they switch off the heating current. If the heating current is too great to be controlled by the contacts KK', it is switched off by a relay, which is controlled by the contacts on the bimetal.

Let us now estimate the deflection of a heated bi-metal strip. We suppose that the component strips have the same thickness d, and the same length l at a temperature θ_1 (Fig. 174 (a)). When they are heated, they are distorted, but to a first approximation we may assume that the mid-line of each, shown dotted, has the length which it would naturally have (Fig. 174 (b)). The difference in length of the mid-lines, p, is then the difference in their expansions. At a temperature θ_2,

$$p = l\lambda(\theta_2 - \theta_1) - l\lambda'(\theta_2 - \theta_1)$$
$$= l(\lambda - \lambda')(\theta_2 - \theta_1).$$

The difference is taken up by the curvature of the strip. If α is the angle through which it bends, then, from the figure,

$$\alpha = \frac{p}{d} = \frac{l}{d}(\lambda - \lambda')(\theta_2 - \theta_1).$$

(The expansion of d is negligible, to a very good approximation.)

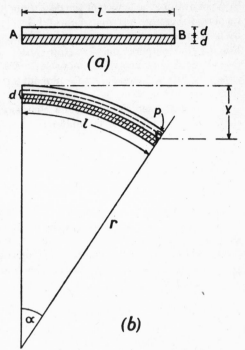

FIG. 174. Expansion of bimetal strip (exaggerated).

To find the radius r of the arc formed by the strip, we assume that the length of the arc is l; this we may do because the expansions in length are all small. Then

$$\alpha = \frac{l}{r};$$

and, by the above equation,

$$\frac{l}{r} = \frac{l}{d}(\lambda - \lambda')(\theta_2 - \theta_1),$$

whence

$$r = \frac{d}{(\lambda - \lambda')(\theta_2 - \theta_1)}.$$

The deflection y of the end of the strip is given by the approximate equation

$$2ry = l^2,$$

from the geometry of the circle.

Thus

$$y = \frac{l^2}{2r} = \frac{l^2(\lambda - \lambda')(\theta_2 - \theta_1)}{2d}.$$

9. Temperature Compensation.

The rate of a clock varies considerably with temperature, unless arrangements are made to prevent its doing so. If the clock is governed by a pendulum, the length of the pendulum increases with temperature, its period therefore also increases, and the clock loses. A clock governed by a balance-wheel and hair-spring also loses as the temperature rises. For, as the temperature rises, the spring becomes less stiff, and the period of the balance-wheel increases. Also the spokes of the wheel expand a little, increasing the moment of inertia of the wheel, and thus further increasing its period.

A balance-wheel clock may be compensated against temperature changes by making the circumference of the wheel in the form of two or three bimetal strips, as shown in Fig. 175. The strips carry small weights W, to give the wheel the necessary moment of inertia. As the temperature rises, the strips curl inwards, and bring the weights nearer to the axle; thus the moment of inertia of the wheel decreases. In a correctly designed timing-system, the decrease in moment of inertia just offsets the decrease in stiffness of the spring, and then the period of the balance-wheel does not change with temperature.

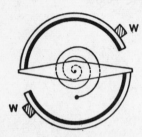

FIG. 175. Bimetal balance-wheel.

Many modern watches are not compensated. Their balance-wheels are made of invar, which, as we have seen, has a very small coefficient of expansion. Another nickel-steel, of slightly different composition, is used for their hair-springs. This alloy changes its elasticity very little with temperature, and is called *elinvar*. The combination of invar balance-wheel and elinvar hair-spring gives a rate which is nearly enough independent of temperature for everyday purposes.

10. Pendula.

To compensate a pendulum clock against changes of temperature, the pendulum must be so made that its effective length remains constant. Fig. 176 (a) shows one way of doing this, in the so-called grid-iron pendulum (Harrison, 1761). Brass and steel rods are arranged so that the expansion of the brass rods raises the bob B of the pendulum, while the expansion of the steel rods lowers it. As explained on p. 273, the expansions can be made to cancel if

$$\frac{l_B}{l_S} = \frac{\lambda_S}{\lambda_B};$$

here l_B and l_S are the total lengths of brass and steel respectively, and λ_B, λ_S, are their coefficients of linear expansion.

Fig. 176 (b) shows the same principle applied to a pendulum with a wooden rod and a cylindrical metal bob. To a first approximation the effective length of the pendulum, l, is the distance from its support

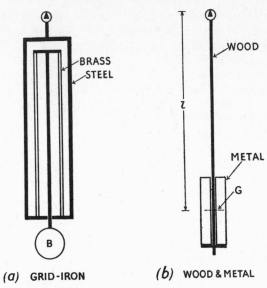

(a) GRID-IRON   (b) WOOD & METAL

FIG. 176. Compensated pendula.

to the centre of gravity, G, of the bob. The condition for constant period is then

$$\frac{\text{length of rod}}{\frac{1}{2}\text{ length of bob}} = \frac{\lambda_{\text{wood}}}{\lambda_{\text{metal}}}.$$

The bob may be made of lead or zinc, either of which is much more expansible than is wood, along its grain.

11. Metal-Glass Seals.

In radio valves and many other pieces of physical apparatus, it is necessary to seal metal cones into glass tubes, with a vacuum-tight joint. The seal must be made at about 400° C., when the glass is soft; as it cools to room temperature, the glass will crack unless the glass and metal contract at the same rate. This condition requires that the metal and the glass have the same coefficient of expansion at every temperature between room temperature and the melting-point of glass. It is satisfied nearly enough by platinum and soda glass (mean $\lambda = 9$ and $8 \cdot 5 \times 10^{-6}$ per °C., respectively), and by tungsten and some types of hard glass similar to pyrex (mean linear coefficient $\lambda = 3-4 \times 10^{-6}$ per °C.).

Modern seals through soft glass are not made with platinum, but with a wire of nickel-iron alloy, which has about the same linear coefficient as the glass. The wire has a thin coating of copper, which adheres to glass more firmly than the alloy. Also, being soft, the copper takes up small differences in expansion between the alloy and the glass.

In transmitting valves, and large vacuum plants, glass and metal tubes several inches in diameter must be joined end-to-end. The metal tubes are made of copper, chamfered to a fine taper at the end where the joint is to be made. The glass is sealed on to the edge of the chamfer; the copper there is thin enough to distort, with the difference in contraction, without cracking the glass.

12. Superficial Expansion.

The increase in area of a body with temperature change is called the *superficial expansion* of the body. A rectangular plate, of sides a, b, at a given temperature, has an area

$$S_1 = ab.$$

If its temperature is increased by θ its sides become $a(1 + \lambda\theta)$, $b(1 + \lambda\theta)$ where λ is its mean coefficient of linear expansion. Thus its area becomes

$$S_2 = a(1 + \lambda\theta)\, b(1 + \lambda\theta)$$
$$= S_1(1 + \lambda\theta)^2$$
$$= S_1(1 + 2\lambda\theta + \lambda^2\theta^2).$$

In this expression, the term $\lambda^2\theta^2$ is small compared with $2\lambda\theta$; if λ is of the order of 10^{-5}, and θ of the order of 100, then $\lambda\theta \backsimeq 10^{-3}$, and $\lambda^2\theta^2 \backsimeq 10^{-6}$. Therefore we may neglect $\lambda^2\theta^2$ and write

$$S_2 = S_1(1 + 2\lambda\theta).$$

The coefficient of superficial expansion of the material of the plate is defined as

$$\frac{\text{increase of area}}{\text{original area} \times \text{temp. rise}} = \frac{S_2 - S_1}{S_1\theta}.$$

Its value is hence equal to 2λ, twice the coefficient of linear expansion. A hole in a plate changes its area by the same amount as would a plug that fitted the hole.

13. Cubical Expansion.

Cubical expansion is expansion in volume. Consider a rectangular block of sides a, b, c, and therefore of volume

$$V_1 = abc.$$

If the block is raised in temperature by θ its sides expand, and its volume becomes

$$V_2 = a(1 + \lambda\theta)\, b(1 + \lambda\theta)\, c(1 + \lambda\theta) = abc(1 + \lambda\theta)^3$$
$$= abc(1 + 3\lambda\theta + 3\lambda^2\theta^2 + \lambda^3\theta^3).$$

Since $\lambda^2\theta^2$ and $\lambda^3\theta^3$ are small compared with $\lambda\theta$, we may in practice neglect them. We then have

$$V_2 = abc(1 + 3\lambda\theta) = V_1(1 + 3\lambda\theta).$$

The coefficient of cubical expansion of the solid is

$$\beta = \frac{\text{increase in volume}}{\text{original volume} \times \text{temp. rise}}$$

$$= \frac{V_2 - V_1}{V_1 \theta}$$

$= 3\lambda$, to a very good approximation.

Thus the coefficient of cubical expansion is *three* times the coefficient of linear expansion.

By imagining a block cut out of a larger block, we can see that the cubical expansion of a hollow vessel is the same as that of a solid plug which would fit into it.

LIQUIDS

14. Cubical Expansion.

The temperature of a liquid determines its volume, but its vessel determines its shape. The only coefficient of expansion which we can define for a liquid is therefore its coefficient of cubical expansion, β. Most liquids, like most solids, do not expand uniformly, and β is not constant over a wide range of temperature. Over a given range θ_1 to θ_2, the *mean coefficient* β is defined as

$$\beta = \frac{V_2 - V_1}{V_1(\theta_2 - \theta_1)},$$

where V_1 and V_2 are the volumes of a given mass of liquid at the temperatures θ_1 and θ_2.

MEAN COEFFICIENTS OF EXPANSION OF LIQUIDS

(Near room temperature)

Liquid	β (°C.$^{-1}$)	Liquid	β (°C.$^{-1}$)
	$\times 10^{-4}$		$\times 10^{-4}$
Alcohol (methyl) .	12·2	Water: 5–10° C. .	0·53
,, (ethyl) .	11·0	10–20° C. .	1·50
Aniline . .	8·5	20–40° C. .	3·02
Ether (ethyl) .	16·3	40–60° C. .	4·58
Glycerine . .	5·3	60–80° C. .	5·87
Olive oil . .	7·0	Mercury: 0–30° C. .	1·81
Paraffin oil . .	9·0	0–100° C. .	1·82
Toluene . .	10·9	0–300° C. .	1·87

15. True and Apparent Expansion : Change of Density.

If we try to find the coefficient of expansion of a liquid by warming it in a vessel, the vessel also expands. The expansion which we observe is the difference between the increases in volume of the liquid and the vessel. This is true whether we start with the vessel full, and catch the overflow, or observe the creep of the liquid up the vessel (Fig. 177). The expansion we observe we call the *apparent expansion*; it is always less than the true expansion of the liquid.

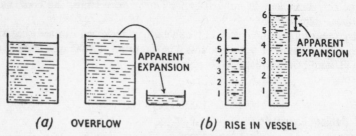

(a) OVERFLOW   *(b)* RISE IN VESSEL

Fig. 177. Apparent expansion of a liquid.

Most methods of measuring the expansion of a liquid, whether true or apparent, depend on the change in density of the liquid when it expands. We therefore consider this change, before describing the measurements in detail. The mean coefficient of true or absolute expansion of a liquid β, is defined in the same way as the mean co-efficient of cubical expansion of a solid:

$$\beta = \frac{\text{increase in volume}}{\text{initial volume} \times \text{temperature rise}}.$$

Thus, if V_1 and V_2 are the volumes of unit mass of the liquid at θ_1 and θ_2, then

$$V_2 = V_1\{1 + \beta(\theta_2 - \theta_1)\}.$$

The densities of the liquid at the two temperatures are

$$\rho_1 = \frac{1}{V_1},$$

$$\rho_2 = \frac{1}{V_2};$$

so that

$$\frac{1}{\rho_2} = \frac{1}{\rho_1}\{1 + \beta(\theta_2 - \theta_1)\}$$

or

$$\rho_2 = \frac{\rho_1}{1 + \beta(\theta_2 - \theta_1)} \qquad \cdots \cdots \quad (5)$$

16. Measurement of Coefficient of True (Absolute) Expansion.

The first measurement of the true expansion of a liquid was made by Dulong and Petit in 1817. A simple form of their apparatus is shown in Fig. 178. It consists of a glass tube ABCD, a foot or two high, containing mercury, and surrounded by glass jackets XY. The jacket X contains ice-water, and steam is passed through the jacket Y.

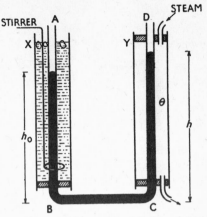

FIG. 178. Apparatus for true (absolute) coefficient of mercury.

For the mercury to be in equilibrium, its hydrostatic pressure at B must equal its hydrostatic pressure at C. Let h_0 be the height of the mercury in the limb at 0° C. and ρ_0 its density; and let h and ρ be the corresponding quantities at the temperature θ of the steam.

Then

$$g\rho_0 h_0 = g\rho h,$$

where g is the acceleration of gravity.

Hence

$$\frac{\rho}{\rho_0} = \frac{h_0}{h}.$$

But, by equation (5),

$$\frac{\rho}{\rho_0} = \frac{1}{1 + \beta\theta}.$$

$$\therefore \frac{h_0}{h} = \frac{1}{1 + \beta\theta}$$

or

$$h_0 + h_0\beta\theta = h.$$

$$\therefore \beta = \frac{h - h_0}{h_0\theta}.$$

The height $h - h_0$ is measured with a cathetometer (a travelling telescope on a vertical column).

This simple apparatus is inaccurate because :

(i) the expansion of CD throws BC out of the horizontal;

(ii) the wide separation of A and D makes the measurement of $(h - h_0)$ inaccurate;

(iii) surface tension causes a difference of pressure across each free surface of mercury; and these do not cancel one another, because the surface tensions are different at the temperatures of the hot and cold columns.

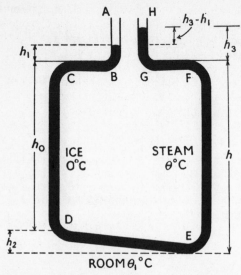

FIG. 179. Modified apparatus for true expansion coefficient.

Regnault got round these difficulties with the apparatus shown, somewhat simplified, in Fig. 179. The points B and G are fixed at the same horizontal level, the join DE is made of flexible iron tubing, and the difference in height between its ends, h_2, is measured. The parts AB, GH are at room temperature θ_1; and to a fair approximation, the average temperature of DE is also θ_1. Suppose θ is the steam temperature.

If the density of mercury at θ_1, θ is ρ_1, ρ, respectively then equating the pressures on both sides at the horizontal level of E, we have

$$g\rho_1 h_1 + g\rho_0 h_0 + g\rho_1 h_2 = g\rho h + g\rho_1 h_3.$$

Therefore *

$$\frac{\rho_0 h_1}{1 + \beta\theta_1} + \rho_0 h_0 + \frac{\rho_0 h_2}{1 + \beta\theta_1} = \frac{\rho_0 h}{1 + \beta\theta} + \frac{\rho_0 h_3}{1 + \beta\theta_1} \quad . \quad . \quad (6)$$

The uncertainty in the temperature of DE is not important, since the height h_2 is very small. Equation (6) gives

$$h_0 + \frac{h_2}{1 + \beta\theta_1} = \frac{h}{1 + \beta\theta} + \frac{h_3 - h_1}{1 + \beta\theta_1} \quad . \quad . \quad . \quad (7)$$

Equation (7) can be solved for β: the quantities which need to be known accurately are h_0, h, and the difference $h_3 - h_1$. This difference can be measured accurately, because AB and GH are close together; and because they are at the same temperature there is no error due to surface tension. The heights h_0 and h are 1 or 2 metres, and so are easy to measure accurately.

* Strictly, equation (6) should be written

$$\frac{\rho_0 h_1}{1 + \beta_1\theta_1} + \rho_0 h_0 + \frac{\rho_0 h_2}{1 + \beta_1\theta_1} = \frac{\rho_0 h}{1 + \beta\theta} + \frac{\rho_0 h_3}{1 + \beta_1\theta_1},$$

where β_1 is the mean coefficient between $0°$ C. and θ_1, and β is that between $0°$ C. and θ. This equation can be solved for β by successive approximations. (See Roberts, *Heat and Thermodynamics*, Chapter X. Blackie.)

Callender and Moss used six pairs of hot and cold columns, each 2 metres long, to increase the difference in level of the liquid. In this way they avoided the complication due to density change of the liquid under high pressure. All the hot columns were beside one another in a hot oil bath kept at a constant high temperature, while the cold columns were similarly placed in a bath of melting ice. Platinum resistance thermometers were used to measure the temperatures, and a cathetometer to measure the heights and difference in level.

17. Apparent Expansion : Weight Thermometer Method.

The method of balancing columns for the absolute expansion of a liquid is slow and awkward; it has only been applied to mercury. Routine measurements are more conveniently made by measuring the apparent expansion; from this, as we shall see, the absolute expansion can be calculated.

A *weight thermometer* is a bulb of fused quartz fitted with a fine stem (Fig. 180). It is filled with liquid at a low temperature, and then warmed; the liquid ex-pands, and from the mass which flows out the apparent expansion of the liquid can be found. The weight ther-mometer is filled by warming it to expel air, and then dipping the stem into the liquid. The process has to be repeated many times;

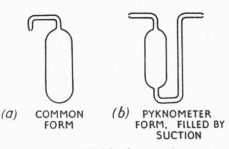

(a) COMMON FORM   *(b)* PYKNOMETER FORM, FILLED BY SUCTION

Fig. 180. Weight thermometers.

and for accurate work the liquid in the thermometer should be boiled at intervals during the filling, to expel dissolved air. In a laboratory experiment, a glass density bottle may be used, filled in the usual way.

The weight thermometer must be filled at a temperature slightly below the lower limit, θ_1, of the range over which the expansion is to be measured. It is then kept in a bath at θ_1, until no more liquid flows out. Next it is weighed, and from its known weight when empty the mass of liquid in it is found. Let this be m_1. The weight thermo-meter is then placed in a bath at the higher temperature of the range, θ_2, and the mass remaining in it, m_2, is found by weighing.

If V_1 and V_2 are the volumes of the weight thermometer at θ_1 and θ_2, then

$$V_2 = V_1\{1 + 3\lambda(\theta_2 - \theta_1)\},$$

where λ is the linear coefficient of quartz, the material of the weight thermometer. Now, if ρ denotes the density of the liquid, whose cubical coefficient is β, we have

$$m_1 = V_1\rho_1,$$
$$m_2 = V_2\rho_2,$$

and

$$\frac{\rho_2}{\rho_1} = \frac{1}{1 + \beta(\theta_2 - \theta_1)}.$$

Therefore

$$\frac{m_2}{m_1} = \frac{V_2\,\rho_2}{V_1\,\rho_1}$$

$$= \frac{1 + 3\lambda(\theta_2 - \theta_1)}{1 + \beta(\theta_2 - \theta_1)}.$$

Hence

$$m_2 + m_2\beta(\theta_2 - \theta_1) = m_1 + 3\lambda(\theta_2 - \theta_1)m_1$$

or

$$m_2\beta(\theta_2 - \theta_1) = m_1 - m_2 + 3\lambda m_1(\theta_2 - \theta_1)$$

and

$$\beta = \frac{m_1 - m_2}{m_2(\theta_2 - \theta_1)} + 3\lambda\frac{m_1}{m_2} \quad \ldots \ldots \quad (11)$$

If we ignore the expansion of the solid, we obtain the coefficient of apparent expansion of the liquid, β_a, relative to the solid.

Thus

$$\beta_a = \frac{m_1 - m_2}{m_2(\theta_2 - \theta_1)} \quad \ldots \ldots \ldots \quad (12)$$

The expression for the apparent coefficient may be expressed in words:

$$\beta_a = \frac{\text{mass expelled}}{\text{mass left in} \times \text{temp. rise}}.$$

Attention is often drawn to the fact that the mass in the denominator is the mass at the higher temperature, and not the lower.

From equation (11),

$$\beta = \beta_a + \frac{m_1}{m_2}\beta_g \quad \ldots \ldots \ldots \quad (13a)$$

where $\beta_g = 3\lambda =$ the cubical coefficient of the solid. Since m_1 and m_2 are nearly equal, then, to a good approximation,

$$\beta = \beta_a + \beta_g \quad \ldots \ldots \ldots \quad (13b)$$

Thus after the apparent coefficient has been calculated, the absolute coefficient is given to a good approximation by

absolute coeff. = apparent coeff. + cubical coeff. of vessel.

18. Coefficient of Weight-thermometer Material.

The cubical coefficient of a glass weight-thermometer may not be accurately known, because glasses differ considerably in their physical properties. Also the coefficient may be changed when the glass is heated in the blowing of the bulb. The coefficient can conveniently be measured, however, by using the weight thermometer to find the apparent coefficient of mercury; and then subtracting the value found from the known value of the absolute coefficient of mercury.

19. Expansion of a Powder.

The weight thermometer can be used to find the cubical coefficient of a granular or powdery solid, such as sand. The procedure is the same as in finding the relative density of the solid, but is gone through at two known temperatures. From the change in relative density, and a knowledge of the expansions of the liquid and the weight thermometer, the change in absolute density of the powder can be found, and hence its cubical expansion.

20. The Dilatometer.

A dilatometer is an instrument for rapidly—but roughly—measuring the expansion of a liquid. It consists of a glass bulb B, with a graduated stem S (Fig. 181). The volume V_b of the bulb, up to the zero of S, is known, and S is graduated in cubic millimetres or other small units. The volume of the bulb, and the value of one scale division, vary with temperature; the dilatometer therefore measures apparent expansion.

FIG. 181. Dilatometer.   FIG. 182. Compensated dilatometer.

The dilatometer is filled with the liquid under test to a point just above the zero of the stem, at a temperature θ_1. The volume V_1 of the liquid is found by adding V_b to the stem-reading v_1. Next the dilatometer is warmed to θ_2, and the liquid rises to v_2. Then $(v_2 - v_1)$ is the apparent expansion of the liquid, and hence

$$\beta_a = \frac{v_2 - v_1}{V_1(\theta_2 - \theta_1)}.$$

If β_g is the cubical coefficient of the glass, then

$$\beta = \beta_a + \beta_g.$$

For demonstration work, a dilatometer can be compensated so that it shows roughly the true expansion of a liquid. Mercury is introduced into the bulb, until it occupies 1/7th of the bulb's volume (Fig. 182).

The expansion of the mercury is then about equal to the expansion of the glass, so that the free volume in the bulb is roughly constant. The cubical coefficients of mercury and glass are given respectively by

$$\beta_{Hg} = 18 \cdot 1 \times 10^{-5} \text{ °C.}^{-1}$$

and $\qquad \beta_g = 3\lambda_g = 3 \times 8 \cdot 5 \times 10^{-6} = 2 \cdot 55 \times 10^{-5} \text{ °C}^{-1};$

Thus $\qquad \dfrac{\beta_{Hg}}{\beta_g} = \dfrac{18 \cdot 1}{2 \cdot 55} = 7 \cdot 1.$

Thus the expansion of the mercury offsets that of the glass, within about $1\frac{1}{2}$ per cent.

The space above the mercury, whose volume is constant, is filled with the liquid to be examined. When the bulb is warmed, the movement of the liquid up the stem shows the liquid's true expansion. This device may be used to show the anomalous expansion of water (p. 289).

21. Mathiessen's Method.

In Mathiessen's method, a cube of fused quartz is hung, from the arm of a balance so that it is completely immersed in the liquid. From its weight in air, the upthrust which the liquid exerts on the cube can be found. If V is the volume of the solid, the upthrust is

$$U = V\rho g$$

where ρ is the density of the liquid. The upthrust is measured at the temperatures θ_1 and θ_2 between which the coefficient of expansion of the liquid, β, is to be found. If λ is the coefficient of linear expansion of fused quartz, the volumes of the bulb are related by the equation

$$V_2 = V_1\{1 + 3\lambda(\theta_2 - \theta_1)\}.$$

The upthrusts are the weights of liquid displaced:

$$U_1 = V_1\rho_1 g,$$
$$U_2 = V_2\rho_2 g,$$

where ρ_1 and ρ_2 are the densities of the liquid at θ_1 and θ_2. We have, from equation (5)

$$\frac{\rho_2}{\rho_1} = \frac{1}{1 + \beta(\theta_2 - \theta_1)}.$$

Therefore $\qquad \dfrac{U_2}{U_1} = \dfrac{V_2\rho_2}{V_1\rho_1} = \dfrac{1 + 3\lambda(\theta_2 - \theta_1)}{1 + \beta(\theta_2 - \theta_1)} \quad \cdots \quad (8)$

In this equation every quantity except β is known, and β can therefore be calculated.

If we re-arrange equation (8), we obtain

$$U_2\{1 + \beta(\theta_2 - \theta_1)\} = U_1\{1 + 3\lambda(\theta_2 - \theta_1)\}$$

or $\qquad U_2\beta(\theta_2 - \theta_1) = U_1 - U_2 + 3\lambda(\theta_2 - \theta_1)U_1$

whence $\qquad \beta = \dfrac{U_1 - U_2}{U_2(\theta_2 - \theta_1)} + 3\lambda\dfrac{U_1}{U_2} \quad \cdots \quad (9)$

If we ignored the expansion of the cube, then λ would be zero, and the coefficient of the liquid, β_a, would have the value

$$\beta_a = \frac{U_1 - U_2}{U_2(\theta_2 - \theta_1)} \quad \ldots \ldots \ldots (10)$$

This quantity is called the *coefficient of apparent expansion* of the liquid, relative to fused quartz.

The quantity 3λ is the coefficient of cubical expansion, β_g, of quartz. Thus

$$\beta = \beta_a + \frac{U_1}{U_2}\beta_g.$$

In practice, U_2 is very nearly equal to U_1, so that their ratio is almost unity, and we may, to a good approximation, write

$$\beta = \beta_a + \beta_g.$$

In a laboratory, Mathiessen's method can be carried out with a glass sinker, weighted with lead shot or mercury. The liquid is warmed in a beaker to the highest temperature required, and measurements of U are made as it cools. In this way the coefficient β may be measured over several temperature ranges in one experiment.

22. Correction of the Barometer.

The hydrostatic pressure of a column of mercury, such as that in a barometer, depends on its density as well as its height. When we speak of a pressure of 76 cm. mercury, therefore, we must specify the temperature of the mercury; we choose 0° C. In practice barometers are generally warmer than that, and their readings must therefore

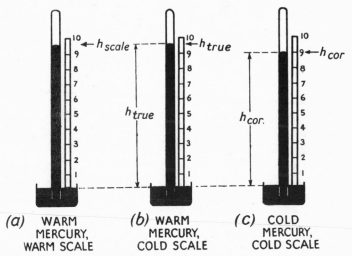

FIG. 183. Reduction of barometer height to 0° C.

be reduced to what they would be at $0°$ C. Also we must allow for the expansion of the scale with which the height is measured.

The scale of a barometer may be calibrated at $0°$ C. At any higher temperature, θ, the height which it indicates, h_{scale}, is less than the true height, h_{true}, of the mercury meniscus above the free surface in the reservoir (Fig. 183 (a) (b)). The true height is given by equation (3) of p. 272:

$$h_{true} = h_{scale} (1 + \lambda\theta) \quad . \quad . \quad . \quad . \quad . \quad (13)$$

where λ is the coefficient of linear expansion of the scale. If ρ_θ is the density of mercury at θ, then the pressure of the atmosphere is

$$p = g\rho_\theta h_{true}.$$

The height of a mercury column at $0°$ C. which would exert the same pressure is called the *corrected height*, $h_{cor.}$ (Fig. 183 (b) (c)). It is given by

$$p = g\rho_0 h_{cor.,}$$

where ρ_0 is the density of mercury at $0°$ C.

Therefore

$$\rho_\theta h_{true} = \rho_0 h_{cor.}.$$

If β is the coefficient of expansion of mercury, then

$$\rho_\theta = \frac{\rho_0}{1 + \beta\theta}.$$

Hence

$$\frac{\rho_0}{1 + \beta\theta} h_{true} = \rho_0 h_{cor.}.$$

and

$$h_{cor.} = \frac{h_{true}}{1 + \beta\theta}$$

Therefore, by equation (13),

$$h_{cor.} = \frac{h_{scale} (1 + \lambda\theta)}{1 + \beta\theta}.$$

Let us write this as

$$h_{cor.} = h_{scale} (1 + \lambda\theta)(1 + \beta\theta)^{-1}.$$

Then, if we ignore $\beta^2\theta^2$ and higher terms, we may write

$$h_{cor.} = h_{scale} (1 + \lambda\theta)(1 - \beta\theta).$$

Hence

$$h_{cor.} = h_{scale} (1 + \lambda\theta - \beta\theta + \beta\lambda\theta^2),$$

and ignoring $\beta\lambda\theta^2$ we find

$$h_{cor.} = h_{scale}\{1 + (\lambda - \beta)\theta\}.$$

The coefficient β is greater than λ, and the corrected height is less than the scale height. It is convenient therefore, to write

$$h_{cor.} = h_{scale}\{1 - (\beta - \lambda)\theta\}.$$

The reader should notice that the correction depends on the difference between the cubical coefficient of the mercury, and the linear coefficient of the scale; as in Dulong and Petit's experiment, there is no question of apparent expansion.

23. The Anomalous Expansion of Water.

If we nearly fill a tall jar with water, and float lumps of ice on it, the water at the base of the jar does not cool below 4° C., although the water at the top soon reaches 0° C. At 4° C. water has its greatest density; as it cools to this temperature it sinks to the bottom. When the water at the top cools below 4° C., it becomes less dense than the water below, and stays on the top. Convection ceases, and the water near the bottom of the jar can lose heat only by conduction. Since water is a bad conductor, the loss by conduction is extremely small, and in practice the water at the bottom does not cool below 4° C. The same happens in a pond, cooled at the top by cold air. Ice forms at the surface, but a little below it the water remains at 4° C., and life in the pond survives. It could not if the water contracted in volume continuously to 0° C.; for then convection would always carry the coldest water to the bottom, and the pond would freeze solid. In fact, lakes and rivers, unless they are extremely shallow, never do freeze solid; even in arctic climates, they take only a crust of ice.

Fig. 184 shows how the volume of 1 gm. of water varies with temperature. The decrease from 0° C. to 4° C. is called *anomalous expansion*; it can be shown with a compensated dilatometer (p. 285). Water also has the unusual property of expanding when it freezes, hence burst

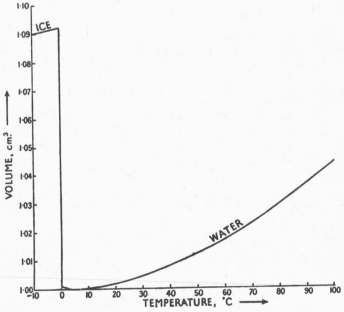

Fig. 184. Volume variation of 1 gm. of water.

pipes. As the figure shows, the expansion is about 9 per cent. If ice were not less dense than water, it would sink, and so, despite the anomalous expansion of water, lakes and rivers would freeze solid in winter.

The following table gives the densities of ice and water at various temperatures. Accurate experiments show that the temperature of maximum density is 3·98° C.

DENSITY OF ICE AND WATER *

Temperature °C.	0	2	4	6	8
ρ_{water} gm./cm.³ .	0·99984	0·99994	0·99997	0·99994	0·99985
ρ_{ice} gm./cm.³ .	0·9160 (volume of 1 gm. ice at 0° C. = 1·092 cm.³)				
Temperature °C.	10	20	40	60	80	100
ρ_{water} gm./cm.³ .	0·99970	0·99820	0·9922	0·9832	0·9718	0·9584

The temperature of maximum density was first measured in 1804, by Hope, whose apparatus is shown in Fig. 185. Both vessels are made of metal; the inner one contains water, and the outer one contains a mixture of ice and salt, which has a temperature below 0° C. After several hours, the water at the top cools to 0° C.—it may even freeze— but the water at the bottom does not fall below 4° C.

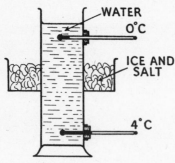

The contraction of water from 0 to 4° C. is explained by supposing that the molecules form clusters, such as H_4O_2, H_6O_3. At first, the contraction due to the formation of these more than offsets the expansion due to the rise of temperature; but above 4° C. the expansion prevails. The metal bismuth behaves like water; it expands on freezing, and contracts at first when warmed above its melting-point. Because it expands on freezing, it makes sharp castings, and is used as a constituent of type-metal.

WATER
0°C
ICE AND SALT
4°C

FIG. 185. Hope's experiment.

* Volumes of liquids are often expressed in millilitres (ml.). A litre is defined as the volume of 1 kg. of water at 4° C. and a pressure of 760 mm. mercury. It was originally intended to be 1,000 cm.³, but accurate measurements of the density of water give:

$$1 \text{ litre} = 1000·028 \text{ cm.}^3$$
$$1 \text{ ml.} = 1·000028 \text{ cm.}^3$$

EXAMPLES

1. Describe how you would use a specific gravity bottle to find the coefficient of expansion of paraffin oil relative to glass between 0° and 50° C.

A specific gravity bottle contains 44·25 gm. of a liquid at 0° C. and 42·02 gm. at 50° C. Assuming that the coefficient of linear expansion of the glass is 0·00001 per deg. C., (a) compare the densities of the liquid at 0° and 50° C., (b) deduce the coefficient of real expansion of the liquid. Prove any formula employed. (*N.*)

First part. See text.

Second part. The apparent coefficient of the liquid, β_a, is given by

$$\beta_a = \frac{\text{mass expelled}}{\text{mass left} \times \text{temp. rise}} = \frac{44\cdot25 - 42\cdot02}{42\cdot02 \times 50}.$$

$$\therefore \ \beta_a = \frac{2\cdot23}{42\cdot02 \times 50} = 0\cdot00106° \text{ C.}^{-1}$$

Now cubical coefficient, β_g, of glass $= 3 \times 0\cdot00001 = 0\cdot00003°$ C.$^{-1}$

$\therefore$ real coefficient, $\beta, = \beta_a + \beta_g = 0\cdot00106 + 0\cdot00003 = 0\cdot00109°$ C.$^{-1}$

Also, if ρ_0, ρ_t are the densities at 0° C., 50° C. respectively,

$$\frac{\rho_0}{\rho_t} = 1 + \beta t$$
$$= 1 + 0\cdot00109 \times 50$$
$$= 1\cdot055.$$

2. Distinguish between the coefficients of real and apparent expansion of a liquid and describe an experiment to determine the coefficient of apparent expansion of paraffin in glass.

A glass vessel holds 40 gm. of paraffin at 0° C. What mass of paraffin will it hold at 70° C.? The coefficient of volume expansion of paraffin is 9×10^{-4} per deg. C. and that of glass 24×10^{-6} per deg. C. (*N.*)

First part. See text.

Second part. Mass of paraffin at 70° C. $= V_{70}\rho_{70}$, where V_{70} is the volume of the glass vessel at 70° C. and ρ_{70} is the density of the paraffin at 70° C.

Now $\qquad\qquad V_{70} = V_0(1 + 24 \times 10^{-6} \times 70) \qquad \ldots \ldots$ (i)

and $\qquad\qquad \dfrac{\rho_0}{\rho_{70}} = 1 + 9 \times 10^{-4} \times 70.$

$$\therefore \ \rho_{70} = \frac{\rho_0}{1 + 9 \times 10^{-4} \times 70} \qquad \cdots \ \cdots \ \cdots \ \cdots \quad \text{(ii)}$$

Multiplying (i) by (ii) we have

$$V_{70}\rho_{70} = V_0\rho_0 \left(\frac{1 + 24 \times 10^{-6} \times 70}{1 + 9 \times 10^{-4} \times 70}\right).$$

But $\qquad\qquad V_0\rho_0 = $ mass of paraffin at 0° C. $= 40$ gm.

$$\therefore \ \text{mass at } 70° \text{ C.} = V_{70}\rho_{70} = 40 \left(\frac{1 + 24 \times 10^{-6} \times 70}{1 + 9 \times 10^{-4} \times 70}\right)$$

$$= \frac{40 \times 1\cdot00168}{1\cdot063} = 37\cdot7 \text{ gm.}$$

3. A clock has a brass pendulum, and keeps correct time at 20° C. How many seconds does it lose per day at 30° C.? λ for brass $= 19 \times 10^{-6}$ per deg. C.

Let l_1 cm. = length of pendulum at 20° C. (θ_1); then period of pendulum

$$= T_1 = 2\pi\sqrt{\frac{l_1}{g}}\ \text{secs.,}$$

where g = acceleration of gravity.

Now let l_2 = length at 30° C. (θ_2); then

$$l_2 = l_1\{1 + \lambda(\theta_2 - \theta_1)\}$$

and new period is

$$T_2 = 2\pi\sqrt{\frac{l_2}{g}} = 2\pi\sqrt{\frac{l_1\{1 + \lambda(\theta_2 - \theta_1)\}}{g}}$$

$$= 2\pi\sqrt{\frac{l_1}{g}}\sqrt{1 + \lambda(\theta_2 - \theta_1)}$$

$$= T_1\sqrt{1 + \lambda(\theta_2 - \theta_1)}.$$

Each beat of the pendulum, however, still moves the clock's hands forward by T_1 apparent seconds. In 24 true hours the pendulum makes N beats, where

$$N = \frac{24 \times 60 \times 60}{T_2}.$$

The number of apparent seconds which the clock records in 24 true hours is therefore

$$NT_1 = \frac{24 \times 60 \times 60}{T_2}.T_1$$

$$= \frac{24 \times 60 \times 60}{\sqrt{1 + \lambda(\theta_2 - \theta_1)}}.$$

Thus: apparent seconds per 24 hr.

$$= \frac{24 \times 60 \times 60}{\sqrt{1 + 19 \times 10^{-6} \times 10}}$$

$$= \frac{24 \times 60 \times 60}{\sqrt{1 \cdot 00019}}$$

$$= \frac{24 \times 60 \times 60}{1 \cdot 000095}.$$

$\therefore$ seconds lost per 24 hr. $= 24 \times 60 \times 60 - \dfrac{24 \times 60 \times 60}{1 \cdot 000095}$

$$= 8 \cdot 2.$$

4. Define the coefficient of linear expansion of a solid, and show how it is related to the coefficient of cubical expansion. Describe an accurate method of determining the coefficient of expansion of a solid.

In order to make connexion to the carbon anode of a transmitting valve it is required to thread a copper wire (2 mm. in diameter at 20° C.) through a smaller hole in the carbon block. If the process can just be carried out by immersing both specimens in dry ice (solid CO_2) at $-80°$ C. and the coefficients of linear expansion of copper and carbon are 17×10^{-6} and 5×10^{-6} per deg. C., calculate the size of the hole at 20° C. (O. & C.)

First part. The coefficient of linear expansion is the increase in length per unit length per degree rise in temperature. It is one-third of the cubical coefficient, proved on p. 278. An accurate method of measuring the linear coefficient is the comparator method, described on p. 270.

Second part. Suppose r cm. is the diameter of the hole at 20° C. Then, from the formula

$$l_2 = l_1[1 + \lambda(\theta_2 - \theta_1)], \text{ where } (\theta_2 - \theta_1) = -80 - 20 = -100° \text{ C.,}$$

diameter at $-80°$ C. $= r(1 - 5 \times 10^{-6} \times 100) = 0.9995\, r$ cm.

Similarly, the diameter of the copper wire at $-80°$ C.

$$= 0.2(1 - 17 \times 10^{-6} \times 100) = 0.19966 \text{ cm.}$$

$$\therefore\ 0.9995\, r = 0.19966$$

$$\therefore\ r = \frac{0.19966}{0.9995} = 0.19976 \text{ cm.} = 1.998 \text{ mm.}$$

5. Describe in detail how the coefficient of expansion of a liquid may be determined by the weight thermometer method.

The height of the mercury column in a barometer provided with a brass scale correct at 0° C. is observed to be 749·0 mm. on an occasion when the temperature is 15° C. Find (a) the true height of the column at 15° C., (b) the height of a column of mercury at 0° C. which would exert an equal pressure. Assume that the coefficients of volume expansion of brass and of mercury are respectively 0·000054 and 0·000181 per deg. C. (*N.*)

First part. The weight thermometer method gives the apparent coefficient of the liquid, which is calculated from:

$$\frac{\text{mass expelled}}{\text{mass left} \times \text{temperature rise}}.$$

The true coefficient is obtained by adding the volume coefficient of the container's material to the apparent coefficient.

Second part. (a) The linear coefficient of brass, λ,

$$= \tfrac{1}{3} \times \text{volume coefficient}$$

$$= \tfrac{1}{3} \times 0.000054 = 0.000018 \text{ per deg. C.}$$

$$\therefore\ \text{true height, } h_\theta, = 749.0\,(1 + \lambda\theta) = 749.0\,(1 + 0.000018 \times 15)$$

$$= 749.2 \text{ mm.}$$

(b) Suppose h_0 is the required height at 0° C. Then, since pressure $= h\rho g$,

$$h_0\rho_0 g = h_\theta\rho_\theta g$$

$$\therefore\ h_0 = h_\theta\frac{\rho_\theta}{\rho_0}.$$

But

$$\frac{\rho_\theta}{\rho_0} = \frac{1}{1 + \beta\theta} = \frac{1}{1 + 0.000181 \times 15} = \frac{1}{1.0027}$$

$$\therefore\ h_0 = 749.0 \times \frac{1.00027}{1.0027}$$

$$= 749\,[1 - (0.0027 - 0.00027)]$$

$$= 747.2 \text{ mm.}$$

6. Define the various coefficients of expansion of a substance which are appropriate to each of its three physical states. Comment on the relation (a) between the coefficients in the solid state, (b) between the coefficients in the liquid state.

An iron rod of cross-sectional area 0·72 sq. cm. is heated so that its temperature is increased by 100° C. What force will be required to hold the rod at its expanded length when the rod is cooled to its original temperature? Express your answer in kilogram-wt. (Take the coefficient of linear expansion of iron as $1 \cdot 1 \times 10^{-5}$ per deg. C. and Young's modulus for iron as $2 \cdot 0 \times 10^{12}$ dynes per sq. cm.) (N.)

First part. The coefficients of expansion in the *gaseous* state are the volume coefficient and pressure coefficient, defined on p. 223 ; the coefficient in the *liquid* state is the volume coefficient, true and apparent coefficients (p. 280) ; the coefficients in the *solid* state are the linear, superficial (areal), and volume coefficients (p. 268). The relations in the solid state are : volume coefficient = 3 × linear coefficient and superficial (areal) coefficient = 2 × linear coefficient. The relation in the liquid state is: true coefficient = apparent coefficient + volume coefficient of container's material.

Second part. Suppose the original length of the rod is l cm. Then expansion for a temperature rise of $\theta°$ C. = $\lambda l \theta$, where λ is the linear coefficient. Now

$$\text{Young's modulus, } E, = \frac{\text{stress}}{\text{strain}} = \frac{F/S}{\lambda l \theta / l}.$$

$$\therefore F = ES\lambda\theta$$

$$= 2 \times 10^{12} \times 0 \cdot 72 \times 1 \cdot 1 \times 10^{-5} \times 100 \text{ dynes}$$

$$= \frac{2 \times 10^{12} \times 0 \cdot 72 \times 1 \cdot 1 \times 100}{10^{5} \times 980 \times 1,000}$$

$$= 1,600 \text{ kilogram-wt. (approx.).}$$

EXERCISES XIII

1. Describe and explain how the coefficient of absolute expansion of a liquid may be determined without a previous knowledge of any other coefficient of expansion.

Aniline is a liquid which does not mix with water, and when a small quantity of it is poured into a beaker of water at 20° C. it sinks to the bottom, the densities of the two liquids at 20° C. being $1 \cdot 021$ and $0 \cdot 998$ gm. cm.$^{-3}$ respectively. To what temperature must the beaker and its contents be uniformly heated so that the aniline will form a globule which just floats in the water? (The mean coefficients of absolute expansion of aniline and water over the temperature range concerned are $0 \cdot 00085$ and $0 \cdot 00045$ deg.$^{-1}$ C., respectively.) (L.)

2. Define the *coefficient of linear expansion* of a solid, and describe a method by which it may be measured.

Show how the coefficient of superficial expansion can be derived from this value.

A "thermal tap" used in certain apparatus consists of a silica rod which fits tightly inside an aluminium tube whose internal diameter is 8 mm. at 0° C. When the temperature is raised, the fit is no longer exact. Calculate what change in temperature is necessary to produce a channel whose cross-section is equal to that of a tube of 1 mm. internal diameter. [Coefficient of linear expansion of silica = 8×10^{-6} per deg. C. Coefficient of linear expansion of aluminium = 26×10^{-6} per deg. C.] (O. & C.)

3. Distinguish between the real and apparent expansion of a liquid. Show that the temperature at which water attains its apparent minimum volume in a glass vessel is not the temperature of maximum density.

Given a glass sinker of known coefficient of cubical expansion, explain how it can be used to find the coefficient of real expansion of water at a given temperature. (O. & C.)

4. A weight thermometer has a mass m when empty and m_0 and m_t when full with a liquid at 0° C. and $t°$ C. respectively. If α is the coefficient

of absolute expansion of the liquid, α_a the coefficient of apparent expansion of the liquid in the thermometer and β the coefficient of volume expansion of the material of the thermometer, find the relation between α, α_a, and β.

Assuming that the masses of liquid filling the thermometer at 0° C. and 6° C. are within 5 per cent. of each other, calculate the percentage error introduced by using the approximate relation between these quantities in the calculation of α.

[α_a = 0·00085 deg.$^{-1}$ C. and β = 0·000025 deg.$^{-1}$ C.] (L.)

5. Define the coefficients of linear and cubical expansion, and derive the relation between them for a particular substance. Describe, and give the theory of, a method for finding *directly* the absolute coefficient of expansion of a liquid. The bulb of a mercury-in-glass thermometer has a volume of 0·5 c.c. and the distance between processive degree marks is 2 mm. If the coefficient of linear expansion of glass is 10^{-5} per deg. C., and the coefficient of cubical expansion of mercury is 1·8 $\times$ 10^{-4} per deg. C., find the cross-sectional area of the bore of the stem. (C.)

6. Define the terms "apparent" and "absolute" coefficients of expansion of a liquid, and show how the former is found by means of a weight thermometer. A litre flask, which is correctly calibrated at 4° C., is filled to the mark with water at 80° C. What is the weight of water in the flask? [Coefficient of linear expansion of the glass of the flask = 8·5 $\times$ 10^{-6}; mean coefficient of cubical expansion of water = 5·0 $\times$ 10^{-4}.] (O. & C.)

7. Show how in general the density of a liquid at a temperature $t°$ C. is related to that at 0° C. for small values of t. Describe and illustrate, by reference to experiments, the anomalous behaviour of water in this respect. A glass sinker has a mass M in air. When weighed in a liquid at temperature t_1 the apparent mass is M_1, and when weighed in the same liquid at temperature t_2 the apparent mass is M_2. If the coefficient of cubical expansion of the glass is β, find α, the real coefficient of expansion of the liquid. (L.)

8. Describe how to measure the coefficient of apparent expansion of a liquid using a weight thermometer. Show how the result can be calculated from the observations.

A specific gravity bottle of volume 50·0 c.c. at 0° C is filled with glycerine at 20° C. What mass of glycerine is contained in the bottle if the density of glycerine at 0° C. is 1·26 gm. per c.c., and its coefficient of real expansion is 5·2 $\times$ 10^{-4} per deg. C.? Assume that the coefficient of linear expansion of the glass is 8 $\times$ 10^{-6} per deg. C. (N.)

9. Describe an accurate method for determining the coefficient of thermal expansion of a solid in the form of a rod. The pendulum of a clock is made of brass whose coefficient of linear expansion is 1·9 $\times$ 10^{-5} per deg. C. If the clock keeps correct time at 15° C., how many seconds per day will it lose at 20° C.? (O. & C.)

10. A steel wire 8 metres long and 4 mm. in diameter is fixed to two rigid supports. Calculate the increase in tension when the temperature falls 10° C. [Linear coefficient of expansion of steel = 12 $\times$ 10^{-6} per deg. C., Young's modulus for steel = 2 $\times$ 10^{12} dynes per sq. cm.] (O. & C.)

11. How can you show that the density of water does not fall steadily as the temperature is raised from 0° C. to 100° C.? What does your experiment indicate about the expansion of water? What importance has this result in nature? (C.)

12. Why is mercury used as a thermometric fluid? Compare the advantages and disadvantages of the use of a mercury-in-glass thermometer and a platinum resistance thermometer to determine the temperature of a liquid at about 300°C.

A dilatometer having a glass bulb and a tube of uniform bore contains 150 gm. of mercury which extends into the tube at 0°C. How far will the meniscus rise up the tube when the temperature is raised to 100°C. if the area of cross-section of the bore is 0·8 sq. mm. at 0°C.? Assume that the density of mercury at 0°C. is 13·6 gm. per c.c., that the coefficient of expansion of mercury is 1·82 × 10⁻⁴ per deg. C., and that the coefficient of linear expansion of glass is 1·1 × 10⁻⁵ per deg. C. (*N.*)

13. Describe in detail how you would determine the coefficient of linear expansion of a metal rod or tube. Indicate the chief sources of error and discuss the accuracy you would expect to obtain.

A steel cylinder has an aluminium alloy piston and, at a temperature of 20°C. when the internal diameter of the cylinder is exactly 10 cm., there is an all-round clearance of 0·05 mm. between the piston and the cylinder wall. At what temperature will the fit be perfect? (The coefficients of a linear expansion of steel and the aluminium alloy are 1·2 × 10⁻⁵ and 1·6 × 10⁻⁵ per deg. C. respectively.) (*O. & C.*)

14. Explain the statement: *the coefficient of absolute expansion of mercury is* 1·81 × 10⁻⁴ *deg.*⁻¹ *C.* Describe an experiment to test the accuracy of this value. Why is a knowledge of it important?

Calculate the volume at 0°C. required in a thermometer to give a degree of length 0·15 cm. on the stem, the diameter of the bore being 0·24 mm. What would be the volume of this mercury at 100°C.? [The coefficient of linear expansion of the glass may be taken as 8·5 × 10⁻⁶ deg.⁻¹ C.] (*L.*)

15. Describe and give the theory of a method for finding the coefficient of real expansion of a liquid which does not require a knowledge of the coefficient of expansion of a sinker or containing vessel.

A weighted glass bulb is weighed in air and then when suspended so as to be totally immersed in a bath of oil maintained at a steady temperature *t*. The apparent loss of weight is found to be 29·861 gm. when *t* = 30·0°C., and 29·085 gm. when *t* = 60·0°C.

Determine the coefficient of real expansion of the oil between 30°C. and 60°C. given that the coefficient of linear expansion of the glass over the same range of temperature is 9·0 × 10⁻⁶ deg.⁻¹ C. Derive the formula used in your calculation. (*L.*)

CHAPTER XIV

CHANGES OF STATE. VAPOURS

SOLID TO LIQUID : FUSION

1. The Solid State.

Substances exist in the solid, liquid or gaseous state. In the *solid state*, a body has a regular, geometrical structure. Sometimes this structure gives the body a regular outward form, as in a crystal of alum; sometimes, as in a strand of wool, it does not. But X-rays can reveal to us the arrangement of the individual atoms or molecules in a solid; and whether the solid is wool or alum, we find that its atoms or molecules are arranged in a regular pattern. This pattern we call a *space-lattice*; its form may be simple, as in metals, or complicated, as in wool, proteins, and other chemically complex substances.

We consider that the atoms or molecules of a solid are vibrating about their mean positions in its space-lattice. And we consider that the kinetic energy of their vibrations increases with the temperature of the solid: its increase is the heat energy supplied to cause the rise in temperature. When the temperature reaches the melting-point, the solid liquefies. Lindemann has suggested that, at the melting-point, the atoms or molecules vibrate so violently that they collide with one another. The attractive forces between them can then no longer hold them in their pattern, the space-lattice collapses, and the solid melts. The work necessary to overcome the forces between the atoms or molecules of the solid, that is, to break-up the space-lattice, is the latent heat of melting or fusion.

2. The Liquid State.

In the liquid state, a body has no form, but a fixed volume. It adapts itself to the shape of its vessel, but does not expand to fill it. We consider that its molecules still dart about at random, as in the gaseous state, and we consider that their average kinetic energy rises with the liquid's temperature. But we think that they are now close enough together to attract one another—by forces of a more-or-less gravitational nature. Any molecule approaching the surface of the liquid experiences a resultant force opposing its escape (Nelkon, *Mechanics and Properties of Matter*, p. 112; Surface Tension). Nevertheless, some molecules do escape, as is shown by the fact that the liquid evaporates: even in cold weather, a pool of water does not last for ever. The molecules which escape are the fastest, for they have the greatest kinetic energy, and therefore the greatest chance of over-coming the attraction of the others. Since the fastest escape, the slower, which remain, begin to predominate: the average kinetic energy of the molecules falls, and the liquid cools. The faster a liquid evaporates, the colder it feels on the hand—petrol feels colder than water, water feels colder than paraffin. To keep a liquid at constant temperature as it evaporates, heat must be supplied to it; the heat required is the latent heat of evaporation.

3. Melting and Freezing.

When a solid changes to a liquid, we say it undergoes a *change of state* or *phase*. Pure crystalline solids melt and freeze sharply. If, for example, paradichlorbenzene is warmed in a test tube until it melts, and then allowed to cool, its temperature falls as shown in Fig. 186 (a).

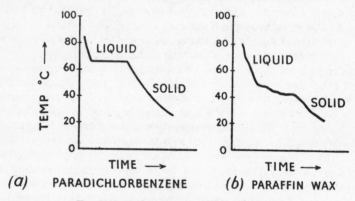

Fig. 186. Cooling curves, showing freezing.

A well-defined plateau in the cooling curve indicates the freezing (or melting) point. While the substance is freezing, it is evolving its latent heat of fusion, which compensates for the heat lost by cooling, and its temperature does not fall. An impure substance such as paraffin wax, on the other hand, has no definite plateau on its cooling curve; it is a mixture of several waxes, which freeze out from the liquid at slightly different temperatures (Fig. 186 (b)).

4. Supercooling.

If we try to find the melting-point of hypo from its cooling curve, we generally fail; the liquid goes on cooling down to room temperature. But if we drop a crystal of solid hypo into the liquid the temperature rises to the melting-point of hypo, and the hypo starts to freeze. While the hypo is freezing, its temperature stays constant at the melting-point; when all the hypo has frozen, its temperature starts to fall again (Fig. 187).

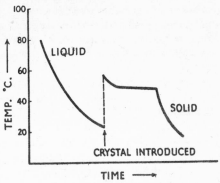

FIG. 187. Cooling curve of hypo.

The cooling of a liquid below its freezing-point is called *supercooling*; the molecules of the liquid lose their kinetic energy as it cools, but do not take up the rigid geometric pattern of the solid. Shaking or stirring the liquid, or dropping grit or dust into it, may cause it to solidify; but dropping in a crystal of its own solid is more likely to make it solidify. As soon as the substance begins to solidify, it returns to its melting (or freezing) point. *The melting-point is the only temperature at which solid and liquid can be in equilibrium.*

No one has succeeded in warming a solid above its melting-point— or, if he has, he has failed to report his success. We may therefore suppose that to superheat a solid is not possible; and we need not be surprised. For the melting-point of a solid is the temperature at which its atoms or molecules have enough kinetic energy to break up its crystal lattice: as soon as the molecules are moving fast enough, they burst from their pattern. On the other hand, when a liquid cools to its melting-point, there is no particular reason why its molecules should spontaneously arrange themselves. They may readily do so, however, around a crystal in which their characteristic pattern is already set up.

5. Pressure and Melting.

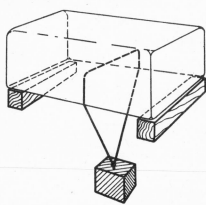

FIG. 188. Melting of ice under pressure.

The melting-point of a solid is affected by increase of pressure. If we run a copper wire over a block of ice, and hang a heavy weight from it, as in Fig. 188, we find that the wire slowly works through the block. It does not cut its way through, for the ice freezes up behind it; the pressure of the wire makes the ice under it melt, and above the wire, where the pressure is released, the ice freezes again. The freezing again after melting by pressure is called *regelation*.

This experiment shows that increasing the pressure on ice makes it melt more readily; that is to say, *it lowers the melting-point* of the ice. We can understand this effect when we remember that ice shrinks when it melts (see p. 208); pressure encourages shrinking, and therefore melting.

The fall in the melting-point of ice with increase in pressure is small: 0·0072° C. per atmosphere. It is interesting, because it explains the slipperiness of ice; skates for example, are hollow ground, so that the pressure on the line of contact is very high, and gives rise to a lubricating film of water. Ice which is much colder than 0° C. is not slippery, because to bring its melting-point down to its actual temperature would require a greater pressure than can be realized.* Most substances swell on melting; an increase of pressure opposes the melting of such substances, and raises their melting-point.

6. Freezing of Solutions.

Water containing a dissolved substance freezes below 0° C. The depression of the freezing-point increases at first with the concentration, but eventually reaches a maximum. The lowest freezing-point of common salt solution is − 22° C., when the solution contains about one-quarter of its weight of salt. When a solution does freeze, pure ice separates out; an easy way of preparing pure water is therefore to freeze it, remove the ice, and then melt the ice. The water which is mixed with the ice in determining the ice-point of a thermometer must be pure, or its temperature will not be 0° C.

When ice and salt are mixed, the mixture cools below 0° C., but remains liquid. As the proportion of salt is increased, the temperature of the mixture falls, until it reaches a minimum at − 22° C. A mixture of ice and salt provides a simple means of reaching temperatures below 0° C., and is called a "freezing mixture".

The phenomena of the freezing of solutions are important in chemistry, and particularly in metallurgy. We shall give a brief explanation of them later in this chapter.

LIQUID TO GAS: EVAPORATION

Evaporation differs from melting in that it takes place at all temperatures; as long as the weather is dry, a puddle will always clear up. In cold weather the puddle lasts longer than in warm, as the rate of evaporation falls rapidly with the temperature.

Solids as well as liquids evaporate. Tungsten evaporates from the filament of an electric lamp, and blackens its bulb; the blackening can be particularly well seen on the headlamp bulb of a bicycle dynamo

* For a discussion of the physics of ice, see Perutz, "Glaciers", *Penguin Science News*, 6.

set, if it has been frequently over-run through riding down-hill. **The rate** of evaporation of a solid is negligible at temperatures well below its melting-point, as we may see from the fact that bars of metal do not gradually disappear.

7. Saturated and Unsaturated Vapours.

Fig. 189 (*a*) shows an apparatus with which we can study vapours and their pressures. A is a glass tube, about a yard long, dipping in a

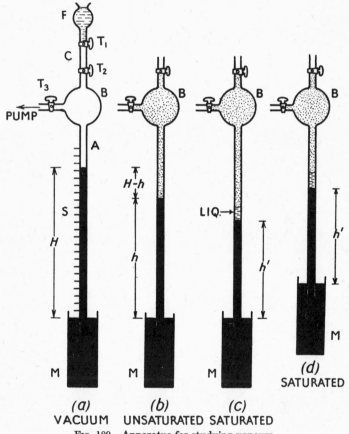

(a)
VACUUM

(b)
UNSATURATED

(c)
SATURATED

(d)
SATURATED

FIG. 189. Apparatus for studying vapours.

mercury trough and backed by a scale S. Its upper end carries a bulb B, which is fitted with three taps T, of which T_1 and T_2 should be as close together as possible. Above T_1 is a funnel F. With T_1 closed but T_2 open, we evacuate the bulb and tube through T_3, with a rotary pump. If the apparatus is clean, the mercury in A rises to the barometer height H. Meanwhile we put some ether in the funnel F. When the apparatus is evacuated, we close T_3 and T_2. We now open and close T_1, so that a little ether flows into the space C. Lastly, we open T_2, so that the ether evaporates into the bulb B. As it does so, the mercury in A falls, showing that the ether-vapour is exerting a pressure (Fig. 189 (b)). If h is the new height of the mercury in A, then the pressure of the vapour in mm. of mercury is equal to $H - h$.

By closing T_1, opening and closing T_2, and then opening T_1 again, we can introduce more ether into the space B. At first, we find that, with each introduction, the pressure of the vapour, $H - h$, increases. But we reach a point at which the introduction of more ether does not increase the pressure, the height of the mercury column remains constant at h'. At this point we notice that liquid ether appears above the mercury in A (Fig. 189 (c)). We say that the vapour in B is now *saturated*; a *saturated vapour* is one that is in contact with its own liquid.

Before the liquid appeared in the above experiment, the pressure of the vapour could be increased by introducing more ether, and we say that the vapour in B was then *unsaturated*.

8. Behaviour of Saturated Vapour.

To find out more about the saturated vapour, we may try to expand or compress it. We can try to compress it by raising the mercury reservoir M. But when we do, we find that the height h' does not change: the pressure of the vapour, $H - h'$, is therefore constant (Fig. 189 (d)). The only change we notice is an increase in the volume of liquid above the mercury. We conclude, therefore, that reducing the volume of a saturated vapour does not increase its pressure, but merely makes some of it condense to liquid.

Similarly, if we lower the reservoir M, to increase the volume of the vapour, we do not decrease its pressure. Its pressure stays constant, but the volume of liquid above the mercury now decreases; liquid evaporates, and keeps the vapour saturated. If we increase the volume of the vapour until all the liquid has evaporated, then the pressure of the vapour begins to fall, because it becomes unsaturated (see Fig. 190 (a)).

9. Effect of Temperature : Validity of Gas-laws for Vapours.

We cannot heat the apparatus of Fig. 189 through any great rise of temperature. But we can warm it with our hands, or by pointing an electric fire at it. If we do warm it, we find that the ether above the mercury evaporates further, and the pressure of the vapour increases. Experiments which we shall describe later show that the pressure of a saturated vapour rises, with the temperature, at a rate much greater than that given by Charles's law. Its rise is roughly exponential.

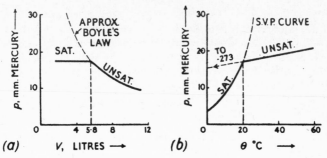

FIG. 190. Effect of volume and temperature on pressure of water vapour.

PROPERTIES OF SATURATED VAPOURS

Temperature °C.	Water Pressure, mm. mercury	Mercury Pressure, mm. mercury	Ethyl Ether Pressure, mm. mercury
−20	0·784 (ice)		
−10	1·96 ,,		112
0	4·56	0·00016	185
10	9·20	0·00043	291
20	17·5	0·0011	440
30	31·7	0·0026	
34·6			760
40	55·1	0·0057	921
50	92·3	0·0122	
60	149	0·0246	1,734
70	234		
80	355	0·0885	2,974
90	526		
100	760	0·276	4,855
150	3,569	2·88	
200	11,647	17·8	
250	29,770	75·8	
300	67,620	249	
356·7		760	

To Boyle's law, saturated vapours are indifferent: *their pressure is independent of their volume.* Unsaturated vapours obey Boyle's law roughly, as they also obey roughly Charles's law. Fig. 190 (*a*). Vapours, saturated and unsaturated, are gases in that they spread throughout their vessels; but we find it convenient to distinguish them by name from gases such as air, which obey Charles's and Boyle's laws closely. We shall elaborate this distinction later.

Fig. 190 (*b*) shows the effect of heating a saturated vapour. More and more of the liquid evaporates, and the pressure rises very rapidly.

As soon as all the liquid has evaporated, however, the vapour becomes unsaturated, and its pressure rises more sedately.

Fig. 191 (a) shows isothermals for a given mass of liquid and vapour at two temperatures, $\theta_1 = 10°$ C., and $\theta_2 = 21°$ C. The temperatures are chosen so that the saturated vapour pressure at θ_2 is double that at θ_1. The absolute temperatures are $T_1 = 273 + \theta_1 = 283°$ K, and and $T_2 = 273 + \theta_2 = 294°$ K. Because the saturated vapour pressure

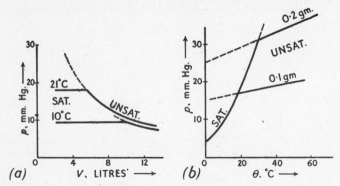

(a) *(b)*

Fig. 191. Relationship between pressure, temperature, total mass, and volume, for water-vapour and liquid.

rises so rapidly with temperature, the absolute temperature T_2 is not nearly double the absolute temperature T_1. Consequently the isothermals for the unsaturated vapour are fairly close together, as shown; and the transition from saturated to unsaturated vapour occurs at a smaller volume at the higher temperature.

Fig. 191 (b) shows pressure-temperature curves for a vapour, initially in contact with different amounts of liquid, in equal total volumes. The more liquid present, the greater is the density of the vapour when it becomes unsaturated, and therefore the higher the pressure and temperature at which it does so.

10. Kinetic Theory of Saturation.

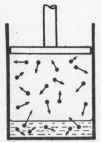

Fig. 192. Dynamic equilibrium.

Let us consider a vapour in contact with its liquid, in an otherwise empty vessel which is closed by a piston (Fig. 192). The molecules of the vapour, we suppose, are rushing randomly about, like the molecules of a gas, with kinetic energies whose average value is determined by the temperature of the vapour. They bombard the walls of the vessel, giving rise to the pressure of the vapour, and they also bombard the surface of the liquid.

The molecules of the liquid, we further suppose,

are also rushing about with kinetic energies determined by the temperature of the liquid. The fastest of them escape from the surface of the liquid. At the surface, therefore, there are molecules leaving the liquid, and molecules arriving from the vapour. To complete our picture of the conditions at the surface, we suppose that the vapour molecules bombarding it are not reflected—as they are at the walls of the vessel—but are absorbed into the liquid. We may expect them to be, because we consider that molecules near the surface of a liquid are attracted towards the body of the liquid.

We shall assume that the liquid and vapour have the same temperature. Then the proportions of liquid and vapour will not change, if the temperature and the total volume are kept constant. Therefore, at the surface of the liquid, molecules must be arriving and departing at the same rate, and hence evaporation from the liquid is balanced by condensation from the vapour. This state of affairs is called a *dynamic equilibrium*. In terms of it, we can explain the behaviour of a saturated vapour.

The rate at which molecules leave unit area of the liquid depends simply on their average kinetic energy, and therefore on the temperature. The rate at which molecules strike unit area of the liquid, from the vapour, likewise depends on the temperature; but it also depends on the concentration of the molecules in the vapour, that is to say, on the density of the vapour. The density and temperature of the vapour also determine its pressure; the rate of bombardment therefore depends on the pressure of the vapour.

Now let us suppose that we decrease the volume of the vessel in Fig. 192 by pushing in the piston. Then we momentarily increase the density of the vapour, and hence the number of its molecules striking the liquid surface per second. The rate of condensation thus becomes greater than the rate of evaporation, and the liquid grows at the expense of the vapour. As the vapour condenses its density falls, and so does the rate of condensation. The dynamic equilibrium is restored when the rate of condensation, and the density of the vapour, have returned to their original values. The pressure of the vapour will then also have returned to its original value. *Thus the pressure of a saturated vapour is independent of its volume.* The proportion of liquid to vapour, however, increases as the volume decreases.

Let us now suppose that we warm the vessel in Fig. 192, but keep the piston fixed. Then we increase the rate of evaporation from the liquid, and increase the proportion of vapour in the mixture. Since the volume is constant, the pressure of the vapour rises, and increases the rate at which molecules bombard the liquid. Thus the dynamic equilibrium is restored, at a higher pressure of vapour. The increase of pressure with temperature is rapid, because the rate of evaporation of the liquid increases rapidly—almost exponentially—with the temperature. A small rise in temperature causes a large increase in the proportion of molecules in the liquid moving fast enough to escape from it.

11. Boiling.

A liquid boils when its saturated vapour pressure is equal to the atmospheric pressure. To see that this is true, we take a closed J-shaped tube, with water trapped in its closed limb (Fig. 193 (*a*)). We heat the tube in a beaker of water, and watch the water in the J-tube. It remains trapped as at (*a*) until the water in the beaker is boiling. Then the water in the J-tube comes to the same level in each limb, showing that the pressure of the vapour in the closed limb is equal to the pressure of the air outside (Fig. 193 (*b*)).

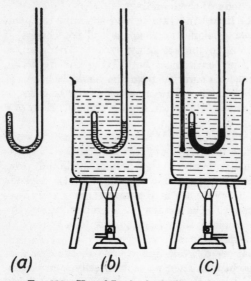

(a)   *(b)*   *(c)*

Fig. 193.   Use of J-tube for boiling-point.

The J-tube gives a simple means of measuring the boiling-point of a liquid which is inflammable, or which has a poisonous vapour, or of which only a small quantity can be had. A few drops of the liquid are imprisoned by mercury in the closed limb of the tube, all entrapped air having been shaken out (Fig. 193 (*c*)). The tube is then heated in a bath, and the temperature observed at which the mercury comes to the same level in both limbs. The bath is warmed a little further, and then a second observation made as the bath cools; the mean of the two observations is taken as the boiling-point of the liquid.

Boiling differs from evaporation in that a liquid evaporates from its surface alone, but it boils throughout its volume. If we ignore the small hydrostatic pressure of the liquid itself, we may say that the pressure throughout a vessel of liquid is the atmospheric pressure. Therefore, when the saturated vapour pressure is equal to the atmospheric pressure, a bubble of vapour can form anywhere in the liquid. Generally the bottom of the liquid is the hottest part of it, and bubbles form there and rise through the liquid to the surface. Just before the liquid boils, its bottom part may be at the boiling-point, and its upper part below. Bubbles of vapour then form at the bottom, rise in to the colder liquid, and then collapse. The collapsing gives rise to the singing of a kettle about to boil.

12. Further Consideration of Boiling.

The account of boiling which we have just given is crude because in it we ignored the effect of surface-tension. Because of surface tension, a bubble can exist in a liquid only if there is an excess pressure inside it. If T is the surface-tension of the liquid, and r the radius of the bubble, the excess pressure is $2T/r$. If the bubble is formed at a depth h below the surface of the liquid, as in Fig. 194, the external pressure acting on it is

$$P = P_a + h\rho g,$$

where P_a = atmospheric pressure, ρ = density of liquid, g = acceleration of gravity.

Therefore a bubble, of radius r, can form at a depth h only if its vapour pressure, p, satisfies the equation

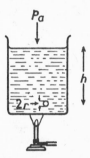

FIG. 194. Boiling.

$$p = P + \frac{2T}{r}$$

$$= P_a + h\rho g + \frac{2T}{r}.$$

If the radius r is small, the term $2T/r$ is great, and the bubble cannot form unless the vapour pressure is considerably above atmospheric. In fact the equation shows that a bubble can never start from zero radius, because it would require an infinite vapour pressure to do so. Bubbles actually form on roughnesses in the vessel, or specks of solid suspended in the liquid. Very clean water in a very smooth beaker may not boil until it is well above 100° C.; its bubbles then grow violently, and the liquid 'bumps' in the beaker. A piece of broken pipe-clay prevents bumping, by presenting fine points for the bubbles to form on.

Thus the temperature of a boiling liquid is not definite—it depends on the conditions of boiling. But the temperature of the vapour is definite. The vapour escaping is in equilibrium with the liquid at the surface, and is at atmospheric pressure. Its temperature, therefore, is the temperature at which the saturated vapour pressure is equal to the atmospheric pressure. This idea is important in defining the upper fixed point of the temperature scale (p. 184). We say that the upper fixed point is the temperature of the steam from water boiling under a pressure of 760 mm. mercury. We must not refer to the temperature of the water, and we must specify the atmospheric pressure because as we have just seen, it determines the temperature of the steam.

TEMPERATURE OF SATURATED STEAM AT PRESSURES NEAR NORMAL
ATMOSPHERIC

Barometer height, H, mm.	680	690	700	710	720	730	740	750	751
Temperature, θ, °C.	96·910	97·312	97·709	98·102	98·490	98·874	99·254	99·629	·666

Barometer height, H, mm.	752	753	754	755	756	757	758	759	760	761
Temperature, θ, °C.	·704	·741	·778	·815	·852	·889	·926	·963	100·000	·037

Barometer height, H, mm.	762	763	764	765	766	767	768	769	770	780
Temperature, θ, °C.	·074	·110	·147	·184	·220	·257	·294	·330	·367	·729

In general, around $H = 760$ mm., the temperature is given by

$$\theta = 100 + 0{\cdot}036\,(H - 760) - 2{\cdot}3 \times 10^{-5}\,(H - 760)^2.$$

13. Variation of Saturated Vapour Pressure with Temperature.

We can now see how the relationship between the pressure of a
saturated vapour and its temperature can be measured. We must
apply various known air pressures to the liquid, heat the liquid, and
measure the temperature of its vapour. Fig. 195 shows a suitable
apparatus, due to Regnault. The flask F contains the liquid, water in

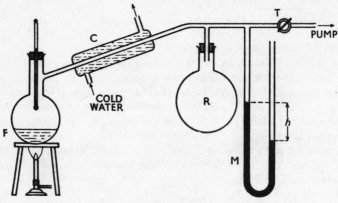

FIG. 195. Apparatus for variation of S.V.P. with temperature.

a laboratory experiment, and the flask R is an air reservoir. The
pressure of the air in R is shown by the mercury manometer M; if its
height is h, the pressure in mm. mercury is

$$p = H - h,$$

where H is the barometer height.

We first withdraw some air from R through the tap T, with a filter
pump, until p is about 700 mm. We then close T and heat the water
gently. The water vapour condenses in the condenser, and runs back

to the flask. After a few minutes the water boils steadily. The temperature of the vapour, θ, and the pressure, p, become constant and we record their values. We next remove the flame from the flask F, and let the apparatus cool for a minute or two. Then we withdraw some more air from R, close T again, and repeat the observations.

If we wish to find the saturated vapour pressure when it is above atmospheric, that is to say, when the temperature is above the normal boiling-point of the liquid, air is pumped into the reservoir R—with a bicycle pump—instead of drawing it out. The manometer M then shows the excess pressure, and

$$p = H + h.$$

With simple glass apparatus we cannot go far in this direction.

14. Boiling Point of a Solution.

At a given pressure, the boiling-point of water containing a dissolved substance is higher than that of pure water. The temperature of the steam evolved from the solution, however, is the temperature of saturated steam at the prevailing pressure. Traces of dissolved substances in the water therefore do not affect the steam point in thermometry.

Since a liquid boils when its saturated vapour pressure is equal to the atmospheric pressure, we must conclude that dissolving a substance in water lowers its saturated vapour pressure, at a given temperature (Fig. 196). We may explain this by supposing that the mole-

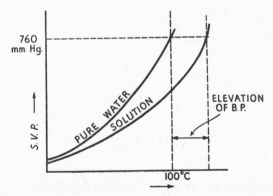

Fig. 196. Effect of solute on saturated vapour pressure.

cules of the dissolved substance, which do not evaporate, hinder the escape of the molecules of the water.

The lowering of the vapour pressure of water by a dissolved solid gives striking support to the kinetic theory of evaporation. For measurements of the vapour pressure show that reduction does not depend on the nature of the solute; it depends only on the number of dissolved particles in the solution expressed as a fraction of the total number of particles (solute plus water molecules). In fact, if there are n solute particles to every 100-n water molecules, then

$$\frac{\Delta p}{p} = \frac{n}{100},$$

where p is the saturated vapour pressure of water, and Δp is the lowering by solution. Thus the lowering simply depends on the number of particles hindering evaporation.

15. Effect of Altitude on Boiling Point.

The pressure of the atmosphere decreases with increasing height above the earth's surface, because the thickness, and therefore the weight, of the belt of air above the observer decreases. The rate of fall in pressure is almost uniform over fairly small heights—about 85 mm. mercury per km., or 1 in. mercury per 1,000 ft. But at great altitudes the rate of fall diminishes. At the height of Everest, 29,000 ft., the atmospheric pressure is about 11 in. of mercury, or 28 cm. On account of the fall in atmospheric pressure, the boiling point of water falls with increasing height. Cooking-pots for use in high mountainous districts, such as the Andes, are therefore fitted with clamped lids. As the water boils, the steam accumulates in the pot, and its pressure rises above atmospheric. At about 760 mm. mercury a safety valve opens, so that the pressure does not rise above that value, and the cooking is done at 100° C.

The fall in the boiling-point with atmospheric pressure gives a simple way of determining one's height above sea-level. One observes the steam point with a thermometer and hypsometer (p. 184). Knowing how the steam point falls with pressure, and how atmospheric pressure falls with increasing height, one can then find one's altitude. The hypsometer was, in fact, devised for this purpose, and takes its name from it; *hypsos* is Greek for height. Hypsometers have been carried up Himalayan peaks; and one was found by Scott and his companions in Amundsen's abandoned tent at the South Pole.

16. Variation of Latent Heat with Temperature.

When we speak of the latent heat of evaporation of a liquid, we usually mean the heat required to vaporize unit mass of it at its normal boiling-point, that is to say, under normal atmospheric pressure. But since evaporation takes place at all temperatures, the latent heat has a value for every temperature. Regnault measured the latent heat of steam over a range of temperatures, by boiling water at controlled pressures, as in measuring its saturated vapour pressure. His apparatus was in principle similar to Berthelot's (Fig. 137); but he connected the outlet tube to an air reservoir, manometer, and pump, as in Fig. 195. Modern measurements give, approximately,

$$L = 600 - 0.6\theta,$$

where L is the latent heat in calories per gm. at $\theta°$ C.

17. Internal and External Latent Heats.

The volume of 1 gm. of steam at 100° C. is 1,672 cm.^{3} Therefore when 1 gm. of water turns into steam, it expands by 1,671 cm.^{3}; in doing so, it does work against the atmospheric pressure. The heat equivalent of this work is that part of the latent heat which must be supplied to the water to make it overcome atmospheric pressure as it evaporates; it is called the "external latent heat". The rest of the latent heat—the internal part—is the equivalent of the work done in separating the molecules, against their mutual attractions.

The work done, W, in the expansion of 1 gm. from water to steam is the product of the atmospheric pressure p and the increase in volume ΔV:
$$W = p.\Delta V.$$

Normal atmospheric pressure corresponds to a barometer height H of 76 cm.; therefore
$$p = g\rho H = 981 \times 13.6 \times 76$$
$$= 1.013 \times 10^6 \text{ dynes/cm.}^2$$
and
$$W = p.\Delta V = 1.013 \times 10^6 \times 1,671.$$

The heat equivalent of this is W/J, where J is the mechanical equivalent of heat (4.19×10^7 ergs/calorie); the external latent heat is therefore
$$L_{ex} = \frac{W}{J} = \frac{1.013 \times 10^6 \times 1,671}{4.19 \times 10^7}$$
$$= 41 \text{ cal./gm.}$$

This result shows that the external part of the latent heat is much less than the internal part. Since the total latent heat L is 540 cal./gm., the internal part is
$$L_{in} = L - L_{ex} = 540 - 41$$
$$= 499 \text{ cal./gm.}$$

18. Density of a Saturated Vapour.

In any experiment to measure the density of a saturated vapour, the vessel containing the vapour must also contain some liquid, to ensure that the vapour is saturated. The problem is therefore to find how much of the total mass is vapour, and how much is liquid. Fig. 197 shows one method of solving this problem, due to Cailletet and Mathias.

A, B are two glass tubes, which have

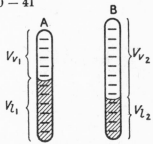

Fig. 197. Determination of density of a saturated vapour.

been calibrated with volume scales, and then evacuated. Known masses m_1, m_2 of liquid are introduced into the tubes, which are then sealed off. The tubes are warmed to the same temperature in a bath, and the volumes of liquid V_{l_1}, V_{l_2} and of vapour $V_{v_1}V_{v_2}$ are observed. Then if ρ_l and ρ_v are the densities of liquid and vapour respectively:

$$m_1 = \rho_l V_{l_1} + \rho_v V_{v_1}$$
$$m_2 = \rho_l V_{l_2} + \rho_v V_{v_2}.$$

From these equations ρ_l can be eliminated, and ρ_v found. The equations can also, of course, be made to give ρ_l; this method is useful for finding the density of a liquid "gas"—e.g. liquid oxygen (p. 329).

19. Density of an Unsaturated Vapour.

We have seen that the molecular weight of a gas, μ, is given very nearly by $\mu = 2\Delta$, where Δ is the density of the gas relative to that of hydrogen (p. 230). The proof that $\mu = 2\Delta$ depends on Avogadro's principle, which says that equal volumes of all gases at the same temperature and pressure contain equal numbers of molecules. This principle is true only of those gases which we normally call "perfect"—which obey Boyle's and Charles's laws accurately (p. 226). It is not true of saturated vapours, but it is roughly true of vapours which are far from saturation. To find the molecular weight of a substance which is liquid at room temperature, therefore, we must vaporize it, and measure the density of its vapour when it is as far from saturation as we can conveniently get it.

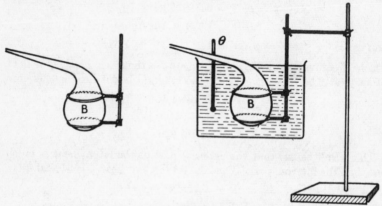

Fig. 198. Determination of density of an unsaturated vapour.

Several methods have been devised for doing this, one of which, Dumas's of 1827, is illustrated in Fig. 198. A glass bulb B, with a long thin stem, is weighed and then partly filled with liquid by warming and dipping. The amount of liquid introduced must be great enough to ensure that all the air in the bulb will be driven out by vapour when the liquid evaporates. The liquid is made to evaporate by plunging the bulb into a bath at a temperature θ about 40° C. above its boiling-point. It then evaporates rapidly, and its vapour sweeps the air out of the bulb. When vapour has stopped coming out, the stem is sealed with a flame: the bulb now contains nothing but the vapour, at the temperature θ and under atmospheric pressure.

The bulb is removed, allowed to cool, dried, and weighed. The stem is then broken at the tip under water; since nearly all the vapour has condensed, at the room temperature, water rushes in and fills the bulb.

Let m_1 = mass of bulb full of air, at room temperature.

$m_2 =$ „ „ „ vapour.

$m_3 =$ „ „ „ water.

Since the mass of air in the bulb is negligible compared with that of water, we have, *numerically*,

Volume of bulb in cm.^{3}, V_1, $= m_3 - m_1$ in gm.

The mass of air in the bulb at room temperature is

$$m_a = V \rho_a,$$

where ρ_a is the density of air at room temperature and atmospheric pressure. The mass of the bulb itself is

$$m_b = m_1 - m_a,$$

and the mass of vapour which filled it when hot is

$$m_v = m_2 - m_b.$$

This mass of vapour occupied the volume V_1 at the temperature θ; its density was therefore

$$\rho_v = \frac{m_v}{V_1}.$$

Since the temperature was well above the boiling-point, the vapour was far from saturated; Boyle's and Charles's laws can therefore be used to reduce its density to s.t.p., for comparison with that of hydrogen.

WATER-VAPOUR IN THE ATMOSPHERE: HYGROMETRY

The water vapour in the atmosphere is important because it affects our comfort. Except in cold weather, we sweat continuously: the water in the sweat evaporates, draws its latent heat of evaporation from the skin, and so keeps us cool. Beads of sweat appear only when the water cannot evaporate as fast as it reaches the surface of the skin; we then feel uncomfortably hot.

On the other hand, if water evaporates from the skin too rapidly, the skin feels parched and hard; around the mucous membranes—at the mouth and nose—it tends to crack.

The rate at which water evaporates, from the skin or anywhere else, depends on the pressure of the water vapour surrounding it. If the water vapour above the skin is far from saturated, evaporation is swift. If the vapour is already saturated, water reaching the skin comes immediately into dynamic equilibrium with it; individual molecules are exchanged between liquid and vapour, but no mass of liquid is lost, and water accumulates.

20. The Partial Pressure of Atmospheric Water.

The atmosphere contains other gases besides water-vapour, such as oxygen and nitrogen. In speaking of the water-vapour, therefore, we must refer to its "partial pressure", as explained on p. 222.

Water-vapour in the atmosphere is also important because it affects the weather. Let us suppose that the atmosphere has a temperature of 20° C.—a warm day—and that the water vapour in it has a partial pressure of 12 mm. mercury. It will have a density of about 12 mg. per litre. The density of *saturated* water vapour at 20° C. is 17·3 mg. per litre, and its pressure 17·5 mm. mercury. The water vapour in the atmosphere is therefore not saturated.

Now let us suppose that the atmosphere cools to 14° C., without changing its composition. The 6°C. fall in temperature will hardly affect the density of the water vapour, but it will bring the atmosphere to saturation. For the pressure of saturated water vapour at 14° C. is 12 mm. mercury, and its density about 12 mg. per litre. If the atmosphere cools any further, water vapour will condense out of it, forming drops of liquid water—that is, of fog or cloud.

21. Relative Humidity.

The dampness of the atmosphere, besides affecting the weather and our comfort, is important also in storage and manufacture of many substances—tobacco and cotton, for example. From what we have said already, we can see that the important factor is not the actual proportion of water vapour in the atmosphere, but its nearness to saturation. In the above example, the density of the vapour remained almost constant, but we would have felt the atmosphere becoming much damper as it cooled from 20° C. to 14° C.

The dampness of the atmosphere is expressed by its *relative humidity*, *R.H.*, which is defined as follows:

$$R.H. = \frac{\text{mass of water-vapour in a given volume of atmosphere}}{\text{mass of an equal volume of saturated water-vapour at the same temperature}} \quad \cdot \quad (1)$$

In other words,

$$R.H. = \frac{\text{density of water-vapour in atmosphere}}{\text{density of saturated water-vapour at the same temperature}}$$

Because an unsaturated vapour roughly obeys Boyle's law, its density is roughly proportional to its pressure; the relative humidity as defined above is therefore roughly given by

$$R.H. = \frac{\text{partial pressure of water-vapour present}}{\text{S.V.P. at temperature of atmosphere}}.$$

where S.V.P. stands for "saturated vapour pressure".

Before describing the methods of measurement, we must warn the reader against thinking that the atmosphere "takes up" water vapour. The atmosphere is not a sponge. Water-vapour exists in it in its own right; and our knowledge of vapours makes us feel sure that, if we could live in an atmosphere of water-vapour alone, we would have just the same experiences of humidity as we now have in our happily richer surroundings.

22. Dew-point.

In the evening, the earth cools more rapidly, by radiation, than the air above it. Then, on smooth surfaces such as metals, we often find a thin film of moisture. The surface has cooled to such a temperature that the water vapour in contact with it has become saturated, and has begun to condense. No fog has formed because the atmosphere in general is warmer than the cold solid, and the vapour in it is not saturated. The temperature of a cold surface on which dew just appears is called the *dew-point*: it is *the temperature at which the saturated vapour-pressure of water is equal to the partial pressure of the water-vapour present in the atmosphere.*

If we know the dew-point, we can find the corresponding pressure of saturated water-vapour, p_1, from tables. From the same tables we can find the pressure of saturated water-vapour at the temperature of the atmosphere. If this is p_2, then, from p. 314, the relative humidity, *R.H.*, is given by

$$R.H. = \frac{p_1}{p_2} \quad \cdot \quad \cdot \quad \cdot \quad \cdot \quad \cdot \quad \cdot \quad (2)$$

23. Dew-point Hygrometers.

Hygrometry is the measurement of relative humidity, and a *hygrometer* is an instrument for measuring it. Many forms of dew-point hygrometer have been devised; we shall describe only the one due, like so much apparatus in Heat, to Regnault. It consists of two glass tubes, A, B, with silver-plated thimbles C, D cemented on to their lower ends. C contains ether, into which dips a thermometer T and a glass tube R (Fig. 199). To use the hygrometer, we first place a sheet of glass between it and ourselves, to prevent our breath from adding to the humidity of the air around it. We then gently blow air through the ether, by means of a scent-spray bulb connected through a rubber tube to R. (Alternatively, we may pass

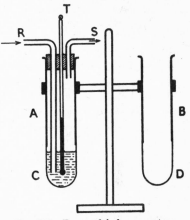

FIG. 199. Regnault's hygrometer.

in a gentle stream of coal-gas, and burn it at the end of a long tube connected to the outlet S.) The gas or air passing through the ether carries away its vapour, and makes it evaporate continuously. In doing so it cools, since it must provide its latent heat of evaporation from its own heat content. When the ether has cooled to the dew-point, a film of mist appears on the thimble C; the thimble D enables us to notice this more sharply, by contrast. At the moment when the dew appears, the thermometer T is read. The flow of air or gas through the ether is stopped, and the ether allowed to warm up. The temperature at which the dew vanishes is noted, and the mean of this and the temperature at which it appeared is taken as the dew-point, θ_1 say. By so doing we correct reasonably well for any difference of temperature between the ether and the outer surface of the tube. Lastly, we take the temperature of the room, θ_2, often from a thermometer (not shown) in B, and look up the saturation pressures at θ_1, θ_2 respectively. These are given in the following table. Then

$$\text{relative humidity} = \frac{\text{S.V.P. at } \theta_1}{\text{S.V.P. at } \theta_2} \times 100 \text{ per cent.}$$

PRESSURE AND DENSITY OF SATURATED WATER VAPOUR

$\theta°$ C.	0	2	4	6	8	10	12	14	16	18	20
p, mm. mercury . .	4·58	5·29	6·10	7·01	8·04	9·21	10·5	12·0	·13·6	15·5	17·5
ρ, mg./litre (or gm./metre³)	4·84	5·54	6·33	7·22	8·21	9·33	10·6	12·0	13·5	15·2	17·1

$\theta°$ C.	22	24	26	28	30	32	34	36	38	40
p, mm. mercury . .	19·8	22·3	25·1	28·3	31·7	35·5	39·8	44·4	49·5	55·1
ρ, mg./litre (or gm./metre³)	19·2	21·5	24·1	26·9	30·0	33·5	37·2	41·3	45·8	51·1

24. The Wet-and-dry-bulb Hygrometer.

A piece of wet cloth feels cold, because the moisture evaporating from it takes latent heat, and cools the remaining liquid. This effect is used in the *wet-and-dry-bulb hygrometer*. A piece of muslin is tied round the bulb of a thermometer, and allowed to dip into a small

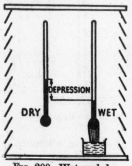

FIG. 200. Wet-and-dry bulb hygrometer.

jar of water. It is mounted, with a second, dry-bulb, thermometer, in a louvred draught-shield (Fig. 200). The rate at which water evaporates from the muslin increases as the relative humidity of the atmosphere falls; the cooling of the wet bulb therefore also increases. The greater the difference in reading of the two thermometers, the less is the relative humidity. By calibration against a chemical hygrometer, tables and charts have been prepared which give the relative humidity in terms of the thermometer readings.

Dry-bulb reading °C.	Difference (depression of wet-bulb), °C.									
	1	2	3	4	5	6	8	10	12	14
0	82	65	48	31%						
5	85	72	58	45	32%					
10	88	76	65	54	44	34%				
15	90	80	71	61	52	44	27	12%		
20	91	83	74	66	59	51	37	24	12%	
25	92	84	77	70	63	57	44	33	22	12%
30		86	79	73	67	61	50	39	30	21%

The wet-and-dry-bulb hygrometer is not very reliable when used in a simple screen. It is more accurate if a steady stream of air is driven past it by a fan, or by whirling the thermometers around in a frame like a football-fan's rattle. The hygrometer is then said to be ventilated.

25. The Hair Hygrometer.

Human hair expands in length in damp air. A hair hygrometer is one consisting of a bundle of hairs fixed to a spring at one end, and wrapped round a spindle at the other. The expansion of the hair turns the spindle and moves a pointer over a scale, which is directly calibrated in relative humidities. Such instruments need to be re-calibrated frequently, because the hair shows elastic fatigue.

THE BEHAVIOUR OF REAL GASES; CRITICAL PHENOMENA

A perfect, or ideal, gas is one which obeys Boyle's law and Charles's exactly, and whose internal energy is independent of its volume. No such gas exists, but at room temperature, and under moderate pressures, many gases approach the ideal closely enough for most purposes.

We shall consider now the departures of gases from perfection; in doing so we shall come to appreciate better the relationship between liquid, vapour, and gas, and we shall see how gases such as air can be liquefied.

26. Departures from Boyle's Law.

In 1847 Regnault measured the volumes of various gases at pressures of several atmospheres. Using the apparatus of Fig. 201, he found that, to halve the volume of the gas, he did not have quite to double the pressure on it. The product pV, therefore, instead of being constant, decreased slightly with the pressure. He found one exception

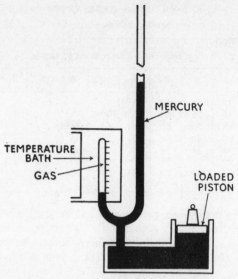

FIG. 201. Regnault's apparatus for isothermals at high pressure.

to this rule: hydrogen. By compressing the gases further, Regnault found the variation of pV with p at constant temperature, and obtained results which are represented by the early parts of the curves in Fig. 202.

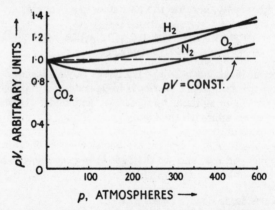

FIG. 202. Isothermals for various gases, at room temperature and high pressure.

The complete curves in the figure show some of the results obtained by Amagat in 1892. Amagat's apparatus for nitrogen is shown in Fig. 203. To get high pressures, he put the apparatus at the bottom of a coal-mine, and made the manometer tube out of rifle barrels, screwed together and standing up the shaft. He reached a pressure of 3,000 atmospheres.

Having found the volume-pressure relationship for nitrogen, Amagat used it to measure high pressures in the laboratory, without having to resort to the mine. His method was similar to that of Andrews, which we are about to describe; by means of it he found the pressure-volume relationships for other gases.

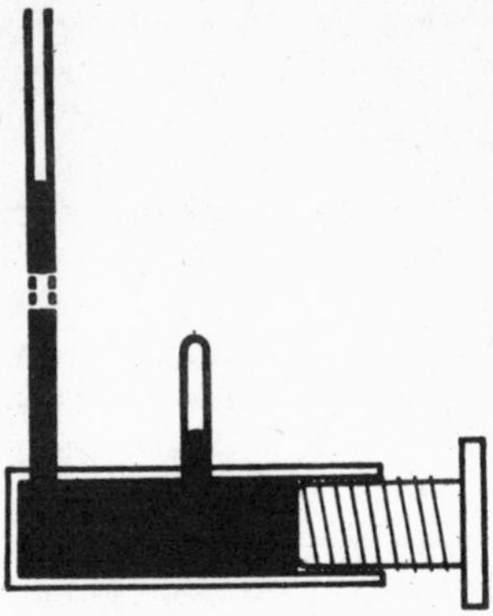

FIG. 203. Amagat's apparatus for isothermals at high pressure.

27. Andrews's Work on Carbon Dioxide.

In 1863 Andrews made experiments on carbon dioxide which have become classics. Fig. 204 shows his apparatus. In the glass tube A he trapped carbon dioxide above the pellet of mercury X. To do this, he started with the tube open at both ends and passed the gas through it for a long time. Then he

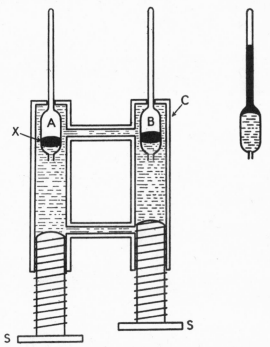

FIG. 204. Andrews's apparatus for isothermals of CO_2 at high pressures.

sealed the end of the capillary. He introduced the mercury pellet by warming the tube, and allowing it to cool with the open end dipping into mercury. Similarly, he trapped nitrogen in the tube B.

Andrews then fitted the tubes into the copper casing C, which contained water. By turning the screws S, he forced water into the lower parts of the tubes A and B, and drove the mercury upwards. The wide parts of the tubes were under the same pressure inside and out, and so were under no stress. The capillary extensions were strong enough to withstand hundreds of atmospheres. Andrews actually reached 108 atmospheres.

When the screws S were turned far into the casing, the gases were forced into the capillaries, as shown on the right of the figure, and greatly compressed. From the known volumes of the wide parts of the tubes, and the calibrations of the capillaries, Andrews determined the volumes of the gases. He estimated the pressure from the compression of the nitrogen, assuming that it obeyed Boyle's law.

For work above and below room temperature, Andrews surrounded the capillary part of A with a water bath, which he maintained at a constant temperature between about 10° C. and 50° C.

Fig. 205 shows some of Andrews's results, corrected for the departure of nitrogen from Boyle's law; it also shows the results of similar experiments over a wider range of temperature, by Amagat in 1893.

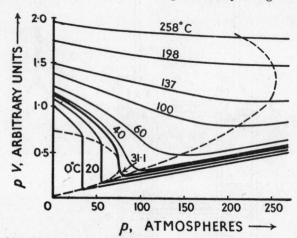

FIG. 205. Isothermals for CO_2, as pV/p curves, at various temperatures. The small dotted loop passes through the ends of the vertical parts; the large dotted loop is the locus of the minima of pV.

28. Critical Temperature.

Before we can interpret Andrews's results for carbon dioxide, we must describe a simple experiment, made by Cagniard de la Tour in

1822. De la Tour made a tube of strong glass, as shown in Fig. 206. In the bulb he had water, round the bend mercury, and at the top —where the tube was sealed off—air. He heated the tube in a bath to over 300° C. The expansion of the liquids was taken up by the compression of the air, from which de la Tour estimated the pressure; it went beyond 100 atmospheres. Above about 100° C. he observed what we would expect; that a meniscus formed in the bulb, showing that steam was present as well as water. But above

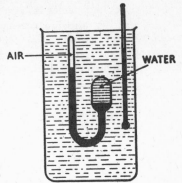

FIG. 206. Cagniard de la Tour's experiment.

about 300° C. he noticed that the meniscus vanished: that there was no observable distinction between liquid and vapour. The temperature at which the meniscus vanished he called the *critical temperature*.

If we consider the nature of a saturated vapour, the phenomenon of the critical temperature need not surprise us. For as its temperature rises a saturated vapour becomes denser, whereas a liquid becomes less dense. The critical temperature is, we may suppose, the temperature at which liquid and saturated vapour have the same density. Fig. 207 supports this view: it shows the results of measurements made on liquid oxygen by the method of Cailletet and Mathias (p. 311).

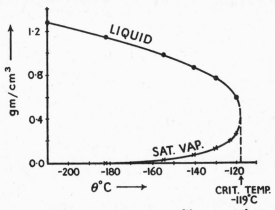

FIG. 207. Densities of liquid oxygen, and its saturated vapour.

29. Behaviour of Carbon Dioxide near the Critical Point.

Now let us turn to Andrews's isothermals for carbon dioxide. These are shown again, this time as a simple pressure-volume diagram, in

Fig. 208. Let us consider the one for 21·5° C., ABCD. Andrews noticed that, when the pressure reached the value corresponding to B, a meniscus appeared above the mercury in the capillary containing the carbon dioxide. He concluded that the liquid had begun to form. From B to C, he found no change in pressure as the screws were turned,

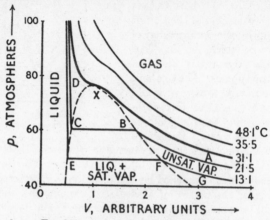

FIG. 208. Andrews's isothermals for CO_2.

but simply a decrease in the volume of the carbon dioxide. At the same time the meniscus moved upwards, suggesting that the proportion of liquid was increasing. At C the meniscus disappeared at the top of the tube, suggesting that the carbon dioxide had become wholly liquid. Beyond C the pressure rose very rapidly; this confirmed the idea that the carbon dioxide was wholly liquid, since liquids are almost incompressible.

Thus the part CBA of the isothermal for 21·5° C. is a curve of volume against pressure for a liquid and vapour, showing saturation at B; it is like the isothermal for water given in Fig. 190 (a), p. 303. And the curve GFE is another such isothermal, for the lower temperature 13·1° C.; the two curves are like the two in Fig. 191 (a), p. 304.

The isothermal for 31·1° C. has no extended plateau; it merely shows a point of inflection at X. At that temperature, Andrews observed no meniscus; he concluded that it was the critical temperature. The isothermals for temperature above 31·1° C. never become horizontal, and show no breaks such as B or F. At temperatures above the critical, no transition from gas to liquid can be observed.

The isothermal for 48·1° C. conforms fairly well to Boyle's law; even when the gas is highly compressed its behaviour is not far from ideal.

The point X in Fig. 208 is called the critical point. The pressure and volume (of unit mass) corresponding to it are called the *critical pressure* and *volume*; the reciprocal of the critical volume is the critical density.

CRITICAL CONSTANTS OF GASES AND BOILING POINTS
(At atmospheric pressure)

Substance	Critical			Boiling-point °C.
	Temperature °C.	Pressure, atmospheres	Density gm./cm.³	
Argon . . .	— 122	48	0·53	— 186
Neon . . .	— 229	27	0·48	— 246
Helium . . .	— 268	2·26	0·069	— 269
Chlorine . . .	146	76	0·57	— 34
Hydrogen . . .	— 240	12·8	0·031	— 253
Nitrogen . . .	— 146	33	0·31	— 196
Oxygen . . .	— 118	50	0·43	— 183
Air	— 140	39	0·35	
Ammonia . . .	130	115	0·24	— 33·5
Carbon dioxide . .	31·1	73	0·46	— 78·2
Ethylene . . .	10	52	0·22	— 102·7
Freon, CCl_2F_2 . .	112	40	0·56	
Sulphur dioxide .	155	79	0·52	— 10·8
Water . . .	374	219	0·4	100

The above account of the phenomena near the critical point is over-simple, and may create the impression that these phenomena are fully understood. They are not; but this is not the place to say much about the matter. We may just point out that, even at temperatures well above the critical, and when no meniscus can be seen, considerable differences of density can be found in a so-called gas. They have been shown by includ-ing, in a sealed tube of liquid and vapour, a number of small glass balls of different densities. When the tube was heated above the critical tempera-ture, each ball floated at a point where the substance had a density equal to that of the ball.

30. Gases and Vapours.

A gas above its critical temperature cannot be liquefied. Early attempts to liquefy gases such as air, by compression without cooling, failed; and the gases were wrongly called "permanent" gases. We still, for convenience, refer to a gas as a vapour when it is below its critical temperature, and as a gas when it is above it. But the distinc-tion is not the same as that between an ideal gas and one which is far from ideal. For a gas which is near its critical point, though it may be a little above its critical temperature, does not obey Boyle's law, as Fig. 208 shows. On the other hand, a vapour which is far from satura-tion obeys Boyle's law fairly well.

31. Refrigeration.

The action of a refrigerator depends on the absorption of its latent heat by a liquid—the working substance—in evaporating.   The working substance must be one whose vapour has a critical temperature above normal atmospheric temperatures, so that it can be liquefied by compression alone. Common working substances are ammonia, carbon dioxide, sulphur dioxide, and specially developed compounds such as the two varieties of Freon: CCl_2F_2, and $C_2Cl_2F_4$. The working substance is compressed by a pump, P, in Fig. 209, and passed through a metal pipe C; there the heat of compression is carried away by circulating water, and the substance liquefies. The liquid passes to a reservoir R. From the reservoir, liquid escapes through a throttle valve V into the coil D, which is connected to the low pressure side of the pump. The coil D lies round the walls of the space to be cooled (not shown).

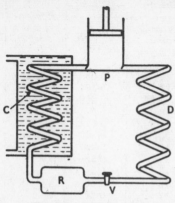

FIG. 209. Refrigeration.

When the liquid escapes from the reservoir, it starts to evaporate, because of the low pressure. It draws its latent heat from its own heat content, and cools. Not all of the liquid evaporates as it emerges, and the mixture of cool liquid and vapour passes round the metal coil D. If the atmosphere in the chamber containing D is warmer than the liquid, the liquid evaporates further. The latent heat which it requires is furnished by the surroundings of D, which are therefore cooled.

THE EQUILIBRIUM OF SOLID, LIQUID AND VAPOUR

We have pointed out that solids as well as liquids evaporate (p. 300). A solid thus has saturated vapour over it, just as a liquid has, and the pressure of the saturated vapour depends on the temperature. The table on p. 303 shows the pressure of saturated water vapour over ice, at — 10° C. and — 20° C.

32. The Triple Point.

In Fig. 210, the curve AP relates the saturated vapour pressure of ice to its temperature; at any point on the curve, ice and water-vapour are in equilibrium. BP is the saturated-vapour-pressure curve of water; at any point on it, water and water-vapour are in equilibrium. CP is the curve relating the melting-point of ice with the pressure: at any point on it, ice and water are in equilibrium. The three curves meet at the point P, whose co-ordinates are $p = 4.6$ mm. mercury, $\theta = 0.01°$ C. These are the only conditions in which ice, water, and water-vapour can exist together: if either the temperature or pressure is altered, at least one phase vanishes. If, when the pressure and temperature are altered, their new values happen to lie on one of the curves, then the two corresponding phases survive, liquid and solid along PC, for example. But if the new conditions lie in one of the three sectors of the diagram—say in PAC—

then the only phase which survives is the one corresponding to that sector: solid, in PAC. The point P is called the *triple point*.

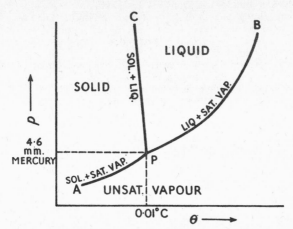

Fig. 210. Triple point for water (*not to scale*).

The curve AP, which gives the saturated vapour pressure of ice, is steeper at P than the curve BP for water. It is steeper because a solid evaporates less readily than a liquid—molecules escape from it less easily. Therefore the saturated-vapour-pressure of the solid falls more rapidly with the temperature.

Fig. 211 shows the triple point for carbon dioxide. Its co-ordinates are $p = 3,880$ mm. mercury, $\theta = -56.6°$ C. At atmospheric pressure, 760

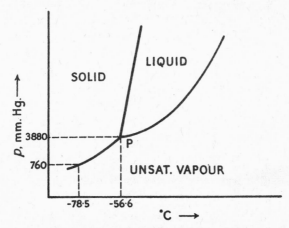

Fig. 211. Triple point for carbon dioxide (*not to scale*).

mm. mercury, therefore, solid carbon dioxide (CO_2) can be in equilibrium with its vapour, but not with liquid CO_2. It is therefore dry, and in America it is called "dry ice"; in England it is called "carbon-dioxide snow". At atmospheric pressure its temperature is — 78·5° C., and it is much used as a coolant—in ice-cream trucks, for example.

Solid carbon dioxide is prepared by simply opening the valve of a cylinder containing carbon dioxide at high pressure. The gas rushes out, and does work in acquiring kinetic energy of mass motion. Since the expansion is rapid, it is adiabatic, and the gas cools. As it does so, it goes over directly to the solid phase.

When solid carbon dioxide is warmed, it goes over directly into vapour. So, incidentally, do solid iodine and a few other substances, at atmospheric pressure. The change from solid to vapour is called sublimation. As the diagram shows, liquid CO_2 cannot exist at any temperature at all, if the pressure is below 3,880 mm. mercury (5·1 atmospheres).

33. Freezing of Solutions.

We have seen that dissolving a solid in water lowers its vapour pressure, and also its freezing-point (p. 300). To explain the lowering of the freezing-point, let us draw, as in Fig. 212, the curves of the saturated vapour pressures

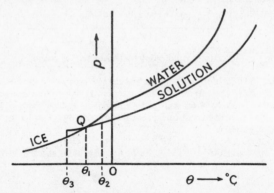

Fig. 212. Equilibrium between ice and a solution in water.

of ice, water and solution. We see that the curve for the solution cuts the ice curve at a point Q which corresponds to a temperature θ_1, below 0° C. This is the only temperature at which ice and solution can be in equilibrium. At a higher temperature, θ_2, ice has the higher vapour pressure: it therefore sublimes faster than water evaporates from the solution, and, on the whole, vapour from the ice condenses into the solution. At a lower temperature θ_3, the solution has the higher vapour pressure; water therefore evaporates from it faster than the ice sublimes, and, on the whole, water from the solution condenses on the ice. Thus the temperature θ_1 is the freezing-point of the solution. It is the temperature at which solution and ice exchange water molecules one for one, and neither grows at the expense of the other.

We can now see why ice and salt, for example, form a freezing mixture. When salt is mixed with ice, it dissolves in the water clinging to the ice, and forms a solution. Since this is above its melting-point, being at 0° C., it has a lower saturation vapour pressure than the ice (Fig. 212). Therefore the ice sublimes and condenses in the solution. In effect, the ice becomes water. And in doing so it abstracts its latent heat of fusion from its surroundings. Thus the mixture changes from solid ice and salt to a liquid solution of salt, and its temperature falls below 0° C.

LIQUEFACTION OF GASES

If one of the so-called permanent gases, hydrogen or nitrogen, is to be liquefied, it must first be cooled below its critical temperature. There are three principal ways of doing this: (i) the gas may be passed through a cold bath containing a more easily liquefied gas, which is boiling at a reduced pressure and therefore has a very low temperature; (ii) the gas may be allowed to expand adiabatically and do work, losing its heat-energy in the process; (iii) the gas may be cooled by a method depending on the fact that, for a real gas, the internal energy is not independent of the volume.

The third of these is the commonest nowadays, and the only one which we shall describe. First we must explain the phenomenon on which it depends.

34. The Joule-Kelvin Effect.

We have already described, on p. 241, Joule's crude experiments on the expansion of a gas into a vacuum—a "free expansion", as it is called. These experiments suggested that in such an expansion the

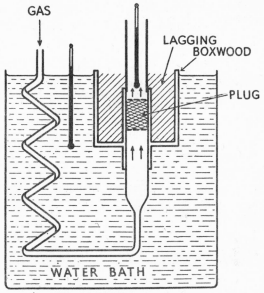

Fig. 213. Joule-Kelvin apparatus.

gas lost no internal energy, and therefore did no work. We concluded that the molecules of a gas had negligible attraction for one another, since otherwise work would have had to be done against their attractions whenever the gas expanded.

In 1852, Joule and Kelvin made more delicate experiments of essentially the same kind. They allowed a gas at high pressure to expand into a vacuum through a plug of cotton wool (Fig. 213). The plug prevented eddies from forming in the gas, so that the gas did not acquire any kinetic energy of motion in bulk. Neither did the gas do any external work, since it pushed back no piston. Nevertheless, Joule and Kelvin found that the gas was cooled slightly in its passage through the porous plug. Therefore work must have been done in separating its molecules; and this work must have been done at the expense of their kinetic energy, the heat-energy of the gas.

The magnitude of the cooling in the Joule-Kelvin effect depends on the temperature at which the gas enters the plug; for air at room temperature it has the order of $0 \cdot 1°$ C. per atmosphere pressure difference.

It is not essential for the gas to expand into a vacuum. Whenever a gas expands from high pressure to low, its volume increases, and some work is done against its inter-molecular attractions. If heat cannot enter the gas, the work is done at the expense of the gas's internal energy, and the gas cools. The cooling is analogous to that which takes place in an adiabatic expansion, but in a normal adiabatic expansion most of the work is done externally against a piston (compare p. 251). An ideal gas would cool in an adiabatic expansion with external work, but not in a free expansion—it would show no Joule-Kelvin effect.

35. The Linde Process.

The cooling of a gas in a free expansion is small, but Linde devised an ingenious arrangement for making it cumulative, and so producing a great temperature fall. His apparatus is shown diagrammatically in Fig. 214. When air is to be liquefied, it must first be freed of carbon dioxide and water, which would solidify and choke the pipes; both are removed by solid caustic soda in a vessel not shown in the figure. The pure air is compressed to about 150 atmospheres by the pump P, and the heat of compression is removed in the water-cooled copper coil C. The air then passes down the copper coil D, which runs within another copper coil E. It emerges through the nozzle N whose opening can be adjusted from outside. The nozzle lies inside a Dewar vessel or thermos flask F. The air expands on emerging, and is cooled by the Joule-Kelvin effect. It then passes upwards through the outer coil E, and as it does so, cools the incoming gas. The incoming gas is thus cooled before making its expansion, and after its expansion becomes cooler still. On escaping through E it cools the following gas yet further. Thus the cooling of the escaping gas continuously helps the cooling of the arriving gas, and the cooling is said to be *regenerative*. Eventually the gas emerging from the nozzle cools below the critical temperature; and since the actual pressure, 150 atmospheres, is well above the critical pressure, 39 atmospheres, the gas liquefies and collects in the flask. The liquefier is heavily lagged with insulating material, G, to prevent heat coming in from the outside.

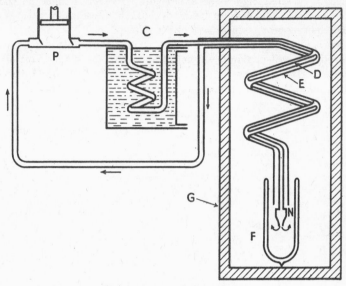

FIG. 214. Liquefaction of air.

The reader should appreciate that the regenerative cooling takes place only in the double coil. At all stages in the process the air enters the inner coil at the temperature of the cooling water around C. But as time goes on it passes through ever-cooler gas coming up from the nozzle, until liquid begins to form and the system reaches equilibrium.

36. Liquid Nitrogen and Oxygen.

As the table on p. 323 shows, the boiling-point of nitrogen, at atmospheric pressure, is − 196° C., whereas that of oxygen is − 183° C. When liquid air is exposed to the atmosphere, therefore, the nitrogen boils off faster and the proportion of liquid oxygen increases. The so-called liquid air sold commercially is mostly liquid oxygen. It is more dangerous than true liquid air, particularly if there is hydrogen about.

37. Hydrogen and Helium.

At ordinary temperatures, the Joule-Kelvin effect is reversed for helium and hydrogen, that is, a free expansion causes warming. We cannot go into the explanation of that here, but we may say that it is connected with the fact that the pV/p curves of hydrogen and helium rise with increasing pressure, instead of falling at first (Fig. 202, p. 318).

These gases show a Joule-Kelvin cooling, however, if they are sufficiently cooled before the expansion. Hydrogen must be cooled below − 83° C. and helium below − 240° C.; these temperatures are called the *inversion temperatures* of the gases.

Hydrogen can be cooled below its inversion temperature by passing it through a coil in liquid air before it enters the double coil of the liquefier. Helium must be passed through a coil in liquid hydrogen, boiling under reduced pressure.

EXAMPLES

1. Describe an experiment which demonstrates that the pressure of a vapour in equilibrium with its liquid depends on the temperature.

A narrow tube of uniform bore, closed at one end, has some air entrapped by a small quantity of water. If the pressure of the atmosphere is 76 cm. of mercury, the equilibrium vapour pressure of water at 12° C. and at 35° C. is 10·5 mm. of mercury and 42·0 mm. of mercury respectively, and the length of the air column at 12° C. is 10 cm., calculate its length at 35° C. (*L.*)

First part. See text.

Second part. For the given mass of air,

$$\frac{p_1 V_1}{T_1} = \frac{p_2 V_2}{T_2}$$

$p_1 = 76 - 1·05 = 74·95$ cm., $V_1 = 10$, $T = 273 + 12 = 285°$ K;

$p_2 = 76 - 4·2 = 71·8$ cm., $T_2 = 273 + 35 = 308°$ K;

$$\therefore \frac{74·95 \times 10}{285} = \frac{71·8 \, V_2}{308}$$

$$\therefore V_2 = \frac{74·95 \times 10 \times 308}{285 \times 71·8} = 11·3.$$

2. State Dalton's law of partial pressures; how is it explained on the kinetic theory? A closed vessel contains air, saturated water-vapour, and an excess of water. The total pressure in the vessel is 760 mm. of mercury when the temperature is 25° C.; what will it be when the temperature has been raised to 100° C.? (Saturation vapour pressure of water at 25° C. is 24 mm. of mercury.) (*C.*)

First part. See text.

Second part. From Dalton's law, the pressure of the air at 25° C. = 760 − 24 = 736 mm. of mercury. Suppose the pressure is *p* mm. at 100° C. Then, since pressure is proportional to absolute temperature for a fixed mass of air, we have

$$\frac{p}{736} = \frac{373}{298},$$

from which $p = 921$ mm.

Now the saturation vapour pressure of water at 100° C. = 760 mm.

∴ total pressure in vessel = 921 + 760 = 1,681 mm. mercury.

3. Define *relative humidity* and *dew-point*. Describe an instrument with which the dew-point can be determined. The relative humidity in a closed room at 15° C. is 60 per cent. If the temperature rises to 20° C., what will the relative humidity become? On what assumptions is your calculation based? (Saturation vapour pressure of water-vapour at 15° C. = 12·67 mm. of mercury, at 20° C. = 17·36 mm.) (*L.*)

First part. See text.

Second part. Suppose p is the actual water vapour pressure in mm. mercury in the air at 15° C.

Then

$$\frac{p}{12\cdot67} = \text{relative humidity} = 60 \text{ per cent.}$$

$$\therefore p = \frac{60}{100} \times 12\cdot67 = 7\cdot60 \text{ mm.}$$

Assuming the pressure of the water-vapour is proportional to its absolute temperature, the pressure p_1 at 20° C. is given by

$$\frac{p_1}{7\cdot60} = \frac{273 + 20}{273 + 15}.$$

$$\therefore p = \frac{7\cdot60 \times 293}{288} = 7\cdot73 \text{ mm.}$$

$$\therefore \text{ relative humidity at } 20° \text{ C.} = \frac{7\cdot734}{17\cdot36} \times 100 \text{ per cent.} = 45 \text{ per cent.}$$

4. What is meant by *saturation pressure of water vapour, dew-point*? Describe *briefly* the principles underlying two *different* methods for the determination of the relative humidity in the laboratory.

A barometer tube dips into a mercury reservoir and encloses a mixture of air and saturated water vapour above the mercury column in the tube, the height of the column being 70 cm. above the level in the reservoir. If the atmospheric pressure and the saturation pressure of water vapour are respectively 76 cm. and 1 cm. of mercury, determine the height of the column when the tube is depressed in the reservoir to reduce the air volume to half its initial value. (*L.*)

First part. The saturation pressure of water vapour is the pressure of water vapour in contact with water in a closed space. The dew-point is the temperature at which the air is just saturated with the water-vapour present. The different methods for measuring relative humidity concern the dew-point (Regnault) hygrometer and the wet-and-dry bulb hygrometer, discussed on pp. 315, 316.

Second part. We apply the gas laws to the *air* only, as the mass of the air remains constant. From Dalton's law,

pressure of air = total pressure — pressure of water-vapour

$$= (76 - 70) - 1 = 5 \text{ cm. mercury.}$$

The volume of the air changes from V, say, to $V/2$. Hence the new pressure, p, of the air is given, from Boyle's law, by

$$5 \times V = p \times \frac{V}{2}$$

$$\therefore p = 10 \text{ cm.}$$

$$\therefore \text{ new total pressure of mixture of gases} = 10 + 1 = 11 \text{ cm.}$$

$$\therefore \text{ new height of mercury column} = 76 - 11 = 65 \text{ cm.}$$

5. What is meant by the *relative humidity* of the air? Describe in detail a good method for finding it.

Air at 19·5° C. has a relative humidity of 75 per cent. Calculate its dew-point and the mass of water vapour contained in 1 litre, being given that the boiling-points of water under pressures of 12 mm., 14 mm., 16 mm. and 18 mm. of mercury are 14° C., 16·45° C., 18·55° C. and 20·45° C. respectively. Assume that water vapour behaves as an ideal gas, that its density at s.t.p. is 0·00080 gm. per c.c. (N.)

First part. The relative humidity of the air is the ratio of the mass of water-vapour in a given volume of the air to the mass of water-vapour required to saturate that volume. A good method for finding it is by the dew-point (Regnault) hygrometer, described on p. 315.

Second part.

$$\text{Relative humidity} = \frac{\text{s.v.p. of water at dew-point}}{\text{s.v.p. of water at } 19 \cdot 5^\circ \text{ C.}} \times 100 \text{ per cent.}$$

$$\therefore \ 75 = \frac{\text{s.v.p. at dew-point}}{17 \text{ mm. mercury}} \times 100$$

$$\therefore \text{ s.v.p. at dew-point} = \tfrac{3}{4} \times 17 = 12 \cdot 75 \text{ mm. mercury.}$$

$$\therefore \text{ dew-point} = 14^\circ \text{ C.} + \frac{0 \cdot 75}{2} \times 2 \cdot 45^\circ \text{ C.}$$

$$= 14 \cdot 9^\circ \text{ C.,}$$

as s.v.p. at 14° C. = 12 mm., at 16·45° C. = 14 mm.

To find the mass of water-vapour in 1 litre. The pressure of water-vapour = s.v.p. at dew-point = 12·75 mm. = 1·275 cm. mercury; the absolute temperature = 273 + 19·5 = 292·5° K.

$$\therefore \text{ vol. in c.c. at s.t.p.} = 1,000 \times \frac{1 \cdot 275}{76} \times \frac{273}{292 \cdot 5}$$

$$\therefore \text{ mass of water-vapour} = 1,000 \times \frac{1 \cdot 275}{76} \times \frac{273}{292 \cdot 5} \times 0 \cdot 0008$$

$$= 0 \cdot 013 \text{ gm.}$$

EXERCISES XIV

1. Compare the properties of saturated and unsaturated vapours. By means of diagrams show how the pressure of (*a*) a gas, and (*b*) a vapour, vary with change (i) of volume at constant temperature, and (ii) of temperature at constant volume.

The saturation vapour pressure of ether vapour at 0° C. is 185 mm. of mercury and at 20° C. it is 440 mm. The bulb of a constant volume gas thermometer contains dry air and sufficient ether for saturation. If the observed pressure in the bulb is 1,000 mm. at 20° C., what will it be at 0° C.? (*L.*)

2. Explain the terms *relative humidity, dew-point.* Describe in detail an experiment to determine the dew-point.

Find the mass of air and water-vapour in a room of 20 × 10 × 5 cubic metres capacity, the temperature being 20° C. and the pressure 750 mm. of mercury. Assume that the saturation pressure of water-vapour at the dew-point is 9·0 mm. of mercury; that the density of dry air at s.t.p. is 1·30 gm. per litre; that the density of water vapour is 5/8 that of air under the same conditions of pressure and temperature. (*L.*)

3. Define *pressure of a saturated vapour, critical temperature.* Give an account of the isothermal curves for carbon dioxide at temperatures above and below its critical temperature.

Some liquid ether is sealed in a thick-walled glass tube, leaving a space containing only the vapour. Describe what is observed as the temperature of the tube and its contents is raised above 197° C., which is the critical temperature for ether. (Assume that the vessel is strong enough to withstand the internal pressure.) (*L.*)

4. Define *dew-point* and explain what is meant by *relative humidity*. Describe how you would determine the dew-point of the atmosphere.

What is the relative humidity of an atmosphere whose temperature is 16·3° C. if its dew-point is 12·5° C.? The following table gives the saturation pressure, *p*, of water-vapour in mm. of mercury at various temperatures, *t*.

$t°$ C.	10	12	14	16	18	20
p mm.	9·20	10·51	11·98	13·62	15·46	17·51

(*N.*)

5. Distinguish between saturated and unsaturated vapours. Sketch the isothermals for water and water-vapour at 100° C. and 50° C. and point out their more important characteristics. Describe how the saturation vapour pressure of water at 50° C. may be determined. (*L.*)

6. State Boyle's law and describe how you would verify it for air over a range of pressures from about half an atmosphere to 2 atmospheres.

Describe how the behaviour of carbon dioxide at various temperatures deviates from Boyle's law. Sketch graphs to illustrate your answer. (*L.*)

7. Define *relative humidity, absolute humidity.*

Describe and explain how the relative humidity of the air may be determined at an exposed position by a method involving a determination of the dew-point.

Briefly describe the experiments you would carry out in order to determine *all* the necessary data. (*L.*)

8. Give an account of *two* methods by which the maximum pressure of aqueous vapour at various temperatures has been measured.

One litre of hydrogen at 0° C. and 760 mm. pressure weighs 0·0894 gm. Find the weight of 500 c.c. of hydrogen collected over water at 20° C. and 765 mm. pressure if the maximum pressure of aqueous vapour at 20° C. is 17·4 mm. (*C.*)

9. It is often stated that burning a gas-fire in a room makes the air "dry". How do you interpret this statement, and how would you test its truth experimentally?

A sealed room, 4·5 m. by 4 m. by 3 m., is initially at a temperature of 13° C., the relative humidity being 50 per cent. Calculate the volume of water which must be evaporated in the room in order to maintain the relative humidity at 50 per cent. when the temperature is raised to 20° C. [Saturation vapour pressures of water at 13° C. and 20° C. are 11·23 mm. and 17·51 mm. of mercury respectively; density of air at N.T.P. is 1·29 gm. per litre; density of water-vapour relative to air is 0·6.] (*W.*)

10. Describe a constant-volume gas thermometer. How would you calibrate such an instrument for use over a range of about −20 to 150° C.? The bulb of a constant-volume gas thermometer contains air and sufficient alcohol to keep the air saturated. The pressure in the bulb is 1,168 mm. at 60° C. when the saturated vapour pressure of alcohol is 350 mm. What will be the pressure in the bulb at 20° C. when the saturated vapour pressure of alcohol is 44 mm.? (*C.*)

11. Give briefly the principles of one method each for liquefying (a) chlorine, (b) hydrogen.

Describe a suitable container for liquid air. Point out carefully the physical principles involved. (*C.*)

12. Give an account of three methods used to obtain temperatures below 0° C. Describe a method for liquefying air. How must the procedure be modified in order to liquefy hydrogen? (*N. Schol.*)

13. Describe the construction and use of *either* (a) Bunsen's ice calorimeter *or* (b) Joly's steam calorimeter. Explain how the result is calculated.

If 1 gm. of water at 100° C. forms 1,670 c.c. of steam at standard atmospheric pressure, find the ratio of internal work to external work done when water is converted into steam. (Latent heat of steam = 540 cal. gm.$^{-1}$) (*L.*)

14. Describe in detail the method you would use to find (a) the melting-point of lead, and (b) the boiling-point of brine.

An alloy of copper and silver is made with different percentage composition. For each mix the melting-point is measured, with the following results:—

M.P. deg. C.	960	810	760	740	760	790	900	1,080
Per cent. of copper in alloy	0	20	30	40	50	60	80	100

Plot a curve showing the relation between the melting-point in degrees Centigrade and the percentage of copper present. Comment on the curve. (*L.*)

CHAPTER XV

TRANSFER OF HEAT

CONDUCTION

1. Conduction.

If we put a poker into the fire, and hold on to it, then heat reaches us along the metal. We say the heat is *conducted*; and we soon find that some substances—metals—are good conductors, and others—such as wood or glass—are not. Good conductors feel cold to the touch on a cold day, because they rapidly conduct away the body's heat.

2. Temperature Distribution along a Conductor.

In order to study conduction in more detail consider Fig. 215 (a), which shows a metal bar AB whose ends have been soldered into the

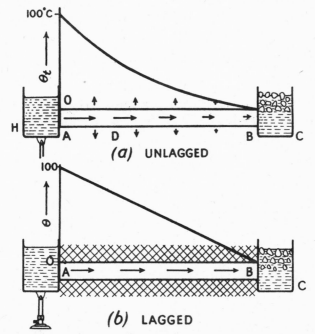

Fig. 215. Temperature fall along lagged and unlagged bars.

walls of two metal tanks, H, C; H contains boiling water, and C contains ice-water. Heat flows along the bar from A to B, and *when conditions are steady* the temperature θ of the bar is measured at points along its length; the measurements may be made with thermojunctions, not shown in the figure, which have been soldered to the rod. The curve in the upper part of the figure shows how the temperature falls along the bar, less and less steeply from the hot end to the cold.

The figure 215 (*b*) shows how the temperature varies along the bar, if the bar is *well lagged* with a bad conductor, such as asbestos wool. It now falls uniformly from hot to cold.

The difference between the temperature distributions is due to the fact that, when the bar is unlagged, heat escapes from its sides, by convection in the surrounding air. Thus the heat flowing past D per second, is less than that entering the bar at A by the amount which escapes from the surface AD. The arrows in the figure represent the heat escaping per second from the surface of the bar, and the heat flowing per second along its length. The heat flowing per second along the length decreases from the hot end to the cold. But when the bar is lagged, the heat escaping from its sides is negligible, and the flow per second is constant along the length of the bar.

We thus see that the temperature gradient along a bar is greatest where the heat flow through it is greatest. We also see that the temperature gradient is uniform only when there is a negligible loss of heat from the sides of the bar.

3. Thermal Conductivity.

Let us consider a thick bar, of which AB in Fig. 216 (i) is a part, and along which heat is flowing steadily. We suppose that the loss of

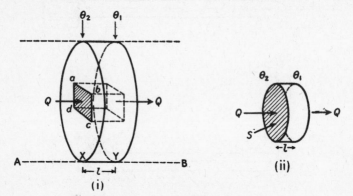

Fig. 216. Definition of thermal conductivity.

heat from the sides of the bar is made negligible by lagging. XY is a slice of the bar, of thickness l, whose faces are at temperatures θ_2 and θ_1. Then the *temperature gradient* over the slice is

$$\frac{\theta_2 - \theta_1}{l}.$$

We now consider an element *abcd* of the slice, whose cross-sectional area is 1 cm.², and we denote by Q the heat flowing through it per second. The value of Q depends on the temperature gradient, and, since some substances are better conductors than others, it also depends on the material of the bar.

We therefore write $$Q = K \frac{\theta_2 - \theta_1}{l}$$

where K is a factor depending on the material.

To a fair approximation the factor K is a constant for a given material; that is to say, it is independent of θ_2, θ_1, and l. It is called the *thermal conductivity* of the material concerned. To put its definition into words, we let $\theta_2 - \theta_1$ be 1° C., and l be 1 cm., so that

$$Q = K.$$

We then say:

Consider a cube of material, whose faces are 1 cm. apart, and have a temperature difference of 1° C. If heat flows in the steady state through the cube at right angles to its faces, and none is lost from its sides, then the heat flow per unit area, in calories per second, is numerically equal to the conductivity of the material.

This definition leads to a general equation for the flow of heat through any parallel-sided slab of the material, when no heat is lost from the sides of the slab. As in Fig. 216 (ii), we denote the cross-sectional area of the slab by S, its thickness by l, and the temperature of its faces by θ_1 and θ_2. Then the heat Q flowing through it per second is

$$Q = \frac{KS(\theta_2 - \theta_1)}{l} \quad \cdots \cdots \quad (1)$$

A useful form of this equation is

$$\frac{Q}{S} = K \frac{\theta_2 - \theta_1}{l} \quad \cdots \cdots \quad (2)$$

or

heat flow per cm.² per sec.=conductivity×temperature gradient. (2*a*)

In terms of the calculus, (2) may be re-written

$$\frac{1}{S}\frac{dQ}{dt} = -K\frac{d\theta}{dl}, \quad \cdots \cdots \quad (3)$$

the temperature gradient being negative since θ diminishes as l increases.

4. Units and Magnitude of Conductivity.

Equation (2) enables us to find the unit of thermal conductivity.

We have $$K = \frac{Q/S \text{ (cal./cm.}^2\text{/sec.)}}{(\theta_2 - \theta_1)/l \text{ (°C./cm.)}}.$$

Thus the unit of thermal conductivity

$$= \frac{\text{cal. cm.}}{\text{cm.}^2 \text{ sec. } °C.} = \text{cal. cm.}^{-1} \text{ sec.}^{-1} °C.^{-1},$$

or, for short, a *c.g.s. unit* (centimetre-gramme-second, the degree centigrade being understood).

THERMAL CONDUCTIVITIES

SOLIDS
(Mean values, c. 0–100° C.)

Substance	K cal. sec.$^{-1}$ cm.$^{-1}°C.^{-1}$	Substance	K	Substance	K
Ag	1·00	Asbestos	0·0003	Ice	0·005
Al	0·50	Brick	0·0003	Marble	0·0071
Cu	0·91	Cardboard	0·0005	(white)	
Fe pure	0·18	Cork	0·0001	Mica	0·0018
wrought	0·14	Cotton	0·00055	Paraffin	
Hg	0·02	Cotton		wax	0·0006
Ni	0·14	wool	0·000006	Silica	0·0033
Pb	0·08	Ebonite	0·0004	(fused)	
Pt	0·17	Felt	0·00009	Rubber	0·00045
Brass	0·26	Flannel	0·00023	(para)	
Duralumin	0·31	Glass	0·0025	Sand	0·00013
Steel	0·11	(window)		Silk	0·00022
		Graphite	0·3	Slate	0·0047
				Wood	c. 0·0005

LIQUIDS AND GASES

Liquid	K	Gas	K
Alcohol (25° C.)	0·00043	Air (0° C.)	0·000058
Glycerine (20° C.)	0·00068	(100° C.)	0·000076
Olive oil (0° C.)	0·0004	CO_2 (0° C.)	0·000035
Paraffin oil (0° C.)	0·0003	H_2 (0° C.)	0·00041
Water (10° C.)	0·00147	N_2 (0° C.)	0·000058
(80° C.)	0·0016	O_2 (0° C.)	0·000058

To a rough approximation we may say that the conductivities of metals are about 1,000 times as great as those of other solids, and of liquids; and that they are about 10,000 times as great as those of gases.

5. Effect of Thin Layer of Bad Conductor.

Fig. 217 shows a lagged copper bar AB, whose ends are pressed against metal tanks at 0° and 100° C., but are separated from them by

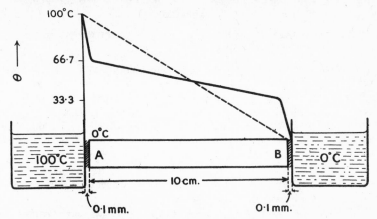

FIG. 217. Temperature gradients in good and bad conductors.

layers of dirt. The length of the bar is 10 cm., and the dirt layers are 0·1 mm. thick. Assuming that the conductivity of dirt is 1/1,000 that of copper, let us find the temperature of each end of the bar.

Suppose K = conductivity of copper,

S = cross-section of copper,

θ_2, θ_1 = temperature of hot and cold ends.

Since the bar is lagged, the heat flow per second Q is constant from end to end. Therefore,

$$Q = \frac{K}{1,000}S\frac{100 - \theta_2}{0 \cdot 01} = KS\frac{\theta_2 - \theta_1}{10} = \frac{K}{1,000}S\frac{\theta_1 - 0}{0 \cdot 01}.$$

Dividing through by K, these equations give

$$\frac{100 - \theta_2}{10} = \frac{\theta_2 - \theta_1}{10} = \frac{\theta_1}{10},$$

or $\qquad 100 - \theta_2 = \theta_2 - \theta_1 = \theta_1,$

whence $\qquad \theta_2 = 66 \cdot 7° \text{ C.},$

$$\theta_1 = 33 \cdot 3° \text{ C.}$$

Thus the total temperature drop, 100° C., is divided equally over the two thin layers of dirt and the long copper bar. The heavy lines in the figure show the temperature distribution; the broken line shows what it would be if there were no dirt.

6. Good and Bad Conductors.

The foregoing example shows what a great effect a thin layer of a bad conductor may have on thermal conditions; 0·1 mm. of dirt causes as great a temperature fall as 10 cm. of copper. We can generalize this result with the help of equation (2a):

heat flow/cm.^{2}/sec. = conductivity × temperature gradient.

The equation shows that, if the heat flow is uniform, the temperature gradient is inversely proportional to the conductivity. If the conductivity of dirt is 1/1,000 that of copper, the temperature gradient in it is 1,000 times that in copper; thus 1 mm. of dirt sets up the same temperature fall as 1 metre of copper. In general terms we express this result by saying that the dirt prevents a good thermal contact, or that it provides a bad one. .The reader who has already studied electricity will see an obvious analogy here. The flow of heat can, in fact, be treated mathematically in the same way as the flow of electricity; we may say that a dirt layer has a high thermal resistance, and hence causes a great temperature drop.

Boiler plates are made of steel, not copper, although copper is about eight times as good a conductor of heat. The material of the plates makes no noticeable difference to the heat flow from the furnace outside the boiler to the water inside it, because there is always a layer of gas between the flame and the boiler-plate. This layer may be very thin, but its conductivity is about 1/10,000 that of steel; if the plate is a centimetre thick, and the gas-film 1/1,000 centimetre, then the temperature drop across the film is ten times that across the plate. Thus the rate at which heat flows into the boiler is determined mainly by the gas.

If the water in the boiler deposits scale on the plates, the rate of heat flow is further reduced. For scale is a bad conductor, and, though it may not be as bad a conductor as gas, it can build up a much thicker layer. Scale must therefore be prevented from forming, if possible; and if not, it must from time to time be removed.

Badly conducting materials are often called *insulators*. The importance of building dwelling-places from insulating materials hardly needs to be pointed out. Window-glass is a ten-times better conductor than brick, and it is also much thinner; a room with large windows therefore requires more heating in winter than one whose walls are more modestly pierced. Wood is as bad a conductor (or as good an insulator) as brick, but it also is thinner. Wooden houses therefore have double walls, with an air-space between them; air is an excellent insulator, and the walls prevent convection. In polar climates, wooden huts must not be built with steel bolts going right through them; otherwise the inside ends of the bolts grow icicles from the moisture in the explorer's breath.

7. Measurement of High Conductivity : Metals.

When the thermal conductivity of a metal is to be measured, two conditions must usually be satisfied: heat must flow through the specimen at a measurable rate, and the temperature gradient along the specimen must be measurably steep. These conditions determine the form of the apparatus used.

When the conductor is a metal, it is easy to get a fast enough heat flow; the problem is to build up a temperature gradient. It is solved by having as the specimen a bar long compared with its diameter. Fig. 218 shows the apparatus, which is due to Searle. AB is the speci-

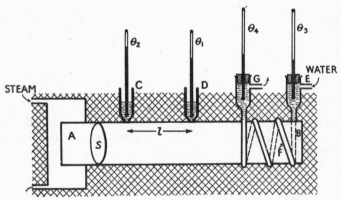

Fig. 218.   Apparatus for thermal conductivity of a metal.

men, about 4 cm. diameter and 20 cm. long. In one form of apparatus it is heated by steam at A, and cooled by circulating water at B. The whole apparatus is heavily lagged with felt. To measure the temperature gradient, thermometers are placed in the two mercury-filled cups C, D; the cups are made of copper, and are soldered to the specimen at a known distance apart. Alternatively, thermometers are placed in holes bored in the bar, which are filled with mercury. In this way errors due to bad thermal contact are avoided.

The cooling water flows in at E, round the copper coil F which is soldered to the specimen, and out at G. The water leaving at G is warmer than that coming in at E, so that the temperature falls continuously along the bar: if the water came in at G and out at E, it would tend to reverse the temperature gradient at the end of the bar, and might upset it as far back as D or C.

The whole apparatus is left running, with a steady flow of water, until all the temperatures have become constant: the temperature θ_2 and θ_1, at C and D in the bar, and θ_4 and θ_3 of the water leaving and entering. The steady rate of flow of the cooling water is measured with a measuring cylinder and a stop-clock.

If S is the cross-sectional area of the bar and K its conductivity, then the heat flow per second through it is

$$Q = KS\frac{\theta_2 - \theta_1}{l}.$$

This heat is carried away by the cooling water; if m gm. flow through F in 1 sec., the heat carried away is $m(\theta_4 - \theta_3)$.

Therefore $KS\dfrac{\theta_2 - \theta_1}{l} = m(\theta_4 - \theta_3).$

With this apparatus we can show that the conductivity K is a constant over small ranges of temperature. To do so we increase the flow of cooling water, and thus lower the outflow temperature θ_4. The gradient in the bar then steepens, and $(\theta_2 - \theta_1)$ increases. When the new steady state has been reached, the conductivity K is measured as before. Within the limits of experimental error, it is found to be unchanged.

8. Measurement of Low Conductivity : Non-metallic Solids.

In measuring the conductivity of a bad conductor, the difficulty is to get an adequate heat flow. The specimen is therefore made in the form of a thin disc, D, about 10 cm. in diameter and a few milli-metres thick (Fig. 219 (a)). It is heated by a steam-chest C, whose bottom is thick enough to contain a hole for a thermometer.

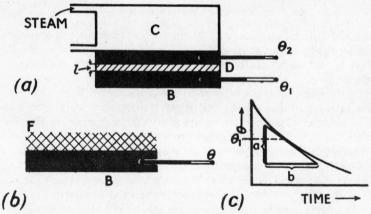

Fig. 219.   Apparatus for thermal conductivity of a bad conductor.

The specimen rests on a thick brass slab B, also containing a thermo-meter. The whole apparatus is hung in mid air by three strings attached to B.

To ensure good thermal contact, the adjoining faces of C, D and B must be flat and clean; those of C and B should be polished. A trace of vaseline smeared over each face improves the contact.

When the temperatures have become steady, the heat passing from C through D escapes from B by radiation and convection. Its rate of escape from B is roughly proportional to the excess temperature of B over the room (Newton's law). Thus B takes up a steady temperature θ_1 such that its rate of loss of heat to the outside is just equal to its gain through D. The rate of loss of heat from the sides of D is negligible, because their surface area is small.

This apparatus is derived from one due to Lees, and simplified for elementary work. If we use glass or ebonite for the specimen, the temperature θ_1 is generally about 70° C.; θ_2 is, of course, about 100° C. After these temperatures have become steady, and we have measured them, the problem is to find the rate of heat loss from B. To do this, we take away the specimen D and heat B directly from C until its temperature has risen by about 10° C. We then remove C, and cover the top part of B with a thick layer of felt F (Fig. 219 (b)). At intervals of a minute—or less—we measure the temperature of B, and afterwards plot it against the time (Fig. 219 (c)).

While the slab B is cooling it is losing heat by radiation and convection. It is doing so under the same conditions as in the first part of the experiment, because the felt prevents heat escaping from the top surface. Thus when the slab B passes through the temperature θ_1, it is losing heat at the same rate as in the first part of the experiment. The heat which it loses is now drawn from its own heat content, whereas before it was supplied from C via D; that is why the temperature of B is now falling, whereas before it was steady. The rate at which B loses heat at the temperature θ_1 is given by:

$$\text{heat lost/sec.} = Ms \times \text{temperature fall/sec.},$$

where M, s are respectively the mass and specific heat of the slab.

To find the rate of fall of temperature at θ_1, we draw the tangent to the cooling curve at that point. If, as shown in Fig. 102 (c), its gradient at θ_1 would give a fall of a deg. C. in b secs., then the rate of temperature fall is a/b deg. C per sec.

We then have, if S is the cross-sectional area of the specimen, l its thickness, and K its conductivity,

$$KS\frac{\theta_2 - \theta_1}{l} = Ms\frac{a}{b}.$$

Thus K can be calculated.

9. Liquids.

In finding the conductivity of a liquid, the liquid must be heated at the top and cooled at the bottom, to prevent convection. Lees' apparatus is therefore suitable. The liquid is held in a narrow glass ring, R, Fig. 220, sandwiched between the plates (not shown) of the Lees' disc apparatus. Let K_g, K_l be the conductivities of the glass

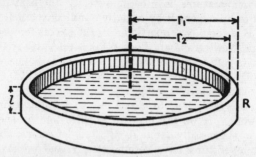

and liquid respectively, and r_2 and r_1 the inner and outer radii of the ring.   Then the downward heat flow per second is

$$Q = K_g\pi(r_1{}^2 - r_2{}^2)\frac{\theta_2 - \theta_1}{l} + K_l\pi r_2{}^2\frac{\theta_2 - \theta_1}{l},$$

where θ_2 and θ_1 are the temperatures above and below the specimen and l is its thickness.   The conductivity K_g need not be known; the heat flow through the ring may be determined in a preliminary experiment with the ring, but without the liquid.

10. Conduction through a Tube.

The conductivity of glass tubing may be measured in the laboratory with the apparatus shown in Fig. 221 (a).   The glass tube AB is surrounded by a steam jacket J, and water flows through it from A to B at a measured rate of m gm./sec.   Thermometers measure the inflow and outflow temperatures of the water, θ_2 and θ_3, which eventually become steady.   In the steady state, the heat flowing through the walls of the tubing is equal to the heat carried away by the water, $m(\theta_3 - \theta_2)$ cal./sec.

To find the conductivity, we must know the area through which the heat flows.   If r_1, r_2, are the inner and outer radii of the tube, and L is its length, then the areas of the inner and outer walls are $2\pi r_1 L$ and $2\pi r_2 L$ respectively (Fig. 221 (b)).   If the tube is thin, we may take the area as constant and equal to its average value.

Thus $$S = 2\pi L\frac{r_1 + r_2}{2}.$$

At the entrance of the tube, the temperature gradient is $(\theta_1 - \theta_2)/(r_2 - r_1)$, where θ_1 is the temperature of the steam; at the exit end the gradient is $(\theta_1 - \theta_3)/(r_2 - r_1)$.

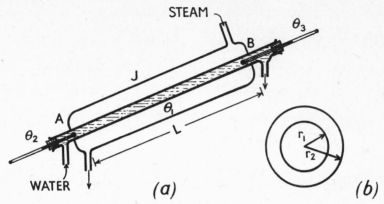

Fig. 221. Apparatus to measure conductivity of glass in form of tubing.

If θ_3 and θ_2 differ by not more than about 10° C., we may take the gradient as constant and equal to its average value:

$$\text{temp.-gradient} = \frac{1}{2}\left(\frac{\theta_1 - \theta_2}{r_2 - r_1} + \frac{\theta_1 - \theta_3}{r_2 - r_1}\right)$$

$$= \frac{\theta_1 - \dfrac{\theta_2 + \theta_3}{2}}{r_2 - r_1}.$$

The conductivity K therefore is given by

$$K \times 2\pi L \frac{r_1 + r_2}{2} \times \frac{\theta_1 - \dfrac{\theta_2 + \theta_3}{2}}{r_2 - r_1} = m(\theta_3 - \theta_2) \quad . \quad . \quad . \quad (4)$$

The conductivity of *rubber tubing* can be found by a modification of this method. A measured length of the tubing is submerged in a calorimeter of water, and steam passed through for a measured time t. The rise in temperature of the water must be corrected for cooling, as in the measurement of the specific heat of a bad conductor (p. 198). The heat flow through the rubber is given by the left-hand side of equation (4) with θ_2 and θ_3 standing for the initial and final temperature of the water. If w is the mass of water, and W the water equivalent of the calorimeter, the right-hand side of the equation is

$$(w + W)\,(\theta_3 - \theta_2)/t.$$

11. Comparison of Conductivities.

Fig. 222 (a) shows an apparatus due to Ingenhousz for comparing the conductivities of solids. Metal, wood, glass, and other rods, of equal lengths and cross-sections, are stuck into a tank through corks. The rods are painted with the same paint, and coated with wax over

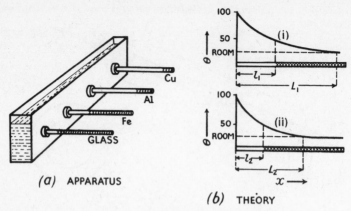

(a) APPARATUS

(b) THEORY

FIG. 222. Comparison of conductivities.

their whole projecting lengths. The tank is filled with water, leaks are stopped as well as possible, and the water is boiled. As the rods warm up, the wax melts off them. Eventually a steady state is reached, and the best conductor is the one from which wax has melted off the greatest length.

If the experiment is to give a quantitative comparison of the conductivities, the rods must be so long that the far end of each of them is at room temperature. Otherwise the following argument will not be true.

At the points where melted wax gives way to solid, each bar is at the melting-point of wax—let us call it $50°$ C. The temperature distributions along any two bars are therefore as shown in Fig. 222 (*b*); they have similar shapes, but at a given distance from the tank, (ii) is steeper than (i). If l_1 is the distance along (i) to the $50°$ C. point, and l_2 the corresponding distance along (ii), then the curve (ii) is the same as curve (i) except that it is horizontally contracted in the ratio l_2/l_1. Therefore the gradient of (ii), at any distance x, is steeper than that of (i) in the ratio l_1/l_2. The temperature gradient at the tank end of each rod determines the rate at which heat flows into it from the hot water.

Now $\qquad Q \propto K \times$ temp. grad. at hot end,

where K is the conductivity of the rod. Therefore, for rods (i) and (ii)

$$\frac{Q_1}{Q_2} = \frac{K_1}{K_2} \times \frac{\text{temp. grad. at end of (i)}}{\text{temp. grad. at end of (ii)}}$$

$$= \frac{K_1}{K_2} \times \frac{l_2}{l_1} \qquad \cdots \cdots \cdots \quad (5)$$

The heat passing into a rod at the hot end escapes by convection from its sides. The lengths l_1 and l_2 respectively, of rods (i) and (ii), have the same average temperatures, $75°$ C. Over the lengths l_1 and l_2, therefore, each rod loses heat at the same rate per unit area, since each has the same surface (p. 349). The heat lost from either rod per second, *between the $100°$ C. and the $50°$ C. points*, is therefore proportional to the area of the rod between those points. It is therefore proportional to the distance l between them.

Since the temperature curves differ only in scale, the distance to the 50° C. point on either rod is proportional to the distance L to the point where the rod reaches room temperature (Fig. 222 (b)). Beyond this point, the bar loses no heat. Therefore, by the above argument, the distance L is proportional to the *total* heat lost per second by the bar. The distance L is therefore proportional to the total heat per second lost by the bar, and this heat is the heat Q entering the bar at the hot end.

Therefore $$Q \propto L \propto l$$

or $$\frac{Q_1}{Q_2} = \frac{L_1}{L_2} = \frac{l_1}{l_2}.$$

But we have seen that $$\frac{Q_1}{Q_2} = \frac{K_1 l_2}{K_2 l_1} \qquad \cdots \cdots \cdots \quad (5)$$

Therefore $$\frac{K_1 l_2}{K_2 l_1} = \frac{l_1}{l_2}$$

or $$\frac{K_1}{K_2} = \frac{l_1^2}{l_2^2}.$$

Thus the conductivity of a given rod is proportional to the square of the distance along it to the melting-point of the wax.

12. The Cracking of Glass.

Glass is a bad conductor of heat. Therefore, when a piece of glass is heated in one place, the neighbouring parts of the glass do not at first warm up with it. Consequently they resist the expansion of the heated part, and the force set up cracks the glass (p. 271). To avoid cracking the glass, care must be taken to warm the whole region around the place to be made hot. Similarly, glass which has been heated must be made to cool slowly and uniformly by playing the flame over it now and then, for shorter and shorter times as it cools.

EXAMPLES

1. Define thermal conductivity and explain how the conductivity of a metal may be measured. Three bars of the same length and cross-section and well-lagged are arranged end to end with thermal contact at the junctions. The two ends of the composite bar are kept at 100° C. and 0° C. respectively. If the thermal conductivity of the metal at the hot end is 1·0 c.g.s. units, that of the metal in the middle 0·5 c.g.s. units, and that of the metal at the cold end 0·25 c.g.s. units, find the temperatures of the two junctions. (C.)

First part. See text.

Second part. Suppose θ_1, θ_2 are the temperatures at the warmer and colder junctions respectively. In the steady state, the heat per sq. cm. per sec. passing through each bar is the same, i.e. the magnitude of $K \times$ *temperature gradient* is the same for each bar. Thus, if the length of each bar is l,

$$1 \cdot 0 \times \frac{100 - \theta_1}{l} = 0 \cdot 5 \times \frac{\theta_1 - \theta_2}{l} \qquad \cdots \cdots \quad \text{(i)}$$

and $$1 \cdot 0 \times \frac{100 - \theta_1}{l} = 0 \cdot 25 \times \frac{\theta_2 - 0}{l} \qquad \cdots \cdots \quad \text{(ii)}$$

Cancelling l from equations (i) and (ii), and solving the simultaneous equations in θ_1, θ_2 thus obtained, we find

$$\theta_1 = 85 \cdot 7^\circ \text{ C.}; \quad \theta_2 = 57 \cdot 1^\circ \text{ C.}$$

2. Define *thermal conductivity*. How would you determine the thermal conductivity of glass using *either* a glass plate or a glass tube?

Find the heat conducted per sq. metre per hour (a) through a brick wall 12 cm. thick, (b) through the same wall covered on one side with a layer of cork 3 cm. thick, if, in each case, the difference of temperature between the exposed surface is 20° C. Assume that the thermal conductivities of cork and brick are $1 \cdot 0 \times 10^{-4}$ and 12×10^{-4} c.g.s. centigrade units respectively. (*N.*)

First part. See text.

Second part. (a) The heat conducted per square metre per hour is given by

$$H = KA \times \text{temperature gradient} \times 3,600 \text{ seconds}$$

$$= \frac{12}{10^4} \times 100^2 \times \frac{20}{12} \times 3,600$$

$$= 72,000 \text{ cal.}$$

(b) Suppose θ is the difference between the temperature of the junction of the brick and cork and that of the exposed surface in the steady state. Then, since the quantity of heat per second per sq. cm. passing through each is the same,

$$\frac{12}{10^4} \times 1 \times \frac{20 - \theta}{12} = \frac{1}{10^4} \times 1 \times \frac{\theta}{3}$$

$$\therefore 3(20 - \theta) = \theta$$

$$\therefore \theta = 15^\circ \text{ C.}$$

$\therefore$ heat conducted per sq. metre per hour

$$= KA \times \text{temperature gradient} \times 3,600$$

$$= \frac{12}{10^4} \times 100^2 \times 3,600 \times \frac{20 - 15}{12}$$

$$= 18,000 \text{ cal.}$$

3. Define *thermal conductivity*. Describe and give the theory of a method of measuring the thermal conductivity of copper.

A sheet of rubber and a sheet of cardboard, each $0 \cdot 20$ cm. thick, are pressed together and their outer faces are maintained respectively at 0° C. and 25° C. If the thermal conductivities of rubber and cardboard are respectively $3 \cdot 1 \times 10^{-4}$ and $1 \cdot 2 \times 10^{-4}$ cal. cm.$^{-1}$ sec.$^{-1}$ (deg. C.)$^{-1}$, find the quantity of heat which flows in 1 hour across a piece of the composite sheet of area 100 cm.^{2} (*L.*)

First part. The thermal conductivity of a substance is the quantity of heat per second flowing in the steady state through opposite faces of a unit cube of the material when a temperature difference of 1 degree is maintained across these faces. The thermal conductivity of copper can be measured by Searle's method (p. 341).

Second part. We must first find the temperature, θ° C., of the junction of the rubber and cardboard. The temperature gradient across the rubber $= (\theta - 0)/0 \cdot 2$; the temperature gradient across the cardboard $= (25 - \theta)/0 \cdot 2$.

$\therefore Q$/sec. across 1 sq. cm. of the rubber $= 3 \cdot 1 \times 10^{-4} \times (\theta - 0)/0 \cdot 2$,

and Q/sec. across 1 sq. cm. of the cardboard $= 1 \cdot 2 \times 10^{-4} \times (25 - \theta)/0 \cdot 2$.

But, in the steady state, the quantity of heat per sec. per sq. cm. through the rubber and the cardboard is the same.

$$\therefore \frac{3 \cdot 1 \times 10^{-4} \times (\theta - 0)}{0 \cdot 2} = \frac{1 \cdot 2 \times 10^{-4} \times (25 - \theta)}{0 \cdot 2}$$

$$\therefore \ 31\theta = 12(25 - \theta)$$

$$\therefore \ \theta = \frac{300}{43} = 7° \text{ C. (to a good approxn.)}$$

$\therefore$ quantity across 100 sq. cm. in 1 hour (3,600 sec.)

$$= \frac{3 \cdot 1 \times 10^{-4} \times 7}{0 \cdot 2} \times 100 \times 3,600$$

$$= 3,906 \text{ cal.}$$

RADIATION

13. Radiation:

All heat comes to us, directly or indirectly, from the sun. The heat which comes directly travels through 93 million miles of space, mostly empty, and travels in straight lines, as does the light: the shade of a tree coincides with its shadow. Both heat and light travel with the same speed because they are cut off at the same instant in an eclipse. Since light is propagated by waves of some kind we conclude that the heat from the sun is propagated by similar waves, and we say it is "radiated".

As we show later, radiation is more copious from a dull black body than from a transparent or polished one. Black bodies are also better absorbers of radiation than polished or transparent ones, which either allow radiation to pass through themselves, or reflect it away from themselves. If we hold a piece of white card, with a patch of black drawing ink on it, in front of the fire, the black patch soon comes to feel warmer than its white surround.

14. Reflection and Refraction.

If, with either a convex lens or a concave mirror, we focus the sun's light on our skin, we feel heat at the focal spot. The heat from the sun has therefore been reflected or refracted in the same way as the light.

If we wish to show the reflection of heat unaccompanied by light, we may use two search-light mirrors, set up as in Fig. 223. At the focus of one, F_1, we put an iron ball heated to just below redness. At the focus of the other, F_2, we put the bulb of a thermometer, which has been blackened

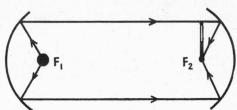

FIG. 223. Reflection of radiant heat.

with soot to make it a good absorber (p. 356).   The mercury rises in
the stem of the thermometer.   If we move either the bulb or the ball
away from the focus, the mercury falls back; the bulb has therefore
been receiving heat from the ball, by reflection at the two mirrors.
We can show that the foci of the mirrors are the same for heat as for
light if we replace the ball and thermometer by a lamp and screen.
(In practice we do this first, to save time in finding the foci for the
main experiment.)

To show the refraction of heat apart from the refraction of light is
more difficult.   It was first done by the astronomer Herschel in 1800.
Herschel passed a beam of sunlight through a prism, as shown diagrammatically in Fig. 224, and explored the spectrum with a sensitive

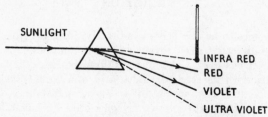

FIG. 224.   Infra-red and ultra-violet (diagrammatic).

thermometer, whose bulb he had blackened.   He found that in the
visible part of the spectrum the mercury rose, showing that the light
energy which it absorbed was converted into heat.   But the mercury
also rose when he carried the bulb into the darkened portion a little
beyond the red of the visible spectrum; the sun's rays therefore carried
energy which was not light.

15. Ultra-violet and Infra-red.

The radiant energy which Herschel found beyond the red is now
called *infra-red* radiation, because it is less refracted than the red.
Radiant energy is also found beyond the violet and it is called *ultra-
violet* radiation, because it is refracted more than the violet.

Ultra-violet radiation is absorbed by the human skin and causes
sun-burn; more importantly, it stimulates the formation of vitamin D,
which is necessary for the assimilation of calcium and the prevention
of rickets.   It is also absorbed by green plants; in them it enables water
to combine with carbon dioxide to form carbohydrates.   This process
is called photo-synthesis; we have already, on p. 191, discussed its
importance to animals and man.   Ultra-violet radiation causes the
emission of electrons from metals, as in photo-electric cells; and it
excites a latent image on a photographic emulsion.   It is harmful to
the eyes.

Ultra-violet radiation is strongly absorbed by glass—spectacle-wearers do not sunburn round the eyes—but enough of it gets through to affect a photographic film. It is transmitted with little absorption by quartz.

Infra-red radiation is transmitted by quartz, and rock-salt, but most of it is absorbed by glass. A little, that which lies near the visible red, passes fairly easily through glass—if it did not, Herschel would not have discovered it. When infra-red radiation falls on the skin, it gives the sensation of warmth. It is what we usually have in mind when we speak of heat radiation, and it is the main component of the radiation from a hot body; but it is in no essential way different from the other components, visible and ultra-violet radiation, as we shall now see.

16. Wavelengths of Radiation.

In books on optics, it is shown how the wavelength of light can be measured with a diffraction grating—a series of fine close lines ruled on glass. The wavelength ranges from $4,000 \times 10^{-8}$ cm. for the violet, to $7,500 \times 10^{-8}$ cm. for the red. The first accurate measurements of wavelength were published in 1868 by Angstrom, and in his honour a distance of 10^{-8} cm. is called an *Angstrom unit* (A.U.). The wavelengths of infra-red radiation can be measured with a grating made from fine wires stretched between two screws of close pitch. They range from 7,500 A.U. to about 1,000,000 A.U. Often they are expressed in a longer unit than the Angstrom: this unit is the micron (μ), which is 1/1,000 mm.

Thus $1\mu = 10^{-4}$ cm. $= 10^4$ A.U.

We denote wavelength by the symbol λ; its value for visible light ranges from $0\cdot4$ μ to $0\cdot75$ μ, and for infra-red radiation from $0\cdot75$ μ to about 100 μ.

We now consider that X-rays and radio waves also have the same nature as light, and that so do the γ-rays from radio-active substances. For reasons which we cannot here discuss, we consider all these waves to be due to oscillating electric and magnetic fields. Fig. 225 shows the

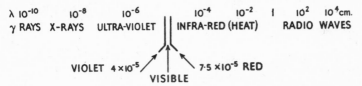

FIG. 225. The electromagnetic spectrum.

range of their wavelengths: it is called a diagram of the *electromagnetic spectrum*.

17. Detection of Heat Radiation.

A thermometer with a blackened bulb is a sluggish and insensitive detector of radiant heat. More satisfactory detectors, however, are

less direct; they are of two main kinds, both electrical. One kind consists of a long thin strip of blackened platinum foil, arranged in a compact zigzag (Fig. 226). On this the radiation falls. The foil is connected in a Wheatstone bridge, to measure its electrical resistance. When the strip is heated by the radiation, its resistance increases, and the increase is measured on the bridge. The instru-

FIG. 226. Bolometer strip.

ment was devised by Langley in 1881; it is called a bolometer, *bole* being Greek for a ray.

The other, commoner, type of radiation detector is called a thermopile (Nobili and Melloni, *c.* 1830). Its action depends on the electromotive force, which appears between the junctions of two different metals, when one junction is hot and the other cold. The modern thermopile is due to Coblenz (1913). It consists of many junctions between fine wires, as shown diagrammatically in Fig. 227; the wires are of silver and bismuth, 0·1 mm. or less in diameter. Their junctions are attached to thin discs of tin, about 0·2 mm. thick, and about 1 mm. square. One set of discs is blackened and mounted behind a slit, through which radiation can fall on them; the junctions attached to them become the hot junctions of the thermopile. The other, cold, junctions are shielded from the radiation to

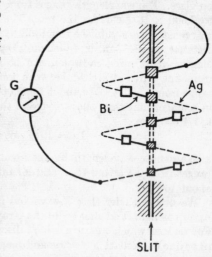

FIG. 227.   Thermopile.

be measured; the discs attached to them help to keep them cool, by increasing their surface area.

Older types of thermopile are made from bars of metal about a millimetre thick. They are slow to warm up when radiation falls upon them, but are more rugged than the modern type.

When radiation falls on the blackened discs of a thermopile, it warms the junctions attached to them, and sets up an e.m.f. This e.m.f. can be measured with a potentiometer, or, for less accurate work, it can be used to deflect a galvanometer, G, connected directly to the ends of the thermopile (Fig. 227).

18. Reflection and Refraction Observed with Thermopile : Inverse Square Law.

With a thermopile and galvanometer, we can repeat Herschel's experiment more strikingly than with a thermometer. And with the simple apparatus of Fig. 228 we can show that, when heat is reflected,

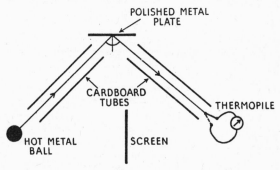

Fɪɢ. 228.   Demonstration of reflection.

the angle of reflection is equal to the angle of incidence. We can also show the first law of reflection; that the incident and reflected rays are in the same plane as the normal to the reflector at the point of incidence.

If heat is radiant energy, its intensity should fall off as the inverse square of the distance from a point source. We can check that it does so by setting up an electric lamp, with a compact filament, in a dark room preferably with black walls. When we put a thermopile at different distances from the lamp, the deflection of the galvanometer is found to be inversely proportional to the square of the distance.

If we wish to do this experiment with radiation that includes no visible light, we must modify it. Instead of the lamp, we use a large blackened tank of boiling water, A, and we fit the thermopile, B, with a conical mouthpiece, blackened on the inside. The blackening prevents any radiation from reaching the pile by reflection at the walls of the mouthpiece. We now find that the deflection of the galvanometer, G, does not vary with the distance of the pile from the tank, *provided that the tank occupies the whole field of view of the cone* (Fig. 229). The area S of the tank from which radiation can reach the thermopile is then proportional to the square of the distance d. And since the deflection is unchanged when the distance is altered, the total radiation from each element of S must therefore fall off as the inverse square of the distance d.

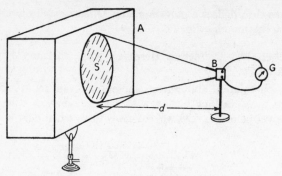

FIG. 229. Proof of inverse square law.

19. The Infra-red Spectrometer.

Infra-red spectra are important in the study of molecular structure. They are observed with an infra-red spectrometer, whose principle is shown in Fig. 230 Since glass is opaque to the infra-red, the radiation

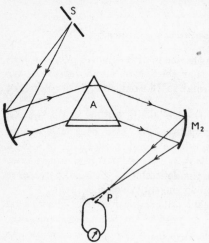

is focused by concave mirrors instead of lenses; the mirrors are plated with copper or gold on their front surfaces. The source of light is a Nernst filament, a metal filament coated with alkaline-earth oxides, and heated electrically. The radiation from such a filament is rich in infra-red. A carbon arc, or a gas-mantle, may be used, however.

The slit S of the spectrometer is at the focus of one mirror which acts as a collimator. After passing through the rock-salt prism, A, the radiation is focused on to the thermopile P by the mirror M_2, which replaces

FIG. 230. Infra-red spectrometer.

the telescope of an optical spectrometer. Rotating the prism brings different wavelengths on to the slit; the position of the prism is calibrated in wavelengths with the help of a grating.

To a fair approximation, the deflection of the galvanometer is proportional to the radiant power carried in the narrow band of wavelengths which fall on the thermopile. If an absorbing body, such as a solution of an organic compound, is placed between the source and the slit, it weakens the radiation passing through the spectrometer, in the wavelengths which it absorbs. These wavelengths are therefore shown by a fall in the galvanometer deflection.

20. Reflection, Transmission, Absorption.

Measurements whose description is outside our scope give the amount of radiant energy approaching the earth from the sun. At the upper limit of our atmosphere, it is about 1·9 cal. per cm.² per min.

At the surface of the earth it is always less than this because of absorption in the atmosphere. Even on a cloudless day it is less, because the ozone in the upper atmosphere absorbs much of the ultra-violet.

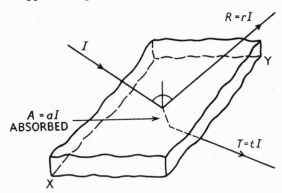

FIG. 231. Reflection, transmission, and absorption.

In Fig. 231, XY represents a body on which radiant energy is falling. The symbol I denotes the latter's intensity: to fix our ideas we may take

$$I = 1 \text{ cal./cm.}^2/\text{min.}$$

$$= 4\cdot2 \text{ joule/cm.}^2/\text{min.}$$

$$= \frac{4\cdot2}{60} \text{ joule/cm.}^2/\text{sec.}$$

$$= 0\cdot07 \text{ watt/cm.}^2$$

Some of this energy is reflected by the glass (R), some is absorbed (A), and some is transmitted (T). The total energy transmitted, absorbed and reflected per cm.² per sec. is equal to the energy falling on the body over the same area and in the same time :

$$T + A + R = I.$$

If we denote by t, a, and r, the fractions of energy which are respectively transmitted, absorbed, and reflected by the body, then

$$tI + aI + rI = I$$

or $$t + a + r = 1 \quad \dots \quad \dots \quad \dots \quad (6)$$

This equation expresses common knowledge: if a body is transparent ($t \to 1$), it is not opaque, and it is not a good reflector ($a \to 0$, $r \to 0$). But also, if the body is a good absorber of radiation ($a \to 1$), it is not transparent, and its surface is dull ($t \to 0$, $r \to 0$). And if it is a good reflector ($r \to 1$), it is neither transparent nor a good absorber ($t \to 0$,

$a \rightarrow 0$). The term opaque, as commonly used, simply means not transparent; we see that it does not necessarily mean absorbent.

Equation (6), as we have written it above, is over-simplified. For a body may transmit some wavelengths (colours, if visible) and absorb or reflect others. If we now let I denote the intensity of radiation of a particular wavelength λ, then by repeating the argument we get

$$t_\lambda + a_\lambda + r_\lambda = 1 \qquad \ldots \ldots \quad (7)$$

where the coefficients t_λ, etc., all refer to the wavelength λ.

The truth of equation (7) is well shown by the metal gold, which reflects yellow light better than other colours. In thin films, gold is partly transparent, and the light which it transmits is green. Green is the colour complementary to yellow; gold removes the yellow from white light by reflection, and passes on the rest by transmission.

21. Radiation and Absorption.

We have already pointed out that black surfaces are good absorbers and radiators of heat, and that polished surfaces are bad absorbers and radiators. This can be demonstrated by the apparatus in Fig. 232,

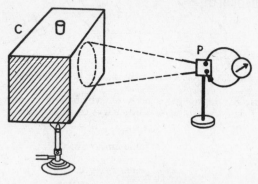

Fig. 232.   Comparing radiators.

in which is a cubical metal tank whose sides have a variety of finishes: dull black, dull white, highly polished. It contains boiling water, and, therefore, has a constant temperature. Facing it is a thermopile, P, which is fitted with the blackened conical mouth-piece described on p. 352.

Provided that the face of the cube occupies the whole field of view of the cone, its distance from the thermopile does not matter (p. 353). The galvanometer deflection is greatest when the thermopile is facing the dull black surface of the cube, and least when it is facing the highly polished surface. The highly polished surface is therefore the worst radiator of all, and the dull black is the best.

This experiment was first done by Leslie in 1804. There were no thermopiles in those days, and Leslie detected the radiant heat with an instrument depending on the expansion of air, which we shall not describe. The tank with different surfaces is called *Leslie's cube*.

Leslie's cube can also be used in an experiment to compare the absorbing properties of surfaces, due to Ritchie (1833). A modern version of it is shown in Fig. 233. The cube C, full of boiling water, is placed between two copper plates, A, B, of which A is blackened and B is polished. The temperature difference between A and B is measured by making each of them one element in a thermo junction: they are joined by a constantan wire, XY, and connected to a galvanometer, by copper wires, AE, DB. If A is hotter than B, the junction, X, is hotter than the junction, Y, and a current flows through the galvanometer in one direction. If B is hotter than A, the current is reversed.

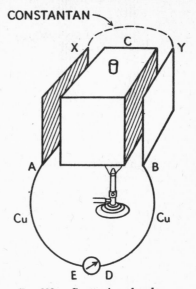

Fig. 233. Comparing absorbers.

The most suitable type of Leslie's cube is one which has two opposite faces similar—say grey—and the other two opposite faces very dissimilar—one black, one polished. At first the plates A, B are set opposite similar faces. The black-ened plate, A, then becomes the hotter, showing that it is the better absorber.

The cube is now turned so that the blackened plate, A, is opposite the polished face of the cube, while the polished plate, B, is opposite the blackened face of the cube. The galvanometer then shows no deflection; the plates thus reach the same temperature. It follows that the good radiating property of the blackened face of the cube, and the bad absorbing property of the polished plate, are just compensated by the good absorbing property of the blackened plate, and the bad radiating property of the polished face of the cube.

22. The Thermos Flask.

A thermos flask—sometimes called a *Dewar flask* after its inventor (c. 1894)—is a device for reducing the transfer of heat to a minimum. It consists of a double walled glass vessel, as shown in Fig. 234; the space between the walls is exhausted to as high a vacuum as possible, and the insides of the walls are silvered. Silvered surfaces are good reflectors, but bad absorbers and radiators. Heat therefore passes

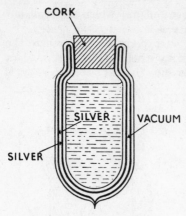

FIG. 234. A thermos flask.

very slowly from the outer wall to the inner by radiation. If the vacuum is good, convection is almost inhibited—the goodness of the vacuum determines the goodness of the flask. Conduction through the glass is slight, because the conduction paths are long. In a good flask, the main cause of heat loss is conduction through the cork.

23. The Black Body.

The experiments described before lead us to the idea of a perfectly black body; one which absorbs all the radiation that falls upon it, and reflects and transmits none. The experiments also lead us to suppose that such a body would be the best possible radiator.

A perfectly black body can be very nearly realized—a good one can be made in half a minute, simply by punching a small hole in the lid of an empty tin. The hole looks almost black, although the shining tin is a good reflector. The hole looks black because the light which enters through it is reflected many times round the walls of the tin, before it meets the hole again (Fig. 235). At each reflection, about 80 per cent. of the light energy is reflected, and 20 per cent. is absorbed. After two reflections, 64 per cent. of the original light goes on

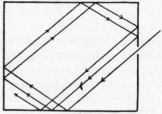

FIG. 235.   Multiple reflections make a black body.

to be reflected a third time; 36 per cent. has been absorbed. After ten reflections, the fraction of the original energy which has not been absorbed is 0.8^{10}, or 0.1.

FIG. 236.   A black body.

Any space which is almost wholly enclosed approximates to a black body. And, since a good absorber is also a good radiator, an almost closed space is the best radiator we can find.

A form of black-body which is used in radiation measurements is shown in Fig. 236. It consists of a porcelain sphere, S, with a small hole in it. The inside is blackened with soot to make it as good a radiator and as bad a reflector as possible. (The effect of multiple reflections is then to convert the body from nearly black to very nearly black indeed.) The sphere is surrounded by a high-temperature bath of, for example, molten salt (the melting-point of common salt is 801° C.).

The deepest recesses of a coal or wood fire are black bodies. Anyone who has looked into a fire knows that the deepest parts of it look brightest—they are radiating most power. Anyone who has looked into a fire also knows that, in the hottest part, no detail of the coals or wood can be seen. That is to say, the radiation from an almost enclosed space is uniform; its character does not vary with the nature of the surfaces of the space. This is so because the radiation coming out from any area is made up partly of the radiation emitted by that area, and partly of the radiation from other areas, reflected at the area in question. If the surface of the area is a good radiator, it is a bad reflector, and vice-versa. And if the hole in the body is small, the radiations from every area inside it are well mixed by reflection before they can escape; the intensity and quality of the radiation escaping thus does not depend on the particular surface from which it escapes.

When we speak of the *quality* of radiation we mean the relative intensities of the different wavelengths that it comprises; the proportion of red to blue, for example. The quality of the radiation from a perfectly black body depends only on its temperature. When the body is made hotter, its radiation becomes not only more intense, but also more nearly white; the proportion of blue to red in it increases. Because its quality is determined only by its temperature, black-body radiation is sometimes called "temperature radiation".

24. Properties of Temperature Radiation.

The quality of the radiation from a black body was examined by Lummer and Pringsheim in 1899. They used a black body represented by B in Fig. 237 and measured its temperature with a thermocouple; they took it to 2,000° C. To measure the intensities of the various wavelengths, Lummer and Pringsheim used an infrared spectrometer and a bolometer (p. 352) consisting of a single platinum strip.

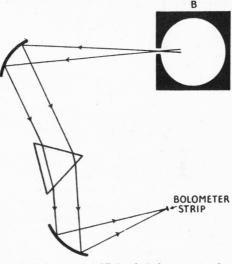

Fig. 237. Lummer and Pringsheim's apparatus for study of black body radiation (diagrammatic).

The results of experiments such as these are shown in Fig. 238 (a).
Each curve gives the relative intensities of the different wavelengths,
for a given temperature of the body. The curves show that, as the
temperature rises, the intensity of every wavelength increases, but the
intensities of the shorter wavelengths increase more rapidly. Thus
the radiation becomes, as we have already observed, less red, that is

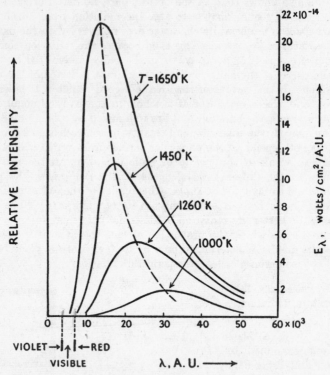

FIG. 238 (a).   Distribution of intensity in black-body radiation.

to say, more nearly white. The curve for sunlight has its peak at about
5,000 A.U., in the visible green; from the position of this peak we
conclude that the surface temperature of the sun is about 6,000° K.
Stars which are hotter than the sun, such as Sirius and Vega, look
blue, not white, because the peaks of their radiation curves lie further
towards the visible blue than does the peak of sunlight.

The actual intensities of the radiations are shown on the right of the
graph in Fig. 238 (a). To speak of the intensity of a single wavelength
is meaningless because there is an infinite number of wavelengths, but
the total intensity of the radiation is finite. The slit of the spectrometer always gathers a band of wavelengths—the narrower the slit

the narrower the band—and we always speak of the intensity of a given band. We express it as follows:

$$\text{energy radiated/cm.}^2\text{/sec., in band } \lambda \text{ to } \lambda + \delta\lambda = E_\lambda\delta\lambda \qquad . \qquad (8)$$

The quantity E_λ is called the *emissive power* of a black body for the wavelength λ and at the given temperature; its definition follows from equation (8):

$$E_\lambda = \frac{\text{energy radiated/cm.}^2\text{/sec., in band } \lambda \text{ to } \lambda + \delta\lambda}{\text{bandwidth, } \delta\lambda}.$$

The expression "energy per second" can be replaced by the word "power", whose unit is the watt. Thus

$$E_\lambda = \frac{\text{power radiated/cm.}^2 \text{ in band } \lambda, \lambda + \delta\lambda}{\delta\lambda}.$$

In the figure E_λ is expressed in watts per cm.² per Angstrom unit.

The quantity $E_\lambda\delta\lambda$ in equation (8) is the area beneath the radiation curve between the wavelengths λ and $\lambda + \delta\lambda$ (Fig. 238 (b)). Thus the energy radiated per cm.² per second between those wavelengths is proportional to that area. Similarly the total radiation emitted per cm.² per second over all wavelengths is proportional to the area under the whole curve.

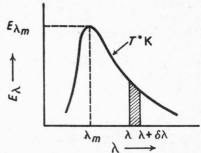

Fig. 238 (b).   Definitions of E_λ, λ_m, and E_{λ_m}.

25. Laws of Black Body Radiation.

The curves of Fig. 238 (a) can be explained only by the quantum theory of radiation, which is outside our scope. Both theory and experiment lead to three generalizations, which together describe well the properties of black-body radiation :

(i) If λ_m is the wavelength of the peak of the curve for $T°$ K., then

$$\lambda_m T = \text{constant} \qquad . \qquad . \qquad . \qquad . \qquad . \qquad (9)$$

The value of the constant is 0.29×10^8 A.U.-°K., or 0.29 cm.-°K. In Fig. 238 (a) the dotted line is the locus of the peaks of the curves for different temperatures.

(ii) If E_{λ_m} is the height of the peak of the curve for the temperature $T°$ K., then

$$E_{\lambda_m} \propto T^5 \qquad . \qquad . \qquad . \qquad . \qquad . \qquad . \qquad (10)$$

The relationships (10) and (9) are particular cases of a general law given by Wien in 1894; (9) is sometimes called *Wien's displacement law*.

(iii) If E is the *total* energy radiated per cm.^{2} per second at $T°$ K., represented by the area under the curve, then

$$E = \sigma T^4,$$

where σ is a constant. This result is called **Stefan's law,** and the constant σ is called *Stefan's constant.* Its value is

$$\sigma = 5\cdot7 \times 10^{-12} \text{ watt/cm.}^2/°\text{K}^4.$$

26. Prévost's Theory of Exchanges.

In 1792 Prévost applied the idea of dynamic equilibrium to radiation. He asserted that a body radiates heat at a rate which depends only on its surface and its temperature, and that it absorbs heat at a rate depending on its surface and the temperature of its surroundings. When the temperature of a body is constant, the body is losing heat by radiation, and gaining it by absorption, at equal rates.

It is easy to think of experiments which seem to support Prévost's theory, and the reader will certainly grasp the general idea of it if he imagines hot pies and cold ice-creams put into the same cupboard. But in such experiments it is difficult to get rid of the possibility of convection. Let us rather take an old-fashioned, high vacuum, electric lamp, and put it in a can of water (Fig. 239 (a)). We can find the

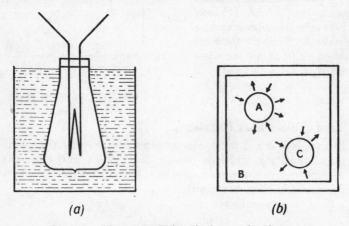

(a)   *(b)*

Fig. 239. Illustrating Prévost's theory of exchanges.

temperature of the lamp's filament by measuring its resistance. We find that, whatever the temperature of the water, the filament comes to that temperature, if we leave it long enough. When the water is cooler than the filament, the filament cools down; when the water is hotter, the filament warms up.

In the abstract language of theoretical physics, Prévost's theory is easy enough to discuss. If a hot body A (Fig. 239 (*b*)) is placed in an evacuated enclosure B, at a lower temperature than A, then A cools until it reaches the temperature of B. If a body C, cooler than B, is put in B, then C warms up to the temperature of B. We conclude that radiation from B falls on C, and therefore also on A, even though A

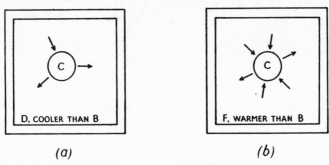

(a)   *(b)*

Fig. 240. Illustrating Prévost's theory.

is at a higher temperature. Thus A and C each come to equilibrium at the temperature of B when each is absorbing and emitting radiation at equal rates.

Now let us suppose that, after it has reached equilibrium with B, one of the bodies, say C, is transferred from B to a cooler evacuated enclosure D (Fig. 240 (*a*)). It loses heat and cools to the temperature of D. Therefore it is radiating heat. But if C is transferred from B to a warmer enclosure F, then C gains heat and warms up to the temperature of F (Fig. 240 (*b*)). It seems unreasonable to suppose that C stops radiating when it is transferred to F; it is more reasonable to suppose that it goes on radiating but, while it is cooler than F, it absorbs more than it radiates.

27. Emissivity.

Let us consider a body B, in equilibrium with an enclosure A, at a temperature $T°$ K. (Fig. 241). If the body is perfectly black, it emits radiation characteristic of the temperature T; let us write the total intensity of this radiation over all wavelengths as E watts/cm.[2] Since the body is in equilibrium with the enclosure, it is absorbing as much as it radiates. And since it absorbs all the radiation that falls upon it, the energy falling on it per cm.[2] per second must be equal to E. This conclusion need not surprise us, since the enclosure A is full of black body radiation characteristic of its temperature T.

Now let us consider, in the same enclosure, a body C which is not black. On each square centimetre of the body's surface, E watts of radiation fall (Fig. 241). Of this, let us suppose that the body absorbs a fraction a, that is to say, it absorbs aE watts per cm.[2] We may call a the total absorp-

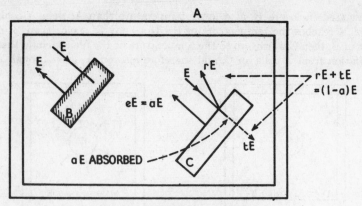

FIG. 241. Equilibria in an enclosure.

tion factor of the body C, "total" because it refers to the total radiation. The radiation which the body does not absorb, $(1 - a)E$, it reflects or transmits.

Thus: $\left.\begin{array}{l}\text{power reflected or}\\\text{transmitted/cm.}^2\end{array}\right\} = E - aE.$

For equilibrium, the total power leaving the body per cm.² must be equal to the total power falling upon it, E watts/cm.² The power emitted by the body, which must be added to that reflected and transmitted, is therefore:

$$\text{total power radiated/cm.}^2 = aE \qquad . \quad . \quad . \quad (12)$$

The ratio of the total power radiated per cm.² by a given body, to that emitted by a black body at the same temperature, is called the *total emissivity* of the given body. Hence, by equation (12),

$$e = \frac{aE}{E} = a.$$

We have therefore shown that the total emissivity of a body is equal to its total absorption factor.

This is a formal expression of the results of Ritchie's experiment (p. 357). If we combine it with Stefan's law, we find that the total energy E radiated per cm.² per second by a body of emissivity e at a temperature $T°$ K. is

$$E = eE = e\sigma T^4.$$

28. Spectral Emissivity; Kirchhoff's Law.

Most bodies are coloured; they transmit or reflect some wavelengths better than others. We have already seen that they must absorb these wavelengths weakly; we now see that, because they absorb them weakly, they must also radiate them weakly. To show this, we have only to repeat the foregoing argument, but restricting it to a narrow band of wavelengths between λ and $\lambda + \delta\lambda$. The energy falling per cm.² per second on the body, in this band, is $E_\lambda \delta\lambda$ where E_λ is the emissive power of a blackbody in the neighbourhood of λ, at the temperature of the enclosure. If the body C absorbs a fraction a_λ of this, we call a_λ the spectral absorption factor of the body, for the wavelength λ. In equilibrium, the body emits as much radiation in the neighbourhood of λ as it absorbs; thus:

energy radiated/cm.²/sec. $= a_\lambda E_\lambda \delta\lambda$ watts per cm.²

We define the spectral emissivity of the body e_λ, by the equation

$$e_\lambda = \frac{\text{energy radiated/cm.}^2\text{/sec. by body in range } \lambda, \lambda + \delta\lambda}{\text{energy radiated/cm.}^2\text{/sec. in same range, by black body at same temperature}}$$

$$= \frac{\text{energy radiated/cm.}^2\text{/sec. by body in range } \lambda, \lambda + \delta\lambda}{E_\lambda \delta\lambda}$$

$$= \frac{a_\lambda E_\lambda \delta\lambda}{E_\lambda \delta\lambda}.$$

Thus
$$e_\lambda = a_\lambda \quad . \quad . \quad . \quad . \quad . \quad . \quad . \quad . \quad (13)$$

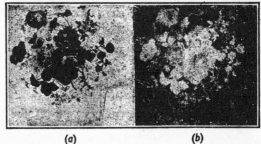

FIG. 242. Photographs showing how a piece of incandescent decorated crockery appears (a) by reflected light and (b) by its own emitted light.

(a)   (b)

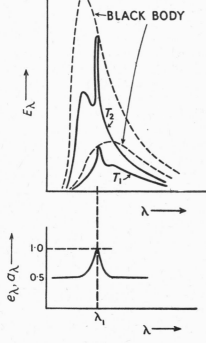

FIG. 243. Illustrating Kirchhoff's law of radiation.

Equation (13) expresses a law due to Kirchhoff:

The spectral emissivity of a body, for a given wavelength, is equal to its spectral absorption factor for the same wavelength.

Kirchhoff's law is not easy to demonstrate by experiment. One reads that a plate, which when cold shows a red pattern on a blue ground, glows blue on a red ground when heated in a furnace. But not all such plates do this, because the spectral emissivities of many coloured pigments vary with their temperature. However, Fig. 242 shows two photographs of a piece of pottery, one taken by reflected light at room temperature (left), the other by its own light when heated (right).

Fig. 243 illustrates Kirchhoff's law, by showing how the

spectral emissivity and absorption factor of a coloured body may vary with wavelength, and how its emissive power E_λ does likewise. It is assumed that e_λ rises to unity at the wavelength λ_1 (which is not likely), and that it does not vary with the temperature. A body for which e_λ is the same for all wavelengths, but is less than unity, is said to be "grey".

29. Absorption by Gases.

An experiment which shows that, if a body radiates a given wavelength strongly, it also absorbs that wavelength strongly, can be made with sodium vapour. A sodium vapour lamp runs at about 220° C.; compared with the sun, or even an arc-lamp, it is cool. The experiment consists of passing sunlight or arc-light through a spectroscope, and observing its continuous spectrum. The sodium lamp is then placed in the path of the light, and a black line appears in the yellow. If the white light is now cut off, the line which looked black comes up brightly—it is the sodium yellow line.

The process of absorption by sodium vapour—or any other gas— is not, however, the same as the process of absorption by a solid. When a solid absorbs radiation, it turns it into heat—into the random kinetic energy of its molecules. It then re-radiates it in all wavelengths, but mostly in very long ones, because the solid is cool. When a vapour absorbs light of its characteristic wavelength, however, its atoms are excited; they then re-radiate the absorbed energy, in the same wavelength (5,893 A.U. for sodium). But they re-radiate it in all directions, and therefore less of it passes on in the original direction than before (Fig. 244). Thus the yellow component of the original beam is weakened, but the yellow light radiated sideways by the sodium is strengthened. The sideways strengthening is hard to detect, but it was shown by R. W. Wood in 1906. He used mercury vapour instead of sodium. The phenomenon is called *optical resonance*, by analogy with resonance in sound.

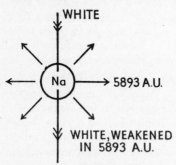

FIG. 244. Absorption by sodium vapour.

CONVECTION

Liquids—except mercury, which is a molten metal—are bad conductors of heat. If we hold a test-tube full of water by the bottom, we can boil the water near the top in a Bunsen flame, without any discomfort. But if we hold the tube at the top, and heat it at the bottom, then the top becomes unbearably hot long before the water boils. The heat is brought to the top by *convection*; the warm water at the bottom expands, becomes less dense, and rises; the cold water sinks to take its place. If we heat a beaker of water at one side, and drop in a crystal of potassium permanganate, we can see the currents of hot water rising, and cold descending. Central-heating systems rely on convection to bring hot water from the boiler, in the basement, to the so-called radiators, and to take the cooler water back to the boiler.

The radiators of a central-heating system are wrongly named; they are convectors. They warm the air around them, which rises, and gives way to cooler air from cooler parts of the room. Gases are even worse conductors of heat than liquids, and for most practical purposes we can neglect conduction through them altogether. Woollen clothes keep us warm because they contain pockets of air, which hardly conduct at all, and cannot convect because they cannot move. The wool fibres themselves are much better conductors than the air they imprison.

Convection by air is important in ventilation: the fire in a room maintains a draught of hot air up the chimney, and cool fresh air from outside comes in under the door. The draught also helps to keep the fire supplied with oxygen; as we shall see, factory chimneys are made tall to stimulate convection and increase the draught.

30. Forced and Free (Natural) Convection.

A gas or a liquid may carry away heat from a hot body by convection. If the flow of liquid or gas is simply due to its being heated by the body, and hence rising, the convection is said to be *free*, or natural. But if the gas or liquid is flowing in a stream maintained by some other means, then the convection is said to be *forced*. Thus cooling one's porridge in the obvious way is an example of forced convection; it causes a more rapid loss of heat than does natural convection.

31. Critical Diameter of Pipes.

Hot-water and steam pipes are often lagged with asbestos to reduce the loss of heat from them. The temperature drop across the lagging makes the outside cooler than the pipe, and so, by Newton's law, tends to reduce the rate at which heat escapes from it. However, the lagging increases the outside diameter of the whole, and so increases its area of contact with the atmosphere. The increase in area tends to make convection more vigorous, by enabling the pipe to heat a greater mass of air. If the diameter of the pipe is small, the increase in area may more than offset the reduction temperature of the outside, and so increase the rate of heat loss. Thus there is a critical diameter of pipe; if the diameter is less than the critical value, the pipe should not be lagged. The critical diameter depends on many factors, but is commonly of the order of 1 cm.

32. The Greenhouse.

A greenhouse keeps plants warm by inhibiting convection. The glass allows radiant heat to reach the plants from the sun, but prevents the warm air in the greenhouse from escaping. In winter, when there is little sunshine, the heat is provided by hot water pipes. In summer the temperature is regulated by opening or closing the roof and windows, and so adjusting the loss of heat by convection.*

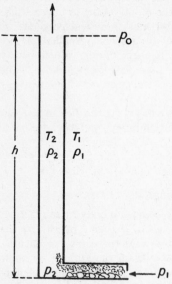

FIG. 245. The action of a chimney.

33. Chimneys.

The taller the chimney, the fiercer is the draught. As the fire burns, it fills the chimney with hot air (Fig. 245); this air is less dense than the colder air outside the chimney, and so the pressure at the bottom of the chimney, p_2, is less than the pressure at the grate, p_1; the excess pressure drives air through the fire and up the chimney.

By making some simplifying assumptions, we can estimate the excess pressure. Let T_1, ρ_1, and T_2, ρ_2, be the respective absolute temperatures, and the densities, of the air outside and inside the chimney. (We assume that T_2 and ρ_2 are uniform). And let p_0 be the atmospheric pressure at the chimney mouth. Then the pressure p_2 at the foot is

$$p_2 = p_0 + g\rho_2 h,$$

where g is the acceleration of gravity and h is the height of the chimney. And the pressure p_1 at the grate is

$$p_1 = p_0 + g\rho_1 h.$$

Then the excess pressure is

$$p_1 - p_2 = g(\rho_1 - \rho_2)h.$$

We shall assume that the difference in pressure is so small that it does not affect the density; the result of the calculation will justify us. The difference in density is then due solely to the difference in temperature.

Thus

$$\frac{\rho_2}{\rho_1} = \frac{T_1}{T_2}.$$

* This theory of the greenhouse is due to R. W. Wood. See *Phil. Mag.*, Series VI, vol. 17, p. 319 (1909); also Abbot, *ibid.*, vol. 18, p. 32 (1909).

Let us take $T_1 = 273°$ K.—a chilly day—and $T_2 = 546°$ K. Then, if $p_1 = 760$ mm. mercury the density of the cold air is the value at s.t.p.:

$$\rho_1 = 0.0013 \text{ gm./cm.}^3$$

And $$\rho_2 = \frac{T_1}{T_2} \rho_1 = \frac{273}{546} \times 0.0013 = 0.00065 \text{ gm./cm.}^3$$

If the chimney is 100 metres high, then

$$h = 100 \times 100 \text{ cm.} = 10^4 \text{ cm.,}$$

and the pressure difference is

$$\begin{aligned} p_1 - p_2 = g(\rho_1 - \rho_2)h &= 980 \times (0.0013 - 0.00065) \times 10^4 \\ &= 980 \times 0.00065 \times 10^4 \\ &= 6,300 \text{ dynes/cm.}^2 \end{aligned}$$

To make this mean something to us, let us convert it into a height of mercury. If h' is the height of mercury equivalent to this pressure, then

$$g\rho h' = 6,360,$$

where ρ is the density of mercury, 13·6 gm./cm.³

Thus

$$\begin{aligned} h' &= \frac{6,360}{13.6 \times 980} \\ &= 0.57 \text{ cm.} \\ &= 5.7 \text{ mm.} \end{aligned}$$

This pressure is about the same as that of the domestic gas supply.

WEATHER

The phenomena of convection and radiation, and of change of state, govern weather and climate. The following brief account of them is greatly simplified.

34. Winds

The great wind currents over the earth are largely due to convection; warm air rises from the equator, and cold air moves in from the poles. But the motion of the air is complicated by the rotation of the earth, and its study is a branch of dynamics rather than of heat.

In the northern hemisphere for instance, the cold air from the north travels roughly south-west; the warm air from the tropics

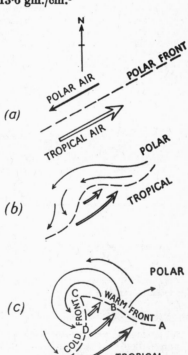

FIG. 246. Development of a depression on the polar front in the northern hemisphere (plan). (From a figure by Pack: *Weather Forecasting*, Longmans, 1948.)

travels roughly north-east (Fig. 246 (*a*)). Where the two streams meet there is a sharp change of temperature, called the polar front. The interface of the two air streams is not vertical, but slopes up towards the pole, at an angle of about ½°; the warm tropical air rides over the cold polar air.

35. Depressions.

A depression is a region of low pressure where a tongue of tropical air protrudes into the polar air (Fig. 246 (*b*) and (*c*)). The boundary AC is called a warm front, because the temperature rises as it passes; the boundary CE is called a cold front. The warm air rises over the cold, so that the system has the cross-section shown in Fig. 247. Usually the whole system moves in the direction of the tropical air-stream.

As a depression approaches, the atmospheric pressure falls because warm air is less dense than cold, and the layer of warm air thickens towards the warm front. Similarly, after the cold front has passed, the pressure rises again.

At each front of the depression, cloud is formed. The air from the tropics is more humid than that from the pole, and the water-vapour in it condenses when it is cooled by adiabatic expansion caused by ascent. The cloud formed has a layer-like form, called stratus, and is divided, according to its height, into the three types indicated in Fig. 247. From the lowest cloud, nimbo-stratus, rain falls. Well ahead of the depression feathery cirrus cloud is formed.

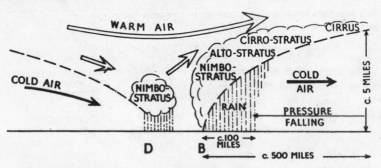

Fig. 247. Section of a depression (after Pack, and Bjedenes and Solber).

Fig. 246 (*c*) shows that the wind circulates counter-clockwise round a depression. In the southern hemisphere it circulates clockwise.

36. Anticyclones.

An anticyclone is a closed region of high pressure. From its boundaries, the air is displaced outwards, so that the air within the region sinks slowly and is compressed adiabatically, thus becoming warmer. This warming tends to prevent the formation of cloud so that the weather in an anticyclone is generally fine. Round an anticyclone, the wind circulates in the opposite sense to the wind round a depression; thus in the northern hemisphere it circulates clockwise.

Changes in the weather are due mainly to the approach and retreat of anticyclones and depressions. Weather forecasts are made, therefore, with the help of charts showing among other things, the barometric pressure, temperature, humidity, and the wind direction and strength, at various points. These charts are made several times a day, and they are considered in conjunction with data on the " upper air " (i.e. up to 100,000 ft.) when forecasts are prepared.

37. Sunrise and Sunset.

Over land, nights are more often windless than days, because the absence of the sun's radiation means no local heating, and therefore no convection. Slow currents of air, however, are common about the time of sunset. In the mountains, streams of mist can often be seen pouring over ridges, from one valley into another.

As soon as the sun sets, the land begins to cool by radiation. Hill-tops cool most rapidly, because they expose a relatively greater area, for a given mass, than do plains or valleys. The air on the top cools by contact, flows downwards, and accumulates as a cold layer—often not many feet thick—in the valleys. Even in gentle country, like that of Kent, this may happen, and may be disastrous to fruit trees in the spring. To prevent it, the air must be stirred, to mix the warm with the cold; both bonfires and huge fans have been used.

38. Temperature Lapse.

During the daytime, in warm sunny weather, the surface of the earth warms up, and starts convection currents. As the warm air rises, it expands, because the pressure of the atmosphere decreases with increasing height above the earth. The rising air can draw no heat from any source and so it expands adiabatically. (It cannot draw heat from the sun's radiation, because air is an extremely poor absorber.) As the air expands adiabatically, it cools. Thus the temperature falls off vertically. If the air is not saturated with moisture, and is not disturbed by local winds, theory shows that its temperature should fall at the rate of 9·8° C. per km., or 5·5° F. per 1,000 ft. This rate is called the dry adiabatic lapse-rate.

Although it is not saturated, the rising air generally contains some water-vapour. When the air has risen to a height at which the temperature is below the dew-point, the water-vapour in it condenses, and forms cumulus cloud. This has two main forms; one like cotton-wool, and the other like cauliflower-heart. Up to the base of the cloud, the temperature lapses at the dry adiabatic rate. Within the cloud, however, the air contains saturated water-vapour. It therefore cools more slowly with height, because as the temperature falls the vapour condenses. The latent heat released by the condensing vapour partly offsets the cooling by expansion. Thus the temperature falls more slowly; the saturated adiabatic lapse rate averages about 6° C. per km. or 3° F. per 1,000 ft.

Local heating, or the inflow of warm air from another region, may interfere with the temperature lapse of the atmosphere. Also in the settled weather of an anticyclone the warm air caused by " settling " may appear at a height of several thousand feet. It rests on the cooler air below, and at their interface the temperature lapse ceases. The abrupt rise in temperature from the lower air to the upper is called a *temperature inversion*.

When a temperature inversion appears, convection stops. For the rising air now meets warmer, less dense air, through which it cannot rise further. Thus smoke tends to accumulate below the level of the inversion, and to form the so-called heat haze. During spells of fine weather in North Wales, haze appears if the wind is from the East, bringing smoke from the Midlands; but not if the wind is from the West, where there is no smoke for it to bring.

39. Water in the Atmosphere: Rain.

The sun's warmth evaporates the seas, rivers and lakes, and the warm moist air rises. As it does so it cools, and the water-vapour becomes saturated. Further cooling makes the vapour condense, and droplets of water appear, forming a cloud. The droplets are so small that they sink through the air very slowly; their diameter is about 0·001 in., and they fall about 100 ft. in an hour.

How the droplets in a cloud become larger, and fall as rain, is an unsolved problem. One theory of it starts from the observation that a cloud gives rain only when it enters a region of the atmosphere below the freezing-point.* The water droplets then start to turn into ice crystals. As soon as a crystal is formed it grows, because water evaporates from the liquid drops around it, and condenses on the crystal. (The water does this because the temperature is below that of the critical point, 0·01° C., and the vapour-pressure of water is then greater than that of ice (see p. 324).)

In this way the crystals become large enough to fall rapidly through the air. As they do so, they enter regions above the freezing-point, and melt. Being large, they continue to fall, as raindrops. If the temperature is everywhere below freezing-point the ice crystals do not melt, but fall as snow.

If moist air is carried into a region where the temperature is below that of the triple-point, without first condensing, then the water-vapour goes over directly into ice. The ice forms feathery crystals, which appear as cirrus cloud. A thickening layer of cirrus often runs before a warm front, and so is a sign of bad weather to come; the front may be 500 miles or more behind the cloud, and so may take a day, or longer, to arrive.

Mountains not only receive weather from afar; they often make their own—usually bad. They force warm moist air into regions of lower pressure, where adiabatic expansion leads often to cooling below the dew-point. The moisture first forms cloud, and then, if it is cooled below 0° C., comes down as rain.

40. Hail and Snow.

Snow consists of ice crystals, formed directly from vapour which has condensed below the triple-point. Hail is generally supposed to be rain which has been carried, by strong convection currents, upwards through a region below the freezing-point; after freezing it has been carried down again, and then fallen as hail.

41. Condensation at Ground-level : Dew, Hoar-frost, Fog.

Water-vapour often condenses on solid surfaces at night. Usually it appears as drops of dew, when the temperature of the surface falls below the dew-point. But if the ground temperature is below that of the triple-point, the vapour goes directly over to fine ice crystals, known as hoar-frost.

---

* This theory, due to Bergeron, can apply only to temperate regions; in the tropics, rain does fall from clouds above freezing point.

Hoar-frost or dew forms more readily on clear, calm nights than on windy or cloudy ones. For clouds radiate heat back to the earth, and so make it cool less at night; and wind breaks up the layer of air above the ground, and so prevents it from being cooled by contact. Cloudless nights occur in anticyclones (p. 370); thus fine warm days are often accompanied by cold dewy nights and misty dawns.

Mist or fog is cloud at ground level. It appears when the temperature of the air falls below the dew-point. Fog appears only in calm weather; wind carries the moist air near ground-level to higher regions, where it condenses and then falls as rain.

In very clean air, water-vapour does not readily condense. This is because a sharply curved surface, such as that of a very small drop, favours evaporation. A molecule near the surface of such a drop is surrounded by fewer other molecules than is a molecule near a flat or gently-curved surface. Thus the molecule near the more sharply curved surface can more easily escape. In other words, the saturated vapour-pressure over a small drop is greater than over a large one or a plane surface. For this reason, in clean air water-vapour may have several times its normal saturation pressure before condensing. In dirty air, however, the solid particles provide nuclei on which drops of fair size can readily form.

In the cleanest country or seaside districts, fog forms readily as described above; there are always enough minute particles in the air to provide nuclei for the drops. In towns one notices the nuclei more because they are dirty. In the upper atmosphere, however, water vapour may have several times the normal saturation pressure corresponding to its temperature, and yet not condense. It is then said to be super-saturated. When an aircraft passes through it, however, it is immediately furnished with nuclei for condensation. Hence the so-called vapour trails; they are not vapour, but drops of water or crystals of ice.

EXERCISES XV

1. Define *coefficient of thermal conductivity*. Describe a method of measuring this coefficient for a metal.

Assuming that the thermal insulation provided by a woollen glove is equivalent to a layer of quiescent air 3 mm. thick, determine the heat loss per minute from a man's hand, surface area 200 sq. cm. on a winter's day when the atmospheric air temperature is $-3°$ C. The skin temperature is to be taken as $34°$ C. and the thermal conductivity of air as $5·7 \times 10^{-5}$ c.g.s. centigrade units. (*L.*)

2. Enumerate and briefly describe the various processes causing a jug of hot water to cool. Discuss methods which can be adopted to lessen the rate at which it cools.

If the thermal capacity of the vessel and its contents is 500 cal./deg. C. and it cools at the rate of $3°$ C. per minute, what current would have to be passed through a heating coil of 600 ohms resistance incorporated in the jug to keep the temperature steady? If the coil consisted of two equal parts in series, at what rate would heating take place if the two parts were put in parallel and the applied voltage not altered? (4·2 joules = 1 cal.) (*L*.)

3. One end of an iron bar is placed in molten metal at a constant temperature. Describe and account for the temperature changes which take place in the bar. Illustrate graphically the final distribution of temperature along the bar. What difference would there be if the sides of the bar were lagged with a non-conducting material?

Draw a labelled diagram of an apparatus for determining the thermal conductivity of a good conductor. Explain why a different form of apparatus is necessary for determining the conductivity of a poor conductor. (*L*.)

4. Discuss the differences in the techniques for the measurement of the thermal conductivity of good and bad conductors.

A copper disc, of radius 10 cm. and thickness 1·0 cm., acquires a steady temperature of 70° C. when placed on top of an ebonite disc, of radius 10 cm. and thickness 2 mm., whose lower face is maintained at 100° C. Suspended in air, the copper disc cools from 80° C. to 50° C. in 5·0 min. In each experiment the temperature of the "surroundings" is 15° C. Assuming that the rate of loss of heat from the copper disc, in cal. cm.$^{-2}$ min.$^{-1}$ is C $\theta^{5/4}$, where θ is the excess temperature above the "surroundings" and C is a constant, calculate the thermal conductivity of the ebonite. Assume that the density of the copper is 8·8 gm. cm.$^{-3}$ and that its specific heat is 0·1 cal. gm.$^{-1}$ deg.$^{-1}$ C. (*N. Schol.*)

5. How can the temperature of a furnace be determined from observations on the radiation emitted?

Calculate the apparent temperature of the sun from the following information:

> Sun's radius : 4·4 × 10⁵ miles.
> Distance from earth : 9·2 × 10⁷ miles.
> Solar constant : 0·14 watt per sq. cm.
> Stefan's constant : 5·7 × 10⁻⁵ ergs cm.$^{-2}$ sec.$^{-1}$ deg.$^{-4}$ (*N*.).

6. Define the coefficient of thermal conductivity of a substance. Describe an accurate method of measuring the conductivity of a poor conductor, indicating the way in which you would calculate the conductivity from the measurements. Explain the difficulties which arise if the same method is applied to a good conductor such as copper. (*O. & C*.)

7. Explain Prévost's theory of exchanges and describe an experiment which can be used to illustrate it.

What is Stefan's law and how may it be tested experimentally? (*C*.)

8. State the laws of heat conduction, and describe a method for the measurement of the specific conductivity of a good conductor. A boiler supplies steam to a 100 h.p. turbine, whose efficiency is 15 per cent. The temperature of the water is 150° C. and that of the outer boiler-wall 300° C. What is the minimum surface of the boiler exposed to the furnace if the thickness of the wall is 4 mm.? [Conductivity of the material of the boiler = 0·9 cal. per sec. per sq. cm. per unit temperature gradient; 1 h.p. = 746 watts; mechanical equivalent of heat 4·2 × 10⁷ ergs per cal.] (*O. & C*.)

9. Define thermal conductivity. Water contained in a closed thin-walled cylindrical copper tank, of radius 30 cm. and height 1 metre, is maintained at 60° C. by means of an electric heater immersed in the water, the outside temperature being 20° C. The tank is lagged over its curved surface by a layer of felt 1 cm. thick. If the drop in temperature in the thin copper walls is neglected, and the thermal conductivity of felt is 9 × 10⁻⁵ c.g.s. units, find the wattage of the heating element. What will

be the cost of running the heater for a week if the cost of electrical energy is 1d. per Board of Trade Unit (kilowatt-hour)? [$J = 4\cdot18$ joules per cal.] (W.)

10. Describe one experiment to show that a polished metal surface is a poor absorber of heat, and one experiment to show that such a surface reflects a high proportion of a beam of light falling on it. Briefly compare heat and light radiations from the standpoint of (a) velocity, (b) effect at a distance, (c) simple refraction, (d) transmission through material substances. (N.)

11. A block of metal is heated and (a) exposed to ordinary atmospheric conditions, or (b) placed in a high vacuum. State concisely the factors that govern the rate at which its temperature falls under conditions (a) and (b). Energy is supplied at the rate of 165 watts to a closed cylindrical canister 5 cm. in radius and 15 cm. high, filled with water and exposed to the air of the room, which is at 15° C. It is found that the temperature of the water remains steady at 80° C. Find the rate of heat loss per unit area of the vessel per deg. C. excess temperature. Estimate also the fall of temperature in a minute, when the energy supply is shut off. Neglect the weight of the canister itself. (L.)

12. Describe an experiment to show (a) that the spectrum of an incandescent solid includes both visible and invisible radiations, (b) how the fraction of incident radiation transmitted by glass depends on the temperature of the source of the radiation.

The sun's rays are focused by a concave mirror of diameter 12 cm. fixed with its axis towards the sun on to a copper calorimeter, where they are absorbed. If the thermal capacity of the calorimeter and its contents is 59 cal. per deg. C. and the temperature rises 8° C. in 2 min., calculate the heat received in 1 min. by a square metre of the earth's surface when the rays are incident normally. (N.)

13. Give an account of Stefan's law of radiation, explaining the character of the radiating body to which it applies and how such a body can be experimentally realized.

If each square cm. of the sun's surface radiates energy at the rate of $1\cdot5 \times 10^3$ cal. sec.$^{-1}$ cm.$^{-2}$ and Stefan's constant is $5\cdot7 \times 10^{-5}$ erg sec.$^{-1}$ cm.$^{-2}$ deg. abs.$^{-4}$, calculate the temperature of the sun's surface in degrees centigrade, assuming Stefan's law applies to the radiation. (L.)

14. Define *thermal conductivity*. Outline the basic principles of the methods used to find the thermal conductivity of solids.

A thin copper rod projects from a steam chest and supports a mass of 168 gm. of copper. The length of the rod from the chest to the copper is 10 cm. All is originally at room temperature, 10° C., and the rod is effectively jacketed. When steam is passed into the chest the initial rate of rise of temperature of the mass of copper is 1° C. per min.

What is the rate at which heat passes along the rod per second and what is the diameter of the circular cross-section of the rod? (Thermal conductivity of copper is 0·9 c.g.s. centigrade units and specific heat of copper is 0·09 cal. gm.$^{-1}$ deg.$^{-1}$ C.) (L.)

15. State Stefan's law of radiation. What is meant by a perfectly black body, and how may it be realized in practice?

Establish the value of Stefan's constant if the temperature of the filament of a 40-watt tungsten lamp is 2,170° C. and the effective surface area of the filament is 0·66 sq. cm. You are to assume that the energy radiated is 0·31 of that from a black body in similar conditions and that any effect due to radiation from the glass envelope is negligible. (L.)

CHAPTER XVI

THERMOMETRY AND PYROMETRY

REALIZATION OF TEMPERATURE SCALE

In Chapter I we discussed the general idea of a temperature scale. To establish such a scale we need

(i) some physical property of a substance—such as the volume of a particular liquid—which increases continuously with increasing hotness, but is constant at constant hotness;

(ii) two standard degrees of hotness—the fixed points (ice and steam)—which can be accurately reproduced.

1. The Fixed Points and Fundamental Interval.

The temperature of melting ice and saturated steam are chosen as the fixed points, because they are easy to realize. We have seen that the atmospheric pressure must be specified in defining the steam point, but this is not necessary in defining the ice point, because the melting-point of ice changes very little with pressure (p. 299). On the other hand impurities in water do not affect the temperature of saturated steam, but impurities in ice do affect its melting-point (p. 144); the ice used in realizing the lower fixed point must therefore be prepared from pure water.

Then, if P is the chosen temperature-measuring quantity, its values P_0 at the ice point, and P_{100} at the steam point determine the fundamental interval of the thermometer: $P_{100} - P_0$. And the temperature θ_P on the P-scale, which corresponds to a value P_θ of P is, *by definition*,

$$\theta_P = \frac{P_\theta - P_0}{P_{100} - P_0} \times 100.$$

2. The Thermometric Substance and Property.

Most thermometers are of the liquid-in-glass type, because it is simple and cheap; they contain either mercury or alcohol. Water is unsuitable because, among other disadvantages, it contracts from the ice point to the temperature of maximum density so that its volume does not increase continuously with increasing hotness.

The mercury and alcohol scales agree fairly well with one another, and with either of the gas scales. The gas scales depend on the change of volume at constant pressure and of pressure at constant volume (p. 226). In practice the constant volume scale is always used, because a change of pressure is easier to measure accurately than a change of volume.

376

The mercury scale agrees better with the gas scales than does the alcohol scale. However, even the best mercury thermometers disagree slightly amongst themselves. The discrepancies may arise because the bores of the tubes are not uniform, or the mercury is impure, or the glass is not homogeneous.

In the most accurate work, therefore, temperatures are measured by the changes in pressure of a gas at constant volume. At pressures of the order of one atmosphere, different gases give slightly different temperature scales, because none of them obeys the gas laws perfectly. But as the pressure is reduced, the gases approach closely to the ideal, and their temperature scales come together. By observing the departure of a gas from Boyle's law at moderate pressures it is possible to allow for its departure from the ideal; temperatures measured with the gas in a constant volume thermometer can then be converted to the values which would be given by the same thermometer if the gas were ideal.

3. The Constant-Volume Gas Thermometer.

Fig. 248 shows a constant volume hydrogen thermometer, due to Chappuis (1884). B is a bulb of platinum-iridium, holding the gas.

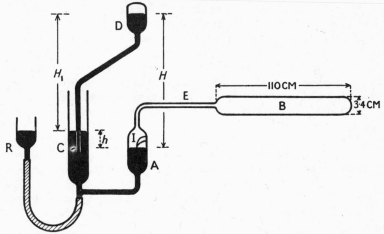

Fig. 248.   Constant volume hydrogen thermometer (*not to scale*).

The volume is defined by the level of the index I in the glass tube A. The pressure is adjusted by raising or lowering the mercury reservoir R. A barometer CD is fitted directly into the pressure-measuring system; if H_1 is its height, and h the difference in level between the mercury surfaces in A and C, then the pressure H of the hydrogen, in mm. mercury is

$$H = H_1 + h.$$

H is measured with a cathetometer.

The glass tubes A, C, D, all have the same diameter to prevent errors due to surface tension; and A and D are optically worked to prevent errors due to refraction (as in looking through common window-glass).

Observations made with a constant-volume gas thermometer must be corrected for the following errors:

(i)   the expansion of the bulb B;
(ii) the temperature of the gas in the tube E and A, which lies between the temperature of B and the temperature of the room;
(iii) the temperature of the mercury in the barometer and mano-meter.

The expansion of the bulb can be estimated from its coefficient of cubical expansion, by using the temperature shown by the gas thermo-meter. Since the expansion appears only as a small correction to the observed temperature, the uncorrected value of the temperature may be used in estimating it. The tube E is called the "dead-space" of the thermometer. Its diameter is made small, about 0·7 mm., so that it contains only a small fraction of the total mass of gas. Its volume is known, and the temperatures at various points in it are measured with mercury thermometers. The effect of the gas in it is then allowed for in a calculation similar to that used to calculate the pressure of a gas in two bulbs at different temperatures (p. 262). Mercury thermometers may be used to measure the temperatures because the error due to the dead-space is small; any error in allowing for it is of the second order of small quantities. For the same reason, mercury thermometers may be used to measure the temperature of the manometer and barometer.

A gas thermometer is a cumbersome instrument, demanding much skill and time, and useless for measuring changing temperatures. In practice, gas thermometers are used only for calibrating electrical thermometers—resistance thermometers and thermocouples. The readings of these, when they are used to measure unknown tempera-tures can then be converted into temperatures on the ideal gas scale.

4. The International Temperature Scale.

Because of the wide use of electrical thermometers, a scale of tempera-ture based on them is used throughout the laboratories of the world. It is called the *international scale of temperature*, and is defined so that temperatures expressed on it agree, within the limits of experimental accuracy, with the same temperatures expressed on the ideal gas scale.

For the purpose of calibrating electrical thermometers, subsidiary fixed points, in addition to the fundamental fixed points of ice and steam, have been determined with the constant-volume gas thermometer. They are all measured at an atmospheric pressure of 760 mm. mercury.

Their values are given, with those of the fundamental fixed points, in the following table.

FIXED POINTS OF THE INTERNATIONAL TEMPERATURE SCALE

(a) Boiling point of liquid oxygen	. .	$-182 \cdot 970°$ C.
(b) Ice point (fundamental)	. . .	$0 \cdot 000°$ C.
(c) Steam point (fundamental)	. . .	$100 \cdot 000°$ C.
(d) Boiling-point of sulphur	. . .	$444 \cdot 600°$ C.
(e) Freezing-point of silver	. . .	$960 \cdot 8°$ C.
(f) Freezing-point of gold	. . .	$1,063 \cdot 0°$ C.

The methods of interpolating between these fixed points will be described below.

5. Electrical Thermometers.

Electrical thermometers have great advantages over other types. They are more accurate than any except gas thermometers, and are quicker in action and less cumbersome than those.

The measuring element of a *thermo-electric thermometer* is the welded junction of two fine wires. It is very small in size, and can therefore measure the temperature almost at a point. It causes very little disturbance wherever it is placed, because the wires leading from it are so thin that the heat loss along them is usually negligible. It has a very small heat capacity, and can therefore follow a rapidly changing temperature. To measure such a temperature, however, the e.m.f. of the junction must be measured with a galvanometer, instead of a potentiometer, and some accuracy is then lost.

The measuring element of a *resistance thermometer* is a spiral of fine wire. It has a greater size and heat capacity than a thermojunction, and cannot therefore measure a local or rapidly changing temperature. But, over the range from about room temperature to a few hundred degrees Centigrade, it is more accurate.

6. Resistance Thermometers.

Resistance thermometers are usually made of platinum. The wire is wound on two strips of mica, arranged crosswise as shown in Fig. 249 (a). The ends of the coil are attached to a pair of leads A, for connecting them to a Wheatstone bridge. A similar pair of leads B is near to the leads from the coil, and connected in the adjacent arm

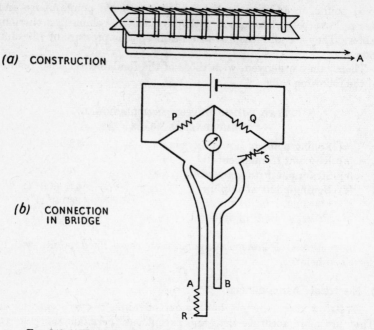

(b) CONNECTION
IN BRIDGE

Fig. 249. Platinum resistance thermometer ($P = Q$, so that B compensates A; and $S = R$).

of the bridge (Fig. 249 (b)). At the end near the coil, the pair of leads B is short-circuited. If the two pairs of leads are identical, their resistances are equal, whatever their temperature. Thus if $P = Q$ the dummy pair, B, just compensates for the pair A going to the coil; and the bridge measures the resistance of the coil alone.

The platinum resistance thermometer is used to measure temperatures on the international scale between the boiling-point of oxygen and 630° C. (630° C. is approximately the freezing-point of antimony, but it is not a fixed point on the scale). The platinum used in the coil must be of high purity. Its purity is judged by the increase in its resistance from the ice point to the steam point. Thus if R_0 and R_{100} are the resistances of the coil at these points, then the coil is fit to reproduce the international temperature scale if

$$\frac{R_{100}}{R_0} > 1.3910.$$

From the boiling-point of oxygen (− 182·970° C.) to the ice-point, the temperature θ, on the international scale, is given by the equation

$$R_\theta = R_0[1 + A\theta + B\theta^2 + C(\theta - 100)^3] \quad . \quad . \quad . \quad (1)$$

Here R_θ is the resistance of the coil, and A, B, C are constants. The constants A and B are determined in a way which we shall describe shortly. When they are known the constant C can be determined from the value of R_θ at the boiling-point of oxygen.

From the ice-point to $630°$ C. the temperature θ is given by

$$R_\theta = R_0(1 + A\theta + B\theta^2).$$

The constants A and B are the same as A and B in equation (1); they can be determined by measuring R_θ at the steam point and the sulphur point ($444\cdot600°$ C.).

At temperatures below the boiling-point of oxygen the resistance of platinum changes rather slowly with temperature. The resistance of lead changes more rapidly, and resistance thermometers of lead wire have been used.

7. Thermocouples.

Between $630°$ C. and the gold point ($1,063\cdot0°$ C.) the international temperature scale is expressed in terms of the electromotive force of a thermocouple. The wires of the thermocouple are platinum, and platinum-rhodium alloy (90 per cent. Pt.: 10 per cent. Rh.). Since the

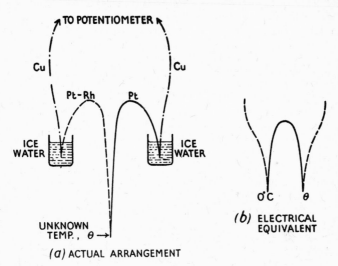

FIG. 250. Use of thermocouples.

e.m.f. is to be measured on a potentiometer, care must be taken that thermal e.m.f.'s are not set up at the junctions of the thermocouple wires and the copper leads to the potentiometer. To do this three junctions are made, as shown in Fig. 250 (a). The junctions of the copper leads to the thermocouple wires are both placed in melting ice. The electromotive force of the whole system is then equal to the e.m.f. of two platinum/platinum-rhodium junctions, one in ice and the other at the unknown temperature (Fig. 250 (b)).

The international temperature θ corresponding to an e.m.f. E is given by
$$E = a + b\theta + c\theta^2,$$

where a, b and c are constants. The values of the constants are determined by measurements at the gold point (1,063·0° C.), the silver point (960·8° C.), and the temperature of freezing antimony (about 630·3° C.). Since the freezing-point of antimony is not a fixed point on the international scale, its value in a given experiment is directly measured with a resistance thermometer. This temperature therefore serves to link the resistance and thermo-electric regions of the temperature scale.

8. Other Thermocouples.

Because of their convenience, thermocouples are used to measure temperatures outside their range on the international scale, when the highest accuracy is not required. The arrangement of three junctions and potentiometer may be used, but for less accurate work the potentiometer may be replaced by a galvanometer G, in the simpler arrangement of Fig. 251 (a). The galvanometer scale may be calibrated to

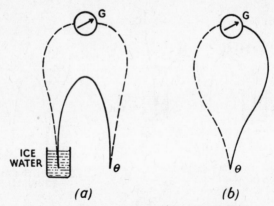

FIG. 251. Simple thermojunction thermometer.

read directly in temperatures, the known melting-points of metals like tin and lead being used as subsidiary fixed points. For rough work, particularly at high temperatures, the cold junction may be omitted (Fig. 251 (b)). An uncertainty of a few degrees in a thousand is often of no importance.

E.M.F.'S OF THERMOJUNCTIONS

(In millivolts, cold junction at 0° C.)

Temp. of hot junction °C.	Pt./Pt.– 10% Rh.	Chromel [1]/ Alumel [2]	Copper/ Constantan[3]	Iron/ Constantan
100	0·64	4·1	4	5
200	1·44	8·1	9	11
300	2·32	12·2	15	16
400	3·25	16·4	21 [5]	22
500	4·22	20·6		27
600	5·22	24·9		33
700	6·26	29·1		39
800	7·33	33·3		45
900	8·43	37·4		
1,000	9·57	41·3		
1,200	11·92 [4]	48·8		
1,400	14·31	55·8		
1,600	16·67			

1. Cr-Ni alloy.
2. Al-Ni alloy.
3. 60 per cent. Cu, 40 per cent. Ni (sometimes called Eureka).
4. Liable to a change of fundamental interval if heated above 1,100° C.
5. Cu starts to oxidize.

9. Intermediate Metals.

Fig. 252 (a) shows two metals of a thermocouple, A, B, separated by a third metal, C. The metal C may be, for example, a film of the solder used to join A and B. At a given temperature θ, the e.m.f. E of the couple

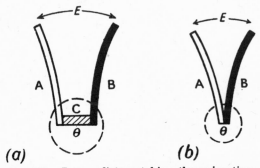

FIG. 252.   Intermediate metal in a thermojunction.

ACB is found, by measurement, to be equal to that of a simple couple AB, formed by twisting or welding the wires together (Fig. 252 (b)). This is true provided that the junctions of A to C, and C to B, are both at the temperature θ. An intermediate metal, at a uniform temperature, does not therefore affect the e.m.f. of a thermojunction.

10. Expanding-liquid Thermometers : Mercury-in-glass.

Mercury freezes at − 39° C. and boils, under atmospheric pressure, at 357° C. Mercury thermometers can be made to read up to about 550° C., however, by filling the space above the liquid with nitrogen, which is compressed as the mercury expands, and raises its boiling-point.

A mercury thermometer has a much greater heat capacity than a thermocouple, and cannot follow a rapidly changing temperature. Also glass, when it has been warmed and then cooled, does not immediately contract back to its original volume at the lower temperature. If a low temperature is measured immediately after a high one, the value given by a mercury thermometer tends to be too low. With modern hard glass (Jena glass) this effect is small; but with a cheap thermometer the ice point may be as much as half a degree low if taken immediately after the steam point has been checked.

A mercury thermometer is filled by warming and dipping, as a weight thermometer (p. 283). The mercury in its bulb is then boiled, to drive out air. It is then allowed to cool and draw in the requisite amount of mercury. Finally it is warmed a little above the highest temperature it is to measure, sealed off, and left for about a year—to age. During the ageing period the glass slowly contracts after its strong heating, and at the end of the period the thermometer is calibrated.

11. Clinical Thermometers.

A clinical thermometer has a fine stem, divided into fifths or tenths of a degree, and calibrated over only a small range: 95°–110° F. or 35°–45° C. (Fig. 253). The stem is thickened on the side remote from

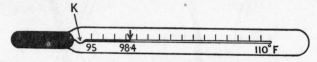

Fig. 253.   Clinical thermometer.

the graduations so that it acts as a lens, to magnify the fine mercury thread. At room temperature the mercury retreats right into the bulb. Between the bulb and the graduations is a fine kink K. When the bulb is warmed the mercury is forced through the kink into the stem. But when the bulb is cooled, the mercury does not flow back past the kink—it stays in the stem, so that the temperature can be read at leisure. It is then shaken back into the bulb.

12. Mercury-in-steel Thermometers.

For industrial purposes mercury-in-steel thermometers are used. They consist of a steel bulb B, connected by a long steel capillary S to a coiled steel tube C (Fig. 254). The whole is filled with mercury,

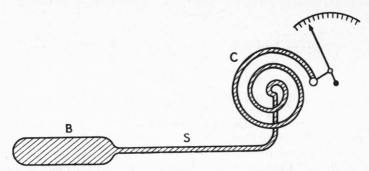

FIG. 254.   Mercury-in-steel thermometer (*diagrammatic*).

and when the bulb is warmed the expansion of the mercury makes the coil unwind. The unwinding of the coil actuates a pointer, and indicates the temperature of the bulb. The distance between the bulb and the indicating dial may be many feet.

13. Alcohol Thermometers.

Ethyl alcohol boils at 78° C., and freezes at — 115° C.   Alcohol thermometers are therefore used in polar regions.   Alcohol is also used in some of the maximum and minimum thermometers which we are about to describe.

14. Maximum and Minimum Thermometers.

Meteorologists observe the highest and lowest temperatures reached by the air day and night. They use a *maximum thermometer* which is a mercury thermometer containing a small glass index I (Fig. 255 (*a*)). The thermometer is laid horizontally, in a louvred screen. When the temperature rises the mercury pushes the index along, but when the temperature falls the mercury leaves the index behind. The maximum temperature is therefore shown by the end of the index nearer the mercury. After each observation, the index is brought back to the mercury by tilting the thermometer.

A *minimum thermometer* is similar to a maximum, except that it contains alcohol instead of mercury. When the alcohol expands it flows past the index, but when it contracts it drags the index back, because of its surface tension (Fig. 255 (*b*)). The end of the index

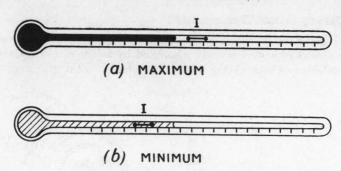

(a) MAXIMUM

(b) MINIMUM

Fig. 255. Meteorological thermometers.

nearer the meniscus therefore shows the minimum temperature. The index is re-set by tilting.

A combined *maximum and minimum thermometer* was invented by Six in 1782. Its construction is shown in Fig. 256. The bulb A, and

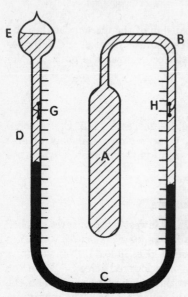

Fig. 256. Combined maximum and minimum thermometer.

the part B of the stem, contain alcohol; so does the part D of the stem, and the lower part of the bulb E. The part C of the stem contains mercury, and the upper part of the bulb E contains air and saturated alcohol vapour. The indices G and H are made of iron, and are fitted with springs pressing against the walls of the stem. When the temperature rises, the expansion of the large volume of alcohol in A forces the mercury round, and compresses the gases in E. The mercury pushes the index G up the tube. When the temperature falls, the alcohol in A contracts, and the mercury retreats. But the spring holds the index G, and the alcohol flows past it. Thus the bottom of G shows the maximum temperature. Similarly, the bottom of H shows the minimum. The indices are re-set by dragging them along from the outside with a magnet.

15. Bimetal Strip Thermometers.

If a bimetal strip is wound into a spiral, with the more expansible metal on the inside, then the spiral will uncoil as the temperature rises. The movement of the spiral can be made to turn a pointer, and to act as a thermometer. Instruments of this kind do not hold their calibration as well as liquid-in-glass thermometers.

PYROMETERS

High temperatures are usually measured by observing the radiation from the hot body, and the name *Pyrometry* is given to this measurement. Before describing pyrometers, however, we may mention some other, rough, methods which are sometimes used. One method is to insert in the furnace a number of ceramic cones, of slightly different compositions; their melting-points increase from one to the next by about 20° C. The temperature of the furnace lies between the melting-points of adjacent cones, one of which softens and collapses, and the other of which does not.

The temperature of steel, when it is below red heat, can be judged by its colour, which depends on the thickness of the oxide film upon it. Temperatures below red heat can also be estimated by the use of paints, which change colour at known temperatures.

Radiation pyrometers can be used only above red-heat (about 600° C.). They fall into two classes:

  (i) *total radiation pyrometers*, which respond to the total radiation from the hot body, heat and light;
 (ii) *optical pyrometers*, which respond only to the visible light.

16. Optical Pyrometers.

Fig. 257 illustrates the principle of the commonest type of optical pyrometer, called a *disappearing filament pyrometer*. It consists

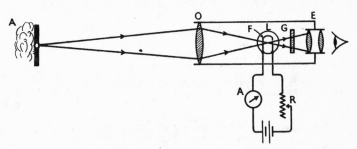

FIG. 257.   Optical radiation pyrometer (*not to scale*).

essentially of a low power telescope, OE, and a tungsten filament lamp L. The eyepiece E is focused upon the filament F. The hot body A whose temperature is to be found is then focused by the lens O so that its image lies in the plane of F. The light from both the filament and the hot body passes through a filter of red glass G before reaching the eye. If the body is brighter than the filament, the filament appears dark on a bright ground. If the filament is brighter than the body, it appears bright on a dark ground. The temperature of the filament is adjusted, by adjusting the current through it, until it merges as nearly as possible into its background. It is then as bright as the body. The rheostat R which adjusts the current is mounted on the body of the pyrometer, and so is the ammeter A which measures the current. The ammeter is calibrated directly in degrees Centigrade or Fahrenheit. A pyrometer of this type can be adjusted to within about 5° C. at 1,000° C.; more elaborate types can be adjusted more closely.

The range of an optical pyrometer can be extended by introducing a filter of green glass between the objective O and the lamp L; this reduces the brightness of the red light. A second scale on the ammeter is provided for use when the filter is inserted.

The scale of a radiation pyrometer is calibrated by assuming that the radiation is black-body radiation (p. 359). If—as usual—the hot body is not black, then it will be radiating less intensely than a black body at the same temperature. Conversely, a black body which radiates with the same intensity as the actual body will be cooler than the actual body. Thus the temperature indicated by the pyrometer will be lower than the true temperature of the actual, not black, body. A correction must be applied to the pyrometer reading, which depends on the spectral emissivity of the body for red light. The wavelength λ for which the spectral emissivity e_λ must be known is the average wavelength of light transmitted by the red filter—usually about 6,500 A.U.

The following tables give e_λ for various substances, and the corrections to be added for various values of e_λ.

SPECTRAL EMISSIVITIES, e_λ

(At 6,500 A.U.)

Substance	Solid	Liquid	Substance	Solid	Liquid
Carbon . .	0·85	—	Nickel . .	0·35	—
Copper . .	0·1	0·15	„ oxidized .	0·9	—
„ oxidized .	0·7	—	Platinum . .	0·35	0·35
Gold . .	0·15	0·2	Silver . .	0·1	—
Iron . .	0·35	0·35	Slag . .	—	0·65
„ oxidized .	0·95	—	Tungsten . .	0·45	—
Nichrome . .	0·9	—			

OPTICAL PYROMETER CORRECTIONS

($\lambda = 6,500$ A.U.)

[*To be added to observed temperature*]

Observed temp., °C.	e_λ						
	0·3	0·4	0·5	0·6	0·7	0·8	0·9
600	44	34	26	18	13	8	4
800	67	50	37	27	19	12	6
1,000	95	71	53	39	27	17	8
1,200	129	96	71	52	36	22	10
1,400	169	125	93	67	46	28	13
1,600	214	159	117	85	58	35	17
1,800	265	196	145	105	72	44	20
2,000	322	238	176	127	87	53	25
2,500	495	362	266	190	131	78	38
3,000	713	516	377	269	183	110	53

17. Total Radiation Pyrometers.

Total radiation pyrometers are less common than optical pyrometers. As we shall see, they can only be used when the source of radiation is of considerable size—such as the open door of a furnace—whereas an optical pyrometer can be used on a very small body such as a lamp-filament.

Fig. 258 illustrates the principle of a Féry total radiation pyrometer. The blackened tube A is open at the end B; at the other end C it carries

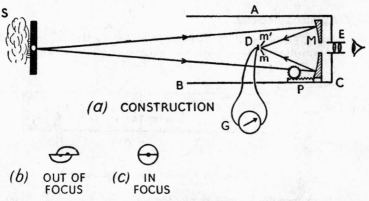

(a) CONSTRUCTION

(b) OUT OF FOCUS   (c) IN FOCUS

Fig. 258.   Féry total radiation pyrometer.

an eye-piece E. D is a thermocouple attached to a small blackened disc of copper, which faces the end C of the tube and is shielded from direct radiation. M is a gold-plated mirror, pierced at the centre to allow light to reach the eye-piece, and moveable by a rack and pinion P.

In use, the eyepiece is first focused upon the disc D. The mirror M is then adjusted until the furnace is also focused upon D. Since a body which is black or nearly so shows no detail, focusing it upon D by simply looking at the image would be almost impossible. To make the focusing easier, two small plane mirrors m', m are fitted in front of D. They are inclined with their normals at about 5° to the axis of the tube, and are pierced with semi-circular holes to allow radiation from M to reach the disc. The diameter of the resulting circular hole is less than that of the disc. When the source of heat is not focused on the disc, the two mirrors appear as at (b) in the figure; when the focusing is correct, they appear as at (c). The source must be of such a size that its image completely fills the hole.

The radiation from the source warms the junction and sets up an electromotive force. A galvanometer G connected to the junction is then deflected, and can be calibrated to read directly the temperature of the source.

The calibration gives the correct temperature if the source is a black body. If the source is not black, its total radiation is equal to that of a black body at some lower temperature; the pyrometer therefore reads too low. If the total emissivity of the source is known, a correction can be made for it. This correction is greater than it would be if an optical pyrometer were used, that is to say, departure from perfect blackness causes less error in an optical pyrometer than in a total radiation one.

18. The Foster Pyrometer.

Another type of total radiation pyrometer is the Foster fixed-focus instrument (Fig. 259); it also uses a thermojunction with blackened

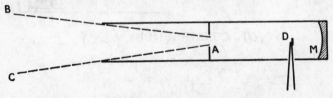

FIG. 259.   Fixed focus total radiation pyrometer.

disc. A is an open diaphragm, so placed that it and the thermojunction D are at conjugate foci of the mirror M. The thermojunction then collects all the radiation entering through A but, since it is much smaller than A, it is raised to a higher temperature than if its disc were the size of A. The radiation entering through A is limited to that within the cone ABC; as long as the whole of this cone is intersected by the hot source, the amount of radiation reaching the thermocouple is independent of the distance to the source (compare the use of a cone with a thermopile, p. 356).

19. Comparison of Pyrometers : the International Scale.

Total radiation and optical pyrometers agree within the limits of experimental error—$\frac{1}{2}$° at 1,750° C., about 4° at 2,800° C. The choice between them is decided solely by convenience. The international temperature scale above the gold-point (1,063·0° C.) is defined in terms of an optical pyrometer.

20. Extension of Range by Sectored Disc.

The range of a radiation pyrometer can be extended by cutting down the radiation admitted to it. A disc from which an angle θ radians has been cut out is rotated in front of the pyrometer, as shown in Fig. 260, so that the radiation entering is cut down in the ratio $\theta/2\pi$. The pyrometer then indicates a temperature T_1, which is less than the true temperature T_2 of the source. The temperatures T are expressed in °K. to simplify the calculation which follows.

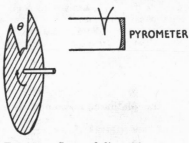

FIG. 260. Sectored disc with radiation pyrometer.

If the pyrometer is of the total radiation type, then we can use Stefan's law. The radiation from a body at T_2°K. is proportional to $T_2{}^4$. The pyrometer receives radiation represented by the temperature T_1, and therefore proportional to $T_1{}^4$.

Therefore

$$\frac{\theta}{2\pi} = \frac{T_1{}^4}{T_2{}^4},$$

whence

$$T_2 = T_1\left(\frac{2\pi}{\theta}\right)^{\frac{1}{4}}.$$

In this way the surface temperature of the sun has been estimated. The value found agrees with that estimated from the wavelength of the sun's most intense radiation (p. 360); it is about 6,000° K.

A sectored disc can be used to extend the range of an optical pyrometer, but the calculation is more difficult than for a total radiation pyrometer.

EXAMPLES

1. How is centigrade temperature defined (a) on the scale of a constant-pressure gas thermometer, (b) on the scale of a platinum resistance thermometer? A constant mass of gas maintained at constant pressure has a volume of 200·0 c.c. at the temperature of melting ice, 273·2 c.c. at the temperature of water boiling under standard pressure, and 525·1 c.c. at the normal boiling-point of sulphur. A platinum wire has resistances of 2·000, 2·778 and 5·280 ohms at the same temperatures. Calculate the values of the boiling-point of sulphur given by the two sets of observations, and comment on the results. (*N.*)

First part (a). The temperature θ on the gas thermometer scale is given by

$$\theta = \frac{V_\theta - V_0}{V_{100} - V_0} \times 100,$$

where V_θ, V_0, V_{100} are the respective volumes of the gas at constant pressure at the temperature concerned, the temperature of melting ice, and the temperature of steam at 76 cm. mercury pressure. (b) The temperature θ_p on the platinum resistance thermometer scale is given by

$$\theta_p = \frac{R_\theta - R_0}{R_{100} - R_0} \times 100,$$

where R_θ, R_0, R_{100} are the respective resistances of the platinum at the temperature concerned, the temperature of melting ice, and the temperature of steam at 76 cm. mercury.

Second part. On the gas thermometer scale, the boiling-point of sulphur is given by

$$\theta = \frac{525\cdot 1 - 200\cdot 0}{273\cdot 2 - 200\cdot 0} \times 100$$

$$= 444\cdot 1^\circ \text{ C.}$$

On the platinum resistance thermometer scale, the boiling-point is given by

$$\theta_p = \frac{5\cdot 280 - 2\cdot 000}{2\cdot 778 - 2\cdot 000} \times 100$$

$$= 421\cdot 6^\circ \text{ C.}$$

The temperatures recorded on the thermometers are therefore different. This is due to the fact that the variation of gas pressure with temperature at constant volume is different from the variation of the electrical resistance of platinum with temperature.

2. Explain how a centigrade temperature scale is defined, illustrating your answer by reference to a platinum resistance thermometer.

The resistance R_t of a platinum wire at temperature t° C., measured on the gas scale, is given by $R_t = R_0 (1 + at + bt^2)$, where $a = 3\cdot 800 \times 10^{-3}$ and $b = -5\cdot 6 \times 10^{-7}$. What temperature will the platinum thermometer indicate when the temperature on the gas scale is 200° C.? (*O. & C.*)

First part. The temperature θ_p in °C. on a resistance thermometer scale is defined by the relation

$$\theta_p = \frac{R_\theta - R_0}{R_{100} - R_0} \times 100,$$

where R_θ, R_0, R_{100} are the respective resistances at the temperature concerned, at 0° C., and at 100° C.

Second part. $\qquad R_t = R_0(1 + at + bt^2)$

$$\therefore R_{200} = R_0(1 + 200a + 200^2 b)$$

and
$$R_{100} = R_0(1 + 100a + 100^2b).$$

$$\therefore \quad \theta_p = \frac{R_{200} - R_0}{R_{100} - R_0} \times 100$$

$$= \frac{R_0(1 + 200a + 200^2b) - R_0}{R_0(1 + 100a + 100^2b) - R_0} \times 100$$

$$= \frac{200a + 200^2b}{a + 100b} = \frac{200(a + 200b)}{a + 100b}$$

$$= 200 \frac{(3 \cdot 8 \times 10^{-3} - 11 \cdot 2 \times 10^{-5})}{3 \cdot 8 \times 10^{-3} - 5 \cdot 6 \times 10^{-5}}$$

$$= \frac{200 \times 0 \cdot 003688}{0 \cdot 003744} = 197° \text{ C.}$$

EXERCISES XVI

1. Give a brief account of the principles underlying the establishment of a scale of temperature and explain precisely what is meant by the statements that the temperature of a certain body is (a) $t°$ C. on the constant volume air scale, (b) $t_P°$ C. on the platinum resistance scale, and (c) $t_T°$ C. on the Cu-Fe thermocouple scale. Why are these three temperatures usually different?

Describe an optical pyrometer and explain how it is used to measure the temperature of a furnace. (N.)

2. What is the general method of calibrating any type of thermometer? Describe *briefly* the method of using *three* of the following temperature measuring devices, and give the temperature range in which they are most usefully employed: (i) platinum resistance thermometer, (ii) mercury-in-glass thermometer, (iii) helium gas thermometer, (iv) optical pyrometer. (L.)

3. Explain the precautions taken in verifying the position of the fixed points on the stem of a mercury-in-glass thermometer.

Describe a constant volume air thermometer. How could such a thermometer be used to determine the melting-point of a solid such as naphthalene? What advantage has the gas thermometer and for what purpose is it used? (L.)

4. Tabulate various physical properties used for measuring temperature. Indicate the temperature range for which each is suitable.

Discuss the fact that the numerical value of a temperature expressed on the scale of the platinum resistance thermometer is not the same as its value on the gas scale except at the fixed points.

If the resistance of a platinum thermometer is 1·500 ohms at 0° C., 2·060 ohms at 100° C. and 1·788 ohms at 50° C. on the gas scale, what is the difference between the numerical values of the latter temperature on the two scales? (N.)

5. Explain how a centigrade temperature scale is defined, illustrating your answer by reference to a platinum resistance thermometer.

The resistance R_t of a platinum wire at temperature $t°$ C., measured on the gas scale, is given by $R_t = R_0(1 + at + bt^2)$, where $a = 4 \cdot 000 \times 10^{-3}$ and $b = -6 \cdot 0 \times 10^{-7}$. What temperature will the platinum thermometer indicate when the temperature on the gas scale is 300° C.?

6. Describe any two types of thermometer which depend on principles other than that of thermal expansion, and indicate how you would use the thermometers in practice.

A piece of iron of mass 200 gm. is rapidly removed from a muffle furnace and immersed in 1,200 gm. of water contained in a copper calorimeter of mass 260 gm. If the initial temperature of the water was 14° C. and it rises to a maximum of 27° C., estimate the approximate temperature of the furnace. State the sources of error in such an experiment. (Specific heat of copper = 0·10 cal./gm./deg. C.; specific heat of iron = 0·13 cal./gm./deg. C.) (*L*.)

7. (*a*) Explain the method of measuring temperature by means of a resistance thermometer, giving a description of the apparatus required. For what range of temperature is the method suitable?

(*b*) 100 c.c. of water and 100 c.c. of paraffin in similar calorimeters, are allowed to cool under identical conditions. Over a certain temperature range the water takes 5 min. to cool and the paraffin 3 min. If the density of paraffin is 0·8 gm./c.c., what is its specific heat? The water equivalent of each of the calorimeters is 10 gm. (*C*.)

8. Explain what is meant by a centigrade temperature.

Describe how the temperature (θ) of an oven may be measured (*a*) approximately when the only thermometer available has a maximum reading less than θ, and (*b*) accurately when some form of electrical thermometer is used. (*L*.)

9. A copper sphere weighing 200 gm. is placed in an oven and, when it has attained the temperature of the latter, it is quickly transferred to a copper calorimeter weighing (with its copper stirrer) 165 gm. and containing 55 gm. of ice and 230 gm. of water at 0° C. The highest common temperature reached is 9° C , and a final weighing of the calorimeter and contents reveals a loss of 1·5 gm. Assuming this loss to be due to the boiling away of 1·5 gm. of water at 100° C. immediately following the immersion of the sphere, calculate the temperature of the oven. (*L* = 80 and 540 cal./gm. respectively.)

Describe briefly *two* thermometers which could be used to determine this oven temperature directly. (*L*.)

10. Describe how you would use *either* (i) a constant-volume *or* (ii) a constant-pressure air thermometer to calibrate a mercurial thermometer. If the difference of mercury level in a constant-volume air thermometer is − 2 cm. when the temperature of the bulb is 10° C. and + 22 cm. when the bulb is at 100° C., what is the height of the barometer? (*L*.)

11. Discuss heat exchange by radiation and explain the term "black body radiation". Describe and explain how such radiation may be realized in practice. State two laws pertaining to black body radiation and illustrate in a qualitative diagram the distribution of energy in the spectrum of black body radiation for different temperatures.

Describe a method, based on optical pyrometry, for measuring the temperature of a furnace. Illustrate your answer by a diagram of the apparatus and give a brief account of the calibration of any direct reading instrument which is employed. (*N. Schol.*)

PART THREE

LIGHT AND SOUND

LIGHT

CHAPTER XVII

INTRODUCTION

IF you wear spectacles you will appreciate particularly that the science of Light, or *Optics* as it is often called, has benefited people all over the world. The illumination engineer has developed the branch of Light dealing with light energy, and has shown how to obtain suitable lighting conditions in the home and the factory, which is an important factor in maintaining our health. Microscopes, used by medical research workers in their fight against disease; telescopes, used by seamen and astronomers; and a variety of optical instruments which incorporate lenses, mirrors, or glass prisms, such as cameras, driving mirrors, and binoculars, all testify to the scientist's service to the community.

In mentioning the technical achievements in Light, however, it must not be forgotten that the science of Light evolved gradually over the past centuries; and that the technical advances were developed from the experiments and theory or the *fundamental* principles of the subject, made by scientists such as NEWTON, HUYGHENS, and FRESNEL.

1. Light Travels in Straight Lines. Eclipses and Shadows

When sunlight is streaming through an open window into a room, observation shows that the edges of the beam of light, where the shadow begins, are straight. This suggests that *light travels in straight lines*, and on this assumption the sharpness of shadows and the formation of eclipses can be explained. Fig. 261 (i) illustrates the eclipse of the

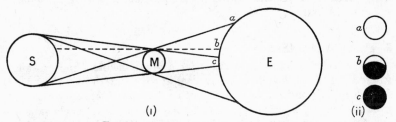

FIG. 261. Eclipse of Sun, (not to scale).

sun, S, our natural source of light, when the moon, M, passes between the sun and the earth, E. The moon is a non-luminous object which does not allow light to pass through it, and hence the boundaries of the shadows formed by M on the earth are obtained by drawing lines from

S which touch the edge of **M**. Consequently there is a total eclipse of the sun at *c* on the earth, a partial eclipse at *b*, and no eclipse at *a*. Fig. 261 (ii) illustrates the appearance of the sun in each case.

2. Light Rays and Beams

Light is a form of energy. We know this is the case because plants and vegetables grow when they absorb sunlight. Further, electrons are ejected from certain metals when light is incident on them, showing that there was some energy in the light; this phenomenon is the basis of the *photo-electric cell* (p. 614). Substances like wood or brick which allow no light to pass through them are called "opaque" substances; unless an opaque object is perfectly black, some of the light falling on it is reflected (p. 401). A "transparent" substance, like glass, is one which allows some of the light energy incident on it to pass through, the remainder of the energy being absorbed and (or) reflected.

A ray of light is the direction along which the light energy travels; and though rays are represented in diagrams by straight lines, in practice a ray has a finite width. A **beam** of light is a collection of rays. A searchlight emits a *parallel beam* of light, and the rays from a point

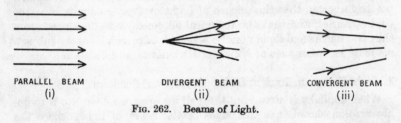

PARALLEL BEAM   DIVERGENT BEAM   CONVERGENT BEAM
      (i)   (ii)   (iii)

Fig. 262.   Beams of Light.

on a very distant object like the sun are substantially parallel, Fig. 262 (i). Lamps emit a *divergent beam* of light; while a source of light behind a lens, as in a projection lantern, can provide a *convergent beam*, Fig. 262 (ii), (iii).

3. The Velocity of Light

The velocity of light is constant for a given medium, such as air, water or glass, and has its greatest magnitude, about 186,000 miles per second, in a vacuum. The velocity of light in air differs only slightly from its velocity in a vacuum, so that the velocity in air is also about 186,000 miles per second. The velocity of light in glass is about 124,000 miles per second; in water it is about 140,000 miles per second. On account of the difference in velocity in air and glass, light changes its direction on entering glass from air (see *Refraction*, p. 429). Experiments to determine the velocity of light are discussed later, p. 588.

4. The Human Eye

When an object is seen, light energy passes from the object to the observer's eyes and sets up the sensation of vision. The eye is thus sensitive to light (or luminous) energy. The eye contains a *crystalline lens*, L, made of a gelatinous transparent substance, which normally throws an image of the object viewed on to a sensitive "screen" R at the back of the eye-ball, called the *retina*, Fig. 263. Nerves on the retina are joined to the *optic nerve*, O, which carries the sensation produced by the image to the brain. The *iris*, I, is a diaphragm with a circular hole in the middle called the *pupil*, P, which contracts when the light received by the eye is excessive and painful to the eye. The colour of

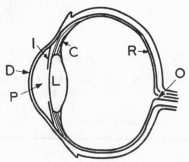

FIG. 263. The eyeball.

a person's eyes is the colour of the iris; the pupil is always black because no light returns from the interior of the eye-ball. A weak salt solution, called the *aqueous humour*, is present on the left of the lens L, and between L and the retina is a gelatinous substance called the *vitreous humour*. The transparent spherical bulge D in front of L is made of tough material, and is known as the *cornea*.

The *ciliary muscles*, C, enable the eye to see clearly objects at different distances, a property of the eye known as its "power of accommodation". The ciliary muscles are attached to the edge of the lens L, and when they contract, the lens' surfaces are pulled out so that they bulge more; in this way a near object can be focused clearly on the retina and thus seen distinctly. When a very distant object is observed the ciliary muscles are relaxed, and the lens' surfaces are flattened.

The use of two eyes gives a three-dimensional aspect of the object or scene observed, as two slightly different views are imposed on the retinæ; this gives a sense of distance not enjoyed by a one-eyed person.

5. Direction of Image seen by Eye

When a fish is observed in water, rays of light coming from a point such as O on it pass from water into air, Fig. 264 (i). At the boundary of the water and air, the rays OA, OC proceed along new directions AB, CD respectively and enter the eye. Similarly, a ray OC from an object O observed in a mirror is reflected along a new direction CD and enters the eye, Fig. 264 (ii). These phenomena are studied more fully later, but

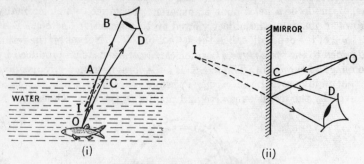

FIG. 264.   Images observed by eye.

the reader should take careful note that the eye sees an object *in the direction in which the rays enter the eye*. In Fig. 264 (i), for example, the object O is seen in the water at I, which lies on BA and DC produced; in Fig. 264 (ii), O is seen behind the mirror at I, which lies on DC produced. In either case, all rays from O which enter the eye appear to come from I, which is called the image of O.

6. Reversibility of Light

If a ray of light is directed along DC towards a mirror, experiment shows that the ray is reflected along the path CO, Fig. 264 (ii). If the ray is incident along OC, it is reflected along CD, as shown. Thus if a light ray is reversed it always travels along its original path, and this is known as *the principle of the reversibility of light*. In Fig. 264 (i), a ray BA in air is refracted into the water along the path AO, since it follows the reverse path to OAB. We shall have occasion to use the principle of the reversibility of light later in this book.

CHAPTER XVIII

REFLECTION AT PLANE SURFACES

HIGHLY-POLISHED metal surfaces reflect about 80 to 90 per cent of the light incident on them; *mirrors* in everyday use are therefore usually made by depositing silver on the back of glass. In special cases the front of the glass is coated with the metal; for example, the largest reflector in the world is a curved mirror nearly 18 feet across, the front of which is coated with aluminium (p. 559). Glass by itself will also reflect light, but the percentage reflected is small compared with the case of a silvered surface, being about 5 per cent for an air-glass surface.

1. Laws of Reflection

If a ray of light, AO, is incident on a plane mirror XY at O, the angle AON made with the *normal* ON to the mirror is called the "angle of incidence", i, Fig. 265. The angle BON made by the reflected ray OB with the normal is called the "angle of reflection", r; and experiments with a ray-box and a plane mirror, for example, show that:

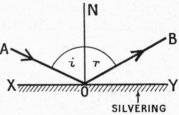

FIG. 265. Plane mirror.

(1) *The reflected ray, the incident ray, and the normal to the mirror at the point of incidence all lie in the same plane.*

(2) *The angle of incidence = the angle of reflection.*

These are called the two *laws of reflection*, and they were known to PLATO, who lived about 430 B.C.

2. Regular and Diffuse Reflection

In the case of a plane mirror or glass surface, it follows from the laws of reflection that a ray incident at a given angle on the surface is reflected in a definite direction. Thus a parallel beam of light incident on a plane mirror in the direction AO is reflected as a parallel beam in the direction OB, and this is known as a case of *regular reflection*, Fig. 266 (i). On the other hand, if a parallel beam of light is incident on a sheet of paper in a direction AO, the light is reflected in all different directions from the paper; this is an example of *diffuse reflection*, Fig. 266 (ii). Objects in everyday life, such as flowers, books, people, are seen by light diffusely reflected from them. The explanation of the diffusion of light is that the surface of paper, for example, is not

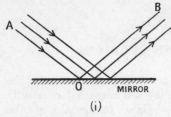

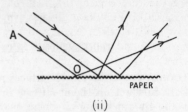

FIG. 266 (i) **Regular reflection.**   FIG. 266 (ii). **Diffuse reflection.**

perfectly smooth like a mirrored surface; the "roughness" in a paper surface can be seen with a microscope. At each point on the paper the laws of reflection are obeyed, but the angle of incidence varies, unlike the case of a mirror.

3. Deviation of Light at Plane Mirror Surface

Besides other purposes, plane mirrors are used in the sextant (p. 405), in simple periscopes, and in signalling at sea. These instruments utilise the property of a plane mirror to deviate light from one direction to another.

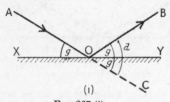

FIG. 267 (i).
Deviation of light at plane mirror.

Consider a ray AO incident at O on a plane mirror XY, Fig. 267 (i). The angle AOX made by AO with XY is known as the *glancing angle*, *g*, with the mirror; and since the angle of reflection is equal to the angle of incidence, the glancing angle BOY made by the reflected ray OB with the mirror is also equal to *g*.

The light has been deviated from a direction AO to a direction OB. Thus if OC is the extension of AO, the *angle of deviation*, *d*, is angle COB. Since angle COY = vertically opposite angle XOA, it follows that

$$d = 2g \quad . \quad . \quad . \quad . \quad . \quad (1);$$

so that, in general, *the angle of deviation of a ray by a plane surface is twice the glancing angle.*

4. Deviation of Reflected Ray by Rotated Mirror

Consider a ray AO incident at O on a plane mirror M_1, a being the glancing angle with M_1, Fig. 267 (ii). If OB is the reflected ray, then, as shown above, the angle of deviation COB = $2g = 2a$.

Suppose the mirror is rotated through an angle θ to a position M_2, the direction of the incident ray AO being *constant*. The ray is now reflected from M_2, in a direction OP, and the glancing angle with M_2 is $(a + \theta)$. Hence the new angle of deviation COP $= 2g = 2\,(a + \theta)$. The reflected ray

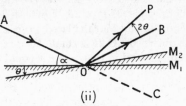

Fig. 267 (ii). Rotation of reflected ray.

has thus been rotated through an angle BOP when the mirror rotated through an angle θ; and since

$$\angle \text{BOP} = \angle \text{COP} - \angle \text{COB},$$

then

$$\angle \text{BOP} = 2\,(a + \theta) - 2a = 2\theta.$$

Thus, *if the direction of an incident ray is constant, the angle of rotation of the reflected ray is twice the angle of rotation of the mirror.* If the mirror rotates through 4°, the reflected ray turns through 8°, the direction of the incident ray being kept unaltered.

5. Optical Lever in Mirror Galvanometer

In a number of instruments a beam of light is used as a "pointer", which thus has a negligible weight and is sensitive to deflections of the moving system inside the instrument. In a mirror galvanometer, used for measuring very small electric currents, a small mirror M_1 is rigidly attached to a system which rotates when a current flows in it, and a beam of light from a fixed lamp L shines on the mirror, Fig. 268. If the light is incident normally on the mirror at A, the beam is reflected directly back, and a spot of light is obtained at O on a graduated scale S

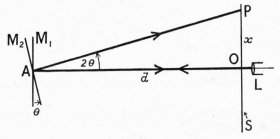

Fig. 268. Optical lever principle.

placed just above L. Suppose that the moving system, to which the mirror is attached, undergoes a rotation θ. The mirror is then rotated through this angle to a position M_2, and the spot of light is deflected through a distance x, say, to a position P on the scale.

Since the direction OA of the incident light is constant, the rotation of the reflected ray is twice the angle of rotation of the mirror (p. 403). Thus angle OAP = 2θ. Now tan $2\theta = x/d$, where d is the distance OA. Thus 2θ can be calculated from a knowledge of x and d, and hence θ is obtained. If 2θ is small, then tan 2θ is approximately equal to 2θ in radians, and in this case θ is equal to $x/2d$ radians.

In conjunction with a mirror, a beam of light used as a "pointer" is known as an "optical lever". Besides a negligible weight, it has the advantage of magnifying by two the rotation of the system to which the mirror is attached, as the angle of rotation of the reflected light is twice the angle of rotation of the mirror. An optical lever can be used for measuring small increases of length due to the expansion or contraction of a solid.

6. Deviation by Successive Reflections at Two Inclined Mirrors

Before we can deal with the principle of the sextant, the deviation of light by successive reflection at two inclined mirrors must be discussed.

Consider two mirrors, XO, XB, inclined at an angle θ, and suppose AO is a ray incident on the mirror XO at a *glancing* angle α, Fig. 269 (i). The reflected ray OB then also makes a glancing angle α with OX, and from our result on p. 405, the angle of deviation produced by XO in a clockwise direction (angle LOB) = 2α.

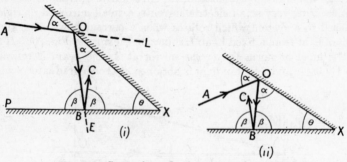

FIG. 269. Successive reflection at two plane mirrors.

Suppose OB is incident at a glancing angle β on the second mirror XB. Then, if the reflected ray is BC, the angle of deviation produced by this mirror (angle EBC) = 2β, in an anti-clockwise direction. Thus the net deviation D of the incident ray AO produced by both mirrors, = $2\beta - 2\alpha$, in an anti-clockwise direction.

Now from triangle OBX,

$$\text{angle PBO} = \text{angle BOX} + \text{angle BXO},$$

i.e., $$\beta = \alpha + \theta$$

Thus $\theta = \beta - \alpha$, and hence

$$D = 2\beta - 2\alpha = 2\theta.$$

But θ is a *constant* when the two mirrors are inclined at a given angle. *Thus, no matter what angle the incident ray makes with the first mirror, the deviation D after two successive reflections is constant and equal to twice the angle between the mirrors.*

Fig. 269 (ii) illustrates the case when the ray BC reflected at the second mirror travels in an opposite direction to the incident ray AO, unlike the case in Fig. 269 (i). In Fig. 269 (ii), the net deviation, D, after two successive reflections in a clockwise direction is $2\alpha + 2\beta$. But $\alpha + \beta = 180° - \theta$. Hence $D = 2\alpha + 2\beta = 360° - 2\theta$. Thus the deviation, D, in an anti-clockwise direction is 2θ, the same result as obtained above.

7. Principle of the Sextant

The *sextant* is an instrument used in navigation for measuring the angle of elevation of the sun or stars. It consists essentially of a fixed glass B, silvered on a vertical half, and a silvered mirror O which can be rotated about a horizontal axis. A small fixed telescope T is directed towards B, Fig. 270.

Suppose that the angle of elevation of the sun, S, is required. Looking through T, the mirror O is turned until the view H' of the horizon seen directly through the unsilvered half of B, and also the view of it, H,

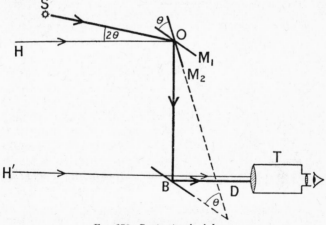

Fig. 270. Sextant principle.

seen by successive reflection at O and the silvered half of B, are coincident. The mirror O is then parallel to B in the position M_1, and the ray HO is reflected along OB and BD to enter the telescope T.

The mirror O is now rotated to a position M_2 until the image of the sun S, seen by successive reflections at O and B, is on the horizon H', and the angle of rotation, θ, of the mirror is noted, Fig. 270.

The ray SO from the sun is now reflected in turn from O and B so that it travels along BD, the direction of the horizon, and the angle of deviation of the ray is thus angle SOH. But the angle between the mirrors M_2 and B is θ. Thus, from our result for successive reflections at two inclined mirrors, angle SOH $= 2\theta$. Now the angle of elevation of the sun, S, is angle SOH. Hence *the angle of elevation is twice the angle of rotation of the mirror O*, and can thus be easily measured from a scale (not shown) which measures the rotation of O.

Since the angle of deviation after two successive reflections is independent of the angle of incidence on the first mirror (p. 9), the image of the sun S through T will continue to be seen on the horizon once O is adjusted, no matter how the ship pitches or rolls. This is an advantage of the sextant.

8. Images in Plane Mirrors

So far we have discussed the deviation of light by a plane mirror. We have now to consider the *images* in plane mirrors.

Suppose that a **point object** A is placed in front of a mirror M, Fig. 271. A ray AO from A, incident on M, is reflected along OB in such a way that angle AON $=$ angle BON, where ON is the normal at O to the mirror. A ray AD incident normally on the mirror at D is reflected back along DA. Thus the rays reflected from M appear to

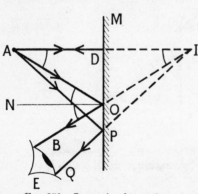

FIG. 271. Image in plane mirror.

come from a point I *behind* the mirror, where I is the point of intersection of BO and AD produced. As we shall prove shortly, any ray from A, such as AP, is also reflected as if it comes from I, and hence an observer at E sees the image of A at I.

Since angle AON $=$ alternate angle DAO, and angle BON $=$ corresponding angle DIO, it follows that angle DAO $=$ angle DIO. Thus in the triangles ODA, ODI, angle DAO $=$ angle DIO, OD is common, and angle ADO $= 90° =$ angle IDO. The two triangles are hence congruent, and therefore AD $=$ ID. For a given position of the object, A and D are fixed points. Consequently, since AD $=$ ID, the point I is a fixed point; and hence *any* ray reflected from the mirror must pass through I, as was stated above.

We have just shown that *the object and image in a plane mirror are at equal perpendicular distances from the mirror*. It should also be noted that AO = OI in Fig. 271, and hence the object and image are at equal distances from any point on the mirror.

9. Image of Finite-sized Object. Perversion

If a right-handed batsman observes his stance in a plane mirror, he appears to be left-handed. Again, the words on a piece of blotting-paper become legible when the paper is viewed in a mirror. This

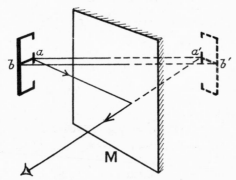

FIG. 272.   Perverted (laterally inverted) image

phenomenon can be explained by considering an E-shaped object placed in front of a mirror M, Fig. 272. The image of a point *a* on the object is at *a'* at an equal distance behind the mirror, and the image of a point *b* on the left of *a* is at *b'*, which is on the *right* of *a'*. The left-hand side of the image thus corresponds to the right-hand side of the object, and vice-versa, and the object is said to be *perverted*, or *laterally inverted* to an observer.

10. Virtual and Real Images

As was shown on p. 406, an object O in front of a mirror has an image I behind the mirror. The rays reflected from the mirror do not actually pass through I, but only *appear* to do so, and the image cannot be received on a screen because the image is behind the mirror, Fig. 273 (i). This type of image is therefore called an unreal or **virtual** image.

It must not be thought, however, that only virtual images are obtained with a plane mirror. If a *convergent* beam is incident on a plane mirror M, the reflected rays pass through a point I *in front of* M, Fig. 273 (ii). If the incident beam converges to the point O, the latter is termed a "virtual" object; I is called a **real** image because it can be received on a screen. Fig. 273 (i) and (ii) should now be compared. In

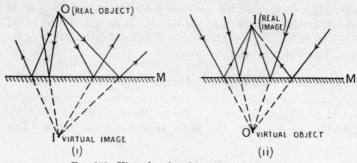

FIG. 273. Virtual and real image in plane mirror.

the former, it can be seen that a real object gives rise to a virtual image; in the latter, a virtual object gives rise to a real image. In each case the image and object are at equal distances from the mirror.

11. Location of Images by No Parallax Method

A virtual image can be located by the *method of no parallax*, which we shall now describe.

Suppose O is a pin placed in front of a plane mirror M, giving rise to a virtual image I behind M, Fig. 274. A pin P behind the mirror is then moved towards or away from M, each time moving the head from side to side so as to detect any relative motion between I and P. When the

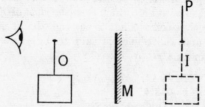

FIG. 274. Location of image by no parallax method.

latter appear to move together they are coincident in position, and hence P is at the place of the image I, which is thus located. When P and I do not coincide, they appear to move relative to one another when the observer's head is moved; this relative movement is called "parallax". It is useful to note that the nearer object moves in the opposite direction to the observer.

The method of no parallax can be used, as we shall see later, to locate the positions of real images, as well as virtual images, obtained with lenses and curved mirrors.

12. Images in Inclined Mirrors.

A *kaleidoscope*, produced as a toy under the name of "mirrorscope", consists of two inclined pieces of plane glass with some coloured tinsel between them. On looking into the kaleidoscope a beautiful series of coloured images of the tinsel can often be seen, and the instrument is used by designers to obtain ideas on colouring fashions.

Suppose OA, OB are two mirrors inclined at an angle θ, and P is a point object between them, Fig. 275 (i). The image of P in the mirror OB is B_1, and $OP = OB_1$ (see p. 407). B_1 then forms an image B_2 in the mirror OA, with $OB_2 = OB_1$, B_2 forms an image B_3 in OB, and so on. All the images thus lie on a circle of centre O and radius OP. Another set of images, A_1, A_2, A_3 . . ., have their origin in the image A_1 formed by P in the mirror OA. When the observer looks into the

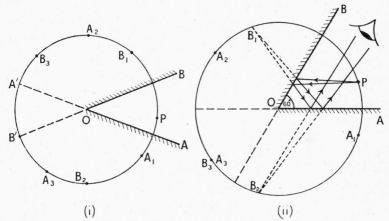

(i) (ii)

Fig. 275. Images in inclined mirrors.

mirror OB he sees the series of images B_1, A_2, B_3 . . . ; when he.looks into the mirror OA he sees the series of images A_1, B_2, A_3 . . . A finite series of images is seen in either mirror, the last image (not shown) being the one formed on the arc $A'B'$, because it is then *behind* the silvering of the next mirror.

When the mirrors are inclined at an angle of 60°, the final image of P, A_3, B_3, of each series coincide, Fig. 275 (ii). The total number of images is now 5, as the reader can verify. Fig. 275 (ii) illustrates the cone of light received by the pupil of the eye when the image B_2 is observed, reflection occurring successively at the mirrors. The drawing is started by joining B_2 to the boundary of the eye, then using B_1, and finally using P.

EXAMPLE

State the laws of reflection of light and describe how you would verify these laws.

A man 6 ft. tall, whose eye level is 5 ft. 6 in. above the ground, looks at his image in a vertical mirror. What is the minimum vertical length of the mirror if the man is to be able to see the whole of himself? Indicate its position accurately in a diagram. (*W.*)

First part. See text. A ray-box can be used to verify the laws.

Second part. Suppose the man is represented by HF, where H is his head and F is his feet; suppose that E represents his eyes, Fig. 276. Since the man

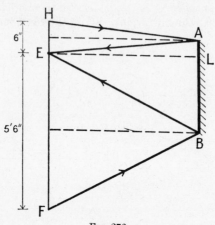

FIG. 276.

sees his head H, a ray HA from H to the top A of the mirror is reflected to E. Thus A lies on the perpendicular bisector of HE, and hence AL = ½ HE = 3 in., where L is the point on the mirror at the same level as E. Since the man sees his feet F, a ray FB from F to the bottom B of the mirror is also reflected to E. Thus the perpendicular bisector of EF passes through B, and hence BL = ½ FE = 2 ft. 9 in.

∴ length of mirror = AL + LB = 3 in. + 2 ft. 9 in. = 3 ft.

EXERCISES XVIII

1. Prove the relation between the angle of rotation of a mirror and the angle of deflection of a reflected ray, when the direction of the incident ray is constant.

2. Two plane mirrors are inclined at an angle of 35°. A ray of light is incident on one mirror at 60°, and undergoes two successive reflections at the mirrors. Show by accurate drawing that the angle of deviation produced is 70°.

Repeat with an angle of incidence of 45°, instead of 60°, and state the law concerning the angle of deviation.

3. Two plane mirrors are inclined to each other at a fixed angle. If a ray travelling in a plane perpendicular to both mirrors is reflected first from one and then from the other, show that the angle through which it is deflected does not depend on the angle at which it strikes the first mirror.

Describe and explain the action of *either* a sextant *or* a rear reflector on a bicycle. (*L*.)

4. State the laws of reflection of light. Two plane mirrors are parallel and face each other. They are *a* cm. apart and a small luminous object is placed *b* cm. from one of them. Find the distance from the object of an image produced by four reflections. Deduce the corresponding distance for an image produced by 2*n* reflections. (*L*.)

5. Two vertical plane mirrors *A* and *B* are inclined to one another at an angle *a*. A ray of light, travelling horizontally, is reflected first from *A* and then from *B*. Find the resultant deviation and show it is independent of the original direction of the ray. Describe an optical instrument that depends on the above proposition. (*N*.)

6. State the laws of reflection for a parallel beam of light incident upon a plane mirror.

Indicate clearly by means of diagrams (*a*) how the position and size of the image of an extended object may be determined by geometrical construction, in the case of reflection in a plane; (*b*) how the positions of the images of a small lamp, placed unsymmetrically between parallel reflecting planes, may be graphically determined. (*W*.)

7. Describe the construction of the *sextant* and the *periscope*. Illustrate your answer by clear diagrams and indicate the optical principles involved. (*L*.)

CHAPTER XIX

REFLECTION AT CURVED MIRRORS

CURVED mirrors are reputed to have been used thousands of years ago. Today motor-cars and other vehicles are equipped with driving mirrors which are curved, searchlights have curved mirrors inside them, and the largest telescope in the world utilises a huge curved mirror (p. 559).

1. Convex and Concave Mirrors. Definitions

In the theory of Light, we are mainly concerned with curved mirrors which are parts of *spherical* surfaces. In Fig. 277 (*a*), the mirror APB is part of a sphere whose centre C is in front of the reflecting surface; in Fig. 277 (*b*), the mirror KPL is part of a sphere whose centre C is behind its reflecting surface. To a person in front of it APB curves inwards and is known as a **concave** mirror, while KPL bulges outwards and is known as a **convex** mirror.

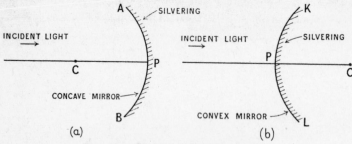

FIG. 277. Concave and convex mirrors.

The mid-point, P, of the mirror is called its *pole*; C, the centre of the sphere of which the mirror is part, is known as the *centre of curvature*; and AB is called the *aperture* of the mirror. The line PC is known as the *principal axis*, and plays an important part in the drawing of images in the mirrors; lines parallel to PC are called *secondary axes*.

2. Narrow and Wide Beams. The Caustic

When a very narrow beam of rays, parallel to the principal axis and close to it, is incident on a concave mirror, experiment shows that all the reflected rays converge to a point F on the principal axis, which is therefore known as the *principal focus* of the mirror, Fig. 278 (i). On this account a concave mirror is better described as a "converging"

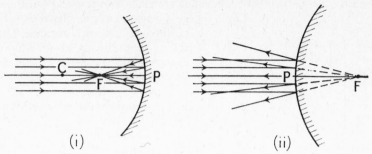

FIG. 278. Focus of concave and convex mirrors.

mirror. An image of the sun, whose rays on the earth are parallel, can hence be received on a screen at F, and thus a concave mirror has a *real* focus.

If a narrow beam of parallel rays is incident on a convex mirror, experiment shows that the reflected rays form a divergent beam which appear to come from a point F *behind* the mirror, Fig. 278 (ii). A convex mirror has thus a *virtual* focus, and the image of the sun cannot be received on a screen using this type of mirror. To express its action on a parallel beam of light, a convex mirror is often called a "diverging" mirror.

When a *wide* beam of light, parallel to the principal axis, is incident on a concave spherical mirror, experiment shows the reflected rays do not pass through a single point, as was the case with a narrow beam. The reflected rays appear to touch a surface known as a *caustic surface*, S, which has an apex, or cusp, at F, the principal focus. Fig. 279. Similarly, if a wide beam of parallel light is incident on a convex mirror, the reflected rays do not appear to diverge from a single point, as was the case with a narrow beam.

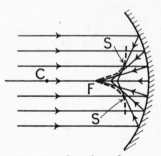

FIG. 279. Caustic surface.

3. Parabolic Mirrors

If a small lamp is placed at the focus, F, of a concave mirror, it follows from the principle of the reversibility of light (p. 400) that rays striking the mirror round a small area about the pole are reflected parallel. See Fig. 278 (i). But those rays from the lamp which strike the mirror at points well away from P will be reflected in different directions, because a *wide* parallel beam is not brought to a focus at F, as shown in Fig. 279. The beam of light reflected from the mirror thus diminishes

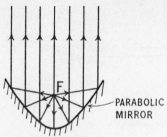

in intensity as its distance from the mirror increases, and a concave spherical mirror is hence useless as a searchlight mirror.

A mirror whose section is the shape of a parabola (the path of a cricket-ball thrown forward into the air) is used in searchlights. A parabolic mirror has the property of reflecting the wide beam of light from a lamp at its focus F as a perfectly parallel beam, in which case the intensity of the reflected beam is practically undiminished as the distance from the mirror increases, Fig. 280.

Fig. 280. Parabolic mirror.

4. Focal Length (f) and Radius of Curvature (r)

From now onwards we shall be concerned with curved spherical mirrors of small aperture, so that a parallel incident beam will pass through the focus after reflection. The diagrams which follow are exaggerated for purposes of clarity.

The distance PC from the pole to the centre of curvature is known as the *radius of curvature* (r) of a mirror; the distance PF from the pole to the focus is known as the *focal length* (f) of the mirror. As we shall now prove, there is a simple relation between f and r.

Consider a ray AX parallel to the principal axis of either a concave or a convex mirror, Fig. 281 (i), (ii). The normal to the mirror at X is

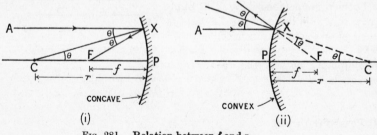

Fig. 281. Relation between f and r.

CX, because the radius of the spherical surface is perpendicular to the surface, and hence the reflected ray makes an angle, θ, with CX equal to the incident angle θ. Taking the case of the concave mirror, angle

AXC = angle XCP, alternate angles, Fig. 281 (i). Thus triangle FXC is isosceles, and FX = FC. As X is a point very close to P we assume to a very good approximation that FX = FP.

$$\therefore \quad FP = FC, \text{ or } FP = \tfrac{1}{2} CP.$$

$$\therefore \quad f = \frac{r}{2} \quad . \quad . \quad . \quad . \quad . \quad (2).$$

This relation between f and r is the same for the case of the convex mirror, Fig. 281 (ii), as the reader can easily verify.

5. Images in Concave Mirrors

Concave mirrors produce images of different sizes; sometimes they are inverted and real, and on other occasions they are erect (the same way up as the object) and virtual. As we shall see, the nature of the image formed depends on the distance of the object from the mirror.

Consider an object of finite size OH placed at O perpendicular to the principal axis of the mirror, Fig. 282 (i). The image, R, of the top point H can be located by the intersection of two reflected rays coming initially from H, and the rays usually chosen are two of the following:

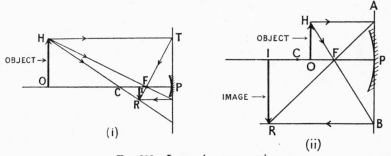

FIG. 282.   Images in concave mirrors.

(1) The ray HT parallel to the principal axis, which is reflected to pass through the focus, F, (2) the ray HC passing through the centre of curvature, C, which is reflected back along its own path because it is a normal to the mirror, (3) the ray HF passing through the focus, F, which is reflected parallel to the principal axis. Since the mirror has a small aperture, and we are considering a narrow beam of light, the mirror must be represented in accurate image drawings by a *straight* line. Thus PT in Fig. 282 (i) represents a perfect mirror.

When the object is a very long distance away (at infinity), the image is small and is formed inverted at the focus (p. 413). As the object approaches the centre of curvature, C, the image remains real and inverted, and is formed in front of the object, Fig. 282 (i). When the object is between C and F, the image is real, inverted, and larger than the object; it is now further from the mirror than the object, Fig. 282 (ii).

As the object approaches the focus, the image recedes further from the mirror, and when the object is at the focus, the image is at infinity. When the object is nearer to the mirror than the focus the image IR becomes *erect* and *virtual*, as shown in Fig. 283 (i). In this case the image is *magnified*, and the concave mirror can thus be used as a shaving mirror.

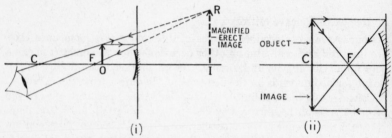

FIG. 283. Images in concave mirrors.

A *special case* occurs when the object is at the centre of curvature, C. The image is then real, inverted, and the same size of the object, and it is also situated at C, Fig. 283 (ii). This case provides a simple method of locating the centre of curvature of a concave mirror (p. 423).

6. Images in Convex Mirrors

Experiment shows that the image of an object in a convex mirror is erect, virtual, and diminished in size, no matter where the object is

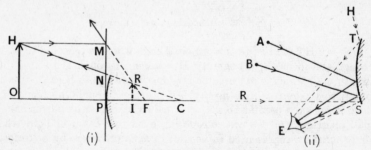

FIG. 284. Images in convex mirrors.

situated. Suppose an object OH is placed in front of a convex mirror, Fig. 284 (i). A ray HM parallel to the principal axis is reflected as if it appeared to come from the virtual focus, F, and a ray HN incident towards the centre of curvature, C, is reflected back along its path. The two reflected rays intersect *behind* the mirror at R, and IR is a virtual and erect image.

Objects well outside the principal axis of a convex mirror, such as A, B in Fig 284 (ii), can be seen by an observer at E, whose *field of view* is that between HT and RS, where T, S are the edges of the mirror. Thus in addition to providing an erect image the convex mirror has a wide field of view, and is hence used as a driving mirror.

7. Formulæ for Mirrors. Sign Convention

Many of the advances in the uses of curved mirrors and lenses have resulted from the use of *optical formulæ*, and we have now to consider the relation which holds between the object and image distances in mirrors and their focal length. In order to obtain a formula which holds for both concave and convex mirrors, a *sign rule* or *convention* must be obeyed, and we shall adopt the following:

A real object or image distance is a positive distance.
A virtual object or image distance is a negative distance.

In brief "real is positive, virtual is negative". The focal length of a concave mirror is thus a positive distance; the focal length of a convex mirror is a negative distance.

8. Concave Mirror

Consider a point object O on the principal axis of a concave mirror. A ray OX from O is reflected in the direction XI making an equal angle θ with the normal CX; a ray OP from O, incident at P, is reflected

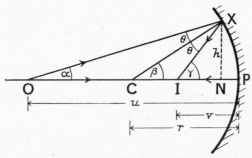

Fig. 285.   Mirror formula.

back along PO, since CP is the normal at P. The point of intersection, I, of the two rays is the image of O. Fig. 285.

Suppose a, β, γ are the angles made by OX, CX, IX respectively with the axis. Since we are considering a mirror of small aperture these angles are small in practice, Fig. 285 being exaggerated. As β is the exterior angle of triangle CXO, we have $\beta = \alpha + \theta$.

$$\therefore \theta = \beta - \alpha \qquad . \qquad . \qquad . \qquad . \qquad \text{(i)}$$

Since γ is the exterior angle of triangle IXC, we have $\gamma = \beta + \theta$.

$$\therefore \theta = \gamma - \beta \qquad . \qquad . \qquad . \qquad . \qquad \text{(ii)}$$

From (i) and (ii), it follows that

$$\beta - \alpha = \gamma - \beta$$
$$\therefore \alpha + \gamma = 2\beta \qquad . \qquad . \qquad . \qquad . \qquad . \qquad \text{(iii)}$$

We can now substitute for α, β, γ in terms of h, the height of X above the axis, and the distances OP, CP, IP. In so doing (a) we assume N is practically coincident with P, as X is very close to P in practice, (b) the appropriate sign, $+$ or $-$, must precede all the numerical values of the distances concerned. Also, as $\alpha = \tan \alpha$ in radians when α is very small, we have

$$\alpha = \frac{XN}{ON} = \frac{XN}{+\,OP} = \frac{h}{+\,OP},$$

where OP is the distance of the real object O from the mirror in centimetres, say, and $XN = h$. Similarly,

$$\beta = \frac{XN}{CN} = \frac{XN}{+\,CP} = \frac{h}{+\,CP},$$

as CP, the radius of curvature of the concave mirror, is real.

Also,

$$\gamma = \frac{XN}{IN} = \frac{XN}{+\,IP} = \frac{h}{+\,IP},$$

where IP is the distance of the real image I from the mirror. Substituting for α, β, γ in (iii),

$$\therefore \frac{h}{(+\,IP)} + \frac{h}{(+\,OP)} = 2\,\frac{h}{(+\,CP)}.$$

Dividing by h,

$$\therefore \frac{1}{IP} + \frac{1}{OP} = \frac{2}{CP}$$

If we let v represent the image distance from the mirror, u the object distance from the mirror, and r the radius of curvature, we have

$$\frac{1}{v} + \frac{1}{u} = \frac{2}{r} \qquad . \qquad . \qquad . \qquad . \qquad \text{(3)}$$

Further, since $f = r/2$, then $\dfrac{2}{r} = \dfrac{1}{f}$

$$\therefore \; \frac{1}{v} + \frac{1}{u} = \frac{1}{f} \qquad \cdots \qquad (4)$$

The relations (3), (4) are standard formulæ for curved mirrors; and when they are used the appropriate sign for v, u, f, or r must always precede the corresponding numerical value.

9. Convex Mirror

We now obtain a relation for object distance (u), image distance (v), and focal length (f) of a convex mirror. In this case the incident rays OX, OP are reflected as if they appear to come from the point I behind the mirror, which is therefore a virtual image, and hence the image distance IP is *negative*, Fig. 286. Further, CP is negative, as the centre of curvature of X a convex mirror is behind the mirror.

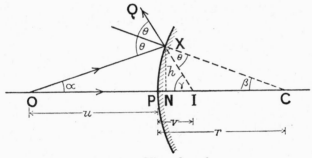

Fig. 286. Mirror formula.

Since θ is the exterior angle of triangle COX, $\theta = a + \beta$. As γ is the exterior angle of triangle CIX, $\gamma = \theta + \beta$, or $\theta = \gamma - \beta$.

$$\therefore \gamma - \beta = a + \beta$$
$$\therefore \gamma - a = 2\beta \qquad \cdots \qquad (i)$$

Now $\gamma = \dfrac{h}{\text{IN}} = \dfrac{h}{(-\text{IP})}$, as I is virtual; $a = \dfrac{h}{\text{ON}} = \dfrac{h}{(+\text{OP})}$, as O is real

$\beta = \dfrac{h}{\text{NC}} = \dfrac{h}{(-\text{PC})}$, as C is virtual. Substituting in (i),

$$\therefore \quad \frac{h}{(-\text{IP})} - \frac{h}{(+\text{OP})} = \frac{2h}{(-\text{CP})}$$
$$\therefore \quad \frac{1}{\text{IP}} + \frac{1}{\text{OP}} = \frac{2}{\text{CP}}$$

$$\therefore \quad \frac{1}{v} + \frac{1}{u} = \frac{2}{r}$$

and $$\therefore \quad \frac{1}{v} + \frac{1}{u} = \frac{1}{f}$$

Thus, using the sign convention, the same formula holds for concave and convex mirrors.

10. Formula for Magnification

The lateral magnification, m, produced by a mirror is defined by

$$m = \frac{height\ of\ image}{height\ of\ object}$$

Suppose IR is the image of an object OH in a concave or convex mirror, Fig. 287 (i), (ii). Then a ray HP from the top point H of the

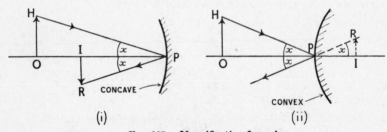

FIG. 287. Magnification formula.

object passes through the top point R of the image after reflection from the mirror. Now the normal to the mirror at P is the principal axis, OP. Thus angle OPH = angle IPR, from the law of reflection.

$$\therefore \quad \tan OPH = \tan IPR$$

$$i.e., \quad \frac{OH}{OP} = \frac{IR}{IP}$$

$$\therefore \quad \frac{IR}{OH} = \frac{IP}{OP}$$

But IP = image distance = v, and OP = object distance = u

$$\therefore \quad \frac{IR}{OH} = \frac{v}{u}$$

$$\therefore \quad m = \frac{v}{u} \qquad . \qquad . \qquad . \qquad . \qquad (5)$$

Thus if the image distance is half the object distance, the image is half the length of the object.

Since
$$\frac{1}{v} + \frac{1}{u} = \frac{1}{f}$$

$$\therefore \frac{v}{v} + \frac{v}{u} = \frac{v}{f},$$

multiplying throughout by v.

$$\therefore 1 + \frac{v}{u} = \frac{v}{f}$$

$$\therefore 1 + m = \frac{v}{f}$$

$$\therefore \qquad m = \frac{v}{f} - 1$$

11. Some Applications of Mirror Formulæ

The following examples will assist the reader to understand how to correctly apply the formulæ $\dfrac{1}{v} + \dfrac{1}{u} = \dfrac{1}{f}$ and $m = \dfrac{v}{u}$:

1. An object is placed 10 cm. in front of a concave mirror of focal length 15 cm. Find the image position and the magnification.

Since the mirror is concave, $f = + 15$ cm. The object is real, and hence $u = + 10$ cm. Substituting in $\dfrac{1}{v} + \dfrac{1}{u} = \dfrac{1}{f}$,

$$\therefore \frac{1}{v} + \frac{1}{(+10)} = \frac{1}{(+15)}$$

$$\therefore \qquad \frac{1}{v} = \frac{1}{15} - \frac{1}{10} = -\frac{1}{30}$$

$$\therefore \qquad v = -30$$

Since v is negative in sign the image is *virtual*, and it is 30 cm. from the mirror. See Fig. 283 (i). The magnification, m, $= \dfrac{v}{u} = \dfrac{30}{10} = 3$, so that the mage is three times as high as the object.

2. The image of an object in a convex mirror is 4 cm. from the mirror. If the mirror has a radius of curvature of 24 cm., find the object position and the magnification.

The image in a convex mirror is always virtual (p. 416). Hence $v = -4$ cm. The focal length of the mirror $= \frac{1}{2} r = 12$ cm.; and since the mirror is convex, $f = -12$ cm. Substituting in $\dfrac{1}{v} + \dfrac{1}{u} = \dfrac{1}{f}$,

$$\therefore \frac{1}{(-4)} + \frac{1}{u} = \frac{1}{(-12)}$$

$$\therefore \qquad \frac{1}{u} = -\frac{1}{12} + \frac{1}{4} = \frac{1}{6}$$

$$\therefore \qquad u = 6$$

Since u is positive in sign the object is real, and it is 6 cm. from the mirror. The magnification, m, $= \dfrac{v}{u} = \dfrac{4}{6} = \dfrac{2}{3}$, and hence the image is two-thirds as high as the object. See Fig. 284 (i).

3. An erect image, three times the size of the object, is obtained with a concave mirror of radius of curvature 36 cm. What is the position of the object?

If x cm. is the numerical value of the distance of the object from the mirror, the image distance must be $3x$ cm., since the magnification $m = \dfrac{\text{image distance}}{\text{object distance}} = 3$. Now an *erect* image is obtained with a concave mirror only when the image is *virtual* (p. 416).

$$\therefore \quad \text{image distance, } v, = -3x.$$

Also, object distance, u, $= +x$

and focal length, f, $= \tfrac{1}{2}r = +18$ cm.

Substituting in $\dfrac{1}{v} + \dfrac{1}{u} = \dfrac{1}{f}$,

$$\therefore \quad \frac{1}{(-3x)} + \frac{1}{(+x)} = \frac{1}{(+18)}$$

$$\therefore \quad -\frac{1}{3x} + \frac{1}{x} = \frac{1}{18}$$

$$\therefore \quad \frac{2}{3x} = \frac{1}{18}$$

$$\therefore \quad x = 12$$

Thus the object is 12 cm. from the mirror.

12. Virtual Object and Convex Mirror

We have already seen that a convex mirror produces a virtual image of an object in front of it, which is a real object. A convex mirror may sometimes produce a real image of a *virtual* object.

As an illustration, consider an incident beam of light bounded by AB, DE, converging to a point O *behind* the mirror, Fig. 288. O is

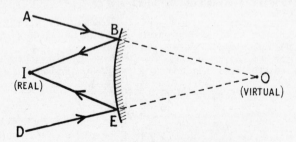

Fig. 288. Real image in convex mirror.

regarded as a virtual object, and if its distance from the mirror is

10 cm., then the object distance, u, $= -10$. Suppose the convex mirror has a focal length of 15 cm., i.e., $f = -15$.

Since

$$\frac{1}{v} + \frac{1}{u} = \frac{1}{f}$$

$$\frac{1}{v} + \frac{1}{(-10)} = \frac{1}{(-15)}$$

$$\therefore \quad \frac{1}{v} = -\frac{1}{15} + \frac{1}{10} = +\frac{1}{30}$$

$$\therefore \quad v = +30$$

The point image, I, is thus 30 cm. from the mirror, and is *real*. The beam reflected from the mirror is hence a convergent beam, Fig. 288; a similar case with a plane mirror is shown in Fig. 273 (ii).

13. Object at Centre of Curvature of Concave Mirror

Suppose an object is placed at the centre of curvature of a concave mirror. Then $u = +r$, where r is the numerical value of the radius of curvature. Substituting in $\dfrac{1}{v} + \dfrac{1}{u} = \dfrac{2}{r}$ to find the image distance v,

$$\therefore \quad \frac{1}{v} + \frac{1}{(+r)} = \frac{2}{(+r)}$$

$$\therefore \quad \frac{1}{v} = \frac{2}{r} - \frac{1}{r} = \frac{1}{r}$$

$$\therefore \quad v = r$$

The image is therefore also formed at the centre of curvature. The magnification in this case is given by $m = \dfrac{v}{u} = \dfrac{r}{r} = 1$, and hence the object and image are the same size. This case is illustrated in Fig. 273 (ii) to which the reader should now refer.

SOME METHODS OF DETERMINING FOCAL LENGTH AND
RADIUS OF CURVATURE OF MIRRORS

14. Concave Mirror

Method 1. A pin O is placed above a concave mirror M so that an inverted image of the pin can be seen, Fig. 289. If the pin is moved up and down with its point on the axis of the mirror, and an observer E moves his eye perpendicularly to the pin at the same time, a position of O is

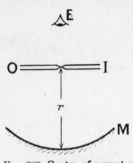

FIG. 289. Centre of curvature of concave mirror.

reached when the image I remains perfectly in line with O as E moves; i.e., there is no parallax (no relative displacement) between pin and image. The pin is now at exactly the same place as its image I, Fig. 289. Since an object and image coincide in position at the centre of curvature of a concave mirror (p. 424), the distance from the point of the pin to the mirror is equal to its radius of curvature, r.

The focal length, f, which is $\dfrac{r}{2}$, is then easily obtained.

If an illuminated object is available, instead of a pin, the object is moved to or from the mirror until a clear image is obtained beside the object. The distance of the object from the mirror is then equal to r. In general, the method of no parallax, using a pin, gives a higher degree of accuracy in locating an image.

Method 2. By using the method of no parallax, or employing an illuminated object, several, say six, values of the image distance, v, can be obtained with the concave mirror, corresponding to six different values of the object distance u. Substituting for u, v in the formula $\dfrac{1}{v} + \dfrac{1}{u} = \dfrac{1}{f}$, six values of f can be calculated, and the average value taken.

A better method of procedure, however, is to plot the magnitudes of

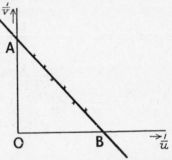

FIG. 290. Graph of $\dfrac{1}{v}$ against $\dfrac{1}{u}$.

$\dfrac{1}{v}$ against $\dfrac{1}{u}$; a straight line BA can be drawn through the points thus obtained, Fig. 290. Now $\dfrac{1}{v} + \dfrac{1}{u} = \dfrac{1}{f}$. Hence, when $\dfrac{1}{v} = 0$, $\dfrac{1}{u} = \dfrac{1}{f}$.

But $\qquad\qquad OB = \dfrac{1}{u}$ when $\dfrac{1}{v} = 0$

$\therefore \qquad OB = \dfrac{1}{f}$, i.e., $f = \dfrac{1}{OB}$

Thus the focal length can be determined from the reciprocal value of the intercept OB on the axis of $\dfrac{1}{u}$.

From $\dfrac{1}{v} + \dfrac{1}{u} = \dfrac{1}{f}$, $\dfrac{1}{v} = \dfrac{1}{f}$ when $\dfrac{1}{u} = 0$. Thus $OA = \dfrac{1}{f}$, Fig. 290, and

hence $f = \dfrac{1}{OA}$. It can thus be seen that (i) f can also be calculated from

the reciprocal of the intercept OA on the axis of $\dfrac{1}{v}$, (ii) OAB is an isosceles

triangle if the same scale is employed for $\dfrac{1}{v}$ and $\dfrac{1}{u}$.

15. Convex Mirror

Method 1. By using a convex lens, L, a real image of an object O can be formed at a point C on the other side of L, Fig. 291. The convex mirror, MN, is then placed between L and C with its reflecting face facing the lens, so that a convergent beam of rays is incident on the mirror. When the latter is moved along the axis OC a position will be reached when the beam is incident *normally* on the mirror, in which case the rays are reflected back along the incident path. *A real inverted image is then formed at O.*

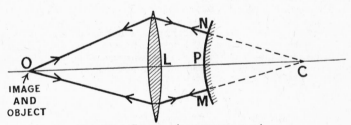

Fig. 291.   Convex mirror measurement.

Since the rays incident on the mirror, for example at N or M, are normal to the mirror surface, they will, if produced, pass through the centre of curvature, C, of the mirror. Thus the distance $PC = r$, the radius of curvature. Since $PC = LC - LP$, this distance can be obtained from measurement of LP and LC, the latter being the image distance from the lens when the mirror is taken away.

Method 2. A more difficult method than the above consists of positioning a pin O in front of the convex mirror, when a virtual image, I, is formed, Fig. 292. A small plane mirror M is then moved between O and P until the image I' of the lower part of O *in M* coincides in position with the upper part of the image of O in the convex mirror. The distances OP, MP are then measured.

Since M is a plane mirror, the image I' of O in it is such that $OM =$

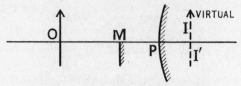

FIG. 292. Convex mirror measurement.

MI'. Thus PI = MI' − MP = OM − MP, and hence PI can be calculated. But PI = v, the image distance of O in the convex mirror, and OP = u, the object distance. Substituting for the virtual distance v, and u, in $\dfrac{1}{v} + \dfrac{1}{u} = \dfrac{1}{f}$, the focal length of the convex mirror can be found.

EXAMPLES

1. Show that a concave spherical mirror can produce a focused image of an object when certain conditions are observed, and prove the usual relation between the object and image distances. A linear object, 10 cm. long, lies along the axis of a concave mirror whose radius of curvature is 30 cm., the near end of the object lying 18 cm. from the mirror. Find the magnification of the image. (*W.*)

First part. The condition for a focused image is that the light from the object must be incident as a narrow beam round the pole of the mirror. This implies that the object must be small (p. 412). The usual relation between the object and image distances is proved on p. 417.

Second part. Suppose Q is the near end of the object, which is 18 cm. from the mirror. The distance of the image of Q is given by

$$\frac{1}{v} + \frac{1}{(+\,18)} = \frac{1}{(+\,15)}$$

since $f = \dfrac{r}{2} = \dfrac{30}{2} = 15$ cm.

$$\therefore \frac{1}{v} = \frac{1}{15} - \frac{1}{18}$$

from which $\qquad v = 90$ cm.

The other end P of the object is (10 + 18) cm. from the mirror, or 28 cm. The image of P is given by

$$\frac{1}{v} + \frac{1}{(+\,28)} = \frac{1}{(+\,15)}$$

$$\therefore \frac{1}{v} = \frac{1}{15} - \frac{1}{28}$$

from which $\qquad v = 32\cdot3$ cm.

$\therefore$ length of image = 90 − 32·3 = 57·7 cm.

$\therefore$ magnification of image = $\dfrac{57\cdot7}{10} = 5\cdot77$

2. PBCA is the axis of a concave spherical mirror, A being a point object, B its image, C the centre of curvature of the mirror and P the pole. Find a relation between PA, PB, and PC, supposing the aperture of the mirror to be small. A concave mirror forms, on a screen, a real image of twice the linear dimensions of the object. Object and screen are then moved until the image is three times the size of the object. If the shift of the screen is 25 cm., determine the shift of the object and the focal length of the mirror. (*N.*)

First part. See text.

Second part. Suppose *v* is the distance of the screen from the mirror when the image is twice the length of the object. Since the magnification, *m*, is given by

$$m = \frac{v}{f} - 1 \quad . \quad . \quad . \quad . \quad . \quad \text{(i)}$$

where *f* is the focal length of the mirror (see p. 421),

$$\therefore 2 = \frac{v}{f} - 1 \quad . \quad . \quad . \quad . \quad . \quad \text{(ii)}$$

When $m = 3$, the image distance is $(v + 25)$ cm. Substituting in (i),

$$\therefore 3 = \frac{v + 25}{f} - 1 \quad . \quad . \quad . \quad . \quad \text{(iii)}$$

Subtracting (ii) from (iii), we have

$$1 = \frac{25}{f}$$

$$\therefore f = 25 \text{ cm.}$$

From (ii), $2 = \dfrac{v}{25} - 1$, or $v = 75$ cm. The object distance, *u*, is thus given by $\dfrac{1}{75} + \dfrac{1}{u} = \dfrac{1}{25}$, from which $u = 37\frac{1}{2}$ cm. From (iii), $v = 100$ cm. The object distance, *u*, is then given by $\dfrac{1}{100} + \dfrac{1}{u} = \dfrac{1}{25}$, from which $u = 33\frac{1}{3}$ cm. Thus the shift of the object $= 37\frac{1}{2} - 33\frac{1}{3} = 4\frac{1}{6}$ cm.

EXERCISES XIX

1. An object is placed (i) 10 cm., (ii) 4 cm. from a concave mirror of radius of curvature 12 cm. Calculate the image position in each case, and the respective magnifications.

2. Repeat Q. 1 by accurate drawings to scale. (*Note.*—The mirror must be represented by a straight line.)

3. An object is placed 15 cm. from a convex mirror of focal length 10 cm. Calculate the image distance and the magnification produced. Draw an accurate diagram to scale, and verify your drawing from the calculated results.

4. Explain with the aid of diagrams why a curved mirror can be used (i) as a driving mirror, (ii) in a searchlight, (iii) as a shaving mirror. Why is a special form of mirror required in the searchlight?

5. Describe and explain a method of finding the focal length of (*a*) a concave mirror, (*b*) a convex mirror.

6. A pole 4 ft. long is laid along the principal axis of a convex mirror of focal length 1 ft. The end of the pole nearer the mirror is 2 ft. from it. Find the length of the image of the pole.

7. Deduce a formula connecting u, v and r, the distances of object, image and centre of curvature from a spherical mirror.

A mirror forms an erect image 30 cm. from the object and twice its height. Where must the mirror be situated? What is its radius of curvature? Assuming the object to be real, determine whether the mirror is convex or concave. (*L.*)

8. Establish the formula $\dfrac{1}{v} + \dfrac{1}{u} = \dfrac{1}{f}$ for a concave mirror.

In an experiment with a concave mirror the magnification m of the image is measured for a series of values of v, and a curve is plotted between m and v. What curve would you expect to obtain, and how would you use it to deduce the focal length of the mirror? (*C.*)

9. Derive an approximate relation connecting the distances of an object and its image from the surface of a convex spherical mirror.

A small object is placed at right angles to the axis of a concave mirror so as to form (*a*) a real, (*b*) a virtual image, twice as long as the object. If the radius of curvature of the mirror is R what is the distance between the two images? (*L.*)

10. Deduce a formula connecting the distances of object and image from a spherical mirror. What are the advantages of a concave mirror over a lens for use in an astronomical telescope?

A driving mirror consists of a cylindrical mirror of radius 10 cm. and length (over the curved surface) of 10 cm. If the eye of the driver be assumed at a great distance from the mirror, find the angle of view. (*O. & C.*)

11. Find the relation connecting the focal length of a convex spherical mirror with the distances from the mirror of a small object and the image formed by the mirror.

A convex mirror, radius of curvature 30 cm., forms a real image 20 cm. from its surface. Explain how this is possible and find whether the image is erect or inverted. (*L.*)

CHAPTER XX

REFRACTION AT PLANE SURFACES

1. Laws of Refraction

WHEN a ray of light AO is incident at O on the plane surface of a glass medium, observation shows that some of the light is reflected from the surface along OC in accordance with the laws of reflection, while the rest of the light travels along a new direction, OB, in the glass, Fig. 293

On account of the change in direction the light is said to be "refracted" on entering the glass; and the *angle of refraction, r,* is the angle made by the refracted ray OB with the normal at O.

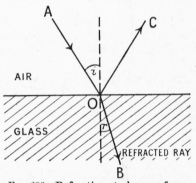

FIG. 293. Refraction at plane surface.

Historical records reveal that the astronomer PTOLEMY, who lived about A.D. 140, measured numerous values of the angle of incidence, i, and the angle of refraction, r, for glass as the angle of incidence was varied. However, he was unable to discover any relation between i and r.

Later scientists were equally unsuccessful, until centuries later SNELL, a Dutch professor, discovered in 1620 that the sines of the angles bear a constant ratio to each other. The *laws of refraction* are:

1. *The incident and refracted rays, and the normal at the point of incidence, all lie in the same plane.*

2. *For two given media,* $\dfrac{\sin i}{\sin r}$ *is a constant, where i is the angle of incidence and r is the angle of refraction.*

2. Refractive Index

The constant ratio $\dfrac{\sin i}{\sin r}$ is known as the **refractive index** for the two given media; and as the magnitude of the constant depends on the colour of the light, it is usually specified as that obtained for yellow light. If the medium containing the incident ray is denoted by 1, and that containing the refracted ray by 2, the refractive index can be denoted by $_1\mu_2$.

Scientists have drawn up tables of refractive index when the incident ray is travelling *in vacuo* and is then refracted into the medium concerned, for example, glass or water. The values thus obtained are known as the *absolute* refractive indices of the media; and as a vacuum is always the first medium, the subscripts for the absolute refractive index, symbol μ, can be dropped. The magnitude of μ for glass is about 1·5, μ for water is about 1·33, and μ for air at normal pressure is about 1·00028. As the magnitude of the refractive index of a medium is only very slightly altered when the incident light is in air instead of a vacuum, experiments to determine the absolute refractive index μ are usually performed with the light incident from air on to the medium; thus we can take $_{air}\mu_{glass}$ as equal to $_{vacuum}\mu_{glass}$ for most practical purposes.

We have already mentioned that light is refracted because it has a different velocity in different media. The Wave Theory of Light, discussed on p. 697, shows that the refractive index $_1\mu_2$ for two given media 1 and 2 is given by

$$_1\mu_2 = \frac{velocity\ of\ light\ in\ medium\ 1}{velocity\ of\ light\ in\ medium\ 2} \qquad . \quad . \quad . \quad (6)$$

and this is a *definition* of refractive index which can be used instead of the ratio $\dfrac{\sin i}{\sin r}$. An alternative definition of the absolute refractive index, μ, of a medium is thus

$$\mu = \frac{velocity\ of\ light\ in\ vacuo}{velocity\ of\ light\ in\ medium} \qquad . \quad . \quad . \quad (7)$$

In practice the velocity of light in air can replace the velocity in vacuo in this definition.

3. Relations Between Refractive Indices

(1.) Consider a ray of light, AO, refracted from *glass to air* along the direction OB; observation then shows that the refracted ray OB is bent away from the normal, Fig. 294. The refractive index from glass to air, $_g\mu_a$, is given by $\sin x / \sin y$, by definition, where x is the angle of incidence in the glass and y is the angle of refraction in the air.

From the principle of the reversibility of light (p. 400), it follows that a ray travelling along BO in air is refracted along OA in the glass. The

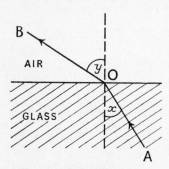

FIG. 294. Refraction from glass to air

refractive index from air to glass, $_a\mu_g$, is then given by $\sin y/\sin x$, by definition. But $_g\mu_a = \dfrac{\sin x}{\sin y}$, from previous.

$$\therefore \quad _g\mu_a = \frac{1}{_a\mu_g} \qquad \cdot \qquad \cdot \qquad \cdot \qquad \cdot \qquad \cdot \qquad \cdot \qquad (8)$$

If $_a\mu_g$ is 1·5, then $_g\mu_a = \dfrac{1}{1\cdot5} = 0\cdot66$. Similarly, if the refractive index from air to water is 4/3, the refractive index from water to air is 3/4.

(2.) Consider a ray AO incident in air on a plane glass boundary, then refracted from the glass into a water medium, and finally emerging along a direction CD into air. *If the boundaries of the media are parallel, experiment shows that the emergent ray CD is parallel to the incident ray AO*, although there is a relative displacement, Fig. 295. Thus the angles made with the normals by AO, CD are equal, and we shall denote them by i_a.

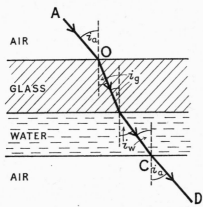

Fɪɢ. 295. Refraction at parallel plane surfaces.

Suppose i_g, i_w are the angles made with the normals by the respective rays in the glass and water media. Then, by definition, $_g\mu_w = \dfrac{\sin i_g}{\sin i_w}$.

But $\qquad \dfrac{\sin i_g}{\sin i_w} = \dfrac{\sin i_g}{\sin i_a} \times \dfrac{\sin i_a}{\sin i_w},$

and $\qquad \dfrac{\sin i_g}{\sin i_a} = {_g\mu_a}, \quad \dfrac{\sin i_a}{\sin i_w} = {_a\mu_w}$

$$\therefore \quad _g\mu_w = {_g\mu_a} \times {_a\mu_w} \qquad \cdot \qquad \cdot \qquad \cdot \qquad \cdot \qquad \cdot \qquad (i)$$

Further, as $_g\mu_a = \dfrac{1}{_a\mu_g}$, we can write

$$_g\mu_w = \frac{_a\mu_w}{_a\mu_g}$$

Since $_a\mu_w = 1\cdot33$ and $_a\mu_g = 1\cdot5$, it follows that $_g\mu_w = \dfrac{1\cdot33}{1\cdot5} = 0\cdot89.$

From (i) on p. 431 it follows that in general

$$_1\mu_3 = {}_1\mu_2 \times {}_2\mu_3 \quad . \qquad . \qquad . \qquad . \qquad . \qquad . \qquad (9)$$

The order of the suffixes enables this formula to be easily memorised.

4. General Relation Between μ and Sin i

From Fig. 295, $\sin i_a / \sin i_g = {}_a\mu_g$

$$\therefore \quad \sin i_a = {}_a\mu_g \sin i_g \qquad . \qquad . \qquad . \qquad . \qquad . \qquad \text{(i)}$$

Also, $\sin i_w / \sin i_a = {}_w\mu_a = 1/{}_a\mu_w$

$$\therefore \quad \sin i_a = {}_a\mu_w \sin i_w \qquad . \qquad . \qquad . \qquad . \qquad . \qquad \text{(ii)}$$

Hence, from (i) and (ii),

$$\sin i_a = {}_a\mu_g \sin i_g = {}_a\mu_w \sin i_w$$

If the equations are re-written in terms of the absolute refractive indices of air (μ_a), glass (μ_g), and water (μ_w), we have

$$\mu_a \sin i_a = \mu_g \sin i_g = \mu_w \sin i_w$$

since $\mu_a = 1$. This relation shows that when a ray is refracted from one medium to another, *the boundaries being parallel,*

$$\mu \sin i = \text{a constant} \qquad . \qquad . \qquad . \qquad . \qquad \text{(10)}$$

where μ is the absolute refractive index of a medium and i is the angle made by the ray with the normal in that medium.

This relation applies also to the case of light passing directly from

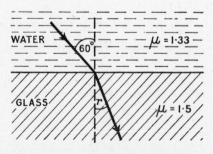

Fig. 296.   Refraction from water to glass.

one medium to another. As an illustration of its use, suppose a ray is incident on a water-glass boundary at an angle of 60°, Fig. 296. Then, applying "$\mu \sin i$ is a constant", we have

$$1 \cdot 33 \sin 60° = 1 \cdot 5 \sin r \quad . \quad . \quad . \quad . \quad . \quad \text{(iii)}$$

where r is the angle of refraction in the glass, and 1·33, 1·5 are the respective values of μ_w and μ_g. Thus $\sin r = 1 \cdot 33 \sin 60°/1 \cdot 5 = 0 \cdot 7679$, from which $r = 50 \cdot 1°$.

5. Multiple Images in Mirrors

If a candle or other object is held in front of a plane mirror, a series of faint or "ghost" images are observed in addition to one bright image. Suppose O is an object placed in front of a mirror with silvering on the back surface M, as shown in Fig. 297. A ray OA from O is then

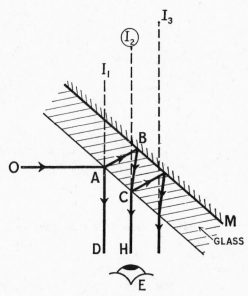

FIG. 297. Multiple images.

reflected from the front (glass) surface along AD and gives rise to a faint image I_1, while the remainder of the light energy is refracted at A along AB. Reflection then takes place at the silvered surface, and after refraction into the air along CH a bright image is observed at I_2. A small percentage of the light is reflected at C, however, and re-enters the glass again, thus forming a faint image at I_3. Other faint images are formed in the same way. Thus a series of *multiple images* is obtained, the brightest being I_2. The images lie on the normal from O to the mirror, the distances depending on the thickness of the glass and its refractive index and the angle of incidence.

6. Drawing the Refracted Ray by Geometrical Construction

Since $\sin i/\sin r = \mu$, the direction of the refracted ray can be calculated when a ray is incident in air at a known angle i on a medium of given refractive index μ. The direction of the refracted ray can also be obtained by means of a geometrical construction. Thus suppose AO is a ray incident in air at a given angle i on a medium of refractive index μ, Fig. 298 (i). With O as centre, two circles, a, b, are drawn whose radii are in the ratio $1 : \mu$, and AO is produced to cut circle a at P. PN is then drawn parallel to the normal at O to intersect circle b at Q. *OQ is then the direction of the refracted ray.*

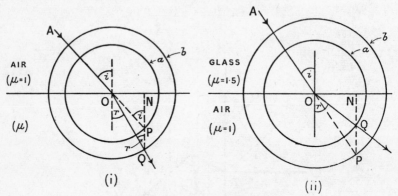

Fig. 298. Drawing of refracted rays.

To prove the construction is correct, we note that angle OPN $= i$, angle OQN $= r$. Thus $\sin i/\sin r = \text{ON/OP} \div \text{ON/OQ} = \text{OQ/OP}$. But OQ/OP $=$ radius of circle b/radius of circle $a = \mu$, from our drawing of the circles. Hence $\sin i/\sin r = \mu$. Thus OQ must be the refracted ray. Although we have taken the case of the incident ray in air, the same construction will enable the refracted ray to be drawn when the incident ray is in any other medium. The radii of the circles are then in the ratio of the absolute refractive indices.

Fig. 298 (ii) illustrates the drawing in the case of a ray AO refracted from a dense medium such as glass ($\mu = 1.5$) into a less dense medium such as air ($\mu = 1$). Circles a, b are again drawn concentric with O, their radii being in the ratio $1 : \mu$. The incident ray AO, however, is produced to cut the *larger* circle b this time, at P, and a line PN is then drawn parallel to the normal at O to intersect the circle a at Q. OQ is then the direction of the refracted ray. The proof for the con-

struction follows similar lines to that given for Fig. 298 (i), and it is left
as an exercise for the reader.

The direction of the incident ray AO in Fig. 298 (ii) may be such that
the line PN does not intersect the circle a. In this case, which is
important and is discussed shortly, no refracted ray can be drawn.
See *Total Internal Reflection*, p. 440.

7. Refractive Index of a Liquid by Using a Concave Mirror

We are now in a position to utilise our formulæ in refraction, and we
shall first consider a simple method of determining roughly the refractive index, μ, of a small quantity of transparent liquid.

If a small drop of the liquid is placed on a concave mirror S, a position
H can be located by the no parallax method where the image of a pin
held over the mirror coincides in position with the pin itself, Fig. 299.

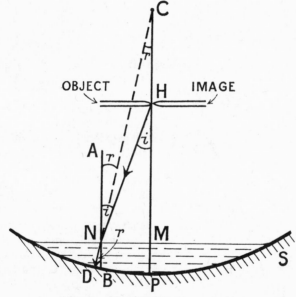

Fig. 299.   (Depth of liquid exaggerated.)

The rays from the pin must now be striking the mirror *normally*, in
which case the rays are reflected back along the incident path and form
an image at the same place as the object. A ray HN close to the axis
HP is refracted at N along ND in the liquid, strikes the mirror normally
at D, and is reflected back along the path DNH. Thus if DN is produced
it passes through the centre of curvature, C, of the concave mirror.

Let ANB be the normal to the liquid surface at N. Then angle

ANH = angle NHM = i, the angle of incidence, and angle BND = angle ANC = angle NCM = r, the angle of refraction in the liquid. From triangles HNM, CNM respectively, $\sin i = $ NM/HN and $\sin r = $ NM/CN. The refractive index, μ, of the liquid is thus given by

$$\mu = \frac{\sin i}{\sin r} = \frac{NM/HN}{NM/CN} = \frac{CN}{HN}.$$

Now since HN is a ray very close to the principal axis CP, HN = HM and CN = CM, to a very good approximation. Thus $\mu = \dfrac{CM}{HM}$. Further, if the depth MP of the liquid is very small compared with HM and CM, CM = CP and HM = HP approximately. Hence, approximately,

$$\mu = \frac{CP}{HP}.$$

HP can be measured directly. CP is the radius of curvature of the mirror, which can be obtained by the method shown on p. 423. The refractive index, μ, of the liquid can thus be calculated.

8. Apparent Depth

Swimmers in particular are aware that the bottom of a pool of water appears nearer the surface than is actually the case; the phenomenon is due to the refraction of light.

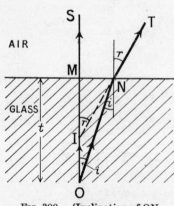

FIG. 300. (Inclination of ON to OM exaggerated.)

Consider an object O at a distance below the surface of a medium such as water or glass, which has a refractive index μ, Fig. 300. A ray OM from O perpendicular to the surface passes straight through into the air along MS. A ray ON very close to OM is refracted at N into the air away from the normal, in a direction NT; and an observer viewing O directly overhead sees it in the position I, which is the point of intersection of SM and TN produced. Though we have only considered two rays in the air, a *cone* of rays, with SM as the axis, actually enters the observer's eye.

Suppose the angle of incidence in the glass is i, and the angle of refraction in the air is r. Then, since "$\mu \sin i$" is a constant (p. 432), we have

$$\mu \sin i = 1 \times \sin r \qquad . \qquad . \qquad . \qquad . \qquad (i)$$

where μ is the refractive index of glass; the refractive index of air is 1.

Since i = angle NOM, and r = angle MIN, $\sin i$ = MN/ON and $\sin r$ = MN/IN. From (i), it follows that

$$\mu \frac{MN}{ON} = \frac{MN}{IN}$$

$$\therefore \quad \mu = \frac{ON}{IN} \quad . \quad . \quad . \quad . \quad . \quad . \quad (ii)$$

Since we are dealing with the case of an observer directly above O, the rays ON, IN are *very* close to the normal OM. Hence to a very good approximation, ON = OM and IN = IM. From (ii),

$$\therefore \quad \mu = \frac{ON}{IN} = \frac{OM}{IM}$$

Since the real depth of the object O = OM, and its apparent depth = IM,

$$\therefore \quad \mu = \frac{\text{real depth}}{\text{apparent depth}} \quad . \quad . \quad . \quad . \quad (11)$$

If the real depth, OM, = t, the apparent depth = $\frac{t}{\mu}$, from (11). The *displacement*, OI, of the object, which we shall denote by d, is thus given by $t - \frac{t}{\mu}$, i.e.,

$$d = t \left(1 - \frac{1}{\mu} \right) \quad . \quad . \quad . \quad . \quad . \quad (12)$$

If an object is 6 ins. below water of refractive index, μ, = $1\frac{1}{3}$, it appears to be displaced upward to an observer in air by an amount, d,

$$= 6 \left(1 - \frac{1}{1\frac{1}{3}} \right) = 1\frac{1}{2} \text{ ins.}$$

9. Object Below Parallel-sided Glass Block

Consider an object O placed some distance in air below a parallel-sided glass block of thickness t, Fig. 301. The ray OMS normal to the surface emerges along MS, while the ray OO_1 close to the normal is refracted along O_1N in the glass and emerges in air along NT in a direction parallel to OO_1 (see p. 431). An observer (not shown) above the glass thus sees the object at I, the point of intersection of TN and SM.

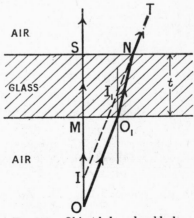

Fig. 301.   Object below glass block.

Suppose the normal at O_1 intersects IN at I_1. Then, since O_1I_1 is parallel to OI and IT is parallel to OO_1, OII_1O_1 is a parallelogram. Thus $OI = O_1I_1$. But OI is the displacement of the object O. Hence O_1I_1 is equal to the displacement. Since the apparent position of an object at O_1 is at I_1 (compare Fig. 300), we conclude that the *displacement OI of O is independent of the position of O below the glass*, and is given by

$$OI = t\left(1 - \frac{1}{\mu}\right), \text{ see p. 437.}$$

10. Measurement of Refractive Index by Apparent Depth Method

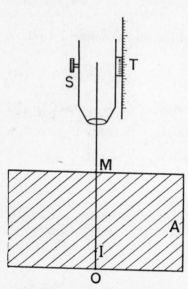

FIG. 302.   Refractive index by apparent depth.

The formula for the refractive index of a medium in terms of the real and apparent depths is the basis of a very accurate method of measuring refractive index. A *travelling microscope*, S (a microscope which can travel in a vertical direction and which has a fixed graduated scale T beside it) is focused on lycopodium particles at O on a sheet of white paper, and the reading on T is noted, Fig. 302. Suppose it is c cm. If the refractive index of glass is required, a glass block A is placed on the paper, and the microscope is raised until the particles are refocused at I. Suppose the reading on T is b cm. Some lycopodium particles are then sprinkled at M on the top of the glass block, and the microscope is raised until they are focused, when the reading on T is noted. Suppose it is a cm.

Then   real depth of O = OM = $(a - c)$ cm.
and   apparent depth = IM = $(a - b)$ cm.

$$\therefore \mu = \frac{\text{real depth}}{\text{apparent depth}} = \frac{a - c}{a - b}$$

The high accuracy of this determination of μ lies mainly in the fact that the objective of the microscope collects only those rays near to its axis, so that the object O, and its apparent position I, are seen by rays very close to the normal OM. The experiment thus fulfils the theoretical conditions assumed in the proof of the formula $\mu = \dfrac{\text{real depth}}{\text{apparent depth}}$ p. (436).

The refractive index of water can also be obtained by an apparent depth method. The block A is replaced by a dish, and the microscope is focused first on the bottom of the dish and then on lycopodium powder sprinkled on the surface of water poured into the dish. The apparent position of the bottom of the dish is also noted, and the refractive index of the water μ_w is calculated from the relation

$$\mu_w = \frac{\text{real depth of water}}{\text{apparent depth of water}}$$

General formula for real and apparent depth. So far we have considered the rays refracted from a medium like glass into air. As a more general case, suppose an object O is in a medium of refractive index μ_1 and the rays from it are refracted at M,N into a medium of refractive index μ_2, Fig. 303. The image of O to an observer in the latter medium is then at I.

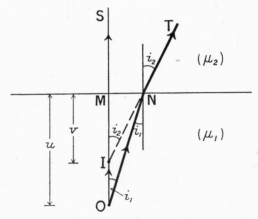

FIG. 303.   Relation between real and apparent depth.

Suppose i_1 is the angle of incidence at N, and i_2 is the angle of refraction as shown. Then, since "$\mu \sin i$" is a constant,

$$\mu_1 \sin i_1 = \mu_2 \sin i_2$$

Now angle MON $= i_1$, and angle MIN $= i_2$.

$$\therefore \quad \mu_1 \frac{MN}{ON} = \mu_2 \frac{MN}{IN}.$$

$$\therefore \quad \frac{\mu_1}{ON} = \frac{\mu_2}{IN} \quad . \quad . \quad . \quad . \quad . \quad (i)$$

If we consider rays very close to the normal, then IN $=$ IM $= v$, say, an ON $=$ OM $= u$, say. Substituting in (i),

$$\therefore \quad \frac{\mu_1}{u} = \frac{\mu_2}{v} \quad . \quad . \quad . \quad . \quad . \quad (ii)$$

This formula can easily be remembered, as the refractive index of a medium is divided by the corresponding distance of the object (or image) *in* that medium.

11. Total Internal Reflection. Critical Angle

If a ray AO in glass is incident at a small angle a on a glass-air plane boundary, observation shows that part of the incident light is reflected along OE in the glass, while the remainder of the light is refracted away from the normal at an angle β into the air. The reflected ray OE is weak, but the refracted ray OL is bright, Fig. 304 (i). This means that

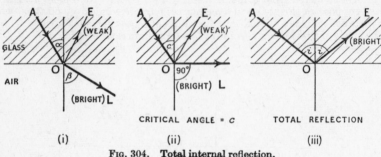

CRITICAL ANGLE = c TOTAL REFLECTION

(i)   (ii)   (iii)

FIG. 304. Total internal reflection.

most of the incident light energy is transmitted, and a little is reflected.

When the angle of incidence, a, in the glass is increased, the angle of emergence, β, is increased at the same time; and at some angle of incidence c in the glass the refracted ray OL travels along the glass-air boundary, making the angle of refraction of 90°, Fig. 304 (ii). The reflected ray OE is still weak in intensity, but as the angle of incidence in the glass is increased slightly the reflected ray suddenly becomes bright, and no refracted ray is then observed, Fig. 304 (iii). Since *all* the incident light energy is now reflected, **total reflection** is said to take place in the glass at O.

When the angle of refraction in air is 90°, a critical stage is reached at the point of incidence O, and the angle of incidence *in the glass* is accordingly known as the **critical angle** for glass and air, Fig. 304 (ii). Since "$\mu \sin i$" is a constant (p. 432), we have

$$\mu \sin c = 1 \times \sin 90°,$$

where μ is the refractive index of the glass. As $\sin 90° = 1$, then

$$\mu \sin c = 1,$$

or, $$\sin c = \frac{1}{\mu} \qquad . \qquad . \qquad . \qquad . \qquad (13)$$

Crown glass has a refractive index of about 1·51 for yellow light, and thus the critical angle for glass to air is given by $\sin c = 1/1·51 = 0·667$.

Consequently $c = 41 \cdot 5°$. Thus if the incident angle in the glass is greater than c, for example $45°$, total reflection occurs, Fig. 304 (iii). The critical angle between two media for blue light is less than for red light, since the refractive index for blue light is greater than that for red light (see p. 464).

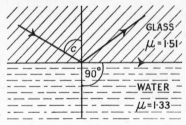

FIG. 305.   Critical angle for water and glass.

The phenomenon of total reflection may occur when light in glass ($\mu_g = 1 \cdot 51$, say) is incident on a boundary with water ($\mu_w = 1 \cdot 33$). Applying "$\mu \sin i$ is a constant" to the critical case, Fig. 305, we have

$$\mu_g \sin c = \mu_w \sin 90°,$$

where c is the critical angle. As $\sin 90° = 1$

$$\mu_g \sin c = \mu_w$$

$$\therefore \qquad \sin c = \frac{\mu_w}{\mu_g} = \frac{1 \cdot 33}{1 \cdot 51} = 0 \cdot 889$$

$$\therefore \qquad c = 63°$$

Thus if the angle of incidence in the glass exceeds $63°$, total internal reflection occurs.

It should be carefully noted that the phenomenon of total internal reflection can only occur when light travels from one medium to another which has a *smaller* refractive index, i.e., which is optically less dense. The phenomenon cannot occur when light travels from one medium to another optically denser, for example from air to glass, or from water to glass, as a refracted ray is then always obtained.

SOME APPLICATIONS OF TOTAL INTERNAL REFLECTION

1. *Reflecting prisms* are pieces of glass of a special shape which are used in prism binoculars and in certain accurate ranging instruments such as submarine periscopes. These prisms, discussed on p. 460, act as reflectors of light by total internal reflection.

2. *The mirage* is a phenomenon due to total reflection. In the desert the air is progressively hotter towards the sand, and hence the density of the air decreases in the direction *bcd*, Fig. 306 (i). A downward ray OA from a tree or the sky is thus refracted more and more away from the normal; but at some layer of air c, a critical angle is reached, and the ray begins to travel in an upward direction along *cg*. A distant observer P thus sees the object O at I, and hence an image of a palm tree, for example, is seen below the actual position of the tree. As an image of part of the sky is also formed by total reflection round the

image of the tree, the whole appearance is similar to that of a pool of water in which the tree is reflected.

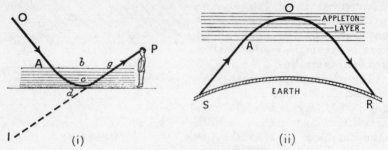

Fig. 306.   Examples of total reflection.

3. *Total reflection of radio waves.* A radio wave is an example of an *electro-magnetic wave* because it comprises electric and magnetic forces. Light waves also are electro-magnetic waves (p. 722). Light waves and radio waves are therefore the same in nature, and a close analogy can be made between the refraction of light and the refraction of a radio wave when the latter enters a medium containing electric particles.

In particular, the phenomenon of total reflection occurs when radio waves travel from one place, S, on the earth, for example England, to another place, R, on the other side of the earth, for example America, Fig. 306 (ii). A layer of considerable density of electrons exists many miles above the earth (at night this is the *Appleton layer*), and when a radio wave SA from a transmitter is sent skyward it is refracted away from the normal on entering the electron layer. At some height, corresponding to O, a critical angle is reached, and the wave then begins to be refracted downward. After emerging from the electron layer it returns to R on the earth, where its presence can be detected by a radio receiver.

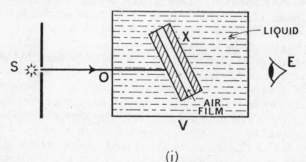

(i)

Fig. 307 (i)   Air-cell method.

12. Measurement of Refractive Index of a Liquid by an Air-cell Method

The phenomenon of total internal reflection is utilised in many methods of measuring refractive index. Fig. 307 (i) illustrates how the refractive index of a liquid can be determined. Two thin plane-parallel glass plates, such as microscope slides, are cemented together so as to contain a thin film of air of constant thickness between them, thus forming an air-cell, X. The liquid whose refractive index is required is placed in a glass vessel V having thin plane-parallel sides, and X is placed in the liquid. A bright source of light, S, provides rays which are incident on one side of X in a constant direction SO, and the light through X is observed by a person on the other side at E.

When the light is incident normally on the sides of X, the light passes straight through X to E. When X is rotated slightly about a vertical axis, light is still observed; but as X is rotated further, the light is suddenly cut off from E, and hence no light now passes through X, Fig. 307 (i).

Fig. 307 (ii) illustrates the behaviour of the light when this happens. The ray SO is refracted along OB in the glass, but at B *total internal reflection begins.* Suppose i_1 is the angle of incidence in the liquid, i_2

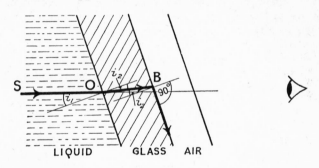

(ii)

FIG. 307 (ii).   Air-cell theory.

is the angle of incidence in the glass, and μ, μ_g are the corresponding refractive indices. Since the boundaries of the media are parallel we can apply the relation "$\mu \sin i$ is a constant", and hence

$$\mu \sin i_1 = \mu_g \sin i_2 = 1 \times \sin 90° \qquad . \qquad . \qquad . \qquad (i)$$

the last product corresponding to the case of refraction in the air-film.

$$\therefore \qquad \mu \sin i_1 = 1 \times \sin 90° = 1 \times 1 = 1$$

$$\therefore \quad \mu = \frac{1}{\sin i_1} \qquad . \qquad . \qquad . \qquad . \qquad . \qquad (14)$$

It should now be carefully noted that i_1 is the angle of incidence in the *liquid* medium, and is thus determined by measuring the rotation of X from its position when normal to SO to the position when the light is cut off. In practice, it is better to rotate X in opposite directions and determine the angle θ between the *two* positions for the extinction of the light. The angle i_1 is then half the angle θ, and hence $\mu = 1/\sin\dfrac{\theta}{2}$.

From equations (i) and (14), it will be noted that i_1 is the critical angle between the liquid and air, and i_2 is the critical angle between the glass and air. We cannot measure i_2, however, as we can i_1, and hence the method provides the refractive index of the *liquid*.

The source of light, S, in the experiment should be a monochromatic source, i.e., it should provide light of one colour, for example yellow light. The extinction of the light is then sharp. If white light is used, the colours in its spectrum are cut off at slightly different angles of incidence, since refractive index depends upon the colour of the light (p. 464). The extinction of the light is then gradual and ill-defined.

13. Pulfrich Refractometer

A *refractometer* is an instrument which measures refractive index by making use of total internal reflection. PULFRICH designed a refractometer enabling the refractive index of a liquid to be easily obtained, which consists of a block of glass G with a polished and vertical face. On top of G is cemented a circular glass tube V, Fig. 308. The liquid L is placed in V, and a convergent beam of monochromatic light is

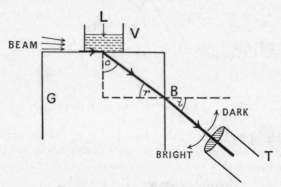

FIG. 308.   Pulfrich refractometer.

directed so that the liquid-glass interface is illuminated. On observing the light refracted through G by a telescope T, a light and dark field of view are seen.

The boundary between the light and dark fields corresponds to the ray which is incident just horizontally on the liquid-glass boundary, as shown in Fig. 308. If c is the angle of refraction in the glass, it follows that

$$\mu \sin 90° = \mu_g \sin c \qquad \qquad \text{(i)}$$

where μ, μ_g are the refractive indices of the liquid and glass respectively
For refraction at B,

$$\mu_g \sin r = \sin i \qquad \qquad \text{(ii)}$$

Also, $\qquad \qquad c + r = 90° \qquad \qquad \text{(iii)}$

From (i), $\sin c = \mu/\mu_g$. Now from (iii), $\sin r = \sin (90° - c) = \cos c$. Substituting in (ii), we have $\mu_g \cos c = \sin i$, or $\cos c = \sin i/\mu_g$.

But $\qquad \qquad \sin^2 c + \cos^2 c = 1$

$$\therefore \qquad \frac{\mu^2}{\mu_g^2} + \frac{\sin^2 i}{\mu_g^2} = 1$$

$$\therefore \qquad \mu^2 + \sin^2 i = \mu_g^2$$

$$\therefore \quad \mu = \sqrt{\mu_g^2 - \sin^2 i}$$

Thus if i is measured and $\mu_g = 1·51$, μ can be calculated. In practice, tables are supplied giving the refractive index in terms of i, and another block is used in place of G for liquids of higher μ than 1·51.

Abbé refractometer. Abbé designed a refractometer for measuring the refractive index of liquids whose principle is illustrated in Fig. 309. Two similar prisms X, Y are placed on a table A, the prism X being hinged at H

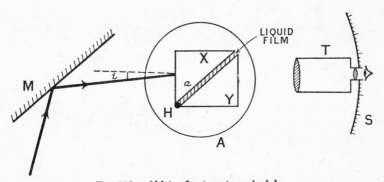

Fig. 309.   Abbé refractometer principle.

so that it could be swung away from Y. A drop of the liquid is placed on the surface a, which is matt, and the prisms are placed together so that the liquid is squeezed into a thin film between them. Light from a suitable source is directed towards the prisms by means of a mirror M, where it strikes the surface a and is scattered by the matt surface into the liquid film. The emergent rays are collected in a telescope T directed towards the prisms, and the field of view is divided into a dark and bright portion. The table A is then turned until the dividing line between the dark and bright fields is on the crosswires of the telescope, which is fixed. The reading on the scale S, which is attached to, and moves with, the table, gives the refractive index of the liquid directly, as explained below.

Theory. The dividing line, BQ, between the bright and dark fields corresponds to the case of the ray DA, incident in the liquid L at grazing incidence on the prism Y, Fig. 310. The refracted ray AB in the prism then

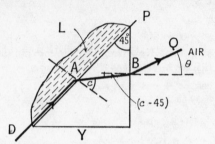

Fig. 310. Theory of refractometer.

makes the critical angle c with the normal at A, where $\mu \sin 90° = \mu_g \sin c$, μ and μ_g being the respective refractive indices of the liquid and the glass.

$$\therefore \quad \mu = \mu_g \sin c \quad . \quad . \quad . \quad . \quad \text{(i)}$$

For simplicity, suppose that Y is a right-angled isosceles prism, so that the angle P of the prism is 45°. The angle of incidence at B in the glass is then $(c - 45°)$, by considering the geometry of triangle PAB, and hence for refraction at B we have

$$\mu_g \sin (c - 45°) = \sin \theta \quad . \quad . \quad . \quad . \quad \text{(ii)}$$

where θ is the angle with the normal at B made by the emerging ray BQ. By eliminating c from (i) and (ii), we obtain finally

$$\mu = \sin 45° \, (\mu_g{}^2 - \sin^2\theta)^{\frac{1}{2}} + \cos 45° \sin \theta$$

$$= \frac{1}{\sqrt{2}} [(\mu_g{}^2 - \sin^2\theta)^{\frac{1}{2}} + \sin \theta]$$

since $\sin 45° = 1/\sqrt{2} = \cos 45°$. Thus knowing μ_g and θ, the refractive index of the liquid, μ can be evaluated. The scale S, Fig. 309, which gives θ, can thus be calibrated in terms of μ.

EXAMPLES

1. Describe a method, based on grazing incidence or total internal reflection, for finding the refractive index of water for the yellow light emitted by a sodium flame.

The refractive index of carbon bisulphide for red light is 1·634 and the difference between the critical angles for red and blue light at a carbon bisulphide–air interface is 0° 56′. What is the refractive index of carbon bisulphide for blue light? (*N.*)

First part. See air-cell method, p. 443.

Second part. Suppose μ_r and c_r are the refractive index and critical angle of carbon bisulphide for red light.

Then
$$\sin c_r = \frac{1}{\mu_r} = \frac{1}{1 \cdot 634} = 0 \cdot 6119$$

$$\therefore \quad c_r = 37° \ 44'$$

The critical angle, c_b, for blue light is less than that for red light.

$$\therefore \quad c_b = 37° \ 44' - 0° \ 56' = 36° \ 48'$$

The refractive index for blue light, μ_b, $= \dfrac{1}{\sin c_b}$

$$\therefore \quad \mu_b = \frac{1}{\sin 36° \ 48'} = 1 \cdot 669$$

2. Find an expression for the distance through which an object appears to be displaced towards the eye when a plate of glass of thickness t and refractive index μ is interposed.

A tank contains a slab of glass 8 cm. thick and of refractive index 1·6. Above this is a depth of 4·5 cm. of a liquid of refractive index 1·5 and upon this floats 6 cm. of water ($\mu = 4/3$). To an observer looking from above, what is the apparent position of a mark on the bottom of the tank? (*O. & C.*)

First part. See text.

Second part. Suppose O is the mark at the bottom of the tank, Fig. 311. Then since the boundaries of the media are parallel, the total displacement of O is the sum of the displacements due to each media.

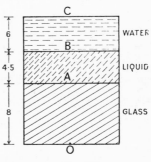

FIG. 311.

For glass, displacement, d, $= t\left(1 - \dfrac{1}{\mu}\right) = 8\left(1 - \dfrac{1}{1 \cdot 6}\right) = 3$ cm.

For liquid, $\qquad d = t\left(1 - \dfrac{1}{\mu}\right) = 4 \cdot 5\left(1 - \dfrac{1}{1 \cdot 5}\right) = 1 \cdot 5$ cm.

For water, $\qquad\qquad\qquad d = 6\left(1 - \dfrac{1}{4/3}\right) = 1 \cdot 5$ cm.

$$\therefore \text{ total displacement} = 3 + 1 \cdot 5 + 1 \cdot 5 = 6 \text{ cm.}$$

$$\therefore \text{ apparent position of O is 6 cm. from bottom.}$$

3. A small object is placed on the principal axis of a concave spherical mirror of radius 20 cm. at a distance of 30 cm. By how much will the position and size of the image alter when a parallel-sided slab of glass, of thickness 6 cm. and refractive index 1·5, is introduced between the centre of curvature and the object? The parallel sides are perpendicular to the principal axis. Prove any formula used. (*N.*)

Suppose O is the position of the object before the glass is placed in position, Fig. 312. The image position is given by $\dfrac{1}{v} + \dfrac{1}{u} = \dfrac{2}{r}$,

$$\therefore \quad \frac{1}{v} + \frac{1}{30} = \frac{2}{20}$$

Solving, $\quad\quad\quad\quad\quad\quad v = 15 \text{ cm.}$

The magnification, m, $= \dfrac{v}{u} = \dfrac{15}{30} = 0.5$

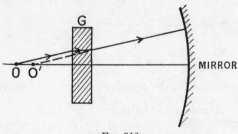

FIG. 312.

When the glass slab G of thickness, t, 6 cm. is inserted, the rays from O appear to come from a point O' whose displacement from O is $t\left(1 - \dfrac{1}{\mu}\right)$, where μ is the glass refractive index. See p. 437. The displacement is thus $6\left(1 - \dfrac{1}{1.5}\right) = 2$ cm. The distance of O' from the mirror is therefore $(30 - 2)$, or 28 cm. Applying the equation $\dfrac{1}{v} + \dfrac{1}{u} = \dfrac{2}{r}$, we find $v = +15\frac{5}{9}$ cm. The image position changes by $(15\frac{5}{9} - 15)$ or $\frac{5}{9}$ cm. The magnification becomes $15\frac{5}{9} \div 28$, or 0.52.

EXERCISES XX

1. A ray of light is incident at 60° in air on an air-glass plane surface. Find the angle of refraction in the glass by calculation and by drawing (μ for glass = 1.5).

2. A ray of light is incident in water at an angle of 30° on a water-air plane surface. Find the angle of refraction in the air by calculation and by drawing (μ for water = 4/3).

3. A ray of light is incident in water at an angle of (i) 30°, (ii) 70° on a water-glass plane surface. Calculate the angle of refraction in the glass in each case. ($_a\mu_g = 1.5$, $_a\mu_w = 1.33$.)

4. (a) Describe the apparent depth method of finding the refractive index of glass, and prove the formula used. (b) What is the apparent position of an object below a rectangular block of glass 6 cm. thick if a layer of water 4 cm. thick is on top of the glass (refractive index of glass and water = $1\frac{1}{2}$ and $1\frac{1}{3}$ respectively)?

5. Describe and explain a method of measuring approximately the refractive index of a small quantity of liquid.

6. Calculate the critical angle for (i) an air-glass surface, (ii) an air-water surface, (iii) a water-glass surface; draw diagrams in each case illustrating the total reflection of a ray incident on the surface. ($_a\mu_g$ = 1·5, $_a\mu_W$ = 1·33.)

7. Explain what happens in general when a ray of light strikes the surface separating transparent media such as water and glass. Explain the circumstances in which total reflection occurs and show how the critical angle is related to the refractive index.

Describe a method for determining the refractive index of a medium by means of critical reflection. (*L*.)

8. Define *refractive index* of one medium with respect to another and show how it is related to the values of the velocity of light in the two media.

Describe a method of finding the refractive index of water for sodium light, deducing any formula required in the reduction of the observations. (*N*.)

9. Explain carefully why the apparent depth of the water in a tank changes with the position of the observer.

A microscope is focused on a scratch on the bottom of a beaker. Turpentine is poured into the beaker to a depth of 4 cm., and it is found necessary to raise the microscope through a vertical distance of 1·28 cm. to bring the scratch again into focus. Find the refractive index of the turpentine. (*C*.)

10. What is meant by *total reflection* and *critical angle*? Describe two methods of measuring the refractive index of a material by determining the critical angle, one of which is suitable for a solid substance and the other for a liquid. (*L*.)

11. (*a*) State the conditions under which total reflection occurs. Show that the phenomenon will occur in the case of light entering normally one face of an isosceles right prism of glass, but not in the case when light enters similarly a similar hollow prism full of water. (*b*) A concave mirror of small aperture and focal length 8 cm. lies on a bench and a pin is moved vertically above it. At what point will image and object coincide if the mirror is filled with water of refractive index 4/3? (*N*.)

12. State the laws of refraction, and define *refractive index*.

Describe an accurate method of determining the refractive index of ɑ transparent liquid for sodium light. Give the theory of the method, and derive any formula you require. Discuss the effect of substituting white light for sodium light in your experiment. (*W*.)

13. Describe an experiment for finding the refractive index of a liquid by measuring its apparent depth.

A vessel of depth 2*d* cm. is half filled with a liquid of refractive index μ_1, and the upper half is occupied by a liquid of refractive index μ_2. Show that the apparent depth of the vessel, viewed perpendicularly, is $d\left(\dfrac{1}{\mu_1} + \dfrac{1}{\mu_2}\right)$.

(*L*.)

14. The base of a cube of glass of refractive index μ_1 is in contact with the surface of a liquid of refractive index μ_2. Light incident on one vertical face of the cube is reflected internally from the base and emerges again from the opposite vertical face in a direction making an angle θ with its normal. Assuming that $\mu_1 > \mu_2$, show that the light has just been totally reflected internally if $\mu_2 = \sqrt{(\mu_1{}^2 - \sin^2 \theta)}$.

Describe how the above principle may be used to measure the refractive index of a small quantity of liquid. (*N.*)

15. Explain the meaning of critical angle and total internal reflection. Describe fully (*a*) one natural phenomenon due to total internal reflection, (*b*) one practical application of it. Light from a luminous point on the lower face of a rectangular glass slab, 2·0 cm. thick, strikes the upper face and the totally reflected rays outline a circle of 3·2 cm. radius on the lower face. What is the refractive index of the glass? (*N.*)

16. What is meant by *index of refraction, total reflection*? State the conditions necessary for total reflection to occur.

Two parallel plates of glass, separated by a layer of air, are immersed vertically in a rectangular trough of liquid. Describe and explain how this apparatus may be used to determine the refractive index of the liquid. (*C.*)

17. Explain the meaning of *critical angle*, and describe how you would measure the critical angle for a water-air boundary.

ABCD is the plan of a glass cube. A horizontal beam of light enters the face AB at grazing incidence. Show that the angle θ which any rays emerging from BC would make with the normal to BC is given by $\sin \theta = \cot a$, where a is the critical angle. What is the greatest value that the refractive index of glass may have if any of the light is to emerge from BC? (*N.*)

18. State the *laws of refraction of light*. Explain how you would measure the refractive index of a transparent liquid available only in *small* quantity, i.e., less than 0·5 c.c.

A ray of light is refracted through a sphere, whose material has a refractive index μ, in such a way that it passes through the extremities of two radii which make an angle a with each other. Prove that if γ is the deviation of the ray caused by its passage through the sphere

$$\cos \tfrac{1}{2} (a - \gamma) = \mu \cos \tfrac{1}{2}a. \qquad (L.)$$

19. Explain what is meant by the terms *critical angle* and *total reflection*. Describe an accurate method of determining the critical angle for a liquid, indicating how you would calculate the refractive index from your measurements.

A man stands at the edge of the deep end of a swimming bath, the floor of which is covered with square tiles. If the water is clear and undisturbed, explain carefully how the floor of the bath appears to him. (*O. & C.*)

CHAPTER XXI

REFRACTION THROUGH PRISMS

In Light, a *prism* is a transparent object usually made of glass which has two plane surfaces, XDEY, XDFZ, inclined to each other, Fig. 313. Prisms are used in many optical instruments, for example prism binoculars, and they are also utilised for separating the colours of the light emitted by glowing objects, which affords an accurate knowledge of their chemical composition. A prism of glass enables the refractive index of this material to be measured very accurately.

The angle between the inclined plane surfaces XDFZ, XDEY is known as the *angle of the prism*, or the *refracting angle*, the line of

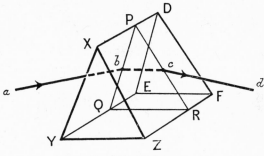

FIG. 313.   **Prism.**

intersection XD of the planes is known as the *refracting edge*, and any plane in the prism perpendicular to XD, such as PQR, is known as a *principal section* of the prism. A ray of light *ab*, incident on the prism at *b* in a direction perpendicular to XD, is refracted towards the normal along *bc* when it enters the prism, and is refracted away from the normal along *cd* when it emerges into the air. From the law of refraction (p. 429), the rays *ab*, *bc*, *cd* all lie in the same plane, which is PQR in this case. If the incident ray is directed towards the refracting angle, as in Fig. 313, the light is always deviated by the prism towards its base.

1. Refraction Through a Prism

Consider a ray HM incident in air on a prism of refracting angle *A*, and suppose the ray lies in the principal section PQR, Fig. 314. Then, if

i_1, r_1 and i_2, r_2 are the angles of incidence and refraction at M, N as shown, and μ is the prism refractive index,

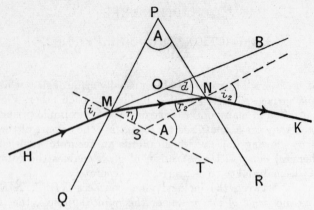

FIG. 314.   Refraction through prism.

$$\sin i_1 = \mu \sin r_1 \quad . \qquad . \qquad . \qquad . \qquad . \qquad . \qquad \text{(i)}$$
$$\sin i_2 = \mu \sin r_2 \quad . \qquad . \qquad . \qquad . \qquad . \qquad . \qquad \text{(ii)}$$

Further, as MS and NS are normals to PM and PN respectively, angle MPN + angle MSN = 180°, considering the quadrilateral PMSN. But angle NST + angle MSN = 180°.

$$\therefore \quad \text{angle NST} = \text{angle MPN} = A$$
$$\therefore \quad A = r_1 + r_2 \qquad . \qquad . \qquad . \qquad . \qquad \text{(iii)}$$

as angle NST is the exterior angle of triangle MSN.

In the following sections, we shall see that the *angle of deviation*, *d*, of the light, caused by the prism, is utilised considerably. The angle of deviation at M = angle OMN = $i_1 - r_1$; the angle of deviation at N = angle MNO = $i_2 - r_2$. Since the deviations at M, N are in the same direction, the total deviation, *d* (angle BOK), is given by

$$d = (i_1 - r_1) + (i_2 - r_2) \qquad . \qquad . \qquad . \qquad . \qquad \text{(iv)}$$

Equations (i) − (iv) are the general relations which hold for refraction through a prism. In deriving them, it should be noted that the geometrical form of the prism base plays no part.

2. Minimum Deviation

The angle of deviation, *d*, of the incident ray HM is the angle BOK in Fig. 314. The variation of *d* with the angle of incidence, *i*, can be obtained experimentally by placing the prism on paper on a drawing board and using a ray AO from a ray-box (or two pins) as the incident ray, Fig. 315 (i). When the direction AO is kept constant and the drawing board is turned so that the ray is always incident at O on the prism, the angle of incidence i is varied; the corresponding

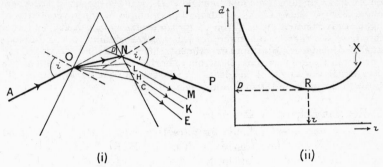

(i)   (ii)

FIG. 315.   Minimum deviation.

emergent rays CE, HK, LM, NP can be traced on the paper. Experiment shows that as the angle of incidence i is increased from zero the deviation d decreases continuously to some value D, and then increases as i is increased further. A *minimum deviation*, corresponding to the emergent ray NP, is thus obtained. A graph of d plotted against i has the appearance of the curve X, which has a minimum value at R, Fig. 315 (ii).

Experiment and theory show that *the minimum deviation, D, of the light occurs when the ray passes symmetrically through the prism.* Suppose this corresponds to the case of the ray AONP in Fig. 315 (i). Then the corresponding incident angle, i, is equal to the angle of emergence, i_1, into the air at N for this special case. See also Fig. 317.

A proof of symmetrical passage of ray at minimum deviation. Experiment shows that minimum deviation is obtained at *one* particular angle of incidence. On this assumption it is possible to prove by a *reductio ad absurdum* method that the angle of incidence is equal to the angle of

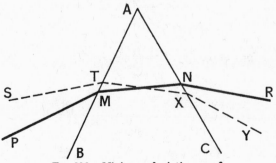

FIG. 316.   Minimum deviation proof.

emergence in this case. Thus suppose that minimum deviation is obtained with a ray PMNR when these angles are *not* equal, so that angle PMB is not equal to angle RNC, Fig. 316. It then follows that a ray YX, incident on AC at an angle CXY equal to angle PMB, will emerge along TS, where angle BTS = angle CNR; and from the principle of the reversibility of light, a ray incident along ST on the prism emerges along XY. We therefore have *two* cases of minimum deviation, corresponding to two different angles of incidence. But, from experiment, this is impossible. Consequently our initial assumption must be wrong, and hence the angle of emergence *does* equal the angle of incidence. Thus the ray passes symmetrically through the prism in the minimum deviation case.

3. Relation Between A, D, and μ

A very convenient formula for refractive index, μ, can be obtained in the minimum deviation case. The ray PQRS then passes symmetrically through the prism, and the angles made with the normal in the air and in the glass at Q, R respectively are equal, Fig. 317.

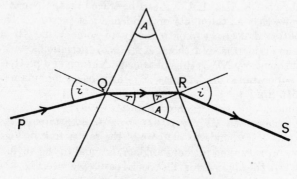

Fig. 317. Formula for μ of prism.

Suppose the angles are denoted by i, r, as shown. Then, as explained on p. 453,

$$i - r + i - r = D \qquad \qquad \text{(i)}$$

and
$$r + r = A \qquad \qquad \text{(ii)}$$

From (ii),
$$r = \frac{A}{2}$$

Substituting for r in (i),
$$2i = A + D$$

$$\therefore \quad i = \frac{A + D}{2}$$

$$\therefore \quad \mu = \frac{\sin i}{\sin r} = \frac{\sin \dfrac{A + D}{2}}{\sin \dfrac{A}{2}} \qquad . \quad . \quad (15)$$

4. The Spectrometer

The spectrometer is an optical instrument which is mainly used to study the light from different sources. As we shall see later, it can be used to measure accurately the refractive index of glass in the form of a prism. The instrument consists essentially of a *collimator*, C, a *telescope*, T, and a *table*, R, on which a prism B can be placed. The lenses in C, T are achromatic lenses (p. 527). The collimator is fixed, but the table and the telescope can be rotated round a circular scale graduated in half-degrees (not shown) which has a common vertical axis with the table, Fig. 318. A vernier is also provided for this scale. The *source of light*, S, used in the experiment is placed in front of a narrow slit at one end of the collimator, so that the prism is illuminated by light from S.

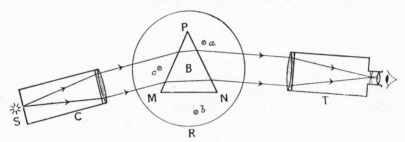

Fig. 318.   Spectrometer.

Before the spectrometer can be used, however, three adjustments must be made: (1) The collimator C must be adjusted so that parallel light emerges from it; (2) the telescope T must be adjusted so that parallel rays entering it are brought to a focus at cross-wires near its eye-piece; (3) the refracting edge of the prism must be parallel to the axis of rotation of the telescope, i.e., the table must be "levelled".

5. Adjustments of Spectrometer

The telescope adjustment is made by first moving its eye-piece until the cross-wires are distinctly seen, and then sighting the telescope on to a *distant* object through an open window. The length of the telescope is now altered by a screw arrangement until the object is clearly seen at the same place as the cross-wires, so that parallel rays now entering the telescope are brought to a focus at the cross-wires.

The collimator adjustment. With the prism removed from the table, the telescope is now turned to face the collimator, C, and the slit in C is illuminated by a sodium flame which provides yellow light. The edges of the slit are usually blurred, showing that the light emerging from the lens of C is not a parallel beam. The position of the slit is now adjusted by moving the tube in C, to which the slit is attached, until the edges of the latter are sharp.

"Levelling" the table. If the rectangular slit is not in the centre of the field of view when the prism is placed on the table, the refracting edge of the prism is not parallel to the axis of rotation of the telescope. The table must then be adjusted, or "levelled", by means of the screws *a*, *b*, *c* beneath it. One method of procedure consists of placing the prism on the table with one face MN approximately perpendicular to the line joining two screws *a*, *b*, as shown in Fig. 318. The table is turned until MN is illuminated by the light from C, and the telescope T is then moved to receive the light reflected from MN. The screw *b* is then adjusted until the slit appears in the centre of the field of view. With C and T fixed, the table is now rotated until the slit is seen by reflection at the face NP of the prism, and the screw *c* is then adjusted until the slit is again in the middle of the field of view. The screw *c* moves MN in its own plane, and hence the movement of *c* will not upset the adjustment of MN in the perpendicular plane.

6. Measurement of the Angle, A, of a Prism

The angle of a prism can be measured very accurately by a spectrometer. The refracting edge, P, of the prism is turned so as to face the collimator lens, which then illuminates the two surfaces containing

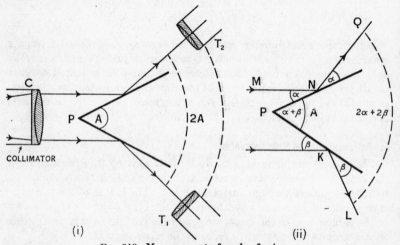

Fig. 319. Measurement of angle of prism.

the refracting angle *A* with parallel light, Fig. 319 (i). An image of the collimator slit is hence observed with the telescope in positions T_1, T_2, corresponding to reflection of light at the respective faces of the prism. It is shown below that the angle of rotation of the telescope from T_1 to T_2 is equal to 2*A*, and hence the angle of the prism, *A*, can be obtained.

Proof. Suppose the incident ray MN makes a glancing angle α with one face of the prism, and a parallel ray at K makes a glancing angle β with the other face, Fig. 319 (ii). The reflected ray NQ then makes a glancing angle α with the prism surface, and hence the deviation of MN is 2α (see p. 402). Similarly, the deviation by reflection at K is 2β. Thus the reflected rays QN, LK are inclined at an angle equal to $2\alpha + 2\beta$, corresponding to the angle of rotation of the telescope from T_1 to T_2. But the angle, A, of the prism $= \alpha + \beta$, as can be seen by drawing a line through P parallel to MN, and using alternate angles. Hence the rotation of the telescope $= 2\alpha + 2\beta = 2A$.

7. Measurement of the Minimum Deviation, D

In order to measure the minimum deviation, D, caused by refraction through the prism, the latter is placed with its refracting angle A pointing *away* from the collimator, as shown in Fig. 320 (i). The telescope is then turned until an image of the slit is obtained on the cross-wires, corresponding to the position T_1. The table is now slowly rotated so that the angle of incidence on the left side of the prism decreases, and the image of the slit is kept on the cross-wires by moving the telescope at the same time. The image of the slit, and the telescope, then slowly

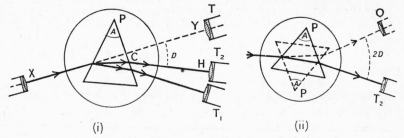

(i)   (ii)

FIG. 320. Measurement of minimum deviation.

approach the fixed line XY. But at one position, corresponding to T_2, the image of the slit begins to move *away* from XY. If the table is now turned in the opposite direction the image of the slit again moves back when the telescope reaches the position T_2. The angle between the emergent ray CH and the line XY is hence the smallest angle of deviation caused by the prism, and is thus equal to D.

The minimum deviation is obtained by finding the angle between the positions of the telescope (i) at T_2, (ii) at T; the prism is removed in the latter case so as to view the slit directly. Alternatively, the experiment to find the minimum deviation is repeated with the refracting angle pointing the opposite way, the prism being represented by dotted lines in this case, Fig. 320 (ii). If the position of the telescope for minimum deviation is now O, it can be seen that the angle between the position O and the other minimum deviation position T_2 is $2D$. The value of D is thus easily calculated.

8. The Refractive Index of the Prism Material

The refractive index, μ, of the material of the prism can be easily calculated once A and D have beeen determined, since, from p. 454,

$$\mu = \sin \frac{A + D}{2} \bigg/ \sin \frac{A}{2}.$$

In an experiment of this nature, the angle A, of a glass prism was found to be 59° 52′, and the minimum deviation, D, was 40° 30′. Thus

$$\mu = \sin \frac{59° \, 52' + 40° \, 30'}{2} \bigg/ \sin \frac{59° \, 52'}{2}$$

$$= \sin 50° \, 11' / \sin 29° \, 56'$$

$$= 1{\cdot}539$$

The spectrometer prism method of measuring refractive index is capable of providing an accuracy of one part in a thousand. The refractive index of a liquid can also be found by this method, using a hollow glass prism made from thin parallel sided glass strips.

9. Grazing Incidence for a Prism

We shall now leave any further considerations of minimum deviation, and shall consider briefly other special cases of refraction through a prism.

When the surface PQ of a prism is illuminated by a source of yellow light placed near Q, the field of view seen through the other surface PR is divided into a bright and dark portion, Fig. 321. If NM is the emergent ray corresponding to the incident ray QH which just grazes the prism surface, the dark portion lies above NM and the bright portion exists below NM. The boundary of the light and dark portions is thus NM.

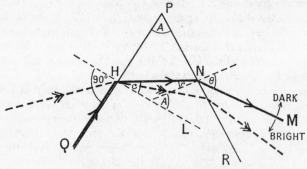

Fig. 321.   Grazing incidence.

Since the angle of incidence of QH is 90°, angle NHL is equal to c, the critical angle for the glass of the prism. From Fig. 321, it follows that $A = c + r$, and hence

$$r = A - c \qquad . \qquad . \qquad . \qquad . \qquad \text{(i)}$$

Further, for refraction at **N**,

$$\sin \theta = \mu \sin r$$

$$\therefore \sin \theta = \mu \sin (A - c) = \mu (\sin A \cos c - \cos A \sin c) . \qquad \text{(ii)}$$

But $\sin c = \dfrac{1}{\mu}$, i.e., $\cos c = \sqrt{1 - \sin^2 c} = \sqrt{1 - \dfrac{1}{\mu^2}} = \dfrac{1}{\mu}\sqrt{\mu^2 - 1}.$

Substituting in (ii) and simplifying, we obtain finally

$$\mu = \sqrt{1 + \left(\frac{\cos A + \sin \theta}{\sin A} \right)^2}$$

Thus if A and θ are measured, the refractive index of the prism material can be calculated.

10. Grazing Incidence and Grazing Emergence

If a ray BM is at grazing incidence on the face of a prism, and the angle A of the prism is increased, a calculation shows that the refracted ray MN in the glass will make a bigger and bigger angle of incidence on the other face PR, Fig. 322. This is left as an exercise for the reader. At a certain value of A, MN will make the critical angle, c, with the normal at N, and the emergent ray NR will then graze the surface PR, as shown

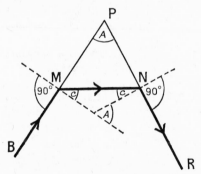

Fig. 322.   Maximum angle of prism.

in Fig. 322. As A is increased further, the rays in the glass strike PR at angles of incidence greater than c, and hence no emergent rays are obtained. Thus Fig. 322 illustrates the largest angle of a prism for which emergent rays are obtained, and this is known as the *limiting angle* of the prism. It can be seen from the simple geometry of Fig. 322 that $A =$

$c + c$ in this special case, and hence *the limiting angle of a prism is twice the critical angle.* For crown glass of $\mu = 1 \cdot 51$ the critical angle c is 41° 30', and hence transmission of light through a prism of crown glass is impossible if the angle of the prism exceeds 83°.

11. Total Reflecting Prisms

When a plane mirror silvered on the back is used as a reflector, multiple images are obtained (p. 433). This disadvantage is overcome by using right-angled isosceles prisms as reflectors of light in optical instruments such as submarine periscopes (see p. 557).

Consider a ray OQ incident normally on the face of AC of such a prism. Fig. 323 (i). The ray is undeviated, and is therefore incident at P in the glass at an angle of 45° to the normal at P. If the prism is made of

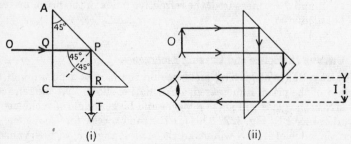

Fig. 323. Images in prisms.

crown glass its critical angle is 41° 30'. Hence the incident angle, 45°, in the glass is greater than the critical angle, and consequently the light is *totally* reflected in the glass at P. A bright beam of light thus emerges from the prism along RT, and since the angle of reflection at P is equal to the incident angle, RT is perpendicular to OQ. The prism thus deviates the light through 90°. If the prism is positioned as shown in Fig. 323 (ii), an inverted bright virtual image I of the object O is seen by total reflection at the two surfaces of the prism.

There is no loss of brightness when total internal reflection occurs at a surface, whereas the loss may be as much as 10 per cent or more in reflection at a silver surface.

EXAMPLES

1. Describe a good method of measuring the refractive index of a substance such as glass and give the theory of the method. A glass prism of angle 72° and index of refraction 1·66 is immersed in a liquid of refractive index 1·33. What is the angle of minimum deviation for a parallel beam of light passing through the prism? (*L.*)

First part. Spectrometer can be used, p. 458.

Second part.

$$\mu = \frac{\sin\left(\dfrac{A + D}{2}\right)}{\sin\dfrac{A}{2}}$$

where μ is the *relative refractive index* of glass with respect to the liquid

But

$$\mu = \frac{1\cdot66}{1\cdot33}$$

$\therefore$

$$\frac{1\cdot66}{1\cdot33} = \frac{\sin\left(\dfrac{72° + D}{2}\right)}{\sin\dfrac{72°}{2}} = \frac{\sin\left(\dfrac{72° + D}{2}\right)}{\sin 36°}$$

$\therefore \quad \sin\left(\dfrac{72° + D}{2}\right) = \dfrac{1\cdot66}{1\cdot33}\sin 36° = 0\cdot7335$

$\therefore \quad \dfrac{72° + D}{2} = 47° \ 11'$

$\therefore D = 22° \ 22'$

2. How would you measure the angle of minimum deviation of a prism? (*a*) Show that the ray of light which enters the first face of a prism at grazing incidence is least likely to suffer total internal reflection at the other face. (*b*) Find the least value of the refracting angle of a prism made of glass of refractive index 7/4 so that no rays incident on one of the faces containing this angle can emerge from the other. (*N.*)

First part. See text.

Second part. (*a*) Suppose PM is a ray which enters the first face of the prism at grazing incidence, i.e., at an angle of incidence of 90°, Fig. 324. The refracted ray MQ then makes an angle of refraction *c*, where *c* is the

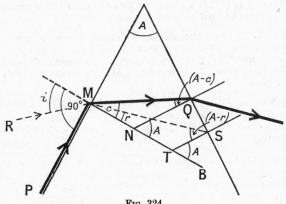

Fig. 324.

critical angle. Suppose QN is the normal at Q on the other face of the prism. Then since angle BNQ = A, where A is the angle of the prism, the angle of refraction MQN at Q = $A - c$, from the exterior angle property of triangle MQN. Similarly, if RM is a ray at an angle of incidence i at the first face less than 90°, the angle of refraction at S at the second face = $A - r$, where r is the angle of refraction BMS.

Now c is the *maximum* angle of refraction in the prism.

Hence MQ makes the minimum angle of incidence on the second face, and thus is least likely to suffer total internal reflection.

(b) The least value of the refracting angle of the prism corresponds to a ray at grazing incidence and grazing emergence, as shown in Fig. 322.

Thus   minimum angle = $2c$

where c is the critical angle (p. 459).

But $$\sin c = \frac{1}{\mu} = \frac{4}{7} = 0.5714$$

$$\therefore \quad c = 34° 51'$$

$$\therefore \text{ minimum angle} = 2c = 69° 42'$$

EXERCISES XXI

1. A ray of light is refracted through a prism of angle 70°. If the angle of refraction in the glass at the first face is 28°, what is the angle of incidence in the glass at the second face?

2. (i) The angle of a glass prism is 60°, and the minimum deviation of light through the prism is 39°. Calculate the refractive index of the glass. (ii) The refractive index of a glass prism is 1·66, and the angle of the prism is 60°. Find the minimum deviation.

3. Draw a labelled diagram of a spectrometer set up for studying the deviation of light through a triangular prism. Describe how you would adjust the instrument and use it to find the refractive index of the prism material.

Indicate briefly how you would show that the radiation from an arc lamp is not confined to the visible spectrum. (*L.*)

4. Show on a diagram the way in which light from a monochromatic source passes through a spectrometer which is in correct adjustment. How may the instrument be used to determine the refractive index of the material of a glass prism for the given light? Prove any formula you use. (*W.*)

5. The refractive index of a prism is 1·6434 for a red line in the lithium spectrum, and 1·6852 for a violet line in the mercury spectrum. Calculate the angle of minimum deviation for each line if the angle of the prism is 60°. (*N.*)

6. How would you investigate the way in which the deviation of a ray of light by a triangular glass prism varies with the angle of incidence on the first face of the prism? What result would you expect to obtain?

The deviation of a ray of light incident on the first face of a 60° glass prism at an angle of 45° is 40°. Find the angle which the emergent ray makes with the normal to the second face of the prism and determine, preferably by graphical construction, the refractive index of the glass of the prism. (L.)

7. A prism has angles of 45°, 45°, and 90° and all three faces polished. Trace the path of a ray entering one of the smaller faces in a direction parallel to the larger face and perpendicular to the prism edges. Assume 1·5 for the refractive index.

If you had two such prisms how would you determine by a simple pin or ray-box method the refractive index of a liquid available only in small quantity? (L.)

8. Under what circumstances does total internal reflection occur? Show that a ray of light incident in a principal section of an equilateral glass prism of refractive index 1·5, can only be transmitted after two refractions at adjacent faces if the angle of incidence on the prism exceeds a certain value. Find this limiting angle of incidence. (W.)

9. Describe and explain a method of measuring the refractive index of a transparent liquid using total internal reflection.

Calculate the angle of incidence of a ray on the face AB of an equilateral triangular glass prism ABC in order that it may be totally reflected at the critical angle at the face BC. The index of refraction of the glass is 1·5. (L.)

10. Draw a graph showing, in a general way, how the deviation of a ray of light when passed through a triangular prism depends on the angle of incidence.

You are required to measure the refractive index of glass in the form of a prism by means of a spectrometer provided with a vertical slit. Explain how you would level the spectrometer table and derive the formula from which you would calculate the refractive index. (You are not required to explain any other adjustment of the apparatus nor to explain how you would find the refracting angle of the prism.) (L.)

11. A ray of monochromatic light passes in the usual way through a triangular glass prism. Indicate by means of a graph how the deviation varies with the angle of incidence. Describe briefly how the refractive index of the glass can be found from the deviation, and derive the formula you use.

[Details of the adjustment of the spectrometer need not be given.]

If the refracting angle of a prism is 60° and the refractive index 1.51, what is the smallest possible angle of incidence of a ray which passes through without suffering total reflection?

Describe what is observed if white light is used and the angle of incidence is varied in the neighbourhood of this minimum. (L.)

CHAPTER XXII

DISPERSION. SPECTRA

1. Spectrum of White Light

In 1666, NEWTON made a great scientific discovery. He found that sunlight, or white light, was made up of different colours, consisting of red, orange, yellow, green, blue, indigo, violet. Newton made a small hole in a shutter in a darkened room, and received a white circular patch of sunlight on a screen S in the path of the light, Fig. 325 (i). But on interposing a glass prism between the hole and the screen he observed

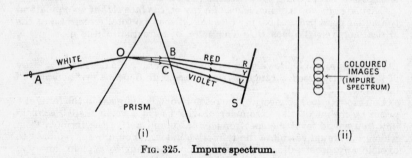

FIG. 325.   Impure spectrum.

a series of overlapping coloured patches in place of the white patch, the total length of the coloured images being several times their width, Fig. 325 (ii). By separating one colour from the rest, Newton demonstrated that the colours themselves could not be changed by refraction through a prism, and he concluded that the colours were not *introduced* by the prism, but were components of the white light. The *spectrum* (colours) of white light are red, orange, yellow, green, blue, indigo, and violet, and the separation of the colours by the prism is known as *dispersion*.

The red rays are the least deviated by the prism, and the violet rays are the most deviated, as shown in the exaggerated sketch of Fig. 65 (i). Since the angle of incidence at O in the air is the same for the red and violet rays, and the angle of refraction made by the red ray OB in the glass is greater than that made by the violet ray OC, it follows from $\sin i/\sin r$ that the refractive index of the prism material for red light is less than for violet light. Similarly, the refractive index for yellow light lies between the refractive index values for red and violet light (see also p. 468).

464

2. Production of Pure Spectrum

Newton's spectrum of sunlight is an *impure spectrum* because the different coloured images overlap, Fig. 325 (ii). A *pure spectrum* is one in which the different coloured images contain light of one colour only, i.e., they are monochromatic images. In order to obtain a pure spectrum (i) the white light must be admitted through a very narrow opening, so as to assist in the reduction of the overlapping of the images, (ii) the beams of coloured rays emerging from the prism must be parallel, so that each beam can be brought to a separate focus.

The spectrometer can be used to provide a pure spectrum. The collimator slit is made very narrow, and the collimator C and the telescope T are both adjusted for parallel light, Fig. 326. A bright source

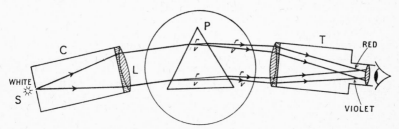

FIG. 326.   Pure spectrum.

of white light, S, is placed near the slit, and the prism P is usually set in the minimum deviation position for yellow light, although this is not essential. The rays refracted through P are now separated into a number of different coloured parallel beams of light, each travelling in slightly different directions, and the telescope brings each coloured beam to a separate focus. A pure spectrum can now be seen through T, consisting of a series of monochromatic images of the slit.

If only one lens, L, is available, the prism P *must* be placed in the

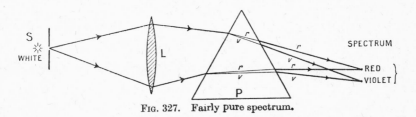

FIG. 327.   Fairly pure spectrum.

minimum deviation position for yellow light in order to obtain a fairly pure spectrum, Fig. 327. The prism is then also approximately in the minimum deviation position for the various colours in the incident convergent beam, and hence the rays of one colour are approximately deviated by the same amount by the prism, thus forming an image of the slit S at roughly the same place.

Infra-red and ultra-violet rays. In 1800 Sir William Herschel moved the blackened bulb of a thermometer into the shadow beyond the red of the visible spectrum of the sun, and observed an increased reading on the thermometer. This led to the discovery of *infra-red rays* (popularly known as "heat-rays"), which are fundamentally the same in nature as the rays of the visible spectrum but do not cause the sensation of vision when incident on the eye. See p. 716. Since they are not scattered by fine particles as much as the rays of the visible spectrum, infra-red rays are able to penetrate fog and mist; and with the aid of filters and special infra-red photographic plates, clear pictures of the countryside have been taken in dense mist. Infra-red photography has also been used at the British Museum to decipher the writing on ancient monuments, and to see clearly pictures of ancient works of art, which have been covered with grime not easily removed.

About 1801 Ritter discovered the existence of invisible rays beyond the violet end of the visible spectrum; these are known as *ultra-violet rays.* Photographic plates are darkened by ultra-violet rays as the rays decompose the silver compound covering them, and they cause certain materials to fluoresce. Metal plates emit electrons when illuminated by ultra-violet light (see *photo-electric effect*, p. 614). Quartz prisms must be used in the investigation of the properties of the rays, as ordinary glass absorbs ultra-violet rays.

3. Deviation Produced by Small Angle Prism for Small Angles of Incidence

Before discussing in detail the colour effect produced when white light is incident on a prism, we must derive an expression for the deviation produced by a *small angle prism.*

Consider a ray PM of monochromatic light incident almost normally on the face TM of a prism of small angle A, so that the angle of incidence, i_1, is small, Fig. 328. Then $\sin i_1/\sin r_1 = \mu$, where r_1 is the angle of refraction in the prism, and μ is the refractive index for the colour of the light. As r_1 is less than i_1, r_1 also is a small angle. Now the sine

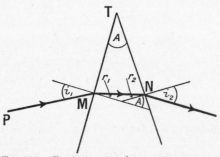

Fig. 328. Deviation through small angle prism.

of a small angle is practically equal to the angle measured in radians. Thus $i_1/r_1 = \mu$, or

$$i_1 = \mu r_1 \qquad \text{.} \qquad \text{.} \qquad \text{.} \qquad \text{.} \qquad \text{.} \qquad \text{.} \qquad \text{(i)}$$

From the geometry of Fig. 328, the angle of incidence r_2 on the face TN of the prism is given by $r_2 = A - r_1$; and since A and r_1 are both small, it follows that r_2 is a small angle. The angle of emergence i_2 is thus also small, and since $\sin i_2/\sin r_2 = \mu$, we may state that $i_2/r_2 = \mu$, or

$$i_2 = \mu r_2 \qquad \text{.} \qquad \text{.} \qquad \text{.} \qquad \text{.} \qquad \text{.} \qquad \text{.} \qquad \text{(ii)}$$

The deviation, d, of the ray on passing through the prism is given by $d = (i_1 - r_1) + (i_2 - r_2)$. Substituting for i_1 and i_2 from (i) and (ii),

$$\therefore d = \mu r_1 - r_1 + \mu r_2 - r_2 = \mu (r_1 + r_2) - (r_1 + r_2)$$
$$\therefore d = (\mu - 1)(r_1 + r_2)$$

But $\qquad r_1 + r_2 = A$

$$\therefore \mathbf{d = (\mu - 1)\,A} \qquad \text{.} \qquad \text{.} \qquad \text{.} \qquad \text{.} \qquad \text{.} \qquad \text{(16)}$$

This is the magnitude of the deviation produced by a *small* angle prism for *small* angles of incidence. If A is expressed in radians, then d is in radians; if A is expressed in degrees, then d is in degrees. If $A = 6°$ and $\mu = 1·6$ for yellow light, the deviation d of that colour for small angles of incidence is given by $d = (1·6 - 1)\,6° = 3·6°$. It will be noted that the deviation is independent of the magnitude of the small angle of incidence on the prism.

4. Dispersion by Small Angle Prism

We have already seen from Newton's experiment that the colours in a beam of white light are separated by a glass prism into red, orange, yellow, green, blue, indigo, violet, so that the emergent light is no longer white but coloured. The separation of the colours by the prism

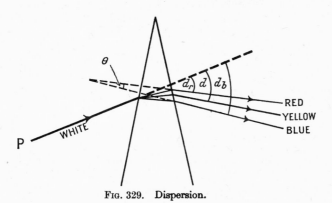

Fig. 329. Dispersion.

is known generally as the phenomenon of *dispersion*, and the *angular dispersion* between the red and blue emergent rays, for example, is defined as the *angle* between these two rays. Thus, in Fig. 329, θ is the angular dispersion between the red and blue rays. Of course, the angular dispersion is also equal to the *difference in deviation* of the two colours produced by the prism; and since we have already derived the expression $d = (\mu - 1) A$ for the deviation of monochromatic light by a small angle prism we can obtain the angular dispersion between any two colours.

Suppose d_b, d_r are the respective deviations of the blue and red light when a ray of white light is incident at a small angle on a prism of small angle A, Fig. 329. Then, if μ_b, μ_r are the refractive indices of the prism material for blue and red light respectively,

$$d_b = (\mu_b - 1) A,$$

and $$d_r = (\mu_r - 1) A.$$

$\therefore$ angular dispersion, $d_b - d_r$, $= (\mu_b - 1) A - (\mu_r - 1) A$

$$\therefore d_b - d_r = (\mu_b - \mu_r) A \qquad . \qquad . \qquad (17)$$

For a particular crown glass, $\mu_b = 1\cdot521, \mu_r = 1\cdot510$. Thus if $A = 8°$, the angular dispersion between the blue and red colours

$$= (\mu_b - \mu_r) A = (1\cdot521 - 1\cdot510)\, 8° = 0\cdot09°$$

The *mean deviation* of the white light by the prism is commonly chosen as the deviation of the *yellow* light, since this is the colour approximately in the middle of the spectrum; the mean refractive index of a material is also specified as that for yellow light. Now the deviation, d, of monochromatic light is given by $d = (\mu - 1) A$, from equation (16), and unless otherwise stated, the magnitudes of d and μ will be understood to be those for yellow light when these symbols contain no suffixes. If $\mu_b = 1\cdot521$ and $\mu_r = 1\cdot510$, then *approximately* the refractive index, μ, for yellow light is the average of μ_b and μ_r, or $\frac{1}{2}(1\cdot521 + 1\cdot510)$; thus $\mu = 1\cdot515$. Thus if the prism has an angle of $8°$, the mean deviation, d, $= (\mu - 1) A = (1\cdot515 - 1)\, 8° = 4\cdot1°$.

5. Dispersive Power,

The *dispersive power*, ω, of the material of a prism for blue and red rays is defined as the ratio

$$\omega = \frac{angular\ dispersion\ between\ blue\ and\ red\ rays}{mean\ deviation} \qquad (18)$$

The dispersive power depends on the material of the prism. As an illustration, suppose that a prism of angle $8°$ is made of glass of a type X, say, and another prism of angle 8° is made of glass of a type Y.

	μ_b	μ_r	μ
Crown glass, X	1·521	1·510	1·515
Flint glass, Y	1·665	1·645	1·655

Further, suppose the refractive indices of the two materials for blue, red, and yellow light are those shown in the above table.

For a small angle of incidence on the prism of glass X, the angular dispersion

$$= d_b - d_r = (\mu_b - 1) A - (\mu_r - 1) A$$
$$= (\mu_b - \mu_r) A = (1·521 - 1·510) 8° = 0·09° \qquad \text{(i)}$$

The mean deviation, $d = (\mu - 1) A = (1·515 - 1) 8° = 4·1°$. (ii)

$\therefore$ dispersive power, $\omega, = \dfrac{0·09}{4·1} = 0·021$ . . . . (iii)

Similarly, for the prism of glass Y,

angular dispersion $= (\mu_b - \mu_r) A = (1·665 - 1·645)\, 8 = 0·16°$

and mean deviation $= (\mu - 1) A = (1·655 - 1) 8 = 5·24°$

$\therefore$ dispersive power $= \dfrac{0·16}{5·24} = 0·03$ . . . . (iv)

From (iii) and (iv), it follows that the dispersive power of glass Y is about 1·5 times as great as that of glass X.

6. General formula for dispersive power

We can now derive a general formula for dispersive power, ω. From the definition in equation 18, it follows that

$$\omega = \frac{d_b - d_r}{d}$$

as d_b, d_r, d denote the deviations of blue, red, and yellow light respectively.

But $\qquad d_b - d_r = (\mu_b - 1) A - (\mu_r - 1) A = (\mu_b - \mu_r) A$

and $\qquad d = (\mu - 1) A.$

$$\therefore \quad \omega = \frac{d_b - d_r}{d} = \frac{(\mu_b - \mu_r) A}{(\mu - 1) A}$$

$$\therefore \quad \omega = \frac{\mu_b - \mu_r}{\mu - 1} \qquad . \qquad . \qquad . \qquad . \qquad . \qquad (19)$$

From this formula, it can be seen that (i) ω depends only on the material of the prism and is independent of its angle, (ii) ω is a number and has therefore no units. In contrast to "dispersive power", it should be noted that "dispersion" is an angle, and that its magnitude depends on the angle A of the prism and the two colours concerned, for

$$d_b - d_r = \text{dispersion} = (\mu_b - \mu_r)\,A.$$

7. Achromatic Prisms

We have seen that a prism separates the colours in white light. If a prism is required to deviate white light without dispersing it into colours, *two* prisms of different material must be used to eliminate the dispersion, as shown in Fig. 330. The prism P is made of crown glass,

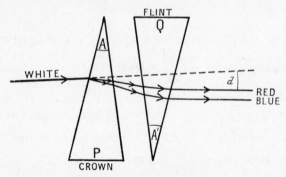

FIG. 330.   Achromatic prisms.

and causes dispersion between the red and blue in the incident white light. The prism Q is inverted with respect to P, and with a suitable choice of its angle A' (discussed fully later), the red and blue rays incident on it can be made to emerge in *parallel* directions. If the rays are viewed the eye-lens brings them to a focus at the same place on the retina, and hence the colour effect due to red and blue rays is eliminated. The dispersion of the other colours in white light still remains, but most of the colour effect is eliminated as the red and blue rays are the "outside" (extreme) rays in the spectrum of white light.

Prisms which eliminate dispersion between two colours, blue and red say, are said to be *achromatic* prisms for those colours. Suppose μ_b, μ_r are the refractive indices of crown glass for blue and red light, and A is the angle of the crown glass prism P. Then, from p. 467,

$$\text{dispersion} = (\mu_b - \mu_r)\,A \qquad . \quad . \quad . \quad . \quad . \quad \text{(i)}$$

If μ_b', μ_r' are the refractive indices of flint glass for blue and red light, and A' is the angle of the flint glass prism Q, then similarly,

$$\text{dispersion} = (\mu_b' - \mu_r')\,A' \qquad . \quad . \quad . \quad . \quad . \quad \text{(ii)}$$

Now prism P produces its dispersion in a "downward" direction since a prism bends rays towards its base, Fig. 330, and prism Q produces its dispersion in an "upward" direction. For achromatic prisms, therefore, the dispersions produced by P and Q must be equal.

$$\therefore (\mu_b - \mu_r) A = (\mu_b' - \mu_r') A' \quad . \quad . \quad . \quad . \quad (20)$$

Suppose P has an angle of 6°. Then, using the refractive indices for $\mu_b, \mu_r, \mu'_b, \mu'_r$ in the table on p. 469, it follows from (20) that the angle A' is given by

$$(1\cdot521 - 1\cdot510)\, 6° = (1\cdot665 - 1\cdot645)\, A'$$

Thus
$$A' = \frac{0\cdot011}{0\cdot02} \times 6° = 3\cdot3°$$

8. Deviation Produced by Achromatic Prisms

Although the colour effects between the red and blue rays are eliminated by the use of achromatic prisms, it should be carefully noted that the incident light beam, as a whole, has been deviated. This angle of deviation, d, is shown in Fig. 330, and is the angle between the incident and emergent beams. The deviation of the mean or yellow light by prism P is given by $(\mu - 1) A$, and is in a "downward" direction. Since the deviation of the yellow light by the prism Q is in an opposite direction, and is given by $(\mu' - 1) A'$, the net deviation, d, is given by

$$d = (\mu - 1) A - (\mu' - 1) A'.$$

Using the angles 6° and 3·3° obtained above, with $\mu = 1\cdot515$ and $\mu' = 1\cdot655$,

$$d = (1\cdot515 - 1)\, 6° - (1\cdot655 - 1)\, 3\cdot3° = 0\cdot93°.$$

9. Direct-vision Spectroscope

The direct-vision spectroscope is a simple instrument used for examining the different colours in the spectrum obtained from a glowing gas in a flame or in a discharge tube. It contains several crown and flint prisms cemented together, and contained in a straight tube having lenses which constitute an eye-piece. The tube is pointed at the

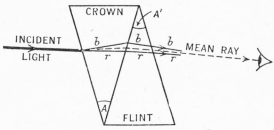

Fig. 331. Dispersion; but no deviation of mean ray.

source of light examined, when various colours are seen on account of the dispersion produced by the prisms, Fig. 331.

In practice, the direct-vision spectroscope contains several crown and flint glass prisms, but for convenience suppose we consider two such prisms, as in Fig. 331. For "direct-vision", the *net deviation of the mean* (yellow) *ray* produced by the prisms must be zero. Thus the mean deviation caused by the crown glass prism in one direction must be equal to that caused by the flint glass prism in the opposite direction. Hence, with the notation already used, we must have

$$(\mu - 1) A = (\mu' - 1) A'.$$

Suppose $A = 6°$, $\mu = 1·515$, $\mu' = 1·655$. Then A' is given by
$$(1·515 - 1) 6° = (1·655 - 1) A'$$

$$\therefore \qquad A' = \frac{0·515}{0·655} \times 6° = 4·7°$$

The *net dispersion* of the blue and red rays is given by

$$(\mu_b - \mu_r) A - (\mu_b' - \mu_r') A'$$
$$= (1·521 - 1·510) 6° - (1·665 - 1·645) 4·7°$$
$$= 0·066 - 0·094 = - 0·028°.$$

The minus indicates that the net dispersion is produced in a "blue-upward" direction, as the dispersion of the flint glass prism is greater than that of the crown glass prism.

SPECTRA

10. The Importance of the Study of Spectra

The study of the wavelengths of the radiation from a hot body comes under the general heading of *Spectra*. The number of spectra of elements and compounds which have been recorded runs easily into millions, and it is worth while stating at the outset the main reasons for the interest in the phenomenon.

It is now considered that an atom consists of a nucleus of positive electricity surrounded by electrons moving in various orbits, and that a particular electron in an orbit has a definite amount of energy. In certain circumstances the electron may jump from this orbit to another, where it has a smaller amount of energy. When this occurs radiation is emitted, and the energy in the radiation is equal to the difference in energy of the atom between its initial and final states. The displacement of an electron from one orbit to another occurs when a substance is raised to a high temperature, in which case the atoms present collide with each other very violently. Light of a definite wavelength will then be emitted, and will be characteristic of the electron energy changes in the atom. There is usually more than one wavelength in the light from a hot body (iron has more than 4,000 different wavelengths in its spectrum), and each wavelength corresponds to a change in energy between two orbits. A study of spectra should therefore reveal much important information concerning the structure and properties of atoms.

Every element has a unique spectrum. Consequently a study of the spectrum of a substance enables its composition to be readily determined. *Spectroscopy* is the name given to the exact analysis of mixtures or compounds by a study of their spectra, and the science has developed to such an extent that the presence in a substance of less than a millionth of a milligram of sodium can be detected.

Types of emission spectra. There are three different types of spectra, which are easily recognised. They are known as (*a*) *line spectra*, (*b*) *band spectra*, (*c*) *continuous spectra*.

(*a*) *Line spectra.* When the light emitted by the atoms of a glowing substance (such as vaporised sodium or helium gas) is examined by a prism and spectrometer, lines of different wavelength are obtained. These lines, it should be noted, are images of the narrow slit of the spectrometer

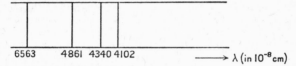

6563   4861 4340 4102 $\longrightarrow \lambda$ (in 10^{-8} cm)

Fig. 332.   Visible line spectra of hydrogen.

on which the light is incident. The spectra of hydrogen, Fig. 332, and helium are line spectra, and it is generally true that line spectra are obtained from *atoms*.

(*b*) *Band spectra.* Band spectra are obtained from *molecules*, and consist of a series of bands each sharp at one end but "fading" at the other end, Fig. 333. The term "fluting" is often used to describe the way in which the bands are spaced. Careful examination reveals that the bands are made up

Fig. 333.   Diagrammatic representation of band spectra.

of numerous fine lines very close to each other. Two examples of band spectra are those usually obtained from nitrogen and oxygen.

(*c*) *Continuous spectra.* The spectrum of the sun is an example of a continuous spectrum, and, in general, the latter are obtained from *solids and liquids*. In these states of matter the atoms and molecules are close together, and electron orbital changes in a particular atom are influenced by neighbouring atoms to such an extent that radiations of all different wavelengths are emitted. In a gas the atoms are comparatively far apart, and each atom is uninfluenced by any other. The gas therefore emits radiations of wavelengths which result from orbital changes in the atom due solely to the high temperature of the gas, and a line spectrum is obtained. When the temperature of a gas is decreased and pressure applied so that the liquid state is approached, the line spectrum of the gas is observed to broaden out considerably.

Production of spectra. In order to produce its spectrum the substance under examination must be heated to a high temperature. There are four main methods of *excitation*, as the process is called, and spectra are classified under the method of their production.

(a) *Flame spectra.* The temperature of a Bunsen flame is high enough to vaporise certain solids. Thus if a piece of platinum wire is dipped into a sodium salt and then placed in the flame, a vivid yellow colour is obtained which is characteristic of the element sodium. This method of excitation can only be used for a limited number of metals, the main class being the alkali and alkaline earth metals such as sodium, potassium, lithium, calcium, and barium. The line spectra produced in each case consist of lines of different colours, but some lines have a greater intensity than others. Thus sodium is characterised by two prominent yellow lines barely distinguishable in a small spectroscope, and lithium by a prominent green line.

(b) *Spark spectra.* If metal electrodes are connected to the secondary of an induction coil and placed a few millimetres apart, a spark can be obtained which bridges the gap. It was discovered that a much more intense and violent spark could be obtained by placing a condenser in parallel with the gap. This spark is known as a *condensed* spark. The solid under investigation forms one of the electrodes, and is vaporised at the high temperature obtained.

(c) *Arc spectra.* This is the method most used in industry. If two metal rods connected to a D.C. voltage supply are placed in contact with each other and then drawn a few millimetres apart, a continuous spark, known as an arc, is obtained across the gap. The arc is a source of very high temperature, and therefore vaporises substances very readily. In practice the two rods are placed in a vertical position, and a small amount of the substance investigated is placed on the lower rod.

(d) *Discharge-tube spectra.* If a gas is contained at low pressure inside a tube having two aluminium electrodes and a high A.C. or D.C. voltage is applied to the gas, a "discharge" occurs between the electrodes and the gas becomes luminous. This is the most convenient method of examining the spectra of gases. The luminous neon gas in a discharge tube has a reddish colour, while mercury vapour is greenish-blue.

11. Absorption Spectra. Kirchhoff's Law

The spectra just discussed are classified as *emission spectra*. There is another class of spectra known as *absorption spectra*, which we shall now briefly consider.

If light from a source having a continuous spectrum is examined after it has passed through a sodium flame, the spectrum is found to be crossed by a dark line; this dark line is in the position corresponding to the bright line emission spectrum obtained with the sodium flame alone. The continuous spectrum with the dark line is naturally characteristic of the absorbing substance, in this case sodium, and it is known as an *absorption spectrum*. An absorption spectrum is obtained when red glass is placed in front of sunlight, as it only allows a narrow band of red rays to be transmitted.

KIRCHHOFF's investigations on absorption spectra in 1855 led him to formulate a simple law concerning the emission and absorption of light by a substance. This states: *A substance which emits light of a certain wavelength at a given temperature can also absorb light of the same wavelength at that temperature.* In other words, a good emitter of a certain wavelength is also a good absorber of that wavelength. From Kirchhoff's law it follows that if the radiation from a hot source emitting a continuous spectrum is passed through a vapour, the absorption spectrum obtained is deficient in those wavelengths which the vapour would emit if it were raised to the same high temperature. Thus if a sodium flame is observed through a spectrometer in a darkened room, a bright yellow line is seen; if a strong white arc light, richer in yellow light than the sodium flame, is placed behind the flame, a dark line is observed in the place of the yellow line. The sodium absorbs yellow light from the white light, and re-radiates it in all directions. Consequently there is less yellow light in front of the sodium flame than if it were removed, and a dark line is thus observed.

12. Fraunhofer Lines

In 1814 FRAUNHOFER noticed that the sun's spectrum was crossed by many hundreds of dark lines. These *Fraunhofer lines*, as they are called, were mapped out by him on a chart of wavelengths, and the more prominent were labelled by the letters of the alphabet. Thus the dark line in the blue part of the spectrum was known as the *F* line, the dark line in the yellow part as the *D* line, and the dark line in the red part as the *C* line.

The Fraunhofer lines indicate the presence in the sun's atmosphere of certain elements in a vapourised form. The vapours are cooler than the central hot portion of the sun, and they absorb their own characteristic wavelengths from the sun's continuous spectrum. Now every element has a characteristic spectrum of wavelengths. Accordingly, it became possible to identify the elements round the sun from a study of the wavelengths of the Fraunhofer (dark) lines in the sun's spectrum, and it was then found that hydrogen and helium were present. This was how helium was first discovered. The *D* line is the yellow sodium line.

The incandescent gases round the sun can be seen as flames many miles high during a total eclipse of the sun, when the central portion of the sun is cut off from the observer. If the spectrum of the sun is observed just before an eclipse takes place, a continuous spectrum with Fraunhofer lines is obtained, as already stated. At the instant when the eclipse becomes total, however, bright emission lines are seen in exactly the same position as those previously occupied by the Fraunhofer lines, and they correspond to the emission spectra of the vapours alone. This is an illustration of Kirchhoff's law, p. 475.

13. Measurement of Wavelengths by Spectrometer

As we shall discuss later (p. 716), the light waves produced by different colours are characterised by different *wavelengths*. Besides measuring refractive index, the spectrometer can be adapted for measuring unknown wavelengths, corresponding to the lines in the spectrum of a glowing gas in a discharge tube, for example.

A prism is first placed on the spectrometer table in the minimum deviation position for yellow (sodium) light, thus providing a reference position for the prism in relation to incident light from the collimator. The source of yellow light is now replaced by a helium discharge tube, which contains helium at a very low pressure, glowing as a result of the high voltage placed across the tube. Several bright lines of various colours can now be observed through the telescope (they are differently coloured images of the slit), and the *deviation*, θ, of each of the lines is obtained by rotating the telescope until the image is on the cross-wires,

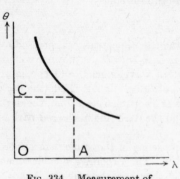

and then noting the corresponding reading on the circular graduated scale. Since the wavelengths, λ, of the different lines in the helium spectrum are known very accurately from tables, a graph can now be plotted between θ and λ. The helium discharge tube can then be replaced by a hydrogen or mercury discharge tube, and the deviations due to other lines of known wavelength obtained. In this way a *calibration curve* for the spectrometer can be obtained, Fig. 334.

Fig. 334. Measurement of wavelength by spectrometer.

The wavelength due to a line Q in the spectrum of an unknown glowing gas can now be easily derived. With the prism still in the minimum deviation position for yellow light, the deviation, θ, of Q is measured. If this angle corresponds to C in Fig. 334, the wavelength λ is OA.

EXAMPLES

1. Show that when a ray of light passes nearly normally through a prism of small angle a and refractive index μ, the deviation δ is given by $\delta = (\mu - 1)\, a$. A parallel beam of light falls normally upon the first face of a prism of small angle. The portion of the beam which is refracted at the second surface is deviated through an angle of $1°\, 35'$, and the portion which is reflected at the second surface and emerges again at the first surface makes an angle of $8°\, 9'$ with the incident beam. Calculate the angle of the prism and the refractive index of the glass. (*C*.)

First part. See text.

Second part. Let θ = angle of prism, μ = the refractive index, and RH the ray incident normally on the face AN, striking the second face at K. Fig. 75.

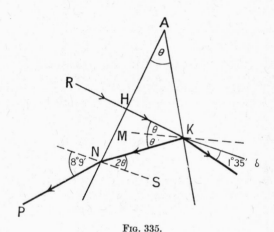

Fig. 335.

Then the angle of incidence at K = θ, and angle HKN = 2θ. By drawing the normal NS at N, which is parallel to HK, it can be seen that angle KNS = 2θ. The angle of emergence from the prism = $8°\, 9'$ since the incident beam was normal to AN.

The angle of deviation, δ, of the beam by the prism is given by

$$\delta = (\mu - 1)\, \theta$$
$$\therefore \quad 1°\, 35' = (\mu - 1)\, \theta \qquad \qquad \text{(i)}$$

For refraction at N, $\mu = \dfrac{\sin 8°\, 9'}{\sin 2\theta}$

Since the angles concerned are small,

$$\mu = \frac{8°\, 9'}{2\theta} \quad . \quad . \quad . \quad . \quad . \quad \text{(ii)}$$

where θ is in degrees.

From (ii), $\qquad \qquad \theta = \dfrac{8°\, 9'}{2\mu}$; substituting in (i),

$$\therefore \qquad 1° 35' = (\mu - 1)\,\frac{8° 9'}{2\mu}$$

$$\therefore \qquad \frac{\mu - 1}{2\mu} = \frac{95}{489}$$

$$\therefore 489\mu - 489 = 190\mu$$

$$\therefore \qquad \mu = 1\cdot63$$

$$\therefore \qquad \theta = \frac{8° 29'}{2\mu} = \frac{8° 29'}{3\cdot26} = 2° 30'$$

2. Define dispersive power. The following table gives the refractive indices of crown and flint glass for three lines of the spectrum.

	C	D	F
Crown	1·514	1·517	1·523
Flint	1·644	1·650	1·664

Calculate the refracting angle of a flint glass prism which, when combined with a crown glass of refracting angle 5°, produces a combination that does not deviate the light corresponding to the D line. What separation of the rays corresponding to the C and F lines will such a compound prism produce? (L.)

For definition, see text.

The D line corresponds to the mean, or yellow, ray, the F and C lines to the blue and red rays respectively. Let μ', μ = the refractive indices for crown and flint glass respectively. A', A = the corresponding angles of the prisms.

For no deviation $\quad (\mu'_D - 1)\,A' - (\mu_D - 1)\,A = 0,$

$$\therefore \quad (1\cdot517 - 1)\,5° - (1\cdot650 - 1)\,A = 0$$

$$\therefore \quad A = \frac{0\cdot517}{0\cdot650} \times 5 = 3\cdot99°$$

The separation of the F and C lines $= (\mu_F - \mu_C)\,A - (\mu'_F - \mu'_C)\,A'$
$$= (1\cdot664 - 1\cdot644)\,3\cdot99° - (1\cdot523 - 1\cdot514)\,5°$$
$$= 0\cdot0798° - 0\cdot045° = 0\cdot0348°$$

3. Prove that for a prism of small angle A the deviation of a ray of light is $(\mu - 1)\,A$, provided that the angle of incidence also is small. A crown glass prism of refracting angle 6° is to be achromatised for red and blue light with a flint glass prism. Using the data below and the formula above find (a) the angle of the flint glass prism, (b) the mean deviation.

	Crown Glass	Flint Glass
μ red	1·513	1·645
μ blue	1·523	1·665

(N.)

First part. See text.

Second part. Let A = the angle of the flint prism,

μ', μ = the refractive indices of the crown and flint glass respectively.

For achromatism, $(\mu'_b - \mu'_r) 6° = (\mu_b - \mu_r) A$

$$\therefore \quad (1\cdot523 - 1\cdot513) 6° = (1\cdot665 - 1\cdot645) A$$

$$\therefore A = \frac{0\cdot010}{0\cdot020} \times 6° = 3°$$

The mean refractive index, μ', for crown glass $= \dfrac{1\cdot523 + 1\cdot513}{2} = 1\cdot518$

and ,, ,, ,, μ, ,, flint ,, $= \dfrac{1\cdot665 + 1\cdot645}{2} = 1\cdot655$

$\therefore$ deviation of mean ray $= (\mu' - 1) 6° - (\mu - 1) 3°$
$$= (1\cdot518 - 1) 6° - (1\cdot655 - 1) 3° = 1\cdot043°$$

EXERCISES XXII

1. Write down the formula for the deviation of a ray of light through a prism of small angle A which has a refractive index μ for the colour concerned. Using the following table, calculate the deviation of (i) red light, (ii) blue light, (iii) yellow light through a flint glass prism of refracting angle $4°$, and through a crown glass prism of refracting angle $6°$.

	Crown glass	Flint glass
μ red	1·512	1·646
μ blue	1·524	1·666

2. Using the above data, calculate the *dispersive powers* of crown glass and flint glass.

3. Explain how it is possible with two prisms to produce dispersion without mean deviation. A prism of crown glass with refracting angle of $5°$ and mean refractive index $1\cdot51$ is combined with one flint glass of refractive index $1\cdot65$ to produce no mean deviation. Find the angle of the flint glass prism. The difference in the refractive indices of the red and blue rays in crown glass is $0\cdot0085$ and in flint glass $0\cdot0162$. Find the inclination between the red and blue rays which emerge from the composite prism. (*L*.)

4. Define *dispersive power* and describe briefly how it may be measured. Draw a diagram showing the construction of a direct vision spectroscope. (*L. Inter.*)

5. What is meant by *total internal reflection*? Describe how this phenomenon may be demonstrated and state the conditions under which it occurs. Derive a formula for the deviation of a ray of light by a wedge of transparent material of small refracting angle. A ray of light, incident on one face of a wedge of refractive index $1\cdot50$ and angle $5°$, is just totally reflected at the second face. Calculate the angle of incidence. (*C*.)

6. Describe and give a diagram of the optical system of a spectrometer. What procedure would you adopt when using the instrument to measure the refractive index of the glass of a prism for sodium light? What additional observations would be necessary in order to determine the dispersive power of the glass?

The refractive index of the glass of a prism for red light is 1·514 and for blue light 1·523. Calculate the difference in the velocities of the red and blue light in the prism if the velocity of light *in vacuo* is 3×10^5 kilometres per sec. (*N*.)

7. Explain, with diagrams, how a "pure" spectrum is produced by means of a spectrometer. What source of light may be used and what readings must be taken in order to find the dispersive power of the material of which the prism is made? (*L*.)

8. (*a*) Explain, giving a carefully-drawn, labelled diagram, the function of the various parts of a spectrometer. How is it adjusted for normal laboratory use? (*b*) Distinguish between a continuous spectrum, an absorption spectrum, a band spectrum, and a line spectrum. State briefly how you would obtain each type with a spectrometer. (*W*.)

9. Describe a prism spectrometer and the adjustment of it necessary for the precise observation of the spectrum of light by a gaseous source.

Compare and contrast briefly the spectrum of sunlight and of light emitted by hydrogen at low pressure contained in a tube through which an electric discharge is passing. (*L*.)

10. Calculate the angle of a crown glass prism which makes an achromatic combination for red and blue light with a flint glass prism of refracting angle 4°. What is the mean deviation of the light by this combination? Use the data given in question 1.

11. State what is meant by *dispersion* and describe, with diagrams, the principle of (i) an achromatic and (ii) a direct-vision prism.

Derive an expression for the refractive index of the glass of a *narrow* angle prism in terms of the angle of minimum deviation and the angle of the prism. If the refractive index of the glass of refracting angle 8° is 1·532 and 1·514 for blue and red light respectively, determine the angular dispersion produced by the prism. (*L*.)

12. Describe the optical system of a simple prism spectrometer. Illustrate your answer with a diagram showing the paths through the spectrometer of the pencils of rays which form the red and blue ends of the spectrum of a source of white light. (Assume in your diagram that the lenses are achromatic.)

The prism of a spectrometer has a refracting angle of 60° and is made of glass whose refractive indices for red and violet are respectively 1·514 and 1·530. A white source is used and the instrument is set to give minimum deviation for red light. Determine (*a*) the angle of incidence of the light on the prism, (*b*) the angle of emergence of the violet light, (*c*) the angular width of the spectrum. (*N*.)

CHAPTER XXIII

REFRACTION THROUGH LENSES

A *lens* is a piece of glass bounded by one or two spherical surfaces. When a lens is thicker in the middle than at the edges it is called a *convex* or *converging lens*, Fig. 336 (i); when it is thinner in the middle than at the edges it is known as a *concave* or *diverging lens*, Fig. 336 (ii). Fig. 344, on p. 489, illustrates other types of convex and concave lenses.

Lenses were no doubt made soon after the art of glass-making was discovered; and as the sun's rays could be concentrated by these curved pieces of glass they were called "burning glasses". ARISTOPHANES, in 424 B.C., mentions a burning glass. To-day, lenses are used in spectacles, cameras, microscopes, and telescopes, as well as in many other optical instruments, and they afford yet another example of the many ways in which Science is used to benefit our everyday lives.

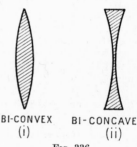

BI-CONVEX (i)   BI-CONCAVE (ii)

FIG. 336.
Convex and concave lenses.

Since a lens has a curved spherical surface, a thorough study of a lens should be preceded by a discussion of the refraction of light through a curved surface. We shall therefore proceed to consider what happens in this case, and defer a discussion of lenses until later, p. 488.

REFRACTION AT CURVED SPHERICAL SURFACE

1. Relation Between Object and Image Distances

Consider a curved spherical surface NP, bounding media of refractive indices μ_1, μ_2 respectively, Fig. 337. The medium of refractive index μ_1 might be air, for example, and the other of refractive index μ_2 might be glass. The centre, C, of the sphere of which NP is part is the centre of curvature of the surface, and hence CP is the radius of curvature, r. The line joining C to the mid-point P of the surface is known as its *principal axis*. P is known as the *pole*.

Suppose a point object O is situated on the axis PC in the medium of refractive index μ_1. The image of O by refraction at the curved surface can be obtained by taking two rays from O. A ray OP passes straight through along PC into the medium of refractive index μ_2, since OP is

normal to the surface, while a ray ON *very close* to the axis is refracted
at N along NI towards the normal CN, if we assume μ_2 is greater than
μ_1. Thus the point of intersection, I, of OP and NI is the image of O,
and we have here the case of a real image.

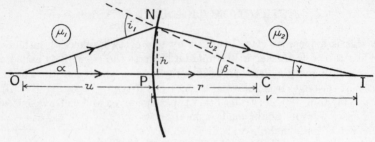

Fig. 337.   Refraction at curved surface.

Suppose i_1, i_2 are the angles made by ON, NI respectively with the
normal, CN, at N, Fig. 337. Then, applying "$\mu \sin i$" is a constant (p. 432),

$$\mu_1 \sin i_1 = \mu_2 \sin i_2 \qquad \cdot \qquad \cdot \qquad \cdot \qquad \cdot \qquad \text{(i)}$$

But if we deal with rays from O very close to the axis OP, i_1 is small;
and hence $\sin i_1 = i_1$ in radians. Similarly, $\sin i_2 = i_2$ in radians.
From (i), it follows that

$$\mu_1 i_1 = \mu_2 i_2 \qquad \cdot \qquad \cdot \qquad \cdot \qquad \cdot \qquad \cdot \qquad \text{(ii)}$$

If a, β, γ are the angles with the axis made by ON, CN, IN respectively, we have

$$i_1 = a + \beta, \text{ from the geometry of triangle ONC,}$$

and $\qquad\qquad i_2 = \beta - \gamma, \text{ from the geometry of triangle CNI.}$

Substituting for i_1, i_2 in (ii), we have

$$\mu_1 (a + \beta) = \mu_2 (\beta - \gamma)$$
$$\therefore \mu_1 a + \mu_2 \gamma = (\mu_2 - \mu_1) \beta \qquad \cdot \qquad \cdot \qquad \cdot \qquad \cdot \qquad \text{(iii)}$$

If h is the height of N above the axis, and N is so close to P that NP
is perpendicular to OP,

$$a = \frac{h}{OP}, \gamma = \frac{h}{PI}, \beta = \frac{h}{PC}$$

From (iii), using our sign convention on p. 417, we have

$$h \left(\frac{\mu_1}{+OP} + \frac{\mu_2}{+PI} \right) = h \frac{(\mu_2 - \mu_1)}{PC},$$

since O is a real object and I is a real image.

$$\therefore \frac{\mu_1}{OP} + \frac{\mu_2}{PI} = \frac{\mu_2 - \mu_1}{PC}$$

If the object distance, OP, from P = u, the image distance, IP, from P = v, and PC = r, then

$$\frac{\mu_1}{u} + \frac{\mu_2}{v} = \frac{\mu_2 - \mu_1}{r} \qquad . \qquad . \qquad . \qquad (21)$$

2. Sign Convention for Radius of Curvature

Equation (21) is the general relation between the object and image distances, u, v, from the middle or pole of the refracting surface, its radius of curvature r, and the refractive indices of the media, μ_2, μ_1. The quantity $(\mu_2 - \mu_1)/r$ is known as the **power** of the surface. If a ray is made to *converge* by a surface, as in Fig. 337, the power will be assumed *positive* in sign; if a ray is made to diverge by a surface, the power will be assumed negative. Since refractive index is a ratio of velocities (p. 430), μ_1 *and* μ_2 *have no sign.* $(\mu_2 - \mu_1)$ on the right side of equation (21) will be taken always as a *positive* quantity, and thus denotes the smaller refractive index subtracted from the greater refractive index. The sign convention for the radius of curvature, r, of a spherical surface is now as follows: If the surface is *convex to the less dense* medium, its radius is *positive*; if it is concave to the less dense medium, its radius is negative. We have thus to view the surface from a point in the less

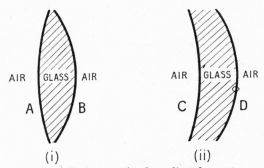

FIG. 338.   Sign convention for radius of curvature.

dense medium. In Fig. 338 (i), the surface A is convex to the less dense medium air, and hence its radius is positive. The surface C is concave to the less dense medium air, and its radius is thus negative, Fig. 338 (ii). The radii of the surfaces B and D are both positive.

3. Special Cases

The general formula $\frac{\mu_1}{u} + \frac{\mu_2}{v} = \frac{\mu_2 \sim \mu_1}{r}$ can easily be remembered on account of its symmetry. The object distance u corresponds to the refractive index μ_1 of the medium in which the object is situated; while the image distance v corresponds to the medium of refractive index μ_2 in which the image is situated.

Suppose an object O in air is x cm. from a curved spherical surface, and the image I is real and in glass of refractive index μ, at a distance of y cm. from the surface, Fig. 339 (i). Then $u = +x$, $v = +y$, $\mu_1 = 1$,

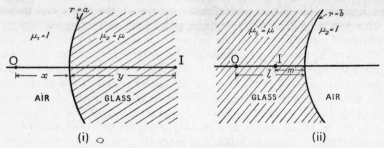

Fig. 339. Special cases of refraction formula.

$\mu_2 = \mu$. If the surface is convex to the less dense medium, as shown in Fig. 339 (i), the radius of curvature, a cm., is given by $r = +a$.

Substituting in
$$\frac{\mu_1}{u} + \frac{\mu_2}{v} = \frac{\mu_2 \sim \mu_1}{r}$$

$$\therefore \quad \frac{1}{x} + \frac{\mu}{y} = \frac{(\mu - 1)}{a}$$

Fig. 339 (ii) illustrates the case of an object O in glass of refractive index μ, the surface being concave to the less dense surface air. The radius, b cm., is then given by $r = -b$. The image I is virtual, and hence its distance $v = -m$. If l is the distance of O, then $u = +l$.

Substituting in
$$\frac{\mu_1}{u} + \frac{\mu_2}{v} = \frac{\mu_2 \sim \mu_1}{r}$$

$$\therefore \quad \frac{\mu}{l} + \frac{1}{-m} = \frac{\mu - 1}{-b}$$

If a surface is *plane*, its radius of curvature, r, is infinitely large. Hence $\dfrac{\mu_2 \sim \mu_1}{r}$ is zero, whatever different values μ_1 and μ_2 may have.

4. Deviation of Light by Sphere

Suppose a ray AO in air is incident on a sphere of glass or a drop of water, Fig. 340 (i). The light is refracted at O, then reflected inside at B, and finally emerges into the air along CD. If i, r are the angles of

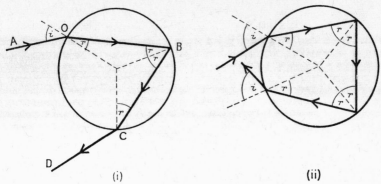

FIG. 340. Deviation of light by sphere.

incidence and refraction at O, the deviation of the light at O and C is $(i - r)$ each time; it is $(180° - 2r)$ at B. The total deviation, δ, in a clockwise direction is thus given by

$$\delta = 2(i - r) + 180° - 2r = 180° + 2i - 4r \qquad . \qquad . \qquad (i)$$

It can be seen that the deviation at each reflection inside the sphere is $(180° - 2r)$ and that the deviation at each refraction is $(i - r)$. Thus if a ray undergoes two reflections inside the sphere, and two refractions, as shown in Fig. 80 (ii), the total deviation in a clockwise direction $= 2(i - r) + 2(180° - 2r) = 360° + 2i - 6r$. After n internal reflections,

$$\text{the total deviation} = 2(i - r) + n(180° - 2r).$$

5. The Rainbow

The explanation of the colours of the rainbow was first given by Newton about 1667. He had already shown that sunlight consisted of a mixture of colours ranging from red to violet, and that glass could disperse or separate the colours (p. 464). In the same way, he argued, water droplets in the air dispersed the various colours in different directions, so that the colours of the spectrum were seen.

The curved appearance of the rainbow was first correctly explained about 1611. It was attributed to refraction of light at a water drop, followed by reflection inside the drop, the ray finally emerging into the air as shown in Fig. 341. The *primary bow* is the rainbow usually seen, and is obtained by two refractions and one reflection at the drops, as in Fig. 341. Sometimes a *secondary bow* is seen higher in the sky, and is formed by rays undergoing two refractions and two reflections at the drop, as in Fig. 341.

The total deviation δ of the light when one reflection occurs in the drop, Fig. 341, is given by $\delta = 180° + 2i - 4r$, as proved before. Now the light emerging from the drop will be intense at those angles of incidence

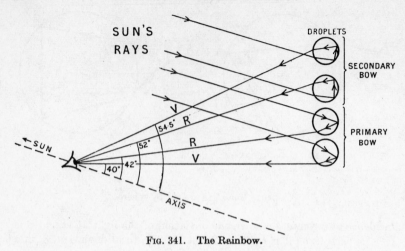

FIG. 341. The Rainbow.

corresponding to the *minimum* deviation position, since a considerable number of rays have about the same deviation at the minimum value and thus emerge almost parallel. Now for a minimum value, $\dfrac{d\delta}{di} = 0$.

Differentiating the expression for δ, we have $2 - 4\dfrac{dr}{di} = 0$.

$$\therefore \qquad \frac{dr}{di} = \frac{1}{2}$$

But $\qquad \sin i = \mu \sin r,$

where μ is the refractive index of water.

$$\therefore \qquad \cos i = \mu \cos r \frac{dr}{di} = \frac{\mu}{2}\cos r$$

$$\therefore \quad 4\cos^2 i = \mu^2 \cos^2 r = \mu^2 - \mu^2 \sin^2 r = \mu^2 - \sin^2 i$$
$$= \mu^2 - (1 - \cos^2 i)$$

$$\therefore \quad 3\cos^2 i = \mu^2 - 1$$

$$\therefore \qquad \cos i = \sqrt{\frac{\mu^2 - 1}{3}} \qquad . \quad . \quad . \quad . \quad \text{(ii)}$$

The refractive index of water for red light is 1·331. Substituting this value in (ii) i can be found, and thus r is obtained. The deviation δ can then be calculated, and the acute angle between the incident and emergent red rays, which is the supplement of δ, is about 42·1°. By substituting the refractive index of water for violet light in (ii), the acute angle between the incident and emergent violet rays is found to be about 40·2°. Thus if a shower of drops is illuminated by the sun's rays, an observer standing with his back to the sun sees a brilliant red light at an angle of 42·1° with the line joining the sun to him, and a brilliant violet light at an angle of 40·2° with this line, Fig. 341. Since the phenomenon is the same in all planes passing through the line, the brightly coloured drops form an arc of a circle whose centre is on the line.

The secondary bow is formed by two internal reflections in the water drops, as illustrated in Fig. 340 (ii) and Fig. 341. The minimum deviation occurs when $\cos i = \sqrt{(\mu^2 - 1)/8}$ in this case. The acute angle between the incident and emergent red rays is then found to be about $51 \cdot 8°$, and that for the violet rays is found to be about $54 \cdot 5°$. Thus the secondary bow has red on the inside and violet on the outside, whereas the primary bow colours are the reverse, Fig. 341

EXAMPLES

1. Obtain a formula connecting the distances of object and image from a spherical refracting surface. A small piece of paper is stuck on a glass sphere of 5 cm. radius and viewed through the glass from a position directly opposite. Find the position of the image. Find also the position of the image formed, by the sphere, of an object at infinity. *(O. & C.)*

First part. See text.

Second part. Suppose O is the piece of paper, Fig. 342 (i). The refracting surface of the glass is at P, and $u = + 10$. Now

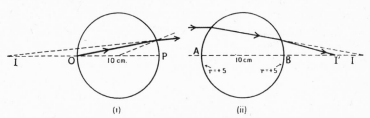

Fig. 342.

$$\frac{\mu_2}{v} + \frac{\mu_1}{u} = \frac{\mu_2 \sim \mu_1}{r}$$

where $\mu_1 = 1 \cdot 5$, $\mu_2 = 1$, $r = + 5$ (p. 483), and v is the image distance from P

Substituting,

$$\frac{1}{v} + \frac{1 \cdot 5}{10} = \frac{1 \cdot 5 - 1}{5}$$

$$\therefore \quad \frac{1}{v} = 0 \cdot 1 - 0 \cdot 15 = - 0 \cdot 05$$

$$\therefore \quad v = - 20 \text{ cm.}$$

Thus the image is virtual, i.e., it is 20 cm. from P on the same side as O.

Third part. Suppose I is the position of the image by refraction at the first surface, A Fig. 342 (ii). Now $\frac{\mu_2}{v} + \frac{\mu_1}{u} = \frac{\mu_2 \sim \mu_1}{r}$, where $u = \infty$, $\mu_1 = 1$, $\mu_2 = 1 \cdot 5$, $r = + 5$.

$$\therefore \quad \frac{1 \cdot 5}{v} = \frac{1 \cdot 5 - 1}{5}$$

$$\therefore \quad v = 15 \text{ cm.} = \text{AI, or BI} = 5 \text{ cm.}$$

I is a virtual object for refraction at the curved surface B. Since $u = -$ BI $= -5$ cm., $\mu_1 = 1{\cdot}5$, $\mu_2 = 1$, $r = +5$, it follows from

$$\frac{\mu_2}{v} + \frac{\mu_1}{u} = \frac{\mu_2 \sim \mu_1}{r}$$

that

$$\frac{1}{v} + \frac{1{\cdot}5}{(-5)} = \frac{1{\cdot}5 - 1}{5}$$

from which

$$v = 2{\cdot}5 \text{ cm.} = \text{BI}'.$$

2. An object is placed in front of a spherical refracting surface. Derive an expression connecting the distances from the refracting surface of the object and the image produced. The apparent thickness of a thick plano-convex lens is measured with (a) the plane face uppermost (b) the convex face uppermost, the values being 2 cm. and $2\frac{2}{3}$ cm. respectively. If its real thickness is 3 cm., calculate the refractive index of the glass and the radius of curvature of the convex face. (L.)

First part. See text.

Second part. With the plane face uppermost, the image I of the lowest point O is obtained by considering refraction at the plane surface D, Fig. 343 (i). Now

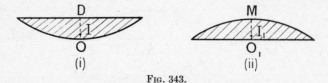

(i) (ii)

Fig. 343.

$$\mu = \frac{\text{real depth}}{\text{apparent depth}}$$

$$\therefore \mu = \frac{3}{2} = 1{\cdot}5$$

With the curved surface uppermost, the image I_1 of the lowest point O_1 is obtained by considering refraction at the curved surface M, Fig. 343 (ii). In this case $MI_1 = v = $ apparent thickness $= -2\frac{2}{3}$ cm., the image I_1 being virtual. Now $u = MO_1 = 3$ cm., $\mu_2 = 1$, $\mu_1 = \mu = 1{\cdot}5$. Substituting in

$$\frac{\mu_2}{v} + \frac{\mu_1}{u} = \frac{\mu_2 \sim \mu_1}{r}$$

we have

$$\frac{1}{-2\frac{2}{3}} + \frac{1{\cdot}5}{3} = \frac{1{\cdot}5 - 1}{r} \ .$$

Simplifying,

$$r = 10 \text{ cm.}$$

REFRACTION THROUGH THIN LENSES

6. Convex (converging) and Concave (diverging) Lenses

At the beginning of the chapter we defined a lens as an object, usually of glass, bounded by one or two spherical surfaces. Besides the convex (converging) lens shown in Fig. 336 (i) on p. 481, Fig. 344 (i) illustrates two other types of convex lenses, which are thicker in the middle than at the edges. Fig. 344 (ii) illustrates two types of concave (diverging) lenses, a concave lens being also shown in Fig. 336 (ii) on p. 481.

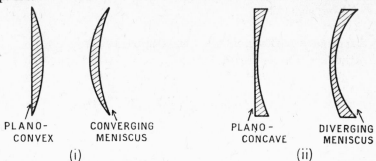

PLANO-   CONVERGING   PLANO-   DIVERGING
CONVEX   MENISCUS   CONCAVE   MENISCUS
   (i)   (ii)

Fig. 344. (i) Convex (converging) lenses. (ii) Concave (diverging) lenses.

The *principal axis* of a lens is the line joining the centres of curvature of the two surfaces, and passes through the middle of the lens. Experiments with a ray-box show that a thin convex lens brings an incident parallel beam of rays to a *principal focus*, F, on the other side of the lens when the beam is narrow and incident close to the principal axis, Fig. 345 (i). On account of the convergent beam obtained with it, the convex lens is better described as a "converging" lens. If a similar parallel beam is incident on the other (right) side of the lens, it converges to a focus F', which is at the same distance from the lens as F when the lens is thin. To distinguish F from F' the latter is called the "first principal focus"; F is known as the "second principal focus".

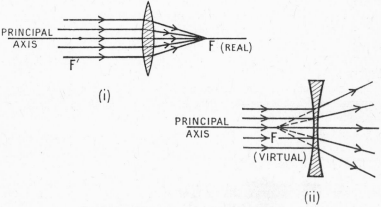

Fig. 345. Focus of convex and concave lenses.

When a narrow parallel beam, close to the principal axis, is incident on a thin concave lens, experiment shows that a beam is obtained which appears to diverge from a point F on the same side as the incident beam, Fig. 345 (ii). F is known as the principal "focus" of the concave lens, Since a divergent beam is obtained, the concave lens is better described as a "diverging" lens.

7. Explanation of Effects of Convex and Concave Lenses

A thin lens may be regarded as made up of a very large number of *small angle prisms* placed together, as shown in the exaggerated sketches of Fig. 346. If the spherical surfaces of the various truncated prisms are imagined to be produced, the angles of the prisms can be

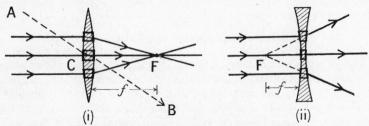

FIG. 346.   Action of convex and concave lenses.

seen to increase from zero at the middle to a small value at the edge of the lens. Now the deviation, d, of a ray of light by a small angle prism is given by $d = (\mu - 1) A$, where A is the angle of the prism, see p. 467. Consequently the truncated prism corresponding to a position further away from the middle of the lens deviates an incident ray more than those prisms nearer the middle. Thus, for the case of the convex lens, the refracted rays converge to the same point or focus F, Fig. 346 (i). It will be noted that a ray AC incident on the middle, C, of the lens emerges parallel to AC, since the middle acts like a rectangular piece of glass (p. 431). This fact is utilised in the drawing of images in convex and concave lenses (p. 496).

Since the concave lens is made up of truncated prisms pointing the opposite way to the convex lens, the deviation of the light is in the opposite direction, Fig. 346 (ii). A divergent beam is hence obtained when parallel rays are refracted by the lens.

8. The Signs of Focal Length, f

From Fig. 346 (i), it can be seen that a convex lens has a real focus; the focal length, f, of a *convex* lens is thus *positive* in sign. Since the focus of a concave lens is virtual, the focal length of a concave lens is negative in sign, Fig. 346 (ii). The reader must memorise the sign of f for a convex and concave lens respectively, as this is always required in connection with lens formulæ.

9. Relation Between Image and Object Distances for Thin Lens

We can now derive a relation between the object and image distances when a lens is used. We shall limit ourselves to the case of a *thin* lens, i.e., one whose thickness is small compared with its other dimensions, and consider narrow beams of light incident on its central portion.

Suppose a lens of refractive index μ_2 is placed in a medium of refractive index μ_1, and a point object O is situated on the principal axis, Fig. 347. A ray from O through the middle of the lens passes straight through as it is normal to both lens surfaces. A ray OM from O, making a *small* angle with the principal axis, is refracted at the first surface in the direction MNI', and then refracted again at N at the second surface so that it emerges along NI.

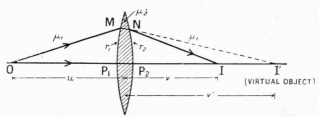

Fig. 347.   (Exaggerated for clarity.)

Refraction at first surface, MP_1. Suppose u is the distance of the object from the lens, i.e., $u = OP_1$, and v' is the distance of the image I' by refraction at the first surface, MP_1, of the lens, i.e., $v' = I'P_1$. Then, since I' is situated in the medium of refractive index μ_2 (I' is on the ray MN produced), we have, if $\mu_2 > \mu_1$,

$$\frac{\mu_2}{v'} + \frac{\mu_1}{u} = \frac{\mu_2 - \mu_1}{r_1} \qquad . \qquad . \qquad . \qquad . \qquad . \qquad \text{(i)}$$

where r_1 is the radius of the spherical surface MP_1, see p. 483.

Refraction at second surface, NP_2. Since MN and P_1P_2 are the incident rays on the second surface NP_2, it follows that I' is a *virtual object* for refraction at this surface (see p. 422). Hence the object distance $I'P_2$ is negative; and as we are dealing with a thin lens, $I'P_2 = -v'$. The corresponding image distance, IP_2 or v, is positive since I is a real image. Substituting in the formula for refraction at a single spherical surface,

$$\therefore \quad \frac{\mu_2}{-v'} + \frac{\mu_1}{v} = \frac{\mu_2 - \mu_1}{r_2} \qquad . \qquad . \qquad . \qquad . \qquad . \qquad \text{(ii)}$$

where r_2 is the radius of curvature of the surface NP_2 of the lens.

Lens equation. Adding (i) and (ii) to eliminate v', we have

$$\frac{\mu_1}{v} + \frac{\mu_1}{u} = (\mu_2 - \mu_1)\left(\frac{1}{r_1} + \frac{1}{r_2}\right);$$

and dividing throughout by μ_1,

$$\frac{1}{v} + \frac{1}{u} = \left(\frac{\mu_2}{\mu_1} - 1\right)\left(\frac{1}{r_1} + \frac{1}{r_2}\right) \quad . \quad . \quad . \quad \text{(iii)}$$

Now parallel rays incident on the lens are brought to a focus. In this case, $u = \infty$ and $v = f$. From (iii),

$$\frac{1}{f} + \frac{1}{\infty} = \left(\frac{\mu_2}{\mu_1} - 1\right)\left(\frac{1}{r_1} + \frac{1}{r_2}\right)$$

$$\therefore \quad \frac{1}{f} = \left(\frac{\mu_2}{\mu_1} - 1\right)\left(\frac{1}{r_1} + \frac{1}{r_2}\right) \quad . \quad . \quad \text{(22)}$$

Substituting $\dfrac{1}{f}$ for the right side of (iii), we obtain the important equation

$$\frac{1}{v} + \frac{1}{u} = \frac{1}{f} \quad . \quad . \quad . \quad . \quad . \quad \text{(23)}$$

This is the "lens equation", and it applies equally to convex and concave lenses if the sign convention is used (see also p. 419).

10. Focal Length Values

Since $\dfrac{1}{f} = \left(\dfrac{\mu_2}{\mu_1} - 1\right)\left(\dfrac{1}{r_1} + \dfrac{1}{r_2}\right)$, it follows that the focal length of a lens depends on the refractive index, μ_2, of its material, the refractive index, μ_1, of the medium in which it is placed, and the radii of curvature, r_1, r_2, of the lens surfaces. The quantity $\dfrac{\mu_2}{\mu_1}$ may be termed the "relative refractive index" of the lens material; if the lens is made of glass of $\mu_2 = 1\cdot5$, and it is placed in water of $\mu_1 = 1\cdot33$, then the relative refractive index $= \dfrac{1\cdot5}{1\cdot33} = 1\cdot13$.

In practice, however, lenses are usually situated in air; in which case $\mu_1 = 1$. If the glass has a refractive index, μ_2, equal to μ, the relative refractive index, $\dfrac{\mu_2}{\mu_1}, = \dfrac{\mu}{1} = \mu$. Substituting in (22), then

$$\frac{1}{f} = (\mu - 1)\left(\frac{1}{r_1} + \frac{1}{r_2}\right) \quad . \quad . \quad . \quad \text{(24)}$$

Fig. 348 illustrates four different types of glass lenses in air, whose refractive indices, μ, are each $1\cdot5$. Fig. 348 (i) is a biconvex lens, whose radii of curvature, r_1, r_2, are each 10 cm. Since a spherical surface convex to a less dense medium has a positive sign (see p. 483), $r_1 = +10$ and $r_2 = +10$. Substituting in (24),

$$\therefore \qquad \frac{1}{f} = (1\cdot5 - 1)\left(\frac{1}{(+10)} + \frac{1}{(+10)}\right) = 0\cdot5 \times \frac{2}{10} = 0\cdot1$$

$$\therefore \qquad f = +10 \text{ cm.}$$

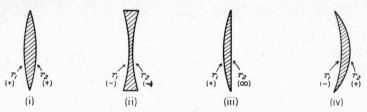

Fig. 348.   Signs of radius of lens surface.

Fig. 348 (ii) is a biconcave lens in air. Since its surfaces are both concave to the less dense medium, $r_1 = -10$ and $r_2 = -10$, assuming the radii are both 10 cm. Substituting in (24),

$$\therefore \qquad \frac{1}{f} = (1\cdot5 - 1)\left(\frac{1}{(-10)} + \frac{1}{(-10)}\right) = 0\cdot5 \times -\frac{2}{10} = -0\cdot1$$

$$\therefore \qquad f = -10 \text{ cm.}$$

In the case of a plano-convex lens, suppose the radius is 8 cm. Then $r_1 = +8$ and $r_2 = \infty$, Fig. 348 (iii). Hence $\dfrac{1}{f} = (1\cdot5 - 1)\left(\dfrac{1}{(+8)} + \dfrac{1}{\infty}\right)$

$= 0\cdot5 \times \dfrac{1}{8} = \dfrac{1}{16}$. Thus $f = +16$ cm.

In Fig. 348 (iv), suppose the radii r_1, r_2 are numerically 16 cm., 12 cm. respectively. Then $r_1 = -16$, but $r_2 = +12$. Hence

$$\frac{1}{f} = (1\cdot5 - 1)\left(\frac{1}{(-16)} + \frac{1}{(+12)}\right) = 0\cdot5\left(-\frac{1}{16} + \frac{1}{12}\right) = +\frac{1}{96}$$

Thus $f = +96$ cm., confirming that the lens is a convex one.

11. Some Applications of the Lens Equation

The following examples should assist the reader in understanding

how to apply correctly the lens equation $\dfrac{1}{v} + \dfrac{1}{u} = \dfrac{1}{f}$:

1. An object is placed 12 cm. from a convex lens of focal length 18 cm. Find the position of the image.

Since the lens is convex, $f = +18$ cm. The object is real, and hence

$u = + 12$ cm. Substituting in $\dfrac{1}{v} + \dfrac{1}{u} = \dfrac{1}{f}$,

$$\therefore \quad \frac{1}{v} + \frac{1}{(+12)} = \frac{1}{(+18)}$$

$$\therefore \quad \frac{1}{v} = \frac{1}{18} - \frac{1}{12} = -\frac{1}{36}$$

$$\therefore \quad v = -36$$

Since v is negative in sign the image is *virtual*, and it is 36 cm. from the lens. See Fig. 351 (ii).

2. A beam of light, converging to a point 10 cm. behind a convex lens, is incident on the lens. Find the position of the point image if the lens has a focal length of 40 cm.

If the incident beam converges to the point O, then O is a *virtual object,*

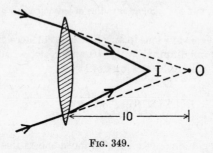

Fig. 349.

Fig. 349. See p. 422. Thus $u = -10$ cm. Also, $f = +40$ cm. since the lens is convex. Substituting in $\dfrac{1}{v} + \dfrac{1}{u} = \dfrac{1}{f}$,

$$\therefore \quad \frac{1}{v} + \frac{1}{(-10)} = \frac{1}{(+40)}$$

$$\therefore \quad \frac{1}{v} = \frac{1}{40} + \frac{1}{10} = \frac{5}{40}$$

$$\therefore \quad v = \frac{40}{5} = 8$$

Since v is positive in sign the image is *real*, and it is 8 cm. from the lens. The image is I in Fig. 349.

3. An object is placed 6 ins. in front of a concave lens of focal length 12 ins. Find the image position.

Since the lens is concave, $f = -12$ ins. The object is real, and hence $u = +6$ ins. Substituting in $\dfrac{1}{v} + \dfrac{1}{u} = \dfrac{1}{f}$,

$$\therefore \frac{1}{v} + \frac{1}{(+6)} = \frac{1}{(-12)}$$

$$\therefore \quad \frac{1}{v} = -\frac{1}{12} - \frac{1}{6} = -\frac{3}{12}$$

$$\therefore \quad v = -\frac{12}{3} = -4$$

Since v is negative in sign the image is virtual, and it is 4 ins. from the lens. See Fig. 352 (i).

4. A converging beam of light is incident on a concave lens of focal length 15 cm. If the beam converges to a point 3 cm. behind the lens, find the position of the point image.

If the beam converges to the point O, then O is a virtual object, as

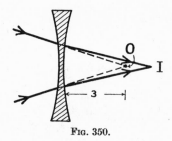

FIG. 350.

in example 2, Fig. 349. Thus $u = -3$ cm. Since the lens is concave, $f = -15$ cm. Substituting in $\dfrac{1}{v} + \dfrac{1}{u} = \dfrac{1}{f}$,

$$\therefore \quad \frac{1}{v} + \frac{1}{(-3)} = \frac{1}{(-15)}$$

$$\therefore \quad \frac{1}{v} = -\frac{1}{15} + \frac{1}{3} = \frac{4}{15}$$

$$\therefore \quad v = \frac{15}{4} = 3\tfrac{3}{4}$$

Since v is positive in sign the point image, I, is *real*, and it is $3\tfrac{3}{4}$ cm. from the lens, Fig. 350.

12. Images in Lenses

Convex lens. (i) When an object is a very long way from a convex lens, i.e., at infinity, the rays arriving at the lens from the object are parallel. Thus the image is formed at the focus of the lens, and is real and inverted.

(ii) Suppose an object OP is placed at O perpendicular to the principal axis of a thin convex lens, so that it is further from the lens than its principal focus, Fig. 351 (i). A ray PC incident on the middle, C, of the lens is very slightly displaced by its refraction through the lens, as the opposite surface near C are parallel (see Fig. 346, which is an exaggerated sketch of the passage of the ray). We therefore consider that PC passes *straight through* the lens, and this is true for any ray incident on the middle of a thin lens.

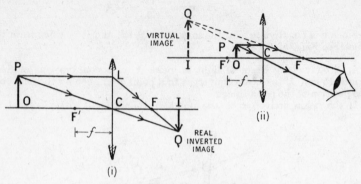

FIG. 351. Images in convex lenses.

A ray PL parallel to the principal axis is refracted so that it passes through the focus F. Thus the image, Q, of the top point P of the object is formed below the principal axis, and hence the whole image IQ is real and inverted. In making accurate drawings the lens should be represented by a straight line, as illustrated in Fig. 351, as we are only concerned with thin lenses and a narrow beam incident close to the principal axis.

(iii) The image formed by a convex lens is always real and inverted until the object is placed nearer to the lens than its focal length, Fig. 351 (ii). In this case the rays from the top point P *diverge* after refraction through the lens, and hence the image Q is *virtual*. The whole image, IQ, is erect (the same way up as the object) and magnified, besides being virtual, and hence the convex lens can be used as a simple "magnifying glass" (see p. 543).

Concave lens. In the case of a convex lens, the image is sometimes real and sometimes virtual. In a concave lens, however, the image is

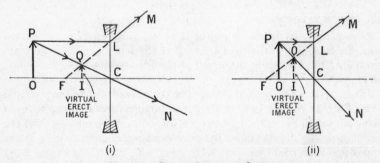

FIG. 352. Images in concave lenses.

always virtual; in addition, the image is always erect and diminished. Fig. 352 (i), (ii) illustrate the formation of two images. A ray PL appears to diverge from the focus F after refraction through the lens, a ray PC passes straight through the middle of the lens and emerges along CN, and hence the emergent beam from P appears to diverge from Q on the same side of the lens as the object. The image IQ is thus *virtual*.

The rays entering the eye from a point on an object viewed through a lens can easily be traced. Suppose L is a convex lens, and IQ is the image of the object OP, drawn as already explained, Fig. 353. If the eye E observes the top point P of the object through the lens, the

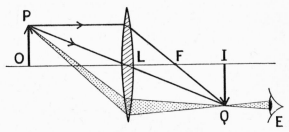

FIG. 353.   Rays entering the eye.

cone of rays entering E are those bounded by the image Q of P and the pupil of the eye. If these rays are produced back to meet the lens L, and the points of incidence are joined to P, the rays entering E are shown shaded in the beam. The method can be applied to trace the beam of light entering the eye from any other point on the object; the important thing to remember is to *work back from the eye*.

Another proof of $\dfrac{1}{v} + \dfrac{1}{u} = \dfrac{1}{f}$. We have already shown how the lens equation $\dfrac{1}{v} + \dfrac{1}{u} = \dfrac{1}{f}$ can be derived by considering refraction in turn at the two curved surfaces (p. 491). A proof of the equation can also be obtained from Fig. 351 or Fig. 352, but it is not as rigid a proof as that already given on page 491.

In Fig. 352, triangles CQI, CPO are similar. Hence IQ/PO = CI/CO. Since triangles FQI, FLC are similar, IQ/CL = FI/FC. Now CL = PO. Thus the left sides of the two ratios are equal.

$$\therefore \quad \frac{CI}{CO} = \frac{FI}{FC}$$

But CI $= -v$; CO $= +u$; FI $= F - IC = -f - (-v) = v - f$; and FC $= -f$.

$$\therefore \quad \frac{-v}{+u} = \frac{v-f}{-f}$$

$$\therefore \qquad vf = uv - uf$$
$$\therefore \quad uf + vf = uv$$

Dividing throughout by uvf and simplifying each term,

$$\therefore \quad \frac{1}{v} + \frac{1}{u} = \frac{1}{f}$$

The same result can be derived by considering similar triangles in Fig. 351, a useful exercise for the student.

13. Lateral Magnification, m

The lateral or linear magnification, m, produced by a lens is defined by

$$m = \frac{height\ of\ image}{height\ of\ object} \qquad \cdots \cdots \quad (25)$$

Thus $m = \dfrac{IQ}{OP}$ in Fig. 351 or Fig. 352. Since triangles QIC, POC are similar in either of the diagrams,

$$\frac{IQ}{OP} = \frac{CI}{CO} = \frac{v}{u},$$

where v, u are the respective image and object distances from the lens.

$$\therefore \qquad \mathbf{m} = \frac{\mathbf{v}}{\mathbf{u}} \qquad \cdot \quad \cdot \quad \cdot \quad \cdot \quad (26)$$

Equation (26) provides a simple formula for the magnitude of the magnification; there is no need to consider the signs of v and u in this case.

Other formulæ for magnification. Since $\dfrac{1}{v} + \dfrac{1}{u} = \dfrac{1}{f}$, we have, by multiplying throughout by v,

$$1 + \frac{v}{u} = \frac{v}{f}$$

$$\therefore \quad 1 + m = \frac{v}{f}$$

$$\therefore \quad m = \frac{v}{f} - 1 \qquad \cdot \quad \cdot \quad \cdot \quad \cdot \quad (27)$$

Thus if a real image is formed 25 cm. from a convex lens of focal length 10 cm., the magnification, m, $= \dfrac{+25}{+10} - 1 = 1.5$.

By multiplying both sides of the lens equation by u, we have

$$\frac{u}{v} + 1 = \frac{u}{f}$$

$$\therefore \quad \frac{1}{m} + 1 = \frac{u}{f}$$

14. Object at Distance 2f from Convex Lens

When an object is placed at a distance of $2f$ from a convex lens, drawing shows that the real image obtained is the same size as the image and is also formed at a distance $2f$ from the lens, Fig. 354. This result

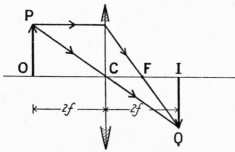

FIG. 354.   Object and image of same size.

can be accurately checked by using the lens equation $\dfrac{1}{v} + \dfrac{1}{u} = \dfrac{1}{f}$.
Substituting $u = +2f$, and noting that the focal length, f, of a convex lens is positive, we have

$$\frac{1}{v} + \frac{1}{2f} = \frac{1}{f}$$

$$\therefore \quad \frac{1}{v} = \frac{1}{f} - \frac{1}{2f} = \frac{1}{2f}$$

$$\therefore \quad v = 2f = \text{image distance.}$$

$\therefore$ lateral magnification, $m, = \dfrac{v}{u} = \dfrac{2f}{2f} = 1$.

showing that the image is the same size as the object.

15. Least Possible Distance Between Object and Real Image with Convex Lens

It is not always possible to obtain a real image on a screen, although the object and the screen may both be at a greater distance from a convex lens than its focal length. The theory given below shows that the distance between an object and a screen must be equal to, or greater than, *four times the focal length* if a real image is required.

Theory. Suppose I is the real image of a point object O in the convex lens. If the image distance = x, and the distance OI = d, the object distance

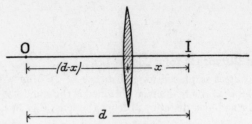

FIG. 355.   Minimum distance between object and image.

$= (d - x)$, Fig. 355. Thus $v = + x$, and $u = + (d - x)$. Substituting in the lens equation $\dfrac{1}{v} + \dfrac{1}{u} = \dfrac{1}{f}$, in which f is positive, we have

$$\frac{1}{x} + \frac{1}{d - x} = \frac{1}{f}$$

$$\therefore \qquad \frac{d}{x(d - x)} = \frac{1}{f}$$

$$\therefore \quad x^2 - dx + df = 0 \qquad . \qquad . \qquad . \qquad . \qquad \text{(i)}$$

For a real image, the roots of this quadratic equation for x must be real roots. Applying to (i) the condition $b^2 - 4ac > 0$ for the general quadratic $ax^2 + bx + c = 0$, then

$$d^2 - 4df > 0$$

$$\therefore \qquad d^2 > 4df$$

$$\therefore \qquad d > 4f$$

Thus the distance OI between the object and screen must be greater than $4f$, otherwise no image can be formed on the screen. Hence $4f$ is the minimum distance between object and screen; the latter case is illustrated by Fig. 354, in which $u = 2f$ and $v = 2f$. If it is difficult to obtain a real image on a screen when a convex lens is used, the possible causes may be (i) the object is nearer to the lens than its focal length, Fig. 351 (ii), or (ii) the distance between the screen and object is less than four times the focal length of the lens.

16. Conjugate Points. Newton's Relation

Suppose that an object at a point O in front of a lens has its image

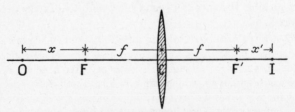

FIG. 356.   Newton's relation.

formed at a point I. Since light rays are reversible, it follows an object placed at I will give rise to an image at O. The points O, I are thus "interchangeable", and are hence called *conjugate points* (or conjugate foci) with respect to the lens. Newton showed that conjugate points obey the relation $xx' = f^2$, where x, x' are their respective distances from the focus on the same side of the lens.

The proof of this relation can be seen by taking the case of the convex lens in Fig. 356, in which $OC = u = x + f$, and $CI = v = x' + f$.

Substituting in the lens equation $\dfrac{1}{v} + \dfrac{1}{u} = \dfrac{1}{f}$,

$$\therefore \quad \frac{1}{x' + f} + \frac{1}{x + f} = \frac{1}{f}$$
$$\therefore \quad f(x' + x + 2f) = (x' + f)(x + f)$$
$$\therefore \quad xx' = f^2 \quad . \quad . \quad . \quad . \quad . \quad (28)$$

Since $x' = f^2/x$, it follows that x' increases as x decreases. The image I thus recedes from the focus F' away from the lens when the object O approaches the lens.

The property of conjugate points stated above, namely that an object and an image at these points are interchangeable, can also be derived from the lens equation $\dfrac{1}{v} + \dfrac{1}{u} = \dfrac{1}{f}$. Thus if $u = 15$ cm. and $v = 10$ cm. satisfies this equation, so must $u = 10$ cm. and $v = 15$ cm.

17. Displacement of Lens when Object and Screen are Fixed

Suppose that an object O, in front of a convex lens at A, gives rise to an image on a screen at I, Fig. 357. Since the image distance AI (v) is

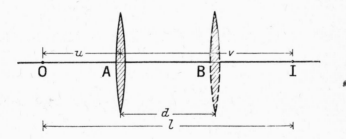

FIG. 357. Displacement of lens.

greater than the object distance AO (u), the image is larger than the object. If the object and the screen are kept fixed at O, I respectively, another clear image can be obtained on the screen by moving the lens from A to a position B. This time the image is smaller than the object, as the new image distance BI is less than the new object distance OB.

Since O and I are conjugate points with respect to the lens, it follows that OB = IA and IB = OA (if this is the case the lens equation will be satisfied by $\frac{1}{IB} + \frac{1}{OB} = \frac{1}{f}$ and by $\frac{1}{IA} + \frac{1}{OA} = \frac{1}{f}$). If the *displacement*, AB, of the lens = d, and the constant distance OI = l, then OA + BI = l − d. But, from above, OA = IB. Hence OA = (l − d)/2. Further, AI = AB + BI = OA + AB = (l − d)/2 + d = (l + d)/2.

But u = OA, and v = AI for the lens in the position A. Substituting for OA and AI in $\frac{1}{v} + \frac{1}{u} = \frac{1}{f}$,

$$\therefore \quad \frac{1}{(l+d)/2} + \frac{1}{(l-d)/2} = \frac{1}{f}$$

$$\therefore \quad \frac{2}{l+d} + \frac{2}{l-d} = \frac{1}{f}$$

$$\therefore \quad \frac{4l}{l^2 - d^2} = \frac{1}{f}$$

$$\therefore \quad f = \frac{l^2 - d^2}{4l} \quad \cdot \quad \cdot \quad \cdot \quad \cdot \quad (29)$$

Thus if the displacement d of the lens, and the distance l between the object and the screen, are measured, the focal length f of the lens can be found from equation (29). This provides a very useful method of measuring the focal length of a lens whose surfaces are inaccessible (for example, when the lens is in a tube), when measurements of v and u cannot be made (see p. 455).

Magnification. When the lens is in the position A, the lateral magnification m_1 of the object $= \frac{v}{u} = \frac{AI}{OA}$, Fig. 357.

$$\therefore \quad \frac{h_1}{h} = \frac{AI}{OA} \quad \cdot \quad \cdot \quad \cdot \quad \cdot \quad (i)$$

where h_1 is the length of the image and h is the length of the object.

When the lens is in the position B, the image is smaller than the object. The lateral magnification, $m_2, = \frac{BI}{OB}$.

$$\therefore \quad \frac{h_2}{h} = \frac{BI}{OB} \quad \cdot \quad \cdot \quad \cdot \quad \cdot \quad (ii)$$

where h_2 is the length of the image. But, from our previous discussion, AI = OB and OA = BI. From (i) and (ii) it follows that, by inverting (i),

$$\frac{h}{h_1} = \frac{h_2}{h}$$

$$\therefore \quad h^2 = h_1\, h_2$$

$$\therefore \quad h = \sqrt{h_1\, h_2} \qquad \cdot \qquad \cdot \qquad \cdot \qquad (30)$$

The length, h, of an object can hence be found by measuring the lengths h_1, h_2 of the images for the two positions of the lens. This method of measuring h is most useful when the object is inaccessible, for example, when the width of a slit in a tube is required.

EXAMPLES

1. A convex lens of focal length 30 cm. is placed 20 cm. away from a concave lens of focal length 5 cm. An object is placed 6 metres distant from the convex lens (which is the nearer to it) and on the common axis of the system. Determine the position, magnification, and nature of the image formed. (*O. & C.*)

Suppose O is the object, Fig. 358.

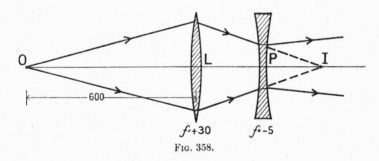

$f = +30 \qquad f = -5$

Fig. 358.

For the convex lens,

$$u = +\ 600 \text{ cm.}, f = +\ 30 \text{ cm.}$$

Substituting in the lens equation,

$$\therefore \qquad \frac{1}{v} + \frac{1}{(+\ 600)} = \frac{1}{(+\ 30)}$$

from which

$$v = \frac{600}{19} = 31\tfrac{11}{19} \text{ cm.} = \text{LI}$$

$$\therefore \qquad \text{PI} = \text{LI} - \text{LP} = 31\tfrac{11}{19} - 20 = 11\tfrac{11}{19} \text{ cm.}$$

For the concave lens, I is a virtual object. Thus $u = PI = -11\frac{11}{19}$. Also, $f = -5$. Substituting in the lens equation, we have

$$\frac{1}{v} + \frac{1}{(-11\frac{11}{19})} = \frac{1}{(-5)}$$

from which $\qquad v = -8\cdot8$ cm.

The image is thus virtual, and hence the rays diverge after refraction through P, as shown. The image is $8\cdot8$ cm. to the left of P.

The magnification, m, is given by $m = m_1 \times m_2$, where m_1, m_2 are the magnifications produced by the convex and concave lens respectively.

But $\qquad m_1 = \frac{v}{u} = 31\frac{11}{19}/600$

and $\qquad m_2 = 8\cdot8/11\frac{11}{19}$

$\therefore \quad m = 31\frac{11}{19}/600 \times 8\frac{4}{5}/11\frac{11}{19} = \frac{1}{25}$

2. Establish a formula connecting object-distance and image-distance for a simple lens. A small object is placed at a distance of 30 cm. from a converging lens of focal length 10 cm. Determine at what distances from this lens a second converging lens of focal length 40 cm. must be placed in order to produce (i) an erect image, (ii) an inverted image, in each case of the same size as the object. (*L.*)

First part. See text.

Second part. Suppose O is the object, Fig. 359. The image I in the convex lens L is formed at a distance v from L given by

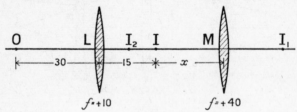

FIG. 359.

$$\frac{1}{v} + \frac{1}{(+30)} = \frac{1}{(+10)}$$

from which $\qquad v = +15$

For an erect image. Since $\dfrac{v}{u} = \dfrac{15}{30} = \dfrac{1}{2}$, the image at I is half the object size; also, the image is inverted, since it is real (see Fig. 351 (i)). If an erect image is required, the second lens, M, must invert the image at I. Further, if the new image, I_1, say, is to be the same size as the object at O, the magnification produced by M of the image at I must be 2. Suppose IM = x

numerically; then, since the magnification $\left(\dfrac{v}{u}\right) = 2$, $MI_1 = 2x$. As I and I_1 are both real, we have, from

$$\frac{1}{v} + \frac{1}{u} = \frac{1}{f},$$

$$\frac{1}{(+\,2x)} + \frac{1}{(+\,x)} = \frac{1}{(+\,40)}$$

$$\therefore \quad \frac{3}{2x} = \frac{1}{40}$$

from which
$$x = 60 \text{ cm.}$$

Thus M must be placed 75 cm. from L for an erect image of the same size as O.

For an inverted image. Since the image at I is inverted, the image I_2 of I in M must be erect with respect to I. The lens M must thus act like a magnifying glass which produces a magnification of 2, and the image I_2 is *virtual* in this case. Suppose $IM = x$ numerically; then $I_2M = 2x$ numerically. Substituting in

$$\frac{1}{v} + \frac{1}{u} = \frac{1}{f}$$

$$\therefore \quad \frac{1}{(-\,2x)} + \frac{1}{(+x)} = \frac{1}{(+40)}$$

$$\therefore \quad x = 20 \text{ cm.}$$

Thus M must be placed 35 cm. from L for an inverted image of the same size as O.

Some Methods of Measuring Focal Lengths of Lenses, and their Radii of Curvature

18. Convex (Converging) Lens

(1) *Plane mirror method.* In this method a plane mirror M is placed on a table, and the lens L is placed on the mirror, Fig. 360. A pin O is then moved along the axis of the lens until its image I is observed to coincide with O when they are both viewed from above, the method of no parallax being used. The distance from the pin O to the lens is then the focal length, f, of the lens, which can thus be measured.

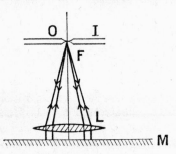

Fig. 360. Plane mirror method.

The explanation of the method is as follows. In general, rays from O pass through the lens, are reflected from the mirror M, and then pass through the lens again to form an image at some place. When O and the image coincide in position, the rays from O incident on M must have returned along their incident path after reflection from the mirror. This is only possible if the rays are incident *normally* on M. Consequently the rays entering the lens after reflection are all parallel, and hence the point to which they converge must be the focus, F, Fig. 360 It will thus be noted that the mirror provides a simple method of obtaining parallel rays incident on the lens.

(2) *Lens formula method.* In this method five or six values of u and v are obtained by using an illuminated object and a screen, or by using two pins and the method of no parallax. The focal length, f, can then be calculated from the equation $\dfrac{1}{v} + \dfrac{1}{u} = \dfrac{1}{f}$, and the average of the values obtained. Alternatively, the values of $\dfrac{1}{u}$ can be plotted against $\dfrac{1}{v}$, and a straight line drawn through the points. When $\dfrac{1}{u} = 0$, $\dfrac{1}{v} =$

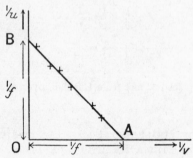

FIG. 361. Graph of $1/u$ against $1/v$.

$OA = \dfrac{1}{f}$, from the lens equation; thus $f = \dfrac{1}{OA}$, and can hence be calculated, Fig. 361. Since $\dfrac{1}{u} = \dfrac{1}{f}$ when $\dfrac{1}{v} = 0$, from the lens equation, $OB = \dfrac{1}{f}$. Thus f can also be evaluated from $\dfrac{1}{OB}$.

(3) *Displacement method.* In this method, an illuminated object O is placed in front of the lens, A, and an image I is obtained on a screen. Keeping the object and screen fixed, the lens is then moved to a position B so that a clear image is again obtained on the screen, Fig. 362. From our discussion on p. 501, it follows that a magnified sharp image is obtained at I when the lens is in the position A, and a diminished sharp image when the lens is in the position B. If the displacement of the lens is d, and the distance between the object and the screen is l, the

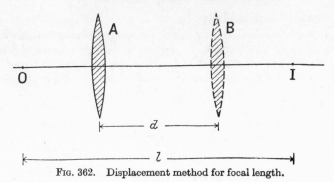

FIG. 362.   Displacement method for focal length.

focal length, f, is given by $f = \dfrac{l^2 - d^2}{4l}$, from p. 502. Thus f can be calculated. The experiment can be repeated by altering the distance between the object and the screen, and the average value of f is then calculated. It should be noted that the screen must be at a distance from the object of at least four times the focal length of the lens, otherwise an image is unobtainable on the screen (p. 500).

Since no measurements need be made to the surfaces of the lens (the "displacement" is simply the distance moved by the holder of the lens), this method can be used for finding the focal length of (i) a thick lens, (ii) an inaccessible lens, such as that fixed inside an eye-piece or telescope tube. Neither of the two methods previously discussed could be used for such a lens.

19. Lateral Magnification Method of Measuring Focal Length

On p. 498, we showed that the lateral magnification, m, produced by a lens is given bv

$$m = \frac{v}{f} - 1 \qquad . \qquad . \qquad . \qquad . \qquad . \qquad . \qquad \text{(i)}$$

where f is the focal length of the lens and v the distance of the image. If an illuminated glass scale is set up as an object in front of a lens, and the image is received on a screen, the magnification, m, can be measured directly. From (i), a straight line graph BA is obtained when m is plotted against the corresponding image distance v, Fig. 363. Further, from (i), $v/f - 1 = 0$ when $m = 0$; thus $v = f$ in this case. Hence, by producing BA to cut the axis of v in D, it follows that $OD = f$; the focal length of the lens can thus be found from the graph.

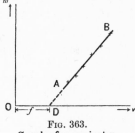

FIG. 363.
Graph of m against v.

20. Concave (Diverging) Lens

(1) *Convex lens method*. By itself, a concave lens always forms a virtual image of a real object (p. 496). A real image may be obtained, however, if a *virtual object* is used, and a convex lens can be used to provide such an object, as shown in Fig. 364. An object S is placed at a

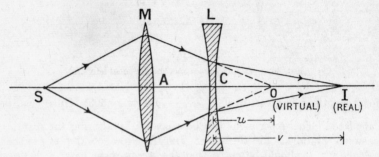

FIG. 364.   Focal length of concave lens.

distance from M greater than its focal length, so that a beam converging to a point O is obtained. O is thus a virtual object for the concave lens L placed as shown in Fig. 364, and a real image I can now be obtained. I is further away from L than O, since the concave lens makes the incident beam on it diverge more.

The image distance, v, from the concave lens is CI and can be measured; v is $+ ve$ in sign as I is real. The object distance, u, from the concave lens $= CO = AO - AC$, and AC can be measured. The length AO is obtained by removing the concave lens, leaving the convex lens, and noting the position of the real image now formed at O by the convex lens. Thus u ($= CO$) can be found; it is a $- ve$ distance, since O is a virtual object for the concave lens. Substituting for u and v in

$\dfrac{1}{v} + \dfrac{1}{u} = \dfrac{1}{f}$, the focal length of the concave lens can be calculated.

(2) *Concave mirror method*. In this method a real object is placed in front of a concave lens, and the position of the virtual image is located with the aid of a concave mirror. An object O is placed in front of the lens L, and a concave mirror M is placed behind the lens so that a divergent beam is incident on it, Fig. 365. With L and M in the same position, the object O is moved until an image is obtained coincident with it in position, i.e., beside O. The distances CO, CM are then measured.

As the object and image are coincident at O, the rays must be incident *normally* on the mirror M. The rays BA, ED thus pass through the centre of curvature of M, and this is also the position of the virtual

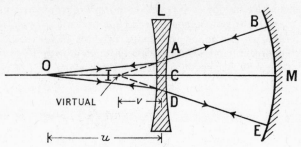

FIG. 365. Focal length of concave lens.

image I. The image distance, v, from the lens $= IC = IM - CM = r - CM$, where r is the radius of curvature; CM can be measured, while r can be determined by means of a separate experiment, as described on p. 423. The object distance, u, from the lens $= OC$, and by substituting for u and v in the formula $\frac{1}{v} + \frac{1}{u} = \frac{1}{f}$, the focal length f can be calculated. Of course, v is negative as I is a virtual image for the lens.

21. Measurement of Radii of Curvature of Lens Surfaces

Concave lens. The radius of curvature of a concave lens surface A can easily be measured by moving an object O in front of it until the image by reflection at A coincides with the object. Since the rays from

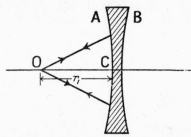

FIG. 366. Radius of concave lens surface.

O are now incident normally on A, its radius of curvature, r_1, $= OC$, the distance from O to the lens, Fig. 366. If the radius of curvature of the surface B is required, the lens is turned round and the experiment is repeated.

Convex lens: Boys' method. Since a convex surface usually gives a virtual image, it is not an easy matter to measure the radius of curvature of such a lens surface. C. V. Boys, however, suggested an ingenious method which is now known by his name, and is illustrated in Fig. 367.

In Boys' method, an object O is placed in front of a convex lens, and it is then moved until an image *by reflection at the back surface* NA is formed beside O. To make the image brighter O should be a well-illuminated object, and the lens can be floated with NA on top of mercury to provide better reflection from this surface.

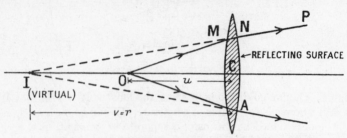

FIG. 367.   Boys' method for radius of convex lens surface.

Since the image is coincident with O, the rays are incident *normally* on NA. A ray OM from O would thus pass *straight through* the lens along NP after refraction at M. Further, as PN produced passes through I, I is a virtual image of O by *refraction in the lens*. On account of the latter fact, we can apply the lens equation $\dfrac{1}{v} + \dfrac{1}{u} = \dfrac{1}{f}$, where $v = IC = r$, the radius of curvature of NA, and $u = OC$. Thus knowing OC and the focal length, f, of the lens, r can be calculated. The same method can be used to measure the radius of curvature of the surface M of the lens, in which case the lens is turned round.

Although reflection from the lens back surface is utilised, the reader should take special pains to note that Boys' method uses the formula $\dfrac{1}{v} + \dfrac{1}{u} = \dfrac{1}{f}$ to calculate the radius of curvature. This is a formula for the *refraction* of light through the lens.

The refractive index of the material of a lens can be found by measuring the radii of curvature, r_1, r_2, of its surfaces and its focal length f. Since $1/f = (\mu - 1)\left(\dfrac{1}{r_1} + \dfrac{1}{r_2}\right)$, where μ is the refractive index, the latter can then be calculated.

22. Combined Focal Length of Two Thin Lenses in Contact

In order to diminish the colouring of the image due to dispersion when an object is viewed through a single lens, the lenses of telescopes and microscopes are made by placing two thin lenses together (see

p. 527). The combined focal length, F, of the lenses can be found by considering a point object O placed on the principal axis of two *thin lenses in contact*, which have focal lengths f_1, f_2 respectively, Fig. 368. A ray OC from O passes through the middle, C, of both lenses undeviated.

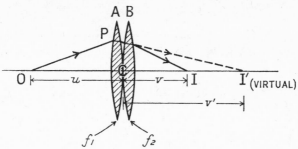

FIG. 368. Focal length of combined lenses.

A ray OP from O is refracted through the first lens A to intersect OC at I', which is therefore the image of O in A. If $OC = u$, $CI' = v'$,

$$\therefore \quad \frac{1}{v'} + \frac{1}{u} = \frac{1}{f_1} \qquad . \qquad . \qquad . \qquad (i)$$

The beam of light incident on the second lens B converges to I', which is therefore a *virtual* object for this lens. The image is formed at I at a distance CI, or v, from the lens. Thus since the object distance CI' is virtual, $u = -v'$ for refraction in this case. For lens B, therefore,

we have

$$\frac{1}{v} + \frac{1}{(-v')} = \frac{1}{f_2} ,$$

or

$$\frac{1}{v} - \frac{1}{v'} = \frac{1}{f_2} \qquad . \qquad . \qquad . \qquad . \qquad (ii)$$

Adding (i) and (ii) to eliminate v',

$$\therefore \quad \frac{1}{v} + \frac{1}{u} = \frac{1}{f_1} + \frac{1}{f_2} .$$

Since I is the image of O by refraction through both lenses,

$$\frac{1}{v} + \frac{1}{u} = \frac{1}{F} ,$$

where F is the *focal length of the combined lenses*. Hence

$$\frac{1}{F} = \frac{1}{f_1} + \frac{1}{f_2} \qquad . \qquad . \qquad . \qquad . \qquad (31)$$

This formula for F applies to any two thin lenses in contact, such as two concave lenses, or a convex and a concave lens. When the formula is used, the signs of the focal lengths must be inserted. As an illustration, suppose that a thin convex lens of 8 cm. focal length is placed in contact with a concave lens of 12 cm. focal length. Then $f_1 = +\ 8$, and $f_2 = -\ 12$. The combined focal length, F, is thus given by

$$\frac{1}{F} = \frac{1}{(+\ 8)} + \frac{1}{(-\ 12)} = \frac{1}{8} - \frac{1}{12} = +\frac{1}{24}$$

$$\therefore \quad F = +\ 24 \text{ cm.}$$

The positive sign indicates that the combination acts like a convex lens.

The focal length of a concave lens can be found by combining it with a convex lens of shorter focal length. The combination then acts like a convex lens, as illustrated by the numerical example just considered, and its focal length F can be found by one of the methods described on p. 505. The concave lens is then taken away, and the focal length f_1 of the convex lens alone is now measured. The focal length f_2 of the concave lens can then be calculated by substituting the values of F and f_1 in the formula $\dfrac{1}{F} = \dfrac{1}{f_1} + \dfrac{1}{f_2}$.

23. Refractive Index of a Small Quantity of Liquid

Besides the method given on p. 435, the refractive index of a small

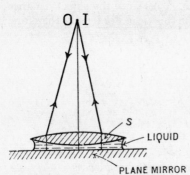

FIG. 369.   Refractive index of liquid.

amount of liquid can be found by smearing it over a plane mirror and placing a convex lens on top of it, as shown in the exaggerated sketch of Fig. 369. An object O is then moved along the principal axis until the inverted image I seen looking down into the mirror is coincident with O in position. In this case the rays which pass through the lens and liquid are incident *normally* on the mirror, and the distance from O to the lens is now the focal length, F, of the *lens and liquid* combination (see p. 505). If the experiment is repeated with the convex lens alone on the mirror, the focal length f_1 of the lens can be measured. But $\dfrac{1}{F} = \dfrac{1}{f_1} + \dfrac{1}{f_2}$, where f_2 is the focal length of the liquid lens. Thus, knowing f_1 and F, f_2 can be calculated.

From Fig. 369, it can be seen that the liquid lens is a plano-concave type; its lower surface corresponds to the plane surface of the mirror, while the upper surface corresponds to the surface S of the convex lens. If the latter has a radius of curvature r, then, from equation (24) on p. 492,

$$\frac{1}{f_2} = (\mu - 1)\left(\frac{1}{r} + \frac{1}{\infty}\right).$$

$$\therefore \qquad \frac{1}{f_2} = (\mu - 1)\frac{1}{r}$$

$$\therefore \quad \mu - 1 = \frac{r}{f_2}$$

$$\therefore \qquad \mu = 1 + \frac{r}{f_2} \qquad . \quad . \quad . \quad . \quad . \quad . \quad \text{(i)}$$

The radius of curvature r of the surface S of the lens can be measured by Boys' method (p. 509). Since f_2 has already been found, the refractive index μ of the liquid can be calculated from (i). This method of measuring μ is useful when only a small quantity of the liquid is available.

EXAMPLES

1. Draw a diagram to illustrate the principle of the convex driving mirror on a motor-car. A convex lens of focal length 24 cm. is placed 12 cm. in front of a convex mirror. It is found that when a pin is placed 36 cm. in front of the lens it coincides with its own inverted image formed by the lens and mirror. Find the focal length of the mirror. (*C.*)

First part. See text.

Second part. Suppose O is the position of the pin, Fig. 370. Since an inverted image of the pin is formed at O, the rays from O strike the convex mirror normally. Thus the image, I, in the lens of O is at the centre of curvature of the mirror.

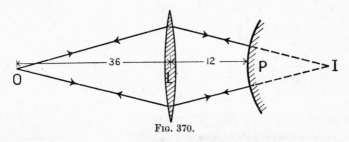

Fig. 370.

Since $u = \text{OL} = + 36, f = + 24$, it follows from the lens equation that

$$\frac{1}{v} + \frac{1}{36} = \frac{1}{24}$$

from which $v = 72$ cm. $= $ LI

∴   PI $= $ LI $- $ LP $= 72 - 12 = 60$.

∴ radius of curvature, r, of mirror $= 60$ cm.

∴   focal length of mirror $= \dfrac{r}{2} = 30$ cm.

2. Give an account of a method of measuring the focal length of a concave lens, preferably without the aid of an auxiliary convex lens. A small luminous object and a screen are placed on an optical bench and a convex lens is placed between them so as to throw a sharp image of the object on the screen; the linear magnification of the image is found to be 2·5. The lens is now moved 30 cm. nearer the screen and a sharp image again formed. Calculate the focal length of the lens. (*N.*)

First part. A concave mirror can be used, p. 508.

Second part. If O, I are the object and screen positions respectively, and L_1, L_2 are the two positions of the lens, then $OL_1 = IL_2$, Fig. 371. See *Displacement method for focal length*, p. 506. Suppose $OL_1 = x = L_2I$.

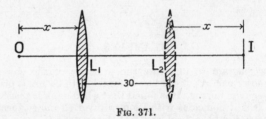

FIG. 371.

For the lens in the position L_1, $u = OL_1 = x$, $v = L_1I = 30 + x$.

But magnification, m, $= \dfrac{v}{u} = 2\cdot5$

∴ $\dfrac{30 + x}{x} = 2\cdot5$

∴ $x = 20$ cm.

∴ $u = OL_1 = 20$ cm.

                 $v = L_1I = 30 + x = 50$ cm.

Substituting in $\dfrac{1}{v} + \dfrac{1}{u} = \dfrac{1}{f}$,

∴ $\dfrac{1}{20} + \dfrac{1}{50} = \dfrac{1}{f}$

from which $f = 14\frac{2}{7}$ cm.

3. Describe two methods for the determination of the focal length of a concave lens. A thin equiconvex lens is placed on a horizontal plane mirror, and a pin held 20 cm. vertically above the lens coincides in position with its own image. The space between the under surface of the lens and the mirror is filled with water (refractive index 1·33) and then, to coincide with its image as before, the pin has to be raised until its distance from the lens is 27·5 cm. Find the radius of curvature of the surfaces of the lens. (*N.*)

First part. See text.

Second part. The focal length, f_1, of the lens = 20 cm., and the focal length, F, of the water and glass lens combination = 27·5 cm. See p. 512 and Fig. 369. The focal length, f, of the water lens is given by

$$\frac{1}{F} = \frac{1}{f} + \frac{1}{f_1}$$

$$\therefore \quad \frac{1}{(+\,27\cdot5)} = \frac{1}{f} + \frac{1}{(+\,20)}$$

Solving, $\qquad \therefore \quad \frac{1}{f} = \frac{1}{27\cdot5} - \frac{1}{20} = -\frac{3}{220}$

the minus showing that the water lens is a concave lens.

But $\qquad\qquad \frac{1}{f} = (\mu - 1)\frac{1}{r},$

where $\mu = 1\cdot33$, and r = radius of the curved face of the lens.

$$\therefore \quad -\frac{3}{220} = (1\cdot33 - 1)\frac{1}{r}$$

$$\therefore \quad r = -\,24\cdot2 \text{ cm.}$$

The glass lens is equiconvex, and hence the radii of its surfaces are the same.

4. Derive an expression for the equivalent focal length of a system of two thin lenses of focal lengths f_1 and f_2 in contact. Two equiconvex lenses of focal length 20 cm. are placed in contact and the space between them filled with water. Find the focal length of the combination ($_a\mu_g = 3/2$, $_a\mu_w = 4/3$). (*L.*)

First part. See text.

Second part. Since the lenses are equiconvex, the radii of curvature, r, of their surfaces are equal. Now

$$\frac{1}{f} = (\mu - 1)\left(\frac{1}{r_1} + \frac{1}{r_2}\right)$$

$$\therefore \quad \frac{1}{20} = \left(\frac{3}{2} - 1\right)\left(\frac{1}{r} + \frac{1}{r}\right)$$

$$\therefore \quad r = 20 \text{ cm.}$$

The water between the lenses forms an equiconcave lens of refractive index 4/3 and radii 20 cm. Its focal length f_1 is thus given by

$$\frac{1}{f_1} = (\mu - 1)\left(\frac{1}{r_1} + \frac{1}{r_2}\right)$$

$$= \left(\frac{4}{3} - 1\right)\left(\frac{1}{-20} + \frac{1}{-20}\right)$$

$$\therefore \qquad f_1 = -\,30 \text{ cm.}$$

The focal length, F, of the combination is given by

$$\frac{1}{F} = \frac{1}{f} + \frac{1}{f_1} + \frac{1}{f} = \frac{2}{f} + \frac{1}{f_1}$$

where f is the focal length of a glass lens.

$$\therefore \qquad \frac{1}{F} = \frac{2}{(+20)} + \frac{1}{(-30)} = \frac{2}{30}$$

$$\therefore \qquad F = \frac{30}{2} = 15 \text{ cm.}$$

EXERCISES XXIII

Refraction at a Single Curved Surface

1. A solid glass sphere has a radius of 10 cm. and a refractive index of 1·5. Find the position from the centre, and, nature, of the image of an object (i) 20 cm., (ii) 40 cm. from the centre due to refraction at the nearest part of the sphere.

2. Obtain a formula connecting the distances of the object and the image from a spherical refracting surface. A transparent sphere of refractive index 4/3 has a radius of 12 cm. Find the positions of the image of a small object inside it 4 cm. from the centre, when it is viewed first on one side and then on the other side of the sphere, in the direction of the line joining the centre to the object.

3. Viewed normally through its flat surface, the greatest thickness of a plano-convex lens appears to be 2·435 cm., and through its curved surface 2·910 cm. Actually it is 3·665 cm. Find (a) the refractive index of the glass, (b) the radius of curvature of the convex surface. Do you consider this is a satisfactory method of finding the radius of curvature? (N.)

4. A large glass sphere is placed immediately behind a small hole in an opaque screen, and a small filament lamp is placed at such a distance u in front of the hole that its image falls within the sphere, and at a distance v behind the hole. (a) Sketch the course taken by the light rays in the formation of this image. (b) Derive a formula connecting the quantities u and v with the refractive index μ of the glass. (c) If $\mu = 1·5$ and $u = 4r$, where r is the sphere's radius, find the image position due to refraction at the nearest part of the glass surface only.

Refraction Through Lenses

5. An object is placed (i) 12 cm., (ii) 4 cm. from a converging (convex) lens of focal length 6 cm. Calculate the image position and the magnification in each case, and draw sketches illustrating the formation of the image.

6. What do you know about the image obtained with a diverging (concave) lens? The image of a real object in a diverging lens of focal length 10 cm. is formed 4 cm. from the lens. Find the object distance and the magnification. Draw a sketch to illustrate the formation of the image.

7. The image obtained with a converging lens is erect and three times the length of the object. The focal length of the lens is 20 cm. Calculate the object and image distances.

8. A beam of light converges to a point 9 cm. behind (i) a converging lens of focal length 12 cm., (ii) a diverging lens of focal length 15 cm. Find the image position in each case, and draw sketches illustrating them.

9. (i) The surfaces of a biconvex lens are 8 cm. and 12 cm. radius of curvature. If the refractive index of the glass is 1·5, calculate the focal length. (ii) The curved surface of a plano-concave lens is 10 cm. radius of curvature, and the refractive index of the glass is 1·6. Calculate the focal length.

10. A thin plano-convex lens is made of glass of refractive index 1·5. When an object is set up 10 cm. from the lens, a virtual image ten times its size is formed. What is (a) the focal length of the lens, (b) the radius of curvature of the lens' surface?

If the lens is floated on mercury with the curved side downwards and a luminous object placed vertically above it, how far must the object be from the lens in order that it may coincide with the image produced by reflection in the curved surface? (*L*.)

11. Deduce an expression for the focal length of a lens in terms of *u* and *v*, the object and image distances from the lens.

A lens is set up and produces an image of a luminous point source on a screen 25 cm. away. *If the aperture of the lens is small*, where must the screen be placed to receive the image when a parallel slab of glass 6 cm. thick is placed at right angles to the axis of the lens and between the lens and the screen, if the refractive index of the glass is 1·6? Deduce any formula you use. (*L*.)

12. Derive an expression for the focal length of a lens in terms of the radii of curvature of its faces and its refractive index.

Find the condition that the distance between the object and image is a minimum, and explain how you would verify your result experimentally. (*C*.)

13. Give an account of a method of finding the focal length of a thin concave lens using an auxiliary convex lens which is not placed in contact with it.

A thin equiconvex lens of refractive index 1·50 is placed on a horizontal plane mirror and a pin fixed 15·0 cm. above the lens is found to coincide in position with its own image. The space between the lens and the mirror is now filled with a liquid and the distance of the pin above the lens when the image and object coincide is increased to 27·0 cm. Find the refractive index of the liquid. (*N*.)

14. Explain clearly what assumptions are made in stating that a simple converging lens can form a focused image of a given object. Write down the usual relation between the object distance (*u*), the image distance (*v*), and the focal length (*f*) of the lens, explaining what rule you use for the signs of these three quantities.

A projecting lantern is required to give an image with a linear magnification not exceeding 20, the distance from the slide to the screen being 25 feet. Projecting lenses with focal lengths 6, 12, and 18 ins. are available; which of these would be most suitable? (*W*.)

15. State the laws of reflection and apply them to find the relation between the distances of object and image from a concave mirror.

An illuminated hole in a screen acts as object and is placed 100 cm. from a concave spherical mirror of radius of curvature 80 cm. Where, between them, must a diverging lens of focal length 120 cm. be placed so that the final image falls upon the screen beside the object? (L.)

16. A lens is mounted in a short draw tube so that it is impossible to make measurements from the lens surfaces. Explain a method you would use to find the focal length of the lens.

A lens mounted as described above is found by experiment to have a focal length of 12 cm. It is set up at such a distance from a luminous object that a real image three times the size of the object is produced on a screen. Where should a concave lens of focal length 18 cm. be placed in order that the final image may be clearly focused on a screen 70 cm. from the luminous object? (L.)

17. Describe in detail how you would determine the focal length of a diverging lens with the help of (a) a converging lens, (b) a concave mirror.

A converging lens of 6 ins. focal length is mounted at a distance of 10 ins. from a screen placed at right angles to the axis of the lens. A diverging lens of 12 ins. focal length is then placed coaxially between the converging lens and the screen so that an image of an object 24 ins. from the converging lens is focused on the screen. What is the distance between the two lenses? Before commencing the calculation state the sign convention you will employ. (N.)

18. (a) Find an expression for the focal length of a combination of two thin lenses in contact. (b) A symmetrical convex glass lens, the radii of curvature of which are 3 cm., is situated just below the surface of a tank of water which is 40 cm. deep. An illuminated scratch on the bottom of the tank is viewed vertically downwards through the lens and the water. Where is the image, and where should the eye of the observer be placed in order to see it? The refractive indices of glass and water may be taken as 3/2 and 4/3 respectively. (O. & C.)

19. Find the relation between the focal lengths of two thin lenses in contact and the focal length of the combination.

The curved face of a plano-convex lens ($\mu = 1.5$) is placed in contact with a plane mirror. An object at 20 cm. distance coincides with the image produced by the lens and reflection by the mirror. A film of liquid is now placed between the lens and the mirror and the coincident object and image are at 100 cm. distance. What is the index of refraction of the liquid? (L.)

20. Show that, in general, there are two coaxial positions of a convergent lens which will give, on a fixed screen, a sharp image of a fixed object.

If the distance between object and screen is 96 cm. and the ratio of the lengths of the two images 4·84, what is the focal length of the lens? (N.)

21. What factors determine the focal length of a thin lens? A plano-concave water lens is formed between a plane glass plate and one surface of a thin double-convex glass lens of focal length 15·8 cm., and the focal length of the convergent combination is found to be 21·6 cm. When the glass lens is turned over, so that the other surface is in contact with the water ($\mu = 4/3$), the focal length of the combination is 21·3 cm. Find the refractive index of the glass. (C.)

22. Describe an optical method of finding the radius of curvature of a surface of a thin convex lens.

An object is placed on the axis of a thin plano-convex lens, and is adjusted so that it coincides with its own image formed by light which has been refracted into the lens at its first surface, internally reflected at the second surface, and refracted out again at the first surface. It is found that the distance of the object from the lens is 20·5 cm. when the convex surface faces the object, and 7·9 cm. when the plane surface faces the object. Calculate (a) the focal length of the lens, (b) the radius of curvature of the surface, (c) the refractive index of the glass. (C.)

23. Describe in detail how you would determine the focal length of a convex mirror with the help of a converging lens. Draw a ray diagram to illustrate the method employed and show how to calculate the result.

A converging lens projects a sharp image of a slit upon a screen placed 50 cm. from the lens. A convex mirror is then placed between the lens and the screen. The light reflected from the mirror forms an image of the slit on a small screen placed half-way between the lens and the mirror, and the image is now twice its former length. Find the separation of the lens and mirror, and the radius of curvature of the mirror. (N.)

24. Define *focal length, conjugate foci, real image*. Obtain an expression for the transverse magnification produced by a thin converging lens.

Light from an object passes through a thin converging lens, focal length 20 cm., placed 24 cm. from the object and then through a thin diverging lens, focal length 50 cm., forming a real image 62·5 cm. from the diverging lens. Find (a) the position of the image due to the first lens, (b) the distance between the lenses, (c) the magnification of the final image. (L.)

25. Describe how you would determine the focal length of a diverging lens if you were provided with a converging lens (a) of shorter focal length, (b) of longer focal length.

An illuminated object is placed at right angles to the axis of a converging lens, of focal length 15 cm., and 22·5 cm. from it. On the other side of the converging lens, and coaxial with it, is placed a diverging lens of focal length 30 cm. Find the position of the final image (a) when the lenses are 15 cm. apart and a plane mirror is placed perpendicular to the axis 40 cm. beyond the diverging lens, (b) when the mirror is removed and the lenses are 35 cm. apart. (N.)

CHAPTER XXIV

DEFECTS OF VISION
DEFECTS OF LENSES

DEFECTS OF VISION

THERE are numerous defects of vision, each necessitating the use of a different kind of spectacles. The use of convex lenses in spectacles was fairly widespread by 1300, but concave lenses were not in common use until about 1550, and were then highly valued. We propose to discuss briefly the essential optical principles of some of the main defects of vision and their "correction", and as a necessary preliminary we must mention certain topics connected with the eye itself.

1. Far and Near Points of Eye. Accommodation

An account of the essential features of the eye was given in Chapter XVII on p. 399, and it was mentioned there that the image formed by the eye-lens L must appear on the retina R, the light-sensitive screen of the eye, in order to be clearly seen, Fig. 372. The ciliary muscles enable the eye to focus objects at different distances from it, a property of the eye known as its power of *accommodation*. The most distant point it can focus (the *"far point"*) is at infinity for a normal eye; and as the ciliary muscles are then completely relaxed, the eye is said to be "unaccommodated", or "at rest". In this case parallel rays entering the eye are focused on the retina, Fig. 372 (i).

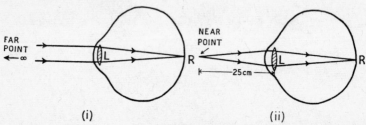

FAR POINT
← ∞

NEAR POINT

25 cm

(i)   (ii)

FIG. 372. Normal eye.

On the other hand, an object is seen in great detail when it is placed as near the eye as it can be while remaining focused; this distance from the eye known as its *least distance of distinct vision*. The point at this distance from the eye is called its *near point*, and the distance is about

25 cm., or 10 ins., for a normal eye, Fig. 372 (ii). The eye is said to be "fully accommodated" when viewing an object at its near point, as the ciliary muscles are then fully strained.

2. Short sight (*myopia*)

If the focal length of the eye is too short, due to the eye-ball being too long, parallel rays will be brought to a focus at a point D in front of the retina, Fig. 373 (i). In this case the far point of the eye is not at infinity, but at a point P nearer to the eye, and the defect of vision is known as *short sight*, or *myopia*.

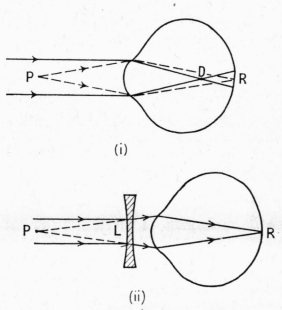

FIG. 373. **Short sight and its correction.**

A suitable *concave* lens, L, is required to correct for short sight, Fig. 373 (ii). Parallel rays refracted through L are now made divergent, and if they appear to come from the far point P of the eye, the rays are brought to a focus on the retina R. From Fig. 373 (ii), it can be seen that the focal length of the required lens is equal to PL, which is practically equal to the distance of the far point from the eye.

3. Far sight (*presbyopia*)

If a person's far point is normal, i.e. at infinity, but his near point is further from the eye than the normal least distance of distinct vision, 25 cm., the person is said to be "far-sighted". In Fig. 374 (i), X is the near point of a person suffering from far sight. Rays from X are brought to a focus on the retina R; whereas rays from the normal near point A, 25 cm. from the eye, are brought to a focus at B behind the retina.

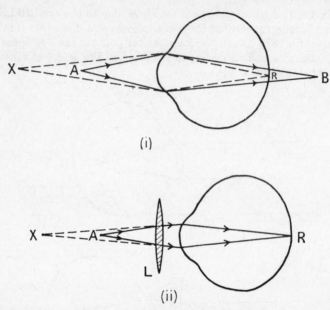

FIG. 374.   Far sight and its correction.

A suitable *convex* lens, L, is required to correct for this defect of vision, Fig. 374 (ii). Rays from A then appear to come from X after refraction through L, and an image is thus now formed on the retina. It can be seen that X is the virtual image of A in the lens L. Thus if XL = 50 cm., and AL = 25 cm., the focal length of L is given from the lens formula by

$$\frac{1}{(-50)} + \frac{1}{(+25)} = \frac{1}{f}$$

$$\therefore \qquad \frac{1}{50} = \frac{1}{f}$$

$$\therefore \qquad f = 50 \text{ cm.}$$

4. Long sight (*hypermetropia*).

Some people are able to focus only those beams of light which converge to a point behind the retina, in which case the far point is virtual. A parallel beam of light is then brought to a focus behind the retina, R, Fig. 375 (i). This defect of vision is known as *long sight*, or

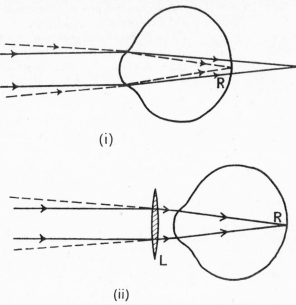

(i)

(ii)

FIG. 375. Long sight, and its correction for far point.

hypermetropia, and is corrected by using a suitable convex lens L, Fig. 375 (ii). This lens is so chosen that it makes a parallel beam converge to the far point, so that the eye can focus it at rest.

The long-sighted eye is unable to focus an object P 25 cm. from the eye (the near point of a normal eye), since a divergent beam is then incident on the eye, Fig. 376 (i). If a convex lens L is used, however,

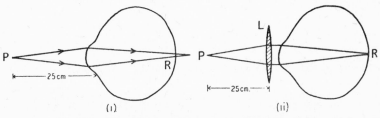

FIG. 376. Long sight, and its correction for near point.

the light from P is made convergent by the lens, and hence an image can now be formed on the retina, Fig. 376 (ii).

5. Astigmatism

If the cornea, the refracting surface in front of the eye (p. 399), has widely varying curvatures in different planes, the rays from an object in one plane will be brought to a focus by the eye at a different place from rays in another plane. In this case the lines in one direction in Fig. 377 will be sharply focused compared with the other lines. A strain is thus imposed on the eye when viewing an object, and this defect of vision is called *astigmatism*. It is corrected by using a *cylindrical lens*, whose curvature compensates for the curvature of the cornea in the particular astigmatic plane.

FIG. 377.
Test of astigmatism.

EXAMPLES

1. Draw diagrams to illustrate *long sight* and *short sight*. Draw also diagrams showing the correction of these defects by suitable lenses. A person can focus objects only when they lie between 50 cm. and 300 cm. from his eyes. What spectacles should he use (a) to increase his maximum distance of distinct vision to infinity, (b) to reduce his least distance of distinct vision to 25 cm.? Find his range of distinct vision using each pair. (N.)

First part. See text.

Second part. (a) To increase the maximum distance of distinct vision from 300 cm. to infinity, the person requires a *concave* lens. See Fig. 373 (ii). Assuming the lens is close to his eye, the focal length PL = 300 cm. as P is 300 cm. from the eye. One limit of the range of distinct vision is now infinity. The other limit is the object distance (u) corresponding to an image distance (v) of 50 cm. from the lens, as the person can see distinctly things 50 cm. from his eyes. In this case, then, $v = -50$ cm., $f = -300$ cm. Substituting in the lens equation, we have

$$\frac{1}{(-50)} + \frac{1}{u} = \frac{1}{(-300)}$$

from which $u = 60$ cm.

The range of distinct vision is thus from 60 cm. to infinity.

(b) To reduce his least distance of distinct vision from 50 cm. to 25 cm., the person requires a *convex* lens. See Fig. 376 (ii). In this case, assuming the lens is close to the eye, $u = +25$ cm., $v = -50$ cm., as the image must be formed 50 cm. from the eye on the same side as the object, making the image virtual. The focal length of the lens is thus given by

$$\frac{1}{(-50)} + \frac{1}{(+25)} = \frac{1}{f}$$

from which $f = +50$ cm.

Objects placed at the focus of this lens appear to come from infinity. The maximum distance of distinct vision, u, is given by substituting $v = -300$ cm. and $f = +50$ cm. in the lens formula.

Thus
$$\frac{1}{(-300)} + \frac{1}{u} = \frac{1}{(+50)}$$

from which
$$u = \frac{300}{7} = 42\tfrac{6}{7} \text{ cm.}$$

The range of distinct vision is thus from 25 to $42\tfrac{6}{7}$ cm.

2. Explain what is meant by the magnifying power of an optical instrument, considering the cases of microscope and telescope. A thin converging lens of focal length 5 cm. is laid on a map situated 60·5 cm. below the eye of an observer whose least distance of distinct vision is 24·5 cm. Describe what is seen (a) then, and when the lens is raised (b) 5 cm., (c) $5\tfrac{1}{2}$ cm., (d) 6 cm. above the map. (L.)

First part. See later text p. 541.

Second part. (a) When the lens is on top of the map, it acts as a thin piece of glass which very slightly raises the map to the observer (p. 436). The map appears unaltered in size and is the same way up.

(b) When the map is 5 cm. from the lens, i.e., at its focal plane, the map is the same way up but now appears bigger. In this case the image is at infinity.

(c) When the map is $5\tfrac{1}{2}$ cm. from the lens, the image is inverted. Its distance v is given by $\dfrac{1}{v} + \dfrac{1}{u} = \dfrac{1}{f}$, from which

$$\frac{1}{v} + \frac{1}{(+5\tfrac{1}{2})} = \frac{1}{(+5)}$$

or
$$v = 55 \text{ cm.}$$

The image is thus $60\cdot5 - (55 + 5\tfrac{1}{2})$ cm. from the observer, i.e., the image is formed at the eye. A blurred image is seen.

(d) When the map is 6 cm. from the lens, the image is inverted and its distance given by

$$\frac{1}{v} + \frac{1}{(+6)} = \frac{1}{(+5)}$$

$$\therefore \qquad v = 30 \text{ cm.}$$

The image is thus $60\cdot5 - (30 + 5\cdot5)$ cm., or 25 cm., from the eye of the observer. The inverted map is thus seen clearly. Since $v/u = 30/6 = 5$, the inverted map is magnified five times.

DEFECTS OF LENSES

We have just considered defects inherent in the eye; we have now to consider defects of an image produced by a lens, which is quite a different matter.

6. Chromatic Aberration

The image of an object formed by a single lens is distorted from a variety of causes. The main defect of the lens is the colouring of the image it produces, which is known as *chromatic aberration*.

Experiment shows that if a parallel beam of white light is incident on a convex lens, the red rays in the light are brought to a focus at R, and the blue rays are brought to a slightly nearer focus at B, Fig. 378.

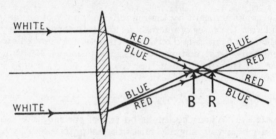

Fig. 378. Chromatic aberration.

Thus a single lens produces coloured images of an object which are at slightly different positions. Because he did not know how to eliminate the chromatic aberration Newton decided to abandon the use of lenses for large telescopes (p. 559).

It has already been noted that the refractive index, μ, of a material varies with the colour of the light (p. 464). Thus since $1/f =$

$(\mu - 1) \left(\dfrac{1}{r_1} + \dfrac{1}{r_2} \right)$, where f is the focal length of a lens, μ is the

refractive index of the material, and r_1, r_2 are the radii of curvature of the surfaces, it follows that f has different values for different colours. For example, the focal length of a lens for blue light, f_b, is

given by $\dfrac{1}{f_b} = (\mu_b - 1) \left(\dfrac{1}{r_1} + \dfrac{1}{r_2} \right)$, where μ_b is the refractive index for

blue light. Suppose the lens in Fig. 378 is made of crown glass, for which $\mu_b = 1.523$, and suppose r_1, r_2 are 15 and 12 cm. respectively. Then

$$\frac{1}{f_b} = (1.523 - 1) \left(\frac{1}{(+15)} + \frac{1}{(+12)} \right)$$

from which $\qquad f_b = 12.86$ cm.

For the same glass, the refractive index μ_r for red light $= 1.513$. The focal length f_r for red light is hence given by

$$\frac{1}{f_r} = (\mu_r - 1)\left(\frac{1}{r_1} + \frac{1}{r_2}\right)$$

$$= (1{\cdot}513 - 1)\left(\frac{1}{(+\ 15)} + \frac{1}{(+\ 12)}\right),$$

from which $\qquad f_r = 13{\cdot}00$ cm.

The separation BR of the two foci is thus given by

$$f_r - f_b = 13{\cdot}00 - 12{\cdot}86 = 0{\cdot}14 \text{ cm.}$$

The *ratio* of the focal lengths for the two colours $= \dfrac{f_r}{f_b} = \dfrac{\mu_b - 1}{\mu_r - 1}$,

since $\dfrac{1}{f_b} = (\mu_b - 1)\left(\dfrac{1}{r_1} + \dfrac{1}{r_2}\right)$ and $\dfrac{1}{f_r} = (\mu_r - 1)\left(\dfrac{1}{r_1} + \dfrac{1}{r_2}\right).$

7. Achromatic Combination of Lenses

A convex lens deviates an incident ray such as AB towards its principal axis, Fig. 379 (i). A concave lens, however, deviates a ray such as PQ away from its principal axis, Fig. 379 (ii). The dispersion

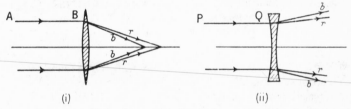

FIG. 379.   Dispersion produced by convex and concave lens.

between two colours produced by a convex lens can thus be annulled by placing a suitable concave lens beside it. Except for the mathematics, the making of *achromatic lenses* is analogous to the case of achromatic prisms, discussed on p. 470. There it was shown that two prisms of different material, with angles pointing in opposite directions can act as an achromatic combination. Fig. 380 illustrates an achromatic lens combination, known as an *achromatic doublet*. The biconvex lens is made of crown glass, while the concave lens is made of flint glass and is a plano-concave lens. So that the lenses can be cemented together with Canada balsam, the radius of curvature of the curved surface of the plano-

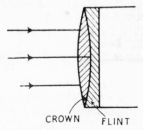

FIG. 380.
Achromatic doublet.

concave lens is made numerically the same as that of one surface of the convex lens. The achromatic combination acts as a convex lens when used as the objective lens in a telescope or microscope.

It should be noted that chromatic aberration would occur if the concave and convex lenses were made of the *same* material, as the two lenses together would then constitute a single thick lens of one material.

8. Condition for an Achromatic Combination

Achromatic lenses were first made about 1729, years after Newton had considered they were impossible to construct. The necessary condition for an achromatic combination of lenses is derived on p. 529. Here we shall accept the result, which states: *Two lenses form an achromatic combination for two colours, if the ratio of their focal lengths is numerically equal to the ratio of the corresponding dispersive powers* (p. 468) *of their materials*. Hence

$$\frac{f_1}{f_2} = \frac{\omega_1}{\omega_2} \qquad \qquad (32)$$

where f_1, f_2 are the mean focal lengths and ω_1, ω_2 are the respective dispersive powers.

If a lens combination of focal length F is required, then f_1, f_2 must satisfy in addition the relation

$$\frac{1}{f_1} + \frac{1}{f_2} = \frac{1}{F} \qquad \qquad \text{(i)}$$

Knowing ω_1, ω_2, and F, the magnitudes of f_1, f_2 can be found by solving the equations (i) and (32).

There still remains, however, the practical matter of fitting the surfaces of the two lenses together, as the lenses must be in good optical contact to function efficiently. Suppose the flint glass lens has one surface plane, as shown in Fig. 380, and has the focal length f_1. Then

$$\frac{1}{f_1} = (\mu - 1) \left(\frac{1}{r_1} + \frac{1}{\infty} \right) = (\mu - 1) \frac{1}{r_1},$$

where μ is the mean refractive index of flint glass and r_1 is the radius of curvature of the lens. Since f_1 and μ are known, r_1 can be calculated. The focal length f_2 of the crown glass convex lens is given by

$$\frac{1}{f_2} = (\mu' - 1) \left(\frac{1}{r_1} + \frac{1}{r_2} \right)$$

where μ' is the mean refractive index of crown glass and r_2 is the radius of curvature of the other lens surface. Knowing f_2, μ', and r_1, the magnitude of r_2 can be calculated. In this way the lens manufacturer knows what the radii of curvature of the crown and flint glass lenses must be to form an achromatic combination of a specified focal length F.

Condition for achromatic lenses. Since $\frac{1}{f} = (\mu - 1)\left(\frac{1}{r_1} + \frac{1}{r_2}\right)$, with the usual notation,

$$\frac{1}{f_b} = (\mu_b - 1)\left(\frac{1}{r_1} + \frac{1}{r_2}\right)$$

and

$$\frac{1}{f_r} = (\mu_r - 1)\left(\frac{1}{r_1} + \frac{1}{r_2}\right)$$

$$\therefore \qquad \frac{1}{f_b} - \frac{1}{f_r} = (\mu_b - \mu_r)\left(\frac{1}{r_1} + \frac{1}{r_2}\right) \qquad . \qquad . \qquad . \qquad \text{(i)}$$

Now the magnitudes of $\frac{1}{f_b}$ and $\frac{1}{f_r}$ are very close to each other, since f_b is nearly equal to f_r. Thus, using the calculus notation, $\frac{1}{f_b} - \frac{1}{f_r} = \delta\left(\frac{1}{f}\right)$; the latter represents the small change in $\frac{1}{f}$ when blue, and then red, rays are incident on the lens. From (i),

$$\delta\left(\frac{1}{f}\right) = (\mu_b - \mu_r)\left(\frac{1}{r_1} + \frac{1}{r_2}\right) \qquad . \qquad . \qquad . \qquad \text{(ii)}$$

But

$$\frac{1}{f} = (\mu - 1)\left(\frac{1}{r_1} + \frac{1}{r_2}\right) \qquad . \qquad . \qquad . \qquad \text{(iii)}$$

where f is the focal length of the lens when yellow light is incident on the lens, and μ is the refractive index for yellow light. Dividing (ii) by (iii) and simplifying for $\delta\left(\frac{1}{f}\right)$, we obtain

$$\delta\left(\frac{1}{f}\right) = \frac{\mu_b - \mu_r}{\mu - 1} \cdot \frac{1}{f}$$

Now the dispersive power, ω, of a material is defined by the relation $\omega = \frac{\mu_b - \mu_r}{\mu - 1}$ (see p. 469).

$$\therefore \qquad \delta\left(\frac{1}{f}\right) = \frac{\omega}{f} \qquad . \qquad . \qquad . \qquad . \qquad \text{(iv)}$$

Combined lenses. Suppose f_1, f_2 are the respective focal lengths of two thin lenses in contact, ω_1, ω_2 are the corresponding dispersive powers of their materials, and F is the combined focal length. If the combination is achromatic for blue and red light, the focal length F_b for blue light is the same as the focal length F_r for red light, i.e., $F_b = F_r$.

$$\therefore \qquad \frac{1}{F_b} = \frac{1}{F_r}$$

$$\therefore \qquad \frac{1}{F_b} - \frac{1}{F_r} = 0$$

$$\therefore \qquad \delta\left(\frac{1}{F}\right) = 0 \qquad . \qquad . \qquad . \qquad . \qquad \text{(v)}$$

But
$$\frac{1}{F} = \frac{1}{f_1} + \frac{1}{f_2}$$

$$\therefore \quad \delta\left(\frac{1}{F}\right) = \delta\left(\frac{1}{f_1}\right) + \delta\left(\frac{1}{f_2}\right)$$

From (v),
$$\therefore \quad 0 = \delta\left(\frac{1}{f_1}\right) + \delta\left(\frac{1}{f_2}\right)$$

$$\therefore \quad \delta\left(\frac{1}{f_1}\right) = -\delta\left(\frac{1}{f_2}\right)$$

Now
$$\delta\left(\frac{1}{f_1}\right) = \frac{\omega_1}{f_1} \quad \text{from equation (iv)}$$

and similarly
$$\delta\left(\frac{1}{f_2}\right) = \frac{\omega_2}{f_2}$$

$$\therefore \quad \frac{\omega_1}{f_1} = -\frac{\omega_2}{f_2} \quad \text{from above}$$

$$\therefore \quad \frac{f_1}{f_2} = -\frac{\omega_1}{\omega_2} \quad . \quad . \quad . \quad . \quad (33)$$

Thus the ratio of the focal lengths is equal to the ratio of the dispersive powers of the corresponding lens materials, as stated on p. 528. Since ω_1, ω_2 are positive numbers, it follows from (33) that f_1 and f_2 must have opposite signs. Thus a concave lens must be combined with a convex lens to form an achromatic combination (see Fig. 380).

Achromatic separated lenses. An achromatic combination can be made with two separated lenses of the *same* material, as we shall now show.

Suppose two lenses of focal lengths f_1, f_2 respectively are situated at a distance d apart. Their combined focal length F is then given by (p. 533).

$$\frac{1}{F} = \frac{1}{f_1} + \frac{1}{f_2} - \frac{d}{f_1 f_2}$$

$$\therefore \quad \delta\left(\frac{1}{F}\right) = \delta\left(\frac{1}{f_1}\right) + \delta\left(\frac{1}{f_2}\right) - \delta\left(\frac{d}{f_1 f_2}\right)$$

$$= \delta\left(\frac{1}{f_1}\right) + \delta\left(\frac{1}{f_2}\right) - \frac{d}{f_1}\delta\left(\frac{1}{f_2}\right) - \frac{d}{f_2}\delta\left(\frac{1}{f_1}\right)$$

For an achromatic combination of two colours, $\delta\left(\dfrac{1}{F}\right) = 0$, as previously shown. Further, $\delta\left(\dfrac{1}{f_1}\right) = \dfrac{\omega}{f_1}$, $\delta\left(\dfrac{1}{f_2}\right) = \dfrac{\omega}{f_2}$, where ω is the dispersive power of the material of the lenses. From above,

$$\therefore \quad 0 = \frac{\omega}{f_1} + \frac{\omega}{f_2} - \frac{\omega d}{f_1 f_2} - \frac{\omega d}{f_1 f_2}$$

$$\therefore \quad 2d = f_1 + f_2$$

$$\therefore \quad d = \frac{f_1 + f_2}{2} \quad . \quad . \quad . \quad . \quad . \quad . \quad (34)$$

Thus the distance between the lenses must be equal to the average of the focal lengths. This condition is utilised in the design of an efficient telescope eye-piece (p. 534).

9. Spherical Aberration

We have now to consider another defect of an image due to a single lens, known as *spherical aberration*.

The lens formula $\dfrac{1}{v} + \dfrac{1}{u} = \dfrac{1}{f}$ has been obtained by considering a narrow beam of rays incident on the central portion of a lens. In this case the angles of incidence and refraction at the surfaces of the lens are small, and sin i and sin r can then be replaced respectively by i and r in radians, as shown on p. 482. This leads to the lens formula and a unique focus, F. If a *wide* parallel beam of light is incident on the lens, however, experiment shows that the rays are not all brought to the same focus, Fig. 381. It therefore follows that the image of an

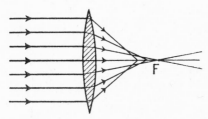

FIG. 381.   Spherical aberration.

object is distorted if a wide beam of light falls on the lens, and this is known as *spherical aberration*. The aberration may be reduced by surrounding the lens with an opaque disc having a hole in the middle, so that light is only incident on the middle of the lens, but this method reduces the brightness of the image since it reduces the amount of light energy passing through the lens.

As rays converge to a single focus for small angles of incidence, spherical aberration can be diminished if the angles of incidence on the lens' surfaces are diminished. In general, then, the *deviation* of the light by a lens should be shared as equally as possible by its surfaces, as each angle of incidence would then be as small as possible. A practical method of reducing spherical aberration is to utilise *two* lenses, when four surfaces are obtained, and to share the deviation equally between the lenses. The lenses are usually plano-convex. It is proved shortly that *the distance between the lenses must be equal to the difference of their focal lengths to reduce spherical aberration* (p. 533).

10. General Formula for Deviation Produced by a Lens

Consider a ray AB incident parallel to, and distant h from, the principal axis CF of a convex lens, Fig 382. After refraction the ray passes through the focus, F, and the angle of deviation, δ, of the ray is

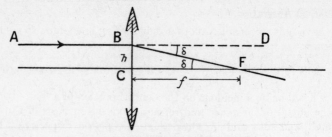

FIG. 382. Deviation produced by lens.

angle DBF. Now angle BFC = angle DBF, and as BC, or h, is small, angle BFC = BC/CF in radians.

$$\therefore \quad \text{deviation by lens} = \frac{h}{f} \qquad . \qquad . \qquad . \qquad . \qquad (35)$$

The same formula is obtained for a concave lens, but the deviation of the incident ray is away from the principal axis.

Focal length of separated lenses. Consider a ray HP incident on a lens O of focal length f_1 parallel to the principal axis, Fig. 383. Since the ray converges to the focus C, the deviation δ of the ray is given by h_1/f_1, where h_1 is the height of P above the axis. If the ray PX is intercepted by a lens

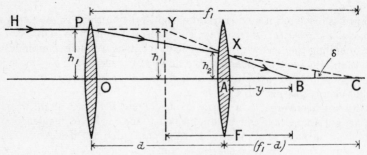

FIG. 383. Focal length of separated lenses.

A distant d from O, the deviation of the ray at X is similarly given by h_2/f_2, where h_2 is the height of X above the axis and f_2 is the focal length of A. The total deviation, δ', of AP by refraction at both lenses is thus given by

$$\delta' = \frac{h_1}{f_1} + \frac{h_2}{f_2} \qquad . \qquad . \qquad . \qquad . \qquad . \qquad (i)$$

If F is the combined focal length of the lenses, the deviation δ' of the ray HP is given by

$$\delta' = \frac{h_1}{F} \qquad . \qquad . \qquad . \qquad . \qquad . \qquad (ii)$$

From (i) and (ii), it follows that

$$\frac{h_1}{F} = \frac{h_1}{f_1} + \frac{h_2}{f_2}$$

$$\therefore \quad \frac{1}{F} = \frac{1}{f_1} + \frac{1}{f_2} \cdot \frac{h_2}{h_1} \quad \cdots \quad \cdots \quad \text{(iii)}$$

Since triangles OPC, AXC are similar,

$$\frac{AX}{OP} = \frac{CA}{CO}$$

$$\therefore \quad \frac{h_2}{h_1} = \frac{f_1 - d}{f_1},$$

as d = distance OA between the lenses, and f_1 = OC.

Substituting for $\frac{h_2}{h_1}$ in (iii),

$$\therefore \quad \frac{1}{F} = \frac{1}{f_1} + \frac{1}{f_2}\left(\frac{f_1 - d}{f_1}\right) = \frac{1}{f_1} + \frac{1}{f_2}\left(1 - \frac{d}{f_1}\right)$$

$$\therefore \quad \frac{1}{F} = \frac{1}{f_1} + \frac{1}{f_2} - \frac{d}{f_1 f_2} \quad \cdots \quad \cdots \quad \text{(36)}$$

It should be noted that F is not measured from either lens.

Condition for equal deviation between two lenses. Consider a ray, parallel to the principal axis, incident at B on two separated lenses O, A, Fig. 384. If OB = h_1, the deviation δ of the light is given by $\frac{OB}{OF}$, or $\frac{h_1}{f_1}$, where f_1 = OF = the focal length of the lens O. Although the ray BD

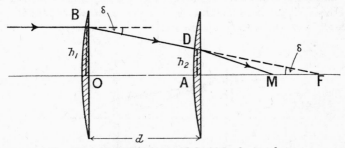

Fig. 384. Condition for equal deviation by two lenses.

incident on the lens A is not parallel to the principal axis, the deviation at this lens is given by a corresponding expression, $\frac{h_2}{f_2}$, where AD = h_2 and f_2 is the focal length of A. If the deviations at the two lenses are equal, it follows that $h_1/f_1 = h_2/f_2$,

$$\text{i.e.,} \quad \frac{h_1}{h_2} = \frac{f_1}{f_2} \quad \cdots \quad \cdots \quad \text{(i)}$$

Now since triangles FBO, FAD **are similar,**

$$\frac{h_1}{h_2} = \frac{FO}{FA} = \frac{f_1}{f_1 - d} \quad \text{.} \quad \text{.} \quad \text{.} \quad \text{.} \quad \text{(ii)}$$

where d is the distance between the lenses. From (i) and (ii), it follows that

$$\frac{f_1}{f_2} = \frac{f_1}{f_1 - d}$$
$$\therefore \quad f_2 = f_1 - d$$
$$\therefore \quad d = f_1 - f_2 \,. \quad \text{.} \quad \text{.} \quad \text{.} \quad \text{.} \quad \text{(37)}$$

Thus the distance between the lenses must be equal to the difference between their focal lengths to reduce spherical aberration.

11. Eye-pieces. Huyghens' Eye-piece

The eye-piece of a telescope should be designed with a view to reducing chromatic and spherical aberration; in practice this can most conveniently be done by using *two* lenses as the eye-piece. We have already shown that such lenses, made of the same material, are achromatic if their distance apart is equal to the average of their focal lengths (p. 530), and that the lenses reduce spherical aberration if their distance apart is equal to the difference between their focal lengths (see above).

Huyghens designed an eye-piece consisting of two plano-convex lenses; one lens, F, had three times the focal length of the other, E, Fig. 385 (i). The lens F pointing to the telescope objective is known as the *field lens*, while the lens E close to the eye is known as the eye lens, and F and E are at a distance $2f$ apart, where f is the focal length of E. Since $3f$ is the focal length of F, it follows from above that the eye-piece eliminates chromatic aberration and reduces spherical aberration.

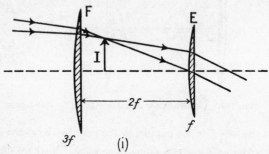

FIG. 385 (i).   Huyghens' eyepiece.

Since the image formed by the objective of a telescope is at a distance equal to, or less than, the focal length of the eye lens E (p. 551), the image **I** formed by the objective must be situated between F and E.

This, then, is the place where cross-wires must be placed if measurement of the final image is required. But the cross-wires are viewed through one lens, E, while the distant object is viewed by rays refracted through both lenses, F, E. The relative lengths of the cross-wires and image are thus rendered disproportionate, and hence cross-wires cannot be used with Huyghens' eye-piece, which is a disadvantage.

12. Ramsden's Eye-piece

Ramsden's eye-piece is more commonly used than Huyghens' eye-piece. It consists of two plano-convex lenses of equal focal length f, the distance between them being $2f/3$, Fig. 385 (ii). The achromatic

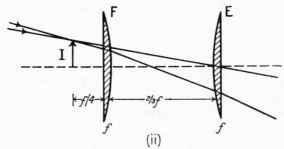

FIG. 385 (ii). Ramsden's eye-piece.

condition requires that the distance between the lenses should be f, the average of the focal lengths. If the field lens F were at the focus of the eye lens E, however, E would magnify any dust on F, and vision would then be obscured. F is placed at a distance $f/4$ from the focus of the objective of the telescope, where the real image is formed, in which case the image in F is formed at a distance from E equal to f, its focal length, and parallel rays emerge from E.

The chromatic aberration of Ramsden's eye-piece is small, as is the spherical aberration. The advantage of the eye-piece, however, lies in the fact that cross-wires can be used with it; they are placed outside the combination at the place where the real image I is formed.

EXAMPLES

1. A thin biconvex lens is placed with its principal axis first along a beam of parallel red light and then along a beam of parallel blue light. If the refractive indices of the lens for red and for blue light are respectively 1·514 and 1·524, and if the radii of curvature of its faces are 30 cm. and 20 cm., calculate the separation of the foci for red and blue light. What relation does the result bear to the dispersive power of the lens for the two kinds of light? (N.)

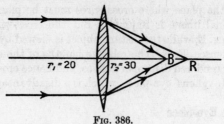

FIG. 386.

(a) $\frac{1}{f} = (\mu - 1)\left(\frac{1}{r_1} + \frac{1}{r_2}\right)$, with the usual notation.

$$\therefore \quad \frac{1}{f_r} = (1.514 - 1)\left(\frac{1}{+20} + \frac{1}{+30}\right)$$

$$\therefore \quad \frac{1}{f_r} = 0.514\left(\frac{1}{20} + \frac{1}{30}\right) = \frac{0.514}{12}$$

$$\therefore \quad f_r = 23.33 \text{ cm.}$$

Also, $\frac{1}{f_b} = (1.524 - 1)\left(\frac{1}{+20} + \frac{1}{+30}\right) = \frac{0.524}{12}$

$$\therefore \quad f_b = 22.90 \text{ cm.}$$

$$\therefore \quad \text{separation} = 23.33 - 22.90 = 0.43 \text{ cm.}$$

(b)   We know that $\dfrac{1}{f_b} - \dfrac{1}{f_r} = \dfrac{\mu_b - \mu_r}{\mu - 1} \cdot \dfrac{1}{f}$ (See p. 529)

i.e., $\dfrac{1}{f_b} - \dfrac{1}{f_r} = \dfrac{\omega}{f}$

$$\therefore \quad f_r - f_b = \frac{\omega}{f} \cdot f_b f_r$$

Now $f_b f_r$ is approximately equal to f^2,

$$\therefore \quad f_r - f_b = \frac{\omega}{f} \cdot f^2 = \omega f$$

$$\therefore \quad \frac{f_r - f_b}{\omega} = f$$

$$\therefore \quad \frac{\text{separation}}{\text{dispersive power}} = \text{focal length,}$$

and is the relation required. The focal length, f, is that for the mean (yellow) light.

2. Define the dispersive power of a medium, and describe, giving the necessary theory, how two thin lenses in contact can be used to form an achromatic combination. A lens of crown glass of dispersive power 0.018 has a focal length of 50 cm. What is the focal length of a flint glass of dispersive power 0.045, which will form an achromatic combination with it? Calculate the focal length of the combination. (C.)

First part. See text.

Second part. The focal lengths of the two lenses must be proportional

to their respective dispersive powers to form an achromatic combination
(p. 528). Thus if f is the focal length of the flint glass lens,

$$\frac{f}{50} = \frac{0\cdot045}{0\cdot018}$$

$$\therefore \ f = 125 \text{ cm}.$$

The flint glass lens must be a concave lens, and the crown glass lens
must be a convex lens; otherwise the combination would not act as an
achromatic convex lens (p. 527). The focal length, F, of the combination is
hence given by

$$\frac{1}{F} = \frac{1}{(+ 50)} + \frac{1}{(- 125)}$$

from which $F = 83\frac{1}{3}$ cm.

3. Explain how it is possible to construct achromatic lenses. Why did
Newton consider it impossible? An achromatic objective of 100 cm. focal
length is to be made, using two lenses of the glasses shown below. Find the
focal length of each lens, stating whether it is convergent or divergent.

	Glass A	Glass B
μ red	1·5155	1·641
μ blue	1·5245	1·659

(N.)

First part. See text. Newton considered it impossible because there was
only a small range of glasses in his time, and the dispersive power of the
different glass materials was about the same.

Second part. Let $f_1, f_2 =$ the focal lengths of the lenses.

$$\therefore \qquad \frac{1}{f_1} + \frac{1}{f_2} = \frac{1}{100} \quad \cdots \quad \cdots \quad \text{(i)}$$

Now the mean refractive index, μ, for glass A $= \dfrac{1\cdot5245 + 1\cdot5155}{2} = 1\cdot52$

$\therefore$ dispersive power, ω_2, for glass A $= \dfrac{\mu_D - \mu_r}{\mu - 1} = \dfrac{1\cdot5245 - 1\cdot5155}{1\cdot52 - 1} = \dfrac{9}{520}$

and mean refractive index, μ, for glass B $= \dfrac{1\cdot659 + 1\cdot641}{2} = 1\cdot65$

$\therefore$ dispersive power, ω_1, for glass B $= \dfrac{1\cdot659 - 1\cdot641}{1\cdot65 - 1} = \dfrac{18}{650}$

The condition for achromatism is $\dfrac{f_1}{f_2} = - \dfrac{\omega_1}{\omega_2}$

$$\therefore \quad \frac{f_1}{f_2} = - \frac{18}{650} \bigg/ \frac{9}{520} \quad \cdots \quad \cdots \quad \text{(ii)}$$

From (ii), $f_1 = - \dfrac{18}{650} \times \dfrac{520}{9} \cdot f_2 = - \dfrac{8}{5} f_2$

Substituting in (i),

$$\therefore \quad - \frac{5}{8f_2} + \frac{1}{f_2} = \frac{1}{100}$$

$$\therefore \quad f_2 = + 37 \cdot 5$$

$$\therefore \quad f_1 = - \frac{8}{5} \times + 37 \cdot 5 = - 60$$

Thus a convex lens of 37·5 cm. focal length should be combined with a concave lens of 60 cm. focal length.

EXERCISES XXIV

Defects of Vision

1. Explain how the eye is focused for viewing objects at different distances. Describe and explain the defects of vision known as *long sight* and *short sight*, and their correction by the use of spectacles.

Explain the advantages we gain by the use of two eyes instead of one.

A certain person can see clearly objects at distances between 20 cm. and 200 cm. from his eye. What spectacles are required to enable him to see distant objects clearly, and what will be his least distance of distinct vision when he is wearing them? (*L.*)

2. Give an account of the common optical defects of the human eye and explain how their effects may be corrected.

An elderly person cannot see clearly, without the use of spectacles, objects nearer than 200 cm. What spectacles will he need to reduce this distance to 25 cm.? If his eyes can focus rays which are converging to points not less than 150 cm. behind them, calculate his range of distinct vision when using the spectacles. (*N.*)

3. Discuss the eye as an optical instrument. Describe the errors of refraction to which it is subject and how they may be corrected by the use of suitable spectacle lenses.

If the spectacles worn by a person for reading consist of a *converging* lens of ½-metre focal length for his right eye and a *diverging* lens of ⅓-metre focal length for his left eye, what qualitative and quantitative deductions do you make concerning his sight? [Assume that the normal reading distance is 25 cm.] (*W.*)

4. Describe the optical system of the eye and explain the meaning of *long sight*, *short sight*, and *least distance of distinct vision*. Illustrate with clear diagrams the two defects of vision mentioned above and show how they are corrected by lenses.

If the range of vision of a short-sighted man is from 10 to 20 cm. from the eye, what lens should be used in order to enable him to see distant objects clearly? What would be the range of accommodation when using this lens? (*L.*)

5. Describe the optical arrangement of the eye, illustrating the description with a labelled diagram.

A person wears bifocal converging spectacles, one surface of each lens being spherical and the other cylindrical. Describe the defects in his vision and explain how the spectacles correct them. (*N.*)

6. Give clear diagrams to illustrate the common optical defects of the human eye.

In a certain case the range of distinct vision is found to be limited to objects distant 15 cm. to 30 cm. from the eye. What lens would be suitable for the distinct vision of distant objects, and what would be the nearer limit of distinct vision when this lens is in use? (W.)

Defects of Lenses

7. Explain the meaning of *dispersion* and *deviation*. Show how a compound prism may be constructed, so that, using white light, (a) deviation may be produced without dispersion, and (b) dispersion may be produced without appreciable deviation.

What is the meaning of *chromatic aberration* as produced by a simple lens? Explain, with the aid of diagrams, a method used to minimise this error. (L.)

8. Explain what is meant by (a) spherical aberration, (b) chromatic aberration. Give an account of ways in which these defects are minimised in optical instruments. (N.)

9. What is the condition for two thin lenses to form an achromatic combination? Draw a diagram of such a combination.

A convex lens of crown glass has a focal length of 40 cm. and a dispersive power of 0·025. Find the focal length of a flint glass lens of dispersive power 0·04 which will form an achromatic convex combination with it? Calculate the focal length of the combination.

10. Explain the dispersion produced by a simple lens, and show how the defect may be corrected.

Why is such correction unnecessary in the case of a simple convex lens used as a magnifying glass held close to the eye? (O. & C.)

11. Derive the expression for the focal length of a thin lens in air in terms of the radii of curvature of the faces and the refractive index of the material of the lens.

A white disc, 1 cm. in diameter, is placed 100 cm. in front of a thin converging lens of 50 cm. mean focal length. The refractive index of the material of the lens is 1·524 for red light and 1·534 for violet light. Calculate the diameters of the images for red and violet light and their distance apart. (W.)

12. Discuss in general terms the defects in the image formed by a single convex lens in a camera and indicate how they may be remedied.

A camera lens forms an image of the same size as the object when the screen is in a certain position. When the screen is moved 10 cm. further from the lens and the object is moved until the image is again in focus, the magnification is found to be 2. What is the focal length of the lens? (C.)

13. Describe the colour effects which you would expect to see in the image of a small source of white light formed on a screen by a lens.

Derive the condition that a combination of two thin lenses in contact shall be nearly free from this defect. (L.)

CHAPTER XXV

OPTICAL INSTRUMENTS

WHEN a telescope or a microscope is used to view an object, the appearance of the final image is determined by the cone of rays entering the eye. A discussion of optical instruments and their behaviour must therefore be preceded by a consideration of the image formed by the eye, and we must now recapitulate some of the points about the eye mentioned in previous pages.

Firstly, the image formed by the eye lens L must appear on the retina R at the back of the eye if the object is to be clearly seen, Fig. 387. Secondly, the normal eye can focus an object at infinity (the "far point" of the normal eye), in which case the eye is said to be "unaccommodated". Thirdly, the eye can see an object in greatest detail when it is placed at a certain distance D from the eye, known as the *least distance of distinct vision*, which is about 25 cm., or 10 ins., for a normal eye (p. 520). The point at a distance D from the eye is known as its "near point".

1. Visual Angle

Consider an object O placed some distance from the eye, and suppose θ is the angle in radians subtended by it at the eye, Fig. 387. Since

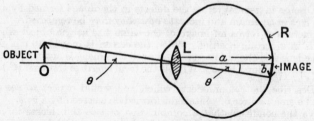

FIG. 387. Length of image on retina, and visual angle.

vertically opposite angles are equal, it follows that the length b of the image on the retina is given by $b = a\theta$, where a is the distance from R to L. But a is a constant; hence $b \propto \theta$. We thus arrive at the important conclusion that *the length of the image formed by the eye is proportional to the* **angle** *subtended at the eye by the object*. This angle is known

540

as the *visual angle*; the greater the visual angle, the greater is the apparent size of the object.

Fig. 388 (i) illustrates the case of an object moved from A to B, and viewed by the eye in both positions. At B the angle β subtended at the eye is greater than the visual angle α subtended at A. Hence the

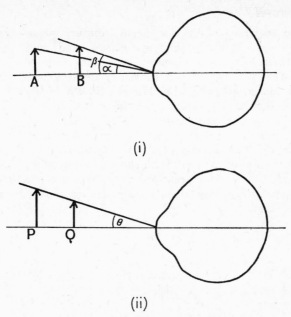

(i)

(ii)

Fig. 388.   Relation between visual angle and length of image.

object appears larger at B than at A, although its physical size is the same. Fig. 388 (ii) illustrates the case of two objects, at P, Q respectively, which subtend the same visual angle θ at the eye. The objects thus appear to be of equal size, although the object at P is physically bigger than that at Q. It should be remembered that an object is not clearly seen if it is brought closer to the eye than the near point.

2. Angular Magnification

Microscopes and telescopes are instruments designed to increase the visual angle, so that the object viewed can be made to appear much larger with their aid. Before they are used the object may subtend a certain angle α at the eye; when they are used the final image may subtend an increased angle α' at the eye. The *angular magnification*, M, of the instrument is defined as the ratio

$$\mathbf{M} = \frac{\alpha'}{\alpha} \qquad . \qquad . \qquad . \qquad . \qquad . \qquad . \qquad (38)$$

and this is also popularly known as the *magnifying power* of the instrument. It should be carefully noted that we are concerned with visual angles in the theory of optical instruments, and not with the physical sizes of the object and the image obtained.

3. Microscopes

At the beginning of the seventeenth century single lenses were developed as powerful magnifying glasses, and many important discoveries in human and animal biology were made with their aid. Shortly afterwards two or more convex lenses were combined to form powerful microscopes, and with their aid HOOKE, in 1648, discovered the existence of "cells" in animal and vegetable tissue.

A microscope is an instrument used for viewing *near* objects. When it is in normal use, therefore, the image formed by the microscope is usually at the least distance of distinct vision, D, from the eye, i.e., at the near point of the eye. With the unaided eye (i.e., without the instrument), the object is seen clearest when it is placed at the near point. Consequently the angular magnification of a microscope in *normal* use is given by

$$M = \frac{a'}{a},$$

where a' is the angle subtended at the eye by the image at the near point, and a is the angle subtended at the unaided eye by the object at the near point.

4. Simple Microscope or Magnifying Glass

Suppose that an object of length h is viewed at the near point, A, by the unaided eye, Fig. 389 (i). The visual angle, a, is then h/D in

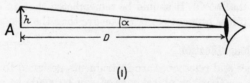

(i)

Fig. 389.　Visual angle at unaided eye.

radian measure. Now suppose that a convex lens L is used as a magnifying glass to view the same object. An erect, magnified image is obtained when the object is nearer to L than its focal length (p. 496), and the observer moves the lens until the image at I is situated at his near point. If the observer's eye is close to the lens at C, the distance

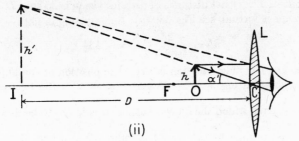

(ii)

FIG. 389. Simple microscope, or magnifying glass.

IC is then equal to D, the least distance of distinct vision, Fig. 389 (ii). Thus the new visual angle a' is given by h'/D, where h' is the length of the virtual image, and it can be seen that a' is greater than a by comparing Fig. 389 (i) with Fig. 389 (ii).

The angular magnification, M, of this simple microscope can be evaluated in terms of D and the focal length f of the lens. From the definition of M (p. 542), $M = a'/a$.

But $$a' = \frac{h'}{D}, \quad a = \frac{h}{D}$$

$$\therefore \quad M = \frac{h'}{D} \bigg/ \frac{h}{D} = h'/h \quad . \quad . \quad . \quad . \quad . \quad \text{(i)}$$

Now h'/h is the "linear magnification" produced by the lens, and is given by $h'/h = v/u$, where v is the image distance CI and u is the object distance CO (see p. 498). Since $\dfrac{1}{v} + \dfrac{1}{u} = \dfrac{1}{f}$, with the usual notation, we have

$$1 + \frac{v}{u} = \frac{v}{f},$$

by multiplying throughout by v.

$$\therefore \quad \frac{v}{u} = \frac{v}{f} - 1 = \frac{D}{f} - 1$$

since $v = \text{CI} = D$.

$$\therefore \quad \frac{h'}{h} = \frac{D}{f} - 1.$$

$$\therefore \quad M = \frac{D}{f} - 1 \quad . \quad . \quad . \quad . \quad \text{(39)}$$

from (i) above.

If the magnifying glass has a focal length of 2 cm., $f = +2$ as it is convex; also, if the least distance of distinct vision is 25 cm., $D = -25$ as the image is virtual, see Fig. 389 (ii). Substituting in (39),

$$\therefore \quad M = \frac{-25}{+2} - 1 = -13\tfrac{1}{2}.$$

Thus the angular magnification is $13\tfrac{1}{2}$. The position of the object O is given by substituting $v = -25$ and $f = +2$ in the lens equation $\frac{1}{v} + \frac{1}{u} = \frac{1}{f}$, from which the object distance u is found to be $+1\cdot86$ cm.

From the formula for M in (39), it follows that a lens of *short* focal length is required for high angular magnification.

5. Magnifying Glass with Image at Infinity

We have just considered the normal use of the simple microscope, in which case the image formed is at the near point of the eye and the eye is accommodated (p. 520). When the image is formed at infinity, however, which is not a normal use of the microscope, the eye is undergoing the least strain and is then unaccommodated (p. 520). In this case the object must be placed at the focus, F, of the lens, Fig. 390.

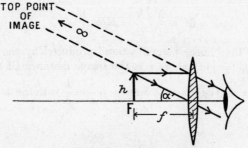

FIG. 390.   Final image at infinity.

Suppose that the focal length of the lens is f. The visual angle a' now subtended at the eye is then h/f if the eye is close to the lens, and hence the angular magnification, m, is given by

$$M = \frac{a'}{a} = \frac{h/f}{h/D},$$

as $a = h/D$, Fig. 389 (i).

$$\therefore \quad M = \frac{D}{f} \qquad . \qquad . \qquad . \qquad . \qquad (40)$$

When $f = +2$ cm. and $D = -25$ cm., $M = -12\tfrac{1}{2}$. The angular magnification was $-13\tfrac{1}{2}$ when the image was formed at the near point

(p. 544). It can easily be verified that the angular magnification varies between $12\frac{1}{2}$ and $13\frac{1}{2}$ when the image is formed between infinity and the near point, and the maximum angular magnification is thus obtained when the image is at the near point.

6. Compound Microscope

From the formula $M = D/f - 1$, M is greater the smaller the focal length of the lens. As it is impracticable to decrease f beyond a certain limit, owing to the mechanical difficulties of grinding a lens of short focal length (great curvature), *two* separated lenses are used to obtain a high angular magnification, and constitute a *compound* microscope. The lens nearer to the object is called the *objective*; the lens through which the final image is viewed is called the *eye-piece*. The objective and the eye-piece are both convex, and both have small focal lengths for a reason explained later (p. 546).

When the microscope is used, the object O is placed at a slightly *greater* distance from the objective than its focal length. In Fig. 391, F_0 is the focus of this lens. An inverted real image is then formed at I_1 in the microscope tube, and the eye-piece is adjusted so that a large virtual image is formed by it at I_2. Thus I_1 is *nearer* to the eye-piece

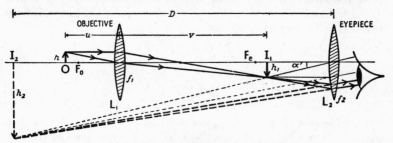

FIG. 391. Compound microscope in *normal* use.

than the focus F_e of this lens. It can now be seen that the eye-piece functions as a simple magnifying glass, used for viewing the image formed at I_1 by the objective .

7. Angular Magnification with Microscope in Normal Use

When the microscope is in normal use the image at I_2 is formed at the least distance of distinct vision, D, from the eye (p. 542). Suppose that the eye is close to the eye-piece, as shown in Fig. 391. The visual angle α' subtended by the image at I_2 is then given by $\alpha' = h_2/D$, where h_2 is the height of the image. With the unaided eye, the object subtends a visual angle α given by $\alpha = h/D$, where h is the height of the object, see Fig. 389 (i).

$\therefore$ angular magnification, $M, = \dfrac{a'}{a}$

$$= \frac{h_2/D}{h/D} = \frac{h_2}{h},$$

Now $\dfrac{h_2}{h}$ can be written as $\dfrac{h_2}{h_1} \times \dfrac{h_1}{h}$, where h_1 is the length of the inter-mediate image formed at I_1.

$$\therefore \quad M = \frac{h_2}{h_1} \cdot \frac{h_1}{h} \qquad \cdots \cdots \quad \text{(i)}$$

The ratio h_2/h_1 is the linear magnification of the "object" at I_1 produced by the *eye-piece*, and we have shown on p. 498 that the linear magnification is also given by $\dfrac{v}{f_2} - 1$, where v is the image distance from the lens and f_2 is the focal length. Since $v = D$ in this case (the image at I_2 is at a distance D from the eye-piece), it follows that

$$\frac{h_2}{h_1} = \frac{D}{f_2} - 1 \qquad \cdots \cdots \quad \text{(ii)}$$

Also, the ratio h_1/h is the linear magnification of the object at O produced by the *objective* lens. Thus if the distance of the image I_1 from this lens is denoted by v, we have

$$\frac{h_1}{h} = \frac{v}{f_1} - 1 \qquad \cdots \cdots \quad \text{(iii)}$$

$$\therefore \quad M = \frac{h_2}{h_1} \cdot \frac{h_1}{h} = \left(\frac{D}{f_2} - 1 \right) \left(\frac{v}{f_1} - 1 \right) \qquad \cdot \quad \text{(41)}$$

It can be seen that if f_1 and f_2 are small, M is large. Thus the angular magnification is high if the focal lengths of the objective and the eye-piece are small.

8. Microscope with Image at Infinity

The compound microscope can also be used with the final image formed at infinity, which is not the normal use of the instrument. In this case the eye is unaccommodated, or "at rest". The image of the object in the objective must now be formed at the focus, F_e, of the eye-piece, as shown in Fig. 392, and the visual angle a' subtended at the eye by the final image at infinity is then given by $a' = h_1/f_2$, where h_1 is the length of the image at I_1 and f_2 is the focal length of the eye-piece.

The angular magnification, M, is given by $m = a'/a$, where $a = h/D$ (p. 542).

$$\therefore \quad M = \frac{a'}{a} = \frac{h_1/f_2}{h/D} = \frac{h_1}{h} \cdot \frac{D}{f_2}$$

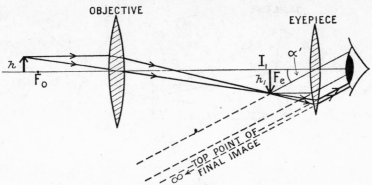

FIG. 392. Microscope with image at infinity.

But, from p. 546, $\dfrac{h_1}{h} = \dfrac{v}{f_1} - 1.$

$$\therefore \qquad M = \left(\dfrac{v}{f_1} - 1\right)\dfrac{D}{f_2} \qquad . \qquad . \qquad . \qquad . \qquad (42)$$

Comparing equations (41) and (42), it can be seen, since D is a negative (virtual) quantity, that the angular magnification is greater when the final image is formed at the near point. Further, it will be noted that the eye-piece is nearer to the image at I_1 in the latter case.

9. The Best Position of the Eye. The Eye-Ring

When an object is viewed by an optical instrument, only those rays from the object which are bounded by the perimeter of the objective lens enter the instrument. The lens thus acts as a *stop* to the light from the object. Similarly, the only rays from the image causing the sensation of vision are those which enter the pupil of the eye. The pupil thus acts as a natural stop to the light from the image; and with a given objective, the best position of the eye is one where it collects as much light as possible from that passing through the objective.

Fig. 393 illustrates three of the rays from a point X on an object at O placed in front of a compound microscope. Two of the rays are refracted at the boundary of the objective L_1 to pass through Y on the real image at I_1, while the ray OC_1 through the middle C_1 of the objective passes straight through to Y. The cone of light is then incident on the eye-piece lens L_2, where it is refracted and forms the point T on the final image, corresponding to X on the object. Now the central ray of the beams of light incident on L_1 from every point on the object passes through C_1, the centre of the objective lens. The central ray of the emergent beams from the eye-piece L_2 thus passes through the image of C_1 in L_2. By similar reasoning, we arrive at the con-

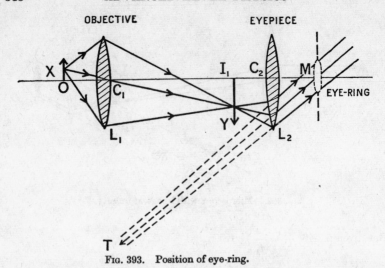

FIG. 393.   Position of eye-ring.

clusion that *all the emergent rays pass through the image M of the objective in the eye-piece.* This image is known as the *eye-ring*, and the best position of the eye is thus at M.

Suppose the objective is 16 cm. from L_2, which has a focal length of 2 cm. The image distance, v in L_2 is given by $\dfrac{1}{v} + \dfrac{1}{(+16)} = \dfrac{1}{(+2)}$, from which $v = 2.3$ cm. Thus M is a short distance from the eye-piece, and in practice the eye should be further from the eye-piece than in Fig. 391. This is arranged in commercial microscopes by having a circular opening fixed at the eye-ring distance from the eye-piece, so that the observer's eye has automatically the best position when it is placed close to the opening.

10. Angular Magnification of Telescopes

Telescopes are instruments used for viewing distant objects, and they are used extensively at sea and at astronomical observatories. The first telescope is reputed to have been made about 1608, and in 1609 Galileo made a telescope through which he observed the satellites of Jupiter and the rings of Saturn. The telescope thus paved the way for great astronomical discoveries, particularly in the hands of KEPLER. Newton also designed telescopes, and was the first person to suggest the use of curved mirrors for telescopes free from chromatic aberration (see p. 559).

If a is the angle subtended at the unaided eye by a distant object, and a' is the angle subtended at the eye by its image when a telescope is used, the angular magnification m of the instrument is given by

$$M = \frac{a'}{a}.$$

It should be carefully noted that a is *not* the angle subtended at the unaided eye by the object at the near point, as was the case with the microscope, because the telescope is used for viewing distant objects.

11. Astronomical Telescope in Normal Adjustment

An astronomical telescope made from lenses consists of an objective of long focal length and an eye-piece of short focal length, for a reason explained on p. 550. Both lenses are convex. *The telescope is in normal adjustment when the final image is formed at infinity*, and the eye is then unaccommodated when viewing the image. The unaided eye is also unaccommodated when the distant object is viewed, as the latter may be considered to be at infinity.

Fig. 394 illustrates the formation of the final image when the telescope is used normally. The image I of the distant object is formed at the focus, F_0, of the objective since the rays incident on the latter are parallel; and since the final image is formed at infinity, the focus F_e of the eye-piece must also be at F_0. Fig. 394 shows three of the many rays from the *top* point of the object, marked a, and three of the many rays from the foot of the object, marked b. These rays pass respectively through the top and foot of the image I, as shown.

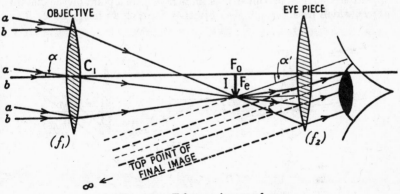

FIG. 394.   Telescope in *normal* use.

We can now obtain an expression for the angular magnification, M, of the telescope; in so doing we shall assume that the eye is close to the eye-piece. Since the length between the objective and the eye-piece is very small compared with the distance of the object from either lens, we can take the angle a subtended at the unaided eye by the object as that subtended at the objective lens, Fig. 394. The angle a' subtended at the eye when the telescope is used is given by $a' = h/f_2$, where h is the length of the image I and f_2 is the focal length of the eye-piece.

But $a = h/f_1$,

where f_1 is the focal length of the objective, since I is at a distance f_1 from C_1.

$$\therefore \quad M = \frac{a'}{a} = \frac{h/f_2}{h/f_1}$$

$$\therefore \quad M = \frac{f_1}{f_2} \quad . \quad . \quad . \quad . \quad . \quad . \quad (43)$$

Thus the angular magnification is equal to the ratio of the focal length of the objective (f_1) to that of the eye-piece (f_2). For high angular magnification, it follows from (43) that the objective should have a long focal length and the eye-piece a short focal length.

It will be noted that the distance between the lenses is equal to the sum $(f_1 + f_2)$ of their focal lengths. This provides a simple method of setting up two convex lenses to form an astronomical telescope when their focal lengths are known.

12. The Eye-Ring, and Relation to Angular Magnification

As we explained in the case of the microscope, the rays which pass through the telescope from the distant object are those bounded by the objective lens. Fig. 395 illustrates three rays from a point on the distant object which pass through the objective, forming an image at Y. The

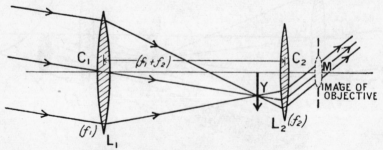

Fig. 395.   Eye-ring relation with magnification.

eye-ring, M, the best position for the eye, is the circular image of the objective in the eye-piece L_2, and we can calculate its position as $C_1 C_2 = f_1 + f_2$, from previous. As the focal length of $L_2 = f_2$, the distance C_2M, or v, is given by $\dfrac{1}{v} + \dfrac{1}{u} = \dfrac{1}{f_2}$,

i.e.,
$$\frac{1}{v} + \frac{1}{+(f_1 + f_2)} = \frac{1}{+(f_2)}$$

from which
$$v = \frac{f_2}{f_1}(f_1 + f_2).$$

Now the objective diameter : eye-ring diameter $= C_1C_2 : C_2M$

$$= u : v = (f_1 + f_2) : \frac{f_2}{f_1}(f_1 + f_2)$$

$$= f_1/f_2.$$

But the angular magnification of the telescope $= f_1/f_2$ (p. 550). Thus the angular magnification, M, is also given by

$$M = \frac{\text{diameter of objective}}{\text{diameter of eye-ring}}, \qquad . \qquad . \qquad (44)$$

the telescope being in normal adjustment.

13. Telescope with Final Image at Near Point

When a telescope is used, the final image can be formed at the near point of the eye instead of at infinity. The eye is then "accommodated", and although the image is still clearly seen, the telescope is *not* in normal adjustment (p. 549). Fig. 396 illustrates the formation of the final image. The objective forms an image of the distant object at its focus F_1, and the eye-piece is moved so that the image is nearer to it than its focus F_2, thus acting as a magnifying glass.

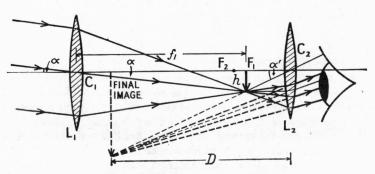

FIG. 396.   Final image at near point.

The angle a subtended at the unaided eye is practically that subtended at the objective L_1. Thus $a = h/f_1$, where h is the length of the image in the objective and f_1 its focal length. The angle a' subtended at the eye by the final image $= h/u$, if the eye is close to the eye-piece, where $u = F_1C_2 =$ the distance of the image at F_1 from the eye-piece.

Thus angular magnification, $M, = \dfrac{a'}{a} = \dfrac{h/u}{h/f_1}$

$$\therefore \quad M = \frac{f_1}{u} \qquad \cdots \cdots \quad \text{(i)}$$

As the final image is formed at a numerical distance D from the eye-piece L_2, we have $v = -D$ when $f = +f_2$. Thus, from $\dfrac{1}{v} + \dfrac{1}{u} = \dfrac{1}{f}$,

$$\frac{1}{-D} + \frac{1}{u} = \frac{1}{+f_2},$$

from which $\qquad\qquad u = \dfrac{f_2 D}{f_2 + D}.$

Substituting in (i) for u,

$$\therefore \quad M = \frac{f_1}{f_2}\left(\frac{f_2 + D}{D}\right)$$

$$\therefore \quad M = \frac{f_1}{f_2}\left(1 + \frac{f_2}{D}\right) \qquad \cdots \cdots \quad \text{(45)}$$

The angular magnification when the telescope is in normal adjustment (i.e., final image at infinity) $= \dfrac{f_1}{f_2}$ (p. 550). Hence, from (45), the angular magnification is increased in the ratio $\left(1 + \dfrac{f_2}{D}\right) : 1$ when the final image is formed at the near point.

14. Terrestrial Telescope

From Fig. 396, it can be seen that the top point of the distant object is above the axis of the lens, but the top point of the final image is below the axis. Thus the image in an astronomical telescope is *inverted*. This instrument is suitable for astronomy because it makes little difference if a star, for example, is inverted, but it is useless for viewing objects on the earth or sea, in which case an erect image is required.

A *terrestrial telescope* provides an erect image. In addition to the objective and eye-piece of the astronomical telescope, it contains a convex lens L of focal length f between them, Fig. 397. L is placed at a distance $2f$ in front of the inverted real image I_1 formed by the objective, in which case, as shown on p. 499, the image I in L of I_1 (i) is inverted, real, and the same size as I_1, (ii) is also at a distance $2f$ from L.

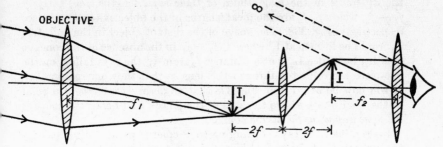

FIG. 397.   Terrestrial telescope.

Thus the image I is now the same way up as the distant object. If I is at the focus of the eye-piece, the final image is formed at infinity and is also erect.

The lens L is often known as the "erecting" lens of the telescope, as its only function is that of inverting the image I_1. Since the image I produced by L is the same size as I_1, the presence of L does not affect the magnitude of the angular magnification of the telescope, which is thus f_1/f_2 (p. 550). The erecting lens, however, reduces the intensity of the light emerging through the eye-piece, as light is reflected at the lens surfaces. Yet another disadvantage is the increased length of the telescope when L is used; the distance from the objective to the eye-piece is now $f_1 + f_2 + 4f$, Fig. 397, compared with $(f_1 + f_2)$ in the astronomical telescope.

15. Galileo's Telescope

About 1610, with characteristic genius, Galileo designed a telescope which provides an erect image of an object with the aid of only two lenses. The *Galilean telescope* consists of an objective which is a convex lens of long focal length, and an eye-piece which is a *concave* lens of short focal length. The distance between the lenses is made equal to

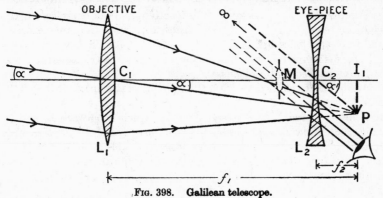

FIG. 398.   Galilean telescope.

the *difference* in the magnitudes of their focal lengths, i.e., $C_1C_2 = f_1 - f_2$, where f_1, f_2 are the focal lengths of the objective and eye-piece respectively, Fig. 398. The image of the distant object in the objective L_1 would be formed at I_1, where $C_1I_1 = f_1$, in the absence of the concave lens L_2; but since L_2 is at a distance f_2 from I_1, the rays falling on the eye-piece are refracted through this lens so that they emerge parallel. It will now be noted from Fig. 398 that an observer sees the top point of the final image above the axis of the lenses, and hence *the image is the same way up as the distant object.*

In Fig. 398, the rays converging to P emerge parallel after passing through the eye-piece L_2. The top point of the image formed at infinity is thus a virtual image in L_2 of the virtual object P. But a ray C_2P through the middle of L_2 passes straight through the lens, and this will also be a ray which passes through the top point of the image at infinity. Thus the three parallel rays shown emerging from the eye-piece in Fig. 398 are parallel to the line PC_2. Hence if the eye is placed close to the concave lens, the angle a' subtended at it by the image at infinity is angle I_1C_2P.

The angle a subtended at the eye by the distant object is practically equal to the angle subtended at the objective, Fig. 398. Now $a = h/C_1I_1 = h/f_1$, where f_1 is the objective focal length and h is the length I_1P; and $a' = h/C_2I_1 = h/f_2$.

∴ angular magnification, $M, = \dfrac{a'}{a} = \dfrac{h/f_2}{h/f_1}$

$$\therefore \qquad M, = \frac{f_1}{f_2} \qquad \cdots \cdots \qquad (46)$$

Thus for high angular magnification, an objective of long focal length (f_1) and an eye-piece of short focal length (f_2) are required, as in the case of the astronomical telescope (see p. 550).

16. Advantage and Disadvantage of Galilean Telescope. Opera Glasses

The distance C_1C_2 between the objective and the eye-piece in the Galilean telescope is ($f_1 - f_2$); the distance between the same lenses in the terrestrial telescope is ($f_1 + f_2 + 4f$), p. 553. Thus the Galilean telescope is a much shorter instrument than the terrestrial telescope, and is therefore used for *opera glasses*.

As already explained (p. 550), the eye-ring is the image of the objective in the eye-piece. But the eye-piece is a concave lens. Thus the eye-ring is virtual, and corresponds to M, which is between L_1 and L_2 (Fig. 398). Since it is impossible to place the eye at M, the best position of the eye in the circumstances is as close as possible to the eye-piece L_2, and consequently the field of view of the Galilean telescope is very limited compared with that of the astronomical or terrestrial telescope. This is a grave disadvantage of the Galilean telescope.

17. Final Image at Near Point

The final image in a Galilean telescope can also be viewed at the near point of the eye, when the telescope is not in normal adjustment. Fig. 399 illustrates the formation of the erect image in this case. The distance C_2I_1 is now more than the focal length f_2 of the eye-piece; and

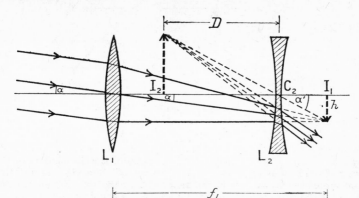

FIG. 399.   Final image at near point.

since $C_2I_2 = D$, the least distance of distinct vision, we have $v = -D$ (the image in L_2 is virtual) and f_2 is negative. Since $\dfrac{1}{v} + \dfrac{1}{u} = \dfrac{1}{f}$, we obtain

$$\frac{1}{-D} + \frac{1}{u} = \frac{1}{-f_2},$$

assuming f_2 is the *numerical* value of the concave lens focal length, from which $u = \dfrac{-f_2 D}{D - f_2}$.

With the usual notation, the angular magnification, M, $= \dfrac{a'}{a}$.

But $a' = h/u$, $a = h/f_1$. Thus $M = f_1/u$.

But
$$u = \frac{-f_2 D}{D - f_2}$$

$$\therefore \qquad M = \frac{f_1}{f_2}\left(\frac{f_2}{D} - 1\right)$$

Measurement of Magnifying Power of Telescope and Microscope

Method 1. *The magnifying power of a telescope* can be measured by placing a well-illuminated large scale S at one end of the laboratory, and viewing it through the telescope at the other end. If the telescope consists of convex lenses O, E acting as the objective and eye-piece respectively, the distance between O, E is the sum of their focal lengths when the instrument is in normal use (p. 550), Fig. 400. By means of a plane mirror M and a plane

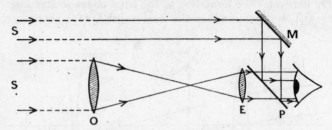

FIG. 400.   Measurement of magnifying power.

piece of glass P, the divisions on the scale S can be superimposed on its image seen through the telescope, and the ratio of the divisions in equal lengths of the field of view can thus be determined. Since the ratio of the angles subtended at the eye by the image and by the scale is equal to the ratio, a, of the divisions, the magnifying power is equal to a. There must be no parallax between the scale and the final image.

Method 2. The magnifying power of a telescope is the ratio of the diameters of the objective and eye-ring (p. 551). The eye-ring is the image of the objective in the eye-piece, and is obtained by pointing the telescope to the sky and holding a ground glass screen near the eye-piece. A circle, which is the image of the objective in the eye-piece, is observed on the screen, and its diameter, d, is measured. The magnifying power is then given by the ratio d_0/d, where d_0 is the diameter of the objective. This method is particularly useful when the telescope is fixed in a tube, as it is in practice. When a telescope is set up as in Fig. 395, a cardboard with a circular hole can be placed round the objective lens to define its diameter, and the eye-ring found by placing a screen near the eye-piece.

The magnifying power of a microscope can be found by placing two similar scales in front of it, one being 25 cm. from the eye. The other scale is placed near the objective, and the eye-piece is moved until the image of this scale coincides with the first scale by the method of no parallax, both eyes being used. The magnifying power is then given by the ratio of the number of divisions occupying the same length.

18. Prism Binoculars

Prism binoculars are widely used as field glasses, and consist of short astronomical telescopes containing two right-angled isosceles prisms between the objective and the eye-piece, Fig. 401. These lenses are both convex, and they would produce an inverted image of the distant object if they were alone used. The purpose of the two prisms is to invert the image and obtain a final *erect* image.

One prism, A, is placed with its refracting edge vertical, while the other, B, is placed with its refracting edge horizontal. As shown in

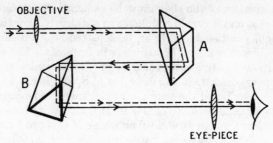

FIG. 401.   Prism binoculars.

Fig. 396, the image formed by the objective alone is inverted. Prism A, however, turns it round in a horizontal direction, while prism B inverts it in a vertical direction, both prisms acting as reflectors of light (see p. 460). The image produced after reflection at B is now the same way up, and the same way round as, the original object. Since the eye-piece is a convex lens acting as a magnifying glass, it produces a final image the same way up as the image in front of it, and hence the final image is the same way up as the distant object.

Fig. 401 illustrates the path of 2 rays through the optical system. Since the optical path of a ray is about 3 times the distance d between the objective and the eye-piece, the system is equivalent optically to an astronomical telescope of length $3d$. The focal lengths of the objective and eye-piece in the prism binoculars can thus provide the same angular magnification as an astronomical telescope 3 times as long. The compactness of the prism binoculars is one of its advantages; another advantage is the wide field of view obtained, as it is an astronomical telescope (p. 354).

19. Projection Lantern

The projection lantern is used for showing slides on a screen, and the *essential features* of the apparatus are illustrated in Fig. 402. S is a slide whose image is formed on the screen A by adjusting the position of an achromatic objective lens L.

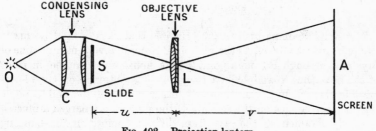

FIG. 402.   Projection lantern.

The illumination of the slide must be as high as possible, otherwise the image of it on the screen is difficult to see clearly. For this purpose a very bright point source of light, O, is placed near a *condensing lens* C, and the slide S is placed immediately in front of C. The condensing lens consists of a plano-convex lens arrangement, which concentrates the light energy from O in the direction of S, and it has a short focal length. The lens L and the source O are arranged to be conjugate foci for the lens C (i.e., the image of O is formed at L), in which case (i) all the light passes through L, and (ii) an image of O is not formed on the screen. Fig. 402 illustrates the path of the beam of light from O which forms the image of S on the screen.

The magnification, m, of the slide is given by $m = \dfrac{v}{u}$, where v, u are the respective screen and slide distances from L. Now $\dfrac{v}{u} = \dfrac{v}{f} - 1$ (see p. 498). Thus the required high magnification is obtained by using an objective whose focal length is small compared with v.

20. Pinhole Camera

The *pinhole camera* consists essentially of a closed box with a pinhole in front and a photographic plate at the back on which the image is formed. The principle was first discovered by PORTA about 1600, who found that clear images were formed on a screen at the back of the box when objects were placed in front of the pinhole.

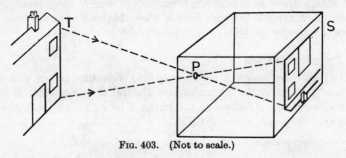

FIG. 403. (Not to scale.)

The simple camera utilises the principle that rays of light normally travel in straight lines. As the pinhole P is small, a very narrow cone of rays pass through P from a point T on a house, for example, in front of the box; thus a well-defined image of T is obtained on the photographic plate S, Fig. 403. Similarly, other points on the building give rise to clear images on the screen. If the pinhole is enlarged a blurred image is obtained, as the rays from different points on the building then tend to overlap.

The pinhole camera is used by surveyors to photograph the outline of buildings, as the image obtained is free from the distortion produced by the lens in a normal camera.

21. Photographic Camera

The photographic camera consists essentially of a *lens system* L, a *light-sensitive film* F at the back, and a *focusing arrangement*, Fig. 404. The latter is usually a concertina-shaped canvas bag D, which adjusts the distance of the lens L from F.

The lens in the camera is an achromatic doublet (p. 527), and the use of two lenses diminishes spherical aberration (p. 531). A *stop* of diameter *d* is provided, so that the light is incident centrally on the lens, thus diminishing distortion. The stop also controls the amount of light incident on the film, and thus controls the exposure. The diameter *d* of the stop is usually given as a fraction of the focal length *f* of the lens system, e.g., $f/4$, or $f/8$; and since the bright-

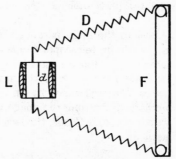

FIG. 404. Photographic camera.

ness of the image of the film is proportional to the area of the stop, which is also proportional to d^2, the brightness when the diameter of the stop is $f/4$ is four times the brightness when the diameter is reduced to $f/8$.

22. The 200-inch (Mount Palomar) Telescope

The construction of the largest telescope in the world is one of the most fascinating stories of scientific skill and invention. The major feature of the telescope is a parabolic *mirror*, 200 ins. across, which is made of pyrex, a low expansion glass. The glass itself took more than six years to grind and polish, having been begun in 1936, and the front of the mirror is coated with aluminium, instead of being covered with silver, as it lasts much longer. The huge size of the mirror will enable enough light from very distant stars and planets to be collected and brought to a focus for them to be photographed. Special cameras are incorporated in the instrument to photograph the universe. This method has the advantage that plates can be exposed for hours, if necessary, to the object to be studied, enabling records to be made. It is hoped to obtain useful information about the building-up and breaking-down of the elements in space, thus assisting in atomic energy research, to investigate astronomical theories of the universe, and to photograph Mars.

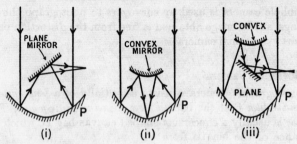

FIG. 405 (i). Newton reflector. (ii). Cassegrain reflector. (iii). Coudé reflector.

Besides the main parabolic mirror P, seven other mirrors are used in the 200-in. telescope. Some are plane, Fig. 405 (i), while others are convex, Fig. 405 (ii), and they are used to bring the light to a more convenient focus, where the image can be photographed, or magnified several hundred times by an eye-piece for observation. The various methods of focusing the image were suggested respectively by *Newton*, *Cassegrain*, and *Coudé*, the last being a combination of the former two methods.

EXAMPLES

1. What do you understand by the magnifying power of an astronomical telescope? Illustrate your answer with a ray diagram depicting the use of the instrument to view stars in the heavens. If such a telescope has an object glass of focal length 50 cm. and an eye lens of focal length 5 cm., what is its magnifying power? If it is assumed that the eye is placed very close to the eye lens and that the pupil of the eye has a diameter of 3 mm., what will be the diameter of the object glass if all the light passing through the object glass is to emerge as a beam which fills the pupil of the eye? Assume that the telescope is pointed directly at a particular star. (*W.*)

First part. See text.

Second part. Assuming the telescope is in *normal* adjustment, the final image is formed at infinity. The magnifying power of the telescope is then $\dfrac{50 \text{ cm.}}{5 \text{ cm.}}$, or 10. See p. 550.

If all the light emerging from the eye-piece fills the pupil of the eye, the pupil is at the eye-ring. See p. 550. The eye-ring is the image of the objective in the eye-piece. Since the distance, u, from the objective to the eye-piece $= 50 + 5 = 55$ cm., the eye-ring distance, v, is given by

$$\frac{1}{v} + \frac{1}{(+\,55)} = \frac{1}{(+\,5)}$$

from which $v = 5\cdot5$ cm.

This is the position of the pupil of the eye. The magnification of the objective is given by

$$\frac{\text{eye-ring diameter}}{\text{objective diameter}} = \frac{v}{u} = \frac{5 \cdot 5}{55} = \frac{1}{10}$$

$$\therefore \quad \frac{3 \text{ mm.}}{\text{objective diameter}} = \frac{1}{10}$$

$$\therefore \quad \text{objective diameter} = 3 \text{ cm.}$$

2. What do you understand by (a) the apparent size of an object, and (b) the magnifying power of a microscope? A model of a compound microscope is made up of two converging lenses of 3 and 9 cm. focal length at a fixed separation of 24 cm. Where must the object be placed so that the final image may be at infinity? What will be the magnifying power if the microscope as thus arranged is used by a person whose nearest distance of distinct vision is 25 cm.? State what is the best position for the observer's eye and explain why. (*L.*)

First part. (a) The apparent size of an object is proportional to the visual angle. See p. 540. (b) The magnifying power of a microscope is defined on p. 541.

Second part. (i) Suppose the objective A is 3 cm. focal length, and the eye-piece B is 9 cm. focal length, Fig. 406. If the final image is at infinity,

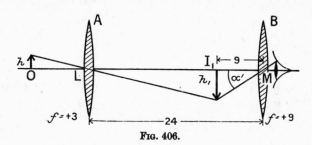

FIG. 406.

the image I_1, in the objective must be 9 cm. from B, the focal length of the eye-piece. See p. 549. Thus the image distance LI_1, from the objective A $= 24 - 9 = 15$ cm. The object distance OL is thus given by

$$\frac{1}{(+ 15)} + \frac{1}{u} = \frac{1}{(+3)}$$

from which $\quad u = OL = 3\frac{3}{4}$ cm.

(ii) The angle a' subtended at the observer's eye is given by $a' = h_1/9$, where h_1 is the height of the image at I_1, Fig. 406. Without the lenses, the object subtends an angle a at the eye given by $a = h/25$, where h is the height of the object, since the least distance of distinct vision is 25 cm.

$$\therefore \quad \text{magnifying power, } M, = \frac{a'}{a} = \frac{h_1/9}{h/25} = \frac{25}{9} \times \frac{h_1}{h}$$

But $\qquad\qquad \dfrac{h_1}{h} = \dfrac{LI_1}{LO} = \dfrac{15}{3\frac{3}{4}} = 4$

$$\therefore \quad M = \frac{25}{9} \times 4 = 11\frac{1}{9}$$

The best position of the eye is at the eye-ring, which is the image of the objective A in the eye-piece B (p. 547).

3. A Galilean telescope has an object-glass of 12 cm. focal length and an eye lens of 5 cm. focal length. It is focused on a distant object so that the final image seen by the eye appears to be situated at a distance of 30 cm. from the eye lens. Determine the angular magnification obtained and draw a ray diagram. What are the advantages of prism binoculars as compared with field glasses of the Galilean type? (N.)

Suppose I_2 is the final image, distant 30 cm. from the eye lens L_2, Fig. 407. The corresponding object is I_1. Since I_2 is a virtual image in L_2'

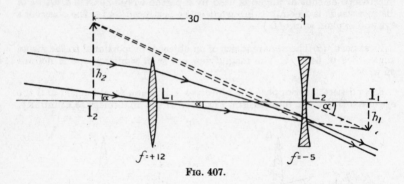

FIG. 407.

$v = I_2L_2 = -30$, $f = -5$, $u = L_2I_1$. From the lens equation for L_2, we have

$$\frac{1}{(-30)} + \frac{1}{u} = \frac{1}{(-5)}$$

from which $u = -6$ cm.

Thus I_1 is a virtual object for L_2.

The angular magnification, M, is given by $M = a'/a$. Now $a' = h_1/L_2I_1$, and $a = h_1/L_1I_1$.

$$\therefore \quad M = \frac{h_1/L_2I_1}{h_1/L_1I_1} = \frac{L_1I_1}{L_2I_1}$$

But $L_2I_1 = 6$ cm., from above, and $L_1I_1 =$ focal length of $L_1 = 12$ cm., since the object is distant.

$$\therefore \quad M = \frac{12}{6} = 2$$

The advantages of the prism binoculars are given on p. 557.

4. Describe the optical system of a projection lantern. A lantern is required for the projection of slides 3 ins. square on to a screen 7 ft. square. The distance between the front of the lantern and the screen is to be 20 ft. What focal length of projection lens (to the nearest inch) would you consider most suitable. (W.)

First part. See text.

Second part. Suppose O is the slide, L is the projection lens, and S is the screen, Fig. 408. The linear magnification, m, due to the lens is given by

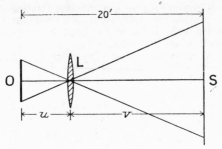

FIG. 408.

$$m = \frac{7 \times 12}{3} = 28$$

$$\therefore \quad LS : LO = 28 : 1$$

$$\therefore \qquad LS = v = \frac{28}{29} \times 20 \text{ ft.}$$

$$\text{and} \qquad LO = u = \frac{1}{29} \times 20 \text{ ft.}$$

Applying the lens equation,

$$\therefore \quad \frac{1}{560/29} + \frac{1}{20/29} = \frac{1}{f}$$

from which $\qquad f = \dfrac{560}{841}$ ft. = 8 ins. (to nearest inch)

EXERCISES XXV

1. An object is viewed with a normal eye at (i) the least distance of distinct vision, (ii) 40 cm., (iii) 100 cm. from the eye. Find the ratio of the visual angles in the three cases, and draw diagrams in illustration.

2. Where should the final image be formed when (a) a telescope, (b) a microscope is in *normal* use? Define the angular magnification (magnifying power) of a telescope and a microscope.

3. Explain the essential features of the astronomical telescope. Define and deduce an expression for the magnifying power of this instrument.

A telescope is made of an object glass of focal length 20 cm. and an eyepiece of 5 cm., both converging lenses. Find the magnifying power in accordance with your definition in the following cases: (a) when the eye is focused to receive parallel rays, and (b) when the eye sees the image situated at the nearest distance of distinct vision which may be taken as 25 cm. (*L.*)

4. Describe the optical principles of the compound microscope. Illustrate your answer with a ray diagram and show how to calculate the magnifying power. Why in an actual microscope do both the objective and the eye-piece each consist of more than one lens? (*N*.)

5. A projection lantern contains a condensing lens and a projection lens. Show clearly in a ray diagram the function of these lenses.

A lantern has a projection lens of focal length 10 ins. and is required to be able to function when the distance from lantern to screen may vary from 20 ft. to 40 ft. What range of movement for the lens must be provided in the focusing arrangement? What is the approximate value of the ratio of the magnifications at the two extreme distances? (*W*.)

6. A convex lens of focal length 20 cm. and a concave lens of focal length 10 cm. are arranged for use as an opera glass. Draw a ray diagram to scale showing how the final image at infinity is produced, describing briefly how you do this, and derive the magnifying power.

When an object is placed 60 cm. in front of the convex lens and the lenses are separated by a distance x, a real image is formed 30 cm. beyond the concave lens. Calculate x. (*C*.)

7. Describe the optical arrangement of an astronomical telescope. Illustrate your description with a ray diagram showing the paths through the telescope of a pencil of rays from a non-axial point on a distant object. Show that, when the instrument is in normal adjustment, the magnifying power is equal to the ratio of the diameter of the object glass to the diameter of the object glass formed by the eye lens. (*L*.)

8. Draw the path of two rays, from a point on an object, passing through the optical system of a compound microscope to the final image as seen by the eye.

If the final image formed coincides with the object, and is at the least distance of distinct vision (25 cm.) when the object is 4 cm. from the objective, calculate the focal lengths of the objective and eye lenses, assuming that the magnifying power of the microscope is 14. (*L*.)

9. An astronomical telescope consisting of an objective of focal length 60 cm. and an eye-piece of focal length 3 cm. is focused on the moon so that the final image is formed at the minimum distance of distinct vision (25 cm.) from the eye-piece. Assuming that the diameter of the moon subtends an angle of $\frac{1}{2}°$ at the objective, calculate (*a*) the angular magnification, (*b*) the actual size of the image seen.

How, with the same lenses, could an image of the moon, 10 cm. in diameter, be formed on a photographic plate? (*C*.)

10. A person whose minimum distance of distinct vision is 20 cm. uses a magnifying glass of 5 cm. focal length held close to the eye. What must be the position of the object examined, and what magnification is obtained? How would you make a compound microscope with two lenses? Discuss the relations between the position of the object, the distance between the lenses, and the distance of distinct vision. (*N*.)

11. Describe the optical system of a pair of prism binoculars, and explain its advantages over (i) a single terrestial telescope, and (ii) other types of binoculars. (*C*.)

12. Describe the construction and mode of action of Galileo's telescope (opera glass). Show by means of a diagram how the concave lens produces a magnified image. (*L.*)

13. Draw a diagram to show how two lenses are arranged to form a microscope, tracing the paths to the eye of two rays from a point on the object not on the axis.

Convex lenses, of focal lengths 3 cm. and 5 cm., are used respectively as the objective and eye-piece of a microscope. If the object is 3·5 cm. from the objective and the final image is 25 cm. from the eye-piece, what is the distance between the centres of the lenses? (*C.*)

14. Define the *angular magnification* (*magnifying power*) of a telescope.

An astronomical telescope consists of two converging lenses of focal lengths 25 cm. and 5 cm. respectively. Find, from first principles, the angular magnification when the final image is formed (i) at infinity, (ii) 25 cm. from the eye-piece. Draw careful ray diagrams illustrating each case.

15. A Galilean telescope has a converging lens of 20 ins. focal length and a diverging lens of 2 ins. focal length. Find, from first principles, the angular magnification when the final image is formed (i) at infinity, (ii) 10 ins. from the eye-piece. Draw careful ray diagrams illustrating each case.

16. Give a detailed description of the optical system of the compound microscope, explaining the problems which arise in the design of an object lens for a microscope.

A compound microscope has lenses of focal length 1 cm. and 3 cm. An object is placed 1·2 cm. from the object lens; if a virtual image is formed 25 cm. from the eye, calculate the separation of the lenses and the magnification of the instrument. (*O. & C.*)

17. A telescope is made up of two thin converging lenses of focal lengths 50 cm. and 5 cm. and used to observe an object 2·5 metres from the objective. If the observer's accommodation is relaxed so that the final image is formed at infinity, what will be the distance between the lenses and the magnifying power, assuming the observer's eye to be close to the eye lens? What would the observer notice if he slowly drew his eye back along the axis of the telescope? Illustrate your answer by ray diagrams and determine the best position for the observer's eye. (*L.*)

CHAPTER XXVI

PHOTOMETRY

Photometry is the science which concerns the measurement of light, and a study of its principles has resulted in considerable benefit to the health of the population. Before the advent of the illumination engineer many factories, shops, and offices were ill-lit, and a strain was thus imposed on the eyes of workers. Streets and roads were also badly lit, resulting in many accidents. Today, standards of illumination have been set up which act as a safeguard against eye-strain, and they have materially assisted in better production in all grades of work, as well as preventing accidents.

Before the measurement of light can be discussed, the meaning of the technical terms used in the subject must be explained.

1. Standard Candle. Candle-Power . The Candela

Light is a form of energy which stimulates the sensation of vision. The sun emits a continuous stream of energy, consisting of ultra-violet, visible, and infra-red radiations (p. 466), all of which enter the eye; but only the energy in the visible radiations, which is called *luminous energy*, stimulates the sensation of vision. In Photometry we are concerned only with the luminous energy emitted by a source of light.

Years ago the luminous energy per second from a candle of specified wax material and wick was used as a standard of luminous energy. This was called the *British Standard Candle*. The luminous energy per second from any other source of light was reckoned in terms of the standard candle, and its value was given at 10 candle-power (10 c.p.) for example. As the standard candle was difficult to reproduce exactly, the standard was altered. It was defined as one-tenth of the intensity of the flame of the *Vernon Harcourt pentane lamp*, which burns a mixture of air and pentane vapour under specified conditions. Later it was agreed to use as a standard the *international standard candle*, which is defined in terms of the luminous energy per second from a particular electric lamp filament maintained under specified conditions, but the precision of this standard was found to be unsatisfactory. In 1948, a unit known as the *candela* was adopted. This is defined as one-sixtieth of the luminous intensity per sq. cm. of a black body (full) radiator at the temperature of solidification of platinum.

2. Intensity of Illumination* and its Units

If a lamp S of 1 candela is placed 1 ft. away from a small area A

---

* The term *illumination* is also used.

and directly in front of it, the *intensity of illumination* of the surface of A is said to be 1 *ft. candle*, Fig. 409. If the same lamp is placed 1 centi-metre away from A, instead of 1 ft., the intensity of illumination of the surface is said to be 1 *cm. candle* (or 1 *phot*); and if the distance of S from A is 1 metre, the intensity of illumination is said to be 1 *metre candle* (or 1 *lux*). These are units of intensity of illum-ination. It is recommended that offices

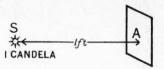

Fig. 409.   Foot-candle.

should have an intensity of illumination of about 8 ft. candles, and that the intensity of illumination for sewing dark materials in work-rooms should be about 20 ft. candles.

3. Luminous Flux, F

In practice a source of light emits a continuous stream of energy, and the name *luminous flux* has been given to the *luminous energy emitted per second*. The unit of luminous flux is the **lumen**. Since the lumen is a certain amount of "energy per second", or "power", there must be a relation between the lumen and the watt, the mechanical unit of power; and experiment shows that 621 lumens of a green light of wavelength $5,540 \times 10^{-8}$ cm. is equivalent to 1 watt.

4. Solid Angle

A lamp radiates luminous flux in all directions round it. If we think of a particular small lamp and a certain direction from it, for example that of the corner of a table, we can see that the flux is radiated towards the corner in a cone whose apex is the lamp. A thorough study of photometry must therefore include a discussion of the measurement of an angle in three dimensions, such as that of a cone, which is known as a *solid angle*.

An angle in two dimensions, i.e., in a plane, is given in radians by the ratio s/r, where s is the length of the arc cut off by the bounding lines of the angle on a circle of radius r. In an analogous manner, the solid angle, ω, of a cone is defined by the relation

$$\omega = \frac{S}{r^2} \qquad . \qquad . \qquad . \qquad . \qquad (47)$$

where S is the area of the surface of a sphere of radius r cut off by the bounding (generating) lines of the cone, Fig. 410 (i). Since S and r^2 both have the dimensions of (length)^2, the solid angle ω is a ratio. When $S = 1$ sq. ft., and $r = 1$ ft., then $\omega = 1$ from equation (47). Thus *unit solid angle* is subtended at the centre of a sphere of radius

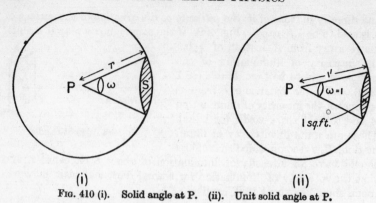

(i)   (ii)

FIG. 410 (i).   Solid angle at P.   (ii).   Unit solid angle at P.

1 ft. by a cap of surface area 1 sq. ft., Fig. 410 (ii). The solid angle all round a point is given from (47) by

$$\frac{\text{total surface area of sphere}}{r^2}$$

i.e., by $\frac{4\pi r^2}{r^2}$, or 4π.

Thus the solid angle all round a point is 4π. The solid angle all round a point on one side of a plane is thus 2π.

5. Luminous Intensity of Source, I

Experiment shows that the luminous flux from a source of light varies in different directions; to be accurate, we must therefore consider the luminous flux emitted in a particular direction. Suppose that we

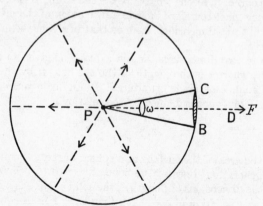

FIG. 411.   Luminous intensity of source.

consider a small lamp P, and describe a cone PCB of small solid angle ω about a particular direction PD as axis, Fig. 411. The *luminous intensity*, I, *of the source in this direction* is then defined by the relation

$$I = \frac{F}{\omega} \quad . \quad . \quad . \quad . \quad . \quad . \quad (48)$$

where F is the luminous flux contained in the small cone. Thus the luminous intensity of the source is the *luminous flux per unit solid angle* in the particular direction. It can now be seen that "luminous intensity" is a measure of the "luminous flux density" in the direction concerned.

The unit of luminous intensity of a source is the *candela*, defined on p. 566; the luminous intensity was formerly known as the *candle-power* of the source. When the luminous flux, F, in the cone in Fig. 411 is 1 lumen (the unit of luminous flux), and the solid angle, ω, of the cone is 1 unit, it follows from equation (48) that $I = 1$ candela. Thus *the lumen can be defined as the luminous flux radiated within unit solid angle by a uniform source of one* candela.

6. Intensity of Illumination of Surface in Terms of Luminous Flux

On p. 567 we encountered the units of the *intensity of illumination of a surface*; these were the ft. candle, the cm. candle, and the metre candle. The intensity of illumination is defined generally as the *luminous flux per unit area* falling on the part of the surface under consideration. Thus if F is the luminous flux incident on a small area A, the intensity of illumination, E, is given by

$$E = \frac{F}{A} \quad . \quad . \quad . \quad . \quad . \quad (49)$$

When $F = 1$ lumen and $A = 1$ sq. ft., then $E = 1$ ft. candle. Thus 1 ft. candle of illumination is equivalent to an illumination of 1 lumen per sq. ft. of the surface. Similarly, 1 cm. candle (p. 567) is equivalent to an illumination of 1 lumen per sq. cm. of the surface.

The reader should take pains to distinguish carefully between "luminous intensity" and "intensity of illumination". The former refers to the *source* of light and is measured in candelas (formerly candle-power); the latter refers to the *surface* illuminated and is measured in cm. candles or ft. candles. Further, "luminous intensity" is defined in terms of unit solid angle, which concerns three dimensions, whereas "intensity of illumination" is defined in terms of unit area, which concerns two dimensions.

7. Relation Between Luminous Intensity (I) and Intensity of Illumination (E)

Consider a *point* source of light of uniform intensity and a small part X of a surface which it illuminates. If the source of light is doubled, the intensity of illumination of X is doubled because the luminous flux incident on it is twice as much. Thus

$$E \propto I \qquad \text{. . . . . (i)}$$

where E is the intensity of illumination due to a point source of luminous intensity I.

The intensity of illumination also depends on the distance of X from the source. Suppose spheres of radii r_1, r_2 are drawn round a point source of candle-power I, such as S in Fig. 412 (i). The same amount of luminous flux F spreads over the surface area ($4\pi r^2$) of both spheres, and hence $E_1 : E_2 = F/4\pi r_1{}^2 : F/4\pi r_2{}^2$, where E_1, E_2 are the intensities of illumination at the surface of the smaller and larger spheres respectively. Thus $E_1 : E_2 = r_2{}^2 : r_1{}^2$. It can hence be seen that the intensity of illumination due to a given source varies inversely as the square of the distance from the source, i.e.,

$$E \propto \frac{1}{r^2} \qquad \text{. . . . . (ii)}$$

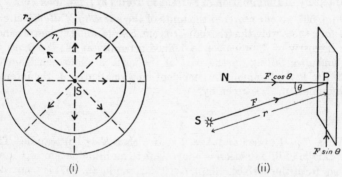

Fig. 412 (i). Inverse square law. (ii). Lambert's cosine rule.

In the eighteenth century LAMBERT showed that the intensity of illumination round a point P on a surface is proportional to cos θ, where θ is the angle between the normal PN at P to the surface and the line SP joining the source S to P, Fig. 412 (ii). A rigid proof of Lambert's law is given shortly, but we can easily see qualitatively why the cosine rule is true. The luminous flux F illuminating P is in the direction SP, and thus has a component F cos θ along NP and a component F sin θ parallel to the surface, Fig. 412. The latter does not illuminate the surface. Hence the effective part of the flux F is F cos θ.

From equations (i) and (ii) and the cosine law, it follows that the intensity of illumination E round P due to the source S of luminous intensity I is given by

$$E = \frac{I \cos \theta}{r^2} \qquad . \quad . \quad . \quad . \quad (50)$$

where $SP = r$. This is a fundamental equation in Photometry, and it is proved rigidly shortly. In applying it in practice one has to take into account that (i) a "point source" is difficult to realise, (ii) the area round the point considered on the surface should be very small so that the flux incident all over it can be considered the same, (iii) the intensity I of a source varies in different directions, (iv) the actual intensity of illumination round a point on a table, for example, is not only due to the electric lamp above it but also to the luminous flux diffusely reflected towards the point from neighbouring objects such as walls.

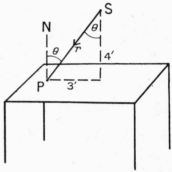

Example: Suppose that we are required to calculate the intensity I of a lamp S fixed 4 ft. above a horizontal table, if the intensity of illumination at a point P on the table 3 ft. to one side of the vertical through the lamp is 6 ft. candles, Fig. 413.

Fig. 413.

The intensity of illumination, E, at P is given by

$$E = \frac{I \cos \theta}{r^2} \qquad . \quad . \quad . \quad . \quad (i)$$

where I is the luminous intensity of S, θ is the angle between SP and the normal PN to the table at P, and $r = SP$.

But $$r^2 = 4^2 + 3^2 = 25, \text{ i.e., } r = 5,$$

$$\cos \theta = \frac{4}{r} = \frac{4}{5},$$

and $$E = 6 \text{ ft. candles.}$$

Substituting in (i),

$$\therefore \quad 6 = \frac{I \times \frac{4}{5}}{25}$$

$$\therefore \quad I = 187 \cdot 5 \quad \text{candelas.}$$

Proof of $E = I \cos \theta/r^2$. Consider a source S of intensity I illuminating a very small area A round a point P on a surface, Fig. 414. If ω is the solid angle at S in the cone obtained by joining S to the boundary of the area, the intensity of illumination at P is given by

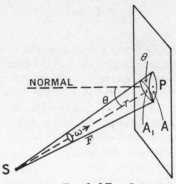

FIG. 414. Proof of $E = I \cos \theta / r^2$.

$$E = \frac{F}{A} = \frac{I\omega}{A}$$

as $I = \dfrac{F}{\omega}$ (p. 567). Now, by definition,

$$\omega = \frac{A_1}{r^2},$$

where A_1 is the area cut off on a sphere of centre S and radius r ($= SP$) by the generating lines of the cone.

$$\therefore \quad E = \frac{I\omega}{A} = \frac{I A_1}{r^2 A}.$$

But $$A_1 = A \cos \theta,$$

since A_1 is the projection of A on the sphere of centre S, and θ is the angle between the areas as well as the angle made by the normal to the surface, Fig. 414.

$$\therefore \quad E = \frac{I A \cos \theta}{r^2 A} = \frac{I \cos \theta}{r^2}$$

8. Brightness of a Surface. Reflection and Transmission Factors

The *brightness** of a surface in a given direction is defined as the luminous flux per sq. cm. *coming from* the surface in the particular direction. The brightness of white paint on the wall of a room is considerably higher than the brightness of a brown-painted panel in the middle of the wall; the brightness of a steel nib is much greater than that of a dark ebonite penholder.

The "brightness" of a surface should be carefully distinguished from the "intensity of illumination" of the surface, which is the luminous flux per sq. cm. *incident on* the surface. Thus the intensity of illumination of white chalk on a blackboard is practically the same as that of the neighbouring points on the board itself, whereas the brightness of

* The term *luminance* is now used by illumination engineers.

the chalk is much greater than that of the board. The difference in brightness is due to the difference in the *reflection factor*, r, of the chalk and board, which is defined by the relation

$$r = \frac{B}{E} \qquad . \quad . \quad . \quad . \quad (51)$$

where B is the brightness of the surface and E is the intensity of illumination of the surface. Thus the brightness, B, is given by

$$B = rE \qquad . \quad . \quad . \quad . \quad (52)$$

Besides reflection, the brightness of a surface may be due to the transmission of luminous flux through it. The brightness of a pearl lamp, for example, is due to the transmission of luminous flux through its surface. The *transmission factor*, t, of a substance is a ratio which is defined by

$$t = \frac{F}{E} \qquad . \quad . \quad . \quad . \quad (53)$$

where F is the luminous flux per sq. cm. transmitted through the substance and E is the luminous flux per sq. cm. incident on the substance. Thus

$$F = tE \qquad . \quad . \quad . \quad . \quad (54)$$

9. The Lummer-Brodhun Photometer

A *photometer* is an instrument which can be used for comparing the luminous intensities of sources of light. One of the most accurate

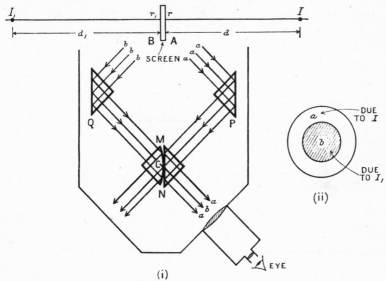

Fig. 415. Lummer-Brodhun photometer

forms of photometer was designed by LUMMER and BRODHUN, and the essential features of the instrument are illustrated in Fig. 155 (i).

A lamp of candle-power I, and a lamp of candle-power I_1, are placed on opposite sides of a white opaque screen, and some of the diffusely-reflected light from the opposite surfaces A, B is incident on two identical totally reflecting prisms P, Q, Fig. 415 (i). The light reflected from the prisms then passes towards the "Lummer-Brodhun cube", which is the main feature of the photometer. This consists of two right-angled isosceles prisms in optical contact at their central portion C, but with the edges of one cut away so that an air-film exists at M, N all round C between the prisms. The rays leaving the prism P are thus transmitted through the central portion C of the "cube", but totally reflected at the edges. Similarly, the rays reflected from the prism Q towards the "cube" are transmitted through the central portion but totally reflected at the edges. An observer of the "cube" thus sees a central circular patch b of light due initially to the light from the source of candle-power I_1, and an outer portion a due initially to the light from the source of candle-power I, Fig. 415 (ii).

10. Comparison of Luminous Intensities

In general, the brightness of the central and outer portions of the field of view in a Lummer-Brodhun photometer is different, so that one appears darker than the other. By moving one of the sources, however, a position is obtained when both portions appear equally bright, in which case they cannot be distinguished from each other and the field of view is uniformly bright. A "photometric balance" is then said to exist.

Suppose that the distances of the sources of c.p. I_1 and I from the screen are d_1, d respectively, Fig. 415. The intensity of illumination, E, due to the source of c.p. I is generally given by $E = I \cos \theta / d^2$ (p. 571). But $\theta = 0$ in this case, as the line joining the source to the screen is normal to the screen. Hence, since $\cos 0° = 1$, $E = I/d^2$. Similarly, the intensity of illumination, E_1, at the screen due to the source of c.p. I_1 is given by $E_1 = I_1/d_1^2$. Now the *brightness* of the surface $B = r_1 E_1$, where r_1 is the reflection factor of the surface (p 573); and the brightness of the surface $A = rE$, where r is the reflection factor of the surface. Hence, for a photometric balance,

$$r_1 E_1 = rE$$

$$\therefore \quad \frac{r_1 I_1}{d_1^2} = \frac{rI}{d^2} \quad \cdots \quad \cdots \quad \text{(i)}$$

If the reflection factors r_1, r of A, B are equal, equation (i) becomes

$$\frac{I_1}{d_1^2} = \frac{I}{d^2}$$

$$\therefore \qquad \frac{I_1}{I} = \frac{d_1{}^2}{d^2}$$

The ratio of the intensities are hence proportional to the squares of the corresponding distances of the sources from the screen.

The reflection factors r_1, r are not likely to be exactly equal, however, in which case another or *auxiliary lamp* is required to compare the candle-powers I_1, I. The auxiliary lamp, of c.p. I_2, is placed on the right side, say, of the screen at a distance d_2, and *one* of the other lamps is placed on the other side. A photometric balance is then

(i)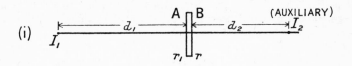

(ii)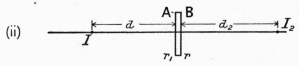

Fig. 416.   Comparison of candle-powers.

obtained, Fig. 416 (i). Then if I_1 is the c.p. of the lamp and d_1 is its distance from the screen,

$$r_1 \frac{I_1}{d_1{}^2} = r \frac{I_2}{d_2{}^2} \qquad . \qquad . \qquad . \qquad . \qquad \text{(ii)}$$

The remaining lamp of c.p. I is then used instead of the lamp of c.p. I_1, and a photometric balance is again obtained by moving this lamp, *keeping the position of the lamp of c.p. I_2 unaltered*, Fig. 416 (ii). Suppose the distance of the lamp of c.p. I from the screen is d. Then

$$r_1 \frac{I}{d^2} = r \frac{I_2}{d_2{}^2} \qquad . \qquad . \qquad . \qquad . \qquad \text{(iii)}$$

From (ii) and (iii), it follows that

$$r_1 \frac{I_1}{d_1{}^2} = r_1 \frac{I}{d^2}$$

$$\therefore \qquad \frac{I_1}{d_1{}^2} = \frac{I}{d^2}$$

$$\therefore \qquad \frac{I_1}{I} = \frac{d_1{}^2}{d^2} \qquad . \qquad . \qquad . \qquad . \qquad . \qquad \text{(55)}$$

The intensities I_1, I are hence proportional to the squares of the corresponding lamp distances from the screen. It should be noted from (55) that the auxiliary lamp's intensity is not required in the comparison of I_1 and I, nor is its constant distance d_2 from the screen required.

11. Flicker Photometer

The Lummer-Brodhun photometer is not reliable when the sources of light have different colours, and for this purpose *flicker photometers* have been developed. The principle of a flicker photometer is illustrated in Fig. 417. A is a white diffusing surface illuminated by light from a source S, while B is a sectored plaster of paris disc illuminated by a source S_1. The light diffused from the surface of B, and the light from A, are viewed by a microscope M, usually against a bright background.

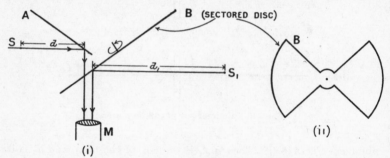

FIG. 417. Principle of flicker photometer.

The sectored disc B is driven by clockwork at a constant low speed, for example 15 revs. per second. The light observed through M is then alternately that diffused from A and that diffused by B, and if the brightnesses of A, B are different experiment shows that a *flicker* effect is produced. When the distance d_1 of the source S_1 is adjusted so that the field of view has a uniform brightness, the flicker effect disappears. This is the case even if the colours are different. S_1 is then replaced by a second lamp S_2 of another colour, and the procedure is repeated, keeping S at the same place. If the distance of S_2 from B is now d_2, it follows that $\dfrac{I_1}{d_1{}^2} = \dfrac{I_2}{d_2{}^2}$, where I_1, I_2 are the are the luminous intensities of S_1, S_2, and hence the intensities can be compared.

12. Bunsen's Grease-Spot Photometer

In 1844 BUNSEN designed a simple photometer which is capable of yielding fairly accurate results. It consists of a grease-spot in the middle of a screen, the remainder, A, of the screen being an opaque sheet of paper, Fig. 418. An auxiliary lamp of c.p. I_2 is placed on the right side of the screen, another lamp of c.p. I_1 is placed on the left side, and the position of the latter is varied until the grease-spot cannot be distinguished from the surrounding screen when it is viewed on one side of the screen, Fig. 418. Suppose the distances of the lamps are

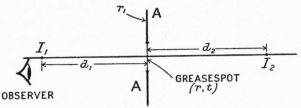

FIG. 418.   Grease-spot photometer principle.

d_1, d_2 respectively. Keeping the auxiliary lamp distance d_2 constant, the lamp of c.p. I_1 is replaced by another of c.p. I, and this is now moved to restore a photometric balance. Suppose the distance of the lamp from the screen is d. Then, as proved below,

$$\frac{I_1}{d_1{}^2} = \frac{I}{d^2}$$

$$\therefore \qquad \frac{I_1}{I} = \frac{d_1{}^2}{d^2} \qquad . \qquad . \qquad . \qquad . \qquad . \qquad (56)$$

This is a similar relation to that obtained using the auxiliary lamp method with the Lummer-Brodhun photometer (p. 575).

Theory of grease-spot photometer. Suppose r_1, r are the respective reflection factors of the opaque screen and the grease-spot surfaces, and t is the transmission factor of the grease-spot, which allows light to pass through it. When the grease-spot cannot be distinguished from the surrounding screen, the brightness B of the grease-spot is equal to the brightness B' of the surrounding screen on the same side.

Now B is due to luminous flux transmitted through the grease-spot from right to left, plus that due to reflection at the left side of the grease-spot, Fig. 418. Since the intensity of illumination of the right side of the spot $= I_2/d_2{}^2$, and that on the left side of the spot $= I_1/d_1{}^2$, it follows that

$$B = t\frac{I_2}{d_2{}^2} + r\frac{I_1}{d_1{}^2} \qquad . \qquad . \qquad . \qquad . \qquad (i)$$

The brightness B' of the left side of the screen is due only to the luminous flux reflected by that side.

$$\therefore \qquad B' = r_1\frac{I_1}{d_1{}^2} \qquad . \qquad . \qquad . \qquad . \qquad . \qquad (ii)$$

Since $B = B'$ for the left side at a photometric balance, it follows from (i) and (ii) that

$$t \frac{I_2}{d_2{}^2} + r \frac{I_1}{d_1{}^2} = r_1 \frac{I_1}{d_1{}^2}$$

$$\therefore \quad \frac{I_1}{d_1{}^2}(r_1 - r) = t \frac{I_2}{d_2{}^2}$$

$$\therefore \qquad \frac{I_1}{d_1{}^2} = \frac{t}{r_1 - r} \cdot \frac{I_2}{d_2{}^2} \qquad . \quad . \quad \text{(iii)}$$

Suppose the lamp of c.p. I_1 is now replaced by a lamp of c.p. I, and the photometric balance is restored, keeping the auxiliary lamp position constant. If the new distance from the screen is d, it follows from (iii) that

$$\frac{I}{d^2} = \frac{t}{r_1 - r} \cdot \frac{I_2}{d_2{}^2} \qquad . \quad . \quad . \quad . \quad \text{(iv)}$$

since $t, r_1, r, I_2, d_2{}^2$ are all constant. From (iii) and (iv),

$$\frac{I_1}{d_1{}^2} = \frac{I}{d^2}$$

$$\therefore \quad \frac{I_1}{I} = \frac{d_1{}^2}{d^2}$$

13. Determination of Reflection Factor

The *reflection factor* of a surface such as glass or a mirror can be measured by means of a grease-spot or a Lummer-Brodhun photometer, using an auxiliary lamp.

A source S of c.p. I is placed on one side of the screen N, and an auxiliary lamp B is placed on the other side, Fig. 419 (i). A photometric balance is now obtained by moving one of the lamps, and we shall suppose that the distance of S from N is now d.

The source S is then placed at A in front of the surface P whose reflection factor r is required, Fig. 419 (ii). If P is inclined at 45° to the line SB, the screen N is illuminated by light reflected from P; and

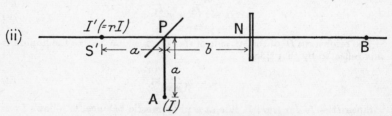

FIG. 419. Determination of reflection factor.

if A and P are moved together, a position can be found when a photo-metric balance is obtained. Suppose the distance $AP = a$ and the distance $PN = b$. The light reflected from P may then be considered to be due to a lamp of reduced candle-power I', where $I' = rI$. As far as the brightness of the screen is concerned, the position of this lamp is at S', at a distance $(a + b)$ from N, since the image of A in P is at S', Fig. 419 (ii). From our previous theory, it follows that

$$\frac{I'}{(a + b)^2} = \frac{I}{d^2}$$

$$\therefore \quad \frac{rI}{(a + b)^2} = \frac{I}{d^2}$$

$$\therefore \qquad r = \frac{(a + b)^2}{d^2} \qquad . \qquad . \qquad . \quad (57)$$

The reflection factor, r, of P can thus be found from measurements of d, a, b.

14. Determination of Transmission Factor

The *transmission factor* of a substance can be measured by using the auxiliary lamp method. A source S of c.p. I is arranged on one side of the screen N and an auxiliary lamp on the other side. A photometric balance is then arranged, and we shall suppose that the distance $SN = d$, Fig. 420 (i).

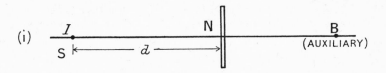

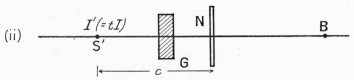

FIG. 420. Determination of transmission factor.

The substance G, whose transmission factor t is required, is now interposed between S and the screen. Since the luminous flux incident on the screen N is less than before, the source must be moved nearer to N to restore the photometric balance, keeping the auxiliary lamp position constant at B. Suppose the new position of the lamp is at S', distant c from N, Fig. 420 (ii). Then, if the luminous flux incident on the screen is now due to a lamp of "effective" c.p. I',

$$\frac{I'}{c^2} = \frac{I}{d^2}.$$

But $$I' = tI,$$

as the luminous flux from the source transmitted through G is reduced by the factor t.

$$\therefore \quad \frac{tI}{c^2} = \frac{I}{d^2}$$

$$\therefore \quad t = \frac{c^2}{d^2} \quad . \quad . \quad . \quad . \quad . \quad (58)$$

The transmission factor can thus be easily calculated from the measurements of c and d.

15. Measurement of Intensity of Illumination

It was pointed out at the beginning of the chapter that the maintenance of standards of illumination plays an important part in safeguarding our health. It is recommended that desks in class-rooms and offices should have an intensity of illumination of 5–10 ft. candles, and workshops an intensity of illumination of 10–15 ft. candles; for sewing dark materials an intensity of 15–25 ft. candles is recommended, while 100 ft. candles is suggested for the operating table in a hospital.

Photo-voltaic cell. There are two types of meters for measuring the intensity of illumination of a surface. The modern type is the photo-voltaic cell, which consists essentially of a cuprous-oxide and copper

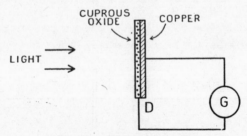

FIG. 421.   Photo-voltaic cell.

plate, made by oxidising one side of a copper disc D, Fig. 421. When the oxide surface is illuminated, electrons are emitted from the surface whose number is proportional to the incident luminous energy, and a current flows in the microammeter or sensitive moving-coil galvanometer G which is proportional to the intensity of illumination. The

galvanometer is previously calibrated by placing a standard lamp at
known distances from the disc D, and its scale reads ft. candles directly.
Fig. 422 illustrates an "Avo Light-meter", which operates on this

FIG. 422.   Avo light-meter.

principle; it is simply laid on the surface whose intensity of illumination
is required and the reading is then taken.

Illumination meter. Another type of illumination meter, which is not
as convenient to use as the photo-voltaic cell, is illustrated in Fig. 163.
L is an electric lamp whose distance from a translucent surface A can
be varied by the screw B, and S is the surface whose intensity of
illumination is required. S and A both illuminate a Lummer-Brodhun
cube (p. 573), and the distance of L from A is varied until the field of

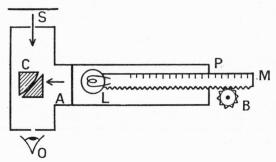

FIG. 423.   Illumination meter.

view is uniformly bright to an observer at O. The position of L is then read at P from a scale M attached to the carriage of L. This scale is calibrated in foot-candles from a previous experiment, in which a standard lamp is placed at known distances from C in the position corresponding to S in Fig. 423.

EXAMPLES

1. Define the terms *illuminating power* and *intensity of illumination*, and describe a method of measuring the illuminating power of a small source of light. A small 60 candle-power lamp is mounted 4 ft. above a horizontal table. Find the intensity of illumination on the table (i) at the point immediately below the lamp, and (ii) at a place 3 ft. away from that point. Reflection from walls, etc., may be neglected. (*L.*)

First part. See text.

Second part. Suppose S is the lamp, O the point immediately below it, and A the point 3 ft. from O, Fig. 424.   (i) The intensity of illumination at O is given by

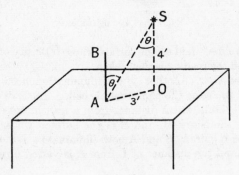

Fig. 424.

$$E = \frac{I}{r^2}$$

since OS is the normal to the surface at O.

$$\therefore \ E = \frac{60}{4^2} = 3\tfrac{3}{4} \text{ ft. candles}$$

(ii) Since the normal at A to the surface is AB, the intensity of illumination at A is given by

$$E = \frac{I \cos \theta}{r^2}$$

where θ = angle SAB, r = AS. Now $SA^2 = 3^2 + 4^2 = 25$, i.e., SA = 5, and hence $\cos \theta = SO/SA = 4/5$.

$$\therefore \quad E = \frac{60 \times 4/5}{25} = 1\cdot92 \text{ ft. candles}$$

2. Describe a simple type of photometer and its use in comparing the illuminating powers of two small sources of light. Mention the precautions to be taken in carrying out such an experiment. After a balance was obtained between two small lamps on a photometer bench, a sheet of plane glass was interposed on one side of the photometer. To restore a balance one of the lamps was moved back through 10 cm. making its distance from the photometer 110 cm. What percentage of light incident on the glass was transmitted by it? (*W.*)

First part. See text.

Second part. Suppose I_1, I_2 are the candle-powers of the two lamps, originally at distances d_1, d_2 respectively from the photometer. Then, from the data, $d_2 = 110 - 10 = 100$ cm., and hence

$$\frac{I_1}{d_1{}^2} = \frac{I_2}{100^2} \quad . \quad . \quad . \quad . \quad . \quad \text{(i)}$$

If the glass is placed between the lamp of candle-power I_1 and the photometer, the effective candle-power $= tI_1$, where t is the transmission factor of the glass.

$$\therefore \quad \frac{t\,I_1}{d_1{}^2} = \frac{I_2}{110^2} \quad . \quad . \quad . \quad . \quad . \quad \text{(ii)}$$

as the lamp of candle-power I_2 is now moved back 10 cm.

From (i) and (ii) it follows by division that

$$t = \frac{100^2}{110^2} = \frac{100}{121} = 0\cdot826$$

$\therefore$ percentage of light transmitted by glass $= 82\cdot6$.

3. Describe some form of accurate photometer, and explain its action. Two lamps, A and B, produce equal illumination on the screen of a photometer when A is 50 cm., and B is 60 cm. from the screen. A plane mirror is placed 6 cm. behind A, the plane of the mirror being approximately at right angles to the line from A to the screen, and it is then found that to restore equality of illumination on the screen the source B must be moved 10 cm. nearer the screen. What is the reflecting power of the mirror? (*C.*)

First part. See text.

Second part. Suppose S is the photometer screen, C is the plane mirror, and I_1, I_2 are the candle-powers of A, B respectively, Fig. 425. Then

$$\frac{I_1}{50^2} = \frac{I_2}{60^2} \quad . \quad . \quad \quad . \quad . \quad \text{(i)}$$

When the mirror C is placed in position, the light reflected from it appears to come from a source of candle-power rI_1, where r is the reflecting power

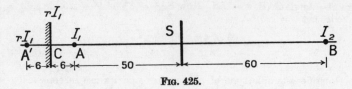

FIG. 425.

of the mirror. The intensity of illumination due to this source is hence $rI_1/62^2$, since the image A' of A in the mirror is 6 cm. from C. The lamp A also contributes an intensity of illumination $I_1/50^2$ to the screen directly.

$$\therefore \ \frac{r\,I_1}{62^2} + \frac{I_1}{50^2} = \frac{I_2}{50^2} \qquad . \qquad . \qquad . \qquad . \qquad \text{(ii)}$$

as B is now 50 cm. from the screen.

From (ii),
$$I_1 \left(\frac{r}{62^2} + \frac{1}{50^2} \right) = \frac{I_2}{50^2}$$

Dividing by equation (i) to eliminate I_1 and I_2, we have

$$50^2 \left(\frac{r}{62^2} + \frac{1}{50^2} \right) = \frac{60^2}{50^2}$$

$$\therefore \ \frac{50^2 r}{62^2} = \frac{60^2}{50^2} - 1$$

from which
$$r = 0.68$$

4. Derive the expression which is used for comparing the luminous intensities of two sources of light by means of a photometer. Two lamps, X and Y, are placed on the axis of a photometer, and their distances from the photometer screen are adjusted so that they produce equal illumination of the two sides of the screen when a slab of material which transmits 80 per cent of the light incident upon it is placed between X and the photometer. The distance of Y is 80 cm. The slab is now placed between the photometer and Y, while the position of X remains unchanged. Calculate the new distance of Y when both sides of the photometer are equally illuminated. (*L.*)

First part. See text.

Second part. Suppose I_1, I_2 are the candle-powers of X, Y respectively, and a is the distance of X from the screen when the material M is placed between it and the screen S, Fig. 426 (i). Then

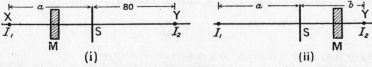

FIG. 426.

$$\frac{t\,I_1}{a^2} = \frac{I_2}{80^2}$$ . . . . . (i)

where t is the transmission factor of M.

When M is placed between Y and S, suppose Y is moved to a distance b from S, Fig. 426 (ii). Then

$$\frac{I_1}{a^2} = \frac{t\,I_2}{b^2}$$ . . . . . (ii)

Dividing (ii) by (i), we have

$$\frac{1}{t} = \frac{t \times 80^2}{b^2}$$

$$\therefore \quad b^2 = t^2 \times 80^2$$

But $t = 80\% = \dfrac{4}{5}$.

$$\therefore \quad b^2 = \frac{4^2}{5^2} \times 80^2$$

$$\therefore \quad b = \frac{4}{5} \times 80 = 64 \text{ cm.}$$

5. Define *lumen, foot-candle,* and show how they are related. Describe and explain how you would make an accurate comparison of the illuminating powers of two lamps of the same type. A photometric balance is obtained between two lamps A and B when B is 100 cm. from the photometer. When a block of glass G is placed between A and the photometer, balance is restored by moving B through 5 cm. Where must B be placed in order to maintain the balance when *two more* blocks, identical with G, are similarly placed between A and the photometer. (*L.*)

First part. See text.

Second part. Suppose I_1, I_2 are the candle-powers of A, B respectively, and d is the distance of A from the photometer P. Then, originally,

$$\frac{I_1}{d^2} = \frac{I_2}{100^2}$$ . . . . . (i)

When G is placed in position, the balance is restored by moving B 105 cm. from P, Fig. 427 (i). If t is the transmission factor of G, the effective candle-power of A is tI_1, and hence

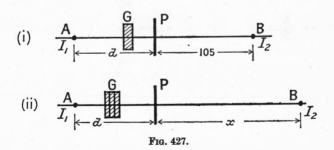

(i)

(ii)

Fig. 427.

$$\frac{t\,I_1}{d^2} = \frac{I_2}{105^2} \qquad \cdot \qquad \cdot \qquad \cdot \qquad \cdot \qquad \text{(ii)}$$

Dividing (ii) by (i),

$$\therefore \quad t = \frac{100^2}{105^2} \qquad \cdot \qquad \cdot \qquad \cdot \qquad \cdot \qquad \text{(iii)}$$

When two more blocks are placed beside G, the effective candle-power of $A = t \times t \times tI_1 = t^3 I_1$, Fig. 427 (ii). Thus if the distance of B from P is now x,

$$\frac{t^3 I_1}{d^2} = \frac{I_2}{x^2} \qquad \cdot \qquad \cdot \qquad \cdot \qquad \cdot \qquad \text{(iv)}$$

Dividing (iv) by (i),

$$\therefore \quad t^3 = \frac{100^2}{x^2}$$

From (iii), $\qquad \therefore \quad \left(\frac{100^2}{105^2}\right)^3 = \frac{100^2}{x^2}$

$$\therefore \quad x^2 = \frac{100^2 \times 105^6}{100^6} = \frac{105^6}{100^4}$$

$$\therefore \quad x = \frac{105^3}{100^2} = 115 \cdot 8 \text{ cm.}$$

EXERCISES XXVI

1. A 30 c.p. lamp X is 40 cm. in front of a photometer screen. What is the illumination directly in front of X on the screen? Calculate the c.p. of a lamp Y which provides the same intensity of illumination when placed 60 cm. from the screen.

2. A lamp of 800 c.p. is suspended 16 ft. above a road. Find the intensity of illumination on the road (i) at a point A directly below the lamp, (ii) at a point B 12 ft. from A.

3. Define *luminous intensity* (*illuminating power*) and *illumination* (*intensity of illumination*). Describe an accurate method of comparing the illuminating powers of two sources of light.

A lamp is fixed 4 ft. above a horizontal table. At a point on the table 3 ft. to one side of the vertical through the lamp, a light-meter is placed flat on the table. It registers 4 ft. candles. Calculate the candle-power of the lamp. (*C.*)

4. What is meant by *illuminating power* and *intensity of illumination*? How are they related?

A small source of 32 c.p. giving out light equally in all directions is situated at the centre of a sphere of 8 ft. diameter, the inner surface of which is painted black. What is the illumination of the surface?

If the inner surface is repainted with a matt white paint which causes it to reflect diffusely 80 per cent of all light falling on it, what will the illumination be? (*L.*)

5. Describe an accurate form of photometer for comparing the candle-powers of lamps.

A lamp is 100 cm. from one side of a photometer and produces the same illumination as a second lamp placed at 120 cm. on the opposite side. When a lightly smoked glass plate is placed before the weaker lamp, the brighter one has to be moved 50 cm. to restore the equality of illumination. Find what fraction of the incident light is transmitted by the plate. (*L.*)

6. How would you compare the candle-powers of two small lamps?

A 100 candle-power lamp is placed 10 ft. above the centre of a horizontal rectangular table measuring 6 ft. by 4 ft. What are the maximum and minimum values of the intensity of illumination on the table due to direct light?

How would your results be changed by the presence of a large horizontal mirror, placed 2 ft. above the lamp, so as to reflect light down on to the table, assuming that only 80 per cent of the light incident on the mirror is reflected? (*W.*)

7. Describe the grease-spot photometer, and explain how you would measure the light loss which results from enclosing a light source by a glass globe. Two 16 candle-power lamps are placed on the same side of a screen at distances of 2 and 5 metres from it. Calculate the distance at which a single 32 candle-power lamp must be placed in order to give the same intensity of illumination on the screen. (*N.*)

8. Define *lumen, foot-candle*. Describe the construction and use of a Lummer-Brodhun photometer.

Twenty per cent of the light emitted by a source of 500 candle-power is evenly distributed over a circular area 5 ft. in diameter. What is the illumination at points within this area? (*L.*)

9. Distinguish between *illuminating power* and *intensity of illumination*. How may the illuminating powers of two sources be accurately compared?

A surface receives light normally from a source at a distance of 3 metres. If the source is moved closer until the distance is only 2 metres, through what angle must the surface be turned to reduce the illumination to its original value? (*O. & C.*)

10. Define *intensity of illumination of a screen, illuminating power of a source of light*. Indicate units in which each of these quantities may be measured.

Describe a reliable photometer, and explain how you would use it to compare the reflecting powers of plaster of paris and ground glass. (*C.*)

11. Describe an accurate form of photometer for comparing the illuminating powers of two sources of light.

Two electric lamps, *A* and *B*, are found to give equal illuminations on the two sides of a photometer when their distances from the photometer are in the ratio 4 : 5. A sheet of glass is then placed in front of *B*, and it is found that equality of illumination is obtained when the distances of *A* and *B* are in the ratio 16 : 19. Find the percentage of light transmitted by the glass. (*C.*)

CHAPTER XXVII

VELOCITY OF LIGHT

FOR many centuries the velocity of light was thought to be infinitely large; from about the end of the seventeenth century, however, evidence began to be obtained which showed that the speed of light, though enormous, was a finite quantity. Galileo, in 1600, attempted to measure the velocity of light by covering and uncovering a lantern at night, and timing how long the light took to reach an observer a few miles away. Owing to the enormous speed of light, however, the time was too small to measure, and the experiment was a failure. The first successful attempt to measure the velocity of light was made by RÖMER, a Danish astronomer, in 1676.

1. Römer's Astronomical Method

Römer was engaged in recording the eclipses of one of Jupiter's satellites or moons, which has a period of 1·77 days round Jupiter. The period of the satellite is thus very small compared with the period of the earth round the sun (one year), and the eclipses of the satellite occur very frequently while the earth moves only a very small distance in its orbit. Thus the eclipses may be regarded as *signals sent out from Jupiter* at comparatively short intervals, and observed on the earth; almost like a bright lamp covered at regular intervals at night and viewed by a distant observer.

The earth makes a complete revolution round the sun, S, in one year. Jupiter makes a complete revolution round the sun in about $11\frac{3}{4}$ years, and we shall assume for simplicity that the orbits of the earth and Jupiter are both circular, Fig. 428. At some time, Jupiter (J_1) and the earth (E_1) are on the same side of the sun, S, and in line with each other, and the earth and Jupiter are then said to be in *conjunction*. Suppose that an eclipse, or "signal", is now observed on the earth E_1. If $E_1 J_1 = x$, and c is the velocity of light, the time taken for the "signal" to reach E_1 is x/c; and if the actual time when the eclipse occurred was a (which is not known), the time T_1 of the eclipse *recorded on the earth* is given by

$$T_1 = a + \frac{x}{c} \qquad . \qquad . \qquad . \qquad . \qquad \text{(i)}$$

The earth and Jupiter now move round their respective orbits, and at some time, about $6\frac{1}{2}$ months later, the earth (E_2) and Jupiter (J_2) are on opposite sides of the sun S and in line with each other, Fig. 168. The earth and Jupiter are then said to be in *opposition*. During the $6\frac{1}{2}$

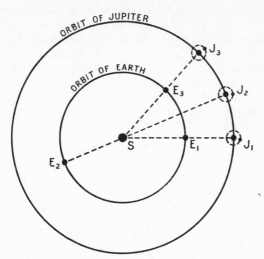

Fig. 428. Römer's method.

months suppose that n eclipses have occured at regular intervals T, i.e., T is the actual time between successive eclipses: the time for the interval between the 1st and nth eclipses is then $(n - 1)\,T$. In the position J_2, E_2, however, the light travels a distance J_2E_2, or $(x + d)$, from Jupiter to the earth, where d is the diameter of the earth's orbit round the sun. The time taken to travel this distance $= (x + d)/c$. Thus the time T' recorded on the earth at E_2 when the nth eclipse occurs is given by

$$T' = a + (n - 1)\,T + \frac{x + d}{c} \qquad . \qquad . \qquad . \qquad \text{(ii)}$$

But, from (i), $\quad T_1 = a + \dfrac{x}{c}$

Subtracting, $T' - T_1 = I = (n - 1)\,T + \dfrac{d}{c},$ $\qquad . \qquad . \qquad . \qquad$ (iii)

where I is the interval recorded on the earth for the time of n eclipses, from the position of conjunction of Jupiter and the earth to their position of opposition. By similar reasoning to the above, the interval I_1 recorded on the earth for n eclipses from the position of opposition (J_2, E_2) to the next position of conjunction (J_3, E_3) is given by

$$I_1 = (n - 1)\,T - \frac{d}{c} \qquad . \qquad . \qquad . \qquad . \qquad . \qquad \text{(iv)}$$

The reason why I_1 is less than I is that the earth is moving towards Jupiter from E_2 to E_3, and *away* from Jupiter from E_1 to E_2.

Römer observed that the nth eclipse between the position J_1, E_1 to the position J_2, E_2 occurred later than he expected by about $16\frac{1}{2}$ minutes; and he correctly deduced that the additional time was due to the time taken by light to travel across the earth's orbit. In (iii), $(n-1)\,T$ was the time expected for $(n-1)$ eclipses, and d/c was the extra time ($16\frac{1}{2}$ minutes) recorded on the earth. Since $d = 186,000,000$ miles approximately, the velocity of light, c, $= 186,000,000/(16\frac{1}{2} \times 60)$ $= 186,000$ miles per second approximately.

Römer also recorded that the time I for n eclipses from the position E_1, J_1 to the position E_2, J_2 was about 33 minutes more than the time I_1 for n eclipses between the position E_2, J_2 to the position E_3, J_3. But, subtracting (iv) from (iii),

$$I - I_1 = \frac{2d}{c} \qquad . \qquad . \qquad . \qquad . \qquad . \qquad . \qquad . \qquad (59)$$

$$\therefore \quad \frac{2d}{c} = 33 \text{ mins.} = 33 \times 60 \text{ secs.}$$

$$\therefore \quad c = 2d/(33 \times 60) = 2 \times 186,000,000/(33 \times 60)$$

$$\therefore \quad c = 186,000 \text{ miles per sec. (approx.)}$$

Maximum and minimum observed periods. When the earth E_1 is moving directly away from Jupiter at J_a, the apparent period T' of the satellite is a maximum. Suppose the earth moves from E_1 to E_2 in the time T', Fig. 429.

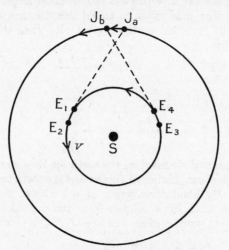

FIG. 429. Maximum and minimum periods.

Then if T is the actual period, v is the velocity of the earth, and c is the velocity of light, it follows that

$$T' = T + \frac{E_1 E_2}{c} = T + \frac{vT'}{c}$$

$$\therefore \quad T'\left(1 - \frac{v}{c}\right) = T \quad . \quad . \quad . \quad . \quad \text{(i)}$$

When the earth is moving directly towards Jupiter at J_b, the apparent period T'' is a minimum. Suppose the earth moves from E_3 to E_4 in this time. Then

$$T'' = T - \frac{E_3 E_4}{c} = T - \frac{vT''}{c}$$

$$\therefore \quad T''\left(1 + \frac{v}{c}\right) = T \quad . \quad . \quad . \quad . \quad \text{(ii)}$$

From (i) and (ii), it follows that

$$T'\left(1 - \frac{v}{c}\right) = T''\left(1 + \frac{v}{c}\right)$$

$$\therefore \quad \frac{T'}{T''} = \frac{1 + \dfrac{v}{c}}{1 - \dfrac{v}{c}} = \text{ratio of maximum and minimum observed periods}$$

2. Bradley's Aberration Method

Römer's conclusions about the velocity of light were ignored by the scientists of his time. In 1729, however, the astronomer BRADLEY observed that the angular elevation of a "fixed" star varied slightly according to the position of the earth in its orbit round the sun. For some time he was puzzled by the observation. But while he was being rowed across a stream one day, he noticed that the boat drifted slightly downstream; and he saw immediately that the difference between the actual and observed angular elevation of the star was due to a combination of the velocity of the earth in its orbit (analogous to the velocity of the stream) with that of the velocity of light (analogous to the velocity of the boat). Thus if the earth were stationary, a telescope would have to point in the true direction AS of a star S to observe it; but since the earth is moving in its orbit round the sun with a velocity v, T would have to be directed along MN to observe the star, where MN makes a small angle a with the direction SA, Fig. 430 (i).

The direction of MN is that of the *relative velocity* between the earth and the light from S, which is found by subtracting the velocity v from the velocity c of the light. This is easily done by drawing the triangle of velocities PBD, in which PB, parallel to SA, represents c in magnitude and direction, while BD represents a velocity equal and opposite to v, Fig. 170 (ii). The resultant of PB and BD is then PD, which is parallel to NM, and PD represents the relative velocity.

The angle a between the true and apparent directions of the star is known as the *aberration*. From Fig. 430 (ii), it follows that

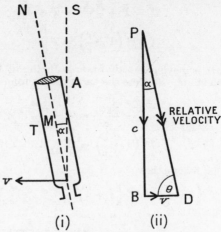

FIG. 430.   Bradley's aberration method.

$$\frac{v}{c} = \frac{\sin a}{\sin \theta},$$

where θ is the apparent altitude of the star.

$$\therefore \quad c = \frac{v \sin \theta}{\sin a} \quad . \quad . \quad . \quad . \quad . \quad (60)$$

Since a is very small, $\sin a$ is equal to a in radians. By using known values of v, θ, and a, Bradley calculated c, the velocity of light, and obtained a value close to Römer's value. The aberration a is given by half the difference between the maximum and minimum values of the apparent altitude, θ, of the star.

3. Fizeau's Rotating Wheel Method. A Terrestrial Method

In 1849 FIZEAU succeeded in measuring the velocity of light with apparatus on the earth, for the first time. His method, unlike Römer's and Bradley's method, is thus known as a *terrestrial method*.

Fizeau's apparatus is illustrated in Fig. 431. A bright source at O emits light which is converged to a point H by means of the lens and the plane sheet of glass F, and is then incident on a lens B. H is at the focus of B, and the light thus emerges parallel after refraction through the latter and travels several miles to another lens C. This lens brings the light to a focus at M, where a silvered plane mirror is positioned, and the light is now returned back along its original path to the glass plate F. An image of O can thus be observed through F by a lens E.

The rim of a toothed wheel, W, which can rotate about a horizontal axis Q, is placed at H, and is the important feature of Fizeau's method.

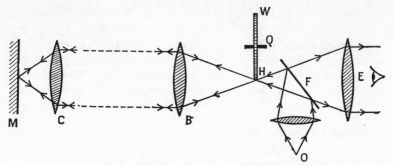

Fig. 431.   Fizeau's rotating wheel method.

The teeth and the gaps of W have the same width, Fig. 432. As W is rotated, an image is observed through E as long as the light passes through the wheel towards E. When the speed of rotation exceeds about 10 cycles per second, the succession of images on the retina causes an image of O to be seen continuously. As the speed of W is further increased, however, a condition is reached when the returning light passing through a gap of W and reflected from M arrives back at the wheel to find that the tooth *next* to the gap has taken the place of the gap. Assuming the wheel is now driven at a constant speed, it can be seen that light continues to pass through a gap in the wheel towards M but always arrives back at W to find its path barred by the neighbouring tooth. The field of view through E is thus dark. If the speed of W is now doubled a bright field of view is again observed, as the light passing through a gap arrives back from M to find the next *gap* in its place, instead of a tooth as before.

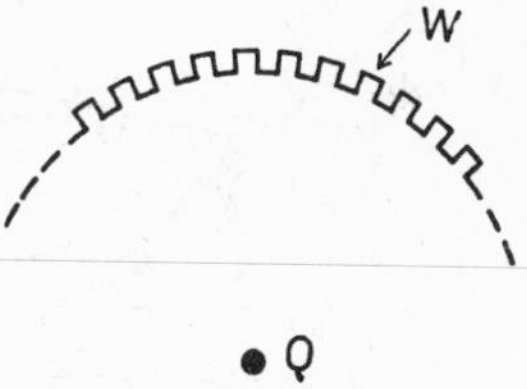

Fig. 432.
Rotating wheel.

Fizeau used a wheel with 720 teeth, and first obtained a dark field of view through E when the rate of revolution was 12·6 revs per second. The distance from H to M was 8,633 metres. Thus the time taken for the light to travel from H to M and back $= 2 \times 8,633/c$ seconds, where c is the velocity of light in metres per second. But this is the time taken by a tooth to move to a position corresponding to a neighbouring gap. Since there are 2×720 teeth and gaps together, the time $= 1/(2 \times 720)$ of the time taken to make one revolution, or $1/(2 \times 720 \times 12·6)$ seconds, as 12·6 revs are made in one second.

$$\therefore \quad \frac{2 \times 8.633}{c} = \frac{1}{2 \times 720 \times 12·6}$$

$$\therefore \quad c = 2 \times 8{,}633 \times 2 \times 720 \times 12{\cdot}6$$
$$= 3{\cdot}13 \times 10^8 \text{ metres per sec.}$$

The disadvantage of Fizeau's method is mainly that the field of view can never be made perfectly dark, owing to the light diffusedly reflected at the teeth towards E. To overcome this disadvantage the teeth of the wheel were bevelled, but a new and more accurate method of determining the velocity of light was devised by FOUCAULT in 1862.

4. Foucault's Rotating Mirror Method

In Foucault's method a plane mirror M_1 is rotated at a high constant angular velocity about a vertical axis at A, Fig. 433. A lens L is placed so that light from a bright source at O_1 is reflected at M_1 and comes to a focus at a point P on a concave mirror C. The centre of curvature of C is at A, and consequently the light is reflected back from C along its original path, giving rise to an image coincident with O_1. In order to observe the image, a plate of glass G is placed at 45° to the axis of the lens, from which the light is reflected to form an image at B_1.

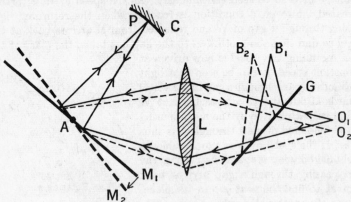

FIG. 433. Foucault's rotating mirror method.

Suppose the plane mirror M_1 begins to rotate. The light reflected by it is then incident on C for a fraction of a revolution, and if the speed of rotation is 2 revs per sec., an intermittent image is seen. As the speed of M_1 is increased to about 10 revs per sec. the image is seen continuously as a result of the rapid impressions on the retina. As the speed is increased further, the light reflected from the mirror flashes across from M_1 to C, and returns to M_1 to find it displaced by a very small angle θ to a new position M_2. An image is now observed at B_2, and by measuring the displacement, $B_1 B_2$, of the image Foucault was able to calculate the velocity of light.

5. Theory of Foucault's Method

Consider the point P on the curved mirror from which the light is always reflected back to the plane mirror, Fig. 434. When the plane mirror is at M_1, the image of P in it is at I_1, where $AI_1 = AP = a$, the radius of curvature of C (see p. 407). The rays incident on the lens L from the plane mirror appear to come from I_1. When the mirror is at M_2 the image of P in it is at I_2, where $AI_2 = AP = a$, and the rays incident on L from the mirror now appear to come from I_2. Now the

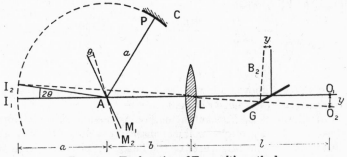

FIG. 434.   Explanation of Foucault's method.

mirror has rotated through an angle θ from M_1 to M_2, and the direction PA of the light incident on it is constant. The angle between the reflected rays is thus 2θ (see p. 403), and hence $I_2AI_1 = 2\theta$.

$$\therefore \quad I_2I_1 = a \times 2\theta = 2a\theta \quad . \quad . \quad . \quad . \quad \text{(i)}$$

The images O_1, O_2 formed by the *lens*, L, are the images of I_1, I_2 in it, as the light incident on L from the mirror appear to come from I_1, I_2. Hence $I_2I_1 : O_1O_2 = I_1L : LO_1$.

$$\therefore \quad \frac{I_2I_1}{y} = \frac{(a + b)}{l}$$

where $y = O_1O_2$, $AL = b$, and $LO_1 = l$.

$$\therefore \quad I_2I_1 = \frac{(a + b)\,y}{l} \quad . \quad . \quad . \quad . \quad \text{(ii)}$$

From (i) and (ii), it follows that

$$2a\theta = \frac{(a + b)\,y}{l}$$

$$\therefore \quad \theta = \frac{(a + b)\,y}{2al} \quad . \quad . \quad . \quad . \quad \text{(iii)}$$

The angle θ can also be expressed in terms of the velocity of light, c, and the number of revolutions per second, n, of the plane mirror. The angular velocity of the mirror is $2\pi n$ radians per second, and hence the time taken to rotate through an angle θ radians is $\theta/2\pi n$ secs. But this is the time taken by the light to travel from the mirror to C and back, which is $2a/c$ secs.

$$\therefore \quad \frac{\theta}{2\pi n} = \frac{2a}{c}$$

$$\therefore \quad \theta = \frac{4\pi na}{c} \qquad . \quad . \quad . \quad . \quad . \quad \text{(iv)}$$

From (iii) and (iv), we have

$$\frac{(a+b)\,y}{2al} = \frac{4\pi na}{c}$$

$$\therefore \quad c = \frac{8\pi na^2 l}{(a+b)\,y} \qquad . \quad . \quad . \quad . \quad \text{(61)}$$

As n, a, l, b are known, and the displacement $y = O_1O_2 = B_1B_2$ and can be measured, the velocity of light c can be measured.

The disadvantage of Foucault's method is mainly that the image obtained is not very bright, making observation difficult. Michelson (p. 597) increased the brightness of the image by placing a large lens between the plane mirror and C, so that light was incident on C for a greater fraction of the mirror's revolution. Since the distance a was increased at the same time, Fig. 434, the displacement of the image was also increased.

The velocity of light in water was observed by Foucault, who placed a pipe of water between the plane mirror and C. He found that, with the number of revolutions per second of the mirror the same as when air was used, the displacement y of the image B was *greater*. Since the velocity of light $= 8\pi na^2 l/(a+b)\,y$, from (61), it follows that the velocity of light in water is *less* than in air. Newton's "corpuscular theory" of light predicted that light should travel faster in water than in air (p. 698), whereas the "wave theory" of light predicted that light should travel slower in water than in air. The direct observation of the velocity of light in water by Foucault's method showed that the corpuscular theory could not be true.

6. Michelson's Method for the Velocity of Light

The velocity of light, c, is a quantity which appears in many fundamental formulæ in advanced Physics, especially in connection with the theories concerning particles in atoms and calculations on atomic (nuclear) energy. EINSTEIN has shown, for example, that the energy W released from an atom is given by $W = mc^2$ ergs, where m is the decrease in mass of the atom in grams and c is the velocity of light in centimetres per second. A knowledge of the magnitude of c is thus important. A. A. MICHELSON, an American physicist, spent many years of his life in measuring the velocity of light, and the method he devised is regarded as one of the most accurate.

The essential features of Michelson's apparatus are shown in Fig. 435. X is an equiangular octagonal steel prism which can be rotated at constant speed about a vertical axis through its centre. The faces of the prism are highly polished, and the light passing through a slit from a very bright source O is reflected at the surface A towards a plane mirror B. From B the light is reflected to a plane mirror L at the focus of a concave mirror HD, where it is reflected towards D. The light

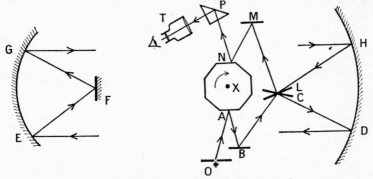

FIG. 435.   Michelson's rotating prism method.

then travels as a parallel beam to another concave mirror GE a long distance away, and it is reflected to a plane mirror F at the focus of GE. The light is then reflected to the mirror, travels back to H, and is there reflected to a plane mirror C placed just below L and inclined to it as shown. From C the light is reflected to a plane mirror M, and is then incident on the face N of the octagonal prism opposite to A. The final image thus obtained is viewed through T with the aid of a totally reflecting prism P.

The image is seen by light reflected from the top surface of the octagonal prism X. When the latter is rotated the image disappears at first, as the light reflected from A when the prism is just in the position shown in Fig. 435 arrives at the opposite face to find this surface in some position inclined to that shown. When the speed of rotation is increased and suitably adjusted, however, the image reappears and is seen in the same position as when the prism X is at rest. *The light reflected from A now arrives at the opposite surface in the time taken for the prism to rotate through 45°, or ⅛th of a revolution*, as in this case the surface on the left of N, for example, will occupy the latter's position when the light arrives at the upper surface of X.

Suppose *d* is the distance in metres travelled by the light in its journey from A to the opposite face; the time taken is then d/c, where c is the velocity of light. But this is the time taken by X to make $\frac{1}{8}$th of a revolution, which is $1/8n$ secs. if the number of revolutions per second is n.

$$\therefore \quad \frac{1}{8n} = \frac{d}{c}$$

$$\therefore \quad c = 8nd \text{ metres per sec.} \quad . \quad . \quad . \quad (62)$$

Thus c can be calculated from a knowledge of n and d.

Michelson performed the experiment in 1926, and again in 1931, when the light path was enclosed in an evacuated tube 1 mile long. Multiple reflections were obtained to increase the effective path of the light. A prism with 32 faces was also used, and Michelson's result for the velocity of light *in vacuo* was 299,774 kilometres per second. Michelson died in 1931 while he was engaged in another measurement of the velocity of light.

EXAMPLES

1. Describe carefully Fizeau's method of determining the speed of propagation of light by means of a toothed wheel. Given that the distance of the mirror is 8,000 yds., that the revolving disc has 720 teeth, and that the first eclipse occurs when the angular velocity of the disc is $13\frac{3}{4}$ revolutions per second, calculate the speed of propagation of light. (*W.*)

First part. See text.

Second part. Suppose c is the speed of light in yards per second.

$$\therefore \text{ time to travel to mirror and back} = \frac{2 \times 8,000}{c} \text{ sec.}$$

But time for one tooth to occupy the next gap's position $= \dfrac{1}{13\frac{3}{4}} \times \dfrac{1}{2 \times 720}$ sec.

$$\therefore \quad \frac{2 \times 8,000}{c} = \frac{1}{13\frac{3}{4} \times 2 \times 720}$$

$$\therefore \quad c = 2 \times 8,000 \times 13\frac{3}{4} \times 2 \times 720$$

$$= 3{\cdot}168 \times 10^8 \text{ yds. per sec.}$$

2. A beam of light is reflected by a rotating mirror on to a fixed mirror. which sends it back to the rotating mirror from which it is again reflected, and then makes an angle of 18° with its original direction. The distance between the two mirrors is 10^6 cm., and the rotating mirror is making 375 revolutions per sec. Calculate the velocity of light. (*L.*)

Suppose OA is the original direction of the light, incident at A on the mirror in the position M_1, B is the fixed mirror, and AC is the direction of the light reflected from the rotating mirror when it reaches the position M_2. Fig. 436.

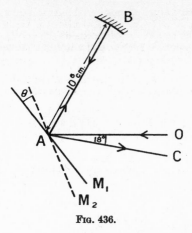

Fig. 436.

The angle θ between M_1, M_2 is $\frac{1}{2} \times 18°$, since the angle of rotation of a mirror is half the angle of deviation of the reflected ray when the incident ray (BA in this case) is kept constant. Thus $\theta = 9°$.

$$\text{Time taken by mirror to rotate } 360° = \frac{1}{375} \text{ sec.}$$

$$\therefore \quad \text{time taken to rotate } 9° = \frac{9}{360} \times \frac{1}{375} \text{ sec.}$$

But this is also the time taken by the light to travel from A to B and back, which is given by $2 \times 10^6/c$, where c is the velocity of light in cm. per sec.

$$\therefore \quad \frac{2 \times 10^6}{c} = \frac{9}{360} \times \frac{1}{375}$$

$$\therefore \quad c = \frac{2 \times 10^6 \times 360 \times 375}{9} = 3 \times 10^{10} \text{ cm. per sec.}$$

EXERCISES XXVII

1. Draw a sketch showing the earth and Jupiter in conjunction and in opposition. How did Römer calculate the velocity of light by observations on one of Jupiter's satellites?

2. Describe briefly how Bradley calculated the velocity of light from the apparent angular displacement (or aberration) of the fixed stars.

3. In Fizeau's rotating wheel experiment the number of teeth was 720 and the distance between the wheel and reflector was 8,633 metres. Calculate the number of revolutions per sec. of the wheel when extinction first occurs, assuming the velocity of light is $3 \cdot 13 \times 10^8$ metres per sec. What are the disadvantages of Fizeau's method?

4. Draw a diagram of Foucault's method of measuring the velocity of light. How has the velocity of light in water been shown to be less than in air? The radius of curvature of the curved mirror is 20 metres and the plane mirror is rotated at 20 revs. per sec. Calculate the angle in degrees between a ray incident on the plane mirror and then reflected from it after the light has travelled to the curved mirror and back to the plane mirror (velocity of light = 3 × 10⁸ metres per sec.).

5. Give an account of a method used for finding the velocity of light in air which makes use of terrestrial measurements only. (*L.*)

6. Draw a diagram showing the arrangement of the apparatus and the path of the rays of light in Fizeau's toothed wheel method for measuring the velocity of light. What are the chief difficulties met with in carrying out the experiment?
If the wheel has 150 teeth and 150 spaces of equal width and its distance from the mirror be 12 kilometres, at what speed, in revolutions per minute, will the first eclipse occur? (*N.*)

7. Describe a terrestrial method by which the velocity of light has been measured. How could the method be modified to show that the velocity of light in water is less than that in air? Briefly discuss the theoretical importance of this fact. (*C.*)

8. Explain fully how the velocity of light has been determined from astronomical observations.
Calculate the ratio of the longest to the shortest interval between successive eclipses of one of Jupiter's moons, being given that the orbital velocity of the earth is v cm./sec. and the velocity of light is V cm./sec. (*L.*)

9. Describe Foucault's (rotating mirror) method of measuring the velocity of light, and the effect upon the displacement of the image of putting a column of water between the rotating and the fixed mirrors. (*L.*)

10. Describe Michelson's method of measuring the velocity of light. What are the advantages of this method compared with Foucault's method?

11. Describe a terrestrial method of determining the velocity of light in air, explaining (without detailed calculation) how the result is obtained.
Why do we conclude that in free space red and blue light travel with the same speed, but that in glass red light travels faster than blue? (*L.*)

12. Explain how the velocity of light was first determined, and describe one more recent method of measuring it.
A beam of light after reflection at a plane mirror, rotating 2,000 times per minute, passes to a distant reflector. It returns to the rotating mirror from which it is reflected to make an angle of 1° with its original direction. Assuming that the velocity of light is 186,000 miles per sec., calculate the distance between the mirrors. (*L.*)

SOUND

CHAPTER XXVIII

WAVE-MOTION. FREQUENCY MEASUREMENT

IF a bicycle bell is rung and then lightly touched, *vibrations* can be felt. Vibrations can also be detected when a sounding tuning-fork is touched, and a light object on the top of a radio set can be seen to tremble when the volume control is turned too far. These and other observations lead to the conclusion that *an object emitting a sound is a vibrating object*, and before proceeding further we must discuss some of the concepts in the topic of vibrations.

1. Simple Harmonic Motion; Frequency, Amplitude, Period

The simplest vibratory motion is *simple harmonic motion*; the bob of a simple pendulum, swinging through a small angle, moves with simple harmonic motion. The displacement, y, of the bob from its central (mean) position is sometimes to the right and sometimes to the left; reckoned from the central position, then, y is sometimes positive and sometimes negative. If the variation of y with time, t, is plotted a sine curve is obtained, as illustrated in Fig. 437; and simple harmonic motion may be defined by the equation

$$y = a \sin \frac{2\pi t}{T} \qquad . \qquad . \qquad . \qquad . \qquad (63)$$

where a, T are constants explained below.

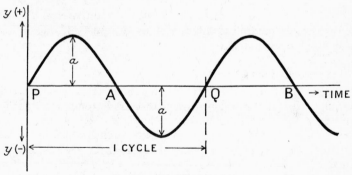

FIG. 437. Sine curve.

A complete to-and-fro movement of a vibrating object is known as a *cycle*; a cycle of changes occurs in the interval PQ or AB, Fig. 437.

601

The *frequency* (*f*) of the vibration is defined as the number of cycles per second (c.p.s.). The voice, instruments, and other sounding objects have vibrations ranging from 15 c.p.s. to 20,000 c.p.s. approximately, which is therefore known as the *audio-frequency* (*A.F.*) range of frequencies.

During a cycle, the vibrating object twice reaches the limit of its oscillation. The maximum distance on either side of its central position is known as the *amplitude*, *a*, of the vibration, Fig. 437; and since the maximum value of the sine of an angle is 1, it follows that the amplitude is the constant *a* in equation (63).

The *period* (*T*) of a vibration is the time taken to go through one cycle. Since the frequency *f* is the number of cycles undergone in 1 sec. then

$$f = \frac{1}{T} \quad . \quad . \quad . \quad . \quad . \quad (64)$$

In practice, the vibration of a sounding *tuning-fork* is the nearest approach to a simple harmonic vibration, which is defined by equation (63). The vibrations in other instruments, such as the violin or piano, are not simple harmonic even when they are sounding a single note (p. 630). But all periodic vibrations, no matter how complex, can be analysed into a number of simple harmonic vibrations, and hence we shall assume the equation $y = a \sin 2\pi t/T$ in discussing mathematically the vibrations of sounding objects, except where otherwise is specified.

2. Sound Requires a Medium

If an electric bell is placed in an air-tight vessel from which the air is gradually removed by a pump, the sound from the bell grows fainter and fainter, until it can hardly be heard. The clapper of the bell can still be seen to be striking the gong, so that the latter is vibrating. This simple experiment shows that *sound can not travel through a vacuum*, unlike light. A material medium, such as air, water, wood, or metal, is necessary to carry sound.

3. Propagation of Sound Waves

Suppose that a tuning-fork is sounding in air. Both prongs are then vibrating, but for convenience we shall consider only the right-hand prong P, Fig. 438. When P moves to the right, the layer of air A next to it moves to the right, and in turn presses on the layer B immediately next to it. B then disturbs the next layer, C. A disturbance of air, started at A, thus travels along from layer to layer until it reaches the diaphragm of the ear, E, of an observer. When the prong P moves back from R to its central position the pressure on A is diminished, and it begins to move to the left. This movement of A causes B to expand to the left in turn, and thus another disturbance (an expansion) is

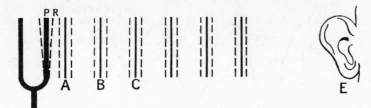

Fig. 438. Propagation of sound wave.

propagated in the air. It can now be seen that a disturbance or *wave* travels in the air as P vibrates, and that the movement of each layer is a vibration of the same frequency as P, with the important difference that many layers are "out of step", or out of *phase*, with each other (see also p. 604). This must be the case because the disturbance takes a finite time to pass from one layer to another, which is another way of saying that the speed of sound is finite. *At a given place,* then, for example at C, the displacement (*y*) of a layer varies simple harmonically with the

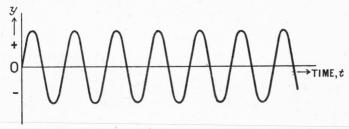

Fig. 439. Variation of displacement (*y*) with time (*t*) *at a given place.*

time (*t*), Fig. 439. The amplitude of the vibration is very small, for example 1/100th in., and depends on the distance of the particular layer from the tuning-fork.

4. Particle Velocities

The velocity of the particles while the wave is passing is the rate of change of the displacement, *y*, with respect to the time, *t*. The particle velocity is thus proportional to the gradient of the displacement-time (*y* − *t*) curve at the corresponding instant. The velocities are hence represented by the dotted curve in Fig. 440, which shows that the maximum velocity occurs when the displacement of the particle is zero. This should occasion no surprise, as the speed of an oscillating object, such as the bob of a pendulum, is fastest when it passes through its original (zero displacement) position.

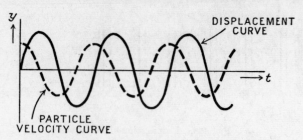

Fig. 440.   Particle velocity and displacement curves.

5. Displacement of Layers at a Given Instant

If we could take an instantaneous picture of the layers of air as the tuning-fork is sounding, it would be something like that shown in Fig. 441 (i), assuming the sound wave travels in a constant direction, *ae*. Some of the layers, for example those at *a*, are just passing through their central (mean) position, while others, such as those at *b*, are just reaching the limit of their vibration. Other layers close to *a*, *b* are at different positions at that instant because their vibrations are out of phase with those of *a*, *b*; but further away, at *d* or *e* for example, a layer is vibrating *in phase* with the layer at *a*.

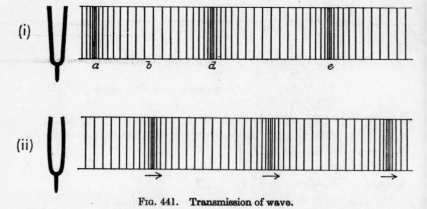

Fig. 441.   Transmission of wave.

At a slightly later instant, the layers have the appearance shown in Fig. 441 (ii); the disturbance, or wave, is thus transmitted along the air. It should be realised that the transmission is due to a transfer of some of the kinetic energy of a vibrating layer to the layer next to it, which in turn transfers some of its kinetic energy to the next layer. The *mean* positions of the vibrating layers while the wave travels along are the same as when the air is undisturbed.

6. Wavelength, and Velocity of Wave

If a graph is made of the magnitudes of the displacements, y, of the layers at some instant t, a sine curve would be obtained, Fig. 442 (i). At a place A, for example, the displacement is a positive maximum at this instant, at B the displacement is zero, and at C the displacement is a negative maximum. A quarter of a period later, at a time $t + T/4$, the magnitudes of the displacements are represented by the sine curve in Fig. 442 (ii). At later instants $t + T/2$, $t + 3T/4$, $t + T$, the magnitudes are represented by the respective sine curves in Fig. 442 (iii), (iv), (v).

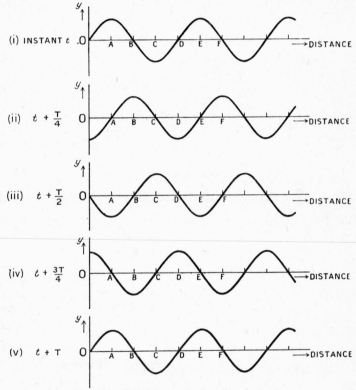

FIG. 442.   Displacements at various instants.

It can now be seen that the variation of the displacements at A, E are "in step", or *in phase*, with each other. The vibrations at B, F are also in phase with each other. The distance between two consecutive places where the vibrations are in phase is defined as the **wavelength** (λ) of the wave; it is also the distance between the positions of successive "crests", or successive "troughs", of any of the curves in Fig. 442.

The *velocity* (*V*) of a wave is the distance it travels in one second. In this time, however, *f* complete waves have passed a given point, where *f* is the frequency of the source, since *f* cycles of changes have occurred at a given point. As the length of one wave is λ, the distance occupied by *f* waves is *f*λ. Hence

$$\mathbf{V} = \mathbf{f}\lambda \qquad . \qquad . \qquad . \qquad . \qquad . \qquad (65)$$

This formula applies to any wave, however it is generated, and should be memorised by the reader as it is used extensively later.

7. Phase Difference, and Path Difference.

A sine wave can be drawn by plotting *angles* along the horizontal axis, instead of times. Thus the sine of 0° is zero, the sine of 90° is 1, the sine of an angle between 180° and 360° is negative, and so on, whence the curve shown in Fig. 443 (i) is obtained. Beyond 360° the

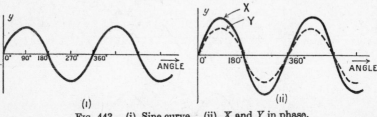

Fig. 443.   (i). Sine curve.   (ii). *X* and *Y* in phase.

curve begins again, and hence the series of values from 0° to 360° constitutes a cycle. The angles thus replace the time, *t*, on the horizontal axis, as can be seen by comparing Fig. 443 (i) with Fig. 440.

When two vibrations, X, Y, of the same frequency are "in step" with each other, X and Y are said to be *in phase*. Their variations are then as shown in Fig. 443 (ii). If the variations of X and Y occur "oppositely", as shown in Fig. 444 (i), X and Y are 180° out of phase. When X and Y vary as shown in Fig. 444 (ii), they are 90° out of phase.

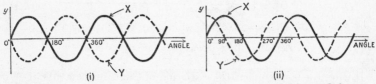

Fig. 444.   (i). *X* and *Y* 180° out of phase.   (ii). *X* and *Y* 90° out of phase.

We encountered an example of two vibrations in phase with each other when defining wavelength, λ (p. 605). Thus the vibrations at

A, E, or at B, F, which are a wavelength apart, are in phase with each other, Fig. 442. The vibrations at B, D are 180° out of phase, and are half a wavelength, $\lambda/2$, apart. The vibrations at A, B, or at C, D, are 90° out of phase, and are a quarter of a wavelength, $\lambda/4$, apart. These relations between path difference and phase difference are important, as they are used to explain many phenomena in Sound and Light, such as those on p. 639 and p. 703.

8. Plane-Progressive Wave Equation

A *plane-progressive wave* travelling in the x-direction is represented by the equation

$$y = a \sin 2\pi \left(\frac{t}{T} - \frac{x}{\lambda} \right) \qquad . \quad . \quad . \quad (66)$$

where y is the magnitude of the varying quantity, a is its maximum value or amplitude, T is its period, λ is the wavelength, t is the time, and x is the distance from some fixed point O. We can understand why the equation represents a *wave* by considering some special values of y. Thus at O, where $x = 0$, $y = a \sin 2\pi t/T$, from (66). At this place, then, y varies simple harmonically with the time t.

At a place which is half a wavelength from O, $x = \lambda/2$. Substituting for x in (66),

$$y = a \sin 2\pi \left(\frac{t}{T} - \frac{1}{2} \right) = a \sin \left(\frac{2\pi t}{T} - \pi \right) = a \sin \left(\frac{2\pi t}{T} - 180° \right)$$

Thus y varies simple harmonically with the time t, and is 180° out of phase with the variation at O, which is at a distance $\lambda/2$ away.

At a place $\lambda/4$ distant from O, $x = \lambda/4$. Substituting in (66),

$$y = a \sin 2\pi \left(\frac{t}{T} - \frac{1}{4} \right) = a \sin \left(\frac{2\pi t}{T} - \frac{\pi}{2} \right) = a \sin \left(\frac{2\pi t}{T} - 90° \right)$$

Thus the variation of y is 90° out of phase with the variation at O. At a distance $x = \lambda$, it can be seen from (66) that

$$y = a \sin \left(\frac{2\pi t}{T} - 2\pi \right) = a \sin \left(\frac{2\pi t}{T} - 360° \right) = a \sin \frac{2\pi t}{T}$$

Thus the variation of y at places distance λ apart are in phase with each other. All these mathematical results have been previously discussed, and are illustrated by the curves in Fig. 444.

9. Pressure Variation Due to Plane-Progressive Wave. Compressions and Rarefactions

Since the layers of air are moving when a wave passes along it, there must be variations of *pressure* in the air. These variations are the cause of the movement of the diaphragm in a microphone when a person speaks into it (p. 610). To understand how the pressure of the air and the displacement of the layers are related to each other, suppose that Fig. 445 (i) represents the positions of the layers *at a given instant*.

The displacement, y, of the layer at L is zero. The layer at a point immediately to the left of L is displaced to the right, since y is then positive, and the layer at a point immediately to the right of L is displaced to the left at that instant, since y is then negative, Fig. 445 (i), (ii). Thus the air at L is *compressed*, and the pressure is hence slightly greater than normal at L, Fig. 445 (iii). The layer on the left

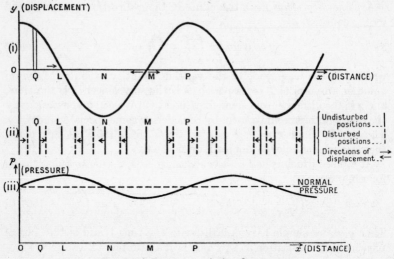

Fig. 445.   Pressure variation due to wave.

of M is displaced to the left, while the layer on the right of M is displaced the other way, Fig. 445 (i), (ii). Consequently the air at M is *rarefied*, and the pressure is hence slightly lower than normal here, Fig. 445 (iii). At N, midway between L and M, the layers on either side are both at the limit of their vibration, i.e., they are displaced by the same amount. The pressure at N is thus *normal*, Fig. 445 (ii). The layer on the left of Q is displaced more to the right than the layer on the right of Q, Fig. 445 (i), (ii), and hence the pressure is slightly greater than normal, though less than at L, Fig. 445 (iii).

Proceeding in this manner, the variation of pressure is similar to that shown in Fig. 445 (iii). It is a simple harmonic variation, with pressures above or below normal at many points in the air, and normal at other points. The condition of the air at L, where the pressure above normal is a maximum, is known as a **compression**; at M, where the pressure below normal is a maximum, the condition of the air is known as a **rarefaction**. As the wave passes along the air, the compressions and rarefactions appear at other points, as illustrated in Fig. 445 (i), (ii). By comparing Fig. 445 (i), (iii), the reader will note that *a compression or a rarefaction occurs at a place where the displacement, y, of the layer is zero*, for example at L or M. The pressure is normal at a place where the displacement, y, is a maximum, for example at N or P. See also Fig. 441.

10. The Ear

The eye can detect colour changes, which are due to the different frequencies of the light waves; it can also detect variations in brightness, which are due to the different amounts of light energy it receives. In the sphere of sound, the ear is as sensitive as the eye; it can detect notes of different pitch, which are due to the different frequencies of sound waves, and it can also detect loud and soft notes, which are due to different amounts of sound energy falling on the ear per second.

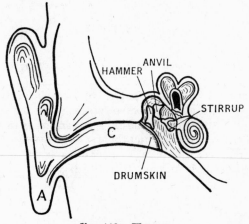

Fig. 446. The ear.

We are not concerned in this book with the complete physiology of the ear. Among other features, it consists of the *outer ear*, A, a canal C leading to the *drumskin*, and bones called the *ossicles*, Fig. 446. The ossicles consist of a bone called the "hammer", fitting into another bone called the "anvil", which is connected to the third bone called the "stirrup". When sound waves occur in the neighbourhood of the ear, they travel down the canal to the drumskin, which is also set into vibration. The part of the hammer in contact with the drumskin then vibrates, and strikes the anvil at the same rate. The motion is thus communicated to the stirrup, and from here it passes by a complicated mechanism to the auditory nerves, which set up the sensation of sound.

In 1843, OHM asserted that the ear perceives a simple harmonic vibration of the air as a simple or pure note. Although the waveforms of notes from instruments are far from being simple harmonic (see p. 630), the ear appears able to analyse a complicated waveform into the sum of a number of simple harmonic waves, which it then detects as separate notes.

11. Longitudinal and Transverse Waves

So far we have discussed waves in which the vibrations of the particles take place in the same direction as that along which the wave travels. Thus if D is a layer of air when a sound wave is transmitted, the vibration of D and the movement of the wave are in the same direction, Fig. 447 (i). This type of wave is called a **longitudinal wave**, and all sound waves are longitudinal.

FIG. 447.   (i). Longitudinal wave.   (ii). Transverse wave.

When a stone is dropped into water, however, the particles of water vibrate up and down while the wave spreads along the water surface. The vibrations of the particles are thus *perpendicular* to the direction along which the wave travels, and this type of wave is called a **transverse wave**, Fig. 447 (ii). We shall meet other examples of transverse waves later, particularly in connection with Light (p. 721).

SOME ELECTRICAL APPLICATIONS IN SOUND

12. Carbon Microphone

The telephone is undoubtedly one of science's great boons to mankind; for example, it enables rapid and efficient communication to be made in matters affecting life and death. The main features of a telephone are the *microphone* and the *telephone earpiece*.

A microphone is an arrangement which converts sound energy to electrical energy. The earliest type was the *carbon microphone*, designed by HUGHES in 1875, which is still used by the Post Office in their modern telephones. It contains carbon granules, C, packed between carbon plates, with a diaphragm D into which a person speaks, Fig. 448. Accumulators, X, at Post Office battery stations maintain a **current** through the carbon granules which depends on the resistance of the circuit.

The granules have a resistance which decreases when they are more closely packed together, and increases when they are more loosely packed. The current in the circuit is originally constant at some value I, Fig. 449; but when a person speaks into the microphone the variation of air-pressure at D causes the diaphragm to vibrate to-and-fro at the same frequency, thus causing a variation in the packing of the granules. When they are more tightly packed, their resistance decreases; the current hence increases. When the granules are more loosely packed, the current decreases. A variation of current is therefore obtained along the telephone wires, as illustrated by S in Fig. 449, and it has exactly the same frequency as the sound waves impinging on the diaphragm of the microphone. Sound energy has thus been converted into electrical energy.

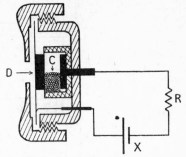

Fig. 448.   Carbon microphone.

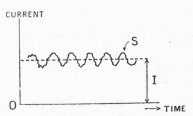

Fig. 449.   Variation of current.

13. Telephone Earpiece

A telephone earpiece converts electrical energy into sound energy, the opposite process to that occurring in the microphone. The essential features of an earpiece are shown in Fig. 450. A permanent magnet A is placed next to two curved pieces of soft-iron B, B, which have coils of insulated wire, C, C, wound round them. The two coils are connected to each other, and the variation of current in the telephone line, obtained by a person speaking into the microphone, flows through the coils.

The free ends of the soft-iron pieces, B, B, are converted into north (N) and south (S) magnetic poles because of the presence of the magnet A, and hence the soft-iron (stalloy) diaphragm D is attracted. Since a current has a magnetic effect, a current in the coils C, C also causes an attraction of D, which is additional to that of B, B if it increases the strengths of their poles. When the current in the coils varies, the attraction on D varies at the same frequency, and hence D

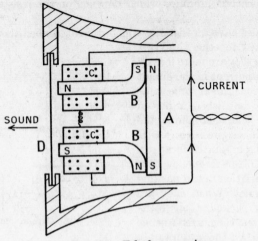

FIG. 450. Telephone earpiece.

vibrates at this frequency. The movement of the diaphragm sets up a sound wave in the air, and hence electrical energy is converted into sound energy by the earpiece.

14. The Moving-Coil Loudspeaker

The loudspeaker in a radio receiver is usually a *moving-coil loud-speaker*; like the telephone earpiece, it converts electrical energy into sound energy, but operates on a different electrical principle. A section of the essential features of the loudspeaker is shown in Fig. 451 (i). It consists of a coil of wire, C, wound round a cylindrical former which is rigidly attached to a paper cone. The cone and the former are loosely

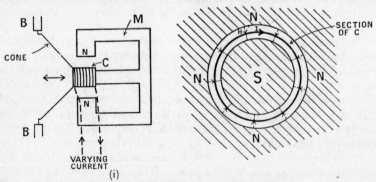

FIG. 451. Moving-coil loudspeaker action.

suspended from a hole in a circular board B. A permanent magnet M has a circular north (N) and south (S) pole, and coil and former are placed round the south pole so that the coil is situated in the magnetic field between the two poles, Fig. 451.

The varying current from the valves in a radio receiver set flows through the coil, C, of the loudspeaker. Suppose the current, I, has the direction shown in Fig. 451. Since the lines of force are radial from the north, N, to the south, S, pole, the magnetic field H is perpendicular to the current. A mechanical force thus acts on the coil which, from Fleming's left-hand rule, is away from the reader. The magnitude of the force is proportional to the current strength, and hence the coil *vibrates* as the varying current flows through it. The cylindrical former, round which the coil is wound, thus vibrates in the direction of its axis, and the paper cone vibrates at this frequency. The large mass of air in contact with the cone also vibrates, and a sound wave is generated in the air. The board B is called a *baffle-board*, and prevents the wave behind the cone from interfering with that in front of it.

15. The Gramophone Disc

In the falling-plate experiment on p. 616 we shall see that the vibrations of a tuning-fork can be "written" with a bristle on a smoked glass plate. One of the earliest devices to record and reproduce a sound consisted of a revolving drum with a steel point, attached to a diaphragm, pressing against it. A wavy groove was indented in the drum when the diaphragm was actuated by sound, and by making a needle with an attached diaphragm retrace the groove the sound could be reproduced.

The modern *gramophone disc* has spiral wavy grooves on it which can be seen under a microscope of high magnifying power. When a gramophone needle is placed on the revolving disc the sideways vibration of the needle in the grooves is communicated to a sensitive diaphragm in the sound-box, which reproduces the sound. The disc is made originally from a soft wax disc on a revolving table. The sound to be recorded is picked up by a microphone and amplified, and the varying current is passed round coils of an electro-magnet which actuates a steel stylus or cutting pen as it moves round the revolving wax disc. Thus wavy grooves of the same frequency as the sound waves are cut into the wax. The disc is then backed by a nickel plate, coated with graphite to make it conduct better, and made the cathode in a copper voltameter through which a current is passed, which results in a copper shell or "negative" used for making the gramophone records. For this purpose the negative is placed in a hydraulic press and pressed firmly on warm soft plastic material, which then has a copy of the wavy trace originally on the wax. On cooling, the plastic hardens, and the familiar gramophone disc is formed. Any future records are made from the copper negative in the same way, the original wax disc being stored in case of damage to the negative. Recordings made at the B.B.C. are originally cut on cellulose-coated aluminium discs, and the metal stamper or "negative" is made from this master disc.

16. Sound Film

Sound can be recorded on film as well as on discs, and the sound track film runs along one side of photographs in motion pictures. In one method the sound track film is made by picking up the sound in a microphone, amplifying it, and then using the varying current to modulate a narrow beam of light incident on a moving film of constant width. The film has then strips of varying density across it when it is developed, according to the intensity and frequency of the original sound.

The *photo-electric cell* is used to reproduce the sound from the film. The cell contains a cæsium surface, S, which emits electrons when it is illuminated, and these are attracted to a metal, A, connected to the positive pole of a battery, Fig. 452. The number of electrons per second

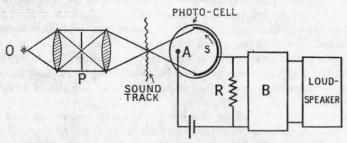

FIG. 452.   Principle of sound track film.

emitted by S is proportional to the intensity of light falling on S, and hence the current in the resistance R, and the potential difference across it, are proportional to the intensity. The moving sound track film is illuminated by a lamp O and a condenser P, and is placed in front of the photo-electric cell. A potential difference is then obtained across R which varies with the same frequency and magnitude as the density of the light passing through the film. The p.d. is amplified by a valve B, and the varying current operates a loudspeaker placed behind the screen on which the pictures are shown.

17. The Cathode-Ray Tube (C.R.T.)

The cathode-ray tube, used in television and radar, is an instrument which enables variations of potential difference, or voltage, to be made visual on a screen. Basically, the instrument contains an emitter of electrons, C, which is a heated filament like that in the thermionic valve, a metal plate G with an opening in the middle, a number of metal plates or cylinders A_1, A_2, A_3, and two pairs of plates, XX, YY, which are respectively vertical and horizontal, Fig. 453 (i). After passing through this system the electrons strike a screen S coated with zinc sulphide, which then glows with a greenish-blue light.

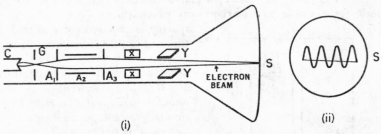

(i)   (ii)

FIG. 453.   Cathode-ray tube principle.

The number of electrons per second passing through G, which affects the *brightness* of the light, is controlled by the electric potential of G with respect to C. The *focusing* of the beam of electrons on the screen is done by altering the potential of the cylinder A_2. When a varying potential difference is applied between the X-plates the beam of electrons is swept horizontally to-and-fro across the tube, and a line is seen on the screen when the frequency is more than 10 cycles per second. A vertical deflection of the beam occurs when a potential difference is applied to the Y-plates. (See also p. 789).

18. Using the Cathode-Ray Tube

The potential difference, V_y, to be examined by the cathode-ray tube is usually connected to the Y-plates. If V_y is obtained from the current flowing in microphone wires when a person is speaking into it, V_y varies continuously (p. 611). Thus if no potential difference is connected to the X-plates, the spot of light on the screen moves rapidly up and down vertically, and a straight line is observed. In order to show the *waveform* of V_y on the screen a potential difference known as the *time-base voltage* is connected between the X-plates, providing, as it were, a "time-axis" for V_y by deflecting the electrons horizontally. A "picture" of the waveform of V_y is then seen on the screen, Fig. 453 (ii).

With the aid of the time-base voltage, the cathode-ray tube can be used to examine visually the waveforms of notes from instruments. Lissajous' figures (p. 623) can be obtained on the screen by disconnecting the time-base voltage, and connecting two potential differences across the X- and Y-plates respectively whose frequencies and phase bear a simple relation to each other.

19. Electrically-Maintained Tuning-Fork

It is sometimes necessary to maintain the vibrations of a tuning-fork; for example, in an experiment where a source of constant frequency is required for a period of time. Fig. 454 illustrates how a battery B can be arranged to maintain the vibrations of a tuning-fork T. B supplies current to a coil wound round a soft-iron core C, the circuit being completed through the fork *via* a platinum style S attached to one prong. S is in contact with a screw at P. When the circuit is completed the electro-magnet created at C attracts the prongs, and the contact at P is broken. The prongs then move back, completing the circuit again, and hence the vibrations of the prongs are maintained.

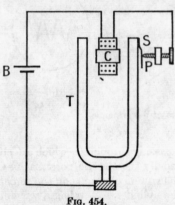

FIG. 454.
Electrically-maintained tuning-fork.

MEASUREMENT OF FREQUENCY OF A TUNING-FORK

20. Falling Plate Method

(1) *Comparison method.* A tuning-fork is often used in experiments in Sound to provide a note of known frequency. One method of measuring the frequency of a fork P is to compare it with the known frequency of another fork Q by a "falling plate method". One end of P is clamped in a vice; a light bristle B is attached to a prong, and rests lightly near the bottom of a smoked glass plate G, Fig. 455. The fork Q is similarly placed, and a bristle C, attached to one of its prongs, rests lightly on G. Both forks are sounded by drawing a bow across them, and the thread S suspending G is now burnt. The glass plate, usually in a groove, falls downward past the horizontally vibrating bristles, which then trace out two clear wavy "tracks" BX, CY on G. Two horizontal lines, M, N, are then drawn across BX, CY, and the

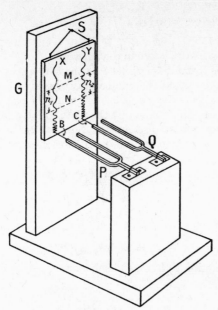

FIG. 455. Falling plate method.

number of complete waves between MN is counted on each trace. Suppose they are n_1, n_2 respectively, and the frequencies of the corresponding forks are f_1, f_2. Then if t is the time taken by the plate to fall a distance MN,

$$f_1 = \text{number of cycles per sec.} = \frac{n_1}{t}$$

and

$$f_2 = \frac{n_2}{t}$$

$\therefore$

$$\frac{f_1}{f_2} = \frac{n_1}{n_2}$$

$$\text{i.e., } f_1 = \frac{n_1}{n_2} \times f_2.$$

Thus knowing n_1, n_2, f_2, the unknown frequency f_1 can be calculated.

(2) *Absolute method.* The unknown frequency f_1 of the tuning-fork P can also be calculated from its own trace. In this case the lengths s_1, s_2 corresponding to an *equal* number of consecutive waves are measured by a travelling microscope. Suppose there are n complete waves between LR, RS, Fig. 456. Then f_1 is given by

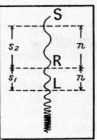

FIG. 456.
(Not to scale.)

$$f_1 = n \sqrt{\frac{g}{s_2 - s_1}} \qquad \cdots \qquad (67)$$

where $g = 980$ when s_1, s_2 are in centimetres.

To prove this formula for f_1, let t be the time taken by the plate to fall a distance LR. Since the number of waves in LR is the same as in RS, the fork has also vibrated for a time t while the plate falls a distance RS. Thus if t is the time taken by the plate to fall a distance LR, $2t$ is the time it takes to fall a distance LS. Suppose u is the velocity of the plate at the instant when the line L on it reaches the vibrating bristle on the fork.

Then $$s_1 = ut + \tfrac{1}{2}gt^2 \qquad \cdots \qquad (i)$$

from the dynamics equation $s = ut + \tfrac{1}{2}ft^2$, since the acceleration, f, of the plate $= g$, the acceleration due to gravity. As the time taken by the plate to fall a distance LS, or $(s_1 + s_2)$, is $2t$, we have

$$s_1 + s_2 = u \cdot 2t + \tfrac{1}{2}g(2t)^2 \qquad \cdots \qquad (ii)$$

Multiplying equation (i) by 2, and subtracting from (ii) to eliminate u,

$$\therefore \quad s_2 - s_1 = gt^2$$

$$\therefore \quad t = \sqrt{\frac{s_2 - s_1}{g}}$$

$$\therefore \quad f_1 = \frac{n}{t} = n \sqrt{\frac{g}{s_2 - s_1}}$$

as given above in equation (67).

The falling-plate method gives only an approximate value of the frequency, as (a) it is difficult to determine an *exact* number of waves; (b) the attachment of a bristle to the tuning-fork prong lowers its frequency slightly (see p. 641); (c) there is friction between the style and the plate.

21. The Stroboscope

A *stroboscope* is an arrangement which makes a vibrating object appear at rest when it is viewed, and thus enables a wave on water, for example, to be studied at leisure. The stroboscopic method can be used to determine the frequency of a tuning-fork, which is electrically maintained for the purpose.

Two light metal plates, A, B, each with a slit S in them, are attached to the prongs of the tuning-fork F so that the slits overlap each other when the fork is not sounded, Fig. 457. Behind the slit is a vertical circular white card C with black dots spaced at equal distances round the circumference, and the dots on the card can be seen through S. The tuning-fork is set into vibration, and the card is rotated by a motor

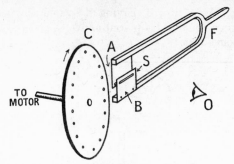

Fig. 457.   Stroboscope method.

about a horizontal axis through its centre with increasing speed. At first an observer O, viewing the dots through S, sees them moving round in an opposite direction to that in which the card is rotated. This is because the intermittent glimpses of the card through S occur quicker than the time taken for one dot to reach the place of the dot in front of it, with the result that the dots appear to be moving slowly back. As the speed of the card is increased further, a stage is reached when the dots appear perfectly stationary, and in this case successive glimpses of the card are made in the time taken by one dot to occupy the position of the next dot.

Suppose that the number of revolutions per second of the card, determined by a revolution counter, is now n, and the number of dots on the card are m. The time taken for one dot to reach the position occupied by the next dot is then $\dfrac{1}{nm}$ seconds. If the frequency of the fork is f, the time for successive glimpses is $\dfrac{1}{2f}$ seconds, since the slits overlap *twice* in one complete vibration. Thus

$$\frac{1}{2f} = \frac{1}{nm}$$

$$\therefore \quad f = \frac{nm}{2} \quad . \quad . \quad . \quad . \quad . \quad (68)$$

If n and m are known, f can hence be calculated.

The metal plates, A, B, attached to the prongs decrease the frequency of the fork, but a correction for them can be made (see p. 641).

22. The Siren

About 1816 DE LA TOUR designed a siren consisting of a chamber A into which air can be blown, with holes drilled all round it at the top,

C, Fig. 358 (i), (ii). A disc B, having the same number of equally-spaced holes bored round it, is placed above C, and the holes in B, C are originally coincident.

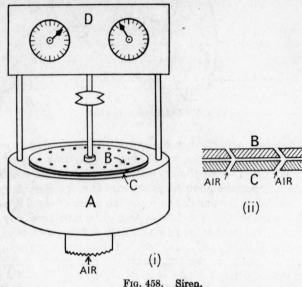

FIG. 458.   Siren.

The holes in B and C are drilled obliquely, sloping in *opposite* directions, Fig. 458 (ii). When a blast of air is blown into the chamber A, the air passing through the hole in C exerts a sideways pressure on the holes in B, and B then begins to rotate. Puffs of air thus emerge through the holes in B and C whenever they coincide in position. A note, due to the successive emerging blasts of air, is now heard, and as the pressure of the air admitted to the chamber A increases, B rotates faster, and the pitch of the note increases.

If there are n holes in each disc, the air emerges from the disc n times in one revolution of the disc. If the latter makes N revolutions per second, it follows that the frequency f of the note is given by

$$f = Nn \text{ cycles per second } . \quad . \quad . \quad . \quad (69)$$

The number of revolutions per second can be read from the counters D, and hence f can be evaluated.

The frequency of a note can be determined with the aid of a siren. The note is sounded, and the speed of the discs is increased until beats are heard, when the unknown frequency is known to be near the frequency of the note from the siren (see p. 641). By carefully adjusting the speed of the discs until the beats occur at a very slow rate, the unknown frequency can be found to a fair degree of accuracy.

23. The Phonic Wheel

LORD RAYLEIGH, a prominent pioneer in investigations on Sound, devised a very accurate method of determining the frequency of a tuning-fork, F, which is electrically maintained for the purpose (p. 616). The intermittent current in the circuit is arranged to energise an electro-magnet D by passing it through coils A, B, and a toothed iron wheel W, which can rotate about a horizontal axis through its centre, is placed centrally between the poles of D, Fig. 459.

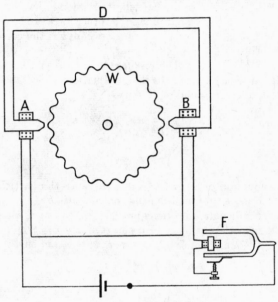

FIG. 459.   Phonic wheel.

If W is pushed so that it begins to rotate, the iron teeth of the wheel are attracted by the poles of D, and the rotation persists. After a time the wheel settles down with a *steady* rotation, and the iron teeth then pass between the poles at the same rate as the intermittent current. Suppose the number of teeth on the wheel is n and that it makes m revolutions per second in its steady rotation. The frequency, f, of the tuning-fork is then given by

$$f = nm \qquad . \qquad . \qquad . \qquad . \qquad . \qquad (70)$$

The number of revolutions per second, m, can be determined to a high degree of accuracy by timing the number of revolutions made by the wheel in a very long interval of time, which is the advantage of the phonic wheel method of determining frequency.

24. Compounding of Perpendicular Vibrations

If a particle is subjected to two periodic forces in perpendicular directions, the path described by the particle will be that of the resultant of the two forces. Suppose, for example, that the two perpendicular forces have the same frequency and phase, and are simple harmonic. The vibration of the particle along the x-axis, due to one force can then be represented by $x = a \sin \omega t$, where a is the amplitude, and the vibration along the perpendicular y-axis due to the other force can be represented by $y = b \sin \omega t$, where b is the corresponding amplitude.

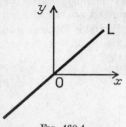

Fig. 460A.
Vibrations in phase.

The *resultant* vibration can be deduced by eliminating the time t from the above equations for x and y. Since $x/a = \sin \omega t$, and $y/b = \sin \omega t$,

$$\therefore \qquad \frac{y}{b} = \frac{x}{a}$$

$$\therefore \qquad y = \frac{b}{a} x$$

This is the equation of a *straight line*, and hence the particle vibrates along a line L whose gradient depends on the ratio b/a, Fig. 460A.

If the perpendicular vibrations are 90° *out of phase*, they can be represented respectively by $x = a \sin \omega t$ and $y = b \sin (\omega t + 90°)$. Thus $y = b \cos \omega t$, and hence $y/b = \cos \omega t$. Now $x/a = \sin \omega t$.

Since $$\sin^2 \omega t + \cos^2 \omega t = 1,$$

$$\therefore \qquad \frac{x^2}{a^2} + \frac{y^2}{b^2} = 1$$

This is the equation of an *ellipse* whose semi-axis are a, b, and hence the particle describes an ellipse E periodically, Fig. 460B (i).

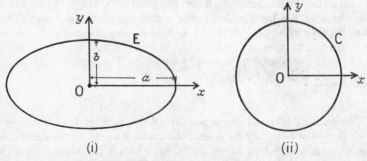

(i)   (ii)

Fig. 460B.   Vibrations 90° out of phase.

If the amplitudes a, b are equal, the equation reduces to $x^2/a^2 + y^2/a^2 = 1$, or to

$$x^2 + y^2 = a^2.$$

This is the equation of a *circle*, C, of radius a, Fig. 460B (ii).

25. Lissajous' Figures

Some very useful information about the frequency and phase of an unknown vibration X can be deduced by combining it with a known vibration Y perpendicular to it, and then studying the resultant figure. If the figure is an ellipse, for example, X has the same frequency as Y and is 90° out of phase with it, as we have just shown. If the figure is a straight line, X has the same frequency as Y and is in phase with it. LISSAJOUS was one of the first to study the combined effect of two perpendicular vibrations, and the figure described, such as the line, circle, or ellipse just discussed, is known as a *Lissajous' figure*.

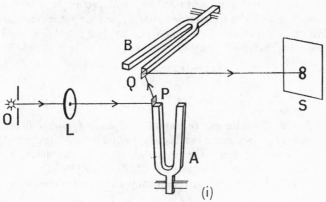

FIG. 461 (i).   Lissajous' figures.

Two tuning-forks, A, B, are arranged so that their vibrations are perpendicular to each other, A being vertical and B horizontal, and small mirrors, P, Q, are attached to their respective prongs, Fig. 461 (i). A beam of light is obtained from a source O behind a circular hole in a screen, and by means of a lens L, the light is reflected in turn from P and Q on to a screen S. The vibrations of A alone would result in a vertical straight line being seen on S, and the vibrations of B alone would result in a horizontal straight line being seen. When both forks vibrate a pattern is observed on S which is a straight line, circle, or ellipse if the frequencies are equal, Fig. 460A,B. The Lissajous' figures when the ratio of the frequencies is 2 : 1 and 3 : 1 respectively are shown in Fig. 461 (ii). Helmholtz used Lissajous' figures to study the vibrations of the violin string and other objects.

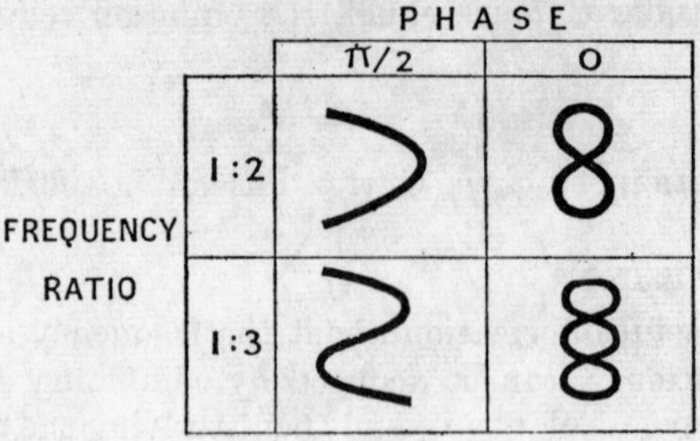

(ii)

Fig. 461 (ii).   Lissajous' figures.

When the frequencies of the forks are slightly different, a pattern is observed which changes continuously, and recurs at definite time intervals. Suppose the frequencies are f_1, f_2 cycles per second, and the time interval is t seconds. Since one fork has then made one more cycle than the other, it follows that

$$f_1 t \sim f_2 t = 1$$

$$\therefore \qquad f_1 \sim f_2 = \frac{1}{t} \quad . \quad . \quad . \quad . \quad . \quad (71)$$

Thus if $f_2 = 256$ cycles per sec. and $t = 5$ secs., $f_1 = 255 \cdot 8$ or $256 \cdot 2$. The correct frequency value can be determined by loading the unknown fork a little, so as to lower the frequency slightly, and noting the new time and interval for the recurrence of the Lissajous' figure. If it is more than 5 secs., the unknown frequency was $256 \cdot 2$ cycles per sec.

EXERCISES XXVIII

1. Define *amplitude*, *frequency*, and *wavelength*. Describe the siren, and explain how you would use it to measure the frequency of a tuning-fork.

2. Describe with the aid of diagrams the features of a *plane-progressive wave* in air. Show how the particle velocity and the pressure vary at different places.

3. Describe the *falling-plate method* of measuring the frequency of a tuning-fork without another fork being available, and give the theory of the method.

4. Describe the *carbon microphone* and the *telephone earpiece*, and explain how each functions.

5. Describe the stroboscopic method of determining the frequency of a tuning-fork, and show how the result is calculated.

6. The beam of a cathode-ray tube is subjected in turn to two vibrations at right angles, represented by (i) $x = 3 \sin \omega t$, $y = 3 \cos \omega t$, (ii) $x = 4 \sin \omega t$, $y = 6 \sin \omega t$, (iii) $x = 4 \cos \omega t$, $y = 8 \sin \omega t$. What is the least *phase difference* between each vibration, and the appearance on the screen of the tube, in the three cases?

7. Draw a diagram showing how Lissajous' figures are obtained with two tuning-forks. What information can be obtained from a study of a Lissajous' figure? Give an example.

8. Describe how a *gramophone disc* and a *sound film* are made. How is the sound reproduced in each case?

9. Describe a determination of the frequency of a tuning-fork by a method which does not require a knowledge of the frequency of another fork or of the velocity of sound in air. Show how the result is calculated.

Two notes are sounded together by apparatus which allows the frequency of one note to be changed continuously. Describe and explain what is heard if the frequencies are equal initially and then one is gradually increased by 50 per cent. (*L.*)

[For second part of question, see p. 639.]

10. In the *falling-plate* experiment of measuring the frequency of a tuning-fork, the successive lengths occupied by 25 complete waves were 9·85 and 14·1 cm. When the experiment was repeated, the successive lengths occupied by 25 complete waves were 9·0 and 13·0 cm. Calculate the frequency of the fork for each experiment, deriving any formula you employ.

11. Describe the nature of the disturbance set up in air by a vibrating tuning fork and show how the disturbance can be represented by a sine curve. Indicate on the curve the points of (*a*) maximum particle velocity, (*b*) maximum pressure.

What characteristics of the vibration determine the pitch, intensity, and quality respectively of the note? (*N.*)

12. Describe with the aid of a diagram how the vibrations of a tuning fork may be electrically maintained.

Describe and explain a stroboscopic method of measuring the frequency of an electrically maintained fork. (*L.*)

CHAPTER XXIX

CHARACTERISTICS, PROPERTIES, AND VELOCITY OF SOUND WAVES

CHARACTERISTICS OF NOTES

NOTES may be similar to or different from each other in three respects: (i) *pitch*, (ii) *loudness*, (iii) *quality*; so that if each of these three quantities of a particular note is known, the note is completely defined or "characterised".

1. Pitch

Pitch is analogous to colour in light, which is characterised by the wavelength, or by the frequency, of the electro-magnetic vibrations (p. 716). Similarly, the pitch of a note depends only on the frequency of the vibrations, and a high frequency gives rise to a high-pitched note. A low frequency produces a low-pitched note. Thus the high-pitched whistle of a boy may have a frequency of several thousand cycles per second, whereas the low-pitched hum of an A.C. radio set when first switched on is a hundred cycles per second. The range of sound frequencies is about 15 to 20,000 cycles per sec.

2. Musical Intervals

If a note of frequency 300 cycles per sec., and then a note of 600 cycles per sec., are sounded by a siren, the pitch of the higher note is recognised to be an upper octave of the lower note. A note of frequency 1,000 cycles per sec. is recognised to be an upper octave of a note of 500 cycles per sec., and thus the *musical interval* between two notes is an upper octave if the ratio of their frequencies is 2 : 1. It can be shown

Note	C doh	D ray	E me	F fah	G soh	A lah	B te	c doh
Natural (Diatonic) Scale Frequency	256	288	320	341	384	427	480	512
Intervals between notes ..		9/8	10/9	16/15	9/8	10/9	9/8	16/15
Intervals above C	1·000	1·125	1·250	1·333	1·500	1·667	1·875	2·000
Equal Temperament Scale intervals above C	1·000	1·122	1·260	1·335	1·498	1·682	1·888	2·000

Note 1.—There are 12 semitones to the octave in the scale of equal temperament; each semitone has a frequency ratio of $2^{1/12}$.

Note 2.—The frequency of C is 256 on the scale of Helmholtz above; in music it is 261·2.

by the siren that the musical interval between two notes depends on the *ratio* of their frequencies, and not on the actual frequencies. The table on p. 626, shows the various musical intervals and the corresponding ratio of the frequencies of the notes.

3. Intensity and Loudness

The *intensity* of a sound at a place is defined as the energy per second flowing through 1 square centimetre held normally at that place to the direction along which the sound travels. As we go further away from a source of sound the intensity diminishes, since the intensity decreases as the square of the distance from the source (see also p. 570).

Suppose the displacement y of a vibrating layer of air is given by $y = a \sin \omega t$, where $\omega = 2\pi/T$ and a is the amplitude of vibration, see equation (63), p. 601. The velocity, v, of the layer is given by

$$v = \frac{dy}{dt} = \omega a \cos \omega t,$$

and hence the kinetic energy, W, is given by

$$W = \tfrac{1}{2} mv^2 = \tfrac{1}{2} m\omega^2 a^2 \cos^2 \omega t \quad . \quad . \quad . \quad \text{(i)}$$

where m is the mass of the layer. The energy of the vibrating layer is partly kinetic and partly potential. Its total energy, W_0, is thus equal to the maximum value of the kinetic energy, when $\cos \omega t = 1$, as the potential energy is then zero. From (i),

$$W_0 = \tfrac{1}{2} m\omega^2 a^2 \quad . \quad . \quad . \quad . \quad . \quad \text{(ii)}$$

In 1 second, the air is disturbed by the wave over a distance V cm., where V is the velocity of sound in *cm.* per sec.; and if the area of cross-section of the air is 1 sq. cm., the volume of air disturbed is V c.c. The mass m of air disturbed per second is thus $V\varrho$ gm., where ϱ is the density of air in gm. per c.c., and hence, from (ii),

$$W_0 = \tfrac{1}{2} m\omega^2 a^2 = \tfrac{1}{2} V\varrho\omega^2 a^2 \quad . \quad . \quad . \quad \text{(iii)}$$

It therefore follows that *the intensity of a sound due to a wave is proportional to the square of its amplitude of vibration.*

It can be seen from (ii) that the greater the mass m of air in vibration, the greater is the intensity of the sound obtained. For this reason the sound set up by the vibration of the diaphragm of a telephone earpiece cannot be heard except with the ear close to the earpiece. On the other hand, the cone of a loudspeaker has a large surface area, and thus disturbs a large mass of air when it vibrates, giving rise to a sound of much larger intensity than the vibrating diaphragm of the telephone earpiece. It is difficult to hear a vibrating tuning-fork a small distance away from it because its prongs set such a small mass of air vibrating. If the fork is placed with its end on a table, however, a much louder sound is obtained, which is due to the large mass of air vibrating by contact with the table.

Loudness is a sensation, and hence, unlike intensity, it is difficult to measure because it depends on the individual observer. Normally, the greater the intensity, the greater is the loudness of the sound (see p.629).

4. The Decibel

We are already familiar with the fact that when the frequency of a note is doubled its pitch rises by an octave. Thus the increase in pitch sounds the same to the ear when the frequency increases from 100 to 200 cycles per second as from 500 to 1,000 cycles per second. Similarly, it is found that increases in loudness depend on the *ratio* of the intensities, and not on the absolute differences in intensity.

If the power of a source of sound increases from 0·1 watt to 0·2 watt, and then from 0·2 watt to 0·4 watt, the loudness of the source to the ear increases in equal steps. The equality is thus dependent on the equality of the *ratio* of the powers, not their difference, and in commercial practice the increase in loudness is registered by taking the *logarithm of the ratio of the powers to the base* 10, which is $\log_{10} 2$, or 0·3, in this case.

Relative intensities or powers are expressed in *bels*, after Graham Bell, the inventor of the telephone. If the power of a source of sound changes from P_1 to P_2, then

$$\text{number of bels} = \log_{10}\left(\frac{P_2}{P_1}\right)$$

In practice the bel is too large a unit, and the **decibel (db)** is therefore adopted. This is defined as one-tenth of a bel, and hence in the above case

$$\text{number of decibels} = 10 \log_{10}\left(\frac{P_2}{P_1}\right)$$

The minimum change of power which the ear is able to detect is about 1 db, which corresponds to an increase in power of about 25 per cent.

5. Calculation of Decibels

Suppose the power of a note from a loudspeaker of a radio receiver is 50 milliwatts, and the volume control is turned so that the power increases to 500 milliwatts. The increase in power is then given by

$$10 \log_{10}\left(\frac{P_2}{P_1}\right) = 10 \times \log\frac{500}{50} = 10 \text{ db.}$$

If the volume control is turned so that the power increases to 1,000 milliwatts, the increase in power compared with the original sound

$$= 10 \log_{10} \left(\frac{1{,}000}{50} \right) = 10 \log_{10} 20 = 13 \cdot 1 \text{ db.}$$

If the volume control is turned down so that the power decreases from 1,000 to 200 milliwatts, the change in power

$$= 10 \log_{10} \left(\frac{200}{1{,}000} \right) = 10 \log_{10} 2 - 10 \log_{10} 10 = -7 \text{ db.}$$

The minus indicates a decrease in power. Besides its use in acoustics the decibel is used by radio and electrical engineers in dealing with changes in electrical power.

The lowest audible sound at a frequency of 1,000 cycles per sec. appears to correspond to a power per sq. cm. of the ear of about 10^{-10} microwatts, which is known as the *threshold of hearing*. Ordinary conversation corresponds to a power of about 10 microwatts, and the peak power of a large bass drum has been estimated at 25 watts.

6. The Phon

The loudness of a sound is a sensation, and thus depends on the observer, whereas power, or intensity, of a sound is independent of the observer. Observations show that sounds which appear equally loud to a person have different intensities or powers, depending on the frequency, f, of the sound. The curves a, b, c represent respectively three values of *equal loudness*, and hence the intensity at X, when the

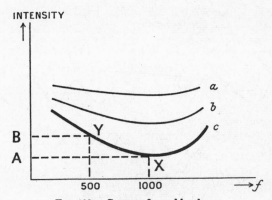

Fig. 462.   Curves of equal loudness.

frequency is 1,000 cycles per second, is less than the intensity at Y, when the frequency is 500, although the loudness is the same, Fig. 462.

In order to measure loudness, therefore, scientists have adopted a "standard" source of frequency 1,000 cycles per second, with which all sounds are compared. The source H whose loudness is required is placed near the standard source, and the latter is then altered until the loudness is the same as H. The intensity or power level of the standard source is then measured, and if this is n decibels above the threshold value (10^{-10} microwatts per sq. cm., p. 629) the loudness is said to be n *phons*. The phon, introduced in 1936, is thus a unit of loudness, whereas the decibel is a unit of intensity or power. *Noise meters*, containing a microphone, amplifier, and meter, are used to measure loudness, and are calibrated directly in phons.

7. Quality or Timbre

If the same note is sounded on the violin and then on the piano, an untrained listener can tell which instrument is being used, without seeing it. We say that the *quality* or *timbre* of the note is different in each case.

The waveform of a note is never simple harmonic in practice; the nearest approach is that obtained by sounding a tuning-fork, which thus produces what may be called a "pure" note, Fig. 463 (i). If the same note is played on a violin and piano respectively, the waveforms produced might be represented by Fig. 463 (ii), (iii), which have the same frequency and amplitude as the waveform in Fig. 463 (i). Now curves of the shape of Fig. 463 (ii), (iii) can be analysed mathematically into the sum of a number of *simple harmonic* curves, whose frequencies are multiples of f_0, the frequency of the original waveform; the amplitudes of these curves diminish as the frequency increases. Fig. 463 (iv),

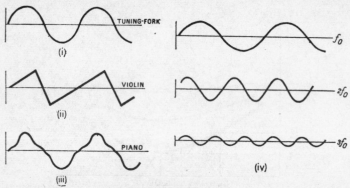

FIG. 463. Wave-forms of notes.

for example, might be an analysis of a curve similar to Fig. 463 (iii), corresponding to a note on a piano. The ear is able to detect simple harmonic waves (p. 610), and thus registers the presence of notes of frequencies $2f_0$ and $3f_0$, in addition to f_0, when the note is sounded on the piano. The amplitude of the curve corresponding to f_0 is greatest, Fig. 463 (iv), and the note of frequency f_0 is heard predominantly because the intensity is proportional to the square of the amplitude (p. 627). In the background, however, are the notes of frequencies $2f_0$, $3f_0$, which are called the *overtones*. The frequency f_0 is called the *fundamental*.

As the waveform of the same note is different when it is obtained from different instruments, it follows that the analysis of each will differ; for example, the waveform of a note of frequency f_0 from a violin may contain overtones of frequencies $2f_0$, $4f_0$, $6f_0$. The musical "background" to the fundamental note is therefore different when it is sounded on different instruments, and hence *the overtones present in a note determine its quality or timbre*.

A *harmonic* is the name given to a note whose frequency is a simple multiple of the fundamental frequency f_0. The latter is thus termed the "first harmonic"; a note of frequency $2f_0$ is called the "second harmonic", and so on. Certain harmonics of a note may be absent from its overtones; for example, the only possible notes obtained from an organ-pipe closed at one end are f_0, $3f_0$, $5f_0$, $7f_0$, and so on (p. 664).

8. Helmholtz Resonators

HELMHOLTZ, one of the greatest scientists of the nineteenth century, devised a simple method of detecting the overtones accompanying the fundamental note. He used vessels, P, Q, of different sizes, containing air which "responded" or *resonated* (see p. 668) to a note of a particular frequency, Fig. 464. When a sound wave entered a small cavity a in

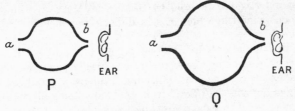

FIG. 464.   Helmholtz resonator.

the resonator, as the vessel was called, an observer at b on the other side heard a note if the wave contained the frequency to which the resonator responded. By using resonators of various sizes, which were themselves singularly free from overtones, Helmholtz analysed the notes obtained from different instruments.

PROPERTIES OF SOUND WAVES

9. Reflection

Like light waves, sound waves are reflected from a plane surface so that the angle of incidence is equal to the angle of reflection. This can be demonstrated by placing a tube T_1 in front of a plane surface AB and blowing a whistle gently at S, Fig. 465. Another tube T_2, directed towards N, is placed on the other side of the normal NQ, and moved until a sensitive flame (see p. 667), or a microphone connected to a cathode-ray tube, is considerably affected at R, showing that the reflected wave passes along NR. It will then be found that angle RNQ = angle SNQ.

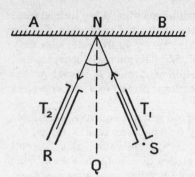

FIG. 465.　Reflection of sound.

It can also be demonstrated that sound waves come to a focus when they are incident on a curved concave mirror. A surface shaped like a parabola reflects sound waves to long distances if the source of sound is placed at its focus (see also p. 414),

The famous whispering gallery of St. Paul's is a circular-shaped chamber whose walls repeatedly reflect sound waves round the gallery, so that a person talking quietly at one end can be heard distinctly at the other end.

10. Acoustics of Rooms. Reverberation

A concert-hall, lecture-room, or a broadcasting studio requires special design to be acoustically effective. The technical problems concerned were first investigated in 1906 by SABINE in America, who was consulted about a hall in which it was difficult for an audience to hear the lecturer.

Generally, an audience in a hall hears sound from different directions at different times. They hear (a) sound *directly* from the speaker or orchestra, as the case may be, (b) sound from *echoes* produced by walls and ceilings, (c) sound *diffused* from the walls and ceilings and other objects present. The echoes are due to regular reflection at a plane surface (p. 402), but the diffused sound is scattered in different directions and reflection takes place repeatedly at other surfaces. When reflection occurs some energy is absorbed from the sound wave, and after a time the sound diminishes below the level at which it can be heard. The perseverance of the sound after the source ceases is known as **reverberation**. In the case of the hall investigated by Sabine the time of reverberation was about $5\frac{1}{2}$ seconds, and the sound due to the first syllable of a speaker thus overlapped the sound due to the next dozen or so syllables, making the speech difficult to comprehend. The quality of a sound depends on the time of reverberation. If the time is very short, for example 0·5 second, the music from an orchestra sounds thin or lifeless; if the time is too long the music sounds muffled. The reverberation time at a B.B.C. concert-hall used for orchestral performances is about $1\frac{3}{4}$ seconds, whereas the reverberation time for a dance-band studio is about 1 second.

11. Sabine's Investigations. Absorptive Power

Sabine found that the time T of reverberation depended on the volume V of the room, its surface area A, and the *absorptive power*, a, of the surfaces. The time T is given approximately by

$$T = \frac{kV}{aA} \; ,$$

where k is a constant. In general some sound is absorbed and the rest is reflected; if too much sound is reflected T is large. If a lot of thick curtains are present in the room too much sound is absorbed and T is small.

Sabine chose the absorptive power of unit area of an open window as the unit, since this is a perfect absorber. On this basis the absorptive power of a person in an audience, or of thick carpets and rugs, is 0·5, linoleum has an absorptive power of 0·12, and polished wood and glass have an absorptive power of 0·01. The absorptive power of a material depends on its pores to a large extent; this is shown by the fact that an unpainted brick has a high absorptive power, whereas the painted brick has a low absorptive power.

From Sabine's formula for T it follows that the time of reverberation can be shortened by having more spectators in the hall concerned, or by using felt materials to line some of the walls or ceiling. The seats in an acoustically-designed lecture-room have plush cushions at their backs to act as an absorbent of sound when the room is not full. B.B.C. studios used for plays or news talks should have zero reverberation time, as clarity is all-important, and the studios are built from special plaster or cork panels which absorb the sound completely. The structure of a room also affects the acoustics. Rooms with large curved surfaces tend to focus echoes at certain places, which is unpleasant aurally to the audience, and a huge curtain is hung from the roof of the Albert Hall to obscure the dome at orchestral concerts.

12. Refraction

Sound waves can be refracted as well as reflected. TYNDALL placed a watch in front of a balloon filled with carbon dioxide, which is heavier than air, and found that the sound was heard at a definite place on the other side of the balloon. The sound waves thus converged to a focus on the other side of the balloon, which therefore has the same effect on sound waves as a convex lens has on light waves (see Fig. 514, p. 700). If the balloon is filled with hydrogen, which is lighter than air, the sound waves diverge on passing through the balloon. The latter thus acts similarly to a concave lens when light waves are incident on it (see p. 699).

The refraction of sound explains why sounds are easier to hear at night than during day-time. In the latter case the upper layers of air are colder than the layers near the earth. Now sound travels faster the higher the temperature (see p. 644), and sound waves are hence refracted in a direction away from the earth. The intensity of the sound waves thus diminish. At night-time, however, the layers of air near the earth are colder than those higher up, and hence sound waves are now refracted towards the earth, with a consequent increase in intensity.

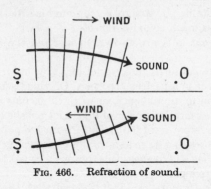

Fig. 466.   Refraction of sound.

For a similar reason, a distant observer O hears a sound from a source S more easily when the wind is blowing towards him than away from him, Fig. 466. When the wind is blowing towards O, the bottom of the sound wavefront is moving slower than the upper part, and hence the wavefronts veer towards the observer, who therefore hears the sound easily. When the wind is blowing in the opposite direction the reverse is the case, and the wavefronts veer upwards away from the ground and O. The sound intensity thus diminishes. This phenomenon is hence another example of the refraction of sound.

13. Interference of Sound Waves

Besides reflection and refraction, sound waves can also exhibit the phenomenon of *interference*, whose principles we shall now discuss.

Suppose two sources of sound, A, B, have exactly the same frequency and amplitude of vibration, and that their vibrations are always in phase with each other, Fig. 467. Such sources are called "coherent" sources. *Their combined effect at a point is obtained by adding algebraically the displacements at the point due to the sources individually;* this is known as the *Principle of Superposition*. Thus their resultant effect at X, for example, is the algebraic sum of the vibrations at X due to the source A alone and the vibrations at X due to the source B alone.

If X is equidistant from A and B, the vibrations at X due to the two sources are *always* in phase as (i) the distance AX travelled by the wave originating at A is equal to the distance BX travelled by the wave originating at B, (ii) the sources A, B are assumed to have the same frequency and to be always in phase with each other. Fig. 468 (i), (ii) illustrate the vibrations at X due to A, B, which have the same amplitude. The resultant vibration at X is obtained by adding the two curves, and has

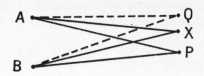

FIG. 467.   Interference of sound.

an amplitude double that of either curve and a frequency the same as either, Fig. 468 (iii). Now the energy of a vibrating source is proportional to the square of its amplitude (p. 627). Consequently the sound energy at X is four times that due to A or B alone, and a loud sound is thus heard at X. As A and B are coherent sources, the loud sound is *permanent*.

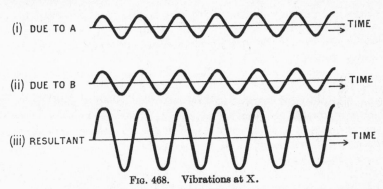

FIG. 468.   Vibrations at X.

If Q is a point such that BQ is greater than AQ by a whole number of wavelengths (Fig. 467), the vibration at Q due to A is in phase with the vibration there due to B (see p. 605). A permanent loud sound is then obtained at Q. Thus a permanent loud sound is obtained at any point *Y* if the *path difference*, BY − AY, is given by

$$BY - AY = n\lambda,$$

where λ is the wavelength of the sources A, B, and n is an integer.

14. Destructive Interference

Consider now a point P in Fig. 467 whose distance from B is half a wavelength longer than its distance from A, i.e., AP − BP = $\lambda/2$. The vibration at P due to B will then be 180° out of phase with the vibration there to A (see p. 606), Fig. 469 (i), (ii). The resultant effect at P is thus zero, as the displacements at any instant are equal and opposite to each other, Fig. 469 (iii). No sound is therefore heard at P, and the permanent silence is said to be due to "destructive interference" between the sound waves from A and B.

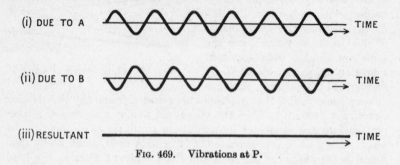

FIG. 469.   Vibrations at P.

If the path difference, AP − BP, were $3\lambda/2$ or $5\lambda/2$, instead of $\lambda/2$, permanent silence would also exist at P as the vibrations there due to A, B would again be 180° out of phase. Summarising, then,

silence occurs if the path-difference is an odd number of half wavelengths, and

a loud sound occurs if the path-difference is a whole number of wavelengths.

The total sound energy in all the positions of loud sound discussed above is equal to the total sound energy of the two sources A, B, from the principle of the conservation of energy. The extra sound at the positions of loud sound thus makes up for the absent sound in the positions of silence.

15. Quincke's Tube. Measurement of Velocity of Sound in a Tube

QUINCKE devised a simple method of obtaining permanent interference between two sound waves. He used a closed tube SAEB which had openings at S, E, and placed a source of sound at S, Fig. 470. A wave then travelled in the direction SAE round the tube, while another wave travelled in the opposite direction SBE; and since these waves are due to the same source, S, they always set out in phase, i.e., they are coherent.

Like a trombone, one side, B, of the tube can be pulled out, thus making SAE, SBE of different lengths. When SAE and SBE are equal in length an observer at E hears a loud sound, since the paths of the two waves are then equal. As B is pulled out the sound dies away and becomes a minimum when the path difference, SBE − SAE, is $\lambda/2$, where λ is the wavelength. In this case the two waves arrive 180° out

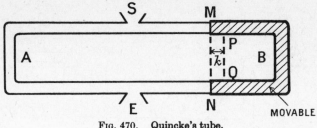

Fig. 470.   Quincke's tube.

of phase (p. 607). If the tube is pulled out further, the sound increases in loudness to a maximum; the path difference is then λ. If k is the distance moved from one position of minimum sound, MN say, to the next position of minimum sound, PQ say, then $2k = \lambda$, Fig. 470. Thus the wavelength of the sound can be simply obtained by measuring k.

The velocity of sound in the tube is given by $V = f\lambda$, where f is the frequency of the source S, and thus V can be found when a source of known frequency is used. In a particular experiment with Quincke's tube, the tube B was moved a distance 4·28 cm. between successive minima of sound, and the frequency of the source was 4,000 cycles per second.

Thus $\lambda = 2 \times 4\text{·}28$ cm.,

and $V = f\lambda = 4{,}000 \times 2 \times 4\text{·}28 = 34{,}240$ cm. per sec.

It can be seen that, unlike reflection and refraction, the phenomenon of interference can be utilised to measure the wavelength of sound waves. We shall see later that interference is also utilised to measure the wavelength of light waves (p. 704).

16. Velocity of Sound in Free Air. Hebb's Method

In 1905 HEBB performed an accurate experiment to measure the velocity of sound in free air which utilised a method of interference. He carried out his experiment in a large hall to eliminate the effect of wind, and obtained the temperature of the air by placing thermometers at different parts of the room. Two parabolic reflectors, R_1, R_2, are placed at each end of the hall, and microphones, M_1, M_2, are positioned at the respective foci S_1, S_2 to receive sound reflected from R_1, R_2, Fig. 471. By means of a transformer, the currents in the microphones are induced into a telephone earpiece P, so that the *resultant* effect of the sound waves received by M_1, M_2 respectively can be heard.

A source of sound of known constant frequency is placed at the focus S_1. The sound waves are reflected from R_1 in a parallel direction (p. 632), and travel to R_2 where they are reflected to the focus S_2 and received by M_2. The microphone M_1 receives sound waves directly

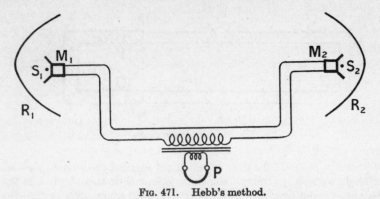

FIG. 471. Hebb's method.

from the source, and hence the sound heard in the telephone earpiece is due to the resultant effect of two coherent sources. With the source and microphone maintained at its focus S_1, R_1 is moved along its axis in one direction. The positions of R_1 are noted when minima of sound are heard; and since the distance between successive minima corresponds to one wavelength, λ, the velocity of sound can be calculated from the relation $V = f\lambda$, as f and λ are known.

17. Other Velocity of Sound Determinations

The velocity of sound in *air* has been determined by many scientists. One of the first accurate determinations was carried out in 1738 by French scientists, who observed the time between the flash and the hearing of a cannon report some 18 miles away. Their results confirmed that the velocity of sound increased as the temperature of the air increased (p. 644), and they obtained the results of 332 metres per second for the velocity at 0° C. Similar experiments were carried out by French scientists in 1822. In 1844 experiments carried out in the Tyrol district, several thousand feet above sea-level, showed that the velocity of sound was independent of the pressure of the air (p. 643).

REGNAULT, the eminent French experimental scientist of the nineteenth century, carried out an accurate series of measurements on the velocity of sound in 1864. Guns were fired at one place, breaking an electrical circuit automatically, and the arrival of the sound at a distant place was recorded by a second electrical circuit. Both circuits actuated a pen or style pressing against a drum rotating at a steady speed round its axis, which is known as a *chronograph*. Thus marks were made on the drum at the instant the sound occurred and the instant it was received. The small interval corresponding to the distance between the marks was determined from a wavy trace made on the drum by a style attached to an electrically-maintained tuning-fork whose frequency was known, and the speed of sound was thus calculated.

The velocity of sound in *water* was first accurately determined in 1826. The experiment was carried out by immersing a bell in the Lake of Geneva, and arranging to fire gunpowder at the instant the bell was struck. Miles away, the interval was recorded between the flash and the later arrival of the sound in the water, and the velocity was then calculated. This and other experiments have shown that the velocity in water is about 1,435 metres per second, or 4,700 ft. per second, more than four times the speed in air.

An objection to all these methods of determining velocity is the unknown time lag between the receipt of the sound by an observer and his recording of the sound. The observer has, as it were, a "personal equation" which must be taken into account to determine the true time of travel of the sound. In Hebb's method, however, which utilises interference, no such personal equation enters into the considerations, which is an advantage of the method.

18. Beats

If two notes of nearly equal frequency are sounded together, a periodic rise and fall in intensity can be heard. This is known as the phenomenon of *beats*, and the frequency of the beats is the number of intense sounds heard per second.

Consider a layer of air some distance away from two tuning-forks of nearly equal frequency, say 312 and 316 cycles per sec., which are sounding. The variation of the displacement, y_1, of the layer due to one fork alone is shown in Fig. 472 (i); the variation of the displacement y_2, of the layer due to the second fork alone is shown in Fig. 472 (ii). According to the Principle of Superposition (p. 634) the variation of the resultant displacement, y, of the layer is the algebraic sum of the two curves, which varies in amplitude in the way shown in Fig. 472 (iii).

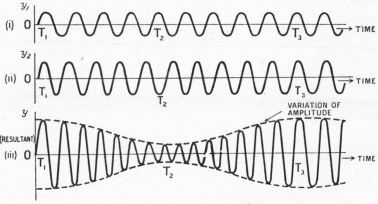

FIG. 472. Beats (not to scale).

To understand the variation of y, suppose that the displacements y_1, y_2 are in phase at some instant T_1, Fig. 472. Since the frequency of the curve in Fig. 472 (i) is 312 cycles per sec., the variation y_1 undergoes 39 complete cycles in $\frac{1}{8}$th second; in the same time, the variation y_2 undergoes $39\frac{1}{2}$ cycles, since its frequency is 316 cycles per second. Thus y_1 and y_2 are 180° out of phase with each other at this instant, and their resultant y is then a minimum at some instant T_2. Thus T_1T_2 represents $\frac{1}{8}$th of a second in Fig. 472 (iii). In $\frac{1}{4}$ of a second from T_1, y_1 has undergone 78 complete cycles and y_2 has undergone 79 complete cycles. The two waves are hence in phase again at T_3, where T_1T_3 represents $\frac{1}{4}$ of a second, and their resultant at their instant is again a maximum, Fig. 472 (iii). In this way it can be seen that a loud sound is heard after every $\frac{1}{4}$ second, and thus the beat frequency is 4 cycles per second. This is the difference between the frequencies, 312, 316, of the two notes, and it is proved below mathematically that *the beat frequency is always equal to the difference of the two nearly equal frequencies.*

It can now be seen that beats are a phenomenon of repeated interference. Unlike the cases in sound previously considered, however, the two sources are not coherent ones.

To show that the beat frequency $= f_2 - f_1$. Suppose that the amplitudes of y_1, y_2 are both equal to a. Then $y_1 = a \sin \omega_1 t$, $y_2 = a \sin (\omega_2 t + \theta)$, where $\omega_1 = 2\pi f_1$, $\omega_2 = 2\pi f_2$, and θ is the constant phase angle between the two variations.

$$\therefore y = y_1 + y_2 = a \left[\sin \omega_1 t + \sin (\omega_2 t + \theta)\right]$$

$$\therefore y = 2a \sin \left(\frac{\omega_1 + \omega_2}{2} t + \frac{\theta}{2}\right) \cdot \cos \left(\frac{\omega_1 - \omega_2}{2} t - \frac{\theta}{2}\right)$$

$$\therefore y = A \sin \left(\frac{\omega_1 + \omega_2}{2} t + \frac{\theta}{2}\right)$$

where $A = 2a \cos \left(\dfrac{\omega_1 - \omega_2}{2} t - \dfrac{\theta}{2}\right)$.

We can regard A as the *amplitude* of the variation of y. The intensity of the resultant note is proportional to A^2, the square of the amplitude (p. 231), and

$$A^2 = 4a^2 \cos^2 \left(\frac{\omega_1 - \omega_2}{2} t - \frac{\theta}{2}\right) = 2a^2 \left[1 + \cos \overline{(\omega_1 - \omega_2) t - \theta}\right]$$

since $2 \cos^2 a = 1 + \cos 2a$. It then follows that the intensity varies at a frequency f given by

$$2\pi f = \omega_1 - \omega_2;$$

But $\omega_1 = 2\pi f_1$, $\omega_2 = 2\pi f_2$.

$$\therefore \quad 2\pi f = 2\pi f_1 - 2\pi f_2$$
$$\therefore \quad f = f_1 - f_2$$

The frequency f of the beats is thus equal to the difference of the frequencies.

19. Uses of Beats

The phenomenon of beats can be used to measure the unknown frequency, f_1, of a note. For this purpose a note of known frequency f_2 is used to provide beats with the unknown note, and the frequency f of the beats is obtained by counting the number made in a given time. Since f is the difference between f_2 and f_1, it follows that $f_1 = f - f$, or $f_1 = f_2 + f$. Thus suppose $f_2 = 1,000$ cycles per sec., and the number of beats per second made with a tuning-fork of unknown frequency f_1 is 4. Then $f_1 = 1,004$ or 996.

To decide which value of f_1 is correct, the end of the tuning-fork prong is loaded with a small piece of plasticine, which diminishes the frequency a little, and the two notes are sounded again. If the beats are *increased*, a little thought indicates that the frequency of the note must originally have been 996 cycles per second. If the beats are decreased, the frequency of the note must originally have been 1,004. The tuning-fork must not be overloaded, as the frequency may decrease, if it was 1,004, to a frequency such as 995, in which case the significance of the beats can be wrongly interpreted.

Beats are also used to "tune" an instrument to a given note. As the instrument note approaches the given note, beats are heard, and the instrument can be regarded as "tuned" when the beats are occurring at a very slow rate.

20. Velocity of Sound in a Medium

When a sound wave travels in a medium, such as a gas, a liquid, or a solid, the particles in the medium are subjected to varying stresses, with resulting strains (p. 608). The velocity of a sound wave is thus partly governed by the *modulus of elasticity*, E, of the medium, which is defined by the relation

$$E = \frac{\text{stress}}{\text{strain}} = \frac{\text{force per unit area}}{\text{change in length (or volume)/original length}}$$
$$\qquad \qquad \qquad \qquad \text{(or volume)} \quad \text{(i)}$$

The velocity, V, also depends on the density, d, of the medium, and it can be shown that

$$\mathbf{V} = \sqrt{\frac{\mathbf{E}}{\varrho}} \qquad . \qquad . \qquad . \qquad . \qquad . \qquad (72)$$

When E is in dynes per sq. cm. and ϱ is in grams per c.c., the velocity V is in centimetres per second. When E is in poundals per sq. ft. and ϱ is in lbs. per cu. ft., V is in ft. per sec. The relation (72) was first derived by Newton.

For a solid, E is Young's modulus of elasticity. The magnitude of E for steel is about 2×10^{12} dynes per sq. cm., and the density ϱ of steel is 7·8 gm. per c.c. Thus the velocity of sound in steel is given by

$$V = \sqrt{\frac{E}{\varrho}} = \sqrt{\frac{2 \times 10^{12}}{7 \cdot 8}} = 5 \cdot 06 \times 10^5 \text{ cm. per sec.}$$

For a liquid, E is the bulk modulus of elasticity. Water has a bulk modulus of $2 \cdot 04 \times 10^{10}$ dynes per sq. cm., and a density of 1 gm. per c.c. The calculated velocity of sound in water is thus given by

$$V = \sqrt{\frac{2 \cdot 04 \times 10^{10}}{1}} = 1 \cdot 43 \times 10^5 \text{ cm. per sec.}$$

The proof of the velocity formula requires advanced mathematics, and is beyond the scope of this book. It can partly be verified by the method of dimensions, however. Thus since density, ϱ, = mass/volume, the dimensions of ϱ are given by $[M]/[L]^3$. The dimensions of force (mass × acceleration) are $[M] \times [L]/[T]^2$, the dimensions of area are $[L]^2$; and the denominator in (i) has zero dimensions since it is the ratio of two similar quantities. Thus the dimensions of modulus of elasticity, E, are given by

$$\frac{[M] [L]}{[T]^2 [L]^2}$$

or $\quad \dfrac{[M]}{[T]^2 [L]}$

Suppose the velocity, V, $= kE^x \varrho^y$, where k is a constant. The dimensions of V are $\dfrac{[L]}{[T]}$.

$$\therefore \quad \frac{[L]}{[T]} = \frac{[M]^x}{[T]^{2x}[L]^x} \times \frac{[M]^y}{[L]^{3y}}$$

using the dimensions of E and ϱ obtained above. Equating the indices of $[M]$, $[L]$, $[T]$ on both sides, then

$$x + y = 0 \quad . \quad . \quad . \quad . \quad . \quad \text{(ii)}$$
$$- x - 3y = 1 \quad . \quad . \quad . \quad . \quad . \quad \text{(iii)}$$
$$- 2x = - 1 \quad . \quad . \quad . \quad . \quad . \quad \text{(iv)}$$

From (iv), $x = 1/2$, from (ii), $y = - 1/2$. Thus, as $V = KE^x \varrho^y$,

$$V = kE^{\frac{1}{2}}\varrho^{-\frac{1}{2}}$$

$$\therefore V = k \sqrt{\frac{E}{\varrho}}$$

It is not possible to find the magnitude of k by the method of dimensions, but a rigid proof of the formula by calculus shows that $k = 1$ since $V = \sqrt{\dfrac{E}{\varrho}}$.

21. Velocity of Sound in a Gas. Laplace's Correction

The velocity of sound in a *gas* is also given by $V = \sqrt{\dfrac{E}{\varrho}}$, where E is the *bulk modulus* of the gas and ϱ is its density. Now it is shown below that $E = p$, the pressure of the gas, if the stresses and strains in the gas take place isothermally. The formula for the velocity then becomes

$V = \sqrt{\dfrac{p}{\varrho}}$; and as the density, ϱ, of air is 0·00129 gm. per c.c. at N.T.P.,

and $p = 76 \times 13\cdot6 \times 980$ dynes/sq. cm.,

$$V = \sqrt{\frac{76 \times 13\cdot6 \times 980}{0\cdot00129}} = 28{,}000 \text{ cm. per sec. (approx.).}$$

This calculation for V was first performed by Newton, who saw that the above theoretical value was well below the experimental value of about 33,000 cm. per sec. The discrepancy remained unexplained for more than a century, when LAPLACE suggested in 1816 that E should be the *adiabatic* bulk modulus of a gas, not its isothermal bulk modulus as Newton had assumed. Alexander Wood in his book *Acoustics* (Blackie) points out that adiabatic conditions are maintained in a gas because of the relative slowness of sound wave oscillations.* It is shown later that the adiabatic bulk modulus of a gas is γp where γ is the ratio of the principal specific heats of a gas (i.e., $\gamma = C_p/C_v$). The formula for the velocity of sound in a gas thus becomes

$$V = \sqrt{\frac{\gamma p}{\varrho}} \qquad . \qquad . \qquad . \qquad . \qquad (73)$$

The magnitude of γ for air is 1·40, and *Laplace's correction*, as it is known, then amends the value of the velocity in air at $0°$ C. to

$$V = \sqrt{\frac{1\cdot40 \times 76 \times 13\cdot6 \times 980}{0\cdot00129}} = 33{,}100 \text{ cm. per sec.}$$

This is in good agreement with the experimental value.

22. Effect of Pressure and Temperature on Velocity of Sound in a Gas

Suppose that the mass of a gas is m, and its volume is v. Its density, ϱ, is then m/v. and hence the velocity of sound, V, is given by

$$V = \sqrt{\frac{\gamma p}{\varrho}} = \sqrt{\frac{\gamma p v}{m}}$$

But $pv = mRT$, where R is the gas constant for 1 gram of the gas and T is its absolute temperature. Thus $pv/m = RT$, and hence

$$V = \sqrt{\gamma R T} \qquad . \qquad . \qquad . \qquad . \qquad \text{(i)}$$

Since γ and R are constants for a given gas, it follows that *the*

---

* It was supposed for many years that the changes are so rapid that there is no time for transfer of heat to occur. The reverse appears to be the case. At ultrasonic (very high) frequencies adiabatic conditions no longer hold.

velocity of sound in a gas is independent of the pressure if the temperature remains constant. This has been verified by experiments which showed that the velocity of sound at the top of a mountain is about the same as at the bottom, p. 638. It also follows from (i) that *the velocity of sound is proportional to the square root of its absolute temperature.* Thus if the velocity in air at 16° C. is 338 metres per sec. by experiment, the velocity, V, at 0° C. is calculated from

$$\frac{V}{338} = \sqrt{\frac{273}{289}} ,$$

from which

$$V = 338 \sqrt{\frac{273}{289}} = 328{\cdot}5 \text{ metres per sec.}$$

Isothermal and adiabatic modulus of elasticity of a gas. The bulk modulus of elasticity, k, is defined by

$$k = \frac{\text{stress}}{\text{strain}} = \frac{\text{force/unit area}}{\text{change in volume/original volume}}$$

Thus for a gas,

$$k = \frac{\delta p}{- \delta v/v}$$

where δp is the increase in pressure, δv is the corresponding change in volume (the minus represents a *decrease* in volume), and v is the original volume. Hence, in the limit,

$$k = - v \frac{dp}{dv}$$

Under isothermal conditions, $pv =$ constant, which is Boyle's law.

$$\therefore \qquad v \frac{dp}{dv} + p = 0$$

$$\therefore \qquad - v \frac{dp}{dv} = p$$

$$\therefore \qquad \text{bulk modulus} = p \text{ (p. 643)}$$

Under adiabatic conditions, $pv^{\gamma} =$ constant, where $\gamma = C_p/C_v$.

$$\therefore \quad p \times \gamma v^{\gamma-1} + v^{\gamma} \frac{dp}{dv} = 0$$

$$\therefore \qquad - v \frac{dp}{dv} = \gamma p$$

$$\therefore \qquad \text{bulk modulus} = \gamma p \text{ (p. 643)}$$

23. Ultrasonics

There are sound waves of higher frequency than 20,000 cycles per second, which are inaudible to a human being. These are known as *ultrasonics*; and since velocity = wavelength × frequency, ultrasonics have short wavelengths compared with sound waves in the audio-frequency range.

In recent years ultrasonics have been utilised for a variety of industrial purposes. They are used on board coasting vessels for depth sounding, the time taken by the wave to reach the bottom of the sea from the surface and back being determined. Ultrasonics are also used to kill bacteria in liquids, and they are used extensively to locate faults and cracks in metal castings, following a method similar to that of radar. Ultrasonic waves are sent into the metal under investigation, and the beam reflected from the fault is picked up on a cathode-ray tube screen together with the reflection from the other end of the metal. The position of the fault can then easily be located.

24. Production of Ultrasonics

In 1881 CURIE discovered that a thin plate of quartz increased or decreased in length if an electrical battery was connected to its opposite faces. By correctly cutting the plate, the expansion or contraction could be made to occur along the axis of the faces to which the battery was applied. When an alternating voltage of ultrasonic frequency was connected to the faces of such a crystal the faces vibrated at the same frequency, and thus ultrasonic sound waves were produced.

Another method of producing ultrasonics is to place an iron or nickel rod inside a solenoid carrying an alternating current of ultrasonic frequency. Since the length of a magnetic specimen increases slightly when it is magnetised, ultrasonic sound waves are produced by the vibrations of the rod.

EXAMPLES

1. How does the velocity of sound in a medium depend upon the elasticity and density? Illustrate your answer by reference to the case of air and of a long metal rod. The velocity of sound in air being 1,100 ft. per sec. at 0° C. and the coefficient of expansion 1/273 per degree, find the change in velocity per degree centigrade rise of temperature. (*L.*)

First part. The velocity of sound, V, is given by $V = \sqrt{E/\varrho}$, where E is the modulus of elasticity of the medium and ϱ is its density. In the case of air, a gas, E represents the bulk modulus of the air under adiabatic conditions, and $E = \gamma p$ (see p. 643). Thus $V = \sqrt{\gamma p/\varrho}$ for air.

For a long metal rod, E is Young's modulus for the metal, assuming the sound travels along the length of the rod.

Second part. Since the coefficient of expansion is 1/273 per degree centigrade, the absolute temperature corresponding to $t°$ C. is given by $(273 + t)$. The velocity of sound in a gas is proportional to the square root of its absolute temperature, and hence

$$\frac{V}{V_0} = \sqrt{\frac{274}{273}},$$

where V is the velocity at 1° C. and V_0 is the velocity at 0° C.

$$\therefore \quad V = V_0 \sqrt{\frac{274}{273}} = 1,100 \times \sqrt{\frac{274}{273}} = 1,102 \text{ ft./sec.}$$

$$\therefore \text{ change in velocity } = 2 \text{ ft./sec.}$$

2. How would you find by experiment the velocity of sound in air? Calculate the velocity of sound in air in cm. per sec. at 100° C. if the density of air at S.T.P. is 0·001293 gm. per c.c., the density of mercury at 0° C. 13·60 gm. per c.c., the specific heat of air at constant pressure 0·2417, and the specific heat of air at constant volume 0·1715. (*L.*)

First part. See Hebb's method, p. 637.

Second part. The velocity of sound in air is given by

$$V = \sqrt{\frac{\gamma p}{\varrho}}$$

with the usual notation. The density, ϱ, of air is 0·001293 gm. per c.c. The pressure p is given by

$$p = h\varrho g$$
$$= 76 \times 13\cdot6 \times 980 \text{ dynes per sq. cm.,}$$

since S.T.P. denotes 76 cm. mercury pressure and 0° C. Also,

$$\gamma = \frac{C_p}{C_v} = \frac{0\cdot2417}{0\cdot1715}$$

$$\therefore \quad V = \sqrt{\frac{0\cdot2417 \times 76 \times 13\cdot6 \times 980}{0\cdot1715 \times 0\cdot001293}}$$

where V is the velocity at 0° C.

But $\qquad\qquad$ velocity $\propto \sqrt{T}$,

where T is the absolute temperature of the air. Thus if V' is the velocity at 100° C.,

$$\frac{V'}{V} = \sqrt{\frac{273 + 100}{273}} = \sqrt{\frac{373}{273}}$$

$$\therefore V' = \sqrt{\frac{373}{273}}V = \sqrt{\frac{373 \times 0\cdot2417 \times 76 \times 13\cdot6 \times 980}{273 \times 0\cdot1715 \times 0\cdot001293}}$$

$$\therefore V' = 38,830 \text{ cm. per sec.}$$

3. State briefly how you would show by experiment that the characteristics of the transmission of sound are such that (*a*) a finite time is necessary for transmission, (*b*) a material medium is necessary for propagation, (*c*) the disturbance may be reflected and refracted. The wavelength of the note emitted by a tuning-fork, frequency 512 vibrations per sec., in air at 17° C. is 66·5 cm. If the density of air at S.T.P. is 1·293 gm. per litre, calculate the ratio of the two principal specific heats of air. Assume that the density of mercury is 13·6 gm. per c.c. (*N.*)

First part. See text.

Second part. Since $V = f\lambda$, the velocity of sound at 17° C. is given by

$$V = 512 \times 66 \cdot 5 \text{ cm. per sec.} \quad . \quad . \quad . \quad \text{(i)}$$

Now
$$\frac{V_\circ}{V} = \sqrt{\frac{273}{290}}$$

where $V_\circ$ is the velocity at $0°$ C., since the velocity is proportional to the square root of the absolute temperature.

$$\therefore \quad V_\circ = \sqrt{\frac{273}{290}} \times V = \sqrt{\frac{273}{290}} \times 512 \times 66 \cdot 5 \quad . \quad . \quad \text{(ii)}$$

But
$$V_\circ = \sqrt{\frac{\gamma p}{\varrho}},$$

where $p = 76$ cm. of mercury $= 76 \times 13 \cdot 6 \times 980$ dynes per sq. cm., and $\varrho = 1 \cdot 293/1,000$ gm. per c.c.

$$\therefore \quad \gamma = \frac{V_\circ{}^2 \times \varrho}{p}$$

$$= \frac{273 \times 512^2 \times 66 \cdot 5^2 \times 1 \cdot 293}{290 \times 1,000 \times 76 \times 13 \cdot 6 \times 980}$$

$$= 1 \cdot 39$$

25. Doppler Effect

The whistle of a train or a jet aeroplane appears to increase in pitch as it approaches a stationary observer; as the moving object passes the observer, the pitch changes and becomes lowered. The apparent alteration in frequency was first predicted by DOPPLER in 1845, who stated that a change of frequency of the wave-motion should be observed when a source of sound or light was moving, and it is accordingly known as the *Doppler effect*.

The Doppler effect occurs whenever there is a *relative velocity* between the source of sound or light and an observer. In light, this effect was observed when measurements were taken of the wavelength of the colour of a moving star; they showed a marked variation. In sound, the Doppler effect can be demonstrated by placing a whistle in the end of a long piece of rubber tubing, and whirling the tube in a horizontal circle above the head while blowing the whistle. The open end of the tube acts as a moving source of sound, and an observer hears a rise and fall in pitch as the end approaches and recedes from him.

A complete calculation of the apparent frequency in particular cases is given shortly, but Fig. 473 illustrates how the change of wavelength, and hence frequency, occurs when a source of sound is moving towards a stationary observer. At a certain instant the position of the moving source is at 4. At four successive seconds *before* this instant the source had been at the positions 3, 2, 1, 0 respectively. If V is the velocity of sound, the wavefront from the source when in the position 3 reaches the surface A of a sphere of radius V and centre 3 when the source is

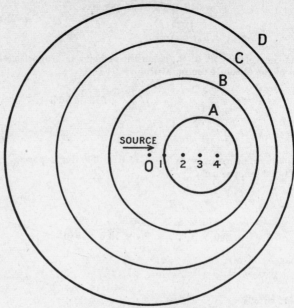

FIG. 473.   Doppler effect.

just at 4. In the same way, the wavefront from the source when it was in the position 2 reaches the surface B of a sphere of radius 2V and centre 2. The wavefront C corresponds to the source when it was in the position 1, and the wavefront D to the source when it was in the position O. Thus if the observer is on the right of S, he receives wavefronts which are relatively more crowded together than if S were stationary; the frequency of S thus appears to increase. When the observer is on the left of S, in which case the source is moving away from him, the wavefronts are further apart than if S were stationary, and hence the observer receives correspondingly fewer waves per second. The apparent frequency is thus lowered.

26. Calculation of Apparent Frequency

Suppose V is the velocity of sound in air, u_s is the velocity of the source of sound S, u_o is the velocity of an observer O, and f is the true frequency of the source.

(i) *Source moving towards stationary observer.* If the source S were stationary, the f waves sent out in one second towards the observer O would occupy a distance V, and the wavelength would be V/f, Fig. 474 (a). If S moves with a velocity u_s towards O, however, the f waves sent out occupy a distance $(V - u_s)$, because S has moved a distance

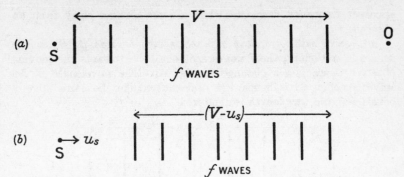

FIG. 474.   Source moving towards stationary observer.

u_s towards O in 1 sec., Fig. 474 (*b*).   Thus the wavelength λ' of the waves reaching O is now $(V - u_s)/f$.

But   velocity of sound waves $= V$.

$\therefore$ apparent frequency, $f' = \dfrac{V}{\lambda'} = \dfrac{V}{(V - u_s)/f}$

$\therefore$ $f' = \dfrac{V}{V - u_s} f$.   .   .   (74)

Since $(V - u_s)$ is less than V, f' is greater than f; the apparent frequency thus appears to increase when a source is moving towards an observer.

(ii) *Source moving away from stationary observer.*   In this case the f waves sent out towards O in 1 sec. occupy a distance $(V + u_s)$, Fig. 475

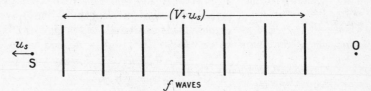

FIG. 475.   Source moving away from stationary observer.

The wavelength λ' of the waves reaching O is thus $(V + u_s)/f$, and hence the apparent frequency f' is given by

$f' = \dfrac{V}{\lambda'} = \dfrac{V}{(V + u_s)/f}$

$\therefore f' = \dfrac{V}{V + u_s} \cdot f$.   .   .   .   (75)

Since $(V + u_s)$ is greater than V, f' is less than f, and hence the apparent frequency decreases when a source moves away from an observer.

(iii) *Source stationary, and observer moving towards it.* Since the source is stationary, the f waves sent out by S towards the moving observer O occupies a distance V, Fig. 476. The wavelength of the waves reaching O is hence V/f, and thus unlike the cases already considered, the wavelength is unaltered.

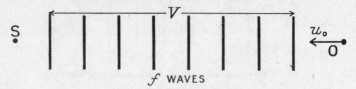

FIG. 476.   Observer moving towards stationary source.

The velocity of the sound waves relative to O is not V, however, as O is moving relative to the source. The velocity of the sound waves relative to O is given by $(V + u_0)$ in this case, and hence the apparent frequency f' is given by

$$f' = \frac{(V + u_0)}{\text{wavelength}} = \frac{V + u_0}{V/f}$$

$$\therefore f' = \frac{V + u_0}{V} \cdot f \qquad . \quad . \quad . \quad . \quad . \quad (76)$$

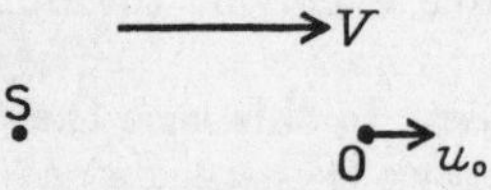

Since $(V + u_0)$ is greater than V, f' is greater than f; thus the apparent frequency is increased.

(iv) *Source stationary, and observer moving away from it*, Fig. 477. As in the case just considered, the wavelength of the waves reaching O is unaltered, and is given by V/f.

FIG. 477.   Observer moving away from stationary source.

The velocity of the sound waves relative to $O = V - u_0$, and hence

$$\text{apparent frequency}, f', = \frac{V - u_0}{\text{wavelength}} = \frac{V - u_0}{V/f}$$

$$\therefore \quad f' = \frac{V - u_0}{V} \cdot f \qquad . \quad . \quad . \quad (77)$$

Since $(V - u_0)$ is less than V, the apparent frequency f' appears to be decreased.

27. Source and Observer Both Moving

If the source and the observer are both moving, the apparent frequency f' can be found from the formula

$$f' = \frac{V'}{\lambda'}$$

where V' is the velocity of the sound waves relative to the observer, and λ' is the wavelength of the waves reaching the observer. This formula can also be used to find the apparent frequency in any of the cases considered before.

Suppose that the observer has a velocity u_0, the source a velocity u_s, and that both are moving in the *same* direction. Then

$$V' = V - u_0$$

and

$$\lambda' = (V - u_s)/f$$

as was deduced in case (i), p. 649.

$$\therefore f' = \frac{V'}{\lambda'} = \frac{V - u_0}{(V - u_s)/f} = \frac{V - u_0}{V - u_s} \cdot f \quad . \tag{i}$$

If the observer is moving towards the source, $V' = V + u_0$, and the apparent frequency f' is given by

$$f' = \frac{V + u_0}{V - u_s} \cdot f \quad . \quad . \quad . \quad . \tag{ii}$$

From (i), it follows that $f' = f$ when $u_0 = u_s$, in which case there is no relative velocity between the source and the observer. It should also be noted that the motion of the observer affects only V', the velocity of the waves reaching the observer, while the motion of the source affects only λ', the wavelength of the waves reaching the observer.

The effect of the wind can also be taken into account in the Doppler effect. Suppose the velocity of the wind is u_w, in the direction of the line SO joining the source S to the observer O. Since the air has then a velocity u_w relative to the ground, and the velocity of the sound waves relative to the air is V, the velocity of the waves relative to ground is $(V + u_w)$ if the wind is blowing in the same direction as SO. All our previous expressions for f' can now be adjusted by replacing the velocity V in it by $(V + u_w)$. If the wind is blowing in the opposite direction to SO, the velocity V must be replaced by $(V - u_w)$.

When the source is moving at an angle to the line joining the source and observer, the apparent frequency changes continuously. Suppose the source is moving along AB with a velocity v, while the observer is stationary at O, Fig. 478. At S, the component velocity of v along OS is $v \cos \theta$, and is *towards* O. The observer thus hears a note of higher pitch whose frequency f' is given by

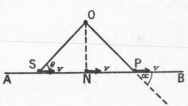

FIG. 478. Source moving at angle to line joining observer and source.

$$f' = \frac{V}{V - v \cos \theta} f,$$

where V is the velocity of sound and f is the frequency of the source of sound. See equation (74), in which u_s now becomes $v \cos \theta$. When the source reaches P, Fig. 478, the component of v is $v \cos \alpha$ *away* from O, and the apparent frequency f'' is hence given by

$$f'' = \frac{V}{V + v \cos \alpha} f,$$

from equation (75). The apparent frequency is thus lower than the frequency f of the source. When the source reaches N, the foot of the perpendicular from O to AB, the velocity v is perpendicular to ON and has thus no component towards the observer O. At this instant, therefore, the observer hears a note of the same frequency f as the source.

EXAMPLES

1. Obtain the formula for the Doppler effect when the source is moving with respect to a stationary observer. Give examples of the effect in sound and light. A whistle giving out 500 vibrations per sec. moves away from a stationary observer in a direction towards and perpendicular to a flat wall with a velocity of 5 ft./sec. How many beats per sec. will be heard by the observer? [Take the velocity of sound as 1,120 ft./sec. and assume there is no wind.] (*C*.)

First part. See text.

Second part. The observer hears a note of apparent frequency f' from the whistle directly, and a note of apparent frequency f'' from the sound waves reflected from the wall.

Now $$f' = \frac{V'}{\lambda'}$$

where V' is the velocity of sound in air relative to the observer and λ' is the wavelength of the waves reaching the observer. Since $V' = 1,120$ ft./sec., and $\lambda' = \frac{1,120 + 5}{500}$ ft.,

$$\therefore \quad f' = \frac{1,120 \times 500}{1,125} = 497 \cdot 8 \text{ cycles per sec.}$$

The note of apparent frequency f'' is due to sound waves moving towards the observer with a velocity of 5 ft. per sec.

$$\therefore \quad f'' = \frac{V'}{\lambda'} = \frac{1,120}{(1,120 - 5)/500}$$

$$= \frac{1,120 \times 500}{1,115} = 502 \cdot 2 \text{ cycles per sec.}$$

$$\therefore \text{ beats per sec.} = f'' - f' = 502 \cdot 2 - 497 \cdot 8 = 4 \cdot 4$$

2. Two observers A and B are provided with sources of sound of frequency 500. A remains stationary and B moves away from him at a velocity of 6 ft. per sec. How many beats per sec. are observed by A and by B, the velocity of sound being 1,100 ft./sec.? Explain the principles involved in the solution of this problem. (L.)

Beats observed by A. A hears a note of frequency 500 due to its own source of sound. He also hears a note of apparent frequency f' due to the moving source B. With the usual notation,

$$f' = \frac{V'}{\lambda'} = \frac{1,100}{(1,100 + 6)/500}$$

since the velocity of sound, V', relative to A is 1,100 ft. per sec., and the wavelength λ' of the waves reaching him is $(1,100 + 6)/500$.

$$\therefore \quad f' = \frac{1,100 \times 500}{1,106} = 497 \cdot 3$$

$\therefore$ beats observed by A = 500 − 497·29 = 2·71 per sec.

Beats observed by B. The apparent frequency f' of the sound from A is given by

$$f' = \frac{V'}{\lambda'}$$

In this case V' = velocity of sound relative to B = 1,100 − 6 = 1,094 ft. per sec., and the wavelength λ' of the waves reaching B is unaltered. Since $\lambda' = 1,100/500$, it follows that

$$f' = \frac{1,094}{1,100/500} = \frac{1,094 \times 500}{1,100} = 497 \cdot 27$$

$\therefore$ beats heard by B = 500 − 497·27 = 2·73

EXERCISES XXIX

1. If the velocity of sound in air is 340 metres per sec. calculate (i) the wavelength in cm. when the frequency is 256 cycles per sec., (ii) the frequency when the wavelength is 85 cm.

2. If the velocity of sound in air at 15° C. is 342 metres per sec. calculate the velocity at (a) 0° C., (b) 47° C. What is the velocity if the pressure of the air changes from 76 cm. to 75 cm. mercury, the temperature remaining constant at 15° C.?

3. Describe a determination (other than resonance) of the velocity of sound in air. How is the velocity dependent upon atmospheric conditions? Give Newton's expression for the velocity of sound in a gas, and Laplace's correction. Hence calculate the velocity of sound in air at 27° C. [Density of air at S.T.P. = 0·00129 gm. cm.$^{-3}$; C_p = 0·24 cal. gm.$^{-1}$. deg.$^{-1}$ C.; C_v = 0·17 cal. gm.$^{-1}$ deg.$^{-1}$ C.] (L.)

4. Describe the factors on which the velocity of sound in a gas depends. A man standing at one end of a closed corridor 190 ft. long blew a short blast on a whistle. He found that the time from the blast to the sixth echo was two seconds. If the temperature was 17° C., what was the velocity of sound at 0° C.? (C.)

5. Describe an experiment to find the velocity of sound in air at room temperature.

A ship at sea sends out simultaneously a wireless signal above the water and a sound signal through the water, the temperature of the water being 4° C. These signals are received by two stations, A and B, 25 miles apart, the intervals between the arrival of the two signals being 16¼ sec. at A and 22 sec. at B. Find the bearing from A of the ship relative to AB. The velocity of sound in water at t° C. = 4,756 + 11t ft. per sec. (N.)

6. Describe how you would demonstrate experimentally *two* of the following: (a) Lissajous' figures, (b) Chladni's figures, (c) Kundt's dust-tube figures. Describe some application of *one* of those which you select. (L.)

7. Explain why sounds are heard very clearly at great distances from the source (a) on still mornings after a clear night, and (b) when the wind is blowing from the source to the observer. (W.)

8. Describe one or two experiments to test each of the following statements: (a) If two notes are recognised by ear to be of the same pitch their sources are making the same number of vibrations per sec. (b) The musical interval between two notes is determined by the ratio of the frequencies of the vibrating sources of the notes. (L.)

9. Describe two methods of measuring the frequency of a tuning-fork neither of which assumes a knowledge of the velocity of sound in air. (L.)

10. Give a brief account of any important and characteristic wave phenomena which occur in sound. Why are sound waves in air regarded as longitudinal and not transverse?

An observer looking due north sees the flash of a gun 4 secs. before he records the arrival of the sound. If the temperature is 20° C. and the wind is blowing from east to west with a velocity of 30 miles per hour, calculate the distance between the observer and the gun. The velocity of sound in air at 0° C. is 1,100 ft. per sec. Why does the velocity of sound in air depend upon the temperature but not upon the pressure? (N.)

11. Explain upon what properties and conditions of a gas the velocity of sound through it depends.

Describe, and explain in detail, a laboratory method of measuring the velocity of sound in air. (L.)

Beats

12. What is meant by (a) the *amplitude*, (b) the *frequency* of a vibration in the atmosphere? What are the corresponding characteristics of the musical sound associated with the vibration? How would you account for the difference in quality between two notes of the same pitch produced by two different instruments, e.g., by a violin and by an organ pipe?

What are "beats"? Given a set of standard forks of frequencies 256, 264, 272, 280, and 288, and a tuning-fork whose frequency is known to be between 256 and 288, how would you determine its frequency to four significant figures? (W.)

13. Explain the production of beats, showing that the frequency of the beats is the difference in the frequencies of the vibrations producing them. (*L.*)

14. Explain the origin of the beats heard when two tuning-forks of slightly different frequency are sounded together. Deduce the relation between the frequency of the beats and the difference in frequency of the forks. How would you determine which fork had the higher frequency?

A simple pendulum set up to swing in front of the "seconds" pendulum ($T = 2$ sec.) of a clock is seen to gain so that the two swing in phase at intervals of 21 secs. What is the time of swing of the simple pendulum? (*L.*)

Doppler Effect

15. Explain why the motion of a source of sound affects its pitch as heard by a stationary observer. How can this phenomenon be demonstrated in a class-room?

What is the velocity of the source along the line joining the source to the observer if, as a result of the motion, the frequency of the note heard is (*a*) increased in the ratio 16 : 15, (*b*) decreased in the ratio 15 : 16? Assume that the velocity of sound is 1,120 ft. per sec. and give the results in ft. per sec. Derive any formula employed. (*N.*)

16. A source of sound, emitting a note of frequency n, is moving with velocity u in a straight line which passes through an observer who is moving with a velocity v in the same straight line and in the same direction as the source. If the velocity of sound in air is V, find the frequency of the note heard by the observer.

If the frequency of a source of sound is 1,000 vibrations per sec., find the frequency of the note heard when (*a*) the observer is stationary and the source approaches at 60 m.p.h., (*b*) the source is stationary and the observer approaches at 60 m.p.h., assuming that the velocity of sound in air is 1,100 ft. per sec. (*W.*)

17. What is the *Doppler effect*? Find an expression for it when the observer is at rest and there is no wind.

A whistle is whirled in a circle of 100 cm. radius and traverses the circular path twice per sec. An observer is situated outside the circle but in its plane. What is the musical interval between the highest and lowest pitch observed if the velocity of sound is 332 metres per sec.? (*L.*)

18. Explain why the frequency of a wave motion appears, to a stationary observer, to change as the component of the velocity of the source along the line joining the source and observer changes. Describe two illustrations of this effect, one with sound and one with light.

A stationary observer is standing at a distance l from a straight railway track and a train passes with uniform velocity v sounding a whistle with frequency n_0. Taking the velocity of sound as V, derive a formula giving the observed frequency n as a function of the time. At which position of the train will $n = n_0$? Give a physical interpretation of the result. (*C.*)

CHAPTER XXX

VIBRATIONS IN PIPES, STRINGS, RODS

1. Introduction

THE music from an organ, a violin, or a xylophone is due to vibrations in the air set up by oscillations in these instruments. In the organ, air is blown into a pipe, which sounds its characteristic note as the air inside it vibrates; in the violin, the strings are bowed so that they oscillate; and in a xylophone a row of metallic rods are struck in the middle with a hammer, which sets them into vibration.

Before considering each of the above cases in more detail, it would be best to consider the feature common to all of them. A violin string is fixed at both ends, A, B, and waves travel along m, n to each end of the string when it is bowed and are there reflected, Fig. 479 (i).

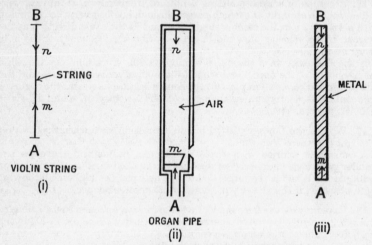

FIG. 479.   Reflection of waves in instruments.

The vibrations of the particles of the string are hence due to *two waves of the same frequency and amplitude travelling in opposite directions.* A similar effect is obtained with an organ pipe closed at one end B, Fig. 479 (ii). If air is blown into the pipe at A, a wave travels along the direction m and is reflected at B in the opposite direction n. The vibrations of the air in the pipe are thus due to two waves travelling in opposite directions. If a metal rod is fixed at its middle in a vice and stroked at one end A, a wave travels along the rod in the direction m

656

and is reflected at the other end B in the direction n, Fig. 479 (iii). The vibrations of the rod, which produce a high-pitched note, are thus due to two waves travelling in opposite directions.

The resultant effect of two waves travelling in opposite directions with equal amplitude and frequency can easily be demonstrated. A light string, or thread, is tied to the end of a clapper, P, of an electric bell, and the other end of the string is passed round a grooved wheel, Fig. 480.

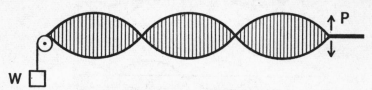

FIG. 480.   Demonstration of stationary wave.

When the clapper vibrates, and a suitable weight W is attached to the string, a number of *stationary loops* is observed along the vibrating string, somewhat as shown in Fig. 480. By altering W a different number of stationary loops can be obtained. The wave along the string is known as a *stationary wave*, and we shall now discuss the formation of a stationary wave in detail.

2. Stationary Waves

Consider a plane-progressive wave a travelling in air along OA, Fig. 481. If it meets a wall at W a reflected wave b is obtained, and the condition of the air along W is due to the combined effects of a, b, Fig. 481 (i).

The layer of air at W must always be at rest since it is in contact with a fixed wall. For convenience, suppose that the displacements of the layers of air due to a at the instant shown are those represented by the sine wave in Fig. 481 (i), so that the displacement of the layer at W due to the incident wave is a maximum. Since the layer at W is always at rest, the displacements of the layers due to the wave *reflected* from the wall must be represented by the curve b at the same instant; otherwise the net displacement at W, which is the algebraic sum of WR, WH, will not be zero. From the curves a, b shown in Fig. 481 (i), it follows that the wave b reflected by the wall is 180° out of phase with the incident wave a.

At the instant t represented in Fig. 481 (i), the algebraic sum, S, of the displacements of the layers *everywhere* along OW is zero if the amplitudes of a, b are equal and the curves have the same wavelength. At an instant $T/4$ later, where T is the period of vibration of the layers, the displacements of the layer due to the incident and reflected waves are

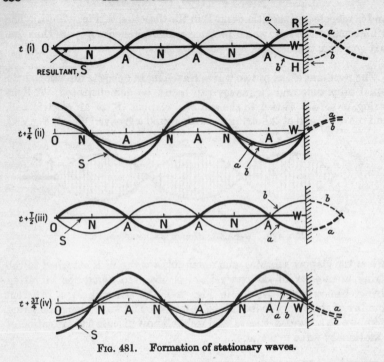

FIG. 481.   Formation of stationary waves.

those shown in Fig. 481 (ii). This can best be understood by imagining the incident wave a to have advanced to the right by $\frac{1}{4}$-wavelength, and the reflected wave to have advanced to the left by $\frac{1}{4}$-wavelength, which implies that the vibrating layers have now reached a displacement corresponding to a time $T/4$ later than t. The algebraic sum S of the displacement is then represented by the curve S in Fig. 481 (ii). At the end of a further time $T/4$, the displacements due to a, b are those shown in Fig. 481 (iii); the waves have now advanced another $\frac{1}{4}$-wavelength in opposite directions. The algebraic sum S of the displacements is again zero everywhere along OW at this instant. After a further time $T/4$, the displacements of the layers, and the resultant displacement S, are those shown in Fig. 481 (iv). The wave in the air represented by S is called a stationary wave.

3. Nodes and Antinodes

We have now sufficient information to deduce the conditions of the layers of air along OW when a stationary wave is obtained. From the curves showing the resultant displacement, S, in Fig. 481, it can be seen that some layers, marked N, are *permanently* at rest; these are known as **nodes**. The layers marked A, however, are vibrating through an amplitude twice as big as the incident or reflected waves, see Fig. 481 (ii) and (iv), and these are known as **antinodes**. Layers between consecutive nodes are vibrating in phase with each other, but the amplitude of vibration varies from zero at a node N to a maximum at the antinode A. Fig. 482 represents the displacement of the layers

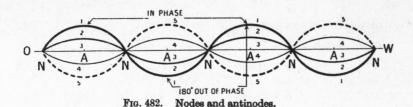

FIG. 482. Nodes and antinodes.

along OW at five different instants 1, 2, 3, 4, 5. It follows that

the distance between consecutive nodes, NN, $= \dfrac{\lambda}{2}$ . . (i)

where λ is the wavelength of the stationary wave;

the distance between consecutive antinodes, AA, $= \dfrac{\lambda}{2}$ . . (ii)

and

the distance from a node to the next antinode, NA, $= \dfrac{\lambda}{4}$ . . (iii)

The importance of the nodes and antinodes in a stationary wave lies in their simple connection with the wavelength.

4. Differences Between Plane-Progressive and Stationary Waves

At the beginning of Chapter XII, we considered in detail the plane-progressive wave and its effect on the medium (pp. 604 and 605). It was then shown that each layer vibrates with constant amplitude at the same frequency, and that each layer is out of phase with others near to it. When a stationary wave is present in a medium, however, some layers (nodes) are permanently at rest; others between the nodes are vibrating in phase with different amplitudes, increasing to a maximum at the antinodes. A stationary wave is always set up when two plane-progressive waves of equal amplitude and frequency travel in opposite directions in the same medium.

Mathematical proof of stationary wave properties. The properties of the stationary wave, already deduced, can be obtained easily from a mathematical treatment. Suppose $y_1 = a \sin 2\pi \left(\dfrac{t}{T} - \dfrac{x}{\lambda} \right)$ is a plane-

progressive wave travelling in one direction along the x-axis (p. 607).
Then $y_2 = a \sin 2\pi \left(\dfrac{t}{T} + \dfrac{x}{\lambda} \right)$ represents a wave of the same amplitude
and frequency travelling in the opposite direction. The resultant dis-
placement, y, is then given by

$$y = y_1 + y_2 = a \left[\sin 2\pi \left(\frac{t}{T} - \frac{x}{\lambda} \right) + \sin 2\pi \left(\frac{t}{T} + \frac{x}{\lambda} \right) \right]$$

from which
$$y = 2a \sin \frac{2\pi t}{T} . \cos \frac{2\pi x}{\lambda} \quad . \quad . \quad . \quad . \quad . \quad \text{(i)}$$

using the transformation of the sum of two sine functions to a product.

$$\therefore \quad y = B \sin \frac{2\pi t}{T} \quad . \quad . \quad . \quad . \quad \text{(ii)}$$

where
$$B = 2a \cos \frac{2\pi x}{\lambda} \quad . \quad . \quad . \quad \text{(iii)}$$

From (ii), B is the magnitude of the *amplitude* of vibration of the various
layers; and from (iii) it also follows that the amplitude is a maximum and
equal to $2a$ at $x = 0$, $x = \lambda/2$, $x = \lambda$, and so on. These points are thus
antinodes, and consecutive antinodes are hence separated by a distance $\lambda/2$.
The amplitude B is zero when $x = \lambda/4$, $x = 3\lambda/4$, $x = 5\lambda/4$, and so on.
These points are thus nodes, and they are hence midway between con-
secutive antinodes.

The particle velocity in a stationary wave is the rate of change of the
displacement (y) of the particle with respect to time (t). The velocity at
the nodes is always zero since the particles there are permanently at rest.
The velocity at an antinode increases from zero (when the particle is
at the end of its oscillation) to a maximum (when the particle passes

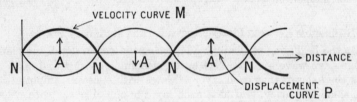

Fig. 483. Particle velocity due to stationary wave.

through its mean or original position). The corresponding displacement
and velocity curves in the latter case are illustrated in Fig. 483 by P, M
respectively. It will be noted that particles at neighbouring antinodes
are moving in opposite directions at any instant.

5. Variation of Pressure in the Stationary Wave

Having considered the variation of the displacements and the
particle velocities when a stationary wave travels in air, we must now
turn our attention to the variation of *pressure* in the air.

Suppose that curve 1 represents the displacements at the antinodes and other points at an instant when they are a maximum, Fig. 484 (i). The layer of air immediately to the left of the node at a is then displaced towards a, since the displacement is positive from curve 1, and the layer immediately to the right of a also displaced towards a. The air at a is thus compressed, and the pressure is thus greater than normal, as represented by curve 1 in Fig. 484 (ii). The displacements of the

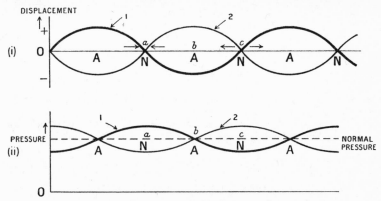

FIG. 484.   Pressure variation due to stationary wave.

layers on either side of the antinode at b are each a maximum to the left, and hence the pressure of the air is normal. The air on the left of the node c is displaced away from a, and the air on the right of c is also displaced away from c. The air is thus rarified here, and hence the pressure is less than normal. By carrying out the same procedure at other points in the air, it can be seen that the pressure variation corresponds to the curve 1 in Fig. 484 (ii).

When the displacements change to those represented by curve 2 in Fig. 484 (i), the variation of pressure at the same instant is shown by curve 2 in Fig. 484 (ii). We can now see that the *pressure variation is always a maximum at a node of the stationary wave, and is always zero at an antinode of the stationary wave.* In a plane-progressive wave, however, the pressure variation is the same at every point in a medium (p. 608).

EXAMPLE

Distinguish between progressive and stationary wave motion. Describe and illustrate with an example how stationary wave motion is produced. Plane sound waves of frequency 100 cycles per sec. fall normally on a smooth wall. At what distances from the wall will the air particles have (a) maximum, (b) minimum amplitude of vibration? Give reasons for your

answer. (The velocity of sound in air may be taken as 1,100 ft./sec.)
(*L. Inter.*)

First part. See p. 659, and p. 657.

Second part. A stationary wave is set up between the source and the
wall, due to the production of a reflected wave. The wall is a node, since
the air in contact with it cannot move; and other nodes are at equal
distances, d, from the wall. But if the wavelength is λ,

$$d = \frac{\lambda}{2} \quad \text{(p. 659).}$$

Also,

$$\lambda = \frac{V}{f} = \frac{1,100}{100} = 11 \text{ ft.}$$

$$\therefore \quad d = \frac{11}{2} = 5\tfrac{1}{2} \text{ ft.}$$

Thus minimum amplitude of vibration is obtained 5½ ft., 11 ft., 16½ ft. . . .
from the wall.

The antinodes are midway between the nodes. Thus maximum amplitude
of vibration is obtained 2¾ ft., 8¼ ft., 13¾ ft., . . . from the wall.

VIBRATIONS OF AIR IN PIPES

6. Closed Pipe

A *closed* or *stopped organ-pipe* consists essentially of a metal pipe
closed at one end Q, and a blast of air is blown into it at the other end
P, Fig. 485 (i). A wave thus travels up the pipe to Q, and is reflected at

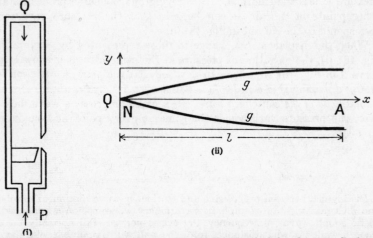

FIG. 485. (i). Closed (stopped) pipe. (ii). Fundamental of closed (stopped) pipe.

this end down the pipe, so that a *stationary wave* is obtained. The end Q of the closed pipe must be a node N, since the layer in contact with Q must be permanently at rest, and the open end A, where the air is free to vibrate, must be an antinode A. The simplest stationary wave in the air in the pipe is hence represented by *g* in Fig. 485 (ii), where the pipe is positioned horizontally to show the relative displacement, *y*, of the layers at different distances, *x*, from the closed end Q; the axis of the stationary wave is Q*x*.

It can now be seen that the length *l* of the pipe is equal to the distance between a node N and a consecutive antinode A of the stationary wave. But NA = $\lambda/4$, where λ is the wavelength (p. 659).

$$\therefore \quad \frac{\lambda}{4} = l$$

$$\therefore \quad \lambda = 4l$$

But the frequency, *f*, of the note is given by $f = V/\lambda$, where *V* is the velocity of sound in air.

$$\therefore \quad f = \frac{V}{4l}$$

This is the frequency of the lowest note obtainable from the pipe, and it is known as its *fundamental*. We shall denote the fundamental frequency by f_0, so that

$$f_0 = \frac{V}{4l} \quad . \quad \quad . \quad \quad . \quad \quad . \quad \quad . \quad (78)$$

7. Overtones of Closed Pipe

If a stronger blast of air is blown into the pipe, notes of higher frequency can be obtained which are simple multiples of the fundamental frequency f_0. Two possible cases of stationary waves are shown in Fig. 486. In each, the closed end of the pipe is a node, and the open

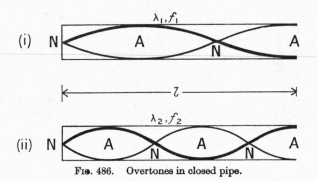

Fig. 486.   Overtones in closed pipe.

end is an antinode. In Fig. 486 (i), however, the length l of the pipe is related to the wavelength λ_1 of the wave by

$$l = \tfrac{3}{4}\lambda_1$$

$$\therefore \quad \lambda_1 = \frac{4l}{3}$$

The frequency f_1 of the note is thus given by

$$f_1 = \frac{V}{\lambda_1} = \frac{3V}{4l} \quad . \quad . \quad . \quad . \quad \text{(i)}$$

But

$$f_0 = \frac{V}{4l}$$

$$\therefore \quad f_1 = 3f_0 \quad . \quad . \quad . \quad . \quad \text{(ii)}$$

In Fig. 486 (ii), when a note of frequency f_2 is obtained, the length l of the pipe is related to the wavelength λ_2 by

$$l = \frac{5\lambda_2}{4}$$

$$\therefore \quad \lambda_2 = \frac{4l}{5}$$

$$\therefore \quad f_2 = \frac{V}{\lambda_2} = \frac{5V}{4l} \quad . \quad . \quad . \quad . \quad \text{(iii)}$$

$$\therefore \quad f_2 = 5f_0 \quad . \quad . \quad . \quad . \quad \text{(iv)}$$

By drawing other sketches of stationary waves, with the closed end as a node and the open end as an antinode, it can be shown that higher frequencies can be obtained which have frequencies of $7f_0$, $9f_0$, and so on. They are produced by blowing harder at the open end of the pipe. The frequencies obtainable at a closed pipe are hence f_0, $3f_0$, $5f_0$, and so on, i.e., the closed pipe gives only odd harmonics, and hence the frequencies $3f_0$, $5f_0$, etc. are possible *overtones*.

8. Open Pipe

An "open" pipe is one which is open at both ends. When air is blown into it at P, a wave m travels to the open end Q, where it is reflected in the direction n on encountering the free air, Fig. 487 (i). A stationary wave is hence set up in the air in the pipe, and as the two ends of the pipe are open, they must both be *antinodes*. The simplest type of wave is hence that shown in Fig. 487 (ii), the x-axis of the wave being drawn along the middle of the pipe, which is horizontal. A node N is midway between the two antinodes.

The length l of the pipe is the distance between consecutive anti-nodes. But the distance between consecutive antinodes $= \lambda/2$, where λ is the wavelength (p. 659).

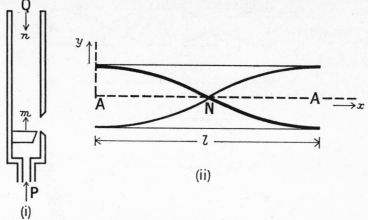

Fig. 487. (i). Open pipe. (ii). Fundamental of open pipe.

$$\therefore \quad \frac{\lambda}{2} = l$$

$$\therefore \quad \lambda = 2l$$

Thus the frequency f_0 of the note obtained from the pipe is given by

$$f_0 = \frac{V}{\lambda} = \frac{V}{2l} \quad . \quad . \quad . \quad . \quad (79)$$

This is the frequency of the fundamental note of the pipe.

9. Overtones of Open Pipe

Notes of higher frequencies than f_0 can be obtained from the pipe by blowing harder. The stationary wave in the pipe has always an anti-node A at each end, and Fig. 488 (i) represents the case of a note of a frequency f_1.

The length l of the pipe is equal to the wavelength λ_1 of the wave in this case. Thus

$$f_1 = \frac{V}{\lambda_1} = \frac{V}{l}$$

But $\qquad f_0 = \frac{V}{2l}$, from (79) above.

$$\therefore \quad f_1 = 2f_0 \quad . \quad . \quad . \quad . \quad . \quad (i)$$

In Fig. 488 (ii), the length $l = \frac{3}{2}\lambda_2$, where λ_2 is the wavelength in the pipe. The frequency f_2 is thus given by

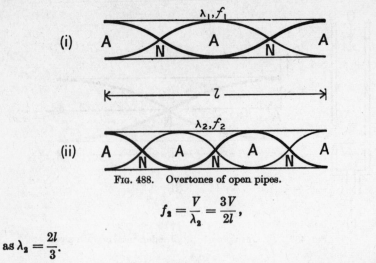

Fig. 488. Overtones of open pipes.

$$f_2 = \frac{V}{\lambda_2} = \frac{3V}{2l},$$

as $\lambda_2 = \dfrac{2l}{3}$.

$$\therefore \qquad f_2 = 3f_0 \qquad . \qquad . \qquad . \qquad . \qquad . \qquad \text{(ii)}$$

The frequencies of the overtones in the open pipe are thus $2f_0$, $3f_0$, $4f_0$, and so on, i.e., all harmonics are obtainable. The frequencies of the overtones in the closed pipe are $3f_0$, $5f_0$, $7f_0$, and so on, and hence the *quality* of the same note obtained from a closed and an open pipe is different (see p. 630).

10. Detection of Nodes and Antinodes, and Pressure Variation, in Pipes

The *nodes and antinodes* in a sounding pipe have been detected by suspending inside it a very thin piece of paper with lycopodium or fine sand particles on it, Fig. 489 (i). The particles are considerably agitated at the antinodes, but they are motionless at the nodes.

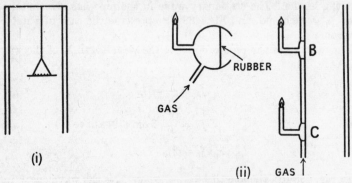

Fig. 489 (i). Detection of nodes and antinodes.
Fig. 489 (ii). Detection of pressure.

The *pressure variation* in a sounding pipe has been examined by means of a sensitive flame, designed by Lord Rayleigh. The length of the flame can be made sensitive to the pressure of the gas supplied, so that if the pressure changes the length of flame is considerably affected. Several of the flames can be arranged at different parts of the pipe, with a thin rubber or mica diaphragm in the pipe, such as at B, C, Fig. 489 (ii). At a place of maximum pressure variation, which is a node (p. 661), the length of flame alters accordingly. At a place of constant (normal) pressure, which is an antinode, the length of flame remains constant.

The pressure variation at different parts of a sounding pipe can also be examined by using a small microphone at B, C, instead of a sensitive flame. The microphone is coupled to a cathode-ray tube (p. 614), and a wave of maximum amplitude is shown on the screen when the pressure variation is a maximum. At a place of constant (normal) pressure, no wave is observed on the screen.

11. End-Correction of Pipes

The air at the open end of a pipe is free to move, and hence the vibrations at this end of a sounding pipe extend a little into the air outside the pipe. The antinode of the stationary wave due to any note is thus a distance c from the open end in practice, known as the *end-correction*, and hence the wavelength λ in the case of a closed pipe is given by $\lambda/4 = l + c$, where l is the length of the pipe, Fig. 490 (i). In the case of an open pipe sounding its fundamental note, the wavelength λ is given by $\lambda/2 = l + c + c$, since *two* end-corrections are required, assuming the end-corrections are equal, Fig. 490 (ii). Thus $\lambda = 2(l+2c)$. See also p. 670.

The mathematical theory of the end-correction was developed independently by Helmholtz and Rayleigh. It is now generally accepted

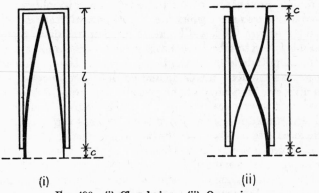

(i)   (ii)

FIG. 490.   (i). Closed pipe.   (ii). Open pipe.

that $c = 0.58r$, or $0.6r$, where r is the radius of the pipe, so that the wider the pipe, the greater is the end-correction. It was also shown that the end-correction depends on the wavelength λ of the note, and tends to vanish for very short wavelengths.

12. Effect of Temperature, and End-Correction, on the Pitch of Pipes

The frequency, f_0, of the fundamental note of a closed pipe of length l and end-correction c is given by

$$f_0 = \frac{V}{\lambda} = \frac{V}{4\,(l+c)} \qquad . \qquad . \qquad . \qquad \text{(i)}$$

with the usual notation, since $\lambda = 4\,(l+c)$. See p. 663. Now the velocity of sound, V, in air at $t°$ C. is related to its velocity V_0 at $0°$ C. by

$$\frac{V}{V_0} = \sqrt{\frac{273+t}{273}} = \sqrt{1 + \frac{t}{273}} \qquad . \qquad . \qquad \text{(ii)}$$

since the velocity is proportional to the square root of the absolute temperature. Substituting for V in (i),

$$\therefore \quad f_0 = \frac{V_0}{4\,(l+c)} \sqrt{1 + \frac{t}{273}} \qquad . \qquad . \qquad \text{(iii)}$$

From (iii), it follows that, with a given pipe, *the frequency of the fundamental increases as the temperature increases*. Also, for a given temperature and length of pipe, the frequency decreases as c increases. Now $c = 0.6r$, where r is the radius of the pipe. Thus *the frequency of the note from a pipe of given length is lower the wider the pipe*, the temperature being constant. The same results hold for an open pipe.

13. Resonance

If a diving springboard is bent and then allowed to vibrate freely, it oscillates with a frequency which is called its *natural frequency*. When a diver on the edge of the board begins to jump up and down repeatedly, the board is forced to vibrate at the frequency of the jumps; and at first, when the amplitude is small, the board is said to be undergoing *forced vibrations*. As the diver jumps up and down to gain increasing height for his dive, the frequency of the periodic downward force reaches a stage where it is practically the same as the natural frequency of the board. The amplitude of the board then becomes very large, and the periodic force is said to have set the board in *resonance*.

A mechanical system which is free to move, like a wooden bridge or the air in pipes, has a natural frequency of vibration, f_0, which depends on its dimensions. When a periodic force of a frequency different from f_0 is applied to the system, the latter vibrates with a small amplitude and undergoes forced vibrations. When the periodic force has a frequency equal to the natural frequency f_0 of the system, the amplitude of vibration becomes a maximum, and the system is then set into

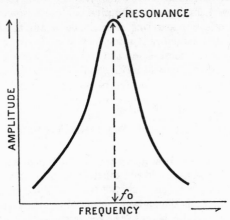

FIG. 491.   Resonance curve.

resonance. Fig. 491 is a typical curve showing the variation of amplitude with frequency. Some time ago it was reported in the newspapers that a soprano who was broadcasting had broken a glass tumbler on the table of a listener when she had reached a high note. This is an example of resonance. The glass had a natural frequency equal to that of the note sung, and was thus set into a vibration sufficiently violent to break it.

The phenomenon of resonance occurs in other branches of Physics than Sound. Electrical circuits, for example, are set into resonance by a periodic electrical force which has the same frequency as the natural frequency of the circuit.

14. Resonance in a Tube or Pipe

If a person blows gently down a pipe closed at one end, the air inside vibrates freely, and a note is obtained from the pipe which is its fundamental (p. 663). A stationary wave then exists in the pipe, with a node N at the closed end and an antinode A at the open end, as explained on p. 663.

FIG. 492.
Resonance in closed pipe.

If the prongs of a tuning-fork are held over the top of the pipe, the air inside it is set into vibration by the periodic force exerted on it by the prongs. In general, however, the vibrations are feeble, as they are *forced* vibrations, and the intensity of the sound heard is correspondingly small. But when a tuning-fork of the same frequency as the fundamental frequency of the pipe is held over the latter, the air inside is set in *resonance* by the periodic force, and the amplitude of the vibrations is large. A loud note, which has the same frequency as the fork, is then heard coming from the pipe, and a stationary wave is set up with the top of the pipe acting as an antinode and the fixed end as a node, Fig. 492. If a sounding tuning-fork is held over a pipe open at both ends, resonance occurs when the stationary wave in the pipe has antinodes at the two open ends, as illustrated by Fig. 487; the frequency of the fork is then equal to the frequency of the fundamental of the open pipe.

15. Resonance Tube Experiment. Measurement of Velocity of Sound and "End-Correction" of Tube

If a sounding tuning-fork is held over the open end of a tube T filled with water, resonance is obtained at some position as the level of water is gradually lowered, Fig. 493 (i). The stationary wave set up is then as shown. If c is the end-correction of the tube (p. 667), and l is the length from the water level to the top of the tube, then

$$l + c = \frac{\lambda}{4} \quad . \quad . \quad . \quad . \quad \text{(i)}$$

But

$$\lambda = \frac{V}{f},$$

where f is the frequency of the fork and V is the velocity of sound in air.

$$\therefore \quad l + c = \frac{V}{4f} \quad . \quad . \quad . \quad . \quad \text{(ii)}$$

If different tuning-forks of known frequency f are taken, and the corresponding values of l obtained when resonance occurs, it follows

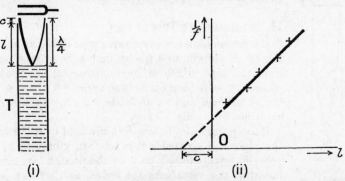

Fig. 493.   Resonance tube experiment.

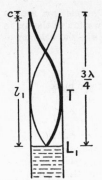

FIG. 494. Resonance at new water level.

from equation (ii) that a graph of $1/f$ against l is a straight line, Fig. 493 (ii). Now from equation (ii), the gradient of the line is $4/V$; thus V can be determined. Also, the negative intercept of the line on the axis of l is c, from equation (ii); hence the end-correction can be found.

If only one fork is available, and the tube is sufficiently long, another method for V and c can be adopted. In this case the level of the water is lowered further from the position in Fig. 493 (i), until resonance is again obtained at a level L_1, Fig. 494. Since the stationary wave set up is that shown and the new length to the top from L_1 is l_1, it follows that

$$l_1 + c = \frac{3\lambda}{4} \qquad \cdots \qquad \text{(iii)}$$

But

$$l + c = \frac{\lambda}{4}, \text{ from (ii).}$$

Subtracting,

$$l_1 - l = \frac{\lambda}{2}$$

$$\therefore \quad \lambda = 2\,(l_1 - l)$$

$$\therefore \quad V = f\lambda = 2f\,(l_1 - l) \qquad \cdots \qquad (80)$$

In this method for V, therefore, the end-correction c is eliminated. The magnitude of c can be found from equations (ii) and (iii). Thus, from (ii),

$$3l + 3c = \frac{3\lambda}{4}$$

But, from (ii),

$$l_1 + c = \frac{3\lambda}{4}$$

$$\therefore \quad 3l + 3c = l_1 + c$$

$$\therefore \quad 2c = l_1 - 3l$$

$$\therefore \quad c = \frac{l_1 - 3l}{2} \qquad \cdots \qquad \cdots \qquad (81)$$

Hence c can be found from measurements of l_1 and l.

EXAMPLES

1. Describe the natural modes of vibration of the air in an organ pipe closed at one end, and explain what is meant by the term "end-correction". A cylindrical pipe of length 28 cm. closed at one end is found to be at resonance when a tuning-fork of frequency 864 vibrations per sec. is sounded near the open end. Determine the mode of vibration of the air in the pipe, and deduce the value of the end-correction. [Take the velocity of sound in air as 340 metres per sec.] (L.)

First part. See text.

Second part. Let λ = the wavelength of the sound in the pipe.

Then
$$\lambda = \frac{V}{f} = \frac{34,000}{864} = 39 \cdot 35 \text{ cm.}$$

If the pipe is resonating to its fundamental frequency f_o, the stationary wave in the pipe is that shown in Fig. 493 and the wavelength λ_o is given by $\lambda_o/4 = 28$ cm. Thus $\lambda_o = 112$ cm. Since $\lambda = 39 \cdot 35$ cm., the pipe cannot be sounding its resonant frequency. The first overtone of the pipe is $3f_o$, which corresponds to a wavelength λ_1 given by $3\lambda_1/4 = 28$ (see Fig. 486 (i)).

$$\therefore \quad \lambda_1 = \frac{112}{3} = 37\tfrac{1}{3} \text{ cm.}$$

Consequently, allowing for the effect of an end-correction, the pipe is sounding its first overtone.

Let c = the end-correction in cm.

Then
$$28 + c = \frac{3\lambda_1}{4}$$

But, accurately,
$$\lambda_1 = \frac{V}{f} = \frac{34,000}{864} = 39 \cdot 35$$

$$\therefore \quad 28 + c = \tfrac{3}{4} \times 39 \cdot 35$$
$$\therefore \quad c = 1 \cdot 51 \text{ cm.}$$

2. Explain the phenomenon of resonance, and illustrate your answer by reference to the resonance-tube experiment. In such an experiment with a resonance tube the first two successive positions of resonance occurred when the lengths of the air columns were 15·4 cm. and 48·6 cm. respectively. If the velocity of sound in air at the time of the experiment was 34,000 cm. per sec., calculate the frequency of the source employed and the value of the end-correction for the resonance tube. If the air column is further increased in length, what will be the length when the next resonance occurs? (C.)

First part. See text.

Second part. Suppose c is the end-correction in cm. Then, from p. 671,

$$48 \cdot 6 + c = \frac{3\lambda}{4} \qquad \qquad \text{. . . . (i)}$$

and
$$15 \cdot 4 + c = \frac{\lambda}{4} \qquad \qquad \text{. . . (ii)}$$

Subtracting,
$$\therefore \quad 33 \cdot 2 = \frac{\lambda}{2}$$

$$\therefore \quad 66 \cdot 4 = \lambda \qquad \qquad \text{. . . . (iii)}$$

$$\text{frequency, } f, = \frac{V}{\lambda} = \frac{34,000}{66 \cdot 4} = 512$$

The end-correction, c, is given by substituting $\lambda = 66\cdot4$ in (i). Thus

$$48\cdot6 + c = \tfrac{3}{4} \times 66\cdot4$$

from which

$$c = 1\cdot2 \text{ cm.}$$

The next resonance occurs when the total length, a, of the stationary wave set up is $5\lambda/4$. From (iii), $a = \tfrac{5}{4} \times 66\cdot4 = 83\cdot0$ cm. Since the end-correction is $1\cdot2$ cm.,

$$\therefore \text{ length of pipe } = 83\cdot0 - 1\cdot2 = 81\cdot8 \text{ cm.}$$

3. Explain, with diagrams, the possible states of vibration of a column of air in (a) an open pipe, (b) a closed pipe. An open pipe 30 cm. long and a closed pipe 23 cm. long, both of the same diameter, are each sounding its first overtone, and these are in unison. What is the end-correction of these pipes? (L.)

First part. See text.

Second part. Suppose V is the velocity of sound in air, and f is the frequency of the note. The wavelength, λ, is thus V/f.

When the open pipe is sounding its first overtone, the length of the pipe plus end-corrections $= \lambda$.

$$\therefore \quad \frac{V}{f} = 30 + 2c \qquad . \qquad . \qquad \text{(i)}$$

since there are two end-corrections.

When the closed pipe is sounding its first overtone,

$$\frac{3\lambda}{4} = 23 + c$$

$$\therefore \quad \frac{3V}{4f} = 23 + c \qquad . \qquad . \qquad \text{(ii)}$$

From (i) and (ii), it follows that

$$23 + c = \tfrac{3}{4}(30 + 2c)$$

$$\therefore \quad 92 + 4c = 90 + 6c$$

$$\therefore \quad c = 1 \text{ cm.}$$

VIBRATIONS IN STRINGS

If a horizontal rope is fixed at one end, and the other end is moved up and down, a wave travels along the rope. The particles of the rope are then vibrating vertically, and since the wave travels horizontally, this is an example of a *transverse* wave (see p. 610). The waves propagated along the surface of the water when a stone is dropped into it are also transverse waves, as the particles of the water are moving up and down while the wave travels horizontally. A transverse wave is also obtained when a stretched string, such as a violin string, is plucked; and before we can study the vibrations in strings, we require to know the velocity of transverse waves along a string.

16. Velocity of Transverse Waves Along a Stretched String

Suppose that a transverse wave is travelling along a thin string of length l and mass s under a constant tension T. If we assume that the string has no "stiffness", i.e., that the string is perfectly flexible, the velocity V of the transverse wave along it depends only on the values of T, s, l. The velocity is given by

$$V = \sqrt{\frac{T}{s/l}} \ ,$$

$$\text{or} \quad \mathbf{V} = \sqrt{\frac{\mathbf{T}}{\mathbf{m}}} \qquad . \quad . \quad . \quad . \quad . \quad (82)$$

where m is the "mass per unit length" of the string.

When T is in *dynes* and m in *gm. per cm.*, then V is in *cm. per sec.*; when T is in poundals and m is in lb. per ft., then V is in ft. per sec.

The formula for V may be partly deduced by the method of dimensions, in which all the quantities concerned are reduced to the fundamental units of mass, [M], length, [L], and time, [T]. Suppose that

$$V = kT^x s^y l^z \qquad . \quad . \quad . \quad . \quad . \quad (i)$$

where k, x, y, z, are numbers. The dimensions of velocity V are [L]/[T], the dimensions of tension T, a force, are [M] [L]/[T²], the dimension of s is [M], and the dimension of l is [L]. As the dimensions on both sides of (i) must be equal, it follows that

$$\frac{[L]}{[T]} = \frac{[M]^x [L]^x}{[T]^{2x}} \cdot [M]^y [L]^z$$

Equating the indices of [M], [L], [T] on both sides, we have

for [M], $\qquad\qquad x + y = 0$

for [L], $\qquad\qquad x + z = 1$

for [T], $\qquad\qquad 2x = 1$

$$\therefore x = \tfrac{1}{2}, z = \tfrac{1}{2}, y = -\tfrac{1}{2}$$

Thus, from (i),

$$V = kT^{\frac{1}{2}} s^{-\frac{1}{2}} l^{\frac{1}{2}}$$

$$\therefore \quad V = k\sqrt{\frac{Tl}{s}} = k\sqrt{\frac{T}{s/l}}$$

A rigid mathematical treatment reveals that $k = 1$, since $V = \sqrt{\frac{T}{s/l}}$. Since s/l is the "mass per unit length" of the string, it follows that

$$V = \sqrt{\frac{T}{m}},$$

where m is the mass per unit length.

17. Modes of Vibration of Stretched String

If a wire is stretched between two points N, N and is plucked in the middle, a transverse wave travels along the wire and is reflected at the fixed end. A *stationary wave* is thus set up in the wire, and the simplest mode of vibration is one in which the fixed ends of the wire are nodes, N, and the middle is an antinode, A, Fig. 495. Since the distance

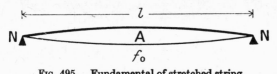

Fig. 495.   Fundamental of stretched string.

between consecutive nodes is $\lambda/2$, where λ is the wavelength of the transverse wave in the wire, it follows that

$$l = \frac{\lambda}{2},$$

where l is the length of the wire. Thus $\lambda = 2l$. The frequency f of the vibration is hence given by

$$f = \frac{V}{\lambda} = \frac{V}{2l},$$

where V is the velocity of the transverse wave. But $V = \sqrt{T/m}$, from previous.

$$\therefore f = \frac{1}{2l}\sqrt{\frac{T}{m}}$$

This is the frequency of the *fundamental* note obtained from the string; and if we denote the frequency by the usual symbol f_0, we have

$$f_0 = \frac{1}{2l}\sqrt{\frac{T}{m}} \qquad . \qquad . \qquad . \qquad . \qquad (83)$$

18. Overtones of Stretched String

The first overtone f_1 of a string plucked in the middle corresponds to a stationary wave shown in Fig. 496, which has nodes at the fixed ends and an antinode in the middle. If λ_1 is the wavelength, it can be seen that

$$l = \frac{3}{2}\lambda_1,$$

$$\text{or} \quad \lambda_1 = \frac{2l}{3}.$$

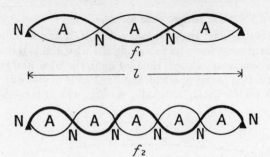

FIG. 496.   Overtones of stretched string plucked in middle.

The frequency f_1 is thus given by

$$f_1 = \frac{V}{\lambda_1} = \frac{3V}{2l} = \frac{3}{2l}\sqrt{\frac{T}{m}} \qquad . \qquad . \qquad . \qquad (i)$$

But the fundamental frequency, $f_0, = \frac{1}{2l}\sqrt{\frac{T}{m}}$, from equation (83).

$$\therefore f_1 = 3f_0$$

The second overtone f_2 of the string when plucked in the middle corresponds to a stationary wave shown in Fig. 496. In this case $l = \frac{5}{2}\lambda_2$, where λ_2 is the wavelength.

$$\therefore \quad \lambda_2 = \frac{2l}{5}$$

$$\therefore \quad f_2 = \frac{V}{\lambda_2} = \frac{5V}{2l}$$

where f_2 is the frequency. But $V = \sqrt{T/m}$.

$$\therefore \quad f_2 = \frac{5}{2l}\sqrt{\frac{T}{m}} = 5f_0$$

The overtones are thus $3f_0$, $5f_0$, and so on.

Other notes than those considered above can be obtained by touching or "stopping" the string lightly at its midpoint, for example, so that the latter becomes a node in addition to those at the fixed ends. If the string is plucked one-quarter of the way along it from a fixed end, the simplest stationary wave set up is that illustrated in Fig. 497 (i). Thus the wavelength, $\lambda, = l$, and hence the frequency f is given by

$$f = \frac{V}{\lambda} = \frac{V}{l} = \frac{1}{l}\sqrt{\frac{T}{m}}$$

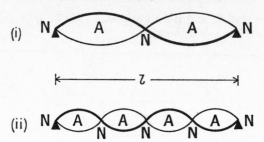

FIG. 497.   Even harmonics in stretched string.

$$\therefore \quad f = 2f_0, \quad \text{since } f_0 = \frac{1}{2l}\sqrt{\frac{T}{m}}.$$

If the string is plucked one-eighth of the way from a fixed end, a stationary wave similar to that in Fig. 496 (ii) may be set up. The wavelength, $\lambda',= l/2$, and hence the frequency $f' = \dfrac{V}{\lambda'} = \dfrac{2V}{l}.$

$$\therefore \quad f' = \frac{2}{l}\sqrt{\frac{T}{m}} = 4f_0$$

19. Verification of the Laws of Vibration of a Fixed String. The Sonometer

As we have already shown (p. 675), the frequency of the fundamental of a stretched string is given by $f = \dfrac{1}{2l}\sqrt{\dfrac{T}{m}}$, writing f for f_0. It thus follows that:

(1) $f \propto \dfrac{1}{l}$ for a given tension (T) and string $(m$ constant$)$.

(2) $f \propto \sqrt{T}$ for a given length (l) and string $(m$ constant$)$.

(3) $f \propto \dfrac{1}{\sqrt{m}}$ for a given length (l) and tension (T).

These are known as the "laws of vibration of a fixed string", first completely given by MERSENNE in 1636, and the *sonometer*, or *monochord*, was designed to verify them

The sonometer consists of a hollow wooden box Q, with a thin horizontal wire attached to A on the top of it, Fig. 498. The wire passes over a grooved wheel P, and is kept taut by a mass M hanging down at the other end. Wooden bridges, B, C, can be placed beneath the wire so that a definite length of wire is obtained, and the length of wire can be varied by moving one of the bridges. The length of wire between

B, C can be read from a fixed horizontal scale S, graduated in centimetres, on the box below the wire.

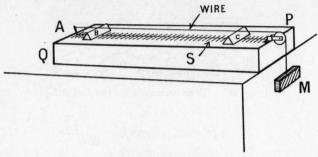

FIG. 498.   Sonometer.

(1) *To verify f ∝ 1/l for a given tension (T) and mass per unit length (m)*,
the mass M is kept constant so that the tension, T, in the wire is
constant. The length, l, of the wire between B, C is varied by moving C
until the note obtained by plucking BC in the middle is the same as
that produced by a sounding tuning-fork of known frequency f. If the
observer has not a musical ear, the "tuning" can be recognised by
listening for beats when the wire and the tuning-fork are both sounding,
as in this case the frequencies of the two notes are nearly equal (p. 640).
Alternatively, a small piece of paper in the form of an inverted V can
be placed on the middle of the wire, and the end of the sounding
tuning-fork then placed on the sonometer box. The vibrations of the
fork are then transmitted through the box to the wire, which vibrates
in resonance with the fork if its length is "tuned" to the note. The
paper will then vibrate considerably and may be thrown off the wire.

Different tuning-forks of known frequency f are taken, and the
lengths, l, of the wire are observed when they are tuned to the corresponding note. A graph of f against $1/l$ is then plotted, and is found to
be a straight line within the limits of experimental error. Thus $f \propto 1/l$
for a given tension and mass per unit length of wire.

(2) *To verify f ∝ √T for a given length and mass per unit length*, the
length BC between the bridges is kept fixed, so that the length of wire
is constant, and the mass M is varied to alter the tension. The experimental difficulty to be overcome is how to find the frequency f of the
note produced when the wire between B, C is plucked in the middle.
For this purpose a second wire, fixed to R, S on the sonometer, is
utilised, usually with a weight (not shown) attached to one end to keep
the tension constant, Fig. 499. This wire has bridges P, N beneath it,
and N is moved until the note from the wire between P, N is the same
as the note from the wire between B, C. Now the tension in PN is

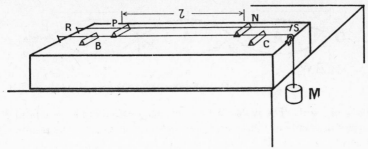

FIG. 499.   Verification of $f \propto \sqrt{T}$.

constant as the wire is fixed to R, S. Thus, since frequency, f, $\propto 1/l$ for a given tension and wire, the frequency of the note from BC is proportional to $1/l$, where l is the length of PN.

If a different mass is attached to the end of the wire BC, the tension in the wire is altered. Keeping BC fixed, the bridge N is moved until the note from PN is the same as that obtained from BC, and the length PN (l) is again noted. Then, as before, the frequency of the new note in BC is proportional to $1/l$. By altering the mass M, and observing the corresponding length l, a graph of $1/l$ can be plotted against $\sqrt{T}$, where T is the weight. The graph is a straight line, within the limits of experimental error, and hence $1/l \propto \sqrt{T}$. Thus $f \propto \sqrt{T}$ for a given length of wire and mass per unit length.

(3) *To verify $f \propto 1/\sqrt{m}$ for a given length and tension*, wires of different material are connected to B, C, and the same mass M and the same length BC are taken. The frequency, f, of the note obtained from BC is again found by using the second wire RS in the way already described. The mass per unit length, m, is the mass per cm. length of the wire, and is given by $\pi r^2 \varrho$ gm. per cm., where r is the radius of the wire in cm. and ϱ is its density in gm. per c.c., as ($\pi r^2 \times 1$) c.c. is the volume of 1 cm. of the wire. Since $f \propto 1/l$, where l is the length on the second wire, a graph of $1/l$ against $1/\sqrt{m}$ should be a straight line; thus a graph of l against $\sqrt{m}$ should be a straight line if $f \propto 1/\sqrt{m}$ for a given length and mass per unit length. Experiment shows this is the case.

20. Melde's Experiment on Vibrations in Stretched String

MELDE gave a striking demonstration of the stationary wave set up in a vibrating string. He used a light thread with one end attached to the prong P of an electrically-maintained tuning-fork, and the other end connected to a weight W after passing over a grooved wheel Q, Fig. 500. With the vibrations of the prong perpendicular to the length of the thread a number of "loops" can be observed, which are due to the rapid movement of the thread as the stationary transverse wave

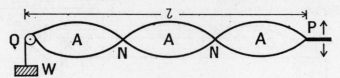

Fig. 500. Melde's experiment.

passes along it. The nodes of the stationary wave are at Q and at P, as the amplitude of vibration of the prong is small, and the number n of the loops depends on the frequency f of the fork, the length l of PQ, the tension T in the thread, and its mass per unit length, m.

The length of a loop $= l/n$. But this is the distance between consecutive nodes, which is $\lambda/2$, where λ is the wavelength of the stationary wave in the thread.

$$\therefore \quad \frac{\lambda}{2} = \frac{l}{n}$$

$$\therefore \quad \lambda = \frac{2l}{n}$$

$$\therefore \quad f = \frac{V}{\lambda} = \frac{n}{2l} V$$

where V is the velocity of the transverse wave. The frequency of the transverse wave is the same as that of the tuning-fork.

But $$V = \sqrt{\frac{T}{m}} \text{ (p. 674)}$$

$$\therefore \quad f = \frac{n}{2l}\sqrt{\frac{T}{m}} \quad , \quad . \quad . \quad . \quad . \quad (84)$$

$$\therefore \quad n\sqrt{T} = \text{constant},$$

if f, T, m are kept constant. In this case, therefore,

$$n = \frac{\text{constant}}{\sqrt{T}}$$

$$\text{or } n^2 \propto \frac{1}{T} \quad . \quad . \quad . \quad . \quad . \quad (85)$$

This relation can be verified by varying the tension T in the thread, and obtaining a corresponding whole number, n, of loops. A graph of n^2 against $1/T$ is then plotted, and is a straight line.

When the prong P of the tuning-fork is vibrating in the same *direction as the length of string*, the latter moves from position 3 to position 2 as the prong moves from one end a of an oscillation to the other end b, Fig. 501. As the string continues from position 2 to position 1, the

Fig. 501.   Melde's experiment.

prong moves back from b to a to complete 1 cycle of oscillation. The fork thus goes through one complete cycle in the same time as the particles of the string go through half a cycle, and hence the frequency of the transverse wave is *half* the frequency f of the fork, unlike the first case considered, Fig. 500. Instead of equation (84), we now have

$$\frac{f}{2} = \frac{n}{2l} \sqrt{\frac{T}{m}}$$

or $n = fl / \sqrt{T/m}$,

and hence with the same tension, thread, and length l, the number of loops n is half that obtained previously (p. 680).

21. Measurement of the Frequency of A.C. Mains

The frequency of the alternating current (A.C.) mains can be determined with the aid of a sonometer wire. The alternating current is passed into the wire MP, and the poles N, S of a powerful magnet are placed on either side of the wire so that the magnetic field due to it is perpendicular to the wire, Fig. 502. As a result of the magnetic effect of the

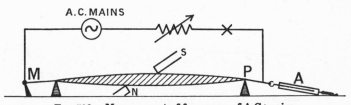

Fig. 502.   Measurement of frequency of A.C. mains.

current, a force acts on the wire which is perpendicular to the directions of both the magnetic field and the current, and hence the wire is subjected to a transverse force. If the current is an alternating one of 50 cycles per second, the magnitude of the force varies at the rate of 50 cycles per second. By adjusting the tension in the sonometer wire, whose magnitude is read on the spring-balance A, a position can be reached when the wire is seen to be vibrating through a large amplitude; in this case the wire is *resonating* to the applied force, Fig. 502.

The length l of wire between the bridges is now measured, and the tension T and the mass per unit length, m, are also found. The frequency f of the alternating current is then given by

$$f = \frac{1}{2l} \sqrt{\frac{T}{m}} \ .$$

22. Velocity of Longitudinal Waves in Wires

If a sonometer wire is stroked along its length by a rosined cloth, a high-pitched note is obtained. This note is due to *longitudinal* vibrations in the wire, and must be clearly distinguished from the note produced when the wire is plucked, which sets up *transverse* vibrations of the wire and a corresponding transverse wave. As we saw on p. 641, the velocity V of a longitudinal wave in a medium is

$$V = \sqrt{\frac{E}{\varrho}} \ ,$$

where E is Young's modulus for the wire and ϱ is its density. The wavelength, λ, of the longitudinal wave is $2l$, where l is the length of the wire, since a stationary longitudinal wave is set up. Thus the frequency f of the note is given by

$$f = \frac{V}{\lambda} = \frac{1}{2l} \sqrt{\frac{E}{\varrho}} \ .$$

The frequency of the note may be obtained with the aid of a siren (p. 619), and thus the velocity of sound in the wire, or its Young's modulus, can be calculated.

EXAMPLES

1. Explain the meaning of the term *resonance*, giving in illustration two methods of obtaining resonance between the stretched string of a sonometer and a tuning-fork of fixed frequency. A sonometer wire of length 76 cm. is maintained under a tension of 4 kg. weight and an alternating current is passed through the wire. A horse-shoe magnet is placed with its poles above and below the wire at its midpoint, and the resulting forces set the wire in resonant vibration. If the density of the material of the wire is 8·8 gm. per c.c. and the diameter of the wire is 1 mm., what is the frequency of the alternating current? (*L*.)

First part. See text.

Second part. The wire is set into resonant vibration when the frequency of the alternating current is equal to its natural frequency, f.

Now $$f = \frac{1}{2l} \sqrt{\frac{T}{m}} \quad \cdot \quad \cdot \quad \cdot \quad \cdot \quad \text{(i)}$$

where $l = 76$ cm., $T = 4,000 \times 980$ dynes, and $m =$ mass per unit length.

Also,   mass of 1 cm., m, = volume × density

$$= (\pi r^2 \times 1) \times 8 \cdot 8 = (\pi \times 0 \cdot 05^2 \times 1) \times 8 \cdot 8,$$

since radius, r, of the wire = $\frac{1}{2}$ mm. = 0·05 cm.

From (i), $\therefore f = \dfrac{1}{2 \times 76} \sqrt{\dfrac{4,000 \times 980}{\pi \times 0 \cdot 05^2 \times 1 \times 8 \cdot 8}}$

$$= 49 \cdot 6 \text{ cycles per sec.}$$

2. What data would be required in order to predict the frequency of the note emitted by a stretched wire (*a*) when it is plucked, (*b*) when it is stroked along its length? A weight is hung on the wire of a vertical sonometer. When the vibrating length of the wire is adjusted to 80 cm. the note it emits when plucked is in tune with a standard fork. On adding a further weight of 100 grams the vibrating length has to be altered by 1 cm. in order to restore the tuning. What is the initial weight on the wire? (*L.*)

First part. When the wire is plucked the vibrations of the particles produce transverse waves, and the frequency of the note is given by $f = \dfrac{1}{2l} \sqrt{\dfrac{T}{m}}$. When the wire is stroked along its length, the vibrations of the particles produce a *longitudinal* wave, and the velocity of the wave is given by $V = \sqrt{E/\varrho}$, where E is Young's modulus for the wire and ϱ is its density. The frequency in the latter case thus depends on the magnitudes of E and ϱ, as well as on the length of the wire.

Second part.   Let W = the initial weight on the wire in gm. wt.,

and f = the frequency of the fork

Since $f = \dfrac{1}{2l} \sqrt{\dfrac{T}{m}}$

we have $= \dfrac{1}{2 \times 80} \sqrt{\dfrac{Wg}{m}}$ . . . . . (i)

When a weight of 100 gm. wt. is added, the frequency increases since the tension increases. The new length of the wire = 81 cm.

$\therefore \qquad f = \dfrac{1}{2 \times 81} \sqrt{\dfrac{(W + 100)g}{m}}$ . . . (ii)

From (i) and (ii), it follows that

$$\frac{1}{160} \sqrt{\frac{Wg}{m}} = \frac{1}{162} \sqrt{\frac{(W + 100)g}{m}}$$

$\therefore \qquad 162^2\, W = 160^2 (W + 100)$

$\therefore \qquad W = \dfrac{160^2 \times 100}{162^2 - 160^2} = 3,975 \text{ gm. wt.}$

VIBRATIONS IN RODS

Sound waves travel through liquids and solids, as well as through gases, and in the nineteenth century an experiment to measure the velocity of sound in iron was carried out by tapping one end of a very long iron tube. The speed of sound in iron is much greater than in air, and the sound through the iron thus arrived at the other end of the pipe before the sound transmitted through the air. From a knowledge of the interval between the sounds, the length of the pipe, and the velocity of sound in air, the velocity of sound in iron was determined. More accurate methods were soon forthcoming for the velocity of sound in substances such as iron, wood, and glass, and they depend mainly on the formation of stationary waves in rods of these materials.

Consider a rod AA fixed by a vice B at its mid-point N, Fig. 503. If the rod is stroked along its length by a rosined cloth, a stationary

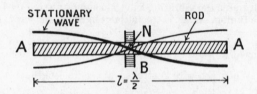

FIG. 503.   Stationary wave in rod.

longitudinal wave is set up in the rod on account of reflection at its ends, and a high-pitched note is obtained. Since the mid-point of the rod is fixed, this is a node, N, of the stationary wave; and since the ends of the rod are free, these are antinodes, A. Thus the length l of the rod is equal to half the wavelength, $\lambda/2$, of the wave in the rod, and hence $\lambda = 2l$. Thus the velocity of the sound in the rod, $V, = f\lambda = f \times 2l$, where f is the frequency of the note from the rod.

23. Kundt's Tube

About 1868, KUNDT devised a simple method of showing the stationary waves in air or any other gas. He used a closed tube T containing the gas, and sprinkled some dry lycopodium powder, or cork dust, along the entire length, Fig. 504. A rod AE, clamped at its mid-point, is placed with one end projecting into T, and a disc E is attached at this end so that it just clears the sides of the tube, Fig. 504.

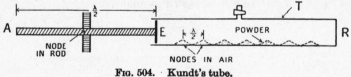

FIG. 504.   Kundt's tube.

When the rod is stroked at A by a rosined cloth in the direction EA, the rod vibrates longitudinally and a high-pitched note can be heard.

The end E acts as a vibrating source of the same frequency, and a sound wave thus travels through the air in T and is reflected at the fixed end R. If the rod is moved so that the position of E alters, a position can be found when the stationary wave in the air in T causes the lycopodium powder to become violently agitated. The powder then settles into definite small heaps at the nodes, which are the positions of permanent rest of the stationary wave, and the distance between consecutive nodes can best be found by measuring the distance between several of them and dividing by the appropriate number.

24. Determination of Velocity of Sound in a Rod

Kundt's tube can be used to determine the velocity of sound, V_r, in the rod. Suppose the length of the rod is l; then $\lambda/2 = l$, or $\lambda = 2l$, where λ is the wavelength of the sound wave *in the rod* (p. 659). Thus the frequency of the high-pitched note obtained from the rod is given by

$$f = \frac{V_r}{\lambda} = \frac{V_r}{2l} \quad . \quad . \quad . \quad . \quad \text{(i)}$$

If l_1 is the distance between consecutive nodes of the stationary wave in the air, we have $\lambda_1/2 = l_1$, where λ_1 is the wavelength of the sound wave *in the air*. Thus $\lambda_1 = 2l_1$, and hence the frequency of the wave, which is also f, is given by

$$f = \frac{V_a}{\lambda} = \frac{V_a}{2l_1} \quad , \quad . \quad . \quad . \quad \text{(ii)}$$

where V_a is the velocity of sound in air. From (i) and (ii) it follows that

$$\frac{V_r}{2l} = \frac{V_a}{2l_1}$$

$$\therefore \quad V_r = \frac{l}{l_1} V_a \quad . \quad . \quad . \quad . \quad \text{(86)}$$

Thus knowing V_a, l, l_1, the velocity of sound in the rod, V_r, can be calculated. By using glass, brass, copper, steel and other substances in the form of a rod, the velocity of sound in these media have been determined. Kundt also used liquids in the tube T instead of air, and employed fine iron filings instead of lycopodium powder to detect the nodes in the liquid. In this way he determined the velocity of sound in liquids.

25. Determination of Young's Modulus of a Rod

On p. 641, it was shown that the velocity of sound, V, in a medium is always given by

$$V = \sqrt{\frac{E}{\varrho}} \, ,$$

where E is the appropriate modulus of elasticity of the medium and ϱ is its density. In the case of a rod undergoing longitudinal vibrations, as in Kundt's tube experiment, E is Young's modulus (see p. 641). Thus if V_r is the velocity of sound in the rod,

$$V_r = \sqrt{\frac{E}{\varrho}}$$

and $\qquad\qquad \therefore \quad E = V_r{}^2\varrho \quad . \quad . \quad . \quad . \quad (87)$

Since V_r is obtained by the method explained on page 685, and ϱ can be obtained from tables, it follows that E can be calculated.

26. Determination of Velocity of Sound in a Gas

If the air in Kundt's tube T is replaced by some other gas, and the rod stroked, the average distance l' between the piles of dust in T is the distance between consecutive nodes of the stationary wave in the gas. The wavelength, λ_g, in the gas is thus $2l'$, and the frequency f is given by

$$f = \frac{V_g}{\lambda_g} = \frac{V_g}{2l'} \ ,$$

where V_g is the velocity of sound in the gas. But the wavelength, λ, of the wave in the rod $= 2l$, where l is the length of the rod (p. 685); hence f is also given by

$$f = \frac{V_r}{\lambda} = \frac{V_r}{2l}$$

$$\therefore \quad \frac{V_g}{2l'} = \frac{V_r}{2l}$$

$$\therefore \quad V_g = \frac{l'}{l} V_r \quad . \quad . \quad . \quad . \quad . \quad (88)$$

Knowing l', l, and V_r, the latter obtained from a previous experiment (p. 685), the velocity of sound in a gas, V_g, can be calculated. See also p. 687.

27. Determination of Ratio of Specific Heats of a Gas, and its Molecular Structure

The velocity of sound in a gas, V_g, is given by

$$V_g = \sqrt{\frac{\gamma p}{\varrho}} \ ,$$

where γ is the ratio (C_p/C_v) of the two principal specific heats of the gas, p is its pressure, and ϱ is its density. See p. 643. Thus

$$\gamma = \frac{V_g{}^2\varrho}{p} \quad . \quad . \quad . \quad . \quad . \quad (89)$$

Now it has already been shown that V_g can be found; and knowing ϱ and p, γ can be calculated. The determination of γ is one of the most important applications of Kundt's tube, as atomic theory shows that $\gamma = 1.66$ for a monatomic gas and 1.40 for a diatomic gas. Thus Kundt's tube provides valuable information about the atomic structure of a gas. When RAMSEY isolated the hitherto-unobtainable argon from the air, Lord Rayleigh in 1895 suggested a Kundt's tube experiment for finding the ratio, γ, of its specific heats. It was then discovered that γ was about 1.65, showing that argon was a monatomic gas. The dissociation of the molecules of a gas at high temperatures has been investigated by containing it in a Kundt's tube surrounded by a furnace, and measuring the magnitude of γ when the temperature was changed.

28. Comparison of Velocities of Sound in Gases by Kundt's Tube

The ratio of the velocities of sound in two gases can be found from a Kundt's tube experiment. The two gases, air and carbon dioxide for example, are contained in tubes B, A respectively, into which the ends of a metal rod R project, Fig. 505. The middle of the rod is clamped.

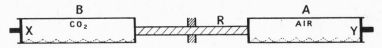

Fig. 505.   Comparison of velocities of sound in gases.

By stroking the rod, and adjusting the positions of the movable discs X, Y in turn, lycopodium powder in each tube can be made to settle into heaps at the various nodes. The average distances, d_a, d_b, between successive nodes in A, B respectively are then measured.

The frequency f of the sound wave in A, B is the same, being the frequency of the note obtained from R. Since $f = V/\lambda$, it follows that

$$\frac{V_g}{\lambda_g} = \frac{V_a}{\lambda_a} , \qquad . \quad . \quad . \quad . \quad \text{(i)}$$

where V_g, V_a are the velocities of sound in carbon dioxide and air respectively, and λ_g, λ_a are the corresponding wavelengths.

Now $$\frac{\lambda_g}{\lambda_a} = \frac{d_b}{d_a} \qquad . \quad . \quad . \quad . \quad . \quad \text{(ii)}$$

since the distance between successive nodes is half a wavelength. From (i),

$$\frac{V_g}{V_a} = \frac{\lambda_g}{\lambda_a}$$

$$\therefore \quad \frac{V_g}{V_a} = \frac{d_b}{d_a} \qquad . \quad . \quad . \quad . \quad \text{(90)}$$

The two velocities can thus be compared as d_b, d_a are known; and if the velocity of sound, V_a, in air is known, the velocity in carbon dioxide can be calculated.

29. Vibrations in Plates. Chladni's Figures

We have already studied the different modes of vibration of the air in a pipe, the particles of a string, and the particles of a rod. About 1790 CHLADNI examined the vibrations of a glass *plate* by sprinkling sand on it. If the plate on a stand is gripped firmly at the corner N and bowed in the middle A of one side, the particles arrange themselves into a symmetrical pattern which shows the nodes of the stationary wave in the plate, Fig. 506 (i). By gripping the plate firmly at other

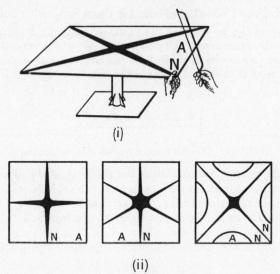

FIG. 506. Chladni's figures.

points N, thus making a node at these points, and bowing at A, a series of different patterns can be obtained. These are known as *Chladni's figures*, Fig. 506 (ii). Each pattern corresponds to a particular mode of vibration, which are not harmonically related in frequency, unlike the case of the vibration of air in pipes and the vibration of strings.

EXAMPLES

1. Describe and explain the way in which a Kundt tube may be used to determine the ratio of the specific heats of a gas. A Kundt tube is excited by a brass rod 150 cm. long and the distance between successive nodes in the tube is 13·6 cm.; what is the ratio of the velocity of sound in brass to that in air? (*L.*)

First part. See text.

Second part. Since both ends of the rod are successive antinodes, the wavelength λ_1 in the rod $= 2 \times 150 = 300$ cm. The wavelength λ_2 in the air $= 2 \times 13·6 = 27·2$ cm.

The frequency *f* of the note in the rod and the air is the same.

$$\therefore \qquad f = \frac{V_1}{\lambda_1} = \frac{V_2}{\lambda_2}$$

where V_1, V_2 are the velocities of sound in the rod and in the air.

$$\therefore \qquad \frac{V_1}{V_2} = \frac{\lambda_1}{\lambda_2} = \frac{300}{27·2} = 11·03$$

2. Describe the dust tube experiment. How may it be used to compare the velocities of sound in different gases? The fundamental frequency of longitudinal vibration of a rod clamped at its centre is 1,500 vibrations per sec. If the mass of the rod is 96·0 gm., find the increase in its total length produced by a stretching force of 10 kgm. wt. (*L.*)

First part. The dust tube is Kundt's tube. See p. 684.

Second part. The wavelength of the wave in the rod $= 2l$, where l is its length, since the ends are antinodes. The velocity, V, of the wave is given by

$$V = f\lambda = 1,500 \times 2l = 3,000\,l \quad . \qquad . \qquad . \qquad \text{(i)}$$

Since the vibrations of the rod are longitudinal,

$$\therefore V = \sqrt{\frac{E}{\varrho}}$$

where E is Young's modulus and ϱ is the density of the rod.

$$\therefore \qquad V = \sqrt{\frac{E}{96·0/v}} = \sqrt{\frac{Ev}{96·0}} \qquad \qquad \text{(ii)}$$

where v is the volume of the rod.

From (i) and (ii),

$$\therefore \qquad \sqrt{\frac{Ev}{96·0}} = 3,000\,l$$

$$\therefore \qquad \frac{Ev}{l^2} = 96 \times 3,000^2$$

$$\therefore \qquad \frac{EA}{l} = 96 \times 3,000^2 \quad . \qquad . \qquad . \qquad \text{(iii)}$$

since $v = Al$, where A is the area of cross-section of the rod. Now if x is the increase in length produced by 10 kgm. wt., it follows from the definition of E that

$$\text{force} = \frac{EAx}{l} = 10,000 \times 980 \text{ dynes}$$

$$\therefore \quad \frac{EA}{l} = \frac{10,000 \times 980}{x}$$

From (iii), $\quad \therefore \; 96 \times 3,000^2 = \dfrac{10,000 \times 980}{x}$

$$\therefore \quad x = \frac{10,000 \times 980}{96 \times 3,000^2} = 0.011 \text{ cm.}$$

EXERCISES XXX

1. Write down in terms of wavelength, λ, the distance between (i) consecutive nodes, (ii) a node and an adjacent antinode, (iii) consecutive antinodes. Find the frequency of the fundamental of a closed pipe 15 cm. long if the velocity of sound in air is 340 metres per sec.

2. What are (a) *progressive waves*, (b) *stationary waves*, (c) *nodes* and *antinodes*? With the help of diagrams show how, under suitable conditions, stationary waves may be produced from two trains of progressive waves. Briefly describe how nodes and antinodes may be demonstrated. (*C.*)

3. Assuming that the frequency of transverse vibration of a stretched string is inversely proportional to its length, describe how you would investigate the relation between the frequency and the tension. How would you plot your observations and what result would you expect?

A stretched string and an air column closed at one end both resound to a tuning-fork of frequency 256 vibrations per sec., the vibration the fundamental in both cases. State briefly the differences between the states of vibration of the string and the air column. What is the next higher frequency to which (a) the string, (b) the air column, will resound without their dimensions or the tension being altered? (*L.*)

4. What is the meaning of *overtone*, *harmonic*? Give an example of a harmonic which is not an overtone.

What is the frequency of the second overtone of the air in a pipe, 1 metre long, closed at one end when the temperature of the air is 20° C.? Assume that the end correction is 1·25 cm. and that the velocity of sound in air at 0° C. is 33,150 cm. per sec. (*L.*)

5. Distinguish between progressive and stationary waves.

Describe an experiment, based on the production of stationary waves, which shows that sound travels more slowly in carbon dioxide than in air at the same temperature. Show how to calculate the ratio of the velocities of sound in these two gases from the experimental measurements. (*N.*)

6. Describe the way in which the air layers in different parts of an open organ pipe are vibrating when the pipe is sounding its fundamental note. What other modes of vibration are possible for this pipe?

An open organ pipe in which the air is at a temperature of 15° C. and a sonometer wire of frequency 512 vibrations per sec., when sounded together, give 5 beats per sec., the organ pipe emitting its fundamental note. If a slight reduction in the tension of the sonometer wire produces unison between the two notes, what change in the temperature of the air in the organ pipe would have produced unison with the original frequency of the sonometer wire? (*W.*)

7. How would you compare the velocity of sound in wood or brass with that of sound in air? Describe the apparatus, method of procedure, and calculation. (L.)

8. Two identical wires stretched on a sonometer under the same tension of 5 kilogrammes wt. emit notes in unison (frequency 300 vibrations per sec.) when plucked. One wire has its tension increased by 100 gm. wt. and then the wires are plucked. Explain the formation of the beats and calculate the number of beats per sec. which would be heard. (L.)

9. How would you (a) demonstrate the presence of overtones in the sound emitted by a stretched string when it is plucked at its centre, (b) verify the relation between the frequency of the fundamental note emitted by a stretched wire, vibrating transversely, and its tension?

Two wires vibrate transversely in unison. The tension in one wire is increased by 1 per cent and now, when they vibrate simultaneously, 3 beats are heard in 2 secs. What was the original frequency of vibration of the two wires? (N.)

10. What is meant by the terms *node*, *antinode*, in respect of sound waves? What are beats, and how are they produced?

Two open organ pipes, 80 and 81 cm. long, are found to give 26 beats in 10 secs. when each is sounding its fundamental note. Find the velocity of sound in air and the frequencies of the two notes. [End corrections may be neglected.] (C.)

11. Describe the motion of the air in an open pipe when it is sounding its first overtone.

Explain how the pitch of the fundamental note of such a pipe is affected by the length and diameter of the pipe and the temperature of the air. (L.)

12. How would you compare (a) the velocities of sound in wood and air, and (b) the velocities of transverse and of longitudinal disturbances in a stretched wire?

A stretched wire 1 metre long gives a note of frequency 2,000 vibrations per sec. when stroked lengthwise with a resined leather. How is the string vibrating and what is the speed of propagation along it of the vibrations? (L.)

13. Describe a laboratory apparatus for investigating the laws of vibration of stretched strings, and give an account of its use.

Explain the fact that the same string under precisely the same physical conditions may emit sounds of different quality, according to the manner in which it is brought into vibration.

Two notes on a piano are four octaves apart. If the lower note is given by a wire 135 cm. long, and the higher by a wire 40 cm. long, and if the tensions are the same, calculate the relative mass of each wire per unit length. (W.)

14. Explain why the velocity of sound in a gas depends upon the ratio of its principal specific heats.

Give a detailed account of a method of determining this ratio for carbon dioxide gas at atmospheric temperature, assuming that the ratio for air is known. Give the theory of the experiment. (W.)

15. Describe, with the aid of diagrams, (a) the stationary waves existing in a sounding organ pipe, (b) the progressive waves by which the sound reaches the ear.

Show that a stationary wave system may be regarded as the resultant of two progressive waves. Use your diagrams to show how the particle velocity and pressure excess are distributed in stationary waves. (*L.*)

16. Describe in detail how to determine the frequency of a tuning-fork by the falling plate method.

Describe how the frequency of an alternating current, such as that from the A.C. mains, may be determined with a sonometer. (*N.*)

17. State the laws of vibration of a stretched string and describe how you would verify them experimentally.

A stretched wire is touched lightly with a feather at a point one-third of its length from one end, and is bowed near that end. It is found to be in unison with a fork of 512 cycles per sec. Find the length of the wire, if the mass per centimetre length is 0·015 gm., and the tension is applied by a load of 10 kilograms. (*L.*)

18. Explain with the aid of diagrams how (i) the pressure and (ii) the amplitude of vibration of the air vary from point to point of an open organ pipe sounding its fundamental tone. Describe experiments you would make to verify your account. (*L.*)

19. Explain *progressive waves, stationary waves:*

How would you determine the velocity of sound in a wooden or a metal rod? (*C.*)

20. A tuning fork is maintained electrically, the prongs oscillating vertically. One end of a horizontal string is attached to one of the prongs and the string passes over a pulley near the other end to which a weight is attached. Describe what is observed as the vibrating length of the string is gradually altered.

Explain the state of motion in the string. How can a similar condition be generated by sound waves in the air and how can the wavelength of such waves be measured? (*L.*)

21. Explain the following terms: *amplitude, antinode, wave length* and *wave form* with reference to sound waves. Draw diagrams showing the positions of the nodes and antinodes in two organ pipes, one with one end open and the other with both ends open, when they are sounding (i) their fundamentals, and (ii) their first overtones.

Describe *briefly* how you would show the presence of nodes in (*a*) a sounding organ pipe, (*b*) a vibrating plate and (*c*) a vibrating string. (*L.*)

22. Describe an experiment in which beats are produced. Explain their formation and how their frequency is related to the frequency of the sources producing them.

An open organ pipe sounding its fundamental note is in tune with a fork of frequency 439. How much must the pipe be shortened in order that two beats per second shall be heard when it is sounded with the fork? Assume the speed of sound is 342 metres per second. (*L.*)

LIGHT

CHAPTER XXXI

WAVE THEORY OF LIGHT

1. Historical

It has already been mentioned that light is a form of energy which stimulates our sense of vision. One of the early theories of light, about 400 B.C., suggested that particles were emitted from the eye when an object was seen. It was realised, however, that something is *entering* the eye when a sense of vision is caused, and about 1660 the great Newton proposed that particles, or corpuscles, were emitted from a luminous object. The *corpuscular theory of light* was adopted by many scientists of the day owing to the authority of Newton, but HUYGHENS, an eminent Dutch scientist, proposed about 1680 that light energy travelled from one place to another by means of a wave-motion. If the *wave theory of light* was correct, light should bend round a corner, just as sound travels round a corner. The experimental evidence for the wave theory in Huyghens' time was very small and the theory was dropped for more than a century. In 1801, however, THOMAS YOUNG obtained evidence that light could bend round a corner (p. 703), and he was among the first to see clearly the close analogy between sound and light waves. As the principles of the subject became understood other experiments were carried out which showed that light could bend round a corner, and Huyghens' wave-theory of light was revived. Newton's corpuscular theory was rejected since it was incompatible with experimental observations (see p. 699), and the wave theory of light has played, and is still playing, an important part in the development of the subject.

We cannot leave the theories of light without mentioning *Einstein's corpuscular theory of light.* In 1905 the great mathematical physicist Einstein suggested that the energy in light could be carried from place to place by particles whose mass depended on the wavelength of the light. Experiments carried out at his suggestion showed that the theory was true, and the particles of light energy are known as "photons". It is now considered that *either* the wave theory *or* the particle theory of light can be used in a problem on light, depending on the circumstances in the problem. In this book we shall only consider Huyghens' wave theory, which was the foundation of many notable advances in the subject.

2. Wavefront. Rays

We have already considered the topic of waves in the Sound section (p. 602). As we shall presently see, close analogies exist between light and sound waves.

Consider a point source of light, S, in air, and suppose that a disturbance, or wave, originates at S as a result of vibrations occurring inside the atoms of the source, and travels outwards. After a time t the wave has travelled a distance ct, where c is the velocity of light in air, and the light energy has thus reached the surface of a sphere of centre S and radius ct, Fig. 507. The surface of the sphere is called the *wavefront* of the light at this instant, and every point on it is vibrating "in step" or *in phase* with every other point. As time goes on the wave travels further and new wavefronts are obtained which are the surfaces of spheres of centre S.

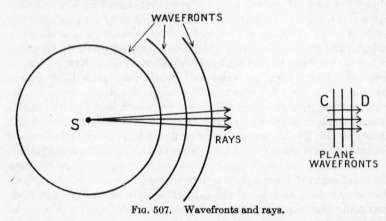

FIG. 507.   Wavefronts and rays.

At points a long way from S, such as C or D, the wavefronts are portions of a sphere of very large radius, and the wavefronts are then substantially *plane*. Light from the sun reaches the earth in plane wavefronts because the sun is so far away; plane wavefronts also emerge from a convex lens when a point source of light is placed at its focus.

The significance of the wavefront, then, is that it shows how the light energy travels from one place in a medium to another. A *ray* is the name given to the direction along which the energy travels, and consequently a ray of light passing through a point is perpendicular to the wavefront at that point. The rays diverge near S, but they are approximately parallel a long way from S, as plane wavefronts are then obtained, Fig. 507.

3. Huyghens' Construction for the New Wavefront

Suppose that the wavefront from a centre of disturbance S has reached the surface AB in a medium at some instant, Fig. 508. To obtain the position of the new wavefront after a further time t, Huyghens postulated that *every point, A, ..., C, ..., E, ..., B, on AB becomes a new or "secondary" centre of disturbance*. The wavelet from A

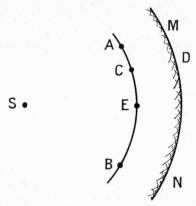

FIG. 508.   Huyghen's construction.

then reaches the surface M of a sphere of radius vt and centre A, where v is the velocity of light in the medium; the wavelet from C reaches the surface D of a sphere of radius vt and centre C; and so on for every point on AB. According to Huyghens, *the new wavefront is the surface MN which touches all the wavelets from the secondary sources*; and in the case considered, it is the surface of a sphere of centre S.

In this simple example of obtaining the new wavefront, the light travels in the same medium. Huyghens' construction, however, is especially valuable for deducing the new wavefront when the light travels from one medium to another, as we shall soon show.

4. Reflection at Plane Surface

Suppose that a beam of parallel rays between HA and LC is incident on a plane mirror, and imagine a plane wavefront AB which is normal to the rays, reaching the mirror surface, Fig. 509. At this instant the point A acts as a centre of disturbance. Suppose we require the new wavefront at a time corresponding to the instant when the disturbance at B reaches C. The wavelet from A reaches the surface of a sphere of radius AD at this instant; and as other points between AC on the mirror, such as P, are reached by the disturbances originating on AB, wavelets of smaller radius than AD are obtained at the instant we are considering. The new wavefront is the surface which touches all the wavelets.

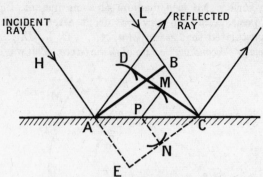

FIG. 509.   Reflection at plane surface.

In the absence of the mirror, the plane wavefront AB would reach the position EC in the time considered. Thus AD = AE = BC, and PN = PM, where PN is perpendicular to EC. The triangles PMC, PNC are hence congruent, as PC is common, angles PMC, PNC are each 90°, and PN = PM. Thus angle PCM = angle ACN. But angle PCN is a constant angle, being equal to angle ACE. As P is *any* point between A, C, it follows that the surface from C touching the wavelets between C, D is a *plane*, and consequently the plane wave AB incident on the mirror is reflected as a plane wave.

Law of reflection. We can now deduce the law of reflection concerning the angles of incidence and reflection. From the above, it can be seen that the triangles ABC, AEC are congruent, and that triangles ADC, AEC are congruent. The triangles ABC, ADC are hence congruent, and therefore angle BAC = angle DCA. Now these are the angles made by the wavefront AB, CD respectively with the mirror surface AC. Since the incident and reflected rays, for example HA, AD, are normal to the wavefronts, these rays also make equal angles with AC. It now follows that the angles of incidence and reflection are equal.

5. Refraction at Plane Surface

Consider a beam of parallel rays between LQ and MD incident on the plane surface of a water medium from air in the direction shown, and suppose that a plane wavefront has reached the position OA at a certain instant, Fig. 510. Each point between O, D becomes a new centre of disturbance as the wavefront advances to the surface of the water, and the wavefront changes in direction when the disturbance enters the liquid.

Suppose that t is the time taken by the light to travel from A to D. The disturbance from O travels a distance OB, or vt, in water in a time t, where v is the velocity of light in water. At the end of the time t, the wavefronts in the water from the other secondary centres between

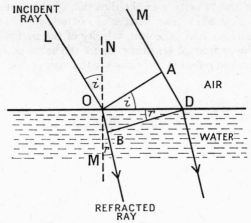

Fig. 510. Refraction at plane surface.

O, D reach the surfaces of spheres to each of which DB is a tangent. Thus DB is the new wavefront in the water, and the ray OB which is normal to the wavefront is consequently the refracted ray.

Since c is the velocity of light in air, $AD = ct$. Now

$$\frac{\sin i}{\sin r} = \frac{\sin LON}{\sin BOM} = \frac{\sin AOD}{\sin ODB}$$

$$\therefore \frac{\sin i}{\sin r} = \frac{AD/OD}{OB/OD} = \frac{AD}{OB} = \frac{ct}{vt} = \frac{c}{v} \quad . \quad . \quad . \quad (i)$$

But c, v are constants for the given media.

$$\therefore \frac{\sin i}{\sin r} \text{ is a constant,}$$

which is one of the laws of refraction (p. 429).

It can now be seen from (i) that the refractive index, μ, of a medium is given by $\mu = \frac{c}{v}$, where c is the velocity of light *in vacuo* and v is the velocity of light in the medium.

6. Newton's Corpuscular Theory of Light

Prior to the wave theory of light, Newton had proposed the corpuscular or particle theory of light (p. 693). According to Newton, particles are emitted by a source of light, and they travel in a straight line until the boundary of a new medium is encountered.

In the case of *reflection at a plane surface*, Newton stated that at some very small distance from the surface M, represented by A B, the particles were acted upon by a repulsive force, which gradually diminished the component of the velocity v in the direction of the normal and then reversed it, Fig. 511. The *horizontal* component of the velocity remained unaltered, and hence the velocity of the particles of light as they moved away from M is again v. Since the horizontal components of the incident and reflected velocities are the same, it follows that

$$v \sin i = v \sin i' \qquad . \qquad . \qquad . \qquad \textbf{(i)}$$

where i' is the angle of reflection.

$$\therefore \ \sin i = \sin i', \ \text{or} \ i = i'$$

Thus the corpuscular theory explains the law of reflection at a plane surface.

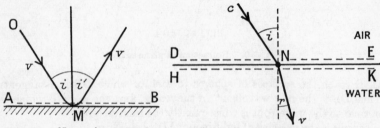

FIG. 511. Newton's corpuscular theory of reflection.

FIG. 512. Newton's corpuscular theory of refraction.

To explain *refraction at a plane surface* when light travels from air to a denser medium such as water, Newton stated that a force of attraction acted on the particles as they approached beyond a line DE very close to the boundary N, Fig. 512. The vertical component of the velocity of the particles was thus increased on entering the water, the horizontal component of the velocity remaining unaltered, and beyond a line HK close to the boundary the vertical component remained constant at its increased value. The resultant velocity, v, of the particles in the water is thus *greater* than its velocity, c, in air.

Suppose i, r are the angles of incidence and refraction respectively. Then, as the horizontal component of the velocity is unaltered,

$$c \sin i = v \sin r$$

$$\therefore \quad \frac{\sin i}{\sin r} = \frac{v}{c}$$

$$\therefore \quad \mu = \frac{v}{c} = \text{the refractive index}$$

Since μ is greater than 1, the velocity of light (v) in water is greater than the velocity (c) in air (as was stated above). This is according to Newton's corpuscular theory. On the wave theory, however, $\mu = \dfrac{c}{v}$

(see p. 697); and hence the velocity of light (v) in water is *less* than the velocity (c) in air according to the wave theory. The corpuscular theory and wave theory are thus in conflict, and Foucault's experimental results showed that the corpuscular theory, as enunciated by Newton, could not be true (p. 596).

7. Power of a Lens

We have now to consider the effect of lenses on the *curvature* of wave-fronts. A plane wavefront has obviously zero curvature and a spherical wavefront has a small curvature if the radius of the sphere is large. *The "curvature" of a spherical wavefront is defined as* $1/r$, where r is the radius of the surface which constitutes the wavefront, and hence the curvature is zero when r is infinitely large, as in the case of a plane wavefront.

When a plane wavefront is incident on a convex lens L, a spherical wavefront, S, of radius f emerges from the lens, where f is the focal length of the lens, Fig. 513 (i). Parallel rays, which are normal to the plane wavefront, are thus refracted towards F, the focus of the lens. Now the curvature of a plane wavefront is zero, and the curvature of the spherical wavefront S is $1/f$. Thus the convex lens impresses a curvature of $1/f$ on a wavefront incident on it, and $1/f$ is accordingly defined as the *converging power* of the lens.

$$\therefore \text{ Power}, P, = \frac{1}{f} \qquad . \qquad . \qquad . \qquad . \qquad (91)$$

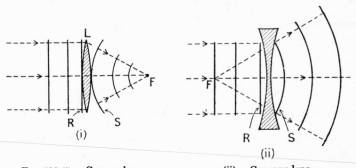

Fig. 513 (i).   Convex lens.   (ii).   Concave lens.

Fig. 513 (ii) illustrates the effect of a *concave* lens on a plane wave-front R. The wavefront S emerging from the lens has a curvature opposite to S in Fig. 253 (i), and it appears to be diverging from a point F behind the concave lens, which is its focus. The curvature of the emerging wavefront is thus $1/f$, where f is the focal length of the lens, and the powers of the convex and concave lens are opposite in sign.

The power of a convex lens is positive, since its focal length is positive, while the power of a concave lens is negative. Opticians use a unit of power called the *dioptre*, *D*, which is defined as the power of a lens of 100 cm. focal length. A lens of focal length f cm. has thus a power P given by

$$P = \frac{1/f}{1/100} \text{ dioptres}$$

$$\text{or} \quad P = \frac{100}{f} \text{ dioptres} \quad . \quad . \quad . \quad (92)$$

A lens of $+8$ dioptres, or $+8D$, is therefore a convex lens of focal length 12·5 cm., and a lens of $-4D$ is a concave lens of 25 cm. focal length.

8. The Lens Equation

Suppose that an object O is placed a distance u from a convex lens, Fig. 514. The spherical wavefront A from O which reaches the lens has a radius of curvature u, and hence a curvature $1/u$. Since the convex lens impresses a curvature of $1/f$ on the wavefront (proved p. 699), the spherical wavefront B emerging from the lens into

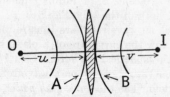

Fig. 514.   Effect of lens on wavefront.

the air has a curvature $\left(\dfrac{1}{u} + \dfrac{1}{f}\right)$. But the curvature is also given by $\dfrac{1}{v}$, where v is the image distance IB from the lens.

$$\therefore \quad \frac{1}{v} = \frac{1}{u} + \frac{1}{f}$$

It can be seen that the curvature of A is of an opposite sign to that of B; and taking this into account, the lens equation $\dfrac{1}{v} + \dfrac{1}{u} = \dfrac{1}{f}$ is obtained.

A similar method can be used for a concave lens, which is left as an exercise for the student.

EXERCISES XXXI

1. Explain how the refraction of light is accounted for on the wave theory, and point out the physical significance of the refractive index. (*C.*)

2. Show how the wave theory of light accounts for the laws of reflection and refraction, and describe a terrestial method of measuring the velocity of light. (*W*.)

3. What do you understand by the wave theory of light? Give some account of its early development and discuss the experimental evidence on which it is based. (*N*.)

4. How did Huyghens explain the reflection of light on the wave theory? Using Huyghens' conceptions, show that a series of light waves diverging from a point source will after reflection at a plane mirror appear to be diverging from a second point, and calculate its position. (*C*.)

5. Explain how the *corpuscular theory* of Newton accounted for the laws of reflection and refraction. What experimental evidence showed that the theory was incorrect?

6. (*a*) Compare the wave theories of light and of sound. (*b*) Describe *one* method for the determination of the velocity of light. (*W*.)

7. How is the refraction of light explained (*a*) on the wave theory, (*b*) on the corpuscular theory of light? Show, in each case, how Snell's law of refraction is derived from the theory.

A spectator on the bank of a swimming-pool sees an object at the bottom of the pool in line with the reflection in the water of the end of a diving-board vertically above it. Assuming that his eyes, and the diving-board, are each 4 ft. above the surface of the water, and that his distance from the diving-board is 24 ft., what is the depth of the pool? [Refractive index of water = 4/3.] (*O*. & *C*.)

CHAPTER XXXII

INTERFERENCE, DIFFRACTION, POLARISATION OF LIGHT

INTERFERENCE OF LIGHT

THE beautiful colours seen in thin films of oil in the road, or in soap bubbles, are due to a phenomenon in light called *interference*. Newton discovered that circular coloured rings were obtained when white light illuminated a convex lens of large radius of curvature placed on a sheet of plane glass (p. 706), which is another example of interference. As we saw in Sound, interference can be used to measure the wavelength of sound waves (p. 636). By a similar method the phenomenon can be used to measure the wavelengths of different colours of light. Interference of light has also many applications in industry.

The essential conditions, and features, of interference phenomena have already been discussed in connection with sound waves. As there is an exact analogy between the interference of sound and light waves we can do no better than to recapitulate here the results already obtained on pp. 634–636:

1. Permanent interference between two sources of light can only take place if they are *coherent* sources, i.e., they must have the same frequency and be always in phase with each other. (This implies that the two sources of light must have the same colour.)

2. If the coherent monochromatic light sources are P, Q, a bright light is observed at B if the path-difference, QB—PB, is a whole number of wavelengths, Fig. 515. (This corresponds to the case of a

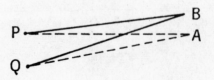

FIG. 515. Interference of light.

loud sound heard at B if P, Q were two coherent sources of sound.) A bright light is observed at A if PA = QA, in which case the path-difference is zero.

3. If the path-difference is an odd number of half wavelengths, darkness is observed at the point under consideration. (This corresponds to silence at the point in the case of two coherent sound sources.)

1. Young's Experiment

From the preceding, it can be understood that two conditions are essential to obtain an interference phenomenon. (i) Two coherent sources of light must be produced, (ii) the coherent sources must be very close to each other as the wavelength of light is very small, otherwise the bright and dark portions in front of the sources tend to overlap and no interference pattern is obtained.

One of the first demonstrations of the interference of light waves was given by YOUNG in 1801. He placed a source, S, of monochromatic light in front of a narrow slit C, and arranged two very narrow slits A, B, close to each other, in front of C. Much to his delight, Young observed bright and dark bands on either side of O on a screen T, where O is on the perpendicular bisector of AB, Fig. 516.

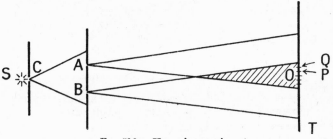

Fig. 516.   Young's experiment.

Young's observations can be explained by considering the light from S illuminating the two holes A, B. Since the light diverging from A has exactly the same frequency as, and is always in phase with, the light diverging from B, A and B act as two close coherent sources. Interference thus takes place in the shaded region, where the light beams overlap, Fig. 516. As AO = OB, a bright band is obtained at O. At a point P close to O, such that BP − AP = $\lambda/2$, where λ is the wavelength of the light from S, a dark band is obtained (p. 703). At a point Q such that BQ − AQ = λ, a bright band is obtained; and so on for either side of O. Young demonstrated that the bands were due to interference by covering A or B, when the bands disappeared.

Young's experiment is not easy to carry out. FRESNEL designed an experiment on similar principles which has the great advantage of enabling the wavelength to be accurately measured.

2. Fresnel's Biprism Experiment

Fresnel used a biprism R which had a very large angle of nearly 180°, and placed a narrow slit S, illuminated by monochromatic light, in front of it so that the refracting edge was parallel to the slit, Fig. 517. The light emerging after refraction from the two halves, L, Q, of the prism can be considered to come from two sources, A, B, which are the virtual images of the slit S in L, Q respectively. Thus A, B are coherent sources; further, as R has a very large obtuse angle, A and B are close together. Thus an interference pattern is observed in the region of O where the emergent light from the two sources overlap, as shown by the shaded portion of Fig. 517, and bright and dark bands can be seen

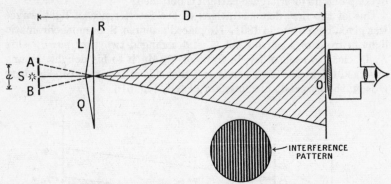

Fig. 517. Fresnel's biprism experiment (not to scale).

through an eye-piece at O directed towards R, Fig. 517. By using cross-wires, and moving the eye-piece by a screw arrangement, the distance y between successive bright bands can be measured. It is shown below that the wavelength λ of the light source S is given by

$$\lambda = \frac{ay}{D} . \qquad . \qquad . \qquad . \qquad . \qquad (93)$$

where a is the distance between A, B, and D is the distance from the slit to the eye-piece. Plate I, B, p. 708.

3. Theory of Fresnel's Biprism Experiment

Suppose P is a point at a distance x from O, Fig. 518. Then BP = $(BN^2 + NP^2)^{\frac{1}{2}}$. Now BN = D, and

$$NP = NO + OP = \frac{a}{2} + x$$

$$\therefore \quad BP = \left[D^2 + \left(\frac{a}{2} + x \right)^2 \right]^{\frac{1}{2}} = D \left[1 + \frac{\left(\frac{a}{2} + x \right)^2}{D^2} \right]^{\frac{1}{2}}$$

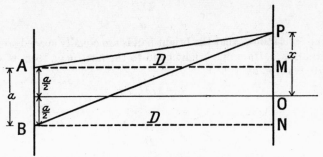

Fig. 518. Theory of biprism experiment.

Now D is very large compared with $(a/2 + x)$. Thus, from the binomial theorem,

$$BP = D\left[1 + \tfrac{1}{2}\frac{\left(\dfrac{a}{2} + x\right)^2}{D^2}\right]$$

$$= D + \frac{\left(\dfrac{a}{2} + x\right)^2}{2D}$$

Also, $\qquad AP = (AM^2 + MP^2)^{\frac{1}{2}}$

But $\qquad MP = OP - PM = x - \dfrac{a}{2}$

$\therefore \qquad AP = \left[D^2 + \left(x - \dfrac{a}{2}\right)^2\right]^{\frac{1}{2}}$

$$= D\left[1 + \frac{\left(x - \dfrac{a}{2}\right)^2}{D^2}\right]^{\frac{1}{2}}$$

$$= D + \frac{\left(x - \dfrac{a}{2}\right)^2}{2D}\text{, using the binomial theorem.}$$

$\therefore \qquad BP - AP = D + \dfrac{\left(\dfrac{a}{2} + x\right)^2}{2D} - D - \dfrac{\left(x - \dfrac{a}{2}\right)^2}{2D}$

$$= \frac{2ax}{2D} = \frac{ax}{D}$$

But $BP - AP = n\lambda$ for a bright band, where n is an integer (p. 307).

$$\therefore \qquad \frac{ax}{D} = n\lambda$$

or $\quad x = \dfrac{n\lambda D}{a}$ . . . . . (i)

From (i) it follows that the bright bands are equally spaced, and that the distance, y, from one bright band to the next (e.g., from $n = 9$ to $n = 10$) is given by

$$y = \frac{\lambda D}{a}$$

$$\therefore \quad \lambda = \frac{ay}{D} \quad\quad \text{. . . . .} \quad \text{(ii)}$$

as stated on p. 704. This relation also holds for Young's experiment, p. 703.

The distance, a, between the images, A, B, of the slit can be measured by placing a suitable convex lens between the biprism and the eye-piece. The distance h_1 between the two slits seen is then measured by moving the eye-piece. If the convex lens is moved again, another position can be obtained when the two slits are again in focus, and the distance h_2 between them is again measured (see "Displacement method", p. 501). Since $\dfrac{h_1}{a} = \dfrac{a}{h_2}$ (see p. 503), it follows that $a^2 = h_1 h_2$, or $a = \sqrt{h_1 h_2}$. Thus a is found; and as y, D can be measured, the wavelength λ can be calculated from (ii).

4. Newton's Rings

Newton discovered an example of interference which is known as "Newton's rings". In this case a lens L is placed on a sheet of plane glass, L having a lower surface of very large radius of curvature, Fig. 519. By means of a sheet of glass G monochromatic light from a

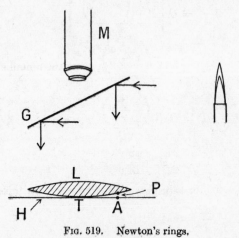

Fig. 519. Newton's rings.

sodium flame, for example, is reflected downwards towards L; and when the light reflected upwards is observed through a microscope M focused on H, a series of bright and dark rings is seen. The circles have increasing radius, and are concentric with the point of contact T of L with H.

Consider the air-film PA between A on the plate and P on the lower lens surface. Some of the incident light is reflected from P to the microscope, while the remainder of the light passes straight through to A, where it is also reflected to the microscope and brought to the same focus. The two rays of light have thus a net path difference of $2t$, where $t = $ PA. The same path difference is obtained at all points round T which are distant TA from T; and hence if $2t = n\lambda$, where n is an integer and λ is the wavelength, we might expect a bright *ring* with centre T. Similarly, if $2t = (n + \frac{1}{2})\lambda$, we might expect a dark ring.

When a ray is reflected from an optically *denser* medium, however, a phase change of 180° occurs in the wave, which is equivalent to its acquiring an extra path difference of $\lambda/2$ (see also p. 657). The truth of this statement can be seen by the presence of the dark spot at the centre, T, of the rings. At this point there is no geometrical path difference between the rays reflected from the lower surface of the lens and H, so that they should be in phase when they are brought to a focus and should form a bright spot. The dark spot means, therefore, that one of the rays suffers a phase change of 180°. Taking the phase change into account, it follows that

$$2t = n\lambda \text{ for a } dark \text{ ring} \quad . \quad . \quad . \quad . \quad (94)$$

and
$$2t = (n + \frac{1}{2})\lambda \text{ for a } bright \text{ ring} \quad . \quad . \quad (95)$$

where n is an integer. Young verified the phase change by placing oil of sassafras between a crown and a flint glass lens. This liquid had a refractive index greater than that of crown glass and less than that of flint glass, so that light was reflected at an optically denser medium at each lens. A bright spot was then observed in the middle of the Newton's rings, showing that no net phase change had now occurred.

The grinding of a lens surface can be tested by observing the appearance of the Newton's rings formed between it and a flat glass plate when monochromatic light is used. If the rings are not perfectly circular, the grinding is imperfect. See Plate I, A, p. 708.

5. Measurement of Wavelength by Newton's Rings

The radius r of a ring can be expressed in terms of the thickness, t, of the corresponding layer of air by simple geometry. Suppose TO is produced to D to meet the completed circular section of the lower surface PQ of the lens, PO being perpendicular to the diameter TD through T, Fig. 520. Then, from the well-known theorem concerning the segments of chords in a circle, TO. OD = QO. OP. But AT = $r = $ PO, QO = OP = r, AP = $t = $ TO, and OD = $2a - $ OT = $2a - t$.

$$\therefore \quad t(2a - t) = r \times r = r^2$$
$$\therefore \quad 2at - t^2 = r^2$$

But t^2 is very small compared with $2at$, as a is large.

$$\therefore \quad 2at = r^2$$

$$\therefore \quad 2t = \frac{r^2}{a} \quad . \quad . \quad . \quad . \quad . \quad . \quad \text{(i)}$$

But
$$2t = (n + \tfrac{1}{2})\lambda \text{ for a bright ring.}$$

$$\therefore \quad \frac{r^2}{a} = (n + \tfrac{1}{2})\lambda \quad . \quad . \quad . \quad . \quad . \quad \text{(96)}$$

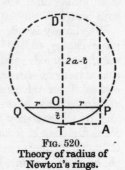

Fig. 520.
Theory of radius of
Newton's rings.

The first bright ring obviously corresponds to the case of $n = 0$ in equation (96); the second bright ring corresponds to the case of $n = 1$. Thus the radius of the 15th bright ring is given from (96) by $r^2/a = 14\tfrac{1}{2}\lambda$, from which $\lambda = 2r^2/29a$. Knowing r and a, therefore, the wave-length λ can be calculated. Experiment shows that the rings become narrower when blue or violet light is used in place of red light, which proves, from equation (96), that the wavelength of violet light is shorter than the wavelength of red light. Similarly it can be proved that the wavelength of yellow light is shorter than that of red light and longer than the wavelength of violet light.

The radius r of a particular ring can be found by using a travelling microscope to measure its diameter. The radius of curvature, a, of the lower surface of the lens can be measured accurately by using light of known wavelength λ', such as the green in a mercury-vapour lamp or the yellow of a sodium flame; since $a = r^2/(n + \tfrac{1}{2})\lambda'$ from (96), the radius of curvature a can be calculated from a knowledge of r, n, λ'.

6. Lloyd's Mirror

In 1834 LLOYD obtained interference bands on a screen by using a plane mirror M, and illuminating it with light nearly at grazing

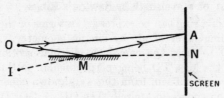

Fig. 521. Lloyd's mirror experiment.

PLATE I

A.—Newton's rings, formed by interference of yellow light between a convex lens and a flat glass plate. (*Page* 707.)

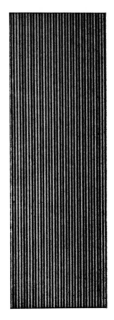

B.—Fresnel's biprism interference bands (magnified). (*Page* 704.)

C.—Diffraction rings in the shadow of a small circular disc. The bright spot is at the centre of the geometrical shadow. (*Page* 714.)

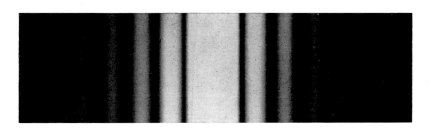

D.—Diffraction bands formed by a single small rectangular aperture. (*Page* 713.)

By permission of the Head of the Physics Department, Northampton College of Advanced Technology, London.

Plate II

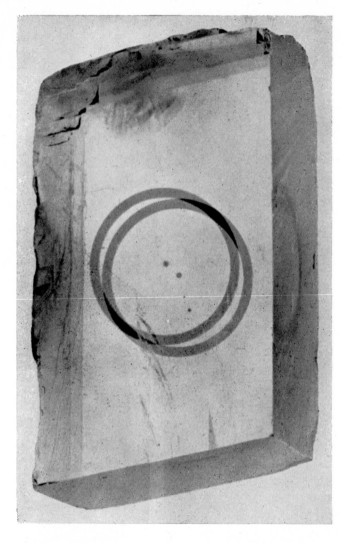

Double Refraction. A ring with a spot in the centre, photographed through a crystal of Iceland spar. The light forms two rings and two spots. (*Page 723.*)

By permission of the Head of the Physics Department, Northampton College of Advanced Technology, London.

incidence, coming from a slit O parallel to the mirror, Fig. 521. A point such as A on the screen is illuminated (i) by a ray OA and (ii) by a ray OM reflected along MA, which appears to come from the virtual image I of O in the mirror. Since O and I are close coherent sources interference bands are obtained on the screen.

Experiment showed that the band at N, which corresponds to the point of intersection of the mirror and the screen, was *dark*; since ON = IN, this band might have been expected, before the experiment was carried out, to be bright. Lloyd concluded that a phase change of 180°, equivalent to half a wavelength, occurred by reflection at the mirror surface, which is a denser surface than air (see p. 707).

7. Interference in Thin Films

If a beam of white light is incident on a thin film of liquid with parallel sides, colours are usually seen. These colours, which can be observed in a soap-bubble or a thin film of oil in the road, are due to an interference phenomenon; they are also obtained in thin transparent films of other substances such as glass. If a beam of *monochromatic* light is incident on a thin film, bright and dark bands can be observed.

Consider a ray AO of monochromatic light incident on a thin parallel-sided film of thickness t and refractive index μ. Fig. 522 is exaggerated for clarity. Some of the light is reflected at O along ON, while the remainder is refracted into the film, where reflection occurs at B. The ray then emerges into the air along CM, which is parallel to ON, and if ON, CM are combined by a lens, or by the eye-lens, a bright or dark band is observed according to the path difference of the rays.

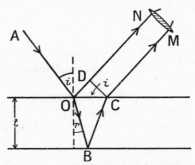

Fig. 522.   Interference in thin plates.

If light travels a distance d in *glass*, it would travel a distance cd/v in *air* in the same time, where c, v are the velocities of light in air and glass respectively. Now $c/v = \mu$ for glass (p. 697). Hence the distance d in glass is equivalent to a distance μd in air, and the latter is called the **optical path** of the distance d in the glass.

Since OB, BC are in a médium of refractive index μ, the optical path difference, p, between ON and OBCM is given by

$$p = \mu\,(OB + BC) - OD \quad . \quad . \quad . \quad . \quad (i)$$

where CD is the perpendicular from C to ON. Suppose r is the angle of refraction in the film at O. By drawing a perpendicular from B to OC, it can be seen that $OB = t/\cos r$; and hence $BC = t/\cos r$, as triangle OBC is isosceles. Also, $OC = 2t \tan r$, from triangle OCB.

$$\therefore \quad OD = OC \sin i = 2t \tan r \sin i,$$

where i is the angle of incidence at O. But $\sin i = \mu \sin r$, from the law of refraction.

$$\therefore \quad OD = 2t \tan r \times \mu \sin r = 2\mu t \sin^2 r/\cos r.$$

From (i), it follows that

$$p = \mu \left(\frac{2t}{\cos r} \right) - \frac{2\mu t \sin^2 r}{\cos r} = \frac{2\mu t\,(1 - \sin^2 r)}{\cos r} = \frac{2\mu t \cos^2 r}{\cos r}$$

$$\therefore p = 2\mu t \cos r \quad . \quad . \quad . \quad . \quad (ii)$$

One other point has not yet been taken into consideration. As stated on p. 707, a phase difference of 180° occurs when a wave is reflected at the surface of a denser medium, which occurs at O in Fig. 522. The phase change is equivalent to a path change of $\lambda/2$, where λ is the wavelength (p. 707), and hence the total path difference, from (ii), is $2\mu t \cos r \pm \lambda/2$.

For a bright band, the total path difference must be a whole number of wavelengths. Taking into account the additional length of $\lambda/2$ caused by the phase change, we can see that

for a bright band, $2\mu t \cos r = (n + \tfrac{1}{2}) \lambda$ . . . . (97)

and *for a dark band*, $2\mu t \cos r = n\lambda$ . . . . . (98)

where n is an integer.

Colours of thin films. The colours of thin films illuminated by white light can now be easily explained. Those colours in the spectrum whose wavelengths satisfy the condition $2\mu t \cos r = n\lambda$ are not seen, and the light observed is thus deficient in that particular colour. If the blue were missing, for example, the colour would be yellow or red. In this way the thin film appears to have colours which depend mainly on the thickness of the film.

8. Broad (Extended) Source and Interference in Thin Parallel Films

If a thin parallel film is illuminated by a *diverging* beam of mono-chromatic light obtained by using an extended or broad source like a bunsen burner sodium flame, a number of *circular* bright and dark curves can be seen. Fig. 523 illustrates how interference is obtained from the light originating from points a, b which is refracted at an angle a into the film.

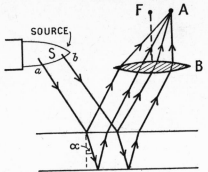

FIG. 523.   Interference with extended source.

The emergent rays are combined by the eye-lens or a glass lens B, and a dark band is formed at A if $2\mu t \cos a = n\lambda$, with the usual notation. If the light is incident on the film in every plane a circular band is obtained, whose centre is F, the focus of B.

When a *parallel* beam of monochromatic light is incident on the thin film, the angle of refraction r in the film and the thickness t are constant. The film thus appears uniformly bright at all points if the condition $2\mu t \cos r = (n + \frac{1}{2})\lambda$ is obeyed, and is uniformly dark if $2\mu t \cos r = n\lambda$. If the film is illuminated by a parallel beam of *white* light, the transmitted light appears to have dark bands across it when viewed through a spectroscope. The latter separates the colours, and a dark band is obtained where the condition $2\mu t \cos r = n\lambda$ is satisfied for the particular colour.

9. Interference in Thin Wedge Films

If a non-parallel thin film, a wedge, is illuminated by a parallel beam of monochromatic light, *straight* bright and dark bands are seen which are parallel to the line of intersection, X, of the two planes forming the wedge. Fig. 524 illustrates how interference is obtained at D when a ray AO is incident at O on the film. The reflected ray interferes with the emergent ray after the latter has traversed a thickness t of the wedge, and a dark band is situated at D if $2\mu t \cos r = n\lambda$. Since t is constant along the line PO which is parallel to X, a straight dark band is observed by the eye-lens, or glass lens, L, focused on D, which is almost on the wedge (compare Newton's rings, p. 707). The formation of other bright and dark bands is due to the variation of t at different parts of the wedge, since r is constant when a parallel beam is incident on the film.

The width of a thin air wedge at any point can be found by illuminating the wedge normally by monochromatic light, and counting the number n of bright bands from that point to the line of intersection of the

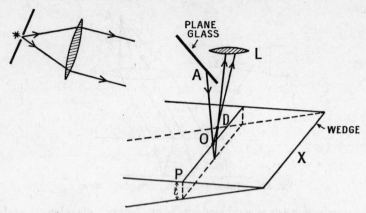

FIG. 524. Interference in thin wedge films (not to scale).

wedge, assuming the wedge closed at one end. Since a change in path difference of the light from one bright band to the next is λ, the wavelength, the thickness t of the wedge is given by $2t = n\lambda$; and as n and λ are known, t can easily be calculated from this relation.

EXAMPLE

What are Newton's rings and under what conditions can they be observed? Explain how they can be used to test the accuracy of grinding of the face of a lens. The face of a lens has a radius of curvature of 50 cm. It is placed in contact with a flat plate and Newton's rings are observed normally with reflected light of wavelength 5×10^{-5} cm. Calculate the radii of the fifth and tenth bright rings. (C.)

First parts. See text.

Second part. With the usual notation, for a bright ring we have

$$2t = (n + \tfrac{1}{2})\lambda \qquad \cdots \qquad \text{(i)}$$

where t is the corresponding thickness of the layer of air.

But, from geometry,
$$2t = \frac{r_n{}^2}{a} \qquad \cdots \qquad \text{(ii)}$$

where r_n is the radius of the ring and a is the radius of curvature of the lens face (p. 708).

$$\therefore \quad \frac{r_n{}^2}{a} = (n + \tfrac{1}{2})\lambda$$

$$\therefore \quad r_n{}^2 = (n + \tfrac{1}{2})\lambda a \qquad \cdots \qquad \text{(iii)}$$

The first ring corresponds to $n = 0$ from equation (iii). Hence the fifth ring corresponds to $n = 4$, and its radius r is thus given by

$$r^2 = (4 + \tfrac{1}{2}) \times 5 \times 10^{-5} \times 50$$

$$\therefore \quad r = \sqrt{\frac{9 \times 5 \times 10^{-5} \times 50}{2}} = 0.106 \text{ cm.}$$

The tenth ring corresponds to $n = 9$ in equation (iii), and its radius is thus given by

$$r^2 = 9\tfrac{1}{2} \times 5 \times 10^{-5} \times 50$$

$$\therefore \quad r = 0.154 \text{ cm.}$$

DIFFRACTION OF LIGHT

In 1665 GRIMALDI observed that the shadow of a very thin wire in a beam of light was much broader than he expected. The experiment was repeated by Newton, but the true significance was only recognised more than a century later, after Huyghens' wave theory of light had been resurrected. The experiment was one of a number which showed that light could bend round corners in certain circumstances.

We have seen how interference patterns, for example, bright and dark bands, can be obtained with the aid of two sources of light close to each other. These sources must be coherent sources, i.e., they must have the same amplitude and frequency, and always be in phase with each other. Consider two points on the *same wavefront*, for example the two points A, B, on a plane wavefront arriving at a narrow slit in a screen, Fig. 525. A and B can be considered as secondary sources of light, an aspect introduced by Huyghens in his wave theory of light (p. 695); and as they are on the same wavefront, A and B have identical amplitudes and frequencies and are in phase with each other. Consequently A, B, are coherent sources, and we can expect to find an interference pattern on a screen S in front of the slit, provided the latter is small compared with the wavelength of light. For a short distance beyond the edges M, N, of the projection of AB, i.e., in the geometrical shadow, observation shows that there are some alternate bright and dark bands. Thus light can travel round corners. The phenomenon is called *diffraction*, and, like interference, it has enabled scientists to measure accurately the wavelength of light. See Plate I, D, p. 708.

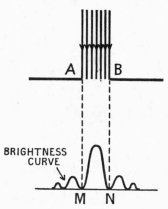

FIG. 525.   Diffraction of light.

If a source of white light is observed through the eyelashes, a series of coloured images can be seen. These images are due to interference between sources on the same wavefront, and the phenomenon is thus an example of diffraction. Another example of diffraction was unwittingly deduced by POISSON at a time when the wave theory was new. Poisson considered mathematically the combined effect of the wavefronts round a circular disc illuminated by a distant small source of light, and he came to the conclusion that the light should be visible beyond the disc in the middle of the geometrical shadow. Poisson thought this was impossible; but experiment confirmed his deduction, and he became a supporter of the wave theory of light. See Plate I, C, p. 708.

10. Diffraction Grating

As we have just seen, the phenomenon of diffraction occurs if the width of an illuminated opening is small compared with the wavelength of the light. The *diffraction grating* is a series of narrow openings, produced by ruling parallel lines close to each other on a transparent substance like a glass plate. The lines, ruled by a special machine, are as many as 15,000 to the inch, and can only be seen under a powerful microscope.

Consider a parallel beam of monochromatic light, such as yellow light, incident normally on a diffraction grating which has clear spaces of width a and opaque lines of thickness b. Fig. 526, which is exaggerated for clarity, shows two of the clear spaces and three of the opaque spaces. Suppose P, Q are two points at the edges of the consecutive clear spaces.

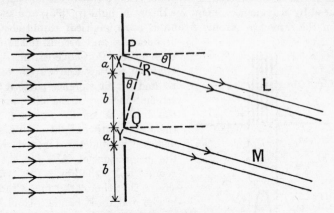

FIG. 526.   Diffraction grating.

Since plane wavefronts arrive at the grating, P and Q act as secondary sources, and we shall suppose PL, QM are rays of light each in a direction θ inclined to the normal to the grating. If the path difference between the rays is a whole number of wavelengths and the rays are brought to a focus, a bright band is obtained. Now the path difference is PR, where QR is the perpendicular from Q to PL, and from Fig. 526, PR = $(a + b) \sin \theta$. Thus a bright band is obtained in the direction θ if

$$(a + b) \sin \theta = n\lambda \quad . \quad . \quad . \quad . \quad (99)$$

where n is an integer.

So far we have only considered the sources P, Q at the *edges* of neighbouring clear spaces. If we take any point X on one space, we can always obtain a point Y on the neighbouring space at a distance $(a + b)$ from it, Fig. 526. X and Y also act as secondary coherent sources on the plane wavefront considered, and hence a bright band is obtained in a direction θ if the condition in (99) is obeyed. By considering all the clear spaces on the grating, it follows that a bright image is formed from all the rays diffracted at an angle θ if $(a + b) \sin \theta = n\lambda$, where n is an integer.

11. Series of Images

The *first order* diffraction image is obtained when $n = 1$. Thus

$$(a + b) \sin \theta = \lambda,$$

or

$$\sin \theta = \frac{\lambda}{a + b}.$$

If the grating has 15,000 lines to the inch, the width, $(a + b)$, of the grating is $\frac{1}{15,000}$ inch, or $\frac{2 \cdot 54}{15,000}$ centimetres, using 2·54 cm. = 1 inch. Suppose yellow light, of wavelength $\lambda = 5,890 \times 10^{-8}$ cm., is used to illuminate the grating. Then

$$\sin \theta = \frac{\lambda}{a + b} = \frac{5,890 \times 10^{-8} \times 15,000}{2 \cdot 54} = 0 \cdot 3478$$

$$\therefore \quad \theta = 20 \cdot 3°$$

The *second order* diffraction image is obtained when $n = 2$. In this case $(a + b) \sin \theta = 2\lambda$.

$$\therefore \quad \sin \theta = \frac{2\lambda}{a + b} = \frac{2 \times 5,890 \times 10^{-8} \times 15,000}{2 \cdot 54} = 0 \cdot 6956$$

$$\therefore \quad \theta = 44 \cdot 1°$$

If $n = 3$, $\sin \theta = 3\lambda/(a + b) = 1 \cdot 043$. Since the sine of an angle cannot be greater than 1, it is impossible to obtain a third order image with this diffraction grating.

12. Measurement of Wavelength

In conjunction with a spectrometer, the diffraction grating provides an easy and accurate measurement of the wavelength of light. The grating, G, is placed vertically on the table, and is illuminated by parallel monochromatic light from a source S placed near the slit of the collimator C, Fig. 527. On placing the telescope T directly opposite

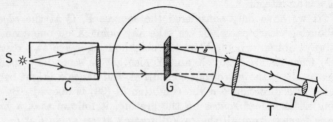

FIG. 527.   Measurement of wavelength by diffraction grating.

C, an image of the slit can be seen. This corresponds to $n = 0$ in the equation $(a + b) \sin \theta = n\lambda$, since $\theta = 0$. When T is rotated from this position, the first order image of the slit is seen at an angle θ given by $(a + b) \sin \theta = \lambda$; from which, knowing $(a + b)$ and θ, the wavelength λ can be calculated. A first order image is also seen on the other side of the normal to the grating, and if the telescope is rotated through an angle a in viewing the two images, $\theta = a/2$.

A second order image is obtained by rotating the telescope to an angle θ_1 given by $(a + b) \sin \theta_1 = 2\lambda$. Thus $\lambda = [(a + b) \sin \theta_1]/2$, and knowing θ_1 and $(a + b)$, the wavelength λ can be calculated.

13. Wavelengths of Electro-magnetic Waves

In this book we have encountered rays which affect the sensation of vision (visible rays), rays which cause heat (infra-red rays, p. 466), and rays which cause chemical action (ultra-violet rays, p. 466). As these rays are all due to electric and magnetic vibrations they are examples of **electro-magnetic** waves (see p. 722). Scientists have measured the wavelengths of these waves by a diffraction grating method, and results show a gradual transition in the magnitudes of the wavelength from one type of ray to another. Thus infra-red rays have a longer wavelength than visible rays, which in turn have a longer wavelength than ultra-violet rays. Radio waves are electro-magnetic waves of

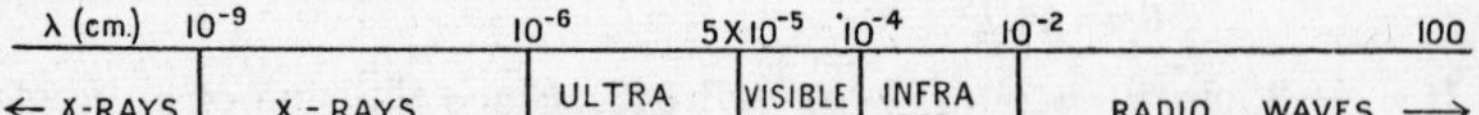

λ (cm.)	10^{-9}		10^{-6}	5×10^{-5}	10^{-4}	10^{-2}		100
← γ-RAYS	X - RAYS		ULTRA VIOLET	VISIBLE SPECTRUM	INFRA RED	RADIO	WAVES →	

FIG. 528.   Spectrum of electromagnetic waves (not to scale).

longer wavelength than infra-red rays, while X-rays and γ-rays, are due to waves of shorter wavelength than ultra-violet waves. The whole spectrum of electro-magnetic waves are shown in Fig. 528; this gives only an approximate value of the limits of the wavelength in the various parts of the spectrum, because these limits are themselves vague.

14. Resolving Power of Telescope Objective

The wave-nature of light limits the sharpness of the image formed by a lens. For simplicity, consider a lens whose aperture is rectangular, of side D, and suppose a plane wave is incident upon the lens, focused at F, Fig. 529. Light spreads out from the wavefront, and some of it reaches the focal plane at points round F. Consider light reaching a point F' from the two halves XY, YZ of the wavefront. If the path-

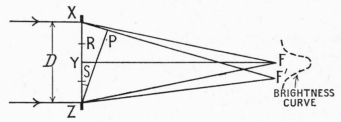

Fig. 529.   Diffraction at rim of lens.

difference XF' − YF' is $\lambda/2$, where λ is the wavelength, light from X destroys that from Y. Similarly, light from a point S midway between X and Y destroys that from R, midway between Y and Z. Thus we can find pairs of points in XY and YZ, the two halves of the wavefronts, such that the light from one point of the pair destroys that from the other. Consequently no light appears at F'. In the case of a circular lens the image formed thus appears as a disc whose brightness diminishes from its centre at F to zero at the circumference of a circle of radius FF' (see brightness curve, Fig. 529). The path difference between XF' and ZF' is λ, and hence if ZP is perpendicular to XF' we may say that XP is equal to λ to a high degree of accuracy. Thus the angle XZP $= \lambda/D$ in radians. Since XZ is perpendicular to FY, and ZP is practically perpendicular to F'Y, angle FYF' = angle XZP $= \lambda/D$. Hence the angle subtended by FF' at the lens $= \lambda/D$, and the radius of the image FF' $= f\lambda/D$, where f is the focal length.

Now consider two parallel beams entering the lens, at an angle a with each other, Fig. 530. The disc images will overlap, but if the centre of one falls on the dark rim of the other, they can *just* be distinguished. For this to happen the angle a must be equal to λ/D. *Thus the*

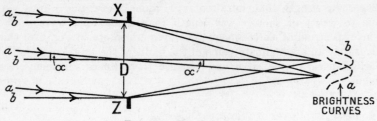

FIG. 530.   Resolving power.

lens cannot "resolve" the images of two distant objects, such as stars, which subtend an angle less than λ/D at the objective. This is called the **resolving power** of the telescope. The expression has to be modified slightly when, as usual, the lens has a circular aperture; the resolving power is then found to be $1.22 \, \lambda/D$. Thus an objective of large diameter increases the resolving power of the telescope.

15. Microscope Condenser and Oil-Immersion Objective

Like the objective and eye-piece of a telescope, the objective and eye-piece of a practical microscope are corrected for chromatic and spherical aberration. In the case of the telescope the object, a star for example, is self-luminous. In the case of the microscope, however, the object, which is usually placed between two glass slides, is non-luminous. Consequently it is illuminated by a condenser, a lens below the object which focuses light reflected by a mirror on to the object, and which is adjusted to get the brightest image.

In microscopes of high magnifying power the object, O, is immersed in cedar oil of refractive index 1·5, and the front surface of the objective, having the same refractive index, dips into the oil, Fig. 531. The **oil-immersion** objective was due to ABBÉ (see p. 445). He showed that the minimum distance between two monochromatic sources of light when they are distinguishable is given by $\lambda/2\mu \sin a$, where λ is the wavelength, $2a$ is the angle subtended by the objective at the objects, and μ is the refractive index of the medium in which the objects

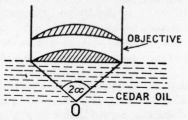

FIG. 531.   Oil-immersion objective.

are situated. Using oil of the same refractive index as the lens Abbé showed that the object could be brought much nearer to the objective than is the case when the object is in air, thus increasing a and hence increasing the resolving power. This arrangement also eliminates spherical aberration.

EXAMPLE

What is meant in optics by (a) interference, (b) diffraction? What part do each of these phenomena play in the production of spectra by a diffraction grating? A parallel beam of sodium light is incident normally on a diffraction grating. The angle between the two first order spectra on either side of the normal is 27° 42'. Assuming that the wavelength of the light is $5,893 \times 10^{-8}$ cm., find the number of rulings per cm. on the grating. (N.)

First part. Briefly, interference is the name given to the phenomena obtained by the combined effect of light waves from two separate coherent sources; diffraction is the name given to the phenomena due to the combined effect of light waves from secondary sources on the same wavefront. In the diffraction grating, production of spectra is due to the interference between secondary sources on the same wavefront which are separated by a multiple of $(a + b)$, where $(a + b)$ is the width of the grating rulings (p. 714).

Second part. The first order spectrum occurs at an angle $\theta = \frac{1}{2} \times 27° 42'$ $= 13° 51'$.

But
$$(a + b) \sin \theta = \lambda$$
$$\therefore \quad a + b = \frac{\lambda}{\sin \theta} = \frac{5,893 \times 10^{-8}}{\sin 13° 51'} \text{ cm.}$$
$$\therefore \text{ number of rulings per cm. } = \frac{1}{(a + b)} = \frac{\sin 13° 51'}{5,893 \times 10^{-8}}$$
$$= 4,062$$

POLARISATION OF LIGHT

We have shown that light is a wave-motion of some kind, i.e., that it is a travelling vibration. For a long time after the wave-theory was revived it was thought that the vibrations of light occurred in the same direction as the light wave travelled, analogous to sound waves. Thus light waves were thought to be longitudinal waves (p. 610). Observations and experiments, however, to be described shortly, showed that the vibrations of light occur in planes *perpendicular* to the direction along which the light wave travels, and thus light waves are *transverse* waves.

16. Polarisation of Transverse Waves

Suppose that a rope ABCD passes through two parallel slits B, C, and is attached to a fixed point at D, Fig. 532 (a). Transverse waves can be set up along AB by holding the end A in the hand and moving it up and down in all directions perpendicular to AB, as illustrated by the arrows in the plane X. A wave then emerges along BC, but unlike the

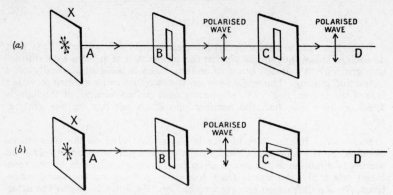

FIG. 532. Formation of plane-polarised waves.

waves along AB, which are due to transverse vibrations in every plane, it is due only to transverse vibrations parallel to the slit at B. This type of wave is called a *plane-polarised* wave. It shows a *lack of symmetry about the direction of propagation*, because a slit C allows the wave to pass through when it is parallel to B, but prevents it from passing when C is perpendicular to B, Fig. 532 (*a*), (*b*). If B is turned so that it is perpendicular to the position shown in Fig. 532 (*a*), a polarised wave is again obtained along BC; but the vibrations which produce it are perpendicular to those shown between B and C in Fig. 532 (*a*).

17. Polarised Light

Years ago it was discovered accidentally that certain natural crystals affect light passing through them. *Tourmaline* is an example of such a crystal, *quartz* and *calcite* or *iceland spar* are others (p. 723). Suppose two tourmaline crystals, P, Q, are placed with their axes, *a*, *b*, parallel, Fig. 533 (i). If a beam of light is incident on P, the light emerging from Q appears slightly darker. If Q is rotated slowly about the line of vision, with its plane parallel to P, the emergent light becomes darker and darker, and at one stage it disappears. In the latter case the axes, *a*, *b* of the crystals are perpendicular, Fig. 533 (ii). When Q is rotated further the light reappears, and becomes brightest when the axes *a*, *b* are again parallel.

This simple experiment leads to the conclusion that light waves are *transverse* waves; otherwise the light emerging from Q could never be extinguished by simply rotating this crystal. The experiment, in fact, is analogous to that illustrated in Fig 532, where transverse waves were set up along a rope and plane-polarised waves were obtained by means of a slit B. Tourmaline is a crystal which, because of its internal molecular structure, transmits only those vibrations of light parallel to its axis. Consequently plane-polarised light is obtained beyond the

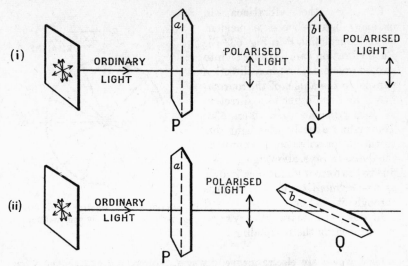

FIG. 533.   Formation of plane-polarised light waves.

crystal P, and no light emerges beyond Q when its axis is perpendicular to P. Fig. 273 should be compared with Fig. 532.

18. Vibrations in Unpolarised and Polarised Light

Fig. 534 (i) is an attempt to represent diagrammatically the vibrations of ordinary or unpolarised light at a point A when a ray travels in a direction AB. X is a plane perpendicular to AB, and ordinary (unpolarised) light may be imagined as due to vibrations which occur in every one of the millions of planes which pass through AB and are perpendicular to X. As represented in Fig. 534 (ii), the amplitudes of the vibrations are all equal.

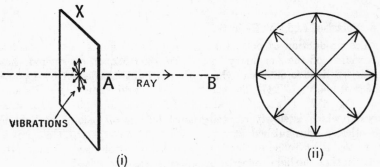

FIG. 534 (i).   Vibrations occur in every plane perpendicular to AB.
        (ii).   Vibrations in ordinary light.

Consider the vibrations in ordinary light when it is incident on the tourmaline P in Fig. 533 (i). Each vibration can be resolved into two components, one in a direction parallel to the axis a of the tourmaline P and the other in a direction m perpendicular to a, Fig. 535. Tourmaline absorbs the light due to the latter vibrations, known as the *ordinary* rays, allowing the light due to the former vibrations, known as the *extraordinary* rays, to pass through it. Thus plane-polarised light, due to the extraordinary rays, is produced by the tourmaline.

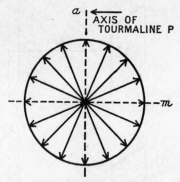

Fig. 535. Production of plane-polarised waves by tourmaline.

Light waves are electro-magnetic waves. Theory and experiment show that the vibrations of light are *electro-magnetic* in origin; a varying electric force E is present, with a varying magnetic force H which has the same frequency and phase. E and H are perpendicular to each other, and are in a plane at right angles to the ray of light, Fig. 536. Experiments recently carried out have shown that the electric force in a light wave affects a photographic plate and causes fluorescence, while the magnetic force, though present, plays no part in this effect of a light wave. On this account the vibrations of the electric force, E, are now chosen as the "vibrations of light", and the planes containing the vibrations shown in Fig. 534 (i), (ii) are those in which only the electric forces are present.

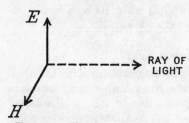

Fig. 536. Electro-magnetic wave.

19. Polarised Light by Reflection

The production of polarised light by tourmaline is due to *selective absorption* of the "ordinary" rays. In 1808 MALUS discovered that polarised light is obtained when ordinary light is reflected by a plane sheet of glass (p. 724). The most suitable angle of incidence is about 56°, Fig. 537. If the reflected light is viewed through a tourmaline crystal which is slowly rotated about the line of vision, the light is practically extinguished at one position of the crystal. This proves that the light reflected by the glass is plane-polarised. Malus also showed that the light reflected by water is plane-polarised.

The production of the polarised light by the glass is explained as follows. Each of the vibrations of the incident (ordinary) light can be

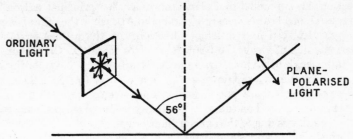

FIG. 537.   Formation of plane-polarised waves by reflection.

resolved into a component parallel to the glass surface and a component perpendicular to the surface. The light due to the components parallel to the glass is reflected, but the remainder of the light, due to the components perpendicular to the glass, is *refracted* into the glass. Thus the light reflected by the glass is plane-polarised.

20. Polarisation by Double Refraction

We have already considered two methods of producing polarised light. The first observation of polarised light, however, was made by BARTHOLINUS in 1669, who placed a crystal of iceland spar on some words on a sheet of paper. To his surprise, two images were seen through the crystal. Bartholinus therefore gave the name of *double refraction* to the phenomenon, and experiments more than a century later showed that the crystal produced plane-polarised light when ordinary light was incident on it. See Plate II, p. 709.

Iceland spar is a crystalline form of calcite (calcium carbonate) which cleaves in the form of a "rhomboid" when it is lightly tapped; this is a solid whose opposite faces are parallelograms. When a beam of unpolarised light is incident on one face of the crystal, its internal molecular structure produces two beams of polarised light, E, O, whose vibrations are perpendicular to each other, Fig. 538. If the incident

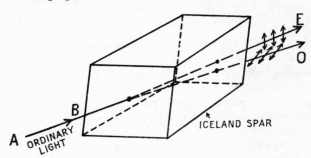

FIG. 538.   Action of iceland spar.

direction AB is parallel to a plane known as the "principal section" of the crystal, one beam O emerges parallel to AB, while the other beam E emerges displaced in a different direction. As the crystal is rotated about the line of vision the beam E revolves round O. On account of this abnormal behaviour the rays in E are called "extraordinary" rays; the rays in O are known as "ordinary" rays (p. 722). Thus two images of a word on a paper, for example, are seen when an iceland spar crystal is placed on top of it; one image is due to the ordinary rays, while the other is due to the extraordinary rays.

With the aid of an iceland spar crystal Malus discovered the polarisation of light by reflection (p. 722). While on a visit to Paris he gazed through the crystal at the light of the sun reflected from the windows of the Palace of Luxemburg, and observed that only one image was obtained for a particular position of the crystal when it was rotated slowly. The light reflected from the windows could not therefore be ordinary (unpolarised) light, and Malus found it was plane-polarised.

21. Nicol Prism

We have seen that a tourmaline crystal produces polarised light, and that the crystal can be used to detect such light (p. 720.) NICOL designed a crystal of iceland spar which is widely used for producing and detecting polarised light, and it is known as a *Nicol prism*. A crystal whose faces contain angles of 72° and 108° is broken into two halves along the diagonal AB, and the halves are cemented together by a layer of canada balsam, Fig. 539. The refractive index of the

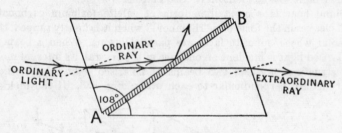

Fig. 539. Action of Nicol prism.

crystal for the ordinary rays is 1·66, and is 1·49 for the extraordinary rays; the refractive index of the canada balsam is about 1·55 for both rays, since canada balsam does not produce polarised light. A critical angle thus exists between the crystal and canada balsam for the ordinary rays, but not for the extraordinary rays. Hence total reflection of the former rays takes place at the canada balsam if the angle of incidence is large enough, as it is with the Nicol prism. The emergent light is then due to the extraordinary rays, and is polarised.

The prism is used like a tourmaline crystal to detect plane-polarised light, namely, the prism is held in front of the beam of light and is rotated. If the beam is plane-polarised the light seen through the Nicol prism varies in intensity, and is extinguished at one position of the prism.

22. Differences Between Light and Sound Waves

We are now in a position to distinguish fully between light and sound waves. The physical difference, of course, is that light waves are due to varying electric and magnetic forces, while sound waves are due to vibrating layers or particles of the medium concerned. Light can travel through a vacuum, but sound can not travel through a vacuum. Another very important difference is that the vibrations of the particles in sound waves are in the same direction as that along which the sound travels, whereas the vibrations in light waves are perpendicular to the direction along which the light travels. Sound waves are therefore *longitudinal* waves, whereas light waves are *transverse* waves. As we have seen, sound waves can be reflected and refracted, and can give rise to interference phenomena; but no polarisation phenomena can be obtained with sound waves since they are longitudinal waves, unlike the case of light waves.

EXERCISES XXXII

1. Describe a method by which the phenomenon of optical interference may be demonstrated experimentally.

Two similar flat rectangular pieces of glass are in contact along one edge, while the opposite edges are separated by a thin piece of tin foil. When examined in sodium light, reflected perpendicularly from the thin air film, 40 bright interference bands are observed. What is the thickness of the foil if its edge just coincides with the centre of the last interference band? [Take the wavelength of sodium light as $5\cdot89 \times 10^{-5}$ cm.] (*C.*)

2. Describe and explain the interference effects produced in light by thin films.

What experimental arrangement would you make in order to obtain accurate measurements of the diameter of Newton's rings seen by reflected sodium light when a plane-convex lens is placed in contact with a plane glass surface? If the diameter of a certain bright ring (call it the nth) is found to be 0·56 cm. and the diameter of the $(n + 20)$th bright ring is found to be 1·34 cm., the wavelength of the sodium light being $5\cdot89 \times 10^{-5}$ cm., calculate the radius of curvature of the surface of the lens. Explain the purpose of measuring the diameter of at least *two* of the rings. (*N.*)

3. What are the main facts which support the following statements: (*a*) that light consists of wave-motion and not a flow of particles; (*b*) that the vibrations of light waves are transverse and not longitudinal; (*c*) that the wavelengths of light waves are much shorter than those of sound? Describe (in brief outline only) *one* experiment which proves that the velocity of light is extremely great. (*W.*)

4. Give an account of the theory of the production of a spectrum by means of a plane diffraction grating. How does it differ from the spectrum produced by means of a prism?

Parallel light consisting of two monochromatic radiations of wavelengths 6×10^{-5} cm. and 4×10^{-5} cm. falls normally on a plane transmission grating ruled with 5,000 lines per cm. What is the angular separation of the second order spectra of the two wavelengths? (*C.*)

5. Describe and account for the interference fringes produced when an air film which is enclosed between two parallel glass plates inclined at a small angle is viewed normally by monochromatic reflected light.

How may the angle of the wedge be determined by measuring the spacing of such fringes? Give a diagram of the apparatus used. (*N.*)

6. Explain the phenomenon of the interference of light, and point out the conditions which must be fulfilled in order to demonstrate the phenomenon.

Describe, and give the theory of, some experiment based on this phenomenon for determining the wavelength of sodium light. (*C.*)

7. Explain fully how the colours of soap-bubbles are formed.

8. Explain what is meant by *interference of light, polarisation of light*. Describe and explain **one** experiment by which **each** of these phenomena may be demonstrated. (*C.*)

9. State the conditions for light waves to interfere. Describe and explain an experiment illustrating how these conditions are realised in practice and show how the wavelength of sodium light may be determined from suitable measurements. (*C.*)

10. What is plane-polarised light?

Explain why two images of an object are seen through a crystal of Iceland Spar. What would be seen if the object were viewed through two crystals, one of which was slowly rotated about the line of vision?

How would you produce a plane-polarised beam of light by reflection from a glass surface? (*C.*)

11. What is meant by the polarisation of light? How is polarisation explained on the hypothesis that light has wave properties?

Describe how polarisation can be produced and detected by reflexion. Mention another way of obtaining polarised light and describe how you would determine which of the two methods is the more effective.

Describe briefly *two* uses of polarised light. (*N.*)

PART FOUR

MAGNETISM AND ELECTRICITY

CHAPTER XXXIII

MAGNETISM

MAGNETIC FIELDS AND FORMULAE

Natural magnets were known some thousands of years ago, and in the eleventh century A.D. the Chinese invented the magnetic compass. This consisted of a magnet, floating on a buoyant support in a dish of water. The respective ends of the magnet, where iron filings are attracted most, are called the north and south poles.

In the thirteenth century the properties of magnets were studied by Peter Peregrinus. He showed that

like poles repel and **unlike poles attract.**

His work was forgotten, however, and his results were rediscovered in the sixteenth century by Dr. Gilbert, who is famous for his researches in magnetism and electrostatics.

1. Ferromagnetism.

About 1823 Sturgeon placed an iron core into a coil carrying a current, and found that the magnetic effect of the current was increased enormously. On switching off the current the iron lost nearly all its magnetism. Iron, which can be magnetized strongly, is called a *ferromagnétic* material. Steel, made by adding a small percentage of carbon to iron, is also ferromagnetic. It retains its magnetism, however, after removal from a current-carrying coil, and is more difficult to magnetize than iron. Nickel and cobalt are the only other ferromagnetic elements in addition to iron, and are widely used for modern magnetic apparatus. A modern alloy for permanent magnets, called *alnico*, has the composition 54 per cent. iron, 18 per cent. nickel, 12 per cent. cobalt, 6 per cent. copper. It retains its magnetism extremely well, and, by analogy with steel, is therefore said to be magnetically very hard. Alloys which are very easily magnetized, but do not retain their magnetism, are said to be magnetically soft. An example is *mumetal*, which contains 76 per cent. nickel, 17 per cent. iron, 5 per cent. copper, 2 per cent. chromium.

2. Force between Poles.

The poles of a magnet are spread over a large area near each end, and single poles cannot exist. Nevertheless, the concept of a "magnetic pole" has been found useful by scientists such as Lord Kelvin and Clerk Maxwell in developing formulae and measurements in magnetism. The *magnetic length* of a magnet, the distance between its poles, is less than its geometrical length.

729

If we wish to make experiments on the forces between magnetic poles, the best we can do is to use magnets consisting of long thin rods of steel, strongly magnetized, and ending in soft iron spheres (Fig. 540). The poles can then be considered as though they are points at the centres of the spheres. Fig. 540 shows two such magnets arranged so that the force between one pair of their poles, N, N', can be measured.

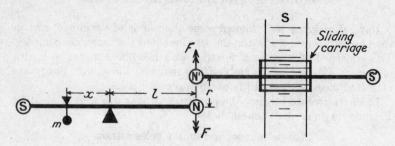

FIG. 540.   Measurement of force between poles (Hibbert's magnetic balance)

As these poles are so much closer together than any of the others, the forces between the others can be neglected in comparison with the force F between N and N'.

Tò measure the force F, we slide the mass m along the magnet NS until it is horizontal. Then, if l is the distance of the pole from the pivot, x the distance of m from the pivot, and g the acceleration due to gravity, we have, by taking moments,

$$F \times l = mg \times x.$$

$$\therefore F = \frac{mgx}{l}.$$

The scale S gives the distance r between the poles N, N'. If F is measured for different values of r, it is found that, to a good approximation,

$$F \propto \frac{1}{r^2}. \qquad \dotfill \quad (1)$$

This is called the *inverse-square law* of magnetism. It can be formally stated as follows:

The force between two given poles varies inversely as the square of the distance between them.

The most accurate experimental verification of the inverse-square law is due to Gauss (see p. 738).

3. Unit Pole-strength. Formula for Force.

The strengths of poles are based on the "unit pole-strength", or briefly "unit pole". The unit pole, a theoretical concept, is defined as *the pole which, placed one centimetre away from a similar pole* in vacuo, *repels it with a force of one dyne.* "Unit poles" are expressed in "c.g.s. units". Laboratory magnets have pole-strengths of the order of 100 to 1,000 c.g.s.

If the poles are in air, the force between them is less than *in vacuo* in the ratio $1 : 1.00000003$; for practical purposes this difference may be neglected. The force F between point poles, of strengths m_1, m_2 c.g.s., r centimetres apart in air or *vacuo* is thus given by

$$F = \frac{m_1 m_2}{r^2} \text{ dynes.} \qquad \ldots \ldots \ldots \quad (2)$$

4. Magnetic Fields.

The region round a magnet, where a magnetic force is experienced, is called a *magnetic field*. The appearance of a magnetic field is quickly obtained by iron filings, and accurately plotted with a small compass, as the reader knows. The *direction* of a magnetic field is taken as the direction which a north pole would move if placed in the field.

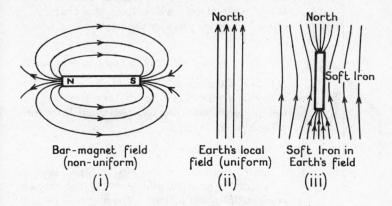

Bar-magnet field (non-uniform) (i)   Earth's local field (uniform) (ii)   Soft Iron in Earth's field (iii)

Fig. 541.   Magnetic fields.

Fig. 541 shows a few typical fields. The field round a bar-magnet is "non-uniform", that is, its strength and direction vary from place to place (Fig. 541 (*i*)). The earth's field locally, however, is uniform (Fig. 541 (*ii*)). A bar of soft iron placed north–south becomes magnetized by induction by the earth's field, and the lines of force become concentrated in the soft iron (Fig. 541 (*iii*)). The tangent to a line of force at a point gives the direction of the magnetic field at that point.

5. Magnetic Field-strength or Intensity.

The strength or intensity H of a magnetic field is defined as *numerically equal to the force in dynes exerted on a unit pole in the field.* Magnetic intensity is expressed in *oersteds*, after Oersted, a pioneer of the magnetic effect of a current. The *earth's horizontal component*, which we shall denote by H_0, is the component of the earth's field in a horizontal direction, and its magnitude is about 0·18 or 0·2 oersted. In moving-coil instruments, powerful fields of the order of thousands of oersteds are used.

Since H dynes is the force exerted on a unit pole in a field of H oersteds, it follows that the force F on a pole of strength m c.g.s. in the field is given by

$$F = Hm \text{ dynes.} \qquad \ldots \ldots \quad (3)$$

6. Couple on Magnet in Field. Magnetic Moment.

When a magnet is placed in a magnetic field, forces act on its poles, each of magnitude Hm dynes from (3), if the field is uniform over the

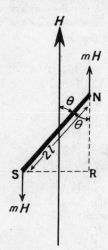

region occupied by the magnet (Fig. 542). If the magnet makes an angle θ with the field, these forces set up a *couple*, which tends to set the magnet along the field. A "couple" is the name given to two equal and opposite forces whose lines of action do not coincide, and they have a turning-effect or moment given by

one force × perpendicular distance between forces.

If $2l$ is the magnetic length of the magnet, that is, l is the magnetic *half*-length, then, from Fig. 542, the perpendicular distance between the forces, $SR = 2l \sin \theta$.

∴ Moment of couple $= Hm \times 2l \sin \theta = 2lmH \sin \theta$.

The product $2ml$ is the product "pole-strength × magnetic length", and is called the *magnetic moment*, M, of the magnet. The magnetic moment is a constant of the magnet. Thus, from above,

Fig. 542. Restoring couple on magnet in uniform field.

$$\text{moment of couple} = MH \sin \theta. \quad . \quad (4)$$

This equation applies to real magnets with diffuse poles, as well as to idealized ones with point poles. For we may regard any real magnet as a bundle of very thin ones, to each of which equation (4) applies. The moment M in equation (4) is then the sum of the products "pole-strength × separation between poles", taken over all the magnets in the bundle. The moment of a magnet is a definite quantity which can be determined by experiment. Since $\sin 90° = 1$, it follows from (4) that the moment M can be defined as numerically equal to *the moment of the couple acting on a magnet placed at right angles to a uniform field of 1 oersted intensity.*

7. Field on Axis of Bar-magnet.

Let us now calculate the intensity H of the field due to a magnet of pole-strength m and magnetic length $2l$ at a point P on its axis, distant

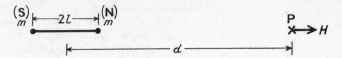

FIG. 543.   Field on axis of thin bar-magnet.

d from the centre of the magnet (Fig. 543). Gauss called this a point in the *end-on* or *A position*. Then, considering a unit pole at P and applying the law of force between poles (p. 731),

$$H = \frac{m \times 1}{(d-l)^2} - \frac{m}{(d+l)^2}$$

$$= \frac{m[(d+l)^2 - (d-l)^2]}{(d-l)^2(d+l)^2} = \frac{m \times 4dl}{(d^2-l^2)^2}.$$

Using magnetic moment $M = 2ml$,

$$\therefore H = \frac{2Md}{(d^2-l^2)^2}. \qquad \cdots \cdots \quad (5)$$

8. Short Bar-magnet.

If a short bar-magnet is considered, and the distance l is small compared with d, then l^2 can be neglected compared with d^2. Thus if $l = d/10$, for example, $l^2 = d^2/100$. In this case an approximate formula for the intensity at P can be given, from (5). Thus

$$H = \frac{2Md}{(d^2)^2} = \frac{2Md}{d^4},$$

$$\therefore H = \frac{2M}{d^3}. \qquad \cdots \cdots \cdots \quad (6)$$

Equations (5) and (6) were first derived by Gauss (1777–1855), who calculated the field due to a bar-magnet at various positions round it.

9. Field on Equator of Bar-magnet.

The equator, or equatorial plane, of a bar-magnet is a plane at right angles to its axis, and passing midway between its poles (Fig. 544). A point P on the equator of a magnet is equidistant from its poles; Gauss called it a point in the *broadside, or B, position*. Let us denote the distance of the point P from either pole by p, its distance from the axis by d, the magnet's pole-strength by m, and its magnetic length by $2l$. Then a unit north pole at P experiences two forces, each of magnitude

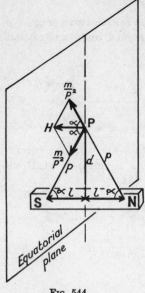

FIG. 544.
The Gauss B position.

m/p^2, in the directions shown, i.e. at an angle a respectively to the axis (Fig. 544). The components of these forces at right angles to the axis are respectively $m \sin a/p^2$, and thus cancel. Their components parallel to the axis are each $m \cos a/p^2$ acting in the same direction, and thus the total field intensity, H, at P of the magnet is *parallel to its axis*.

The magnitude H of the intensity is given by

$$H = \frac{2m \cos a}{p^2}.$$

From Fig. 544 we have $\cos a = l/p$, and $p = (d^2 + l^2)^{1/2}$.

$$\therefore H = \frac{2ml}{p^3} = \frac{2ml}{(d^2 + l^2)^{3/2}},$$

$$\therefore H = \frac{M}{(d^2 + l^2)^{3/2}}, \quad \cdots \quad (7)$$

where M is the magnetic moment.

10. Short Bar-magnet.

If d is at least ten times as great as l, then l^2 can be neglected compared with d^2. From (7) it follows that in this case

$$H = \frac{M}{d^3}. \qquad \cdots \cdots (8)$$

On comparing equation (6) with equation (8), it is seen that, at a given distance d, the field due to a short bar-magnet in the end-on (Gauss A) position is twice that in the broadside (Gauss B) position.

11. Gauss's General Formulae.

If the force F between point poles varies as the nth power of the distance r between them, i.e. $F \propto 1/r^n$, then, at a great distance d from a bar-magnet, or a large distance d from a short magnet, Gauss showed that (see p. 735)

$$H_A = \frac{nM}{d^{n+1}}, \qquad \cdots \cdots (9)$$

where H_A is the field intensity at a point on the axis (Gauss A position). For a point on the equator (Gauss B position), he showed that (see p. 735)

$$H_B = \frac{M}{d^{n+1}}, \qquad \cdots \cdots (10)$$

where H_B is the field intensity. From these equations it follows that

$$\frac{H_A}{H_B} = n. \qquad \ldots \ldots \ldots \quad (11)$$

We shall see later how Gauss used this result to verify the inverse-square law (p. 738).

12. Proof of Gauss's Formulae.

From p. 733 it follows that the intensity H_A at a point on the axis is given, assuming an nth-power law, by

$$H_A = \frac{m}{(d-l)^n} - \frac{m}{(d+l)^n} = \frac{m[(d+l)^n - (d-l)^n]}{(d^2 - l^2)^n}.$$

Expanding the numerator by the binomial theorem, and neglecting squares and higher powers of l, then

$$(d+l)^n = d^n + nd^{n-1}l, \quad \text{and} \quad (d-l)^n = d^n - nd^{n-1}l.$$

$$\therefore H_A = \frac{2mnd^{n-1}l}{(d^2)^n} = \frac{nMd^{n-1}}{d^{2n}} = \frac{nM}{d^{n+1}}.$$

From Fig. 544 (p. 734) it follows that the intensity H_B at a point on the equator is given by

$$H_B = \frac{2m \cos \alpha}{p^n} = \frac{2ml}{p^{n+1}} = \frac{M}{(d^2 + l^2)^{(n+1)/2}}.$$

Neglecting l^2,

$$H_B = \frac{M}{d^{n+1}}.$$

DEFLECTION MAGNETOMETER AND APPLICATIONS

13. Description and Theory.

The deflection magnetometer is used in measurements on magnets and magnetic fields. It consists of a short magnet X or needle pivoted at the centre of a circular graduated scale (Fig. 545). A long aluminium pointer is rigidly attached at right angles to X to measure the magnet's deflection, and parallax is eliminated by means of a mirror below the pointer. When no other magnets are near, the magnetic needle points north–south.

The magnetic field investigated, H, is always placed so that it is *perpendicular to the earth's field*, H_0, that is, east–west, at the small pivoted magnet (Fig. 545). In this case the magnet is deflected from the north–south direction, and comes to rest at an angle θ to its original direction. The moment of the couple due to H is now exactly equal and

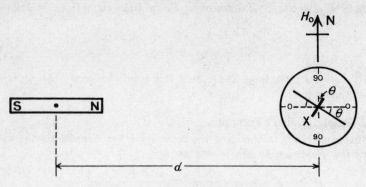

FIG. 545. Deflection magnetometer.

opposite to that due to H_0. Thus if M is the magnetic moment of the magnet, it follows from our formula on p. 732 that

$$MH \sin (90° - \theta) = MH_0 \sin \theta.$$
$$\therefore H \cos \theta = H_0 \sin \theta.$$
$$\therefore H = H_0 \tan \theta. \qquad \ldots \ldots (12)$$

This is the fundamental formula of the deflection magnetometer; it only holds, of course, when H is perpendicular to H_0.

14. Readings of Magnetometer.

Let us suppose that a bar-magnet is set due west of a deflection magnetometer as in Fig. 546 (i). The field H_A due to the magnet then

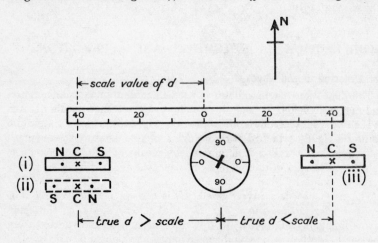

FIG. 546. Use of deflection magnetometer in Gauss A position.

produces a deflection. The following readings are taken to eliminate possible errors:

(1) Both ends of the pointer are read—this corrects for the fact that the pivot of the magnetic needle may not be at the centre of the graduated scale.

(2) Reverse the bar-magnet, into position (ii), and again read both ends of the pointer—this corrects for the fact that the geometrical centre of the magnet, C, may not be midway between its equivalent point-poles.

(3) Place the bar-magnet at the same distance east of the magnetometer, in position (iii), and repeat the four readings—this eliminates the error if the pivot of the magnet is not at the zero of the distance-scales.

The average deflection, θ, is then the average of the eight readings taken (readings in the range 30°–60° only should be taken), and can be tabulated as follows:

END-ON POSITION

Distance d	Magnet W.				Magnet E.				Average Deflection θ_A
	N pole W.		N pole E.		N pole W.		N pole E.		
	θ_1	θ_2	θ_3	θ_4	θ_5	θ_6	θ_7	θ_8	$\dfrac{\theta_1 + \ldots + \theta_8}{8}$

15. Investigations with Magnetometer. Field along Axis of Magnet. End-on or Gauss A position.

(1) Since the field H_A is perpendicular to H_0, as in Fig. 546, then, if θ_A is the deflection,

$$H_A = H_0 \tan \theta_A. \qquad \ldots \ldots \quad (13)$$

Thus, as H_0 is constant, $H_A \propto \tan \theta_A$. We can therefore find how H_A varies with the distance d from the middle of the magnet by plotting $\tan \theta_A$ against d, for varying distances.

(2) For a *short* bar-magnet, $H_A = 2M/d^3$. Thus, from (13),

$$\frac{2M}{d^3} = H_0 \tan \theta_A.$$

$$\therefore \frac{1}{d^3} \propto \tan \theta_A, \quad \text{or} \quad d^3 \propto \cot \theta_A.$$

Thus we can show that the field is proportional to $1/d^3$ by plotting d^3 v. $\cot \theta_A$, and seeing whether a straight-line graph is obtained which passes through the origin.

16. Field along Equator of Magnet. Broadside or Gauss B position.

To investigate the field along the equator or broadside position, we set up the magnetometer and magnet as in Fig. 547. The magnet's field H_B must be perpendicular to the earth's for us to use the magnetometer, and the magnet must therefore lie east–west, but on a north–south line through the magnetometer. We take sets of eight readings

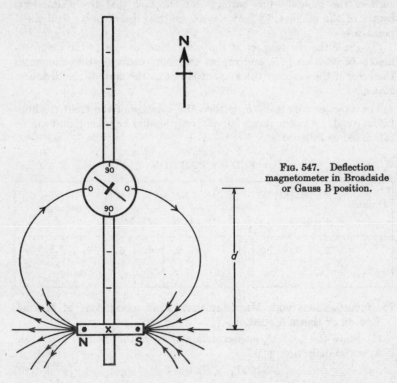

Fig. 547. Deflection magnetometer in Broadside or Gauss B position.

at each distance d, tabulate them as shown on p. 737, and calculate the average deflection θ_B for each distance. Then, since $H_B = H_0 \tan \theta_B$,

$$H_B \propto \tan \theta_B.$$

Thus, as before, the variation of H_B with d can be obtained by plotting $\tan \theta_B$ v. d. Also, for a *short* bar-magnet, $H_B = M/d^3$ (p. 734). We can test this relation by plotting $1/d^3$ v. $\tan \theta_B$, or d^3 v. $\cot \theta_B$, when a straight-line graph passing through the origin should be obtained.

17. Gauss's Method of verifying Inverse-square Law.

On p. 735 we compared the fields H_A and H_B in the end-on (Gauss A) and broadside (Gauss B) positions respectively for a short magnet. It was shown that, assuming an nth-power law,

$$\frac{H_A}{H_B} = n,$$

the distance d being the same for the two cases.

The deflection magnetometer can be used to find n. In the way indicated previously, the average deflections θ_A, θ_B in the end-on and broadside positions respectively are taken at the *same* distance d large compared with l. Now

$$\frac{H_A}{H_B} = \frac{\tan \theta_A}{\tan \theta_B}.$$

On calculating $\tan \theta_A / \tan \theta_B$, it is found that this ratio is equal to 2, within the limits of experimental error. Thus $n = 2$, and hence the law is an inverse-square law.

18. Approximate Method of verifying Inverse-square Law.

An approximate method of verifying the inverse-square law is to use one pole of a long ball-ended magnet (Fig. 548). A wooden stand W holds one pole of the magnet, south pole for example, vertically above the pivot of the magnetometer, so that this pole does not deflect the needle. The other, north, pole of the magnet is placed level with the needle and at a distance d east or west of it.

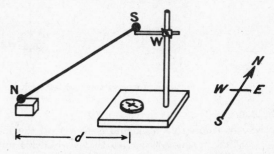

Fig. 548. Testing inverse-square law by deflection.

If H is the field intensity at the needle due to the north pole, then $H = H_0 \tan \theta$, where θ is the deflection. Thus $H \propto \tan \theta$. The distance d is varied by sliding the south pole up and down the stand W, and $\tan \theta$ is plotted against $1/d^2$. A straight line passing through the origin is obtained, showing that $H \propto 1/d^2$.

19. Comparison of Magnetic Moments. Deflection Method.

The moments of two magnets can be compared by placing each of them in turn at a measured distance d from the pivot of a deflection magnetometer, in the Gauss A position (see Fig. 546). The procedure on p. 737 is followed, and the average of the eight readings is taken; the distance d should be such that the deflection is between $40°$ and $50°$.

With the usual notation,

$$H_1 = \frac{2M_1 d_1}{(d_1{}^2 - l_1{}^2)^2} = H_0 \tan \theta_1,$$

and

$$H_2 = \frac{2M_2 d_2}{(d_2{}^2 - l_2{}^2)^2} = H_0 \tan \theta_2.$$

Dividing and rearranging terms,

$$\therefore \quad \frac{M_1}{M_2} = \frac{(d_1{}^2 - l_1{}^2)^2 d_2 \tan \theta_1}{(d_2{}^2 - l_2{}^2)^2 d_1 \tan \theta_2}. \quad \dots \dots \text{(14)}$$

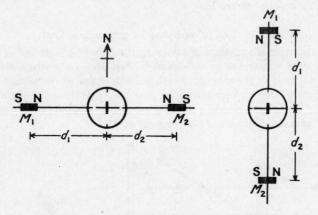

Fig. 549. Comparison of moments by null deflection.

20. Null Method.

Another way of comparing moments is to set up the magnets on opposite sides of the magnetometer, so that their fields oppose each other (Fig. 549). The distance of one magnet is adjusted until the magnetometer shows no deflection, and the respective distances d_1, d_2 are measured. The observations are repeated with each magnet turned end-for-end, and with each magnet on each side of the magnetometer.

Since the field intensities at the magnetometer are equal, it follows that, with the usual notation,

$$\frac{2M_1 d_1}{(d_1{}^2 - l_1{}^2)^2} = \frac{2M_2 d_2}{(d_2{}^2 - l_2{}^2)^2},$$

$$\therefore \quad \frac{M_1}{M_2} = \frac{(d_1{}^2 - l_1{}^2)^2 d_2}{(d_2{}^2 - l_2{}^2)^2 d_1}. \quad \dots \dots \text{(15)}$$

21. Short Magnets.

The deflection and null methods can be used, of course, for comparing the moments of short bar-magnets. Since $H = 2M/d^3$, with the usual notation, the formula in (14) becomes

$$\frac{M_1}{M_2} = \frac{d_1{}^3 \tan \theta_1}{d_2{}^3 \tan \theta_2}, \quad \ldots \ldots \quad (16)$$

and the formula in (15) becomes

$$\frac{M_1}{M_2} = \frac{d_1{}^3}{d_2{}^3}. \quad \ldots \ldots \quad (17)$$

22. Magnetic-length Measurement.

The magnetic length, $2l$, of a magnet can be approximately found by observing the deflection θ in a magnetometer in (a) the end-on or (b) the broadside position, for varying distances d.

(a) *End-on.* In this case we have

$$\frac{2Md}{(d^2 - l^2)^2} = H_0 \tan \theta.$$

$$\therefore \frac{2M}{H_0} d \cot \theta = (d^2 - l^2)^2,$$

$$\therefore \sqrt{\frac{2M}{H_0} d \cot \theta} = (d^2 - l^2).$$

On plotting $\sqrt{d \cot \theta}$ v. d^2, a straight-line graph is obtained (Fig. 550). Since $d^2 = l^2$ when $\sqrt{d \cot \theta} = 0$, the intercept on the d^2-axis gives l^2. Thus l, and hence $2l$, is obtained.

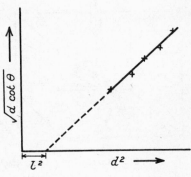

(a) Result

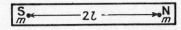

(b) Interpretation

FIG. 550. Testing equation for field along axis of bar-magnet.

(b) *Broadside.* In this case we have

$$\frac{M}{(d^2 + l^2)^{3/2}} = H_0 \tan \theta,$$

$$\therefore d^2 + l^2 = \left(\frac{M}{H_0}\right)^{2/3} (\cot \theta)^{2/3}.$$

On plotting $(\cot \theta)^{2/3}$ v. d^2, a straight-line graph is obtained. (Fig. 551). The intercept on the d^2-axis is $- l^2$, since $d^2 + l^2 = 0$ when $(\cot \theta)^{2/3} = 0$. Thus l, and hence $2l$, is found.

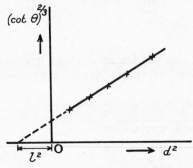

FIG. 551. Broadside to bar-magnet.

VIBRATIONS OF MAGNET. VIBRATION (OSCILLATION) MAGNETOMETER

23. Vibration of Magnet in a Uniform Field.

Consider a magnet suspended from a torsionless silk thread in a draught-shield. If it is gently disturbed, for example by momentarily bringing a piece of iron towards it, the magnet *vibrates* about the magnetic meridian (Fig. 552).

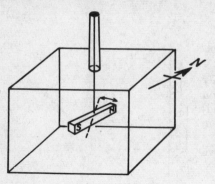

The oscillation occurs because, when the magnet is deflected from the meridian, a couple acts on it, tending to bring it back into the meridian. On p. 732 it was shown that the couple had a moment $MH \sin \theta$, where M is the moment of the magnet, H is the field intensity, and θ is the angle between the magnet and the field. If the angular displacement, θ, is small—say not more than $10°$

Fig. 552. Oscillation of bar-magnet.

—then, to a close approximation, $\sin \theta = \theta$ in radians. The restoring couple C is then given by

$$C = MH\theta. \qquad \ldots \ldots \ldots (18)$$

Thus the restoring couple is proportional to the angular displacement θ, and the magnet therefore makes simple harmonic vibrations (see p. 39).

24. Period of Vibration.

The period of vibration, T, depends on the restoring couple per unit deflection of the magnet; from (18),

$$\frac{C}{\theta} = MH.$$

The period also depends on the moment of inertia K of the magnet, which is determined by its mass, size, and shape. Now from equation (39), p. 70,

$$T = 2\pi \sqrt{\frac{K}{\text{restoring couple per unit deflection}}},$$

$$\therefore T = 2\pi \sqrt{\frac{K}{MH}}. \qquad \ldots \ldots \ldots (19)$$

The number of vibrations made per second, n, or the *frequency* of the vibration, is given by

$$n = \frac{1}{T} = \frac{1}{2\pi} \sqrt{\frac{MH}{K}},$$

$$\therefore n^2 = \frac{MH}{4\pi^2 K},$$

or $\qquad\qquad\qquad H \propto n^2.$ . . . . (20)

This relationship shows that a vibrating magnet may be used to compare magnetic field-strengths, for example, to explore the earth's field over the laboratory. When used in this way it is called a *vibration magnetometer*.

It should be noted that the relations (19) and (20) are true only when the fibre suspending the magnet is torsionless, that is, it exerts a negligible restoring couple when it is twisted. The restoring couple on the magnet is then simply that due to the magnetic field ($MH \sin \theta$), as already assumed. A common material used for the suspension is unspun silk. The magnet must be small so that the whole of it is in the uniform field, and it must be protected from draughts, which would upset the oscillation.

25. Applications of Vibration Magnetometer.

As an illustration of the use of the vibration magnetometer, suppose we wish to investigate the magnetic field H along the equator of a magnet NS (Fig. 553). The magnet is placed with its south pole S

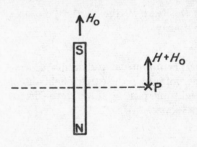

FIG. 553. Field on equator of magnet.

pointing north, in which case the field H at a point P on the equator acts northwards (p. 734). The total field at P is thus $H + H_0$. The number of vibrations per minute, say, of the magnetometer at P is observed.

The vibration magnetometer is then moved along the equator to vary d, and each time the number of vibrations per minute, n, is observed. Finally, the number of vibrations per minute, n_0, in the earth's field is recorded. Now

$$H + H_0 = Kn^2,$$

where K is a constant, from (20), and $H_0 = Kn_0^2$,

$$\therefore H = K(n^2 - n_0^2).$$

Thus $(n^2 - n_0^2)$ is a measure of the field intensity H, and this can be plotted against d to show the variation of H with d.

26. Verification of Inverse-square Law.

The same method can be used to verify the inverse-square law for magnetic poles. A ball-ended magnet is set up in a wooden stand, so that only its north pole creates a horizontal field at the magnetometer (Fig. 554). This pole is placed level with the magnetometer and at a

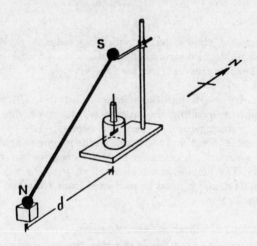

Fig. 554. Verification of inverse-square law with vibration magnetometer.

distance d due south of it, so that the field H due to the pole acts northwards. Then, as explained previously,

$$H \propto (n^2 - n_0^2),$$

where n is the number of vibrations per minute at a distance d, say, from the pole, and n_0 is the number per minute in the earth's field alone. On plotting $(n^2 - n_0^2)$ v. $1/d^2$, a straight line passing through the origin is obtained, thus verifying the inverse-square law.

27. Comparison of Moments.

The method of vibration can be used to compare the moments of two magnets. The magnets are rigidly fixed together, with similar poles adjacent, and allowed to vibrate in the earth's field (Fig. 555(a)). If M_1, M_2, K_1, K_2, are their magnetic moments and moments of inertia respectively, and if H_0 is the earth's horizontal field, then the period of the magnets is

$$T_1 = 2\pi \sqrt{\frac{K_1 + K_2}{(M_1 + M_2)H_0}}.$$

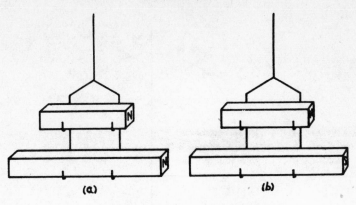

FIG. 555. Comparison of moments by vibration.

The magnets are now fixed together with opposite poles adjacent, and again allowed to vibrate. Fig. 555(b). Their period is now

$$T_2 = 2\pi \sqrt{\frac{K_1 + K_2}{(M_1 - M_2)H_0}}.$$

Therefore

$$\frac{T_2}{T_1} = \sqrt{\frac{M_1 + M_2}{M_1 - M_2}},$$

whence

$$\frac{M_1}{M_2} = \frac{T_2{}^2 + T_1{}^2}{T_2{}^2 - T_1{}^2} \qquad \ldots \ldots \quad (21)$$

EARTH'S MAGNETIC FIELD

28. Earth's Magnetism.

It was Dr. Gilbert who first showed that a magnetized needle, when freely suspended about its centre of gravity, dipped downwards towards the north at about 70° to the horizontal in England. He also found that this *angle of dip* increased with latitude, as shown in Fig. 556, and concluded that the earth itself was, or contained, a magnet. The points where the angle of dip is 90° are called the earth's magnetic poles; they are fairly near to the geographic poles, but their positions are continuously, though slowly, changing. Gilbert's simple idea of the earth as a magnet has had to be rejected. The earth's crust does not contain enough magnetic material to make a magnet of the required strength; the earth's core is, we believe, molten—and molten iron is non-magnetic. The origin of the earth's magnetism is, in fact, one of the great theoretical problems of the present day.

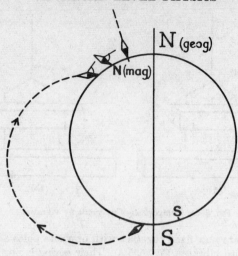

FIG. 556.   Illustrating the angle of dip.

29. Horizontal and Vertical Components.

Since a freely suspended magnetic needle dips downward at some angle δ to the horizontal, the earth's *resultant magnetic field; R*, acts at an angle δ to the horizontal. The "angle of dip", or *inclination*, can thus be defined as the angle between the resultant earth's field and the horizontal. The earth's field has a *vertical component*, V, given by

$$V = R \sin \delta, \qquad \ldots \ldots \quad (22)$$

and a *horizontal component*, H_0, given by

$$H_0 = R \cos \delta. \qquad \ldots \ldots \quad (23)$$

Also,

$$\frac{V}{H_0} = \tan \delta. \qquad \ldots \ldots \quad (24)$$

In previous chapters we have been concerned only with H_0, the horizontal component. This is explained if we consider the forces on the poles of a magnet in a magnetometer, for example, which is pivoted

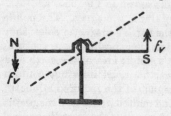

FIG. 557.   A compass-needle is not deflected vertically.

so that it can rotate in a horizontal plane (Fig. 557). Such a magnet can be deflected by the horizontal component of the earth's field, but not by the vertical component. A vertical rotation of the needle would raise its centre of gravity, as shown in Fig. 557, but the forces f_v due to the vertical component of the field are very small compared with the weight of the

needle, and consequently its vertical deflection is too slight to be noticeable. In the earth's field, the needle merely swings horizontally until it
points magnetic north and south.

30. Lines of Force in Combined Fields of Earth and Magnet.

When a magnet is placed in the earth's field, the combined field
contains a *neutral point*, or points, which are places where the resultant
magnetic intensity is zero.

Single Pole. Fig. 558 shows the lines of force round a north pole in
the earth's field—the pole is one end of a very long magnet, which is
held vertical in a wooden clamp. The lines of force of an "isolated" pole
would be radial, by symmetry, that is, they would spread out in straight
lines from the pole. At points north of the pole, however, the earth's
field and that due to the pole are parallel and add (Fig. 558). At points

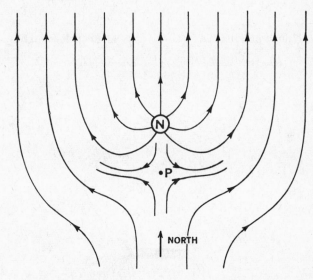

FIG. 558.   Lines of force of north pole in earth's field.

south, the two fields are opposite to each other and subtract. At the
point P the fields are equal, and the resultant field-strength there is
zero. P is a neutral point, and no lines of force pass through P. If *r* is
the distance of P from the pole, of strength *m*, then

$$\frac{m}{r^2} = H_0.$$

Bar-magnet. Fig. 559 shows the lines of force of a bar-magnet in the
earth's field, (*a*) when its north pole points north, (*b*) when its north

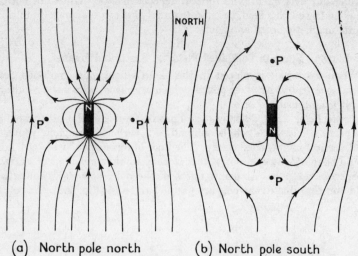

(a) North pole north   (b) North pole south

Fig. 559. Lines of force of bar-magnet in earth's field.

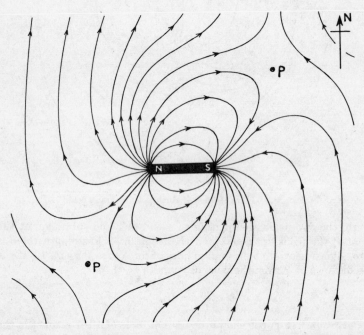

Fig. 560. Magnetic field near bar-magnet with its north pole pointing west

pole points south. Their shapes can be remembered by the fact that a neutral point lies to the north of a south pole, and to the south of a north pole.

If the value of H_0 is known, the moment M of the magnet can be calculated from the position of the neutral point. Thus if d is its distance from the centre of the magnet and l is the half-length, then

$$\frac{2Md}{(d^2 - l^2)^2} = H_0 \quad \text{(Fig. 559}(b)\text{)},$$

and

$$\frac{M}{(d^2 + l^2)^{3/2}} = H_0 \quad \text{(Fig. 559}(a)\text{)}.$$

The lines of force of a bar-magnet lying east–west are shown in Fig. 560.

31. Measurement of Earth's Field and Moment of a Magnet.

By combining vibration and deflection experiments the horizontal component of the earth's magnetic field, H_0, can be obtained from measurements of mass, length, and time. The method of doing this is due to Gauss; before he devised it, there was no way of measuring either the strength of a field or the moment of a magnet.

To start the experiment, we first set up a *deflection magnetometer* at the point P where we wish to determine H_0 (Fig. 561 (a)). A bar-magnet M is placed in the end-on position, and the average deflection θ for a given distance d is found, as explained on p. 737. With the usual notation,

$$\frac{2Md}{(d^2 - l^2)^2} = H_0 \tan \theta \quad \text{(p. 740)}.$$

$$\therefore \; \frac{M}{H_0} = \frac{(d^2 - l^2)^2 \tan \theta}{2d}. \qquad \ldots \ldots \; (i)$$

We now remove the deflection magnetometer, and set up at the point P a draught-case and silk suspension for the magnet (Fig. 561 (b)). We start it vibrating in a horizontal plane with a small amplitude, and find its period T. Then

$$T = 2\pi \sqrt{\frac{K}{MH_0}}, \qquad \ldots \ldots \ldots \; (ii)$$

where K is the moment of inertia of the magnet. $K = $ mass $\times$ $[(l^2/3)+(b^2/12)]$ for a rectangular magnet, where b is the breadth, or mass $\times [(l^2/3)+(r^2/4)]$ for a cylindrical magnet, where r is the cross-section radius.

From (ii), $\qquad MH_0 = \dfrac{4\pi^2 K}{T^2} = x$, say.

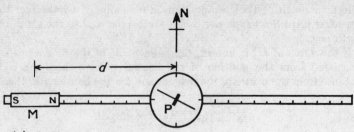

(a) Deflection experiment

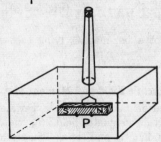

(b) Vibration experiment

FIG. 561. Determination of H_0 and M.

From (i),
$$\frac{M}{H_0} = \frac{(d^2 - l^2)^2 \tan \theta}{2d} = y \text{ say.}$$

$$\therefore MH_0 \div \frac{M}{H_0} = H_0^2 = \frac{x}{y}.$$

$$\therefore H_0 = \sqrt{\frac{x}{y}} = \sqrt{\frac{8\pi^2 K d}{(d^2 - l^2)^2 T^2 \tan \theta}}.$$

Thus H_0 can be calculated. Further,

$$MH_0 \times \frac{M}{H_0} = M^2 = xy, \text{ and thus } M = \sqrt{xy}.$$

Consequently M can also be found.

32. Direction of the Earth's Field; Variation or Declination, and Dip.

To specify the earth's magnetic field at any point, we must state its strength and direction. To specify its direction we must give the direction of the magnetic meridian, and the angle of dip (δ in Fig. 562). In most parts of the world the magnetic meridian does not lie along the geographic meridian (the vertical plane running geographically north–south). The angle between the magnetic and geographic

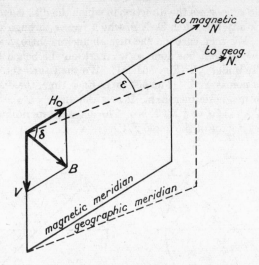

Fig. 562. Magnetic and geographic meridians.

meridians, ε, is called the magnetic variation, or sometimes the declination, at the place concerned; it is shown on the margins of maps.

To specify the strength or intensity of the earth's field we need give only the horizontal component, H_0; the vertical component V, and the total intensity R, are related to it via the angle of dip. Thus

$$\tan \delta = \frac{V}{H_0}, \qquad \cos \delta = \frac{H_0}{R}.$$

We have already seen how to determine H_0; we will see shortly how to measure the variation and dip.

33. Magnetic Meridian; Magnetic Axis.

We cannot take the magnetic meridian simply to be the direction in which a compass needle points, because the needle **may** not be magnetized along the line joining its points (Fig. 563). Of such a magnet we say that its magnetic and geometric axes do not coincide. Let us

Fig. 563. Finding the magnetic meridian.

therefore suppose that we have a body of any shape, which is magnetized in an unknown direction—for example, a disc magnetized along a diameter—and that we have to use it to find the magnetic meridian.

In Fig. 564, NS represents the direction in which the disc is magnetized. First we mark any line, such as XY, which passes through the centre C of the disc. We then suspend the disc about its centre, and allow it to come to rest; when it has done so we mark on the bench the points X'Y' vertically under XY (Fig. 564 (a)). We then turn the disc over, and mark the points X"Y" (Fig. 564 (b)). Each time, the diameter NS lies along the magnetic meridian. If a is the angle between NS and XY, then X'CX" is 2a, and X'CN is a. The magnetic meridian therefore lies along the bisector of the angle X'CX".

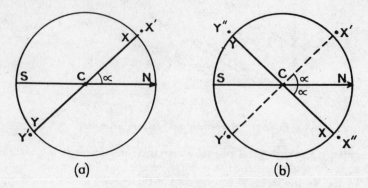

FIG. 564.   A disc magnetised along diameter.

The line NS is called the *magnetic axis* of the disc: if the disc is freely suspended in a uniform magnetic field, then its magnetic axis is the line which sets itself along that field.

34. Angle of Dip Measurement.

The angle of dip can be measured with a magnetized needle suspended so that it can rotate in a vertical plane (Fig. 565). The apparatus is called a *dip circle*. It consists of a vertical divided circle A, which can be rotated about a vertical axis, its orientation being read on a horizontal circle B. At the centre of the vertical circle are agate knife-edges K, on which the axle of the needle rests. The base is fitted with levelling screws S and a spirit level L.

When we are using the dip circle, we first level it. Then we rotate the vertical circle about its vertical axis until the needle points vertically up and down (Fig. 566). This means that the needle is being deflected only by the vertical component of the earth's field, V; the horizontal component H_0 must therefore be acting parallel to the axle of the needle, and the plane of the vertical circle must thus be lying east–west. We now turn the axis through 90° of the vertical circle, using the readings on the horizontal circle; this brings the plane of the

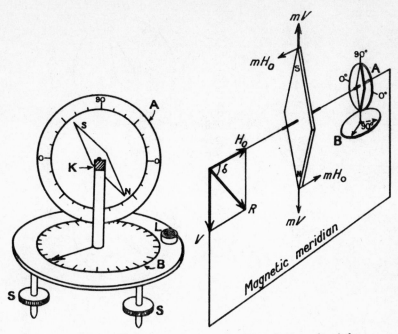

FIG. 565.   A dip-circle.   FIG. 566.   Setting a dip-circle.

vertical circle into the magnetic meridian. If the needle and instrument
are perfect, the ends of the needle, when read against the vertical
circle, give the angle of dip.

35. Errors of Dip-circle.

In practice, the needle and instrument are not perfect. There are
four sources of error:

(*i*) The axle of the needle may not pass through the centre of the
vertical circle (Fig. 567(*a*)). We therefore read both ends of the needle,
as in using a deflection magnetometer.

(*ii*) The 90°–90° line on the vertical circle may not be truly vertical.
If it is tilted as shown on the left of Fig. 567 (*b*), then both ends of the
needle read high. We therefore turn the vertical circle through 180° on
the horizontal circle. Both ends of the needle now read too low, and by
averaging the four readings we get rid of the error.

(*iii*) The magnetic axis of the needle may not coincide with its geometric axis (Fig. 567 (*c*)). This is the error we have already described in
connexion with finding the meridian (p. 752). To allow for it, we turn the
magnet over on its bearings, and repeat the four readings detailed above.

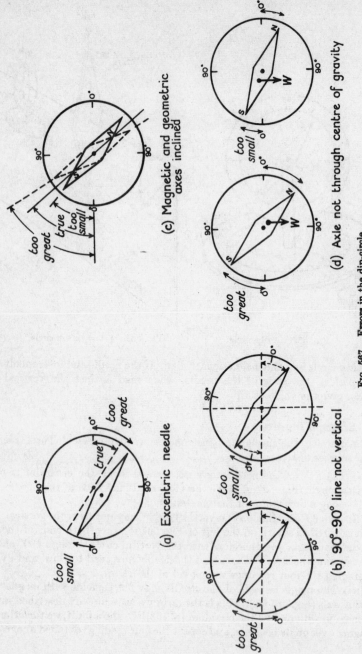

(a) Excentric needle

(b) 90°–90° line not vertical

(c) Magnetic and geometric axes inclined

(d) Axle not through centre of gravity

Fig. 567. Errors in the dip-circle.

(*iv*) The axle of the needle may not pass through its centre of gravity (Fig. 567 (*d*)). If the centre of gravity lies towards the north pole, then the weight of the needle, *W*, makes all the readings too high. We can get rid of this error only by remagnetizing the needle in the opposite direction, and repeating the eight previous readings. Stroking with a bar-magnet will remagnetize the needle strongly enough.

The average of the 16 readings is recorded as the angle of dip.

36. Magnetic Elements, Maps, Changes.

The dip δ, variation ε, and horizontal component H_0 of the earth's field, at any point, are called the *magnetic elements* at that point. Magnetic maps show their values over the earth's surface; they do this by lines joining all points where the value of a given element is the same. The most important of these, to navigators, are the isogonic lines, or isogonals, which join points of equal variation or declination. *Gonia* is Greek for angle; an agonic line is one joining points of zero variation—points, that is to say, where the compass points towards the geographic poles. Lines of equal dip are called isoclinic lines, or iso-clinals; the line of zero dip is called the magnetic equator. Lines of equal horizontal intensity are called isodynamic lines.

The magnetic elements at a given point are not constant. They show small fluctuations with periods of one day, one month, one year, and eleven years. The eleven-year fluctuations are associated with sun-spot activity—the appearance of a new sun-spot is accompanied by great fluctuations, known as magnetic storms. A sun-spot is believed to be a whirling vortex of hydrogen ions, many of which fly off the sun and reach our atmosphere. As they are positively charged, their motion is equivalent to a current, and sets up a magnetic field which is felt on the earth.

The magnetic elements, particularly the variation, also show a very slow change, which is often called the secular change. In 1580 the variation at London was 11° 15′ East, in 1659 it was zero; since then it has been westerly, passing through a maximum value of 24° 30′ in 1820, and in 1945 it was 9° 51′ West. The rate of change is not constant: its average value at present is 8′ a year. These changes are about the same as if the earth's magnetic poles were rotating round its geographic poles in a cone of semi-angle 17°, from east to west, and with a period of about 900 years (Fig. 568).

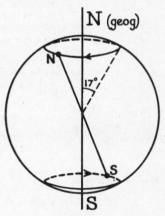

Fig. 568. Apparent motion of earth's magnetic poles.

EXAMPLES ON MAGNETISM

1. Describe an oscillation magnetometer and account for the salient features of its design. A small suspended magnet which makes 20 oscillations per min. in the earth's horizontal field is found to make 30 oscillations per min. at a point due N. and 15 cm. from the centre of a bar-magnet of magnetic length 10 cm. placed horizontally with its axis in the magnetic meridian and with its N. pole towards the N. Calculate the magnetic moment of the magnet (*L.*)

First part (see p. 742).

Second part. Let H = intensity due to the magnet alone,
H_0 = earth's horizontal intensity, 0·2 oersted.

Then since intensity $\propto$ frequency²,

$$\frac{H + H_0}{H_0} = \frac{30^2}{20^2} = \frac{9}{4}.$$

$$\therefore 4H = 5H_0.$$

$$\therefore H = \frac{5}{4} H_0 = \frac{5}{4} \times 0\cdot2 = 0\cdot25 \text{ oersted.}$$

But

$$H = \frac{2Md}{(d^2 - l^2)^2}.$$

$$\therefore \frac{2M \times 15}{(15^2 - 5^2)^2} = 0\cdot25.$$

$$\therefore M = \frac{0\cdot25(15^2 - 5^2)^2}{2 \times 15} = 333 \text{ c.g.s.}$$

2. Prove that the intensity of the magnetic field due to a short bar-magnet at a point on its axis produced is twice the value at a point equally distant in its equatorial plane.

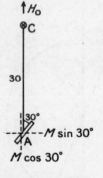

A short bar-magnet of magnetic moment 500 e.m.u. is placed on a horizontal table with its N. pole pointing 30° east of magnetic north. In what direction will a small compass needle set, if it is placed on the table 20 cm. magnetic north of the bar-magnet? (*L.*)

First part. The intensity along the axis can be proved to be $2M/d^3$, and that along the equator to be M/d^3, which is half the former intensity.

Second part. Suppose A is the magnet, and C is the point 20 cm. due north (Fig. 569).

The moment M of the magnet can be resolved along AC and perpendicular to AC. Thus along AC the moment $= M \cos 30°$.

Fig. 569. Example.

$$\therefore \text{ intensity } H_1 \text{ at C, along AC, } = \frac{2M \cos 30°}{20^3} = \frac{2 \times 500 \cos 30°}{20^3}$$

$$= \frac{\cos 30°}{8}. \qquad \qquad \cdots \cdots (i)$$

Perpendicular to AC, the moment $= M \sin 30°$.

$$\therefore \text{ intensity } H_2 \text{ at } C, \text{ perpendicular to AC, } = \frac{M \sin 30°}{20^3} = \frac{500 \sin 30°}{20^3}$$

$$= \frac{\sin 30°}{16}.$$

The direction of the resultant is $\theta°$ to AC (north), given by

$$\tan \theta = \frac{H_2}{H_1} = \frac{\sin 30°}{16} \div \frac{\cos 30°}{8}$$

$$= 0·29 \text{ (approx.)},$$

$$\therefore \ \theta = 16° \text{ (approx.)}.$$

3. What is meant by magnetic dip? Describe and explain how the dip varies along a meridian.

A small dip needle registers 60° when correctly placed relative to the earth's magnetic field. When a short bar-magnet is placed horizontally 20 cm. due S. of, and with its N. pole pointing to, the centre of the needle, the dip changes to 45°. Calculate the magnetic moment of the bar-magnet if the horizontal component of the earth's magnetic field is 0·20 oersted. (*C.*)

First part (see p. 745).

Second part. When the angle of dip is 60°,

$$\frac{V}{H_0} = \tan 60°, \quad \text{or} \quad V = H_0 \tan 60°. \quad \ldots \ldots \ldots \text{ (i)}$$

When the angle of dip is 45°, then

$$\frac{V}{H + H_0} = \tan 45°,$$

where H is the intensity due to the magnet at the needle. Since $\tan 45° = 1$,

$$\therefore \ V = H + H_0.$$

Hence, from (i), $H_0 \tan 60° = H + H_0$, or $0·732 H_0 = H$.

$$\therefore \ H = 0·732 \times 0·2 \text{ oersted.}$$

But

$$H = \frac{2M}{d^3} = \frac{2M}{20^3}.$$

$$\therefore \ \frac{2M}{20^3} = 0·732 \times 0·2.$$

$$\therefore \ M = \frac{0·732 \times 0·2 \times 20^3}{2} = 586 \text{ c.g.s.}$$

4. Describe how a dip circle is set up for use. Why is it necessary to read both ends of the needle when finding the angle of dip?

The actual angle of dip at a place where H_0 is 0·18 c.g.s. is 68°. In an experiment with a dip circle the needle is found to come to rest making an angle of dip 66°. The dip needle weighs 9·5 grammes and measures 10·6 cm. from pole to pole. The strength of each pole is 210 c.g.s. and the needle is pivoted at the mid-point of a line joining its poles, but the centre of gravity of the needle, which is in this line, is a short distance, x, from the point of suspension. If this is the only error in the instrument, find the value of x. (*L.*)

First part (see p. 752). When both ends of the needle are read, "correction" is made for the possibility that the axle of the needle is not at the centre of the graduated scale.

Second part. Let G be the centre of gravity and O the axle. Fig. 570

The couple on the magnet due to the resultant earth's field, R, is given, from $MH \sin \theta$, by

$$RM \sin 2°.$$

The opposing couple due to the weight, 9·5g dynes, is given by

$$9\cdot5g \times x \cos 66°.$$

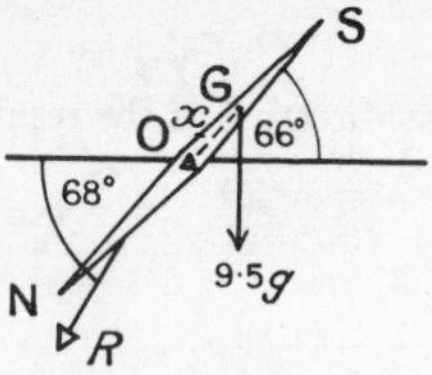

$$\therefore \ RM \sin 2° = 9\cdot5gx \cos 66°.$$

Fig. 570. Example.

But $\qquad R = 0\cdot18 \sec 68°$, and $M = 210 \times 10\cdot6$ c.g.s.

$$\therefore \ x = \frac{RM \sin 2°}{9\cdot5g \cos 66°} = \frac{0\cdot18 \sec 68° \times 210 \times 10\cdot6 \sin 2°}{9\cdot5 \times 981 \times \cos 66°}$$

$$= 0\cdot01 \text{ cm.}$$

EXERCISES XXXIII

1. Find the strength of magnetic field due to a short bar-magnet, (*a*) at a point on the axis, (*b*) at a point on the line bisecting the magnet at right angles.

Assuming that the magnetic moment may be resolved into components as a force may be (or by any other means), find the strength of magnetic field on a line making 45° with the axis of a short magnet of moment 200 c.g.s. and at a distance of 10 cm. from the mid-point of the magnet. (*L.*)

2. A bar-magnet of moment 400 c.g.s. lies with its axis parallel to the magnetic meridian and its north-seeking pole pointing N. When the field is plotted the null points are found to be 13 cm. from the poles. The distance between the poles is 10 cm. Find *by a graphical method* the intensity of the horizontal component of the earth's magnetic field. Sketch a map of the field and explain how the null points arise. (*N.*)

3. Give the theory and experimental details of a satisfactory method of verifying the inverse square law for magnetic poles (e.g. Gauss's method using a short bar-magnet). (*L.*)

4. Describe with full experimental details a method of comparing the values of the horizontal component of the earth's magnetic field at two different places.

A small horizontal magnetic needle suspended by a silk fibre has a period of 5 sec. when vibrating in the earth's magnetic field alone. When a short bar-magnet with its N. pole pointing N. is placed 25 cm. due S. of it and in the magnetic meridian, the orientation of the needle is unchanged but its period is now 4 sec. Find the positions of the neutral points in the field. (*L.*)

5. Describe and explain how you would use a short bar-magnet and a deflection magnetometer to verify the inverse square law of magnetic force.

A short bar-magnet, placed 30 cm. due magnetic E. of a magnetometer needle and pointing towards it, produces a deflection of 45°. The same magnet suspended by a torsionless fibre in a horizontal plane in the place formerly occupied by the magnetometer is found to have a period of oscillation of 2·0 sec. If the moment of inertia of the magnet about the axis of oscillation is 40 gm.-cm.², find the horizontal component of the earth's magnetic field. (*N.*)

6. How would you show by an experiment that the poles of a magnet are equal in magnitude? Describe the method you would use to find out if the poles of a magnet are symmetrically placed.

A short strongly magnetized bar-magnet whose magnet axis coincides with its geometrical axis, the poles being equidistant from its ends, is placed with its axis horizontal in the magnetic meridian. A magnet suspended so that it is free to oscillate in a horizontal plane is placed in the same meridian so that the distance between the centres of the magnets is *x*. The time of the suspended magnet is 2·5 sec. The bar-magnet is then turned end to end about its centre, leaving *x* as before, and the time of vibration of the suspended magnet (which still points north) now becomes 2 × 2·5 sec. What would be the time of vibration of the magnet if the bar-magnet were removed? Also, what is the value of the magnetic field due to the bar-magnet at the distance *x*, in terms of the earth's horizontal field *H*, in the two cases considered? (*L.*)

7. Describe a method of investigating the intensity of the field due to a short bar-magnet at various distances from the centre of the magnet along its axis.

The field intensities at two points on the axis of a bar-magnet at distances of 10 cm. and 20 cm. respectively from its centre are in the ratio of 12·5 to 1. Find the distance between the poles of the magnet. (*N.*)

8. Describe and explain how, if you were provided with a large sheet of paper, a plotting compass, and a suitable bar-magnet, you would determine the magnetic moment of the bar-magnet, given the value of the horizontal component of the earth's magnetic field.

A small powerful bar-magnet lies in the magnetic meridian with its N. pole pointing N. An oscillation magnetometer placed 20 cm. to the N. of the magnet makes 100 oscillations in 100 secs. When the magnet is removed the time of 100 oscillations is found to be 200 secs. Calculate the magnetic moment of the bar-magnet, given that the horizontal component of the earth's magnetic field is 0·2 oersted. (*C.*)

9. Describe an experiment, using a bar-magnet and a deflection magnetometer to investigate the validity of the law of inverses for magnetic poles.

Two *short* bar-magnets M_1 and M_2 are placed on a horizontal table with their magnetic axes lying along two straight lines intersecting at *O*, one line being in the magnetic meridian and the other at right angles to it. A small compass needle is placed at *O*. When M_1 is 30 cm. W. of *O* and M_2 is 20 cm. N. of *O* the needle sets E.–W. If M_2 is removed the needle makes an angle of 45° with the magnetic meridian. Assuming the magnetic moment of M_2 to be 640 unit pole cm., find a value for (*a*) the strength of the horizontal component of the magnetic field, (*b*) the magnetic moment of M_1. (*L.*)

Terrestrial Magnetism.

10. What is meant by *angle of dip* and *angle of declination* at a point on the earth's surface? Indicate in a very general way the value of the dip at different points on the earth's surface.

Describe the method of measuring the angle of dip, using a dip circle and, with the aid of a diagram in each case, explain the reasons for taking the various readings to eliminate the possible errors. (*L.*)

11. State, with reference to a diagram, the quantities which are necessary to define the earth's magnetic field in direction and magnitude at any point of its surface.

Give a brief description of two different methods of determining the horizontal component of the earth's field. (*L.*)

12. Define *magnetic moment* of a magnet and find an expression for the couple acting on a magnet of magnetic moment M when it makes an angle θ with a uniform magnetic field of strength H.

The needle of a dip circle sets with its magnetic axis horizontal when a mass of 0·01 gm. is attached to the needle at a distance of 5·0 cm. from the axis of rotation. On exactly reversing its magnetization the needle sets horizontally when the same small mass is attached at a point 3·0 cm. on the other side of the axis of rotation. Calculate a value for the magnetic moment of the needle. (Assume H_0 is 0·20 oersted and the angle of dip is 65°.) (*L.*)

13. Explain, with the help of diagrams, (*a*) how a dip-circle is set up so that the needle swings in the magnetic meridian, (*b*) why, in order to determine the true value of the angle of dip, it is necessary (among other things) to read both ends of the needle and to reverse the needle on its bearings.

A magnetic needle, suspended so as to oscillate in a horizontal plane, had a time period of 20·0 secs. and a moment of inertia of 13,500 gm.-cm.² about the axis of oscillation. Mounted as a dip needle swinging in the meridian it rested horizontally when a weight of 0·2 gm. was fixed on it at a point 18·0 cm. from its centre. What was the angle of dip at the place where the observations were made? (*N.*)

14. Define the terms magnetic meridian, inclination, declination. Indicate how these quantities vary on the earth's surface.

How would you find the direction of the magnetic meridian if the only piece of steel available were a magnetised flat circular disc? (*O. & C.*).

15. What is meant by (*a*) *declination*, (*b*) *inclination* or *dip*? Give a general account of how these vary with time at any place (e.g. London) on the earth's surface.

A freely suspended magnet oscillates in a horizontal plane at two places, A and B. The time per oscillation at A is 2·8 secs. The horizontal component of the earth's magnetic field at A is 0·158 oersted and the angle of dip is 70° 12′. What will be the time for an oscillation at B where the *total* magnetic intensity of the earth's field is 0·467 oersted and the angle of dip is 66° 0′? What is the magnitude of the earth's magnetic field at A? (*L.*)

CHAPTER XXXIV

ELECTROSTATICS

GENERAL PHENOMENA

If a rod of ebonite is rubbed with fur, or a fountain-pen with a coat-sleeve, it gains the power to attract light bodies, such as pieces of paper or tin-foil or a suspended pith-ball. The discovery that a body could be made attractive by rubbing is attributed to Thales (640–548 B.C.). He seems to have been led to it through the Greeks' practice of spinning silk with an amber spindle; the rubbing of the spindle in its bearings caused the silk to adhere to it. The Greek word for amber is *elektron*, and a body made attractive by rubbing is said to be "electrified". This branch of Electricity, the earliest discovered, is called *Electrostatics*.

1. Conductors and Insulators.

Little progress was made in the study of electrification until the sixteenth century A.D. Then Gilbert (1540–1603), who was physician-in-ordinary to Queen Elizabeth, found that other substances besides amber could be electrified: for example, glass when rubbed with silk. He failed to electrify metals, however, and concluded that to do so was impossible.

More than 100 years later—in 1734—he was shown to be wrong, by du Fay; du Fay found that a metal could be electrified by rubbing with fur or silk, but only if it were held in a handle of glass or amber; it could not be electrified if it were held directly in the hand. His experiments followed the discovery, by Gray in 1729, that electric charges could be transmitted through the human body, water, and metals. These are examples of *conductors*; glass and amber are examples of *insulators*.

2. Positive and Negative Electricity.

In the course of his experiments du Fay also discovered that there were two kinds of electrification: he showed that electrified glass and amber tended to oppose one another's attractiveness. To illustrate how he did so, we may use ebonite instead of amber, which has the same electrical properties. We suspend a pith-ball, and attract it with an electrified ebonite rod E (Fig. 571(a)); we then bring an electrified glass rod G towards the ebonite rod, and the pith-ball falls away (Fig. 571(b)). Benjamin Franklin, a pioneer of electrostatics, gave the name of "positive electricity" to the charge on a glass rod rubbed with silk, and "negative electricity" to that on an ebonite rod rubbed with fur.

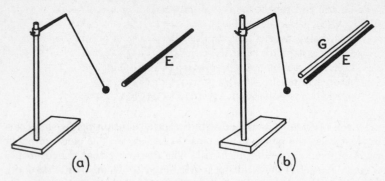

Fig. 571. Demonstrating that electrified glass tends to oppose effect of electrified ebonite.

3. Electrons and Electrostatics.

Towards the end of the nineteenth century Sir J. J. Thomson discovered the existence of the *electron* (p. 1005). This is the lightest particle known—it is about 1/1840th of the mass of the hydrogen atom—and experiments show that it carries a tiny quantity of *negative* electricity. Later experiments showed that electrons are present in all atoms.

The detailed structure of atoms is complicated, but, generally, electrons exist round a minute core or nucleus carrying positive electricity. Normally, atoms are electrically neutral, that is, there is no surplus of charge on them. Consequently the total negative charge on the electrons is equal to the positive charge on the nucleus. In insulators, all the electrons appear to be firmly "bound" to the nucleus under the attraction of the unlike charges. In metals, however, some of the electrons appear to be relatively "free". These electrons play an important part in electrical phenomena concerning metals.

The theory of electrons (negatively charged particles) gives simple explanations of electrification by friction, and of the attraction of uncharged bodies by charged ones. If the silk on which a glass rod has been rubbed is brought near to a charged and suspended ebonite rod it repels it; the silk must therefore have a negative charge. We know that the glass has a positive charge, and therefore we suppose that when the two were rubbed together electrons from the surface atoms were transferred from the glass to the silk. Likewise we suppose that when fur and ebonite are rubbed together, electrons go from the fur to the ebonite.

4. Attraction of Charged Body for Uncharged Bodies.

To explain the attraction of a charged body for an uncharged one, we shall suppose that the uncharged body is a conductor—a metal. If it is brought near to a charged ebonite rod, say, then the negative

charge on the rod repels the free electrons in the metal to its remote
end (Fig. 572). A positive charge is thus left on the near end of the
metal; this, being nearer than the negative charge on the far end, is
attracted more strongly than the negative charge is repelled. On the
whole, therefore, the metal is attracted. If the uncharged body is not
a conductor, the mechanism by which it is attracted is more complicated; we shall postpone its description to a later chapter.

FIG. 572.   Attraction by charged body.

5. Electrostatics Today.

The discovery of the electron has led, in the last twenty or thirty
years, to a great increase in the practical importance of electrostatics.
In devices such as wireless valves and cathode-ray tubes, for example,
electrons are moving under the influence of electrostatic forces. The
problems of preventing sparks and the breakdown of insulators are
essentially electrostatic. There are also difficulties in making measurements at very high voltages. These problems occur in high-voltage
electrical engineering. Later, we shall also describe a modern electrostatic generator, of the type used to provide a million volts or more for
X-ray work and nuclear bombardment. Such generators work on
principles of electrostatics discovered over a hundred years ago.

6. Gold-leaf Electroscope.

One of the the earliest instruments used for testing positive and
negative charges consisted of a metal rod A to which gold leaves L were

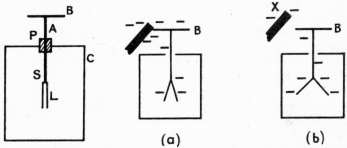

FIG. 573. A gold-leaf electroscope.   FIG. 574. Testing charge with electroscope.

attached (Fig. 573). The rod was fitted with a circular disc or cap B,
and was insulated with a plug P from a metal case C which screened
L from outside influences other than those brought near to B.

When B is touched by an ebonite rod rubbed with fur, some of the negative charge on the rod passes to the cap and L; and since like charges repel, the leaves diverge (Fig. 574(a)). If an unknown charge X is now brought near to B, an increased divergence implies that X is negative (Fig. 574(b)). A positive charge is tested in a similar way; the electroscope is first given a positive charge and an increased divergence indicates a positive charge.

7. Induction.

We shall now show that it is possible to obtain charges, called *induced charges*, without any contact with another charge. An experiment on electrostatic induction, as the phenomenon is called, is shown in Fig. 575(a). Two insulated metal spheres A, B are arranged so that they

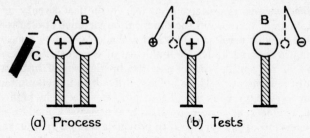

(a) Process   (b) Tests

Fig. 575. Charges induced on a conductor.

touch one another, and a negatively charged ebonite rod C is brought near to A. The spheres are now separated, and then the rod is taken away. Tests with a charged pith-ball now show that A has a positive charge and B a negative charge (Fig. 575(b)). If the spheres are placed together so that they touch, it is found that they now have no effect on a pith-ball held near. Their charges must therefore have neutralized each other completely, thus showing that the induced positive and negative charges are equal. This is explained by the movement of electrons from A to B when the rod is brought near. B has then a negative charge and A an equal positive charge.

8. Charging by Induction.

Fig. 576 shows how a conductor can be given a permanent charge by induction, without dividing it in two. We first bring a charged ebonite rod, say, near to the conductor, (a); next we connect the conductor to earth by touching it momentarily (b); finally we remove the ebonite. We then find that the conductor is left with a positive charge (c). If we use a charged glass rod, we find that the conductor is left with a negative charge; the charge left, called the induced charge, has always the opposite sign to the inducing charge.

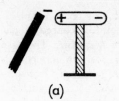
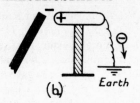

(a)   (b)   (c)

Earth

Fig. 576. Charging permanently by induction.

This phenomenon of induction can again be explained by the movement of electrons. If the inducing charge is negative, then, when we touch the conductor, electrons are repelled from it to earth, as shown in Fig. 576(b), and a positive charge is left on the conductor. If the inducing charge is positive, then electrons are attracted up from the earth to the conductor, which then becomes negatively charged.

9. Induction and the Electroscope.

It is always observed that the leaves of an electroscope diverge when a charged body is brought near its cap, without touching it. This we can now easily understand; if, for example, we bring a negatively charged rod near the cap, it induces a positive charge on the cap, and a negative one on the leaves: the leaves then repel each other. Further, the negative charge on the leaves induces a positive one on the inside of the case, the corresponding negative charge running to the earth, on which the case rests. The positive charge on the case attracts the negative charge on the leaves, and makes them diverge further.

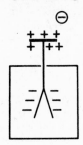
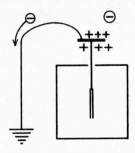
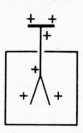

Fig. 577. Charging electroscope by induction.

We can use induction to give a permanent charge to the cap and leaves of an electroscope, by momentarily earthing the cap while holding an inducing charge near it. This is illustrated in Fig. 577.

10. The Electrophorus.

A device which provides an almost unlimited supply of charge, by induction, was invented by Volta about 1800; it is called an *electrophorus*. It consists of an ebonite or sulphur base, E in Fig. 578, and a metal disc D on an insulating handle. The ebonite is charged negatively by rubbing it—or, much better, beating it—with fur. The disc is then laid upon it, and acquires induced charges, positive underneath and negative on top, (*a*). Very little negative charge escapes from the ebonite to the disc, because the natural unevenness of their surfaces prevents them touching at more than a few points; charge escapes from these points only, because the ebonite is a non-conductor. After it has been placed on the ebonite, the disc is earthed with the finger, and the negative charge on its upper surface flows away, (*b*). The disc can then be removed, and carries with it the positive charge which was on its underside, (*c*).

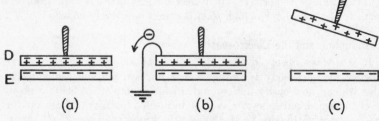

D
E

(a)   (b)   (c)

Fig. 578.   The electrophorus.

An electrophorus produces sufficient charge to give an audible—and sometimes a visible—spark. The disc can be discharged and charged again repeatedly, until the charge on the ebonite has disappeared by leakage. Apparently, therefore, it is in principle an inexhaustible source of energy. However, work is done in raising the disc from the ebonite, against the attraction of their opposite charges, and this work must be done each time the disc is charged; the electrophorus is therefore not a source of energy, but a device for converting it from a mechanical into an electrical form.

The action of the electrophorus illustrates the advantages of charging by induction. First, the supply of charge is almost inexhaustible, because the original charge is not carried away. Second, a great charge —nearly equal to the charge on the whole of the ebonite—can be concentrated on to the conducting disc. As we have seen, only a very small charge could be transferred by contact, because the ebonite is not a conductor.

11. The Action of Points, Van de Graaff Generator.

Sometimes in experiments with an electroscope connected to other apparatus by a wire, the leaves of the electroscope gradually collapse, as though its charge were leaking away. This behaviour can often be traced to a sharp point on the wire—if the point is blunted, the leakage stops. Charge leaks away from a sharp point through the air, being carried by molecules away from the point. This is explained later (p. 777).

Points are used to collect the charges produced in *electrostatic generators*. These are machines for continuously separating charges by induction, and thus building up very great charges and potential differences. Fig. 579 is a simplified diagram of one such machine, due to Van de Graaff. A hollow metal sphere S is supported on an insulating tube T, many feet high. A silk belt B runs over the pulleys shown, of which the lower is driven by an electric motor. Near the bottom and top of its run, the belt passes close to the electrodes E, which are sharply pointed combs, pointing towards the belt. The electrode E_1 is made about 10,000 volts positive with respect to the earth by a battery. Its point then sprays the lower part of the belt with positive charge, which is carried up into the sphere. There it induces a negative charge on the points of electrode E_2 and a positive charge on the sphere to which the blunt end of E_2 is connected. The point sprays the belt

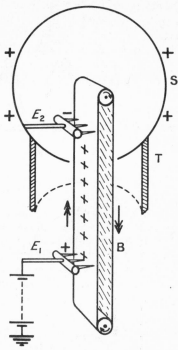

FIG. 579. Principle of Van de Graaff generator.

with negative charge, and discharges it before it passes over the pulley. The sphere gradually charges up positively, until its potential is about a million volts relative to the earth.

Large machines of this type are used with high-voltage X-ray tubes, and for atom-splitting experiments. They have more elaborate electrode systems, stand about 40 ft. high, and have 15-ft. spheres. They can produce potential differences up to 5,000,000 volts and currents of about 50 micro-amperes. The electrical energy which they deliver comes from the work done by the motor in drawing the positively charged belt towards the positively charged sphere, which repels it.

In all types of high-voltage equipment sharp corners and edges must be avoided, except where points are deliberately used as electrodes. Otherwise, corona discharges may break out from the sharp places. All such places are therefore enlarged by metal globes, such as S in Fig. 580; these are called stress-distributors. See also p. 788.

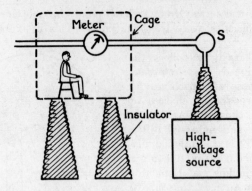

Fig. 580. High-voltage measurement.

12. Ice-pail Experiment.

A famous experiment on electrostatic induction was made by Faraday in 1843. In it he used the ice-pail from which it takes its name; but it was a modest pail, $10\frac{1}{2}$ in. high—not a bucket. He stood the pail on an insulator, and connected it to a gold-leaf electroscope, as in Fig. 581(a). He next held a metal ball on the end of a long silk thread, and charged it positively by a spark from an electrophorus. Then he lowered the ball into the pail, without letting it touch the sides or bottom (Fig. 581(b)).

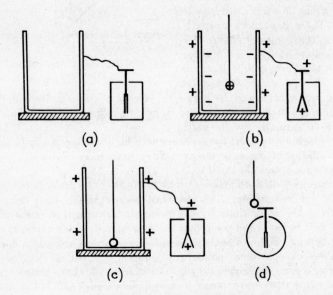

Fig. 581. Faraday's ice-pail experiment.

A positive charge was induced on the outside of the pail and the leaves, and made the leaves diverge. Once the ball was well inside the pail, Faraday found that the divergence of the leaves did not change when he moved the ball about—nearer to or farther from the walls or the bottom. This showed that the amount of the induced positive charge did not depend on the position of the ball, once it was well inside the pail. Faraday then allowed the ball to touch the pail, and noticed that the leaves of the electroscope still did not move (Fig. 581(c)). When the ball touched the pail, therefore, no charge was given to, or taken from, the outside of the pail. Faraday next lifted the ball out of the pail, and tested it for charge with another electroscope. He found that the ball had no charge whatever (Fig. 581(d)). The induced negative charge on the inside of the pail, must therefore have been equal in magnitude to the original positive charge on the ball.

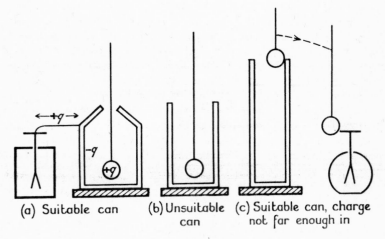

(a) Suitable can   (b) Unsuitable   (c) Suitable can, charge
             can   not far enough in

FIG. 582. Referring to Faraday's ice-pail experiment.

Faraday's experiment does not give these simple results unless the pail—or whatever is used in place of it—very nearly surrounds the charged ball (Fig. 582(a), (b)). If, for example, the ball is allowed to touch the pail before it is well inside, as in Fig. 582(c), then it does not lose all its charge.

13. Conclusions.

The conclusions to be drawn from the experiment therefore apply, strictly, to a *hollow closed conductor*. They are:

(i) When a charged body is enclosed in a hollow conductor it induces on the inside of that conductor a charge equal but opposite to its own; and on the outside a charge equal and similar to its own (Fig. **581** (a)).

(*ii*) The *total* charge inside a hollow conductor is always zero: either there are equal and opposite charges on the inside walls and within the volume (before the ball touches), or there is no charge at all (after the ball has touched).

14. Comparison and Collection of Charges.

Faraday's ice-pail experiment gives us a method of comparing quantities of electric charges. The experiment shows that if a charged body is lowered well inside a tall, narrow can then it gives to the outside of the can a charge equal to its own. If the can is connected to the cap of an electroscope, the divergence of the leaves is a measure of the charge on the body. Thus we can compare the magnitudes of charges, without removing them from the bodies which carry them: we merely lower those bodies, in turn, into a tall insulated can, connected to an electroscope.

Sometimes we may wish to discharge a conductor completely, without letting its charge run to earth. We can do this by letting the conductor touch the bottom of a tall can on an insulating stand. The whole of the body's charge is then transferred to the outside of the can.

15. Charges Produced by Separation; Lines of Force.

The ice-pail experiment suggests that a positive electric charge, for example, is always accompanied by an equal negative charge. Faraday

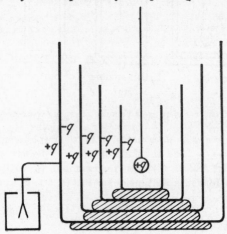

FIG. 583.   Extension of ice-pail experiment.

repeated his experiment with a nest of hollow conductors, insulated from one another, and showed that equal and opposite charges were induced on the inner and outer walls of each (Fig. 583).

Faraday also showed that equal and opposite charges are produced when a body is electrified by rubbing. He fitted an ebonite rod with a fur cap, which he rotated by a silk thread or string wrapped round it (Fig. 583(a)); he then compared the charges produced with an ice-pail and electroscope (Fig. 584(a), (b), (c), (d)).

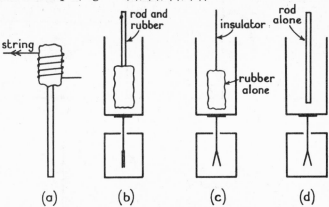

Fig. 584. Stages in showing that equal and opposite charges are produced by friction.

In describing the conclusions from this last experiment, we now say, as indeed we have done already, that electrons flow from the fur to the ebonite, carrying to it a negative charge, and leaving on the fur a positive charge. It appears, therefore, that free charges are always

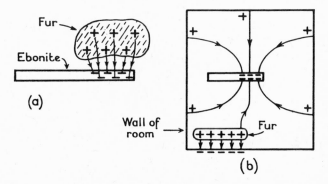

Fig. 585. Charging by friction—lines of force.

produced by separating equal amounts of the opposite kinds of electricity.

The idea that charges always occur in equal opposite pairs affects our drawing of lines of force diagrams. Lines of force radiate outwards from a positive charge, and inwards to a negative one; from any positive charge, therefore, we draw lines of force ending on an equal negative charge. Figs. 585, 586 give some illustrations of this procedure.

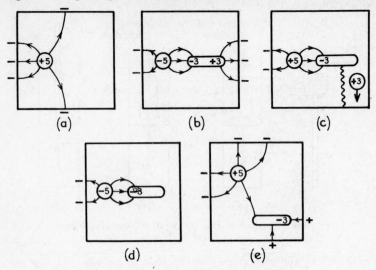

Fig. 586. Charging by induction—lines of force.

16. Distribution of Charge; Surface Density.

By using a can connected to an electroscope we can find how electricity is distributed over a charged conductor of any form—pear-shaped, for example. We take a number of small leaves of tin-foil, all of the same area, but differently shaped to fit closely over the different parts of the conductor, and mounted on ebonite handles (Fig. 587(a)).

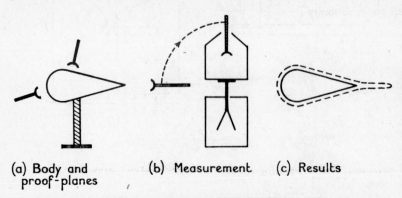

(a) Body and proof-planes   (b) Measurement   (c) Results

Fig. 587. Investigating charge distribution.

These are called *proof-planes*. We charge the body from an electro-phorus, press a proof-plane against the part which it fits, and then lower the proof-plane into a can connected to an electroscope (Fig. 587(b)). After noting the divergence of the leaves we discharge the can and electroscope by touching one of them, and repeat the observation with a proof-plane fitting a different part of the body. Since the proof-planes have equal areas, each of them carries away a charge proportional to the charge per unit area of the body, over the region which it touched. The charge per unit area over a region of the body is called the *surface-density* of the charge in that region. We find that the surface-density increases with the curvature of the body, as shown in Fig. 587(c); the distance of the dotted line from the outline of the body is proportional to the surface-density of charge.

THE ELECTROSTATIC FIELD

17. The Law of Force between two Charges.

The magnitude of the force between two electrically charged bodies was studied by Coulomb in 1875. He showed that, if the bodies were small compared with the distance between them, then the force F was inversely proportional to the square of the distance d, i.e.

$$F \propto \frac{1}{d^2}. \qquad \qquad \cdots \cdots \cdots \quad (1)$$

This result is known as the *inverse square law*, or Coulomb's law.

18. Quantity of Charge.

The force between, let us say, two ebonite rods depends not only on their distance apart; it depends also on how hard they have been rubbed. Thus we get the idea of quantity of electricity: the more vigorously a rod has been rubbed, the greater the force it exerts on another at a given distance—and, we say, the greater the electric charge upon it. That is to say, we define the magnitude of a charge by saying that it is proportional to the mechanical force which it exerts on another charge at a given distance away.

In Fig. 588(a), A and B are two charged bodies. The force f which A exerts upon B is, we say, proportional to the magnitude, q, of the charge on A. But, since action and reaction are equal and opposite, B exerts an equal force f on A. Thus the force which A experiences, as well as the force which it exerts, is proportional to the magnitude q of its charge. Similarly, the force f which A and B exert on each other is proportional to the magnitude q' of the charge on B.

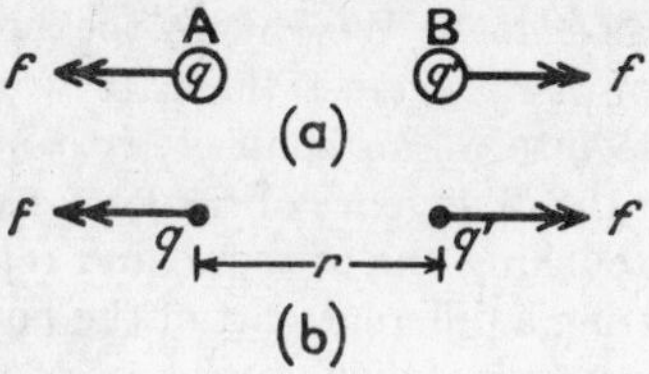

FIG. 588. Force between charges.

The force between two charges is therefore proportional to the magnitude of each:

$$f \propto qq'. \qquad \ldots \ldots \ldots \quad (2)$$

This is not an experimental relationship; it merely expresses, in mathematical shorthand, our decision to measure the charge on a body by the force which it exerts on another charged body.

19. Law of Force.

Let us now combine the relationship (2) with Coulomb's experimental law—which says that the force between point charges is inversely proportional to the square of the distance between them. In Fig. 588 (b)) q and q' are two point charges, separated by a distance r, and exerting a force f upon each other. Combining experiment and definition, we get

$$f \propto \frac{qq'}{r^2},$$

or

$$f = c \, \frac{qq'}{r^2}, \qquad \ldots \ldots \ldots \quad (3)$$

where c is a constant.

20. Unit Charge. Permittivity.

The "unit charge" is defined as *that charge which repels a similar charge one centimetre away in a vacuum with a force of one dyne.* This is called an *electrostatic unit* (*e.s.u.*) of charge. Thus $f = 1$ dyne when $q = 1$ e.s.u., $q' = 1$ e.s.u., and $r = 1$ cm. Substituting in equation (3), we have, when the charges are in a vacuum,

$$1 = c \, \frac{1 \times 1}{1^2}, \qquad \text{or} \qquad c = 1.$$

$$\therefore f = \frac{qq'}{r^2} \text{ dynes}, \qquad \ldots \ldots \ldots \quad (4)$$

where q, q' are in e.s.u. and r in centimetres.

This equation is not strictly correct. On one side we have a force, f; on the other side is a distance, r, and quantities of electricity, q, q'. Now a quantity of electricity is a fundamental thing, ranking the same as a mass, a length, or a time. We therefore include a quantity K on the right-hand side to make the dimensions the same on the two sides, which is called the *permittivity* of the medium. Then, generally,

$$F = \frac{qq'}{Kr^2}. \qquad \ldots \ldots \ldots \quad (5)$$

The permittivity of a vacuum is 1; the permittivity of air at normal pressure and temperature is about 1·0005, and hence we make little error in assuming that equation (4) also applies to air. The permittivity of glass is about 2; the permittivity of water is about 80.

The electrostatic unit of charge defined above is sometimes also called a "statcoulomb". It is much smaller than the practical unit of charge, the coulomb:

$$1 \text{ coulomb} = 3 \times 10^9 \text{ e.s.u.}$$

The e.s.u. of charge, however, is much greater than the charge, e, on an electron:

$$e = 4·80 \times 10^{-10} \text{ e.s.u.}$$

21. Electric Intensity or Field-strength. Lines of Force.

An "electric field" can be defined as a region where an electric force is experienced. As in magnetism, electric fields can be mapped out by electrostatic lines of force, which may be defined as a line such that the tangent to it is in the direction of the force on a small positive charge at that point. Arrows on the lines of force show the direction of the force on a positive charge; the force on a negative charge is in the opposite direction. Fig. 589 shows the lines of force, also called *electric flux*, in some electrostatic fields.

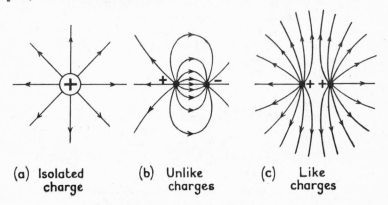

| (a) Isolated charge | (b) Unlike charges | (c) Like charges |

589. Lines of electrostatic force.

The force exerted on a charged body in an electrostatic field depends on the charge of the body and the *intensity* or *strength* of the field. *The intensity of an electrostatic field at any point is defined as numerically equal to the force in dynes which it exerts on a unit charge at that point.* It is expressed in dynes per e.s.u. of charge, and is denoted by the letter E. Its direction at any point is defined as the direction of the force on a positive charge there.

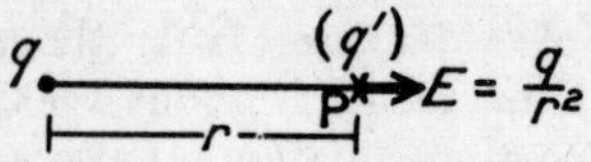

$$q \bullet \underset{\longleftarrow r \longrightarrow}{\underline{\hspace{2cm}}} \overset{(q')}{\underset{P}{\times}} \to E = \frac{q}{r^2}$$

FIG. 590.   Field of point charge.

We can easily find an expression for the strength of the electric field due to a point charge in air (Fig. 590). We start from equation (4) for the force between two such charges:

$$f = \frac{qq'}{r^2} .$$

If the charge q' is situated at the point P in Fig. 590, the electric field strength at that point is given, by definition, by

$$E = \frac{f}{q'} = \frac{q}{r^2}. \qquad \ldots \ldots \ldots (6)$$

The direction of the field is radially outward if the charge q is positive (Fig. 589 (a)); it is radially inward if the charge q is negative.

22. Field Intensity due to Charged Sphere and Plane.

The lines of force due to a *charged sphere* radiate symmetrically from the surface. Since all the lines meet at the centre of the sphere if produced backwards, we can treat the charge q on the sphere as if it were concentrated at a point at the centre to find the field intensity outside the sphere. It follows that the intensity E outside, at a point r cm. from the centre, is given by

$$E = \frac{q}{r^2}. \qquad \ldots \ldots \ldots (7)$$

At any point *inside* the sphere, calculation shows that

$$E = 0. \qquad \ldots \ldots \ldots (8)$$

In this case, the charges on either side of any point inside the sphere have a resultant intensity of zero there.

Outside a charged plane having a surface-density σ e.s.u. per sq. cm., calculation beyond the scope of this book shows that the intensity E is given by

$$E = \frac{4\pi\sigma}{K}, \qquad \ldots \ldots \ldots (9)$$

where K is the permittivity of the medium. Thus for a sphere of radius r carrying a charge q in air, $\sigma = q/\text{area} = q/4\pi r^2$. Hence in this case, the intensity just outside is given by

$$E = 4\pi\sigma = \frac{4\pi q}{4\pi r^2} = \frac{q}{r^2} \text{ (see eqn. (7))}.$$

23. Field round Points.

On p. 773 we saw that the surface-density of charge (charge per unit area) round a point of a conductor is very great. Consequently, the strength of the electric field near the point is very great. The intense electric field breaks down the insulation of the air, and sends a stream of charged molecules away from the point. The mechanism of the breakdown, which is called a "corona discharge", is complicated, and we shall not discuss it here; some of the processes in it are similar to those in conduction through a gas at low pressure, which we shall describe in Chapter XLIII. Corona breakdown starts when the electric field strength is about 100 e.s.u. (a potential gradient of 30,000 volts per cm.). The corresponding surface-density is about 8 e.s.u. per sq. cm.

EXAMPLE

An electron, of charge 4.80×10^{-10} e.s.u., is situated in a uniform electric field of intensity 4 e.s.u. Find the force on it, its acceleration, and the time it takes to travel 2 cm. from rest. (Electronic mass, m, $= 9.10 \times 10^{-28}$ gm.)

Force on electron $P = eE = 4.8 \times 10^{-10} \times 4 = 19.2 \times 10^{-10}$ dyne.

$$\therefore \text{ acceleration}, f, = \frac{P}{m} = \frac{19.2 \times 10^{-10}}{9.1 \times 10^{-28}} = 2.12 \times 10^{18} \text{ cm. per sec.}^2$$

The time t to cover a distance s of 2 cm. is given by $s = \frac{1}{2}ft^2$.

$$\therefore \ t = \sqrt{\frac{2s}{f}}$$

$$= \sqrt{\frac{2 \times 2}{2.12 \times 10^{18}}} = 1.37 \times 10^{-9} \text{ sec.}$$

The extreme shortness of this time is due to the fact that the ratio of charge-to-mass for an electron is very great:

$$\frac{e}{m} = \frac{4.8 \times 10^{-10}}{9.1 \times 10^{-28}} = 5.3 \times 10^{17} \text{ e.s.u. per gm.}$$

In an electric field, the charge e determines the force on an electron, while the mass m determines its inertia. Because of the large ratio e/m, the electron moves almost instantaneously, and requires very little energy to displace it. Also it can respond to changes in an electric field which take place even millions of times per second. Thus it is the large value of e/m for electrons which makes electronic valves, for example, useful in electrical communication and remote control.

ELECTRIC POTENTIAL

24. Potential in Fields.

When an object is held at a height above the earth it is said to have potential energy. A heavy body tends to move under the force of attraction of the earth from a point of great height to one of less, and we say that points in the earth's gravitational field have potential values depending on their height.

Electric potential is analogous to gravitational potential, but this time we think of points in an electric field. Thus in the field round a positive charge, for example, a positive charge moves from points near the charge to points further away. Points round the charge are said to have an "electric potential".

25. Potential Difference.

In mechanics we are always concerned with differences of height; if a point A on a hill is h feet higher than a point B, and our weight is w pounds, then we do wh foot-pounds of work in climbing from B to A (Fig. 591 (a)). Similarly in electricity we are often concerned with differences of potential; and we define these also in terms of work.

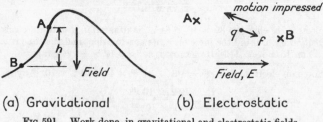

(a) Gravitational   (b) Electrostatic

FIG 591.   Work done, in gravitational and electrostatic fields.

Let us consider two points A and B in an electrostatic field, and let us suppose that the force on a positive charge q has a component f in the direction AB (Fig. 591 (b)). Then if we move a positively charged body from B to A, we do work against this component of the field E. *We define the potential difference between* A *and* B *as the work done in moving a unit positive charge from* B *to* A. We denote it by the symbol V_{AB}.

In the electrostatic system of units, work done is measured in ergs, or dyne-centimetres. Thus we can define the electrostatic unit (e.s.u.) of potential difference, which is sometimes called a statvolt: *the potential difference between two points* A *and* B *is one e.s.u., if the work done in taking one e.s.u. of positive charge from* B *to* A *is one erg.*

An erg is a small amount of work, but an electrostatic unit is a very small amount of charge. Consequently the e.s.u. of potential difference turns out to be, by everyday standards, rather great. The everyday unit of potential difference, which we shall define later, is called a volt; one e.s.u. of potential difference is equal to 300 volts. The potential difference between the two wires of most domestic supply mains is about 240 volts—less than one e.s.u. of potential difference.

26. Potential and Energy.

Let us consider two points A and B in an electrostatic field, A being at a higher potential than B. The potential differences between A and B we denote as usual by V_{AB}. If we take a positive charge q from B to A, we do work on it of amount qV_{AB}: the charge gains this amount of potential energy. If we now let the charge go back from A to B, it loses that potential energy: work is done on it by the electrostatic force, in the same way as work is done on a falling stone by gravity. This work may become kinetic energy, if the charge moves freely, or external work if the charge is attached to some machine, or a mixture of the two.

The work which we must do in first taking the charge from B to A does not depend on the path along which we carry it, just as the work done in climbing a hill does not depend on the route we take. If this were not true, we could devise a perpetual motion machine, in which we did less work in carrying a charge from B to A via X than it did for us in returning from A to B via Y (Fig. 592).

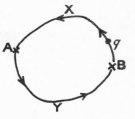

FIG. 592. A closed path in an electrostatic field.

The fact that the potential differences between two points is a constant, independent of the path chosen between the points, is the most important property of potential in general; we shall see why later on. This property can be conveniently expressed by saying that the work done in carrying a charge round a closed path in an electrostatic field, such as $BXAYB$ in Fig. 592 is zero.

27. Potential Difference Formula.

To obtain a formula for potential difference, let us calculate the potential difference between two points in the field of a single point

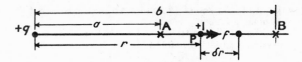

FIG. 593. Calculation of potential.

positive charge, q in Fig. 593. For simplicity we will assume that the points, A and B, lie on a line of force at distances a and b respectively from the charge. When a unit positive charge is at a distance r from the charge q the force on it is

$$f = \frac{q \times 1}{r^2} \text{ dynes.}$$

The work done in taking the charge from B to A, against the force f, is equal to the work which the force f would do if the charge were allowed to go from A to B. Over the short distance δr, the work done by the force f is

$$\delta W = f \delta r.$$

Over the whole distance AB, therefore, the work done by the force on the unit charge is

$$\int_A^B \delta W = \int_{r=a}^{r=b} f dr$$

$$= \int_a^b \frac{q}{r^2} dr$$

$$= \left[-\frac{q}{r} \right]_a^b$$

$$= \frac{q}{a} - \frac{q}{b} \text{ ergs.}$$

This, then, is the value of the work which an external agent must do to carry a unit positive charge from B to A; it is therefore the value of the potential difference between A and B:

$$V_{AB} = \frac{q}{a} - \frac{q}{b}. \qquad \ldots \ldots \ldots (10)$$

EXAMPLE

Two positive point charges, of 12 and 8 e.s.u. respectively, are 10 cm. apart. Find the work done in bringing them 4 cm. closer.

Suppose the 12 e.s.u. charge to be fixed in position. The potential difference between points 6 and 10 cm. from it, by (10), is

$$V = \frac{12}{6} - \frac{12}{10} = 0.8 \text{ e.s.u.}$$

The work done in moving the 8 e.s.u. charge from 10 to 6 cm. away from the other is therefore

$$W = 8 \times V = 8 \times 0.8 = 6.4 \text{ ergs.}$$

28. Zero Potential.

Instead of speaking continually of potential differences between pairs of points, we may speak of the potential at a single point—provided we always refer it to some other, agreed, reference point. This procedure is analogous to referring the heights of mountains to sea-level.

For practical purposes we generally choose as our reference point the electric potential of the surface of the earth. Although the earth is large it is all at the same potential, because it is a good conductor of electricity; if one point on it were at a higher potential than another, electrons would flow from the lower to the higher potential. As a result, the higher potential would fall, and the lower would rise; the flow of electricity would cease only when the potentials became equalized.

In general it is difficult to calculate the potential of a point relative to the earth. This is because the electric field due to a charged body near a conducting surface is complicated, as shown by the lines of force diagram in Fig. 594. In theoretical calculations, therefore, we often find

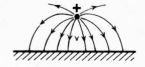

FIG. 594. Electric field of positive charge near earth.

it convenient to consider charges so far from the earth that the effect of the earth on their field is negligible; we call these "isolated" charges. We consequently define the potential at a point A in the field of an isolated charge as *the work done in bringing a unit positive charge from infinity to* A.

29. Potential Formula.

Equation (10) gives the potential difference between two points in the field of an isolated point charge q. If we let the point B retreat to infinity, then $b \gg a$, and the equation gives for the potential at A:

$$V_A = \frac{q}{a}. \qquad \ldots \ldots \ldots (11)$$

The derivation of this equation shows us what we mean by the word "infinity": the distance b is infinite if $1/b$ is negligible compared with $1/a$. If a is 1 cm., and b is 1 m., we make an error of only 1 per cent. in ignoring it; if b is 100 m., then for all practical purposes the point B is at infinity. In atomic physics, where the distances concerned have the order of 10^{-8} cm., a fraction of a millimetre is infinite.

In the neighbourhood of an isolated negative charge, the potential is negative, because q in equation (11) is negative. The potential is also negative in the neighbourhood of a negative charge near the earth: the earth is at zero potential, and a positive charge will tend to move from it towards the negative charge. A negative potential is analogous to the depth of a mine below sea-level. Fig. 595 (a) shows the potential variation near a positive charge C before and after a conductor AB is brought near. Fig. 595 (b) shows the potential variation when AB is earthed.

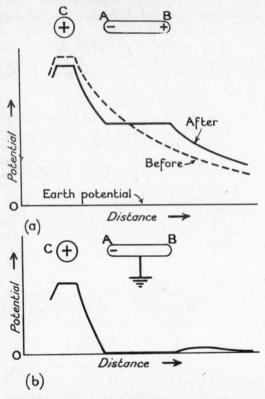

FIG. 595. Potential distribution (a) near a positive charge before and after bringing up an uncharged conductor, (b) near a positive charge in the presence of an earthed conductor.

30. Potential Difference and Intensity.

We shall now see how potential difference is related to intensity or field-strength. Suppose A, B are two neighbouring points on a line of force, so close together that the electric field-intensity between them is constant and equal to E (Fig. 596). If V is the potential at A, $V + \delta V$ is that at B, and the respective distances of A, B from the origin are x and $x + \delta x$, then

$$V_{AB} = \text{potential difference between } A, B$$
$$= V_A - V_B = V - (V + \delta V) = -\delta V.$$

The work done in taking a unit charge from B to A

$$= \text{force} \times \text{distance} = E \times \delta x = V_{AB} = -\delta V.$$

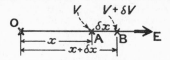

FIG. 596. Field strength and potential gradient.

Hence
$$E = -\frac{\delta V}{\delta x},$$

or, in the limit,

$$E = -\frac{dV}{dx}. \qquad . \quad . \quad . \quad . \quad . \quad . \quad (12)$$

The quantity dV/dx is the rate at which the potential rises with distance, and is called the potential gradient. Equation (12) shows that the strength of the electric field is equal to the negative of the potential gradient, and strong and weak fields in relation to potential are illustrated in Fig. 597.

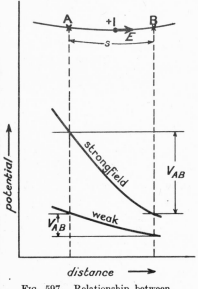

FIG. 597. Relationship between potential and field strength.

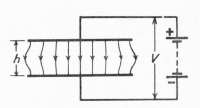

FIG. 598. Electric field between parallel plates.

In Fig. 598 the electric intensity $= V/h$, the potential gradient, and this is uniform in magnitude in the middle of the plates. At the edge of the plates the field becomes non-uniform.

EXAMPLES

1. An electron is liberated from the lower of two large parallel metal plates separated by a distance $h = 2$ cm. The upper plate has a potential of 2,400 volts relative to the lower. How long does the electron take to reach it?

The potential difference between the plates, V, is 8 electrostatic units, because 1 e.s.u. $= 300$ volts. Between large parallel plates, close together, the electric field is uniform except near the edges of the plates, as shown by the lines of force in Fig. 598. Except near the edges, therefore, the potential gradient between the plates is uniform; its magnitude is $V/h = 8/2 = 4$ e.s.u. per cm. The strength of the electric field is consequently 4 dynes per e.s.u. of charge. From the example worked on p. 777, we see that the time taken by the electron to reach the upper plate is 1.37×10^{-9} second.

2. An electron is liberated from a hot filament, and attracted by an anode, of potential 1200 volts positive with respect to the filament. What is the speed of the electron when it strikes the anode?

The kinetic energy which the electron gains from the field is eV, where

$$e = \text{electronic charge} = 4.8 \times 10^{-10} \text{ e.s.u.},$$

$$V = \text{potential difference in e.s.u.} = \frac{1200}{300} = 4.$$

If m and v are the mass and final speed of the electron, then

$$\tfrac{1}{2}mv^2 = eV,$$

where $m = 9.1 \times 10^{-28}$ gm.

Hence

$$v = \sqrt{\frac{2eV}{m}} = 2.1 \times 10^9 \text{ cm. per sec.}$$

31. The Electron-volt.

The kinetic energy gained by an electron which has been accelerated through a potential difference of 1 volt is called an electron-volt. Its value is

$$\text{electronic charge } e \times 1 \text{ volt} = 4.8 \times 10^{-10} \text{ e.s.u.} \times \frac{1}{300} \text{ e.s.u.}$$

$$= 1.6 \times 10^{-12} \text{ erg.}$$

The electron-volt is a useful unit of energy in atomic physics. For example, the work necessary to extract a conduction electron from tungsten is 4.52 electron-volts. This quantity determines the magnitude of the thermionic emission from the metal at a given temperature (p. 974); it is analogous to the latent heat of evaporation of a liquid.

EQUIPOTENTIALS

32. Equipotentials.

We have already said that the earth must have the same potential all over, because it is a conductor. In a conductor there can be no differences of potential, because these would set up a potential gradient or electric field; electrons would then redistribute themselves through-out the conductor, under the influence of the field, until they had destroyed the field. This is true whether the conductor has a net charge, positive or negative, or whether it is uncharged; it is true whatever the actual potential of the conductor, relative to any other body.

Any surface or volume over which the potential is constant is called an *equipotential*. The volume or surface may be that of a material body, or simply a surface or volume in space. For example, as we shall see later, the space inside a hollow charged conductor is an equipoten-tial volume. Equipotential surfaces can be drawn throughout any space in which there is an electric field, as we shall now explain.

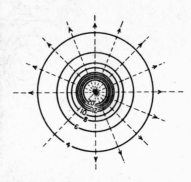

Let us consider the field of an iso-lated point-charge q. At a distance a from the charge, the potential is q/a; a sphere of radius a and centre

FIG. 599. Equipotentials and lines of force round a point charge of $+10$ e.s.u.

at q is therefore an equipotential surface, of potential q/a. In fact, all spheres centred on the charge are equipotential surfaces, whose poten-tials are inversely proportional to their radii (Fig. 599). An equipotential surface has the property that, along any direction lying in the surface, there is no electric field; for there is no potential gradient. *Equipotential surfaces are therefore always at right angles to lines of force*, as shown in the figure. Since conductors are always equipotentials, if any conductors appear in an electric-field diagram the lines of force must aways be drawn to meet them at right angles.

33. Potential due to a System of Charges.

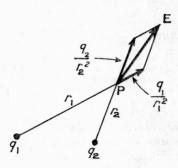

FIG. 600. Finding resultant field of two point-charges.

When we set out to consider the electric field due to more charges than one, then we see the advan-tages of the idea of potential over the idea of field-strength. If we wish to find the field-strength E at the point P in Fig. 600, due to the two charges q_1 and q_2, we have first to find the force exerted by each on a unit charge at P, and then to com-pound these forces by the parallelo-gram method. See Fig. 600. On the other hand, if we wish to find the potential at P, we merely calculate the potential due to each charge, and *add the potentials algebraically.*

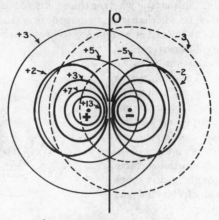

(a) Opposite charges

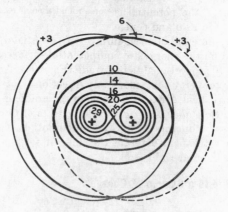

(b) Like charges

Fig. 601. Equipotentials in the field of two point charges. (Light and dotted circles are equipotentials of individual charges in isolation. Each charge of 10 e.s.u., distance apart of 1·6 cm.; potentials in round figures.)

Quantities which can be added algebraically are called "scalars"; they may have signs—positive or negative, like a bank balance—but they have no direction: they do not point north, east, south, or west. Quantities which have direction, like forces, are called "vectors"; they have to be added either by resolution into components, or by the parallelogram method. Either way is slow and clumsy, compared with the addition of scalars. For example, we can draw the equipotentials round a point-charge with compasses; if we draw two sets of them, as in Fig. 601 (*a*) or (*b*), then by simple addition we can rapidly sketch the equipotentials around the two charges together.

And when we have plotted the equipotentials, they turn out to be more useful than lines of force. A line of force diagram appeals to the imagination, and helps us to see what would happen to a charge in the field. But it tells us little about the strength of the field—at the best, if it is more carefully drawn than most, we can only say that the field is strongest where the lines are closest. But equipotentials can be labelled with the values of potential they represent; and from their spacing we can find the actual value of the potential gradient, and hence the field-strength. The only difficulty in interpreting equipotential diagrams lies in visualizing the direction of the force on a charge; this is always at right angles to the curves.

34. Field inside Hollow Conductor. Potential Difference and Gold-leaf Electroscope.

If a hollow conductor contains no charged bodies, then, whatever charge there may be on its outside, there is none on its inside. Inside it, therefore, there is no electric field; the space within the conductor is an equipotential volume. If the conductor has an open end, like a can, then most of the space inside it is equipotential, but near its mouth there is a weak field (Fig. 602).

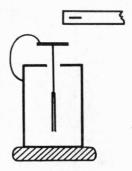

FIG. 602. Equipotentials and lines of force near mouth of an open charged can.

FIG. 603. Electroscope cap joined to case.

The behaviour of the *gold-leaf electroscope* illustrates this point. If we stand the case on an insulator, and connect the cap to it with a wire, then, no matter what charge we give to the cap, the leaves do not diverge (Fig. 603). Any charge we give to the cap spreads over the case of the electroscope, but none appears on the leaves, and there is no force acting to diverge them. When, as usual, the cap is insulated and the case earthed, charging the cap sets up a potential difference between it and the case. Charges appear on the leaves, and the field between them and the case makes them diverge (p. 763). If the case is insulated from earth, as well as from the cap, the leaves diverge less; the charge on them and the cap raises the potential of the case and reduces the potential difference between it and the leaves. The field acting on the leaves is thus made weaker, and the force on the leaves less. We can sum up these observations by saying that *the electroscope indicates the potential difference between its leaves and its case.*

35. Potential of Pear-shaped Conductor.

On p. 773 we saw that the surface-density of the charge on a pear-shaped conductor was greatest where the curvature was greatest. The potential of the conductor at various points can be examined by means of the gold-leaf electroscope, the case being earthed. One end of a wire is connected to the cap; some of the wire is then wrapped round an insulating rod, and the free end of the wire is placed on the conductor. As the free end is moved over the conductor, it is observed that the divergence of the leaf remains constant. This result was explained on p. 784.

36. Electrostatic Shielding.

The fact that there is no electric field inside a closed conductor, when it contains no charged bodies, was demonstrated by Faraday in a

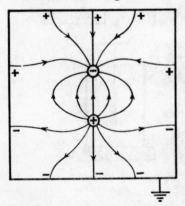

FIG. 604.   Lines of force round charges.

spectacular manner. He made for himself a large wire cage, supported it on insulators, and sat inside it with his electroscopes. He then had the cage charged by an induction machine—a forerunner of the type we described on p. 767—until painful sparks could be drawn from its outside. Inside the cage Faraday sat in safety and comfort, and there was no deflection to be seen on even his most sensitive electroscope.

If we wish to protect any persons or instruments from intense electric fields, therefore, we enclose them in hollow conductors; these are called "Faraday cages", and are widely used in high-voltage measurements. See Fig. 580.

We may also wish to prevent charges in one place from setting up an electric field beyond their immediate neighbourhood. To do this we surround the charges with a Faraday cage, and connect the cage to earth (Fig. 604). The charge induced on the outside of the cage then runs to earth, and there is no external field. (When a cage is used to shield something *inside* it, it does not have to be earthed.)

THE CATHODE-RAY OSCILLOGRAPH

An oscillograph is an instrument for plotting one varying physical quantity—potential difference, sound-pressure, heart-beat—against another—current, displacement, time. A cathode-ray oscillograph, of the kind we are about to describe, plots alternating potential difference against time. It is so called because it traces the desired wave-form with a beam of electrons, and beams of electrons were originally called cathode rays.

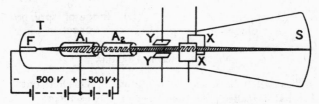

Fig. 605. A cathode-ray oscillograph tube.

A cathode-ray oscillograph is essentially an electrostatic instrument. It consists of a highly evacuated glass tube, T in Fig. 605, one end of which opens out to form a screen S which is internally coated with zinc sulphide. A hot filament F, at the other end of the tube, emits electrons. These are then attracted by the cylinders A_1 and A_2, which have increasing positive potentials with respect to the filament. Many of the electrons, however, shoot through the cylinders and strike the screen; where they do so, the zinc sulphide fluoresces in a green spot. On their way to the screen, the electrons pass through two pairs of metal plates, XX and YY, called the deflecting plates.

37. Deflection; Time-base.

If a battery were connected between the Y-plates, so as to make the upper one positive, the electrons in the beam would be attracted towards that plate, and the beam would be deflected upwards. In the same way, the beam can be deflected horizontally by a potential difference applied between the X-plates. When the oscillograph is in use, the alternating potential difference to be examined is applied between the Y-plates. If that were all, then the spot would be simply drawn out into a vertical line. To trace the wave-form of the alternating potential difference, the X-plates are used to provide a time-axis. A special valve circuit generates a potential difference which rises steadily to a certain value, as shown in Fig. 606 (a), and then falls rapidly to zero; it can be made to go through these changes tens, hundreds, or thousands of times per second. This potential difference is applied between the X-plates, so that the spot is swept steadily to the right,

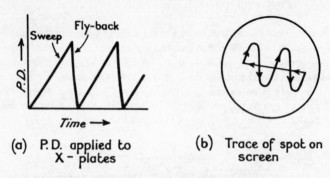

(a)   P.D. applied to
        X - plates

(b)   Trace of spot on
        screen

FIG. 606.   Action of a C.R.O.

and then flies swiftly back and starts out again. This horizontal motion provides what is called the time-base of the oscillograph. On it is superimposed the vertical motion produced by the Y-plates; thus, as shown in Fig. 606 (b), the wave-form of the potential difference to be examined is displayed on the screen

38. Focusing.

To give a clear trace on the screen, the electron beam must be focused to a sharp spot. This is the function of the cylinders A_1 and A_2, called the first and second anodes. Fig. 607 shows the equipotentials of the field between them, when their difference of potential is 500 volts. Electrons entering the field from the filament experience forces from low potential to high at right angles to the equipotentials. They have, however, considerable momentum, because they have been accelerated by a potential difference of about 500 volts, and are travelling fast. Consequently the field merely deflects them, and, because of its cylindrical symmetry, it converges the beam towards the point P. Before they can reach this point, however, they enter the second cylinder. Here the potential rises from the axis, and the electrons are deflected outwards. However, they are now travelling faster than when they were in the first cylinder, because the potential is everywhere higher. Consequently their momentum is greater, and they are less deflected than before. The second cylinder, therefore, diverges the beam less than the first cylinder converged it, and the beam emerges from the second anode still somewhat convergent. By adjusting the potential of the first anode, the beam can be focused upon the screen, to give a spot a millimetre or less in diameter.

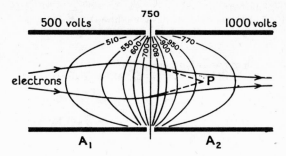

FIG. 607. Focusing in a C.R.O. tube.

Electron-focusing devices are called electron-lenses, or electron-optical systems. For example, the action of the anodes A_1 and A_2 is roughly analogous to that of a pair of glass lenses on a beam of light, the first glass lens being converging, and the second diverging, but weaker.

39. Comparison of Static and Current Phenomena.

Broadly speaking, we may say that in electrostatic phenomena we meet small quantities of charge, but great differences of potential; in the phenomena of current electricity, on the other hand, the potential differences are small but the amounts of charge transported by the currents are great. Sparks and shocks are common in electrostatics, because they require great potential differences; but they are rarely dangerous, because the total amount of energy available is usually small. On the other hand, shocks and sparks in current electricity are rare, but, when the potential difference is great enough to cause them, they are likely to be dangerous.

These quantitative differences make problems of insulation much more difficult in electrostatic apparatus than in apparatus for use with currents. The high potentials met in electrostatics make leakage currents relatively great, and the small charges therefore tend to disappear rapidly. Any wood, for example, ranks as an insulator for current electricity, but a conductor in electrostatics. In electrostatic experiments we sometimes wish to connect a charged body to earth; all we have then to do is to touch it.

EXAMPLES

1. Explain what is meant by the potential at a point in an electric field. Obtain an expression for the potential at a point in a field due to a point charge.

Charges of $-3, 1, 2$ and -4 e.s.u. are placed at the corners, taken in order, of a square ABCD of side 2 cm. Find (a) the work done in taking a point charge of 2 e.s.u. from the mid-point of AB to the centre of the square, (b) the magnitude and direction of the electric field at the centre of the square. (L.)

First part (see pp. 779, 781). .

Second part. (a) The potential, V_1, at the centre O, say, is given by

$$V_1 = -\frac{3}{a} + \frac{1}{a} + \frac{2}{a} - \frac{4}{a} = -\frac{4}{a}, \quad \ldots \ldots \quad \text{(i)}$$

where a is the length of the half-diagonal.

The potential, V_2, at the mid-point N, say, of AB is given by

$$V_2 = -\frac{3}{AN} + \frac{1}{BN} + \frac{2}{CN} - \frac{4}{DN}.$$

But $AN = 1 = BN$,   and $CN = \sqrt{5} = DN.$

$$\therefore \ V_2 = -3 + 1 + \frac{2}{\sqrt{5}} - \frac{4}{\sqrt{5}} = -2 - \frac{2}{\sqrt{5}}.$$

From (i), $V_1 = -\dfrac{4}{a}$, where $a = \frac{1}{2}\sqrt{8} = \sqrt{2}.$

$$\therefore \ V_1 - V_2 = -\frac{4}{\sqrt{2}} - \left(-2 - \frac{2}{\sqrt{5}}\right).$$

$$= 2 + \frac{2}{\sqrt{5}} - \frac{4}{\sqrt{2}} = 0.068.$$

$\therefore$ work done = charge $\times$ p.d. = $2 \times 0.068 = 0.136$ erg.

(b) *Intensity at O.* Due to the charge -3, intensity $E_1 = \dfrac{3}{AO^2}$, towards A.

Due to the charge $+2$, intensity $E_2 = \dfrac{2}{CO^2}$, towards A.

$\therefore$ resultant of E_1 and E_2, R_1, $= E_1 + E_2 = \dfrac{5}{AO^2}$, as AO = CO.

But $AO^2 + OD^2 = AD^2$, or $2AO^2 = 2^2 = 4$. Thus $AO^2 = 2$.

$$\therefore \ R_1 = \frac{5}{2} = 2.5 \text{ e.s.u.} \quad \ldots \ldots \quad \text{(i)}$$

Due to the charge $+1$, intensity $E_3 = \dfrac{1}{BO^2}$, towards D.

Due to the charge -4, intensity $E_4 = \dfrac{4}{DO^2}$, towards D.

$\therefore$ resultant R_2 of E_3 and $E_4 = E_3 + E_4 = \dfrac{5}{DO^2} = \dfrac{5}{2} = 2.5$ e.s.u. . (ii)

From (i) and (ii), since R_1 and R_2 are perpendicular, the resultant intensity at

$O = \sqrt{R_1^2 + R_2^2} = \sqrt{2.5^2 + 2.5^2} = 3.5$ e.s.u., parallel to AB.

2. How are cathode rays produced and what are their properties?

An electron starts from rest and moves freely in an electric field of intensity 0.080 e.s.u. of potential per cm. Determine (a) the force on the electron, (b) its acceleration, (c) the kinetic energy acquired and the velocity attained if the electron moves through a potential difference of 0.300 e.s.u. (Charge on an electron = 4.81×10^{-10} e.s.u., mass of an electron = 9.12×10^{-28} gm.) (L.)

First part (see p. 1004).

Second part. (*a*) Force on electron (F) = intensity (E) × charge (e)
$$= 0 \cdot 080 \times 4 \cdot 81 \times 10^{-10}$$
$$= 0 \cdot 385 \times 10^{-10} \text{ dyne.}$$

(*b*) The acceleration, f, $= \dfrac{\text{Force}}{\text{Mass}}$

$$= \frac{0 \cdot 385 \times 10^{-10}}{9 \cdot 12 \times 10^{-28}} = 4 \cdot 22 \times 10^{16} \text{ cm. per sec.}^2$$

(*c*) Kinetic energy acquired = work done on electron
$$= \text{charge} \times \text{p.d.}$$
$$= 4 \cdot 81 \times 10^{-10} \times 0 \cdot 300$$
$$= 1 \cdot 443 \times 10^{-10} \text{ erg.}$$

Since kinetic energy, W, $= \tfrac{1}{2}mv^2$,

$$v = \sqrt{\frac{2W}{m}}$$

$$= \sqrt{\frac{2 \cdot 886 \times 10^{-10}}{9 \cdot 12 \times 10^{-28}}} = 5 \cdot 6 \times 10^8 \text{ cm. per sec.}$$

EXERCISES XXXIV

1. How has it been shown experimentally that a closed conducting surface screens completely the space inside it from the electrostatic effect of charges outside it?

Three concentric hollow metal spheres of radii 4, 6, and 8 cm. have charges $+8$, -6, and $+4$ units respectively. What are the potentials and the field-strengths at points 2, 5, 7, and 10 cm. from the centre? (*L.*)

2. Explain the process of electrostatic induction. Give clear diagrams to illustrate the process of charging an insulated sphere with a positive charge by this method.

Explain the action of an electrostatic machine (other than an electrophorus or a friction machine) which will produce and maintain a high electrostatic potential difference. (*L.*)

3. Define *electrostatic unit of charge* and *intensity of electric field*. Two small metal spheres of equal size have charges of $+10$ and $+40$ units respectively, and are placed 9 cm. apart. Find the position of the neutral point. They are then connected *momentarily* by a fine wire. Find the *potential* at the point midway between them. Sketch the electric field *before* they are connected. (*N.*)

4. Describe and explain the action of a gold-leaf electroscope. How would you show that the deflection is a measure of potential difference between the leaves and the case?

A sheet of waxed paper rests on a large metal disc which is in contact with the cap of an electroscope. A second disc, to which an insulating handle is attached, is placed on the wax. The two discs are momentarily connected to the terminals of a 12-volt battery and the top one is then withdrawn by means of the handle. Describe and explain what happens. (*C.*)

5. Define electrostatic potential at a point and establish a formula for the potential at a point at a distance r from a charge of Q e.s.u. Charges of $+6$, -5, $+8$, and -10 e.s.u. are placed at points A, B, C, D respectively, where ABCD is a rectangle and AB = 6 cm. and BC = 4 cm. If E and F are the mid-points of AB and CD, find the work done against the electric forces in taking a small charge e from E to F. (*L.*)

6. Define (*a*) electric intensity, (*b*) difference of potential. How are these quantities related?

A charged oil-drop of radius 0·00013 cm. is prevented from falling under gravity by the vertical field between two horizontal plates charged to a difference of potential of 8,340 volts. The distance between the plates is 1·6 cm., and the density of oil is 0·92 gm. per cm. Calculate the magnitude of the charge on the drop (g = 981 cm./sec.²). (*O. & C.*)

7. Define *electric potential* at a point.

How would you show experimentally that the maximum charge that can be induced on a conductor is equal in magnitude and opposite in sign to the inducing charge?

Three thin conducting spherical shells of radii respectively 10, 20, and 40 cm. are mounted concentrically, the two inner ones being insulated and the outer one connected to earth. The innermost shell carries a charge of 30 e.s.u. and the middle one a charge of 50 e.s.u. Calculate (*a*) the potentials of the two inner conductors, (*b*) the charges on each face of each shell. (*L.*)

8. Define *intensity of electric field, potential gradient at a point.* What is the connexion between these quantities? Explain why there is a tendency for electricity to discharge from points.

A surface discharges into the air when the potential gradient is 100 e.s.u. per cm. To what potential can a sphere of radius 3 metres be raised before it begins to lose its charge to the air? (*C.*)

9. Define the terms *electric charge, electric field-strength,* and *electrostatic potential.* In what units are these quantities measured? Derive from your definitions an expression for the potential at a distance r from a point charge q e.s.u.

Charges of $+6$, $+2$, -5 e.s.u. are placed at the corners A, B, D respectively of a rectangle ABCD; AB is 1 cm. and BC $\sqrt{3}$ cm. long. Calculate the work done in moving a charge 0·01 e.s.u. from the centre of the rectangle to the foot of the perpendicular from A to the diagonal of the rectangle BD. (*O. & C.*)

10. Describe simple electrostatic experiments to illustrate *two* of the following: (*a*) the production of equal and opposite charges by induction; (*b*) the action of points; (*c*) the effect on a charged conductor of the approach of an earthed conductor. (*L.*)

11. Discuss the following, giving examples: *Electrostatic induction, electric discharge from points* and *dielectric strength.*

Describe a modern form of apparatus for obtaining a small current at a very high voltage. (*L.*)

12. Show how (*i*) the surface density, (*ii*) the intensity of electric field, (*iii*) the potential, varies over the surface of an elongated conductor charged with electricity. Describe experiments you would perform to support your answer in cases (*i*) and (*iii*).

Describe and explain the action of points on a charged conductor; and give two practical applications of the effect. (*L.*)

13. Describe carefully Faraday's ice-pail experiments and discuss the deductions to be drawn from them. How would you investigate experimentally the charge distribution over the surface of a conductor? (*C.*)

CHAPTER XXXV

CONDENSERS

A condenser, or capacitor, is a device for storing electricity. The earliest condenser was invented—almost accidentally—by van Musschenbroek of Leyden, in about 1746, and became known as a Leyden jar. A present-day form of it is shown in Fig. 608 (a), J is a glass jar, FF are tin-foil coatings over the lower parts of its walls, and T is a knob connected to the inner coating. Modern forms of condenser are shown at (b) and (d) in the figure. Essentially, all condensers consist of two metal plates separated by an insulator. The insulator is called the dielectric; in some condensers it is oil or air. Fig. 608 (c) shows the conventional symbol for a condenser.

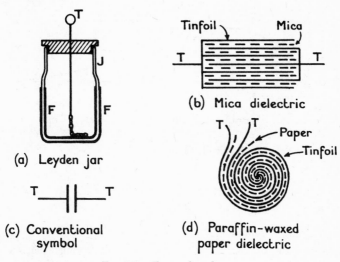

(a) Leyden jar

(b) Mica dielectric

(c) Conventional symbol

(d) Paraffin-waxed paper dielectric

FIG. 608.   Types of condensers.

1. Charging a Condenser.

To study the action of a condenser we need a paper one of about 4 microfarad capacitance (see later), a couple of high-tension batteries D and an electrostatic voltmeter V reading to about 300 volts (1 e.s.u.). We also need a two-way key (K in Fig. 609) and a poor conductor (R). The latter is a short stick of powdered and compressed carbon; it is called a radio resistor, and should have a resistance of about 5 megohms (p. 821). We connect the batteries in series, and measure their total voltage, V_0, with the voltmeter (Fig. 609 (a)). We then connect up all the apparatus as shown in Fig. 609 (b). If we close the key at A, the condenser is connected via the resistor to the battery, and the potential difference across the condenser, V, which is measured by the voltmeter, begins to rise (Fig. 609 (c)). The potential difference becomes steady when it is equal to the battery voltage V_0. If we now open the key, the voltmeter reading stays unchanged (unless the condenser is leaky).

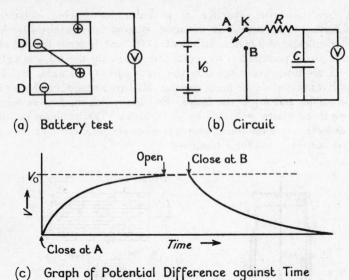

(a) Battery test   (b) Circuit

(c) Graph of Potential Difference against Time

FIG. 609.   Charging and discharging a condenser through a resistor.

The condenser is said to be charged, to the battery voltage; its condition does not depend at all on the resistor, whose only purpose was to slow down the charging process, so that we could follow it on the voltmeter.

2. Discharging a Condenser.

We can show that the charged condenser is storing electricity by discharging it: if we put a piece of wire across its terminals, a fat spark passes just as the wire makes contact, and the voltmeter reading falls to zero.

If we now recharge the condenser and then close the key at B, in Fig. 609 (b), we allow the condenser to discharge through the resistor R. The potential difference across it now falls to zero as slowly as it rose during charging.

3. Charging and Discharging Processes.

When we connect a condenser to a battery, electrons flow from the negative terminal of the battery on to the plate A of the condenser

connected to it (Fig. 610); and, at the same
rate, electrons flow from the other plate B of
the condenser towards the positive terminal of
the battery. Positive and negative charges thus
appear on the plates, and oppose the flow of
electrons which causes them. As the charges
accumulate, the potential difference between the
plates increases, and the charging current falls
to zero when the potential difference becomes
equal to the battery voltage V_0.

When the battery is disconnected and the
plates are joined together by a wire, electrons
flow back from plate A to plate B until the
positive charge on B is completely neutralized.
A current thus flows for a time in the wire, and
at the end of the time the charges on the plates
become zero.

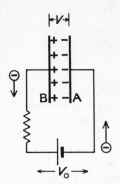

Fig. 610.   A condenser
charging. (Resistance is
shown because some is
always present, even if
only that of the connect-
ing wires.)

4. Condensers in A.C. Circuits.

Condensers are widely used in alternating current and radio circuits,
because they can transmit alternating currents. To see how they do
so, let us consider the circuit of Fig. 611, in which the condenser may
be connected across either of the batteries X, Y. When the key is
closed at A, current flows from the battery X, and charges the plate D
of the condenser positively. If the key is now closed at B instead,
current flows from the battery Y; the plate D
loses its positive charge and becomes negatively charged. Thus if the key is rocked
rapidly between A and B, current surges
backwards and forwards along the wires connected to the condenser. An alternating voltage, as we shall see in Chapter XLI, is one
which reverses many times a second; when
such a voltage is applied to a condenser,
therefore, an alternating current flows in the
connecting wires.

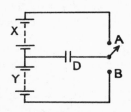

Fig. 611. Reversals of voltage applied to condenser.

5. Capacitance Definition, and Units.

Experiments with a ballistic galvanometer, which measures quantity
of electricity, show that, when a condenser is charged to a potential
difference V, the charges stored on its plates, $\pm q$, are proportional to V.
The ratio of the charge on either plate to the potential difference between
the plates is called the *capacitance*, C, of the condenser:

$$C = \frac{q}{V}. \qquad . \quad . \quad . \quad . \quad . \quad . \quad (1)$$

Thus
$$q = CV, \quad \ldots \ldots \ldots \quad (2)$$

and
$$V = \frac{q}{C}. \quad \ldots \ldots \ldots \quad (3)$$

The practical unit of capacitance is the *farad*; this is the capacitance of a condenser which stores 1 coulomb of charge when a p.d. of 1 volt is applied. Commercially, the *microfarad* (μF) is used; it is one-millionth of a farad.

The electrostatic unit of capacitance is defined as the capacitance of a condenser which stores 1 e.s.u. of charge on its plates when the p.d. between them is 1 e.s.u. To find the relation between the farad and the e.s.u. of capacitance, we note:

$$1 \text{ farad} = \frac{1 \text{ coulomb}}{1 \text{ volt}} = \frac{3 \times 10^9 \text{ e.s.u. (charge)}}{1/300 \text{ e.s.u. (p.d.)}} = 9 \times 10^{11} \text{ e.s.u.}$$

Thus 1 microfarad (μF) $= 9 \times 10^5$ e.s.u. of capacitance.

6. Comparison of Capacitances.

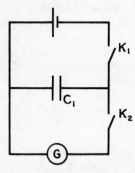

FIG. 612. Comparison of capacitances.

Large capacitances, of the order of micro-farads, can be compared with the aid of a ballistic galvanometer. In this instrument, as explained on p. 937, the first "throw" or deflection is proportional to the quantity of electricity discharged through it.

The circuit required is shown in Fig. 612. The condenser of capacitance C_1 is charged by a battery of e.m.f. V, and then dis-charged through the ballistic galvanometer G. The corresponding first deflection θ_1 is ob-served. The condenser is now replaced by another of capacitance C_2, charged again by the battery, and the new deflection θ_2 is ob-served when the condenser is discharged.

Now
$$\frac{q_1}{q_2} = \frac{\theta_1}{\theta_2}.$$

$$\therefore \frac{C_1 V}{C_2 V} = \frac{\theta_1}{\theta_2}.$$

$$\therefore \frac{C_1}{C_2} = \frac{\theta_1}{\theta_2}. \quad \ldots \ldots \ldots \quad (4)$$

7. Factors determining Capacitance of Condenser. Variable Condenser.

We shall now find out by experiment what factors influence capacitance. To interpret our observations we shall require the formula for potential difference:

$$V = \frac{q}{C}.$$

This shows that, when a condenser is given a fixed charge, the potential difference between its plates is inversely proportional to its capacitance.

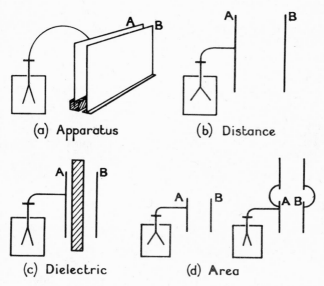

(a) Apparatus   (b) Distance

(c) Dielectric   (d) Area

Fig. 613. Factors determining capacitance.

Distance between plates. In Fig. 613 (a), A and B are two metal plates, B being earthed, while A is insulated and connected to an electroscope. We set the plates close together, but not touching, and charge A from an electrophorus. The leaves of the electroscope diverge by an amount which measures the potential difference between the plates. If we move the plates further apart the leaves diverge further, showing that the potential difference has increased (Fig. 613 (b)). Since we have done nothing to increase the charge on the plates, the increase in potential difference must be due to a decrease in capacitance (see above equation). The capacitance of a condenser therefore decreases when the separation of its plates is increased; we shall see in the next chapter that the capacitance is inversely proportional to the separation.

Dielectric. Let us now put a dielectric—a sheet of glass or ebonite—between the plates. The leaves diverge less, showing that the potential difference has decreased (Fig. 613 (c)). The capacitance has therefore increased, and the increase is due to the dielectric. By using several sheets of it we can show that the effect of the dielectric increases with its thickness. In practical condensers the dielectric completely fills the space between the plates.

Area of plates. To see how the capacitance depends on the area of the plates, we set them at a known distance apart. We then take another pair of plates, at the same distance apart, and connect them to the first pair by wires held on insulating handles (Fig. 613 (d)). The leaves diverge less, showing that the capacitance has increased; it is, in fact, directly proportional to the area of the plates.

A condenser in which the effective area of the plates can be adjusted is called a variable condenser. In the type shown in Fig. 614, the plates are semicircular and one set can be swung into or out of the other. The capacitance of the condenser is proportional to the area of overlap of the plates. The plates are made of brass or aluminium, and the dielectric may be air, oil, or mica.

SUMMARY. We shall see shortly that the capacitance of a condenser having parallel plates with air between them is given by

$$C = \frac{A}{4\pi d},$$

FIG. 614. Variable air condenser.

where C = capacitance in e.s.u.
A = area of overlap of plates in cm.²
d = distance between plates in cm.

With a dielectric between the plates, the capacitance is given by

$$C = \frac{kA}{4\pi d} \text{ e.s.u.} \quad \text{or} \quad \frac{kA}{4\pi d \times 9 \times 10^5} \ \mu\text{F},$$

where k is a constant depending on the nature of the dielectric (p. 802).

8. Capacitance of Condensers. Isolated Sphere.

Suppose a sphere of radius r cm. in air is given a charge q e.s.u. The surface of the sphere then has a potential relative of earth given by

$$V = \frac{q}{r}.$$

$$\therefore \frac{q}{V} = r,$$

$$\therefore \text{ capacitance, } C, = r. \qquad \cdots \cdots \quad (5)$$

An isolated sphere of radius 6 cm. thus has a capacitance of 6 e.s.u. The other "plate" of the condenser is the earth.

9. Concentric Spheres.

Faraday used two concentric spheres to investigate the dielectric constant of liquids. Suppose a, b are the respective radii of the inner and outer spheres (Fig. 615). Let $+q$ be the charge given to the inner sphere and let the outer sphere be earthed, with air between them.

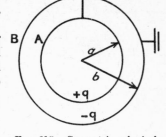

FIG. 615. Concentric spherical condenser.

The induced charge on the outer sphere is $-q$ (see p. 769). The potential V_a of the inner sphere = potential due to $+q$ and potential due to $-q = +\dfrac{q}{a} - \dfrac{q}{b}$, since the potential due to the charge $-q$ is $-q/b$ everywhere inside the larger sphere (see p. 787).

But $V_b = 0$, as the outer sphere is earthed.

$$\therefore \text{ potential difference, } V, = V_a - V_b = \frac{q}{a} - \frac{q}{b}.$$

$$\therefore V = q\left(\frac{b-a}{ab}\right),$$

$$\therefore \frac{q}{V} = \frac{ab}{b-a},$$

$$\therefore C = \frac{ab}{b-a}. \quad \ldots \ldots \ldots \quad (6)$$

10. Parallel-plate Condenser.

Suppose two parallel plates of a condenser have a charge on each numerically equal to q, as in p. 799. The surface-density, σ, is then q/A, where A is the area of either plate, and the intensity between the plates, E, is given (see p. 776) by

$$E = \frac{4\pi\sigma}{K},$$

where K is the permittivity of the medium (Fig. 616).

σ e.s.u./sq.cm

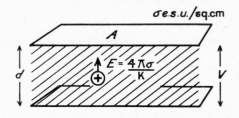

FIG. 616.
Parallel-plate condenser.

Now the work done in taking a unit charge from one plate to the other = force × distance = $E \times d$, where d is the distance between the plates = V, the p.d. between the plates.

$$\therefore \ V = \frac{4\pi\sigma}{K} \times d,$$

$$\therefore \ V = \frac{4\pi q}{KA} \times d,$$

$$\therefore \ \frac{q}{V} = \frac{KA}{4\pi d},$$

$$\therefore \ C = \frac{KA}{4\pi d}. \qquad \cdots \cdots \ (7)$$

This formula for C is approximate, as the field becomes non-uniform at the edges, as illustrated in Fig. 598.

11. Dielectric Constant (Relative Permittivity) and Strength.

To study the effect of the dielectric in a condenser, the capacitance of a given condenser must be measured: first without a dielectric, and then with one. We shall see later how this can be done (p. 812).

The ratio of the capacitance with and without the dielectric between the plates is called the dielectric constant, or relative permittivity of the material used. The expression "without a dielectric" strictly means "with the plates in a vacuum"; but the effect of air on the capacitance of a condenser is so small that for most purposes it may be neglected. The dielectric constant of a substance is denoted by the letter k;* thus

$$k = \frac{\text{capacitance of given condenser, with space between plates filled with dielectric}}{\text{capacitance of same condenser with plates } in \ vacuo}.$$

The following table gives the value of dielectric constant, and also of dielectric strength, for various substances. The strength of a dielectric is the potential gradient at which its insulation breaks down, and a spark passes through it. A solid dielectric is ruined by such a breakdown, but a liquid or gaseous one heals up as soon as the applied potential difference is reduced.

Water is not suitable for a dielectric in practice, because it is a good insulator only when it is very pure, and to remove all matter dissolved in it is almost impossible.

* $K = kK_0$, where K is the permittivity of the medium and K_0 is the permittivity of a vacuum. Thus k (dielectric constant) is a ratio and has no units; K, however, has units.

PROPERTIES OF DIELECTRICS

Substance	Dielectric constant, k	Dielectric strength, kilovolts per mm.
Glass . . .	5–10	30–150
Mica . . .	6	80–200
Ebonite . . .	2·8	30–110
Ice* . . .	94	—
Paraffin wax . .	2	15–50
Paraffined paper .	2	40–60
Paraffin oil ' .	4·7	—
Ethyl alcohol* . .	26	—
Methyl alcohol* . .	32	—
Water* . . .	81	—
Air	1·0005	—
Sulphur dioxide* .	1·01	—

* Polar molecules (see p. 804).

12. Action of Dielectric.

The explanation of dielectric action which we shall now give is similar in principle to Faraday's, but expressed in modern terms—there was no knowledge of electrons in his day.

We regard a molecule as a collection of atomic nuclei, positively charged, and surrounded by a cloud of negative electrons. When a dielectric is in a charged condenser, its molecules are in an electric field; the nuclei are urged in the direction of the field, and the electrons in the opposite direction (Fig. 617 (a)). Thus each molecule is distorted, or polarized: one end has an excess of positive charge, the other an excess of negative. At the surfaces of the dielectric, therefore, charges appear, as shown in Fig. 617 (b). These charges are of opposite sign to the charges on the plates, and so reduce the potential difference between the plates.

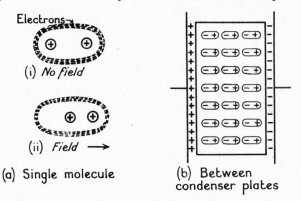

(a) Single molecule   (b) Between condenser plates

Fig. 617.   Polarisation of a dielectric.

If the condenser is connected to a battery, then its potential difference is constant; but the surface charges on the dielectric still increase its capacitance. They do so because they offset the mutual repulsions of the charges on the plates, and so enable greater charges to accumulate there before the potential difference rises to the battery voltage.

Some molecules, we believe, are permanently polarized: they are called polar molecules. For example, the water molecule consists of an oxygen atom, O, with two hydrogen atoms H, making roughly a right-angled structure (Fig. 618 (a)).

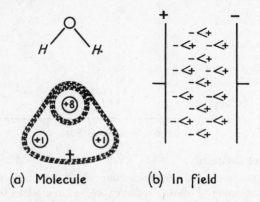

(a) Molecule   (b) In field

Fig. 618.   Water as a dielectric.

Oxygen has a nuclear charge of $+8e$, where e is the electronic charge, and has eight electrons. Hydrogen has a nuclear charge of $+e$, and one electron. In the water molecule, the two electrons from the hydrogen atom move in paths which surround the oxygen nucleus. Thus they are partly added to the oxygen atom, and partly withdrawn from the hydrogen atoms. On the average, therefore, the apex of the triangle is negatively charged, and its base is positively charged. In an electric field, water molecules tend to orient themselves as shown in Fig. 618 (b). The effect of this, in a condenser, is to increase the capacitance in the way already described. The increase is, in fact, much greater than that obtained with a dielectric which is polarized merely by the action of the field.

13. Arrangements of Condensers.

In radio circuits, condensers often appear in arrangements whose resultant capacitances must be known. To derive expressions for these, we need the equation defining capacitance in its three possible forms:

$$C = \frac{q}{V}, \qquad V = \frac{q}{C}, \qquad q = CV.$$

In Parallel. Fig. 619 shows three condensers, having all their left-hand plates connected together, and all their right-hand plates likewise. They are said to be connected in parallel. If a cell is now connected across them, they all have the same potential difference V. (For, if they had not, current would flow from one to another until they had.) The charges on the individual condensers are respectively

$$\left.\begin{array}{l} q_1 = C_1 V \\ q_2 = C_2 V \\ q_3 = C_3 V \end{array}\right\} \quad . \quad . \quad . \quad . \quad . \quad . \quad (8)$$

The total charge on the system of condensers is

$$q = q_1 + q_2 + q_3 = (C_1 + C_2 + C_3)V.$$

And the system is therefore equivalent to a single condenser, of capacitance

$$C = \frac{q}{V} = C_1 + C_2 + C_3.$$

Thus when condensers are connected in parallel, their resultant capacitance is the sum of their individual capacitances. It is greater than the greatest individual one.

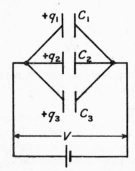

FIG. 619. Condensers in parallel.

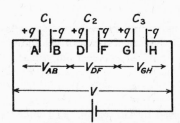

FIG. 620. Condensers in series.

In Series. Fig. 620 shows three condensers having the right-hand plate of one connected to the left-hand of the next, and so on—connected in series. When a cell is connected across the ends of the system, a charge q is transferred from the plate H to the plate A, a charge $-q$ being left on H. This charge induces a charge $+q$ on plate G; similarly, charges appear on all the other condenser plates, as shown in the figure. (The induced and inducing charges are equal because the condenser plates are very large and very close together; in effect, either may be said to enclose the other.) The potential differences across the individual condensers are, therefore, given by

$$\left.\begin{array}{l} V_{AB} = \dfrac{q}{C_1} \\[2mm] V_{DF} = \dfrac{q}{C_2} \\[2mm] V_{GH} = \dfrac{q}{C_3} \end{array}\right\} \quad . \quad . \quad . \quad . \quad . \quad (9)$$

The sum of these is equal to the applied potential difference V because the work done in taking a unit charge from H to A is the sum of the work done in taking it from H to G, from F to D, and from B to A. Therefore

$$V = V_{AB} + V_{DF} + V_{GH}$$
$$= q\left(\frac{1}{C_1} + \frac{1}{C_2} + \frac{1}{C_3}\right). \quad \ldots \ldots \quad (10)$$

The resultant capacitance of the system is the ratio of the charge stored to the applied potential difference, V. The charge stored is equal to q, because, if the battery is removed, and the plates HA joined by a wire, a charge q will pass through that wire, and the whole system will be discharged. The resultant capacitance is therefore given by

$$C = \frac{q}{V}, \quad \text{or} \quad \frac{1}{C} = \frac{V}{q},$$

whence, by equation (7),

$$\frac{1}{C} = \frac{1}{C_1} + \frac{1}{C_2} + \frac{1}{C_3}. \quad \ldots \ldots \quad (11)$$

Thus, to find the resultant capacitance of condensers in series, we must add their reciprocals of the individual capacitances. The resultant is less than the smallest individual.

Comparison of Series and Parallel Arrangements. Let us compare Figs. 619 and 620. In Fig. 620, where the condensers are in series, all the condensers carry the same charge, which is equal to the charge carried by the system as a whole, q. The potential difference applied to the system, however, is divided amongst the condensers, in inverse proportion to their capacitances (equations (9)). In Fig. 619, where the condensers are in parallel, they all have the same potential difference; but the charge stored is divided amongst them, in direct proportion to their capacitances (equations (8)).

EXAMPLE

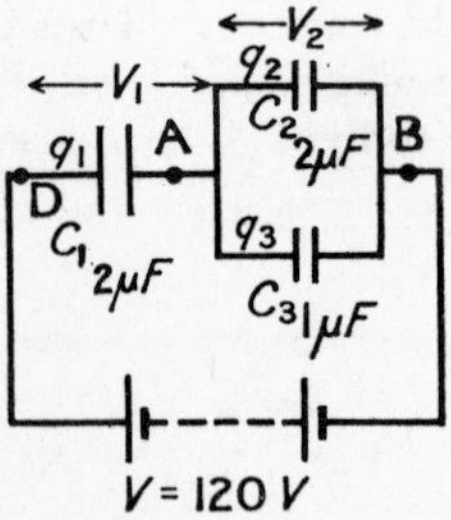

Fig. 621. Example.

Find the charges on the condensers in Fig. 621, and the potential differences across them.

Capacitance between A and B,

$$C' = C_2 + C_3 = 3 \ \mu\text{F}.$$

Overall capacitance A to D,

$$C = \frac{C_1 C'}{C_1 + C'} = \frac{2 \times 3}{2 + 3} = 1 \cdot 2 \ \mu\text{F}.$$

Charge stored in this

$$= q_1 = q_2 + q_3 = CV = 1 \cdot 2 \times 10^{-6} \times 120$$
$$= 144 \times 10^{-6} \text{ coulomb,}$$

$$\therefore \quad V_1 = \frac{q_1}{C_1} = \frac{144 \times 10^{-6}}{2 \times 10^{-6}} = 72 \text{ volts,}$$

$$V_2 = V - V_1 = 120 - 72 = 48 \text{ volts,}$$

$$q_2 = C_2 V_2 = 2 \times 10^{-6} \times 48 = 96 \times 10^{-6} \text{ coulomb,}$$

$$q_3 = C_3 V_2 = 10^{-6} \times 48 = 48 \times 10^{-6} \text{ coulomb.}$$

14. Energy of a Charged Condenser.

A charged condenser is a store of electrical energy, as we may see from the vigorous spark it can give on discharge. To find the energy stored, let us suppose that the condenser, of capacitance C, is already charged to a potential difference V. And let us suppose that we wish to increase the charge on its plates from q to $q + \delta q$, where δq is very small. Then we must transfer a charge δq from the negative plate to the positive. In doing so, we shall increase the potential difference by the amount

$$\delta V = \frac{\delta q}{C}.$$

But if δq is very small compared with q, δV will be very small compared with V, and the potential difference will be almost constant at the value V. Then the work done in displacing the charge δq will be

$$\delta W = V \delta q,$$

from the definition of potential difference. But

$$V = \frac{q}{c},$$

and therefore

$$\delta W = \frac{q}{c} \delta q.$$

If we now suppose that the condenser is at first completely discharged, and then charged until the final charge on the plates has some definite value q_1, then the work done in charging it is

$$\int_{q=0}^{q=q_1} dW = \int_0^{q_1} \frac{q \, dq}{C} = \left[\frac{1}{2} \frac{q^2}{C} \right]_0^{q_1} = \frac{1}{2} \frac{q_1^2}{C}.$$

In general, therefore, the energy stored by a condenser of capacitance C, carrying a charge q, at a potential difference V, is

$$\left. \begin{aligned} W &= \frac{1}{2} \frac{q^2}{C} \\ &= \tfrac{1}{2} q V \\ &= \tfrac{1}{2} C V^2 \end{aligned} \right\} \quad \cdots \cdots \cdots \quad (12)$$

If the quantities C, q, V are all in electrostatic units, then the energy W is in ergs. (See definition of e.s.u. of potential difference, p. 778.) But if C is in farads, q in coulombs, and V in volts, then W is in joules. This follows from the definition of the volt, which we shall give later; but the reader can check it by converting the equation from one set of units to the other, as on p. 798, and using the fact that 1 joule $= 10^7$ ergs.

15. The Quadrant Electrometer.

An electrometer is an electrostatic instrument for measuring potential difference. Fig. 622 illustrates the principles of an electrometer devised

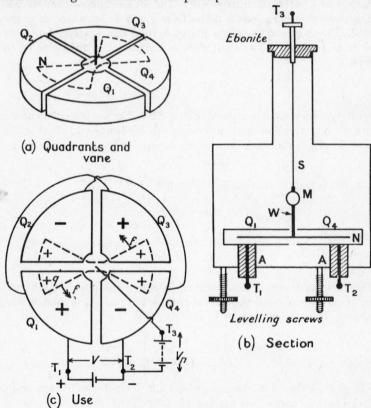

(a) Quadrants and vane

(b) Section

(c) Use

Fig. 622. The quadrant electrometer.

by Kelvin (1824–1907), and improved by Dolezalek; it is called the quadrant electrometer. It consists of four hollow brass quadrants Q, mounted on amber pillars A. Within the quadrants swings a vane of silvered paper N. The vane is attached to a wire W, which is suspended on a fine phosphor-bronze tape S, about 1/1000 in. thick. A small mirror M is attached to the wire W. Fig. 622 (a), (b).

The quadrants and suspension are enclosed in a brass case fitted with a window; through the window a beam of light is shone on to the mirror and reflected on to a scale. As explained in the Light section of this book (p. 403), the movement of the spot of light over the scale measures the deflection of the vane.

The quadrants are connected together in opposite pairs, as shown at (c) in the figure, and brought out to terminals $T_1 T_2$. Between these the potential difference to be measured, V, is applied; in Fig. 622 (c) its source is represented as a single cell. The vane is given a potential V_n, of about 100 volts, relative to one pair of quadrants, by a battery connected between the terminal T_3 and one of the other two terminals. If V_n is positive, then the vane acquires a positive charge q. The potential difference V between the quadrants sets up an electrostatic field between them; and this field urges the vane from the positive pair of quadrants towards the negative, with the forces f, f, in Fig. 622 (c). These forces are proportional to the strength of the field between the quadrants, and hence to the potential difference V.

The forces f, f exert a couple on the vane, whose moment is proportional to f, and therefore to the potential difference V. The vane turns until the restoring couple set up by the twist in the suspension is equal to the couple set up by the electrostatic forces f. Since the restoring couple is proportional to the twist of the suspension, the deflection of the vane is proportional to V, the potential difference to be measured. The corresponding displacement of the spot of light on the scale depends on the distance of the scale from the mirror. When this is 1 m., the displacement of the spot may be about 20 cm. for a potential difference of 1 volt.

The quadrant electrometer is a difficult instrument to use, and is almost obsolete. It must be levelled, so that the vane lies parallel to the quadrants; also the vane must hang symmetrically between the quadrants, and must be equidistant from their upper and lower surfaces. To test the setting-up, the voltage V is applied first in one sense and then in the other: if the deflections of the vane are equal and opposite, the setting-up is correct.

16. The Electrostatic Voltmeter.

The electrostatic voltmeter is a more handy but less sensitive form of electrometer. In it the fibre suspension is replaced by jewelled bearings and hair springs, and the beam of light by an aluminium pointer, as shown in Fig. 623. The bearings support a set of vanes N, which can swing in and out of two sets of fixed vanes Q_1, Q_2. When a potential difference V is applied between the vanes, they acquire opposite charges, and attract one another. The moving vanes swing into the fixed, under the control of the hair springs, and deflect the pointer.

Electrostatic voltmeters are fairly accurate and reliable when used to measure potential differences of the order of 1,000 volts. More delicate models are available, however, which will give full-scale

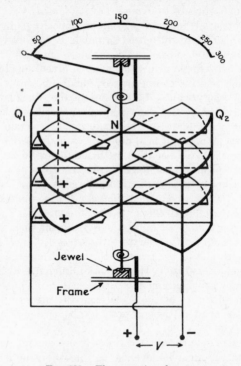

Fig. 623.   Electrostatic voltmeter.

deflection for a few hundred volts or less; these are useful in the study of condensers. The electrostatic voltmeter is less sensitive than the quadrant electrometer, partly because its controlling springs are stiffer than the suspension of the electrometer vane, and partly for another reason which we shall see in a moment.

The electrostatic voltmeter differs from the quadrant electrometer in that it is operated solely by the potential difference to be measured, V. It requires no auxiliary source of potential difference, such as the source of V_n in the quadrant electrometer. Also its deflection is roughly proportional to V^2 instead of being accurately proportional to V. The deflection is roughly proportional to V^2 because the charge on each set of vanes is roughly proportional to V, and the attraction between the vanes is proportional to the product of their charges. (The deflection is not strictly proportional to V^2 because the geometry of the system changes as the moving vanes swing into the fixed.) In the quadrant electrometer the source of the potential difference V_n maintains a constant charge q on the vane. The forces on the vane are proportional to this charge and to the charge placed on either pair of quadrants by the source of the unknown voltage V. The charges on the quadrants are proportional to V and so, therefore, is the deflection.

The quadrant electrometer is sometimes used without a potential difference V_n: the vane is connected to one set of quadrants. When connected in this way, the electrometer behaves in the same way as an electrostatic voltmeter. The charges on the vane and the other set of quadrants are each proportional to V, and the deflection is proportional to V^2. The electrometer is then insensitive, because when V is small V^2 is very small. This is also the second reason for the insensitiveness of the electrostatic voltmeter. Instruments whose deflection is proportional to V^2 deflect in the same direction whatever the sense of V; they are known as 'idiostatic' instruments.

17. Measurement of Capacitance.

Small capacitances can be measured with the quadrant electrometer. In principle the method is to compare the unknown capacitance, C_x, with a standard capacitance, C_s. The latter is the capacitance of a standard condenser, of accurately known dimensions, from which its capacitance has been calculated by equation (7), p. 802.

We first connect the standard condenser in parallel with the electrometer. The electrometer itself has a small capacitance between its quadrants of the order of 10^{-11} farad. But this is so much less than the usual values of C_s and C_x—of the order of 10^{-9} to 10^{-6} farad—that we may ignore it in the calculation that follows. After paralleling the electrometer and the standard condenser, we connect them with the unknown condenser, a two-way key, and

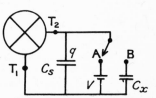

FIG. 624. Comparison of capacitances by electrometer.

a single cell, in the circuit of Fig. 624. We close the key at A for a moment, and thus charge the standard condenser to the cell voltage V. The electrometer gives a steady deflection θ, proportional to V, and the condenser acquires a charge

$$q = C_s V. \qquad \ldots \ldots \ldots \text{(i)}$$

We now close the key at B, and thus connect the unknown condenser in parallel with the standard. The charge q is now shared between the two condensers. Their resultant capacitance is $C_s + C_x$, and the potential difference across them is therefore

$$V' = \frac{q}{C_s + C_x}. \qquad \qquad \text{(ii)}$$

If θ' is the new deflection of the electrometer, then

$$\frac{\theta'}{\theta} = \frac{V'}{V} = \frac{C_s}{C_s + C_x}$$

by equations (i) and (ii). From this equation,

$$\frac{C_s}{C_x} = \frac{\theta}{\theta'} - 1, \qquad \qquad \text{(13)}$$

from which C_x can be calculated.

18. Measurement of Dielectric Constant.

The same method enables us to measure dielectric constants. We take a condenser—such as a parallel-plate one—whose dielectric can easily be withdrawn or introduced. We measure its capacitance as above, first with air between the plates, C_x, and then with the dielectric between the plates, C_x'. The dielectric constant is

$$k = \frac{C_x'}{C_x}.$$

EXAMPLES

1. Define *capacitance* of a conductor. How is it affected by the presence of a neighbouring conductor which is (*a*) unchanged and insulated, (*b*) earthed? How would you demonstrate these effects experimentally?

Assuming the expressions for the potential of an isolated conducting sphere, show that the capacitance of such a sphere will be increased by a factor n if it is enclosed within an earthed concentric sphere, the radii of the spheres being $n/(n-1)$. (*L.*)

First part. In (*a*), the capacitance is slightly increased, in (*b*) it is considerably increased. In the former case there are induced +ve and −ve charges on the neighbouring conductor, but in (*b*) there is only one induced charge, opposite to the inducing charge. The potential is thus lowered slightly in (*a*), and considerably lowered in (*b*).

Second part. The potential V of an isolated sphere $= Q/a$, where a is the radius.

$$\therefore \frac{Q}{V} = a = C_1.$$

With concentric spheres, $V = $ p.d. between spheres $= \dfrac{Q}{a} - \dfrac{Q}{b}$, where a, b are the respective radii.

$$\therefore \frac{Q}{V} = \frac{ab}{b-a} = C_2,$$

$$\therefore \frac{C_2}{C_1} = \frac{b}{b-a}.$$

But $$\frac{b}{a} = \frac{n}{n-1}, \quad \text{or} \quad b = \frac{n}{n-1} \cdot a,$$

$$\therefore \frac{C_2}{C_1} = \frac{\dfrac{na}{n-1}}{\dfrac{na}{n-1} - a} = \frac{na}{a} = n.$$

2. Define *electrical capacitance (capacity)*. Describe experiments to demonstrate the factors which determine its value for a parallel plate condenser.

The plates of a parallel plate air condenser consisting of two circular plates, each of 10 cm. radius, placed 2 mm. apart, are connected to the terminals of an electrostatic voltmeter. The system is charged to give a reading of 100 on the voltmeter scale. The space between the plates is then filled with oil of dielectric constant 4·7 and the voltmeter reading falls to 25. Calculate the capacitance of the voltmeter. You may assume that the voltage recorded by the voltmeter is proportional to the scale reading. (*N*.)

First part (see p. 799).

Second part. Capacitance of air condenser, $C = \dfrac{A}{4\pi d}$ e.s.u.

$$= \frac{\pi \times 10^2}{4\pi \times 0 \cdot 2} = 125 \text{ e.s.u.}$$

Suppose V is the p.d. across the air condenser and voltmeter, and let C_1 be the voltmeter capacitance.

Then total charge $= CV + C_1 V = (C + C_1)V.$ . . . (i)

When the plates are filled with oil the capacitance increases to $4 \cdot 7 C$, and the p.d. falls to V_1. But the total charge remains constant.

$$\therefore 4 \cdot 7 C V_1 + C_1 V_1 = (C + C_1)V, \quad \text{from (i)}.$$
$$\therefore (4 \cdot 7 C + C_1)V_1 = (C + C_1)V,$$
$$\therefore \frac{4 \cdot 7 C + C_1}{C + C_1} = \frac{V}{V_1} = \frac{100}{25} = 4,$$
$$\therefore 0 \cdot 7 C = 3 C_1,$$
$$\therefore C_1 = \frac{0 \cdot 7 C}{3} = \frac{0 \cdot 7 \times 125}{3},$$
$$= 29 \cdot 2 \text{ e.s.u.}$$

3. Define the *capacitance* of a condenser. Explain how, using a condenser in conjunction with a gold-leaf electroscope, the voltage sensitivity of the electroscope may be increased.

Two condensers, of capacitance 4 μF and 2 μF respectively, are joined in series with a battery of e.m.f. 100 volts. The connexions are broken and the like terminals of the condensers are then joined. Find the final charge on each condenser. (*L*.)

First part (see p. 799).

Second part. The combined capacitance, C, of the condensers is given by

$$\frac{1}{C} = \frac{1}{C_1} + \frac{1}{C_2},$$
$$\therefore \frac{1}{C} = \frac{1}{4} + \frac{1}{2} = \frac{3}{4}, \quad \text{or} \quad C = \frac{4}{3} \mu\text{F}.$$

∴ charge on each condenser = charge on "equivalent" condenser

$$= CV = \frac{4}{3} \times 100 = \frac{400}{3} \text{ micro-coulombs.}$$

When like terminals are joined together, the p.d. across each condenser, which is different at first, becomes equalized. Suppose it reaches a p.d. V. Then, as the total charge remains constant,

$$\text{initial total charge} = \frac{400}{3} + \frac{400}{3} = \text{final total charge} = 4V + 2V.$$

$$\therefore \ 6V = \frac{800}{3},$$

$$\therefore \ V = \frac{400}{9} \text{ volts,}$$

$$\therefore \ \text{charge on larger condenser} = 4 \times \frac{400}{9} = \frac{1600}{9} \text{ micro-coulombs,}$$

and charge on smaller condenser $= 2 \times \dfrac{400}{9} = \dfrac{800}{9}$ micro-coulombs.

4. Define the *electrostatic potential* of an isolated conductor. Obtain an expression relating the energy of a charged conductor to the charge on it and its capacity.

Two insulated spherical conductors of radii 5·00 cm. and 10·00 cm. are charged to potentials of 600 volts and 300 volts respectively. Calculate the total energy of the system. Also calculate the energy after the spheres have been connected by a fine wire. Comment on the difference between the two results. (*N.*)

First part (see p. 807).

Second part. The capacitances of the spheres are 5 and 10 e.s.u. respectively. The potentials must be changed to e.s.u. in order to calculate the energy. Now 600 volts $= \dfrac{600}{300}$ e.s.u. $= 2$ e.s.u., and 300 volts $= 1$ e.s.u.

From

$$\text{energy, } W, = \tfrac{1}{2}CV^2,$$

$$\text{total energy} = \tfrac{1}{2} \times 5 \times 2^2 + \tfrac{1}{2} \times 10 \times 1^2 = 15 \text{ ergs.} \qquad . \ . \ \text{(i)}$$

When the spheres are connected by a fine wire, the potentials become equalized. Suppose this is V. Then, since $q = CV$ and *the total charge is constant*,

$$\text{original total charge} = 5 \times 2 + 10 \times 1 = 20$$

$$= \text{final total charge}$$

$$= 5V + 10V = 15V.$$

$$\therefore \ 15V = 20 \quad \text{or} \quad V = \frac{4}{3} \text{ e.s.u.}$$

$$\therefore \ \text{new energy} = \tfrac{1}{2} \cdot 5 \cdot \left(\frac{4}{3}\right)^2 + \tfrac{1}{2} \cdot 10 \cdot \left(\frac{4}{3}\right)^2$$

$$= \tfrac{1}{2} \times 15 \times \left(\frac{4}{3}\right)^2 = 13\tfrac{1}{3} \text{ ergs.} \qquad . \ . \ \text{(ii)}$$

From (i) and (ii), $1\tfrac{2}{3}$ ergs of electrical energy have been converted into heat. This occurred because a current flows in the connecting wire when the two spheres are connected.

EXERCISES XXXV

1. State the factors which determine the capacitance of a condenser. Describe briefly experiments you would perform to verify your statements.

Obtain an expression for the energy of a charged condenser.

Find the energy which may be stored in condensers of 2 and 4 microfarads when taken singly, in series and in parallel, when a potential difference of 100 volts is available. (*L.*)

2. Define *capacitance* (or capacity), *permittivity* (or dielectric constant), microfarad (μF).

Derive an approximate expression for the capacitance of an air condenser consisting of two parallel opposite circular plates of radius r cm. at a distance t cm. apart. Explain on what the degree of approximation depends.

Two condensers of capacitances respectively 2 μF and 3 μF are joined in series between points A and B. What capacitance must be placed in parallel with the 2 μF condenser in order to increase the capacitance from A to B by 0·8 μF? (*L.*)

3. Describe and explain an experiment to demonstrate the change in the capacity of a parallel plate condenser produced by inserting a sheet of dielectric between the plates.

Derive the expression for the energy stored in a condenser of capacity C when a potential difference V is applied across its plates.

A parallel plate condenser in air has a capacity of 100 e.s.u. Calculate the change in energy of the condenser when the space between the plates is filled with an insulator of dielectric constant 5, (*a*) if the potential difference between the plates is kept constant at 2 e.s.u., (*b*) if the charge on the plates is kept constant at 600 e.s.u. State the unit in which the results are expressed. (*N.*)

4. Define *unit charge* and *unit potential difference* in the electrostatic system of units.

Describe *either* a condensing electroscope *or* a quadrant electrometer and show how the instrument you describe may be used to compare the e.m.f.s of two cells (each of the order of 2 volts). (*L.*)

5. Explain how the strength of the electric field at any point is related to the electric potential at and near the point.

A parallel plate condenser consists of two large plates 2 cm. apart, the dielectric on one side of the middle plane between the plates consisting of air, and on the other side of an insulating material of dielectric constant 4·2. Calculate the strength of the electric field in the half occupied by air, if the difference of potential between the plates is 500 volts. (*L.*)

6. Deduce expressions for the combined capacitance of two condensers (*a*) connected in series, (*b*) connected in parallel. Describe how *one* of these expressions may be verified by experiment.

A fixed condenser of capacitance 10^{-4} microfarad is connected in series with a variable condenser the capacitance of which may be varied from zero to 10^{-4} microfarad in steps of 10^{-6} microfarad. These two in series are connected in parallel with a third condenser of capacitance 5×10^{-4} microfarad. Calculate (*i*) the maximum capacitance of the whole combination, (*ii*) the smallest change in this capacitance which can be produced by the arrangement. (*N.*)

7. Define *capacitance* of a condenser.

Describe how you would compare the capacitances of two condensers using an electrometer.

A uniform slab of glass of thickness 0·25 cm. is inserted between the charged insulated plates of a parallel plate air condenser. Will it be necessary to increase or decrease the distance between the plates, and by how much, in order to maintain the same difference of potential between them? You are to assume that the area of the slab is at least equal to that of each of the plates and that the dielectric constant of the glass is 5·0. (L.)

8. Obtain an expression for the capacitance of a parallel plate condenser.

If the area of each plate is 300 cm.^{2} and the distance between the plates is 2 mm., calculate (a) the electric intensity between the plates, (b) the energy of the condenser when the p.d. between the plates is 200 volts and the dielectric is air. Neglect any variation of intensity at the edges of the plates. (1 e.s.u. of potential = 300 volts.) (L.)

9. (a) An uncharged metal sphere is held near to a positively charged spherical conductor. Give a diagram showing the distribution of lines of force and equipotentials in the electric field when the metal sphere is (i) isolated, (ii) earthed.

(b) A condenser consists of two horizontal parallel plates in contact with an intermediate layer of paraffin wax of dielectric constant 2 and thickness t. The upper plate is now raised vertically through a distance t. What will be the effect on the potential difference and charge if (i) the plates are connected across a battery of e.m.f. E, (ii) the plates are charged and then isolated from the battery before movement occurs? (L.)

10. Define *electric intensity* and *potential* at a point in an electric field and state the connection between them.

Derive an expression for the capacitance of an isolated conducting sphere. It may be assumed that, when such a sphere is charged, the electric intensity at points outside the sphere is equal to that which would be produced by the entire charge placed at the centre with no sphere present.

An isolated conducting sphere is surrounded by an air which becomes conducting when the potential gradient at any point exceeds a certain value. Explain how the maximum potential to which the sphere may be raised depends on the radius. If, for a sphere of radius 50 cm., the maximum potential is 9×10^5 volt, calculate the potential gradient for breakdown. (N.)

11. Derive an expression for the energy stored in a charged condenser.

Explain how the energy stored in a parallel plate air condenser changes when the distance between the plates is increased, the condenser having first been connected (a) *permanently*, (b) *momentarily*, to the terminals of a battery.

A battery of e.m.f. 200 volts charges a capacitance of 3,000 microfarads. The battery being removed, the condenser is connected across a discharge tube; 50 per cent of the energy stored in the condenser is used to cause a luminous electrical discharge in the tube lasting 1/300 sec. If the effective potential difference across the tube during discharge is 150 volts, find the effective current passing through the tube. (N.)

CHAPTER XXXVI

CURRENT ELECTRICITY

OHM'S AND JOULE'S LAWS: RESISTANCE AND POWER

1. Discovery of Electric Current.

By the middle of the eighteenth century, electrostatics was a well-established branch of physics. Machines had been invented which could produce by friction great amounts of charge, giving sparks and electric shocks. The momentary current (as we would now call it) carried by the spark or the body was called a "discharge".

In 1786 Galvani, while dissecting a frog, noticed that its leg-muscle twitched when one of his assistants produced an electric spark in

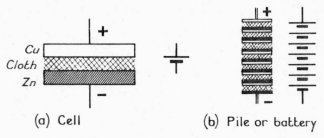

(a) Cell   **(b) Pile or battery**

Fig. 625. Voltaic cell and pile, with conventional symbols.

another part of the room. He also found that, when a frog's leg-muscle was hung by a copper hook from an iron stand, the muscle twitched whenever it swung so as to touch the stand. Galvani supposed that the electricity which caused the twitching was generated within the muscle, but his fellow-Italian Volta believed that it arose from the contact of the two different metals. Volta turned out to be right, and in 1799 he discovered how to obtain from two metals a continuous supply of electricity: he placed a piece of cloth soaked in brine between copper and zinc plates. The arrangement is called a *voltaic cell*, and the metal plates its "poles"; the copper is known as the positive pole, the zinc as the negative cell. Volta increased the power by building a pile of cells, with the zinc of one cell resting on the copper of the other (Fig. 625). From this pile he obtained sparks and shocks similar to those given by electrostatic machines.

Shortly after, it was found that water was decomposed into hydrogen and oxygen when connected to a voltaic pile. This was the earliest discovery of the chemical effect of an electric current. The heating effect was also soon found, but the magnetic effect, the most important effect, was discovered some twenty years later.

2. Ohm's Law.

The properties of an electric circuit, as distinct from the effects of a current, were first studied by Ohm in 1826. He set out to find how the length of wire in a circuit affected the current through it—in modern language, he investigated electrical resistance. In his first experiments he used voltaic piles as sources of current, but he found that the current which they gave fluctuated considerably, and he later replaced them by thermocouples (p. 836). He passed the currents through various lengths of brass wire, 0·015 in. in diameter, and observed them on a torsion balance galvanometer; this is represented by G in Fig. 626 (a). No unit of current had been defined at the time of

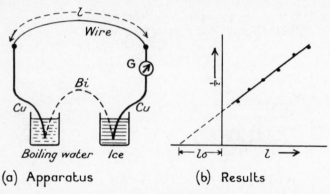

(a) Apparatus   (b) Results

Fig. 626.   Ohm's experiment.

these experiments, but physicists had agreed to take the strength of a current as proportional to its magnetic field. Ohm found that the current in his experiments was almost inversely proportional to the length of wire, l, in the circuit. He plotted the reciprocal of the current (in arbitrary units) against the length l, and got a straight line, as shown in Fig. 626 (b). Thus

$$i \propto \frac{1}{l_0 + l},$$

where l_0 is the intercept of the line on the axis of length. Ohm explained this result by supposing, naturally, that the thermocouples and galvanometer, as well as the wire, offered resistance to the current. He interpreted the constant l_0 as the length of wire equal in resistance to the galvanometer and thermocouples. The *ohm*, symbol Ω, is the unit of electrical resistance (see p. 821).

3. Specific Resistance, or Resistivity.

Ohm showed, by using wires of different length and diameter, that the resistance of a wire, R, is proportional to its length, l, and inversely proportional to its cross-sectional area A. The truth of this can easily be demonstrated today by experiments with a Wheatstone bridge (see p. 867) and suitable lengths of wire. We have, then, for a given wire,

$$R \propto \frac{l}{A} \; ;$$

we may therefore write

$$R = \varrho \frac{l}{A}, \qquad \ldots \ldots \quad (1)$$

where ϱ a is constant for the material of the wire. It is called the specific resistance, or *resistivity*, of that material.

To define it in words, we imagine a rectangular prism of the material, of unit length and unit cross-section. Then $l=1$, $A=1$, and $R=\varrho$. Thus the resistivity of a substance is the resistance between the faces of a rectangular prism of the substance, which is 1 cm. long and whose cross-sectional area is 1 sq. cm. The unit of resistivity is 1 ohm-cm., because, from equation (1),

$$\varrho = R \frac{A}{l}, \qquad \ldots \ldots \quad (2)$$

which has the units

$$\text{ohms} \times \frac{\text{cm.}^2}{\text{cm.}} = \text{ohms} \times \text{cm.}$$

Resistivities are thus often expressed in microhm-centimetres; 1 microhm $= 10^{-6}$ ohm.

RESISTIVITIES

Substance	Resistivity ϱ, ohm-cm. (at 20° C.)	Temperature coefficient a, °C.$^{-1}$
Aluminium . . .	$2{\cdot}82 \times 10^{-6}$	$0{\cdot}0039$
Brass	$c.\ 8 \times 10^{-6}$	$c.\ 0{\cdot}0015$
Constantan[1] . . .	$c.\ 49 \times 10^{-6}$	$0{\cdot}00001$
Copper	$1{\cdot}72 \times 10^{-6}$	$0{\cdot}0043$
Iron	$c.\ 9{\cdot}8 \times 10^{-6}$	$0{\cdot}0056$
Manganin[2] . . .	$c.\ 44 \times 10^{-6}$	$c.\ 0{\cdot}00001$
Mercury	$95{\cdot}77 \times 10^{-6}$	$0{\cdot}00091$
Nichrome[3] . . .	$c.\ 100 \times 10^{-6}$	$0{\cdot}0004$
Silver	$1{\cdot}62 \times 10^{-6}$	$0{\cdot}0039$
Tungsten[4]	$5{\cdot}5 \times 10^{-6}$	$0{\cdot}0058$
Carbon (graphite) . .	33 to 185×10^{-6}	$-0{\cdot}0006$ to $-0{\cdot}0012$

[1] Also called Eureka; 60 per cent. Cu, 40 per cent. Ni.
[2] 84 per cent. Cu, 12 per cent. Mn, 4 per cent. Ni; used for resistance boxes and shunts.
[3] Ni—Cu—Cr; used for electric fires—does not oxidize at 1000° C.
[4] Used for lamp filaments—melts at 3380° C.

The resistivity of a metal is increased by even small amounts of impurity; and alloys, such as Constantan, may have resistivities far greater than any of their constituents.

4. Ohm's Theory of the Circuit.

We have seen that Ohm abandoned the use of voltaic piles in his experiments, because the currents which they gave were not steady. He attributed this to fluctuations in their "exciting force"—electromotive force, as we now call it. Similarly, when he used thermocouples, he found that the current through a given circuit increased when the difference in temperature between the couples was increased. He was thus led to propose a "mathematical law of the galvanic circuit":

$$I = \frac{E}{R} . \qquad . \quad . \quad . \quad . \quad . \quad . \quad (3)$$

Here I stands for the strength of the current, E for the exciting force (e.m.f.), and R for the total resistance of the circuit.

5. Demonstration of Ohm's Law.

Ohm showed that his law applied not only to a complete circuit but to any part of it. To understand this, let us consider an experiment

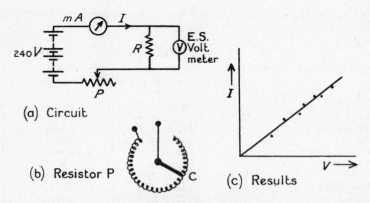

(a) Circuit

(b) Resistor P

(c) Results

Fig. 627.   Demonstration of Ohm's law.

which can easily be done with modern apparatus. As shown in Fig. 627 (a), we connect in series the following apparatus:

(i) two high-tension batteries; of total e.m.f. 240 volts.
(ii) a milliameter reading to 5 milliamp.;
(iii) a radio resistor R of resistance 50,000 ohms (this should be of the "two-watt" type, or larger);

(iv) a variable radio resistor P of about 100,000 ohms resistance. This consists of a circular carbon track with a wiping contact C (Fig. 627 (b)). Across the resistor R we connect an electrostatic voltmeter, reading to 300 volts, to measure the potential difference V across R. By adjusting the resistor P we vary the current I through the circuit, and at each value of I we measure V. On plotting V against I we get a straight line through the origin, as in Fig. 627 (c); this shows that the potential difference across the resistor R is proportional to the current through it:

$$V \propto I. \qquad \ldots \ldots \text{(4)}$$

Thus, taking into account that the resistance of a conductor depends on its temperature and on other physical conditions such as mechanical strain, Ohm's law can be stated as follows:

Under constant physical conditions, the potential difference across a conductor is proportional to the current through it.

The law is obeyed by the most important class of conductors—metals —and by some others, such as carbon. It is not obeyed by some crystals, such as silicon carbide, nor by some conducting solutions. nor by thermionic valves, nor—as in a neon lamp—by gases.

6. Resistance.

From Ohm's law, it follows that

$$\frac{V}{I} = R, \text{ a ccnstant.} \qquad \ldots \ldots \text{(5)}$$

R is *defined* as the "resistance" of the conductor.

The practical unit of potential difference, V, is the *volt*, symbol V; the practical unit of current, I, is the *ampere*, symbol A; the practical unit of resistance, R, is the *ohm*, symbol Ω. The ohm is thus the resistance of a conductor through which a current of one ampere flows when a potential difference (p.d.) of one volt is across it.

From the above equation, it also follows that

$$V = IR, \text{ and } I = \frac{V}{R}. \qquad \ldots \ldots \text{(6)}$$

Smaller units of current are the milliampere (one-thousandth of an ampere), symbol mA. and the micro-ampere (one-millionth of an ampere), symbol μA. Smaller units of p.d. are the millivolt (1/1000 V.) and the microvolt ($1/10^6$ V.). A small unit of resistance is the microhm ($1/10^6$ ohm); larger units are the kilohm (1,000 ohms) and the megohm (10^6 ohms).

HEAT AND POWER

7. Electrical Heating. Joule's Laws.

In 1841 Joule studied the heating effect of an electric current by passing it through a coil of wire in a jar of water (Fig. 628). He used various currents, measured by a form of tangent galvanometer (p. 916), and various lengths of wire, but always the same mass of water. The rise in temperature of the water, in a given time, was then proportional to the heat developed by the current in that time. Joule found that the

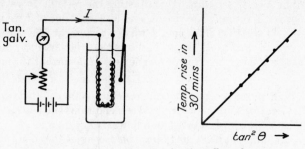

FIG. 628. Joule's experiment on heating effect of current.

heat produced in a given time, with a given wire, was proportional to $\tan^2 \theta$, where θ is the deflection, or to I^2, since $I \propto \tan \theta$ (Fig. 628). If H is the heat produced per second, then

$$H \propto I^2. \qquad \ldots \ldots \ldots \quad (7)$$

Joule also made experiments on the heat produced by a given current in different wires. He used wires of different lengths, but of the same diameter, and of the same material; he found that the rate at which heat was produced, by a given current, was proportional to the length of the wire. That is to say, he found that the rate of heat production was proportional to what Ohm had already called the resistance of the wire:

$$H \propto R. \qquad \ldots \ldots \ldots \quad (8)$$

Relationships (7) and (8) together give

$$H \propto I^2 R. \qquad \ldots \ldots \ldots \quad (9)$$

8. Mechanism of the Heating Effect.

Heat is a form of energy. The heat produced per second by a current in a wire is therefore a measure of the energy which it liberates in one second, as it flows through the wire. The heat is produced, we suppose, by the free electrons as they move through the metal. On their way, they collide frequently with atoms; at each collision they lose some of their kinetic energy, and give it to the atoms which they strike. Thus, as the current flows through the wire, it increases the kinetic energy of vibration of the metal atoms: it generates heat in the wire. The electrical resistance of the metal is due, we say, to its atoms obstructing the drift of the electrons past them: it is analogous to mechanical friction. As the current flows through the wire, the energy lost per second by the electrons is the electrical power supplied by the battery which maintains the current. That power comes, as we shall see later, from the chemical energy liberated by these actions within the battery.

9. Potential Difference and Energy.

On p. 779 we defined the potential difference V_{AB} between two points, A and B, as the work done by an external agent in taking a unit positive charge from B to A (Fig. 629 (a)). This definition applies equally well to points in an electrostatic field and to points on a conductor carrying a current.

In Fig. 629 (b), D represents any electrical device or circuit element: a lamp, motor, or battery on charge, for example. A current of I amperes flows through it from the terminal A to the terminal B; if it flows for t seconds, the charge Q which it carries from A to B is, since a current is the quantity of electricity per second flowing,

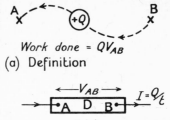

(a) Definition

Work done = QV_{AB}

$\longleftarrow V_{AB} \longrightarrow$ $I = \frac{Q}{t}$

W joules in t secs

(b) Application to a current

Fig. 629. Potential difference and energy.

$$Q = It \text{ coulombs. . . (10)}$$

Let us suppose that the device D liberates a total amount of energy W joules in the time t; this total may be made up of heat, light, sound, mechanical work, chemical transformation, and any other forms of energy. Then W is the amount of electrical energy given up by the charge Q in passing through the device D from A to B.

$$\therefore W = QV_{AB}, \quad \ldots \ldots \quad (11)$$

where V_{AB} is the potential difference between A and B in volts.

The work, in all its forms, which the current I does in t seconds as it flows through the device, is therefore

$$W = IV_{AB}t, \quad \ldots \ldots \quad (12)$$

by equations (10) and (11).

10. Electrical Power.

The energy liberated per second in the device is defined as its electrical *power*. The electrical power, P, supplied is given, from above, by

$$P = \frac{W}{t} = \frac{IV_{AB}t}{t}$$

or
$$P = IV_{AB}. \quad \ldots \ldots \quad (13)$$

When an electric current flows through a wire or "passive" resistor, all the power which it conveys to the wire appears as heat. If I is the current, R is the resistance, then $V_{AB} = IR$, Fig. 630.

$$\therefore P = I^2R. \qquad \dots \dots \quad (14)$$

Also,
$$P = \frac{V_{AB}^2}{R}. \qquad \dots \dots \quad (15)$$

The power, P, is in *watts* when I is in amp., R is in ohms, and V_{AB} is in volts. 1 kilowatt = 1,000 watts.

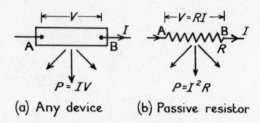

(a) Any device   (b) Passive resistor

FIG. 630.   Power equations.

The formulae for power, $P = I^2R$ or V^2/R, is true only when all the electrical power supplied is dissipated as heat. As we shall see, the formulae do not hold when part of the electrical energy supplied is converted into mechanical work, as in a motor, or into chemical energy, as in an accumulator being charged. A device which converts all the electrical energy supplied to it into heat is called a "passive" resistor; it may be a wire, or a strip of carbon, or a liquid which conducts electricity but is not decomposed by it. Since 4·2 joules = 1 calorie, it follows that, for a resistor, the heat H in it is given by

$$\left.\begin{array}{l} H = IVt \text{ joules} = \dfrac{IVt}{4\cdot2}\,\text{cal.} \\[2mm] H = I^2Rt \text{ joules} = \dfrac{I^2Rt}{4\cdot2}\,\text{cal.} \\[2mm] H = \dfrac{V^2t}{R}\text{ joules} = \dfrac{V^2t}{4\cdot2R}\,\text{cal.} \end{array}\right\} \quad \dots \dots \quad (16)$$

or by

or by

The units of I, V, R are amp., volts, ohms respectively.

11. High-tension Transmission.

When electricity has to be transmitted from a source, such as a power station, to a distant load, such as a factory, the two must be connected by cables. These cables have resistance, which is in effect added to the internal resistance of the generator; power is wasted in them as heat.

If r is the total resistance of the cables, and I the supply current, the power wasted is I^2r. The power delivered to the factory is IV, where V is the potential difference at the factory. Economy requires the waste power, I^2r, to be small; but it also requires the cables to be thin, and therefore cheap to buy and erect. The thinner the cables, however, the higher their resistance r. Thus the most economical way to transmit the power is to make the current, I, as small as possible; this means making the potential difference V as high as possible. When large amounts of power are to be transmitted, therefore, very high voltages are used: 132,000 volts on the main lines of the British grid, 6,000 volts on subsidiary lines. These voltages are much too high to be brought into a house, or even a factory. They are stepped down by transformers, in a way which we shall describe later; stepping-down in that way is possible only with alternating current, which is one of the main reasons why alternating current is so widely used.

EXAMPLE

Define the c.g.s. electromagnetic units of *current, potential difference, resistance.* State the ratio of each to its corresponding practical unit.

Obtain, from first principles, an expression for the heat in calories dissipated in a conductor of resistance R ohms when a potential difference V volts is maintained across it for a time t seconds.

An electric heating element to dissipate 450 watts on 250 volt mains is to be made from Nichrome ribbon of width 1 mm. and thickness 0·05 mm. Calculate the length of ribbon required. (The resistivity of Nichrome is 110×10^{-6} ohm cm.) (*L.*)

First part (see p. 915). 1 amp. = 1/10 e.m.u. of current, 1 volt = 10^8 e.m.u. of p.d., 1 ohm = 10^9 e.m.u. of resistance.

The heat in calories = $I^2Rt/4·2$ calories (see p. 824).

Second part. Since power, P, $= \dfrac{V^2}{R}$,

$$\therefore\ 450 = \frac{250^2}{R},$$

$$\therefore\ R = \frac{250^2}{450} = \frac{1250}{9}\ \text{ohms.}$$

But $$R = \varrho\,\frac{l}{a},$$

$$\therefore\ l = \frac{Ra}{\varrho}$$

$$= \frac{1250 \times 0·1 \times 0·005}{9 \times 110 \times 10^{-6}},$$

$$= 631\ \text{cm.}$$

12. Summary of Formulae Related to Power and Ohm's Law.

In any device whatever (Fig. 630 (*a*)):

Electrical power consumed = power developed in other forms,

$$P = IV,$$

watts = amperes × volts.

In a passive resistor (Fig. 630 (*b*)):

(i) $$V = RI; \quad I = \frac{V}{R}; \quad R = \frac{V}{I},$$

volts = ohms × amperes.

(ii) Power consumed = heat developed per second, in joules:

$$P = I^2R = IV = \frac{V^2}{R}.$$

(iii) Heat developed in time *t*:

Electrical energy consumed = J × heat developed in calories ($J = 4\cdot2$ joules per calorie):

$$Pt = JH.$$

watts × seconds = J × calories

or $$I^2Rt = IVt = \frac{V^2}{R}t = JH.$$

Board of Trade (commercial) unit = kilowatt-hour = kilowatt × hour.

ELECTROMOTIVE FORCE

13. E.M.F. Internal Resistance.

If we take a high-tension battery, and connect an electrostatic voltmeter across it, the meter reads about 120 volts. Across two batteries in series it reads 240 volts. Let us now connect the two batteries in series with two resistors, of resistance 200,000 and 100,000 ohms, as in Fig. 631. By using the voltmeter, we find that the potential difference across the 200,000-ohm resistor is 160 volts, and across the 100,000-ohm resistor 80 volts. These add up to 240 volts; if we inserted a third

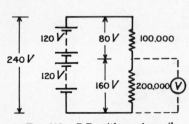

FIG. 631.   P.D. with moving-coil voltmeter.

resistor, we should find that the potential differences across all three added up to the same value. It appears that the batteries always maintain a total potential difference of 240 volts across any circuit to which they are joined. This constant potential difference represents what Ohm called the exciting force of the batteries. Since it is the property which enables the batteries to maintain a flow of electricity in a circuit, we may call it their electromotive force.

Now let us connect a lower resistance across the batteries of Fig. 631—say 10,000 ohms. We find the potential difference across their terminals falls slightly. And if we use a still lower resistance— say 1,000 ohms—then the potential difference falls greatly, perhaps to about $\frac{2}{3}$ of its open-circuit value.

We suppose, therefore, that the batteries have some internal resistance—the resistance r of the chemical solutions between the plates (Fig. 632 (a)). This is analogous to the resistance of the wires of Ohm's thermocouples (p. 818). When an appreciable current I flows from the battery, it sets up a potential difference rI across the internal resistance, and by that amount makes the external potential difference less than the electromotive force, E (Fig. 632 (b)). In a rough-and-ready way we may represent the battery as a source of constant potential difference E, in series with a passive resistor r (Fig. 632 (c)).

14. Electromotive Force and Energy.

To get a rigorous definition of electromotive force, let us first imagine that

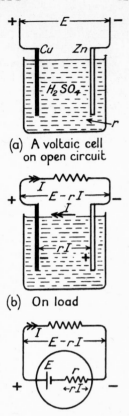

(a) A voltaic cell on open circuit

(b) On load

(c) Representation

FIG. 632. E.m.f. and internal resistance.

we pass a current through the device of Fig. 633 in opposition to its e.m.f. We can do this by connecting its terminals AC, via a resistance R, to a battery D which has a greater e.m.f. (Fig. 633 (a)). If a charge q passes round the circuit in a given time, then the work done in carrying it from A to B, against the potential difference E, is qE joules. This work appears as chemical changes in the source of E. Now suppose that we remove the battery D, and connect a resistor across the terminals AC (Fig. 633 (b)). The potential difference will now send a current round the circuit in the opposite direction to the previous current. And when a charge q has passed, the energy delivered by the source of e.m.f. E will be qE joules. The chemical changes in the source will have been reversed, and will have given up this amount of energy, as electrical energy. The current, in passing round the circuit, will have converted this energy into heat. Some of the heat will have been dissipated in the external resistance R, some in the internal resistance r.

Our picture of a source of current as a constant potential difference in series with a resistance is over-simplified, but it has brought us to the point where we can make a definition of e.m.f. which is both rigorous and intelligible. We shall make it first in terms of charge, later in terms of current.

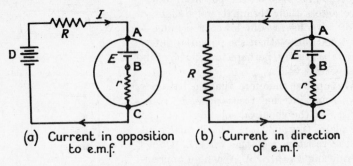

(a) Current in opposition to e.m.f.   (b) Current in direction of e.m.f.

FIG. 633.   Illustrating definition of e.m.f.

In terms of charge: *if a device has an electromotive force E, then, in passing a charge q round a circuit joined to it, it liberates an amount of electrical energy equal to qE.* If a charge q is passed through the source against its e.m.f., then the work done against the e.m.f. is qE. The above definition of e.m.f. does not depend on any assumptions about the nature of its source.

If a device of e.m.f. E passes a steady current I for a time t, then the charge that it circulates is

$$q = It.$$

Thus:

electrical energy liberated, $W, = qE = IEt,$ . . (17)

and electrical power generated, $P, = \dfrac{W}{t} = EI.$ . . (18)

We can now define e.m.f. in terms of power and current, and therefore in a way suitable for dealing with circuit problems. From equation (18)

$$P = EI,$$

or

$$E = \frac{P}{I}.$$

Thus *the e.m.f. of a device is the ratio of the electrical power which it generates, to the current which it delivers.* If current is forced through a device in opposition to its e.m.f.. then equation (18) gives the power consumed in overcoming the e.m.f.

Electromotive force resembles potential difference in that both can be defined as the ratio of power to current. The practical unit of e.m.f. is therefore 1 watt per amp., or 1 volt; and *the e.m.f. of a source, in volts, is numerically equal to the power which it generates when it delivers a current of 1 amp.*

15. Representation of an E.M.F. and Internal Resistance.

Sources of e.m.f. differ widely in their nature. In a thermocouple, the e.m.f. arises at the junction of the two metals—this point is sometimes called the seat of the e.m.f. In a voltaic cell, we believe, the e.m.f. arises at the interfaces of the plates and solutions—part at one interface, the rest at the other. In each of these sources we can distinguish between the seat, or seats, of the e.m.f., and that of the internal resistance, which is in the bulk of the solution or the wires of the thermocouple. The e.m.f. of a dynamo, however, does not arise at a point: it acts along the wires of the armature coil as they move in the magnetic field (p. 952). Here we cannot distinguish between the seats of the e.m.f. and the internal resistance. In solving circuit problems, however, it is helpful to show the e.m.f. and internal resistance separately, although as a rule they are physically inextricable.

16. Ohm's Law for Complete Circuit.

Fig. 634 shows a source of current connected to a passive resistor—called the load—of resistance R. To find the current I, we equate the power generated by the source to the heat developed per second in the resistances:

$$EI = I^2 r + I^2 R.$$

Thus

$$E = Ir + IR, \qquad \ldots \ldots (19)$$

whence

$$I = \frac{E}{R + r}. \qquad \ldots \ldots (20)$$

Equation (20) asserts that the current is equal to the e.m.f. of the source divided by the total resistance of the circuit; it is Ohm's original statement of his law (p. 820). Equation (19) asserts that the sum of the potential differences across the resistances is equal to the e.m.f. The potential difference Ir appears across the internal resistance, and is often called the voltage drop; because of it, the

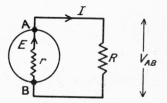

FIG. 634. A complete circuit.

potential difference between the terminals of the cell, V_{AB} falls when the current taken, I, is increased:

$$V_{AB} = E - Ir. \qquad \ldots \ldots (21)$$

17. Terminal Potential Difference.

The quantity V_{AB} is often called the terminal potential difference of the cell; it is also the potential difference across the load. Equations (19) and (21) give

$$V_{AB} = IR, \qquad \ldots \ldots \quad (22)$$

which is Ohm's law for the load alone; we could have written it down directly. Equations (20) and (22) together give the terminal potential difference in terms of the e.m.f. and the resistances:

$$V_{AB} = IR = \frac{E}{R+r} R. \qquad \ldots \ldots \quad (23)$$

18. Output and Efficiency.

The power delivered to the load in Fig. 634 is called the output power, P_{out}; its value is

$$P_{out} = IV_{AB}$$
$$= I^2R. \qquad \ldots \ldots \quad (24)$$

The power generated by the source of current is

$$P_{gen} = IE. \qquad \ldots \ldots \quad (25)$$

The difference between the power generated and the output is the power wasted as heat in the source: I^2r. The ratio of the power output to the power generated is the efficiency, η, of the circuit as a whole:

$$\eta = \frac{P_{out}}{P_{gen}}. \qquad \ldots \ldots \quad (26)$$

By equations (24) and (25), therefore,

$$\eta = \frac{P_{out}}{P_{gen}} = \frac{IV_{AB}}{IE}.$$
$$= \frac{V_{AB}}{E}.$$

Equation (23) now gives

$$\eta = \frac{R}{R+r}. \qquad \ldots \ldots \quad (27)$$

This shows that the efficiency tends to unity (or 100 per cent.) as the load resistance R tends to infinity. For high efficiency the load resistance must be several times the internal resistance of the source. When the load resistance is equal to the internal resistance, the efficiency is 50 per cent. (See Fig. 635 (a).)

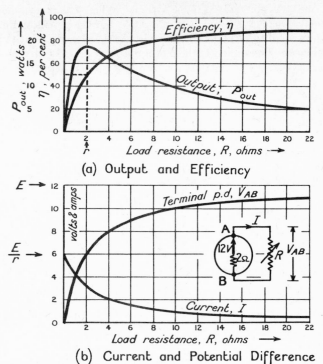

FIG. 635. Effect of varying load resistance.

19. Power Variation.

Now let us consider how the power output varies with the load resistance. Equations (24) and (20) give

$$P_{out} = I^2R,$$

and

$$I = \frac{E}{R + r},$$

whence

$$P_{out} = \frac{E^2R}{(R + r)^2}.$$

If we take fixed values of E and r, and plot P_{out} as a function of R, we find that it passes through a maximum when $R=r$ (Fig. 635 (a)). We can get the same result in a more general way by differentiating P_{out} with respect to R, and equating the differential coefficient to zero. Physically, this result means that the power output is very small when R is either very large or very small, compared with r. When R is very large, the terminal potential difference, V_{AB}, approaches a constant value equal to the e.m.f. E (Fig. 635 (b)); as R is increased the current I

falls, and the power IV_{AB} falls with it. When R is very small, the current approaches the constant value E/r, but the potential difference (which is equal to IR) falls steadily with R; the power output therefore falls likewise. Consequently the power output is greatest for a moderate value of R; the mathematics show that this value is actually $R = r$.

To prove $R = r$, differentiate the expression for P_{out}, given on p. 831, with respect to R. Then

$$E^2 \frac{(R + r)^2 - R \cdot 2(R + r)}{(R + r)^4} = 0, \text{ for a maximum.}$$

From the numerator, $r^2 - R^2 = 0$, or $R = r$.

20. Examples of Loads in Electrical Circuits.

The loading on a dynamo or battery is generally adjusted for high efficiency, because that means greatest economy. Also, if a large dynamo were used with a load not much greater than its internal resistance, the current would be so large that the heat generated in the internal resistance would ruin the machine. With batteries and dynamos, therefore, the load resistance is made many times greater than the internal resistance.

Loading for greatest power output is common in communication engineering. For example, the last valve in a radio receiver delivers electrical power to the loudspeaker, which the speaker converts into mechanical power as sound-waves (p. 612). Because it converts electrical energy into mechanical energy, and not heat, the loudspeaker is not a passive resistor, and the simple equations above do not apply to it. Nevertheless, circuit conditions can be specified which enable the valve to deliver the greatest power to the speaker; these are similar to the condition of equal load and internal resistances, and are usually satisfied in practice.

21. Load not a Passive Resistor.

As an example of a load which is not a passive resistor, we shall take an accumulator being charged. The charging is done by connecting the accumulator X in opposition to a source of greater e.m.f., Y in Fig. 636,

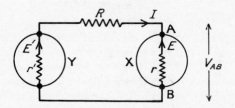

FIG. 636.   Accumulator charging.

via a controlling resistor R. If E, E' and r, r' are the e.m.f. and internal resistances of X and Y respectively, then the current I is given by the equation:

$$\left.\begin{array}{c}\text{power generated}\\\text{in Y}\end{array}\right\} = \left\{\begin{array}{c}\text{power converted to}\\\text{chemical energy}\\\text{in X}\end{array}\right\} + \left\{\begin{array}{c}\text{power dissipated}\\\text{as heat in all}\\\text{resistances}\end{array}\right.$$

$$E'I \qquad = \qquad EI \qquad + I^2R + I^2r' + I^2r.$$
$$\cdots \quad (28)$$

Thus $\qquad\qquad (E' - E)I = I^2(R + r' + r),$

whence $\qquad\qquad I = \dfrac{E' - E}{R + r' + r}.$ $\quad$ . . . . (29)

The potential difference across the accumulator, V_{AB}, is given by

$$\left.\begin{array}{c}\text{power delivered}\\\text{to X}\end{array}\right\} = \left\{\begin{array}{c}\text{power converted to}\\\text{chemical energy}\end{array}\right\} + \left\{\begin{array}{c}\text{power dissipated}\\\text{as heat}\end{array}\right.$$

$$I V_{AB} \qquad = \qquad IE \qquad + \qquad I^2r.$$

Hence $\qquad\qquad V_{AB} = E + Ir.$ $\quad$ . . . . . . (30)

Equation (30) shows that, when current is driven through a generator in opposition to its e.m.f., then the potential difference across the generator is equal to the *sum* of its e.m.f. and the voltage drop across its internal resistance. This result follows at once from energy considerations, as we have just seen.

22. Cells in Series and Parallel.

When cells or batteries are in series and assist each other, then the total e.m.f.

$$E = E_1 + E_2 + E_3 + \ldots, \quad \text{. . . . . (31)}$$

and the total internal resistance

$$r = r_1 + r_2 + r_3 + \ldots, \quad \text{. . . . . (32)}$$

where E_1, E_2 are the individual e.m.f.s and r_1, r_2 are the corresponding internal resistances. If one cell, e.m.f. E_2 say, is turned round "in opposition" to the others, then $E = E_1 - E_2 + E_3 + \ldots$; but the total internal resistance remains unaltered.

When *similar* cells are in parallel, the total e.m.f. $= E$, the e.m.f. of any one of them. The internal resistance r is here given by

$$\frac{1}{r} = \frac{1}{r_1} + \frac{1}{r_1} + \ldots, \quad \text{. . . . . (33)}$$

where r_1 is the internal resistance of each cell. If different cells are in parallel, there is no simple formula for the total e.m.f. and the total internal resistance, and any calculations involving circuits with such cells are dealt with by applying Kirchhoff's laws (see p. 862).

23. Summary of Formulae Involving E.M.F.

(i) *Any load*:

(a) power generated $\Big\}$ = $\Big\{$ power supplied to load $\Big\}$ + $\Big\{$ power dissipated in internal resistance

$$EI \qquad = \qquad IV_{AB} \qquad + \qquad I^2r,$$

(b) terminal p.d. = e.m.f. — voltage drop in internal resistance

$$V_{AB} = E - rI.$$

(ii) *Passive resistance load:*

power equation: $\qquad EI = I^2R + I^2r,$

current: $\qquad\qquad I = \dfrac{E}{R + r},$

terminal p.d.: $\qquad V_{AB} = E - rI = RI$

$$= E\,\frac{R}{R + r}.$$

EXAMPLES

1. What is meant by the *electromotive force* of a cell?

A voltmeter is connected in parallel with a variable resistance, R, which is in series with an ammeter and a cell. For one value of R the meters read 0·3 amp. and 0·9 volt. For another value of R the readings are 0·25 amp. and 1·0 volt. Find the values of R, the e.m.f. of the cell, and the internal resistance of the cell. What assumptions are made about the resistance of the meters in the calculation?

If in this experiment the ammeter had a resistance of 10 ohms and the voltmeter a resistance of 100 ohms and R was 2 ohms, what would the meters read? (*L.*)

First part (see p. 828).

Second part. The voltmeter reads the p.d. across the cell if the resistances of the meters are neglected. Thus, with the usual notation,

$$E - Ir = 0.9, \quad \text{or} \quad E - 0.3r = 0.9 \quad \ldots \ldots \text{(i)}$$

and $\qquad\qquad\qquad E - 0.25r = 1.0. \qquad \ldots \ldots \ldots \text{(ii)}$

Subtracting (i) from (ii),

$$0.05r = 0.1, \quad \text{i.e.} \quad r = 2 \text{ ohms.}$$

Also, from (i),

$$E = 0.3r + 0.9 = 0.6 + 0.9 = 1.5 \text{ volts.}$$

Further, $\qquad\qquad R_1 = \dfrac{V}{I} = \dfrac{0.9}{0.3} = 3 \text{ ohms.}$

and $\qquad\qquad\qquad R_2 = \dfrac{1.0}{0.25} = 4 \text{ ohms.}$

If the voltmeter has 100 ohms resistance and is in parallel with the 2 ohms resistance, the combined resistance R is given by

$$\frac{1}{R} = \frac{1}{2} + \frac{1}{100} = \frac{51}{100}, \quad \text{or} \quad R = \frac{100}{51} \text{ ohms.}$$

$$\therefore \text{ current, } I, = \frac{E}{\text{Total resistance}}$$

$$= \frac{1 \cdot 5}{\dfrac{100}{51} + 10 + 2} = 0 \cdot 11 \text{ amp.}$$

Also, voltmeter reading $= IR = 0 \cdot 11 \times \dfrac{100}{51} = 0 \cdot 21$ volt.

2. Define *internal resistance* of a voltaic cell. Describe one method of finding by experiment the internal resistance of a primary cell.

Two Daniell cells A and B are connected in series with a coil of resistance 9·8 ohms. A voltmeter of very high resistance connected to the terminals of A reads 0·96 volt and when connected to the terminals of B it reads 1·00 volt. Find the internal resistance of each cell. (Take the e.m.f. of a Daniell cell as 1·08 volts.) (*L.*)

First part. The "internal resistance" is the resistance of the chemicals inside the cell between the poles, and is given by (drop in terminal p.d.) ÷ current, when the cell is used. The potentiometer may be used to measure the internal resistance. See p. 855.

Second part. The p.d. across both cells $= 0 \cdot 96 + 1 \cdot 00 = 1 \cdot 96$ volts
$$= \text{p.d. across 9·8 ohms.}$$

$$\therefore \text{ current flowing, } I, = \frac{V}{R} = \frac{1 \cdot 96}{9 \cdot 8} = 0 \cdot 2 \text{ amp.}$$

Now terminal p.d. across each cell $= E - Ir$.

$\therefore$ for cell A, $0 \cdot 96 = 1 \cdot 08 - 0 \cdot 2r$,   or $r = 0 \cdot 6$ ohm.

For cell B, $1 \cdot 00 = 1 \cdot 08 - 0 \cdot 2r$,   or $r = 0 \cdot 4$ ohm.

THE THERMO-ELECTRIC EFFECT

24. Seebeck Effect.

The heating effect of the current converts electrical energy into heat, but we have not so far described any mechanism which converts heat into electrical energy. This was discovered by Seebeck in 1822. In his experiments he connected a plate of bismuth between copper wires

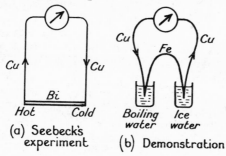

Fig. 637.   The thermo-electric effect.

leading to a galvanometer, as shown in Fig. 637 (*a*). He found that if one of the bismuth-copper junctions was heated, while the other was kept cool, then a current flowed through the galvanometer. The direction of the current was from the copper to the bismuth at the cold junction. We can easily repeat Seebeck's experiment, using copper and iron wires and a galvanometer capable of indicating a few microamperes (p. 932) (Fig. 637 (*b*)).

25. Thermocouples.

Seebeck went on to show that a current flowed, without a battery, in any circuit containing two different metals, with their two junctions at different temperatures. Currents obtained in this way are called thermo-electric currents, and a pair of metals, with their junctions at different temperatures, are said to form a thermocouple. The following is a list of metals, such that if any two of them form a thermocouple, then the current will flow from the higher to the lower in the list, across the cold junction:

> *Antimony, Iron, Zinc, Lead, Copper, Platinum, Bismuth.*

Thermo-electric currents often appear when they are not wanted; they may arise from small differences in purity of two samples of the same metal, and from small differences of temperature—due, perhaps, to the warmth of the hand. They can cause a great deal of trouble in circuits used for precise measurements, or for detecting other small currents, not of thermal origin. As sources of electrical energy, thermo-electric currents are neither convenient nor economical, but they have been used—in gas-driven radio sets. Their only wide application is in the measurement of temperature, and of other quantities, such as radiant energy, which can be measured by a temperature rise.

26. Variation of Thermo-electric E.M.F. with Temperature.

On p. 860 we shall see how thermo-electric e.m.f.s are measured. When the cold junction of a given thermocouple is kept constant at 0°C., and

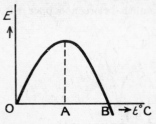

FIG. 638.   Thermo-electric e.m.f. variation with temperature.

the hot junction temperature $t°$C. is varied, the e.m.f. E is found to vary as $E = at + bt^2$, where a, b are constants. This is a parabola-shaped curve (Fig. 638). The temperature A corresponding to the maximum e.m.f. is known as the *neutral temperature*; it is about 250°C. for a copper-iron thermocouple. Beyond the temperature B, known as the *inversion temperature*, the e.m.f. reverses. Thermo-electric thermometers, which utilize thermocouples, are used only as far as the neutral temperature, as the same e.m.f. is obtained at two different temperatures, from Fig. 638.

27. Peltier and Thomson Effects.

When a current flows along the junction A of two metals in series, heat is evolved or absorbed at A depending on the current direction. This is known as the *Peltier effect*. It has no connexion with the usual heating or Joule effect of a current, discussed on p. 821. The Joule effect is irreversible, that is, heat is obtained in both directions of the current. In the Peltier effect, however, the effect is reversed when the current is reversed; that is, a cooling is produced at the junction of two metals in one direction, and an evolution of heat in the other direction.

Sir William Thomson, later Lord Kelvin, also found that heat was evolved or absorbed when a current flows along a metal whose ends are kept at different temperatures. The *Thomson effect*, like the Peltier effect, is also reversible.

EXERCISES XXXVI

1. State the laws of the development of heat when an electric current flows (a) through a wire of uniform material, (b) across the junction between two metals.

An electric heating coil is connected in series with a resistance of X ohms across the 240-volt mains, the coil being immersed in a kilogram of water at 20°C. The temperature of the water rises to boiling-point in 10 minutes. When a second heating experiment is made with the resistance X short-circuited, the time required to develop the same quantity of heat is reduced to 6 minutes. Calculate the value of X. (Heat losses may be neglected.) (*L.*)

2. Deduce an expression for the heat developed in a wire by the passage of an electric current.

The temperature of 300 gm. of paraffin oil in a vacuum flask rises 1·0°C. per min. with an immersion heater of 12·3 watts input. On repeating with 400 gm. of oil the temperature rises by 1·20°C. per min. for an input of 19·2 watts. Find the specific heat of the oil and the water equivalent (assumed constant) of the flask. (4·2 joules = 1 calorie.) (*L.*)

3. Describe an experiment to determine the resistance of a wire by a calorimetric method.

It is desired to construct a 5-amp. fuse from tin wire which has a melting-point of 230°C. and resistivity 22×10^{-6} ohm/cm. at that temperature. Estimate the diameter of the wire required if the emissivity of its surface is 21×10^{-5} cal. per sq. cm. per sec. per °C. excess temperature above the surroundings whose temperature is 20°C. Neglect the heat lost by conduction along the wire. (*N.*)

4. Describe the chief thermo-electric effects which occur in a circuit which includes two metals such as copper and iron.

Make a labelled diagram showing clearly the arrangement of a potentiometer circuit suitable for measuring a thermo-electric e.m.f. of about 2 mV. (*L.*)

5. Indicate, by means of graphs, the relation between the current and voltage (a) for a uniform manganin wire; (b) for a water voltameter; (c) for a diode valve. How do you account for the differences between the three curves?

An electric hot plate has two coils of manganin wire, each 20 metres in length and 0·23 sq. mm. cross-sectional area. Show that it will be possible to **arrange** for three different rates of heating, and calculate the wattage in each case when the heater is supplied from 200-volt mains. The specific resistance of manganin is 4.6×10^{-5} ohm-cm. (O. & C.)

6. Describe an experiment for determining the variation of the resistance of a coil of wire with temperature.

An electric fire dissipates 1 kW. when connected to a 250-volt supply. Calculate to the nearest whole number the percentage change that must be made in the resistance of the heating element in order that it may dissipate 1 kW. on a 200-volt supply. What percentage change in the length of the heating element will produce this change of resistance if the consequent increase in the temperature of the wire causes its resistivity to increase by a factor 1·05? The cross-sectional area may be assumed constant. (N.)

7. What is a thermocouple? Explain the use of a potentiometer to measure the small electromotive forces developed by a thermocouple.

What are the relative advantages and disadvantages of a thermocouple used as a thermometer as compared with the resistance thermometer? (L.)

8. Give a general account of the thermo-electric effect. Describe how you would calibrate a thermocouple for use over the range of 0°–100° C. on the mercury-in-glass scale of temperature. (C.)

9. Derive, from first principles, an expression for the rate at which heat is generated in a resistance of R e.m.u. by the passage of a current of i e.m.u.

An electric lamp takes 60 watts on a 240-volt circuit. How many dry cells, each of e.m.f. 1·45 volts and internal resistance 1·0 ohm, would be required to light the lamp? How much zinc would be consumed by the battery in 1 hour? (1 faraday = 96,500 coulombs; equivalent weight of zinc = 32·5.) (O. & C.)

10. Describe an experimental method of producing a thermo-electric e.m.f.

How may a thermojunction be used to measure temperature?

Why is a copper-iron junction not used to measure temperature above 250° C., although a copper-constantan junction is often so employed? (L.)

11. Describe an instrument which measures the strength of an electric current by making use of its heating effect. State the advantages and disadvantages of this method. *

A surge suppressor is made of a material whose conducting properties are such that the current passing through is directly proportional to the fourth power of the applied voltage. If the suppressor dissipates energy at a rate of 6·0 watts when the potential difference across it is 240 volts, estimate the power dissipated when the potential difference rises to 1,200 volts. (C.)

12. Describe and explain how to determine by experiment the relation between the e.m.f., E, of a thermocouple and the temperature, $\theta°$ C., of its hot junction, the cold junction being maintained at 0° C.

The relation is sometimes given as (a) $E = \alpha\theta + \beta\theta^2$ and sometimes as (b) $E = k\theta^n$, where α, β, k and n are constants. Indicate how you would plot your observations to test these equations and to determine values for the constants. (L.)

CHAPTER XXXVII

APPLICATIONS OF OHM'S LAW.
MEASUREMENTS. NETWORKS

In this chapter we shall apply Ohm's law to circuits more complicated than those of Chapter XXXVI. We shall see that some special types of circuits can be used to make electrical measurements more accurately than with pointer instruments.

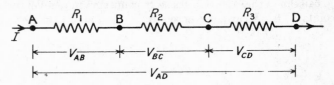

Fɪɢ. 639.   Resistances in series.

RESISTORS AND THEIR ARRANGEMENTS

1. Series Resistors.

The resistors of an electric circuit may be arranged in series, so that the charges carrying the current flow through each in turn (Fig. 639); or they may be arranged in parallel, so that the flow of charge divides between them (Fig. 640, p. 840).

Fig. 639 shows three passive resistors in series, carrying a current I. If V_{AD} is the potential difference across the whole system, the electrical energy supplied to the system per second is IV_{AD}. This is equal to the electrical energy dissipated per second in all the resistors; therefore

$$IV_{AD} = IV_{AB} + IV_{BC} + IV_{CD},$$

whence
$$V_{AD} = V_{AB} + V_{BC} + V_{CD}. \qquad \cdots \cdot (1)$$

The individual potential differences are given by Ohm's law:

$$\left.\begin{aligned} V_{AB} &= IR_1 \\ V_{BC} &= IR_2 \\ V_{CD} &= IR_3 \end{aligned}\right\} . \qquad \cdots \cdots (2)$$

and

Hence, by equation (1),

$$\begin{aligned} V_{AD} &= IR_1 + IR_2 + IR_3 \\ &= I(R_1 + R_2 + R_3). \qquad \cdots \cdot (3) \end{aligned}$$

And the effective resistance of the system is

$$R = \frac{V_{AD}}{I} = R_1 + R_2 + R_3. \qquad \cdots \cdots (4)$$

The physical facts are:

   (i) *Current same through all resistors.*

  (ii) *Total potential difference = sum of individual potential difference (equation (1)).*

 (iii) *Individual potential differences directly proportional to individual resistances (equation (2)).*

 (iv) *Total resistance greater than greatest individual resistance (equation (4)).*

  (v) *Total resistance = sum of individual resistances.*

2. Resistors in Parallel.

Fig. 640 shows three passive resistors connected in parallel, between the points A, B. A current I enters the system at A and leaves at B,

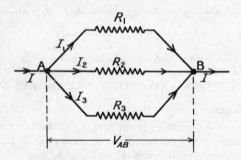

FIG. 640.   Resistances in parallel.

setting up a potential difference V_{AB} between those points. The current branches into I_1, I_2, I_3, through the three elements, and

$$I = I_1 + I_2 + I_3. \quad \cdots \cdots \quad (5)$$

Now
$$I_1 = \frac{V_{AB}}{R_1}, \quad I_2 = \frac{V_{AB}}{R_2}, \quad I_3 = \frac{V_{AB}}{R_3}.$$

$$\therefore I = V_{AB}\left(\frac{1}{R_1} + \frac{1}{R_2} + \frac{1}{R_3}\right).$$

$$\therefore \frac{I}{V_{AB}} = \frac{1}{R} = \frac{1}{R_1} + \frac{1}{R_2} + \frac{1}{R_3}, \quad \cdots \cdots \quad (6)$$

where R is the effective resistance (V_{AB}/I) of the system.

The physical facts about resistors in parallel may be summarized as follows:

   (i) *Potential difference same across each resistor.*

  (ii) *Total current = sum of individual currents (equation (5)).*

 (iii) *Individual currents inversely proportional to individual resistances.*

(iv) *Effective resistance less than least individual resistance* (equation (6)).

3. Resistance Boxes.

In many electrical measurements variable known resistances are required; they are called resistance boxes. As shown in Fig. 641 (*a*) ten coils, each of resistance 1 ohm, for example, are connected in series. A rotary switch with eleven contacts enables any number of these coils to be connected between the terminals AA'. A resistance box contains several sets of coils and switches, the first giving resistances 0–10 ohms in steps of 1 ohm, the next 0–100 ohms in steps of 10 ohms, and so on. These are called decade boxes.

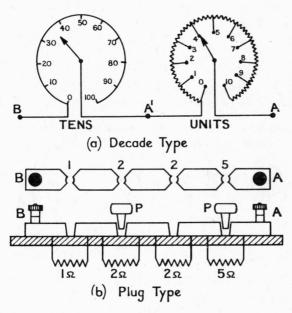

(a) Decade Type

(b) Plug Type

FIG. 641. Resistance boxes.

The switches used in a decade box are of very high quality; their contact resistances are negligible compared with the resistances of the coils which they select. Switches of this kind have been developed only in the last twenty years or so: in older boxes no switches are used. Instead, the resistances are varied by means of plugs. As shown in Fig. 641(*b*), the resistance coils are joined across gaps in a thick brass bar, and the gaps are formed into tapered sockets to receive short-circuiting plugs P. The resistance between the terminals A and B in Fig. 641 (*b*) is the sum of the unplugged resistances between them—3 ohms in this example.

The coils of a resistance box are wound in a particular way, which we shall describe and explain later (p. 967). They are not intended to carry large currents, and must not be allowed to dissipate more than one watt. Therefore, since $P = I^2R$, the greatest safe current for a 1-ohm coil is 1 amp., and for a 10-ohm coil about 0·3 amp. If the one-watt limit is exceeded, the insulation will be damaged, or the wire burnt out.

4. The Potential Divider.

Two resistance boxes in series are often used in the laboratory to provide a known fraction of a given potential difference—for example, of one which is too large to measure easily. Fig. 642 (a) shows the arrangement, which is called a resistance "potential divider". The current flowing, I, is given by

$$I = \frac{V_0}{R_1 + R_2},$$

$$\therefore V_1 = IR_1 = \frac{R_1}{R_1 + R_2} V_0. \quad \ldots \quad (7)$$

A resistor with a sliding contact can similarly be used, as shown in Fig. 642 (b), to provide a continuously variable potential difference, from

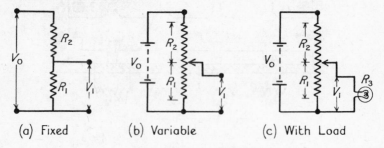

(a) Fixed (b) Variable (c) With Load

Fig. 642. Potential divider.

zero to the full supply value V_0. This is a convenient way of controlling the voltage applied to a load, such as a lamp (Fig. 642 (c)). The resistance of the load, R_3, however, acts in parallel with the resistance R_1; equation (7) is therefore no longer true, and the voltage V_1 must be measured with a voltmeter. It can be calculated, as in the following example, if R_3 is known; but if the load is a lamp its resistance varies greatly with the current through it, because its temperature varies.

EXAMPLE

A load of 2000 ohms is connected, via a potential divider of resistance 4000 ohms, to a 10-volt supply (Fig. 643). What is the potential difference across the load when the slider is (a) one-quarter, (b) half-way up the divider?

Since $\dfrac{1}{R} = \dfrac{1}{2000} + \dfrac{1}{1000}$,

(a) $R_{BC} = \dfrac{2000 \times 1000}{2000 + 1000} = \dfrac{2000}{3}$ ohms.

$\therefore R_{AC} = R_{AB} + R_{BC} = 3000 + \dfrac{2000}{3}$ ohms,

$\therefore V_{BC} = \dfrac{R_{BC}}{R_{AC}} V_{AC}$

$= \dfrac{2000/3}{11,000/3} \times 10 = \dfrac{2}{11} \times 10$

$= 1\cdot8$ volts.

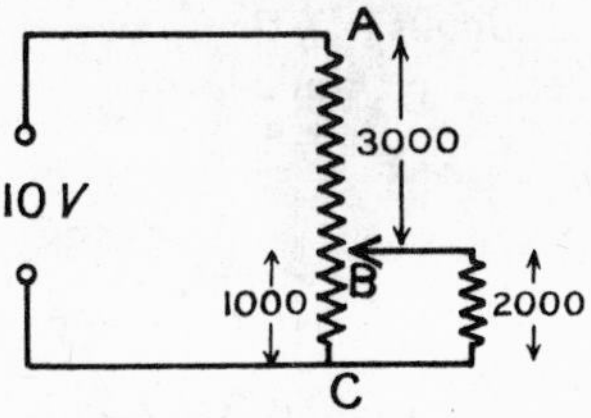

FIG. 643. A loaded potential divider.

If the load were removed, V_{BC} would be 2·5 volts.

(b) It is left for the reader to show similarly that $V_{BC} = 3\cdot3$ volts. Without the load it would be 5 volts.

MEASURING INSTRUMENTS

5. Conversion of a Milliammeter into a Voltmeter.

Ohm's law enables us to use a milliammeter as a voltmeter. Let us suppose that we have a moving-coil instrument which requires 5 milliamperes for full-scale deflection (f.s.d.). And let us suppose that the resistance of its coil, r, is 20 ohms (Fig. 644). Then, when it is fully deflected, the potential difference across it is

$V = rI$

$= 20 \times 5 \times 10^{-3} = 100 \times 10^{-3}$ volt.

$= 0\cdot1$ volt.

Since the coil obeys Ohm's law, the current through it is proportional to the potential difference across it; and since the deflection of the pointer is proportional to the current it is therefore also proportional to the potential difference. Thus the instrument can be used as a voltmeter, giving full-scale deflection for a potential difference of 0·1 volt, or 100 millivolts. Its scale could be engraved as shown at the top of Fig. 644.

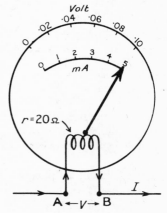

FIG. 644. P.D. across moving-coil meter.

The potential differences to be measured in the laboratory are usually greater than 100 millivolts, however. To measure such a potential difference, we insert a resistor R in series with the coil, as shown in Fig. 645 (*a*). If we wish to measure up to 10 volts we must choose the resistance R so that, when 10 volts are applied between the terminals CD, then a current of 5 milliamperes flows through the moving coil. By Ohm's law

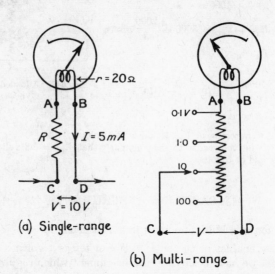

(a) Single-range

(b) Multi-range

FIG. 645. Voltmeters.

$$V = (R + r)I,$$
$$\therefore 10 = (R + 20) \times 5 \times 10^{-3}$$

or

$$R + 20 = \frac{10}{5 \times 10^{-3}} = 2 \times 10^3 = 2000 \text{ ohms.}$$

$$\therefore R = 2000 - 20$$
$$= 1980 \text{ ohms.}$$

The resistance R is called a *multiplier*. Many voltmeters contain a series of multipliers of different resistances, which can be chosen by a switch or plug-and-socket arrangement (Fig. 645 (*b*)).

6. Conversion of a Milliammeter into an Ammeter.

Moving-coil instruments give full-scale deflection for currents smaller than those generally encountered in the laboratory. If we wish to measure a current of the order of an ampere or more we connect a low resistance S, called a shunt, across the terminals of a moving-coil meter (Fig. 646). The shunt diverts most of the current to be measured, I, away from the coil—hence its name. Let us suppose that, as before, the coil of the meter has a resistance r of 20 ohms and is fully deflected by a current, I_C, of 5 milliamperes. And let us suppose that we wish to shunt it so that it gives f.s.d. for 5 amperes to be measured. Then the current through the shunt is

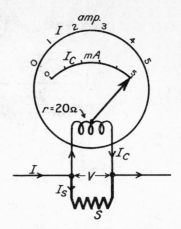

$$I_S = I - I_C$$
$$= 5 - 0\cdot005$$
$$= 4\cdot995 \text{ amp.}$$

The potential difference across the shunt is the same as that across the coil, which is

$$V = rI_C = 20 \times 0\cdot005 = 0\cdot1 \text{ volt.}$$

The resistance of the shunt must therefore be

FIG. 646. Conversion of milliam-meter to ammeter.

$$S = \frac{V}{I_S} = \frac{0\cdot1}{4\cdot995} = 0\cdot02002 \text{ ohms.}$$

The ratio of the current measured to the current through the coil is

$$\frac{I}{I_C} = \frac{5}{5 \times 10^{-3}} = 1000.$$

This ratio is the same whatever the current I, because it depends only on the resistances S and r; the reader may easily show that its value is $(S + r)/r$. The deflection of the coil is therefore proportional to the measured current, as indicated in the figure, and the shunt is said to have a "power" of 1000 when used with this instrument.

The resistance of shunts and multipliers are always given with four-figure accuracy. The moving-coil instrument itself has an error of the order of 1 per cent.; a similar error in the shunt or multiplier would therefore double the error in the instrument as a whole. On the other hand, there is nothing to be gained by making the error in the shunt less than about 0·1 per cent., because at that value it is swamped by the error of the moving system.

7. The Universal Shunt.

It is not as easy to change the shunt of an ammeter with a switch as it is to change the multiplier of a voltmeter. That is because shunts have very low resistances, and minute changes in the resistance of the switch contacts may cause appreciable changes in the total resistance across the moving coil.

Fig. 647 shows how this difficulty is avoided, in the so-called universal shunt. A total resistance R, made up of several resistors, is connected across the coil; the

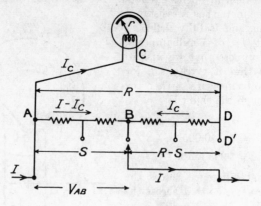

FIG. 647.   Universal shunt.

external circuit is connected across only a part of this, S, which is selected by the switch. Then S acts as a shunt, and $R - S$ as a series resistance. The switch contacts are in series with the external circuit—where their resistance is trivial —but do not add to the resistance across the galvanometer. To find the power of the shunt, we write down the potential difference between the points A and B, in terms of the measured current I, and the coil current I_C. From the figure, we have

$$V_{AB} = S(I - I_C);$$

and also, from the circuit ACDB,

$$V_{AB} = (r + R - S)I_C.$$

Therefore

$$S(I - I_C) = (r + R - S)I_C,$$

or

$$SI = (r + R)I_C,$$

whence

$$\frac{I}{I_C} = \frac{r + R}{S}. \qquad \ldots \ldots \ldots (8)$$

Very often R is made much greater than r—say 1000 ohms—so that, to a fair approximation,

$$\frac{I}{I_C} = \frac{R}{S}. \qquad \ldots \ldots \ldots (9)$$

The switch contacts by which S is chosen are then engraved with the values of R/S: for example, 1, 10, 100; in Fig. 647 the contact "1" would be at D′.

The approximate equation (9) does not contain the resistance of the galvanometer. Therefore the values of multiplying power engraved on the shunt apply to any galvanometer, so long as its resistance is much less than that of the shunt. That is why the shunt is called universal.

8. Universal Instruments.

A universal instrument is one which is adapted for measuring both current and voltage. It has a universal shunt R, and a series of voltage multipliers R' (Fig. 648). The shunt is connected permanently across the coil, and the resistances in R' are adjusted to give the desired full-scale voltages with the shunt in position. A switch or plug enables the various full-scale values of current or voltage to be chosen, but the user does the mental arithmetic. The instrument shown in the figure is reading 1·7 volts; if it were on the 10-volt range, it would be reading 6·4.

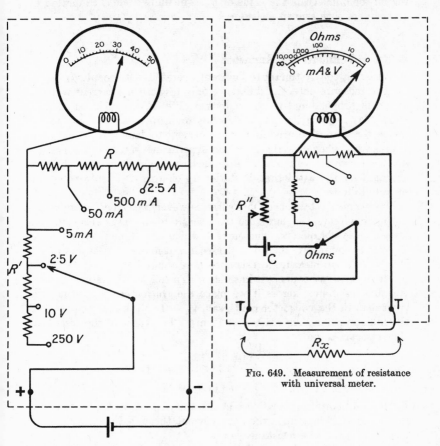

FIG. 649. Measurement of resistance with universal meter.

FIG. 648. A universal meter.

The terminals of a meter, universal or otherwise, are usually marked + and −; the pointer is deflected to the right when current passes through the meter from + to −.

Universal meters are generally arranged to measure resistance as well as current and voltage. An extra position on the switch, marked "R" or "ohms", puts a dry cell C and a variable resistor R'' in series with the moving coil (Fig. 649). Before the instrument is used to measure a resistance, its terminals TT are short-circuited, and R'' is adjusted until the pointer is fully deflected. As shown in the figure, it is then opposite the zero on the ohms scale. The short-circuit is next removed, and the unknown resistance R_x is connected across the terminals. The current falls, and the pointer moves to the left, indicating on the ohms scale the value of R_x. The ohms scale is calibrated by the makers with known resistances.

9. Use of Voltmeter and Ammeter.

A moving-coil voltmeter is a current-operated instrument. It can be used to measure potential difference only because the current which it draws is proportional to the potential difference applied to it, from Ohm's law. Since its action depends on Ohm's law, a moving-coil voltmeter cannot be used in any experiment to demonstrate that law; that is why, when describing such an experiment on p. 820, we specified an electrostatic voltmeter. An electrostatic voltmeter, which is actuated by the attraction of stationary charges, is a truly potential-operated device.

Having once established Ohm's law, however, we can use moving-coil voltmeters freely; they are both more sensitive and more accurate than electrostatic voltmeters. The current which they take does, however, sometimes complicate their use. To see how it may do so, let us suppose that we wish to measure a resistance R of about 100 ohms. As shown in Fig. 650 (a), we connect it in series with a cell, a milliammeter, and a variable resistance; across it we place the voltmeter. We adjust the current until the voltmeter reads, say, $V_1 = 1$ volt; let us suppose that the milliammeter then reads $I = 12$ mA. The value of the resistance then appears to be

$$R = \frac{V_1}{I} = \frac{1}{12 \times 10^{-3}} = \frac{10^3}{12}$$

$$= 83 \text{ ohms (approx.)}.$$

But the milliammeter reading includes the current drawn by the voltmeter. If that is 2 mA., then the current through the resistor, I', is only 10 mA. and its resistance is actually

$$R = \frac{V_1}{I'} = \frac{1}{10 \times 10^{-3}} = \frac{1}{10^{-2}}$$

$$= 100 \text{ ohms}.$$

The current drawn by the voltmeter has made the resistance appear 17 per cent. lower than its true value.

In an attempt to avoid this error, we might connect the voltmeter as shown in Fig. 650 (b): across both the resistor and the milliammeter. But its reading would then include the potential difference across the milliammeter. Let us suppose that this is 0·05 volt when the current through the milliammeter is 10 mA. Then the potential difference V'

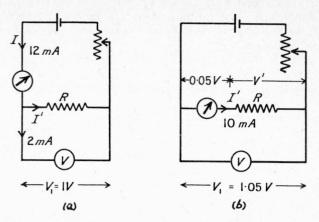

Fig. 650. Use of ammeter and voltmeter.

across the resistor would be 1 volt, and the voltmeter would read 1·05 volt. The resistance would appear to be

$$R = \frac{1·05}{10 \times 10^{-3}} = \frac{1·05}{10^{-2}}$$

$$= 105 \text{ ohms.}$$

Thus the voltage drop across the milliammeter would make the resistance appear 5 per cent. higher than its true value.

Errors of this kind are negligible only when the voltmeter current is much less than the current through the resistor, or when the voltage drop across the ammeter is much less than the potential difference across the resistor. If we were measuring a resistance of about 1 ohm, for example, the current I' in Fig. 650 (a) would be 1 amp., and I would be 1·002 amp. The error in measuring R would then be only 0·2 per cent.—less than the intrinsic error of the meter. But the circuit of Fig. 650 (b) would give the same error as before. It could do so because, as we saw when considering shunts, the shunt across the milliammeter would have been chosen to make the voltage drop still 0·05 volt. Thus V_1 would still be 1·05 volt when V' was 1 volt, and the error would be 5 per cent. as before.

In low-resistance circuits, therefore, the voltmeter should be connected as in Fig. 650 (a), so that its reading does not include the voltage drop across the ammeter. But in high-resistance circuits the voltmeter should be connected as in Fig. 650 (b), so that the ammeter does not carry its current.

10. Measurement of E.M.F.

If a moving-coil voltmeter is connected across a cell, it will not read its true e.m.f., because the current which it draws will set up a voltage drop across the internal resistance of the cell. The drop will be negligible only if the resistance of the voltmeter is very high compared with the internal resistance.

In principle the e.m.f. of cells may be compared with a quadrant electrometer, which is a sensitive but clumsy form of electrostatic voltmeter (p. 808). In practice this method is rarely used, because it has been superseded by the potentiometer method (p. 851). Fig. 651 shows the circuit for the quadrant electrometer method. The potential

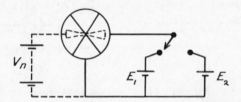

FIG. 651. Comparison of e.m.f.s. with quadrant electrometer.

of the needle, V_n, is maintained at about 100 volts, and the cells, E_1 and E_2, are connected in turn to the quadrants. The deflections θ_1 and θ_2 are proportional to the potential differences between the quadrants; and these are equal to the e.m.f.s because the electrometer draws no current. Therefore

$$\frac{E_1}{E_2} = \frac{\theta_1}{\theta_2}.$$

11. Figure of Merit of a Voltmeter.

If a milliammeter of 1 mA. f.s.d. (full scale deflection) is converted into a voltmeter, then if it is to have 1 volt f.s.d. its total resistance—coil plus multiplier—must be 1000 ohms. (One volt across its terminals will send through it a current of 1/1000 amp. = 1 mA.) If it is to have 10 volts f.s.d., then its total resistance must be 10,000 ohms; for 20 volts f.s.d., 20,000 ohms, and so on. It will have a resistance of 1000 ohms for every volt of its full-scale deflection. Such a meter is said to have a *figure of merit* of 1000 ohms per volt. Similarly, a voltmeter which takes 10 mA, or 1/100 amp., for full-scale deflection has a figure of merit of 100 ohms per volt. The greater the figure of merit of a voltmeter, expressed in this way, the less will it disturb any circuit to which it is connected, and the less error will its current cause in any measurements made with it. On the other hand, the greater the figure of merit, the more delicate the moving system of the meter and the greater its intrinsic error. First-grade, and particularly sub-standard, meters (p. 935) therefore have medium or low figures of merit: from 500 to 66·7 ohms per volt.

When a voltmeter of low figure of merit is being used, it may be necessary to allow for the current which it draws. The allowance is made in the way indicated on pp. 848-9, where the use of a voltmeter and ammeter together was discussed.

THE POTENTIOMETER

Pointer instruments are useless for very accurate measurements: the best of them have an intrinsic error of about 1 per cent. of full scale. Where greater accuracy than this is required, elaborate measuring circuits are used.

One of the most versatile of these, due to Poggendorf, is the potentiometer. It consists of a uniform wire, AB in Fig. 652 (a), about a metre long; through it an accumulator X maintains a steady current I. Since the wire is uniform, its resistance per centimetre, R, is constant; the voltage drop across 1 cm. of the wire, RI, is therefore also constant. The potential difference between the end A of the wire, and any point C upon it, is thus proportional to the length of wire l between A and C:

$$V_{AC} \propto l. \qquad \ldots \ldots \ldots \quad (10)$$

12. Comparison of E.M.F.s

To illustrate the use of the potentiometer, let us suppose that we take a cell, Y in Fig. 652 (b), and join its positive terminal to the point A (to which the positive terminal of X is also joined). We connect the negative terminal of Y, via a sensitive galvanometer, to a slider S, which we can press on to any point in the wire. Let us suppose that the cell Y has an e.m.f. E, which is less than the potential difference V_{AB} across the whole of the wire. Then if we press the slider on B, a current I' will flow through Y in opposition to its e.m.f. (Fig. 652 (c)). This current will deflect the galvanometer G—let us say to the right. If we now press the slider on A, the cell Y will be connected straight across the galvanometer, and will deliver a current I'' in the direction of its e.m.f. (Fig. 652 (d)). The galvanometer will therefore show a deflection to the left. If the deflections at A and B are not opposite, then either the e.m.f. of Y is greater than the potential difference across the whole wire, or we have connected the circuit wrongly. The commonest mistake in connecting up is not joining both positives to A.

Now let us suppose that we place the slider on to the wire at a point a few centimetres from A, then at a point a few centimetres farther on, and so forth. (We do not run the slider continuously along the wire, because the scraping would destroy its uniformity.) When the slider is at a point C near A (Fig. 653 (a)) the potential difference V_{AC} is less than the e.m.f. E of Y; current therefore flows through G in the direction of E, and G may deflect to the left. When the slider is at D near B, V_{AD} is greater than E, current flows through G in opposition to E, and G deflects to the right. By trial and error (but no scraping of the

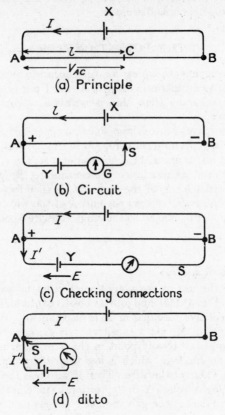

(a) Principle

(b) Circuit

(c) Checking connections

(d) ditto

Fig. 652. The potentiometer.

slider) we can find a point F such that, when the slider is pressed upon it, the galvanometer shows no deflection. The potential difference V_{AF} is then equal to the e.m.f. E; no current flows through the galvanometer because E and V_{AF} act in opposite directions in the galvanometer circuit (Fig. 653 (a)). Because no current flows, the resistance of the galvanometer, and the internal resistance of the cell, cause no voltage drop; the full e.m.f. E therefore appears, between the points, A and S, and is balanced by V_{AF}:

$$E = V_{AF}.$$

If we now take another cell of e.m.f. E_0, and balance it in the same way, at a point H (Fig. 653 (b)), then

$$E_0 = V_{AH}.$$

Therefore

$$\frac{E}{E_0} = \frac{V_{AF}}{V_{AH}}.$$

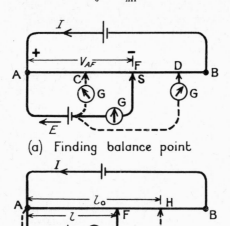

(a) Finding balance point

(b) Comparison of e.m.f.

Fig. 653. Use of potentiometer.

The potential differences V_{AF}, V_{AH} are proportional to the lengths l, l_0 from A to F, and from A to H, respectively. Therefore

$$\frac{E}{E_0} = \frac{l}{l_0}. \qquad \ldots \ldots \ldots (11)$$

13. Accuracy.

When the potentiometer is used to compare the e.m.f.s of cells, no errors are introduced by the internal resistances, because no current flows at the balance-points.

The potentiometer is more accurate than the quadrant electrometer, which, like a moving-coil voltmeter, has an intrinsic error of about 1 per cent. of full-scale. The accuracy of a potentiometer is limited by the non-uniformity of the slide-wire, the uncertainty of the balance-point, and the error in measuring the length l of wire from the balance-point to the end A. With even crude apparatus, the balance-point can be located to within about 0·5 mm.; if the length l is 50 cm., or 500 mm., then the error in locating the balance-point is 1:1000. If the wire has been carefully treated, its non-uniformity may introduce an error of about the same magnitude. The overall error is then about ten times less than that of a pointer instrument. A refined potentiometer has a still smaller error.

The precision with which the balance-point of a potentiometer can be found depends on the sensitivity of the galvanometer—the smallness of the current which will give a just-discernible deflection. A moving-coil galvanometer must be protected by a series resistance R of several thousand ohms, which is shorted out when the balance is nearly reached (Fig. 654). A series resistance is preferable to a shunt, because it reduces the current drawn from the cell under test, when the potentiometer is unbalanced. The process of seeking the balance-point then causes less change in the chemical condition of the cell, and therefore in its e.m.f.

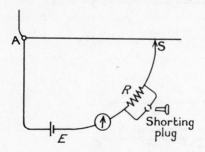

FIG. 654. Use of protective resistance with galvanometer.

It is important to realize that the accuracy of a potentiometer does not depend on the accuracy of the galvanometer, but only on its sensitivity. The galvanometer is used not to measure a current but merely to show one when the potentiometer is off balance. It is said to be used as a null-indicator, and the potentiometer method of measurement, like the bridge methods which we shall describe shortly, is called a null method.

The current through the potentiometer wire must be steady—it must not change appreciably between the finding of one balance-point and the next. The accumulator which provides it should therefore be neither freshly charged nor nearly run-down; when an accumulator is in either of those conditions its e.m.f. falls with time. Errors in potentiometer measurements may be caused by non-uniformity of the wire, and by the resistance of its connexion to the terminal at A. This resistance is added to the resistance of the length l of the wire between A and the balance-point, and if it is appreciable it makes equation (11) invalid. Both these sources of error are eliminated in the Rayleigh potentiometer, which we shall describe later (p. 859).

14. Uses of the Potentiometer. E.M.F. and Internal Resistance.

All the uses of the potentiometer depend on the fact that it can measure potential difference accurately, and without drawing current from the circuit under test.

If one of the cells in Fig. 653 (b) has a known e.m.f., say E_0 then the e.m.f. of the other, E, is given by equation:

$$\frac{E}{E_0} = \frac{l}{l_0}. \qquad \cdots \cdots \cdots \quad (12)$$

A cell of known e.m.f. is called a standard cell. The e.m.f.s of standard cells are determined absolutely—that is to say, without reference to the e.m.f.s of any other cell—by methods which depend, in principle, on the definition of e.m.f. (power/current, p. 828). Standard cells are described on p. 901, along with the precautions which must be taken in their use. For simple experiments a Daniell cell (p. 895), whose e.m.f. is about 1·1 volt, may be used as a standard.

Equation (12) is true only if the current I through the potentiometer wire has remained constant. The easiest way to check that it has done so is to balance the standard cell against the wire before and after balancing the unknown cell. If the lengths to the balance-point are equal—within the limits of experimental error—then the current I may be taken as constant. A check of this kind should be made in each of the experiments to be described.

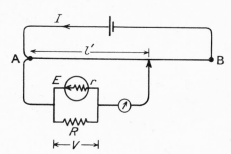

FIG. 655. Measurement of internal resistance.

The internal resistance of a cell, r, can be found with a potentiometer by balancing first its e.m.f., E, and then its terminal potential difference, V, when a known resistance R is connected across it (Fig. 655). Ohm's law for the complete circuit gives

$$\frac{V}{E} = \frac{R}{R + r}. \qquad \cdots \cdots \cdots \quad (13)$$

But

$$\frac{V}{E} = \frac{l'}{l}, \qquad \cdots \cdots \cdots \quad (14)$$

where l and l' are the lengths of potentiometer wire required to balance E and V. From equations (13) and (14), r can be found from

$$r = \left(\frac{l}{l'} - 1\right) R.$$

15. Calibration of Voltmeter.

Fig. 656 shows how a potentiometer can be used to calibrate a voltmeter. A standard cell is first used to find the p.d. per cm. or volts

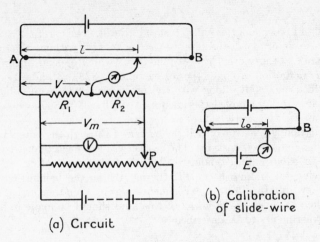

FIG. 656.   Calibration of voltmeter with potentiometer.

per cm. of the wire (Fig. 656 (b)): if its e.m.f. E_0 is balanced by a length l_0, then

$$\text{volts per cm.} = \frac{E_0}{l_0}. \qquad \ldots \ldots (15)$$

Different voltages V_m are now applied to the voltmeter by the adjustable potential divider P (Fig. 656 (a)). The fixed potential divider, comprising R_1R_2, gives a known fraction V of each value of V_m, which is then balanced on the potentiometer:

$$\frac{V}{V_m} = \frac{R_1}{R_1 + R_2}. \qquad \ldots \ldots (16)$$

(The resistances R_1 and R_2 are high—of the order of 1000 to 10,000 ohms, so that the voltage adjustment by P is fairly uniform. Their ratio is chosen so that the greatest value of V is measurable on the potentiometer—about 1·5 volts.) If l is the length of potentiometer wire which balances a given value of V, then

$$V = l \times (\text{volts/cm. of wire})$$

$$= l \frac{E_0}{l_0}.$$

From each value of V, the value of V_m is calculated by equation (16).

If the voltmeter reading is V_{obs}, then the correction to be added to it is $V_m - V_{obs}$. This is plotted against V_{obs}, as in Fig. 657.

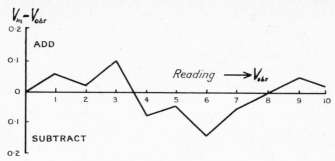

FIG. 657.   Correction curve of voltmeter.

16. Measurement of Current.

A current can be measured on a potentiometer by means of the potential difference which it sets up across a known resistance, R in Fig. 658 (a). The resistance is low, being chosen so that the potential

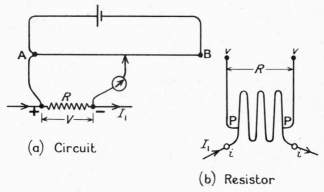

(a) Circuit

(b) Resistor

FIG. 658.   Measurement of current with potentiometer.

difference across it is of the order of 0·1 volt. (A higher value is not chosen, because the voltage drop across the resistor disturbs the circuit in which it is inserted.) Fig. 658 (b) shows in detail the kind of resistor used, which is often called a standard shunt. It consists of a broad strip of alloy, such as manganin, whose resistance varies very little with temperature (p. 819). The current is led in and out at the terminals i, i. The terminals v, v are connected to fine wires soldered to points PP on the strip; they are called the potential terminals. The marked value R of the resistance is the value between the points PP; it is adjusted by making hack-saw cuts into the edges of the strip.

As shown in Fig. 658 (a), the current to be measured, I_1, is passed through the shunt, and the potential difference between its potential terminals, V, is balanced on the potentiometer wire. If l is the length of wire to the balance-point, then

$$\frac{V}{E_0} = \frac{l}{l_0}, \qquad \qquad \ldots \ldots \ldots \quad (17)$$

where E_0 and l_0 refer to a standard cell as before. Equation (17) enables the current to be found in terms of E_0, l_0, l, and R, since

$$V = I_1 R.$$

The resistance of the wires connecting the potential terminals to the points PP, and to the potentiometer circuit, do not affect the result, because at the balance-point the current through them is zero.

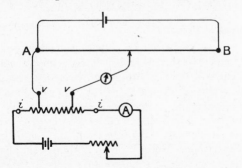

Fig. 659.   Calibration of ammeter with potentiometer.

This method of measuring a current can be used to calibrate an ammeter, A. The circuit is shown in Fig. 659; its principle and use should explain themselves. The results are treated in the same way as in the calibration of a voltmeter.

17. Comparison of Resistances.

A potentiometer can be used to compare resistances, by comparing the potential differences across them when they are carrying the same current I_1 (Fig. 660). This method is particularly useful for very low resistances, because, as we have just seen, the resistances of the connecting wires do not affect the result of the experiment. It can, however, be used for higher resistances if desired. With low resistances the ammeter A′ and rheostat P are necessary to adjust the current to a value which will neither exhaust the accumulator Y, nor overheat the resistors. No standard cell is required. The potential difference across the first resistor, $V_1 = R_1 I_1$, is balanced against a length l_1 of the potentiometer wire, as shown by the full lines in the figure. Both potential terminals of R_1 are then disconnected from the potentiometer, and those of R_2

are connected in their place. If l_2 is the length to the new balance-point, then

$$\frac{l_1}{l_2} = \frac{V_1}{V_2} = \frac{R_1 I_1}{R_2 I_1} = \frac{R_1}{R_2}.$$

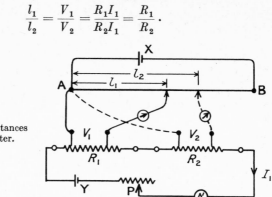

FIG. 660.
Comparison of resistances
with potentiometer.

This result is true only if the current I_1 is constant; as well as the potentiometer current. The accumulator Y, as well as X, must therefore be in good condition. To check the constancy of the current I_1, the ammeter A′ is not accurate enough. The reliability of the experiment as a whole can be checked by balancing the potential V_1 a second time, after V_2. If the new value of l_1 differs from the original, then at least one of the accumulators is running down and must be replaced.

18. The Rayleigh Potentiometer.

Fig. 661 shows a potentiometer devised by Lord Rayleigh (1842–1919), which is free from errors due to non-uniformity of the wire and

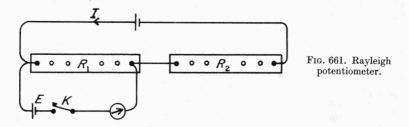

FIG. 661. Rayleigh
potentiometer.

to contact resistance at the end A (p. 854). It consists of two plug-type resistance boxes, R_1, R_2, joined in series. (These boxes may well be the R-sections of two similar Post Office boxes (p. 869)). At the start of a measurement all the plugs of R_1 are inserted, and all of R_2 taken out. Then R_1 is zero, and the main current I sets up no potential difference across it; but when the key K is pressed, the unknown e.m.f. E deflects the galvanometer. R_1 is now increased by, say, 100 ohms, and R_2 is decreased by the same amount. In this way $R_1 + R_2$ is kept constant, and the current I does not change. But there is now a potential difference across R_1, which opposes E. Plugs are taken out of R_1 and put into R_2, so as to keep $R_1 + R_2$ constant, until the galvanometer shows no deflection when K is pressed. If R_1' is the value of R_1 at this point, then

$$E = R_1'I.$$

The procedure is now repeated with a standard cell of e.m.f. E_0, in place of E. Since $R_1 + R_2$ has been kept constant, the current I is the same as before; hence, if R_1'' is the new value of R_1 at balance,

$$E_0 = R_1''I.$$

Consequently,
$$\frac{E}{E_0} = \frac{R_1'I}{R_1''I} = \frac{R_1'}{R_1''}.$$

19. Measurement of Thermal E.M.F.

The e.m.f.s of thermojunctions (p. 836) are small—of the order of a millivolt. If we attempted to measure such an e.m.f. on a simple potentiometer we should find the balance-point very near one end of the wire, so that the end-error would be serious. The Rayleigh potentiometer, although it is free from end-errors, is not suitable for measuring small e.m.f.s: if, in Fig. 661, $R_1 + R_2 = 10,000 \ \Omega$, and the e.m.f. of the accumulator $= 2$ volts, then $I = 2/10,000 = 2 \times 10^{-4}$ amp. $= 0.2$ mA. To balance a thermal e.m.f. of 2 mV, R_1 would therefore have to be 10 Ω; and since R_1 cannot be adjusted in steps smaller than 1 Ω, the e.m.f. cannot be measured to a greater accuracy than 10 per cent.

For accurate measurement of thermal e.m.f.s special potentiometers have been devised, but the simple circuit of Fig. 662 will do for a laboratory experiment. The e.m.f. E is applied via a sensitive galvanometer G across a standard shunt R of about 1 ohm. A current I, of a few milliamperes, is passed through the shunt, and measured on the milliammeter M. Its value is adjusted by the rheostat P until G shows no deflection. The potential difference RI is then equal and opposite to the thermal e.m.f.

$$E = RI.$$

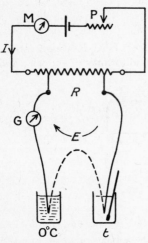

FIG. 662. Measurement of thermal e.m.f.

(If a balance cannot be found, the connexions of the junction to R should be reversed.) A more accurate measurement of E is given on p. 1035.

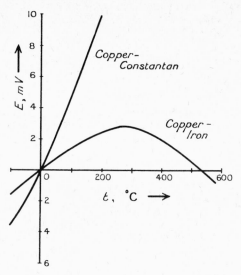

FIG. 663. E.m.f.s of thermocouples. (Reckoned positive when into copper at the cold junction.)

Fig. 663 shows the results of measuring the e.m.f. E when the cold junction is at $0°$C. and the hot is at various temperatures t. The curves approximate to parabolae:

$$E = at + bt^2. \qquad \ldots \ldots \quad (18)$$

THERMO-ELECTRIC E.M.F.s

(E in micro-volts when t is in $°$C.
and cold junction at $0°$C.)

Junction	a	b	Range for a and b, $°C$	Limits of use, $°C$.
Cu/Fe . . .	14	−0·02	0–100	See 1
Cu/Constantan[2] .	41	0·04	−50 to +300	−200 to +300
Pt/Pt—Rh[3] . .	6·4	0·006	0–200	0–1700
Chromel[4]/Alumel[5] .	41	0·00	0–900	0–1300

[1] Simple demonstrations.
[2] See p. 819.
[3] 10 per cent. Rh; used only for accurate work or very high temperatures.
[4] 90 per cent. Ni, 10 per cent. Cr.
[5] 94 per cent. Ni, 3 per cent. Mn, 2 per cent. Al, 1 per cent. Si.

NETWORKS

2 ̇ ̇irchhoff's Laws.

A "network" is usually a complicated system of electrical conductors. Kirchhoff (1824–87) extended Ohm's law to networks, and gave two laws, which together enabled the current in any part of the network to be calculated.

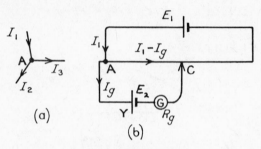

Fig. 664.   Kirchhoff's laws.

The *first law* refers to any point in the network, such as A in Fig. 664 (*a*); it states that the total current flowing into the point is equal to the total current flowing out of it:

$$I_1 = I_2 + I_3.$$

The law follows from the fact that electric charges do not accumulate at the points of a network. It is often put in the form that *the algebraic sum of the currents at a junction of a circuit is zero*, or

$$\Sigma I = 0,$$

where a current, I, is reckoned positive if it flows towards the point, and negative if it flows away from it. Thus at A in Fig. 664 (*a*),

$$I_1 - I_2 - I_3 = 0.$$

Kirchhoff's first law gives a set of equations which contribute towards the solving of the network; in practice, however, we can shorten the work by putting the first law straight into the diagram, as shown in Fig. 664 (*b*) for example, since

$$\text{current along AC} = I_1 - I_g.$$

Kirchhoff's *second law* is a generalization of Ohm's law for the complete circuit. It refers to any closed loop, such as AYCA in Fig. 664 (*b*); and it states that, round such a loop, the algebraic sum of the voltage drops is equal to the algebraic sum of the e.m.f.s:

$$\Sigma RI = \Sigma E.$$

Thus, clockwise round the loop,

$$R_{AC}(I_1 - I_g) - R_g I_g = E_2.$$

We have used the potentiometer to illustrate Kirchhoff's laws merely because it is already familiar to us; we shall not go on and solve it as a network, because we have already dealt with as much of the theory of it as we need.

EXAMPLE

Fig. 665 shows a network which can be solved by Kirchhoff's laws. From the first law, the current in the 8-ohm wire is $(I_1 + I_2)$, assuming I_1, I_2 are the currents through the cells. Taking closed circuits formed by each cell with the 8-ohm wire, we have, from the second law,

$$E_1 = 6 = 3I_1 + 8(I_1 + I_2) = 11I_1 + 8I_2$$

and

$$E_2 = 4 = 2I_2 + 8(I_1 + I_2) = 8I_1 + 10I_2.$$

Solving the two equations, we find $I_1 = \dfrac{14}{23}$

$= 0.61$ amp., $I_2 = -\dfrac{2}{23} = -0.09$ amp.

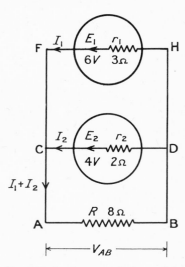

Fig. 665. Load across cells in parallel.

The minus sign indicates that the current I_2 flows in the sense opposite to that shown in the diagram; i.e. it flows against the e.m.f. of the generator E_2. It does so because the potential difference V_{AB} is greater than E_2:

$$V_{AB} = R\left(I_1 + I_2\right) = 8\left(\frac{14}{23} - \frac{2}{23}\right)$$

$$= 8 \times \frac{12}{23} = \frac{96}{23} = 4.2 \text{ volts.}$$

This is equal to the e.m.f. E_2 *plus* the drop across the internal resistance r_2 (p. 833):

$$V_{CD} = 4 + 2 \times \frac{2}{23} = 4 + \frac{4}{23}$$

$$= \frac{96}{23} \text{ volts} = V_{AB}.$$

It is also equal to the e.m.f. E_1 *minus* the drop across r_1, because the current flows through the upper generator in the direction of its e.m.f.:

$$V_{FH} = 6 - 3 \times \frac{14}{23} = 6 - \frac{42}{23} = \frac{138 - 42}{23}$$

$$= \frac{96}{23} \text{ volts} = V_{AB}.$$

WHEATSTONE BRIDGE
MEASUREMENT OF RESISTANCE

21. Wheatstone Bridge Circuit.

About 1843 Wheatstone designed a circuit called a "bridge circuit" which gave an accurate method for measuring resistance. We shall deal later with the practical aspects. In Fig. 666, X is the unknown resistance, and P, Q, R are resistance boxes. One of these—usually R—is adjusted until the galvanometer between A, C, represented by its resistance R_g, shows no deflection: that is to say,

$$I_g = 0.$$

Then, as we shall show,

$$\frac{P}{Q} = \frac{R}{X},$$

whence

$$X = \frac{Q}{P} R.$$

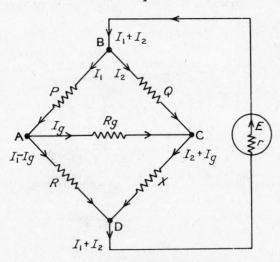

FIG. 666.   Analysis of Wheatstone bridge.

Fig. 666 shows Kirchhoff's first law applied to the circuit. From the second law, we have:

$$\text{loop ACBA:} \quad R_g I_g - Q I_2 + P I_1 = 0, \quad \cdot \quad \ldots \quad \text{(i)}$$

$$\text{loop ACDA:} \quad R_g I_g + X(I_2 + I_g) - R(I_1 - I_g) = 0,$$

or

$$I_g(R_g + X + R) + X I_2 - R I_1 = 0. \quad \ldots \quad \text{(ii)}$$

If we wished to find I_g, we would have to set up a third equation, by going round one of the loops, including the battery (p. 866). But if we wish only to find the condition for no deflection of the galvanometer, we have merely to put $I_g = 0$ in equations (i) and (ii). Then

$$-Q I_2 + P I_1 = 0, \quad \text{or} \quad P I_1 = Q I_2,$$

whence

$$\frac{P}{Q} = \frac{I_2}{I_1};$$

and

$$X I_2 - R I_1 = 0, \quad \text{or} \quad X I_2 = R I_1,$$

whence

$$\frac{R}{X} = \frac{I_2}{I_1}.$$

Therefore, as already stated,

$$\frac{P}{Q} = \frac{R}{X}. \quad \ldots \ldots \ldots \quad \text{(19)}$$

This is the condition for balance of the bridge. It is the same, as the reader may easily show, if the battery and galvanometer are interchanged in the circuit.

22. Alternative Wheatstone Bridge Proof.

Equation (19) for the balance condition can be got without the use of Kirchhoff's laws. At balance, since no current flows through the galvanometer, the points A and C must be at the same potential (Fig. 667). Therefore

$$V_{AB} = V_{CB}$$

and

$$V_{AD} = V_{CD},$$

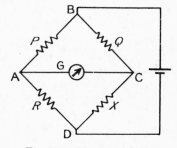

FIG. 667. Wheatstone bridge

whence

$$\frac{V_{AB}}{V_{AD}} = \frac{V_{CB}}{V_{CD}}. \quad \ldots \ldots \ldots \quad \text{(i)}$$

Also, since $I_g = 0$, P and R carry the same current, I_1, and X and Q carry the same current, I_2. Therefore

$$\left.\begin{array}{c} \dfrac{V_{AB}}{V_{AD}} = \dfrac{I_1 P}{I_1 R} = \dfrac{P}{R} \\[3mm] \text{and} \qquad \dfrac{V_{CB}}{V_{CD}} = \dfrac{I_2 Q_2}{I_2 X} = \dfrac{Q}{X} \end{array}\right\} \quad \dots \dots \quad \text{(ii)}$$

Hence, by equations (i) and (ii),

$$\frac{P}{R} = \frac{Q}{X},$$

or

$$\frac{P}{Q} = \frac{R}{X}.$$

23. Galvanometer Position.

We shall now show, by taking a numerical example, how the galvanometer in a bridge circuit can best be positioned.

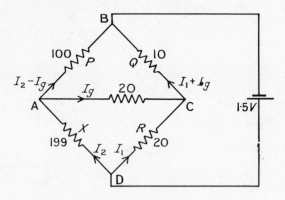

FIG. 668.   An unbalanced Wheatstone bridge.

Fig. 668 shows an unbalanced Wheatstone bridge, fed from a cell of negligible internal resistance. The figures give the resistance in ohms, and I_g is to be found. Applying Kirchhoff's laws:

Loop ACBA: $20I_g + 10(I_1 + I_g) - 100(I_2 - I_g) = 0$

or $130I_g + 10I_1 - 100I_2 = 0$,

whence $I_1 = 10I_2 - 13I_g.$ $\dots \dots$ (i)

Loop ADCA: $-199I_2 + 20I_1 - 20I_g = 0.$

Substituting for I_1: $\quad -199I_2 + 200I_2 - 260I_g - 20I_g = 0,$

or $\qquad\qquad\qquad\qquad I_2 - 280I_g = 0,$

whence $\qquad\qquad\qquad\qquad I_2 = 280I_g.$

$\therefore$ by (i), $\quad I_1 = 2800I_g - 13I_g = 2787I_g.$ $\qquad$ . . (ii)

Loop DCBXD: $\quad 20I_1 + 10(I_1 + I_g) = 1.5,$

or $\qquad\qquad\qquad 30I_1 + 10I_g = 1.5.$

Substituting from (ii) for I_1: $\quad 30 \times 2787I_g + 10I_g = 1.5$

or $\qquad\qquad\qquad\qquad 83620I_g = 1.5,$

whence $\qquad I_g = \dfrac{1.5}{83620} = 1.79 \times 10^{-5}$ amp.

$$= 17.9 \text{ microamperes.}$$

The reader should now show that, if the battery and galvanometer were interchanged, the current I_g would be 13·2 microamperes. This result illustrates an important point¯ in the use of the Wheatstone bridge: with a given unbalance, the galvanometer current is greatest when the galvanometer is connected from the junction of the highest resistances to the junction of the lowest. Therefore, unless $P = Q$, which is unusual, the galvanometer should be connected across PQ.

24. Practical Arrangement.

A practical form of Wheatstone bridge is shown in Fig. 669. The resistances P and Q can be given values of 10, 100, or 1000 ohms by three-point switches. The resistance R has four decade dials by which it can be varied from 1 ohm to more than 10,000 ohms. Pairs of terminals are provided for connecting the unknown resistance, the battery, and the galvanometer, X, B, G; and keys K_1 and K_2 are fitted in the battery and galvanometer circuits.

To measure a resistance, we first set $P = Q = 10\ \Omega$. We set $R = 0$ and press first K_1 then K_2; the small interval between pressing K_1 and K_2 gives time for the currents in the bridge to become steady (Chapter XLI). Let us suppose that, when we press K_2, the galvanometer deflects to the right. We then set $R = 10,000\ \Omega$ and again press K_1, K_2. If the galvanometer deflects to the left we can proceed; if it deflects again to the right, then either we have made a wrong connexion —which with this form of bridge is almost impossible—or X is greater than 10,000 ohms. If the galvanometer deflects to the left, we try again with $R = 1000\ \Omega$· and so on with $100\ \Omega$ and $10\ \Omega$, if necessary. Let us suppose that the galvanometer deflects to the left with $R = 100\ \Omega$, but to the right with $10\ \Omega$. We then adjust the 10's dial until we get, say, a leftward deflection with $40\ \Omega$ and a rightward with

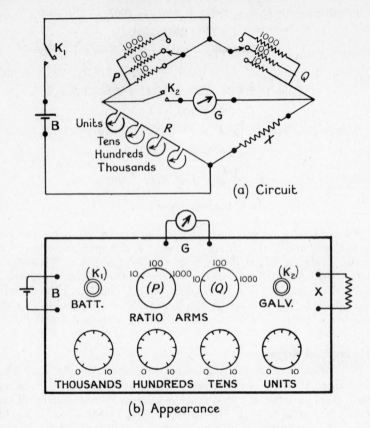

Fig. 669. Practical form of Wheatstone bridge.

30 Ω. With the unit's dial we now narrow the limits to, let us say, 36 Ω (left) and 35 Ω (right). We have

$$\frac{X}{R} = \frac{Q}{P} = \frac{10}{10} = 1.$$

$$\therefore X = R.$$

It follows that X lies between 35 and 36 Ω.

We now set $P = 100$, so that

$$\frac{X}{R} = \frac{Q}{P} = \frac{10}{100} = \frac{1}{10}$$

or

$$X = \frac{R}{10}.$$

The balance-point now lies between $R = 350 \, \Omega$ (right) and $R = 360 \, \Omega$ (left); by using the unit's dial we can now locate it between, say, 353 and 354. Then, from the equation, X lies between 35·3 and 35·4 ohms. If we finally make $P = 1000 \, \Omega$, we have

$$\frac{X}{R} = \frac{Q}{P} = \frac{10}{1000} = \frac{1}{100}$$

or

$$X = \frac{R}{100}.$$

Only a sensitive galvanometer will give considerable deflections near the balance-point in this condition; if it locates the balance-point between $R = 3536 \, \Omega$ and $3537 \, \Omega$ then X lies between 35·36 and 35·37 ohms. If a moving-coil galvanometer is used, it must be protected by a high series resistance while balance is being sought.

25. Range of Measurable Resistance.

The resistors P and Q are often called the ratio arms of the bridge, because their resistances determine the ratio of R to X. If X is greater than the greatest value of R, it can be measured by making $Q = 100$, $P = 10$. Then

$$\frac{X}{R} = \frac{Q}{P} = \frac{100}{10} = 10$$

and

$$X = 10R.$$

A balance-point between $R = 14{,}620$ and $14{,}630$, say, would mean that R lay between 146,200 and 146,300 ohms. Similarly, by making $Q = 1000$, $P = 10$, resistances can be measured up to 100 times the greatest value of R: that is to say, up to a little more than 1,000,000 ohms. With these high resistances, however, the near-balance currents are very small, and a sensitive galvanometer is necessary.

The lowest resistance which a bridge of this type can measure with reasonable accuracy is about 1 ohm; R can be adjusted in steps of 1 ohm, and P/Q can be made 1/100, so that measurements can be made to within 1/100 ohm. Resistances lower than about 1 ohm cannot be measured accurately on a Wheatstone bridge, whatever the ratios available, or the smallest steps in R. They cannot because of the resistances of the wires connecting them to the X terminals, and of the contacts between those wires and the terminals to which they are, at each end, attached. This is the reason why the potentiometer method is more satisfactory for low resistances.

26. The Post Office Box.

An old-fashioned type of Wheatstone bridge, with plugs instead of switches, is called the Post Office box, and is illustrated in **Fig. 670.**

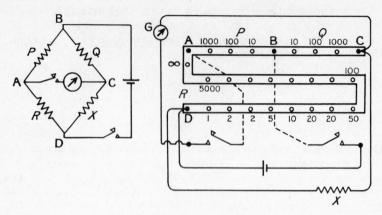

Fig. 670. Post Office box.

It is connected up and used in the same way as the dial type of bridge, but requires far more skill by its operator. Anyone who has to use a Post Office box should observe the following rules:

(i) do not attempt to memorize the wiring-up; the circuit should be worked out from the Wheatstone bridge diagram (Fig. 667);

(ii) take the 10 Ω plugs out of each ratio arm P, Q before testing the circuit;

(iii) test for correct connexions by seeing whether the galvanometer gives opposite deflections with $R = 0$ and $R = \infty$ (for the latter an "infinity" plug is provided, whose gap is not bridged by any resistor—Fig. 670);

(iv) press plugs home firmly, with a half-turn to the right;

(v) never mix the plugs from different boxes—always put loose plugs in the lid of their box, never on the bench.

27. The Slide-wire (Metre) Bridge.

Fig. 671 shows a simple and cheap form of Wheatstone bridge; it is sometimes called a metre bridge, for no better reason than that the wire AB is often a metre long. The wire is uniform, as in a potentiometer, and can be explored by a slider S. The unknown resistance X and a known resistance R are connected as shown in the figure; heavy brass or copper strip is used for the connexions AD, FH, KB, whose resistances are generally negligible. When the slider is at a point C in the wire it divides the wire into two parts, of resistances R_{AC} and R_{CB}; these, with X and R, form a Wheatstone bridge. (The galvanometer and battery are interchanged relative to the circuits we have given earlier; that enables the slider S to be used as the galvanometer

key. We have already seen that the interchange does not affect the
condition for balance (p. 865)). The connexions are checked by

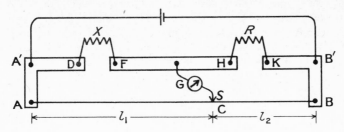

FIG. 671.   Slide-wire (metre) bridge.

placing S first on A, then on B. The balance-point is found by trial
and error—not by scraping S along AB. At balance,

$$\frac{X}{R} = \frac{R_{AC}}{R_{CB}}.$$

Since the wire is uniform, the resistances R_{AC} and R_{CB} are proportional to the lengths of wire, l_1 and l_2. Therefore

$$\frac{X}{R} = \frac{l_1}{l_2}. \qquad \ldots \ldots \quad (20)$$

The resistance R should be chosen so that the balance-point C comes
fairly near to the centre of the wire—within, say, its middle third. If
either l_1 or l_2 is small, the resistance of its end connexion AA′ or BB′
in Fig. 671 is not negligible in comparison with its own resistance;
equation (20) then does not hold. Some idea of the accuracy of a
particular measurement can be got by interchanging R and X, and
balancing again. If the new ratio agrees with the old within about
1 per cent., then their average may be taken as the value of X.

28. Resistance by Substitution.

Fig. 672 illustrates a simple way of measuring a resistance X. It is
connected in series with a rheostat S, an ammeter A, and a cell. S is
adjusted until A gives a large deflection. X is
then replaced by a box of known resistances,
R, which can be selected by plugs or dials.
R is varied until the ammeter gives the
same reading as before. Then, if the e.m.f.
of the cell has not fallen, $R = X$. The
accuracy of this method is limited, by the
inherent error of the ammeter, to about
1 per cent. It does not depend on the accuracy of *calibration* of the ammeter, but

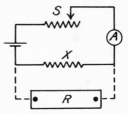

FIG. 672. Measurement of
resistance by substitution.

on the accuracy with which it reproduces a given deflection for a given current. The ammeter is used simply as a "transfer instrument"—to indicate when the current in the second part of the experiment is the same as in the first. This principle is very useful in measurements more difficult than that of resistance by direct method. For example, the power output of a small radio transmitter can be measured by making it light a lamp, which is placed near to a light-meter (p. 581). The lamp is then connected to a source of direct current, and the current through it is adjusted until the light-meter gives the same reading. Simple measurements of the current, and the voltage across the lamp, then give the power supplied to it—which is equal to the power output of the radio transmitter.

29. Resistance and Sensitivity of a Galvanometer.

It is often necessary to know the resistance, R_g, and sensitivity of a suspended-coil galvanometer. To find them, we may use the circuit of Fig. 673 (a). S is a rheostat of about 1000 ohms maximum, r is a standard shunt of about 0·01 ohm, M is a milliammeter, and R is a resistance box.

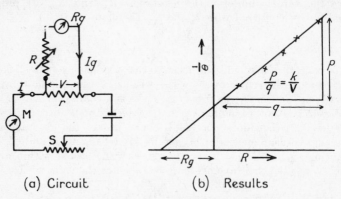

(a) Circuit   (b) Results

Fig. 673.   Galvanometer calibration.

The current in the main circuit, I, is adjusted to a value which can be accurately read on M—say 10 milliamperes. Since r is very small compared with $R + R_g$, the galvanometer current I_g is negligible compared with I, and we may say that the potential difference across r is

$$V = rI.$$

In this example it would be $0·01 \times 10 \times 10^{-3} = 10^{-4}$ volt $= 0·1$ millivolt. The galvanometer current is therefore

$$I_g = \frac{V}{R + R_g}.$$

If $R + R_g$ is 1000 ohms, then $I_g = 10^{-4}/10^3 = 10^{-7}$ amp. = 0·1 micro-ampere, which is a reasonable value for a galvanometer of moderate sensitivity. If θ is the deflection of the galvanometer, then

$$I_g = k\theta,$$

where k is a constant (the reduction factor) which we wish to find.

From the equation for I_g on p. 872,

$$\frac{V}{R + R_g} = k\theta,$$

whence

$$\frac{1}{\theta} = \frac{k}{V}(R + R_g).$$

Therefore, if we vary R and plot $1/\theta$ against it, we get a straight line, as shown in Fig. 673 (b). The line makes an intercept on the R axis, which gives the value of R_g. And its slope p/q is k/V. Since we know V, from page 872, we can hence find k; and $1/k$, the deflection per unit current, is the sensitivity.

30. Temperature Coefficient of Resistance.

We have seen that the resistance of a given wire increases with its temperature. If we put a coil of fine copper wire into a water bath, and use a Wheatstone bridge to measure its resistance at various moderate temperatures t, we find that the resistance, R, increases

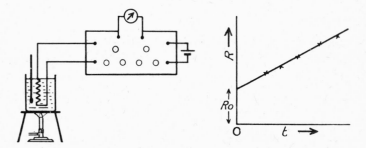

Fig. 674. Measurement of temperature coefficient.

uniformly with the temperature (Fig. 674). We may therefore define a temperature coefficient of resistance, α, such that

$$R = R_0(1 + \alpha t), \qquad \ldots \ldots \quad (21)$$

where R_0 is the resistance at 0°C. In words,

$$\alpha = \frac{\text{increase of resistance per deg. C. rise of temperature}}{\text{resistance at 0°C.}}.$$

If R_1 and R_2 are the resistances at t_1°C. and t_2°C., then

$$\frac{R_1}{R_2} = \frac{1 + \alpha t_1}{1 + \alpha t_2}. \qquad \ldots \ldots \quad (22)$$

Values of a for pure metals are of the order of 0·004 per deg. C. They are much less for alloys than for pure metals, a fact which enhances the value of alloys as materials for resistance boxes and shunts.

Equation (21) represents the change of resistance with temperature fairly well, but not as accurately as it can be measured. More accurate equations are given on pp. 380–1 in the Heat section of this book, where resistance thermometers are discussed.

EXAMPLES

1. How would you compare the resistances of two wires A and B, using (a) a Wheatstone bridge method and (b) a potentiometer? For each case draw a circuit diagram and indicate the method of calculating the result.

In an experiment carried out at 0°C., A was 120 cm. of Nichrome wire of resistivity 100×10^{-6} ohm-cm. and diameter 1·20 mm., and B a German silver wire 0·80 mm. diameter and resistivity 28×10^{-6} ohm-cm. The ratio of the resistances A/B was 1·20. What was the length of the wire B?

If the temperature coefficient of resistance of Nichrome is 0·00040 per deg. C. and of German silver is 0·00030 per deg. C., what would the ratio of the resistances become if the temperature were raised by 100 deg. C. ? (L.)

First part (see pp., 858, 870).

Second part. With usual notation,

for A,
$$R_1 = \frac{\varrho_1 l_1}{a_1},$$

and for B,
$$R_2 = \frac{\varrho_2 l_2}{a_2}.$$

$$\therefore \frac{R_1}{R_2} = \frac{\varrho_1}{\varrho_2} \cdot \frac{l_1}{l_2} \cdot \frac{a_2}{a_1} = \frac{\varrho_1}{\varrho_2} \cdot \frac{l_1}{l_2} \cdot \frac{d_2{}^2}{d_1{}^2},$$

where d_2, d_1 are the respective diameters of B and A.

$$\therefore 1·20 = \frac{100}{28} \times \frac{120}{l_2} \times \frac{0·8^2}{10·2^2}.$$

$$\therefore l_2 = \frac{100 \times 120 \times 0·64}{1·20 \times 28 \times 1·44} = 159 \text{ cm.} \qquad \ldots \ldots \text{(i)}$$

When the temperature is raised by 100°C., the resistance increases according to the relation $R_t = R_0(1 + at)$. Thus

new Nichrome resistance, $R_A, = R_1(1 + a \cdot 100) = R_1 \times 1·04,$

and　new German silver resistance, $R_B = R_2(1 + a' \cdot 100) = R_2 \times 1·03.$

$$\therefore \frac{R_A}{R_B} = \frac{R_1}{R_2} \times \frac{1·04}{1·03} = 1·20 \times \frac{1·04}{1·03} = 1·21. \qquad \ldots \ldots \text{(ii)}$$

2. State Kirchhoff's laws relating to the currents in network of conductors. Two cells of e.m.f. 1·5 volts and 2 volts respectively and internal resistances of 1 ohm and 2 ohms respectively are connected in parallel to an external resistance of 5 ohms. Calculate the currents in each of the three branches of the network. (N.)

First part (see p. 862).

Second part. Suppose x, y amp. are the respective currents through the cells (Fig. 675). Then, from Kirchhoff's first law, the current through the 5-ohm wire is $(x + y)$ amp.

Applying Kirchhoff's second law to the complete circuit with the cell of e.m.f. 1·5 volts and external resistance 5 ohms, we have

$$1·5 = x + 5(x + y) = 6x + 5y. \qquad . \quad . \quad . \quad (i)$$

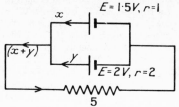

FIG. 675.   Example.

Applying the law to the complete circuit with the cell of e.m.f. 2 volts and external resistance 5 ohms, then

$$2 = 2y + 5(x + y) = 5x + 7y. \qquad . \quad . \quad . \quad . \quad . \quad . \quad (ii)$$

Solving (i) and (ii), we find $y = 9/34$ amp., $x = 1/34$ amp. Thus the current through the 5-ohm resistor $= x + y = 10/34 = 5/17$ amp.

EXERCISES XXXVII

Circuit Calculations.

1. State Ohm's law and describe an experiment to verify it.

A resistance of 1000 ohms and one of 2000 ohms are placed in series with a 100-volt mains supply. What will be the reading on a voltmeter of internal resistance 2000 ohms when placed across (a) the 1000 ohms resistance, (b) the 2000 ohms resistance? (L.)

2. Define the absolute e.m.u. of potential difference and hence show that the rate of production of heat in a wire of constant resistance is proportional to the square of the current passing through it.

A cell A, e.m.f. 1·1 volts and internal resistance 3 ohms, is joined in parallel with another cell B, e.m.f. 1·4 volts and internal resistance 1 ohm, similar poles being connected together. The ends of a wire, of resistance 4 ohms, are joined to the terminals of A. Find (a) the current through the wire, (b) the rate of dissipation of energy in watts in each of the cells A and B. (L.)

3. Twelve cells each of e.m.f. 2 volts and of internal resistance $\frac{1}{2}$ ohm are arranged in a battery of n rows and an external resistance of $\frac{3}{8}$ ohm is connected to the poles of the battery. Determine the current flowing through the resistance in terms of n.

Obtain numerical values of the current for the possible values which n may take and draw a graph of current against n by drawing a smooth curve through the points. Give the value of the current corresponding to the maximum of the curve and find the internal resistance of the battery when the maximum current is produced. (L.)

4. Describe with full experimental details an experiment to test the validity of Ohm's law for a metallic conductor.

An accumulator of e.m.f. 2 volts and of negligible internal resistance is joined in series with a resistance of 500 ohms and an unknown resistance X ohms. The readings of a voltmeter successively across the 500-ohm resistance and X are 2/7 and 8/7 volts respectively. Comment on this and calculate the value of X and the resistance of the voltmeter. (N.)

5. State Ohm's law, and hence define the term "resistance" of an electrical circuit. Describe some form of Wheatstone's bridge and explain fully how it is used to determine the ratio of two resistances.

An approximately balanced Wheatstone's bridge network is constructed as follows. Two equal resistances of 100 ohms, AB, BC, are connected in series, and another two, AD, DC of 200 and 201 ohms respectively, connected in series with each other but as a whole in parallel with ABC. A 2-volt accumulator of negligible resistance is connected to A, C, and a galvanometer of resistance 50 ohms across BD. Find the current through the galvanometer. (*G. & C.*)

6. State Ohm's law and describe how you would test its validity. Why would an experiment involving the use of a moving-coil ammeter and a moving-coil voltmeter be unsatisfactory?

In order to calibrate a galvanometer an accumulator of e.m.f. 200 volts and negligible resistance is connected in series with two resistances P and Q. A resistance R and the galvanometer, resistance G, are joined in series and then connected to the ends of P. The galvanometer is shunted by a resistance S. If $P = 200$ ohms, $Q = 1880$ ohms, $R = 291$ ohms, $S = 10$ ohms, $G = 90$ ohms, and the deflection is 20 divisions, calculate the current sensitivity in micro-amperes per division.

7. State Kirchhoff's laws for flow of electricity through a network containing sources of e.m.f.

Wheatstone bridge with slide wire of 0·5 ohm and length 50 cm. is used to compare two resistances, each of 2 ohms. The cell has an e.m.f. of 2 volts and no internal resistance, and the galvanometer has resistance of 100 ohms. Find the current through the galvanometer when the bridge is 1 cm. off balance. Compare the result with that of approximate calculation. (*L.*)

8. State Ohm's law, and describe the experiments you would make in order to verify it. The positive poles A and C of two cells are connected by a uniform wire of resistance 4 ohms and their negative poles B and D by a uniform wire of resistance 6 ohms. The middle point of BD is connected to earth. The e.m.f.s of the cells AB and CD are 2 volts and 1 volt respectively, their resistances 1 ohm and 2 ohms respectively. Find the potential at the middle point of AC. (*O. & C.*)

9. Describe the Wheatstone net method of comparing two resistances and discuss its accuracy. Outline the method you would adopt when two very low resistances are to be accurately compared.

An accumulator, of 2·05 volts and of negligible internal resistance, is applied to the terminals A and C of a Wheatstone network ABCD. Resistances AB and AD are 2000 ohms each and BC and DC are 2100 ohms each, at balance. The resistances AB and BC are now transposed; calculate the potential difference between the ends of the galvanometer branch BD when it is on open circuit. What value of resistance will now have to be placed in parallel with the arm DC in order to restore the balance of the network? (*L.*)

Measurements.

10. Derive the relation between the four resistances of a balanced Wheatstone bridge. Describe, with experimental details, how you would use a Wheatstone bridge circuit for an accurate determination of the resistivity of the material of a wire.

A Wheatstone bridge is used to check the resistance of a nominal 1-ohm coil. The bridge is balanced with a standard ohm in one arm. When the standard is replaced by the nominal ohm the latter has to be shunted with 2 metres of eureka wire of diameter 0·1 mm. in order to maintain the balance. Calculate the resistance of the nominal ohm. (Resistivity of eureka = 49×10^{-6} ohm/cm.) (*L.*)

11. Describe and explain how you would use a potentiometer (*a*) to compare the electromotive forces of two cells, (*b*) to test the accuracy of the 1-amp. reading of an ammeter.

The e.m.f. of a cell is balanced by the fall in potential along 150 cm. of a potentiometer wire. When the cell is shunted by a resistance of 14 ohms the length required is 140 cm. What is the internal resistance of the cell? (*N*.)

12. Give clearly labelled diagrams of the complete circuits in which a uniform wire 1 metre in length could be used to compare: (*a*) two resistances each of the order 10 ohms; (*b*) two resistances each of the order 0·1 ohm; (*c*) the e.m.f.s of two cells.

Explain in each instance how the result is obtained from the observations. (*L*.)

13. Describe the method you would use to find by experiment the variation of resistance of a wire with temperature indicating graphically the results expected.

If the temperature coefficient of resistance, *a*, of silver is 0·004 per °C., what resistance at 150°C. has a silver wire whose resistance at 0°C. is 1·5 ohms? (*L*.)

14. Describe methods (one in each case) of measuring the resistance of (*a*) a coil of wire of about 100 ohms, (*b*) an ammeter shunt of about 0·05 ohm, (*c*) a saline solution between two platinum electrodes. Give reasons for your choice of method, and explain how you would make the required calculations.

15. Describe a simple stretched wire potentiometer and explain the theory of its use to compare potential differences. Indicate by means of diagrams the modifications and additions required to use it (*a*) to measure a current of about 3 amp., (*b*) to measure the e.m.f. of a thermocouple.

Give reasons why it is permissible to use a potentiometer to measure potential differences in an experiment to verify Ohm's law but fallacious to use it to measure currents in the same experiment. (*L*.)

16. Describe a potentiometer, explaining the principles of its action. Describe briefly how a potentiometer may be used to determine (*a*) the ratio of two electromotive forces (*b*) the ratio of two small resistances. (*C*.)

17. Explain the principle of the potentiometer, and state its advantages for accurate electrical measurements.

How would you use a potentiometer to measure (*a*) the e.m.f. of a thermocouple (about 0·004 volt), (*b*) a current of the order of 100 amperes? Give, in each case, a diagram of the circuit you would employ, and assuming that your potentiometer has a resistance of 4 ohms and is driven by a 2-volt cell of negligible resistance; calculate suitable magnitudes for any components you would require. (*O. & C*.)

18. Calculate the resistivity of mercury if a thread 50 cm. long in a tube of 1 mm. internal diameter has a resistance of 0·61 ohm.

Describe a method suitable for determining the resistivity of mercury supplied in a tube having dimensions of the order of magnitude mentioned. Give reasons for the procedure adopted. (*N*.)

19. Describe the comparison of two resistances using (*a*) a Wheatstone circuit, (*b*) a potentiometer. Proof of formulae are not required, but details of precautions to be taken to obtain an accurate result should be given. What advantages has each method, and for what purposes would each be preferred? (*L*.)

CHAPTER XXXVIII

THE CHEMICAL EFFECT OF THE CURRENT

In this chapter we shall deal both with the effects of an electric current when it is passed through a chemical solution, and with chemical generators of electric current, or cells.

ELECTROLYSIS

The chemical effect of the electric current was first studied quantitatively by Faraday, who introduced most of the technical terms which are now used in describing it. A conducting solution is called an *electrolyte* and the chemical changes which occur when a current passes through it are called *electrolysis* (*lysis* = decomposition). Solutions

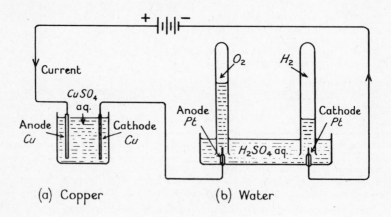

FIG. 676. Voltameters.

in water of acids, bases, and salts are electrolytes, and so are their solutions in some other solvents, such as alcohol. The plates or wires which dip into the electrolyte to connect it to the circuit are called electrodes; the one by which the current enters the solution is called the *anode*, and the one by which it leaves is called the *cathode* (Fig. 676 (*a*)).

The whole arrangement is called a *voltameter*, presumably because it can be used to measure the current delivered by a voltaic cell; if the electrolyte is a solution of a copper or silver salt, the voltameter is called a copper or silver voltameter. If the electrolyte is acidulated

water, then the voltameter is called a water voltameter, because when
a current passes through it, the water, not the acid, is decomposed
(Fig. 676 (b)). We shall see why later.

1. Faraday's Laws of Electrolysis.

When a current is passed through copper sulphate solution with
copper electrodes, copper is deposited on the cathode and lost from the
anode. Faraday showed that the mass dissolved off the anode by a
given current in a given time is equal to the mass deposited on the
cathode. He also showed that the mass is proportional to the product
of the current, and the time for which it flows: that is to say, to the
quantity of electricity which passes through the voltameter. When he
studied the electrolysis of water, he found that the masses of hydrogen
and oxygen, though not equal, were each proportional to the quantity
of electricity that flowed. He therefore put forward his first law of
electrolysis: *the mass of any substance liberated in electrolysis is proportional to the quantity of electricity that liberated it.*

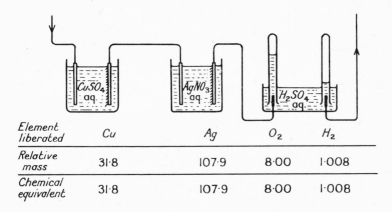

Element liberated	Cu	Ag	O_2	H_2
Relative mass	31·8	107·9	8·00	1·008
Chemical equivalent	31·8	107·9	8·00	1·008

FIG. 677. Voltameters in series (same quantity of electricity
passes through each).

Faraday's second law of electrolysis concerns the masses of different substances liberated by the same quantity of electricity. An
experiment to illustrate it is in Fig. 677. The experiment shows
that *the masses of different substances, liberated in electrolysis by the
same quantity of electricity, are proportional to their chemical equiv-
alents.* This is Faraday's second law; it implies that the same
quantity of electricity is required to liberate the gramme-equivalent
of any substance. Recent measurements give this quantity as
96,500 coulombs; it is called Faraday's constant, or simply one
faraday.

2. Electrochemical Equivalent.

The mass of a substance which is liberated by one coulomb is called its *electrochemical equivalent*, and is expressed in grammes per coulomb. If z is the electrochemical equivalent of a substance, the mass of it liberated by I amperes in t seconds is

$$m = Izt. \qquad \ldots \ldots \ldots \quad (1)$$

Since the chemical equivalent of hydrogen is 1·008 then 1·008 gm. of hydrogen are liberated by 96,500 coulombs, and the electrochemical equivalent of hydrogen is

$$z_H = \frac{1 \cdot 008}{96,500} = 0 \cdot 0000105 \text{ gm./coulomb.}$$

And similarly, since the chemical equivalent of copper is 31·8, its electrochemical equivalent is

$$z_{Cu} = \frac{31 \cdot 8}{96,500} = 0 \cdot 000329.$$

In general, if C is the chemical equivalent of an element, then its electrochemical equivalent is given by

$$z = \frac{C}{96,500} \text{ gm./coulomb.}$$

3. Measurement of Current by Electrolysis.

Until a short time ago the chemical effect of the current was used to define the ampere, because measurements with the current balance (p. 932) could not be made as accurately as simple weighings. (Nowadays they can, and the ampere is defined as on p. 1039.) In those days the ampere was defined as the current which, when flowing steadily,

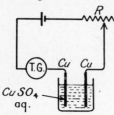

FIG. 678. Current measurement by chemical effect.

would deposit 0·001118 gm. of silver per second. In teaching laboratories, the chemical effect is still used in this way: to find, for example, the reduction factor K of a tangent galvanometer (Fig. 678). A copper voltameter is connected in series with the galvanometer, and a steady current passed for a known time t. The current is kept constant by adjusting the rheostat R to keep the deflection constant. The connexions to the galvanometer are reversed at some point in the experiment to allow for errors in setting (p. 917). The cathode is weighed before and after the experiment. Its increase in mass, m, gives the current I, in terms of the electrochemical equivalent of copper, z:

$$m = Izt,$$

$$I = \frac{m}{zt}. \qquad \ldots \ldots \ldots \quad (2)$$

And if θ is the average deflection of the galvanometer, see p. 916,

$$I = K \tan \theta. \qquad \ldots \ldots \quad (3)$$

From equations (2) and (3), K can be evaluated.

Great care must be taken in this experiment over the cleanliness of the electrodes. They must be cleaned with sandpaper at the start; and, at the finish, the cathode must be rinsed with water and dried with alcohol, or over a gentle spirit flame: strong heating will oxidize the copper deposit.

4. The Mechanism of Conduction; Ions.

The theory of electrolytic conduction is generally attributed to Arrhenius (1859–1927), although Faraday had stated some of its essentials in 1834. Faraday suggested that the current through an electrolyte was carried by charged particles, which he called ions (Greek *ion* = go). A solution of silver nitrate, he supposed, contained silver ions and "nitrate" ions. The silver ions were silver atoms with a

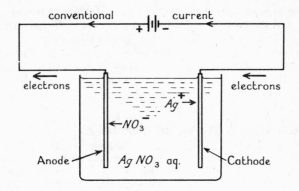

FIG. 679.   Ions in electrolysis.

positive charge; they were positive because silver was deposited at the cathode, or negative electrode (Fig. 679). The nitrate ions were groups of atoms—NO_3 groups—with a negative charge; they travelled towards the anode, or positive electrode, and, when silver electrodes are used, formed silver nitrate.

Nowadays, we consider that a silver ion is a silver atom which has lost an electron; this electron transfers itself to the NO_3 group when the silver nitrate molecule is formed, and gives the nitrate ion its negative charge. We denote nitrate and silver ions, respectively, by the symbols NO_3^- and Ag^+. When the ions appear at the electrodes of a voltameter they are discharged. The current in the external circuit brings electrons to the cathode, and takes them away from the anode (Fig. 679). At the anode silver atoms lose electrons and go into solution as positive ions. *In effect,* the negative charges carried across the cell by the NO_3^- ions flow away through the external circuit. At the cathode, each silver ion gains an electron, and becomes a silver atom, which is deposited upon the electrode.

Ionization.

The splitting up of a compound into ions in solution is called ionization, or ionic dissociation. Faraday does not seem to have paid much attention to how it took place, and the theory of it was given by Arrhenius in 1887. For a reason which we will consider later, Arrhenius suggested that an electrolyte ionized as soon as it was dissolved: that its ions were not produced by the current through it, but were present as such in the solution, before ever the current was passed.

We now consider that salts of strong bases and acids, such as silver nitrate, copper sulphate, sodium chloride, ionize completely as soon as they are dissolved in water. That is to say, a solution contains no molecules of these salts, but only their ions. Such salts are called strong electrolytes; so are the acids and bases from which they are formed, for these also ionize completely when dissolved in water.

Other salts, such as sodium carbonate, do not appear to ionize completely on solution in water. They are the salts of weak acids, and are called weak electrolytes. The weak acids themselves are also incompletely ionized in water.

5. Formation of Ions; Mechanism of Ionization.

In the Heat section of this book we described the structure of the solid state (p. 297). In solid crystalline salts such as sodium chloride the structure is made up of sodium and chlorine ions: not of atoms, nor of NaCl molecules, but of Na^+ and Cl^- ions. In other words, we think today that ions exist in solid crystalline salts, as well as in their solutions. We do so for the reason that the idea enables us to build up a consistent theory of chemical combination, of the solid state, and of electrolytic dissociation.

A sodium atom contains eleven electrons, ten of which move in orbits close to the nucleus, and one of which ranges much more widely; for our present purposes we may represent it as in Fig. 680 (a). A chlorine atom has ten inner electrons and seven outer ones; for our present purposes we may lump these into two groups, as in Fig. 680 (b). The outer electron of the sodium atom is weakly attracted to its nucleus, but the outer electrons of the chlorine atom are strongly attracted (because the ten inner electrons are a more effective shield round the $+11$ nucleus of sodium than round the $+17$ nucleus of chlorine). Therefore, when a sodium and a chlorine atom approach one another, the outer electron of the sodium atom is attracted more strongly by the chlorine nucleus than by the sodium nucleus. It leaves the sodium atom, and joins the outer electrons of the chlorine; the sodium atom becomes a positively charged sodium ion, Fig. 680 (c), and the chlorine atom a negatively charged chlorine ion, Fig. 680 (d). Between these two ions there now appears a strong electrostatic attraction, which holds them together as a molecule of NaCl. In the solid state, the ions are arranged alternately positive and negative; the forces between them bind the whole into a rigid crystal.

When such a crystal is dropped into water, it dissolves and ionizes. We can readily understand this when we remember that water has a very high dielectric constant: 81 (p. 775). It therefore reduces the forces between the ions 81 times, and the crystal falls apart into ions. In the same way we explain the ionization of other salts, and bases and acids. The idea that these dissociate because they are held together by electrostatic forces, which the solvent weakens, is supported

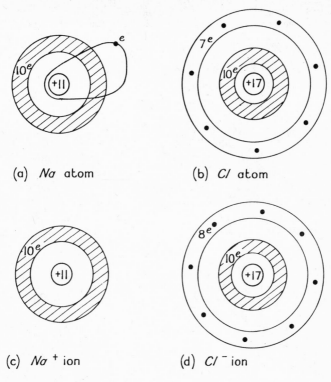

(a) *Na* atom   (b) *Cl* atom

(c) *Na* + ion   (d) *Cl* − ion

FIG. 680.   Sodium and chlorine, atoms and ions.

by the fact that they ionize in some other solvents as well as water. These solvents also are liquids which have a high dielectric constant, such as methyl and ethyl alcohols (32 and 26 respectively). In these liquids, however, it seems that strong electrolytes behave as weak ones do in water: only a fraction of the dissolved molecules, not all of them, dissociate. In the electronic theory of atomic structure, the chemical behaviour of an element is determined by the number of its outer electrons. If it can readily lose one or two it is metallic, and forms positive ions; if it can readily gain one or two, it is acidic, and forms negative ions. Ions are not chemically active in the way that atoms are. Sodium atoms, in the form of a lump of the metal, react violently with water; but the hydroxide which they form ionizes ($NaOH \rightarrow Na^+ + OH^-$), and the sodium ions drift peaceably about in the solution—which is still mainly water.

Pure water is a feeble conductor of electricity, and we consider that it is but feebly ionized into H^+ and OH^- ions. These, we believe, are continually joining up to form water molecules, and then dissociating again in a dynamical equilibrium:

$$H_2O \rightleftharpoons H^+ + OH^-.$$

If, as we shall find in the electrolysis of water, H^+ and OH^- ions are removed from water, then more molecules dissociate, to restore the equilibrium.

The concentrations of H^+ and OH^- in water are so small that they do not contribute appreciably to the conduction of electricity when an electrolyte is dissolved in the water; but, as we shall see, they sometimes take part in reactions at the electrodes.

6. Explanation of Faraday's Laws.

The theory of dissociation neatly explains Faraday's laws and some other phenomena of electrolysis. If an $AgNO_3$ molecule splits up into Ag^+ and NO_3^- ions, then each NO_3^- ion that reaches the anode dissolves one silver atom off it. At the same time, one silver atom is deposited on the cathode. Thus the gain in mass of the cathode is equal to the loss in mass of the anode. Also the total mass of silver nitrate in solution is unchanged; experiment shows that this is true. The mass of silver deposited is proportional to the number of ions reaching the cathode; if all the ions carry the same charge—a reasonable assumption—then the number deposited is proportional to the quantity of electricity which deposits them. This is Faraday's first law.

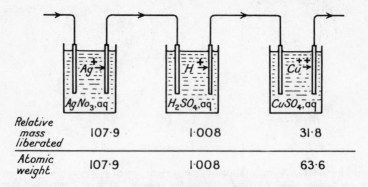

Relative mass liberated	107·9	1·008	31·8
Atomic weight	107·9	1·008	63·6

Fig. 681. Illustrating Faraday's second law.

To see how the ionic theory explains Faraday's second law, let us again consider a number of voltameters in series (Fig. 681). When a current flows through them all, the same quantity of electricity passes through each in a given time. Experiment shows that

$$\frac{\text{mass of silver deposited}}{\text{mass of hydrogen liberated}} = 107{\cdot}0.$$

From experiments on chemical combination, we know that

$$\frac{\text{mass of silver atom}}{\text{mass of hydrogen atom}} = \frac{107 \cdot 9}{1 \cdot 008} = 107 \cdot 0.$$

Therefore we may say that, each time a silver ion is discharged and deposited as an atom, a hydrogen ion is also discharged and becomes an atom. The hydrogen atoms thus formed join up in pairs, and escape as molecules of hydrogen gas. The theory fits the facts, on the simple assumption that the hydrogen and silver atoms carry equal charges: we now say that each is an atom which has lost one electron.

But when we consider the copper voltameter in Fig. 681, we find a complication. For

$$\frac{\text{mass of copper deposited}}{\text{mass of hydrogen liberated}} = \frac{31 \cdot 8}{1 \cdot 008},$$

whereas

$$\frac{\text{mass of copper atom}}{\text{mass of hydrogen atom}} = \frac{63 \cdot 6}{1 \cdot 008}.$$

To explain this result we must suppose that only one copper atom is deposited for every two hydrogen atoms liberated. In terms of the ionic theory, therefore, only one copper ion is discharged for every two hydrogen ions. It follows that a copper ion must have twice as great a charge as a hydrogen ion: it must be an atom which has lost two electrons.

This conclusion fits in with our knowledge of the chemistry of copper. One atom of copper can replace two of hydrogen, as it does, for example, in the formation of copper sulphate, $CuSO_4$, from sulphuric acid, H_2SO_4. We therefore suppose that the sulphate ion also is doubly charged: SO_4^{--}. When sulphuric acid is formed, two hydrogen atoms each lose an electron, and the SO_4 group gains two. When copper sulphate is formed, each copper atom gives up two electrons to an

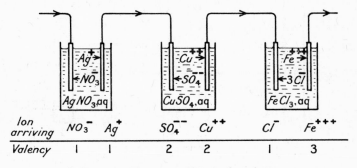

Fig. 682.   Movement of ions in electrolysis.

SO_4 group. And when copper sulphate ionizes, each molecule splits into two doubly charged ions:

$$CuSO_4 \rightarrow Cu^{++} + SO_4^{--}.$$

In general, if we express the charge on an ion in units of the electronic charge, we find that it is equal to the valency of the atom from which the ion was formed. That is to say, it is equal to the number of hydrogen atoms which the atom can combine with or replace. That is illustrated in Fig. 682, explains Faraday's second law (mass deposited $\propto$ chemical equivalent). For if a current I passes through a voltameter for a time t, the total charge carried through it is It. And if q is the charge on an ion, the number of ions liberated is It/q. If M is the mass of an ion, the mass liberated is $M\dfrac{It}{q}$, and is therefore proportional to M/q. But M is virtually equal to the atomic weight, since the mass of an electron is negligible. And q, we have just seen, is equal, in electronic units, to the valency. Therefore the mass liberated is proportional to the ratio of atomic weight to valency, which is the chemical equivalent.

7. Electrolysis of Copper Sulphate Solution.

If copper sulphate solution is electrolysed with platinum or carbon electrodes, copper is deposited on the cathode, but the anode is not dissolved away: instead, oxygen is evolved from it (Fig. 683). The

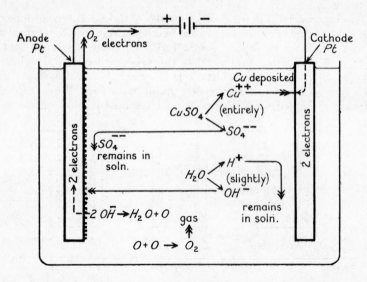

FIG. 683.   Electrolysis of copper sulphate with insoluble electrodes.

SO_4^{--} ions which approach the anode do not attack it: neither carbon nor platinum forms a sulphate, and each is said to be insoluble, in the electrolysis of copper sulphate. As the electrolysis proceeds, the solution becomes paler in colour; chemical tests show that it is gradually losing copper sulphate, but gaining sulphuric acid—Cu^{++} ions are disappearing from the solution, but the SO_4^{--} are remaining in it.

The oxygen which is evolved comes from the water of the solution. We have already seen that water is always slightly ionized, into H^+ and OH^- ions. When copper sulphate is electrolyzed with platinum or carbon electrodes, the OH^- ions of the water are discharged at the anode. Each gives up an electron; they then combine in pairs to give a water molecule and an oxygen atom:

$$2OH^- - 2 \text{ electrons} \rightarrow H_2O + O.$$

The oxygen atoms combine in pairs and come off as molecules:

$$2O \rightarrow O_2\uparrow.$$

As the OH^- ions disappear, an excess of H^+ ions appear in the solution. If the electrolysis were carried to the point where all the copper originally in the solution was deposited on the cathode, the solution would become simply one of sulphuric acid. This would be ionized into H^+ and SO_4^{--} ions, in the proportion two H^+ to one SO_4^{--}.

8. Electrolysis of Water.

When a current is passed through water acidulated with dilute sulphuric acid, and platinum electrodes are used, oxygen and hydrogen are produced at the anode and cathode respectively. The amount of acid in solution remains unaltered, and the net effect is thus the electrolysis of water. The sulphuric acid ionizes into hydrogen and sulphate ions (Fig. 684):

$$H_2SO_4 \rightarrow 2H^+ + SO_4^{--}.$$

The hydrogen ions from the acid greatly outnumber those from the water, but we cannot distinguish between them. All we can say is that, for every SO_4^{--} ion that approaches the anode, two H^+ ions approach the cathode. At the cathode, the H^+ ions collect electrons, join up in pairs, and come off as molecules of hydrogen gas, H_2. At the anode, however, the SO_4^{--} ions remain in solution, and OH^- ions are discharged; as before, they form water and oxygen molecules, and the oxygen comes off as gas.

To produce one molecule of oxygen, four OH^- ions must be discharged:

$$4OH^- \rightarrow 2H_2O + O_2\uparrow + 4 \text{ electrons to circuit.} \quad . \quad . \quad (4)$$

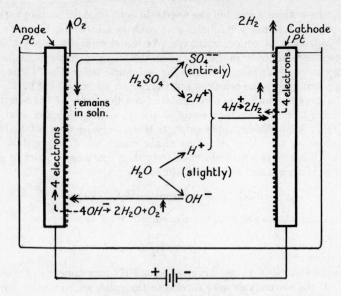

FIG. 684. Electrolysis of water.

And every time four OH⁻ ions are discharged at the anode, four H⁺ ions are discharged at the cathode. (If this were not so, a net positive or negative charge would accumulate in the solution, and we could draw sparks from it.) Thus the reaction is accompanied by

$$4H^+ + 4 \text{ electrons} \rightarrow 2H_2\uparrow \qquad \ldots \quad (5)$$

Equations (4) and (5) agree with the experimental fact that hydrogen and oxygen come off in the proportions in which they are found in water: 2 to 1 by volume. This can be shown by collecting the gases in tubes filled with electrolyte and inverted over the electrodes (Fig. 676 (b)) The electrolysis decomposes the water only, and leaves the acid unchanged. Equal numbers of H⁺ and OH⁻ ions are discharged, and in the solution H⁺ ions remain, in the proportion of two H⁺ to one SO₄⁻⁻.

The only function of the sulphuric acid is to increase the concentration of ions in the solution, and so to enable it to carry a greater current with a given potential difference than would pure water. The greater current discharges H⁺ ions at a greater rate, and so causes the water to dissociate faster into H⁺ and OH⁻. Thus more ions are formed to carry the current.

9. The Electrolytic Condenser.

An electrolytic condenser is one in which the dielectric is formed electrolysis—by a secondary reaction at an insoluble electrode. It is made from two coaxial aluminium tubes, A and K in Fig. 685, with a solution or paste of ammonium borate between them. A current is passed through from A (anode) to K (cathode) and a secondary reaction at A liberates oxygen. The oxygen does not come off as a gas, however, but combines with the aluminium to form a layer of aluminium oxide over the electrode A. This layer is about 1/1000 in. thick, and is an insulator. When the layer has been formed, the whole system can be used as a condenser, one of whose electrodes is the cylinder A, and the other the surface of the liquid or paste adjacent to Λ. Because the dielectric layer is so thin, the capacitance is much greater than that of a paper condenser of the same size.

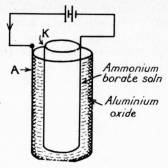

Fig. 685.   Forming an electrolytic condenser.

In the use of an electrolytic condenser, some precautions must be taken. The voltage applied to it must not exceed a value determined by the thickness of the dielectric, and marked on the condenser; otherwise the layer of aluminium oxide will break down (see "dielectric strength", p. 802). And the voltage must always be applied in the same sense as when the layer was being formed. If the plate A is made negative with respect to K, the oxide layer is rapidly dissolved away. Consequently an alternating voltage must never be applied to an electrolytic condenser. This condition limits the usefulness of these condensers.

Electrolytic condensers are not very reliable, because the oxide layer is apt to break down with age. Domestic radio receivers abound in them, but in high-grade apparatus they are avoided.

10. Application of Ohm's Law to Electrolytes.

Fig. 686 (a) shows how the current through an electrolyte, and the potential difference across it, may be measured. If the electrodes are soluble—copper in copper sulphate, for example—then the current is proportional to the potential difference (Fig. 686 (b)). The best results in this experiment are obtained with very small currents. If the current is large, the solution becomes non-uniform: it becomes stronger near the anode, where copper is dissolved by the attack of the SO_4^{--} ions, and weaker near the cathode, where copper is deposited, and SO_4^{--} ions drift away. Near the cathode the solution becomes paler in colour; near the anode it becomes deeper. The total amount of copper sulphate in solution remains constant, but is gradually transferred to the neighbourhood of the anode. As the solution round the cathode becomes weaker, its resistance increases, and more than offsets the decreasing resistance of the solution round the anode; with a given potential difference, therefore, the current gradually falls. A small current makes this effect unimportant, because it makes the electrolysis very slow. But the best way to do the experiment is to use an alternating current; the electrolysis reverses with the current fifty or more times per second, and no changes of concentration build up. Rectifier-type meters (p. 976) are most suitable for measuring the current and potential difference in this case.

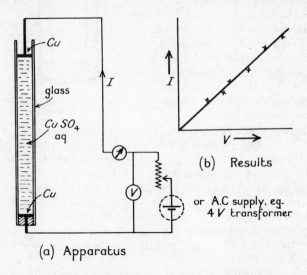

(a) Apparatus

Fig. 686.   Current/Voltage characteristic of electrolyte with soluble electrodes.

When the measurements are properly made they show, as we have said, that the current is proportional to the potential difference: for example, copper sulphate solution, with copper electrodes, obeys Ohm's law. The voltameter behaves as a passive resistor; all the electrical energy delivered to it by the current appears as heat (pp. 823–4); no electrical energy is converted into mechanical or chemical work. In particular, therefore, no electrical energy is used to break up the molecules of copper sulphate into ions. This is the argument which led Arrhenius to suggest that the electrolyte dissociates into ions as soon as it is dissolved; dissociation is a result of solution, not of electrolysis.

1. Measurement of Resistance of Electrolyte.

The resistance of an electrolyte can be measured on a Wheatstone preferably with an alternating current supply (Fig. 687). A

telephone earpiece T is used as the detector, in place of the galvanometer—it gives minimum sound at the balance-point. Fifty-cycle

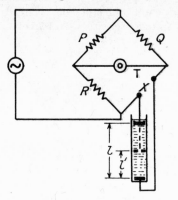

mains give an uncomfortably low-
pitched note for listening, and a
supply of frequency 400 to 1000
cycles per second is more satisfactory. This may be a small induction
coil of a type sold for the purpose,
which has fewer secondary turns
than the common spark-coil, because
a high voltage is not required. By
sliding the upper electrode of the
cell, the resistances of two lengths
of electrolyte, l and l' are measured;
their difference, r, is the resistance
of a length $l-l'$, and is free from

Fig. 687. Measurement of electrolyte resistance.

end-errors. If A is the cross-section
of the tube, then the specific resistance of the electrolyte, ϱ, is given by

$$r = \frac{(l - l')\varrho}{A}.$$

It is usual, however, not to give the resistivity of an electrolyte, but to
give instead its conductivity, σ. This is defined as the reciprocal of its
resistivity, and is expressed in mho per centimetre:

$$\sigma = \frac{1}{\varrho} = \frac{l - l'}{Ar}.$$

12. Electrical Behaviour with Insoluble Electrodes.

If we set out to find the current/voltage
relationship for a water voltameter, using
a d.c. supply, we find that the voltameter
does not obey Ohm's law. If we apply to
it a voltage E less than 1·7 volts, the
current flows only for a short time and
then stops, as though the voltameter were
charged like a condenser. To study the
matter further, we may arrange a two-way
key and a second galvanometer, G, as in
Fig. 688. We first press the key at Y, and
pass a current through the voltameter
until it stops; then we press the key at X,
and connect the galvanometer G straight
across the voltameter. A brief current I

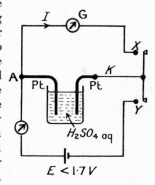

Fig. 688. Demonstrating back-e.m.f. of water voltameter.

flows through G, whose direction shows that the anode of the voltameter is acting as the positive pole of a current supply. It appears, therefore, that the voltameter is setting up a back-e.m.f. which prevents a steady current from flowing, unless the supply voltage is greater than 1·7 volts.

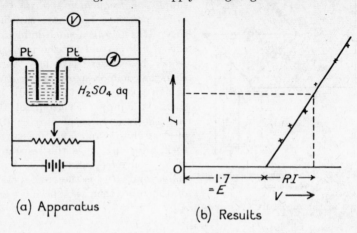

(a) Apparatus

(b) Results

Fig. 689.   Current/Voltage characteristic of water voltameter.

To investigate this behaviour further, let us gradually increase the potential difference across the voltameter, as in Fig. 689 (a). We then find that, if we work with small currents, the current increases linearly with the potential difference V, when the latter is greater than 1·7 volts (Fig. 689 (b)). It follows that the voltameter does indeed exert a back-e.m.f., E, equal to 1·7 volts. If V is the potential difference applied to it, then the current through it obeys the relationship

$$I \propto (V - E).$$

We may write this as

$$I = \frac{V - E}{R},$$

where R is the resistance of the electrolyte.

13. Electrical Energy Consumed in Decomposition.

We have not yet explained the origin of the back-e.m.f. E, but we shall try to do so later. Meanwhile let us notice that the behaviour of the voltameter is somewhat like that of an electric motor. When the armature of a motor rotates, a back-e.m.f. is induced in it, and the current through it is given by an equation similar to that above. The back-e.m.f. in the motor, we shall see, represents the electrical power converted into mechanical work. So here the back-e.m.f. E represents this electrical power converted into chemical work—used in breaking up the water molecules. The potential difference across the voltameter is

$$V = IR + E$$

from the equation for I; the power equation is therefore

$$IV = I^2R + EI.$$

The left-hand term is the electrical power input; the first term on the right is the heat produced per second in the electrolyte; and the second term is the work done per second in decomposing the water.

Chemists tell us that when oxygen and hydrogen combine to form one gramme-molecule of water (18 gm.) then 68,400 calories of heat are evolved. The energy set free is therefore $4 \cdot 19 \times 68,400$ joules. When one gramme-molecule of water is decomposed, this much work must be done. In the process two gramme-atoms of hydrogen are liberated (because the formula for water is H_2O). The quantity of electricity required to decompose one gramme-molecule of water is therefore $2 \times 96,500$ coulombs. If the back-e.m.f. is E, the corresponding amount of energy is $2 \times 96,500 \times E$ joules. Therefore

$$2 \times 96,500 \times E = 4 \cdot 19 \times 68,400,$$

whence
$$E = \frac{4 \cdot 19 \times 68,400}{2 \times 96,500}$$
$$= 1 \cdot 48 \text{ volts.}$$

The lowest value of E which anyone has ever got by experiment is $1 \cdot 67$ volts—from which it appears that we have something yet to learn about what happens in a water voltameter.

CELLS

If we put plates of copper and zinc into a beaker of dilute sulphuric acid, we have a voltaic cell (p. 817). It is often called a simple cell. If we join its plates via a galvanometer, current flows through the galvanometer from the copper to the zinc (Fig. 690); the cell sets up an e.m.f. which acts, in the external circuit, from copper to zinc. Its value is about one volt. The copper plate is at a higher potential than the zinc plate, and is the positive terminal of the cell; the zinc is the negative terminal. Within the cell there must be some agency which carries the current from the zinc to the copper. This is the agency which gives rise to the e.m.f. of the cell; it is analogous to the force exerted by the magnetic field on the moving electrons in the armature winding of a dynamo.

In a voltaic cell, the agency which gives rise to the e.m.f. is not so easy to track down as in a dynamo; there has been much argument about what is called the "seat" of the e.m.f. We may start to seek it by placing a penknife blade into a strong solution of copper sulphate: a pink film of metallic copper is deposited on the blade. It appears, then, that copper ions have a tendency to go out of solution on to iron. In the same way we can show that they tend to go out on to zinc.

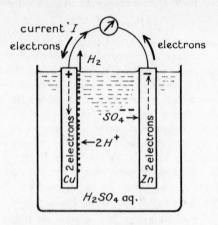

FIG. 690. A simple cell.

Do metal ions ever tend to go the other way—from solid metal into solution? They certainly do if the solution is sulphuric acid and the metal zinc or iron: the metal enters the solution in the form of ions, displaces the hydrogen ions, which are discharged and come off as gas, and turns the solution into one of iron or zinc sulphate. But this happens only if the zinc or iron is impure. Pure zinc in sulphuric acid gives no action at all—no zinc sulphate, no hydrogen.

14. Action in a Simple Cell.

If we want to make pure zinc react with sulphuric acid, we must make it into part of a voltaic cell: we must connect it to a plate of a different metal, such as copper which also dips in the acid. Then the zinc is eaten away, and hydrogen bubbles off; but the hydrogen appears at the copper plate, and not at the zinc (Fig. 690). At the same time the solution becomes one of zinc sulphate—which simply means that it contains zinc ions in place of hydrogen ones. We can now form a picture of what happens when a stick of pure zinc is put alone into dilute sulphuric acid (Fig. 691). At first zinc ions leave the metal, and go into the liquid. But they leave negative charges on the zinc rod, which attract the zinc ions, and prevent any more from leaving. Nothing further happens. But if we introduce a plate of copper, and connect it to the zinc, electrons can flow from the zinc to the copper (Fig. 690). At the copper they can neutralize the charges on hydrogen ions, and to enable molecules to form and come off in bubbles. As the electrons flow away from the zinc, more zinc ions can go into solution, and so the zinc can continuously dissolve in the acid. In doing so, it maintains a continuous electric current in the wire connecting it to the copper. (When the zinc is impure each speck of impurity acts as the other plate of a minute cell, and enables the zinc around it to react with the acid. This "local action", as it is called, makes impure zinc undesirable in voltaic cells, for it consumes the zinc without giving any useful current. It can be prevented by rubbing the zinc with mercury, which dissolves it and presents a surface of pure zinc to the acid. The process is called amalgamating the zinc.)

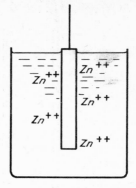

Fig. 691. Pure zinc in dilute sulphuric acid.

To explain the voltaic cell, therefore, we must suppose that zinc ions tend to dissolve from zinc into sulphuric acid, but copper ions do not. This is consistent with the fact that copper does not react chemically with cold dilute sulphuric acid. The passage of ions from metals to solutions, and oppositely, was studied by Nernst about 1889; we shall give a slight account of his theory later.

15. Daniell's Cell.

Fig. 692 shows a cell, developed by Daniell about 1850, which has some advantages over Volta's. Daniell's cell consists of a zinc rod, Zn, in a porous pot, P, containing sulphuric acid; this in turn stands in a strong solution of copper sulphate in a copper vessel, Cu. (Sometimes the copper is just a thin sheet in a glass vessel.) When the copper and zinc are connected by a wire, current flows through the wire from copper to zinc. The copper is therefore the positive terminal of the cell, and the zinc the negative. As in Volta's cell, zinc ions go into solution at the zinc rod, leaving electrons on it. But at the copper plate, copper ions go out of solution—a metallic film of copper is deposited on the vessel. When the zinc and copper are joined by a wire, electrons from the zinc can go along it to the copper vessel, and discharge the copper ions as they reach it. To complete the action of the cell hydrogen ions from the sulphuric acid pass through the porous pot into the copper sulphate solution (Fig. 692). Thus zinc is dissolved, the acid gradually changes to zinc sulphate, the copper sulphate gradually changes to sulphuric acid, and copper is deposited on the copper vessel.

The e.m.f. of a Daniell cell is about 1·08 volts. Its internal resistance depends on its size and condition—the size is usually about that of a plant-pot, and the internal resistance is of the order of several ohms.

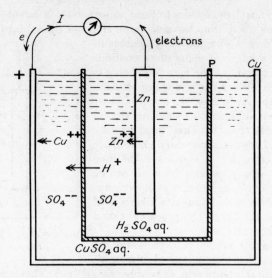

FIG. 692.   A Daniell cell.

16. Polarization.

The great disadvantage of the simple cell is that it does not give a steady current; from the moment of making the circuit, the current starts to fall, and after a minute or two it almost ceases to flow. The current decays because a layer of hydrogen gas forms over the copper

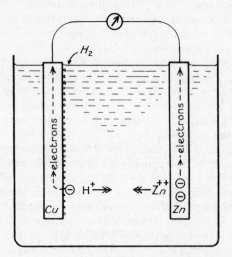

FIG. 693.   Polarization in simple cell.

plate; scraping the plate enables the current to start once more, but it soon decays again. The hydrogen layer increases the internal resistance of the cell, but we do not believe that this is the main reason for the decay of the current. If the copper plate is replaced by one of platinum black (platinum with a finely grained surface), bubbles form on it very easily, and escape readily. The hydrogen layer may then be no more than one molecule thick; but the current decays as before.

To explain this decay of the current we think that the hydrogen layer replaces the copper *as an electrode of the cell*. We suppose that the hydrogen tends to go back into solution as positive hydrogen ions (Fig. 693). In other words, it tends to behave in the same way as the zinc rod, on the other side of the cell, which also goes into solution as positive ions. Thus the hydrogen sets up an e.m.f. which opposes the original e.m.f. of the cell, and cuts down the current; the hydrogen thus sets up a 'back-e.m.f.' in the circuit. This behaviour is called polarization of the cell.

17. Depolarization.

The advantage of Daniell's cell over Volta's is that it does not polarize. Hydrogen ions drift from the acid compartment into the copper sulphate compartment, but they are never discharged, no hydrogen molecules are formed, and no layer of hydrogen appears on the copper electrode. The copper sulphate solution is often called the depolarizer, because it prevents the formation of hydrogen gas.

18. Polarization in Water Voltameter.

We can find support for the idea of polarization in the behaviour of the water voltameter (p. 891). When the potential difference across the voltameter is less than 1·7 volts, the current through it falls to zero in a minute or less. The voltameter itself can then deliver a current for a short time. Its positive terminal, as a source, is that which was its anode, and its negative terminal is that which was its cathode. While current was being sent through the voltameter, the cathode became covered with hydrogen, and the anode with oxygen. When the voltameter acts as a source of current it has, in effect, electrodes of oxygen and hydrogen and the current through the external circuit flows from the oxygen plate to the hydrogen (Fig. 694). In the simple cell, when it is polarized, there is no oxygen plate, but there is a hydrogen one, and this lies over the copper plate. We may therefore suppose that it tends to drive a current, through the external circuit, from zinc to copper; that is to say, it sets up an e.m.f. opposing that of the cell with the copper plate clean.

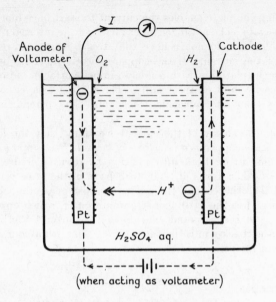

FIG. 694. Polarisation of water voltameter.

19. Nernst's Theory of the Voltaic Cell; Electrode Potentials.

If a metal is in contact with a solution of one of its own salts, it is surrounded by its own ions. Whether the ions deposit themselves on the metal, or the metal goes into solution, depends partly on the particular metal concerned, and partly on the strength of the solution: the stronger the solution the greater its tendency to deposit ions on the metal. If the solution deposits ions, the metal comes to a positive potential with respect to it; if the metal goes into solution as ions, it becomes negative with respect to the solution (Fig. 695 (a)). By methods beyond the scope of this book, the potential difference between a metal and a solution can be measured. These show that copper in normal copper sulphate solution (1 gm.-equivalent weight per litre) becomes 0·08 volt positive with respect to the solution. Zinc in normal zinc sulphate solution becomes 1·03 volts negative. Now let us imagine a Daniell cell in which zinc sulphate replaces the sulphuric acid, and both solutions are normal. If we suppose that the solutions themselves set up no appreciable potential difference at their interface, then we get a potential distribution like that shown in Fig. 695 (a). The difference in potential between the copper and zinc is very nearly equal to the e.m.f. of a Daniell cell: 1·11 volts compared with 1·08. We may attribute the difference to the fact that a Daniell cell in practice has sulphuric acid, not zinc sulphate solution, in contact with the zinc; also the solutions are not normal: the acid is usually 1 to 4 of water, and the copper sulphate is saturated.

These considerations explain a striking experimental fact about all cells: the e.m.f. depends only on the nature and concentration of the constituent chemicals. The size of a cell affects only its internal resistance.

When a current I is drawn from a cell, there is a voltage drop across the internal resistance r, that is to say, across the solution or solutions. This modifies the potential diagram as shown in Fig. 695 (*b*). The terminal voltage V, which is the observed potential difference between the copper and zinc, is now less than its open-circuit value, which is the e.m.f. of the cell.

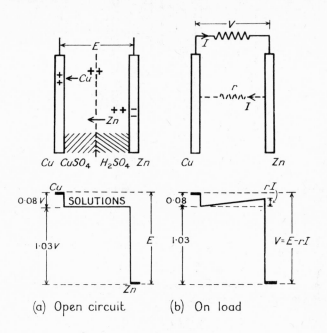

FIG. 695.   Potential differences in voltaic cell.

20. The Leclanché Cell.

Daniell's cell has the great practical disadvantage that it cannot be left set up; the solutions gradually mix by diffusion through the porous pot. It is now used only in teaching laboratories as a simple standard of e.m.f.; its e.m.f. is more nearly constant than that of any other cheap and robust type of cell, and it is remarkably free from polarization.

A practically more useful cell is that devised by Leclanché. Its negative electrode is a zinc rod in a strong solution of ammonium chloride (Fig. 696). Its positive electrode is a carbon plate in a porous pot packed with manganese dioxide, which acts as the depolarizer. Manganese dioxide is a poor conductor of electricity, and powdered carbon is therefore packed in the pot with it.

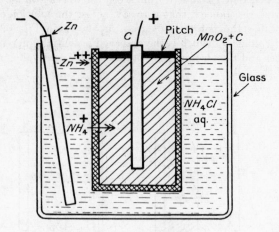

FIG. 696.   Leclanché cell.

The ammonium chloride ionizes into ammonium ions and chlorine ions:

$$NH_4Cl \rightarrow NH_4^+ \text{ and } Cl^-.$$

The zinc goes into solution, as zinc ions, and the ammonium ions drift through the porous pot towards the carbon plate. When a current is drawn from the cell, electrons flow from the zinc to the carbon, and discharge the NH_4^+ ions. The chemical action in this cell is complicated, but may be crudely represented as

$$2NH_4^+ + 2 \text{ electrons} \rightarrow 2NH_3 + H_2.$$

The hydrogen tends to polarize the cell, but is gradually oxidized by the manganese dioxide; again the action is complicated, but it reduces to

$$2MnO_2 + 2H_2O + H_2 \rightarrow 2Mn(OH)_3.$$

The depolarizing action is slow, and a Leclanché cell is therefore not suitable for giving a large current for a long time. A short rest, however, enables the manganese dioxide to remove the hydrogen and restore the e.m.f. of the cell. Thus Leclanché cells are suitable for giving intermittent currents: they are widely used, for example, with electric bells. They are also suitable for Wheatstone bridges, because they cannot give a current large enough to burn out the resistance coils when a wrong connexion is made. The e.m.f. of a Leclanché cell, before polarization sets in, is about 1·5 volts, and its internal resistance about 1 ohm.

21. Dry Cell.

Fig. 697 shows a dry form of Leclanché cell, which has the obvious advantage that it is portable. The ammonium chloride is made into a paste with water, zinc chloride, flour, and gum; and the porous pot is replaced by a muslin bag. A cardboard spacer prevents the bag from touching the zinc and short-circuiting the cell. A dry Leclanché cell has the same e.m.f. as a wet one, but, for a given size, a lower internal resistance, because the thickness of solution between the zinc and carbon is less. It depolarizes better, because the volume of manganese dioxide is greater in relation to the overall size of the cell: the cycle-lamp size will give a useful light continuously for two hours or more.

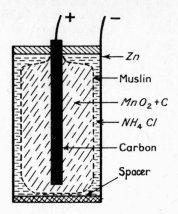

FIG. 697.   A dry cell.

22. Standard Cells.

A standard cell is one whose e.m.f. varies very little with time, and with temperature, so that it can be used as a standard of potential difference in potentiometer experiments. The commonest type is the Weston cadmium cell (Fig. 698). It is housed in an H-shaped glass tube because its electrodes are liquid or semi-liquid. The negative electrode is an amalgam of cadmium in mercury; the solution is of cadmium sulphate; the depolariser is a paste of mercurous sulphate; and the positive electrode is mercury. In some cells, crystals of cadmium sulphate are placed on top of the electrodes to keep the solution saturated. The e.m.f. of one of these, in volts at a temperature $t°C.$, is

$$E = 1 \cdot 01830 - 0 \cdot 0000406 \, (t - 20)$$
$$- 0 \cdot 00000095 \, (t - 20)^2 + 0 \cdot 00000001 \, (t - 20)^3.$$

The e.m.f. of the type without crystals is about $1 \cdot 0186$ volts between $0°C.$ and $40°C.$

A standard cell without crystals of cadmium sulphate is called an unsaturated cell; one with crystals is called a saturated cell, because the crystals keep the solution saturated. Saturated cells give an accurately reproducible e.m.f., because the concentration of the solution is sharply defined at any given temperature. Unsaturated cells do not agree among one another so well, because the solution may vary a little from one to the other. But the e.m.f. of a given unsaturated cell varies less with temperature than that of a saturated cell, because the concentration of the solution is constant.

The depolarizer of a standard cell is effective only for very small currents, and the e.m.f. of the cell will change appreciably if more than about 10 microamperes are drawn from it. *A standard cell must not, in any circumstances, be used as a source of current.* In the early stages of balancing a standard cell against a potentiometer wire, a protective resistance of about 100,000 ohms should be connected in series with the cell.

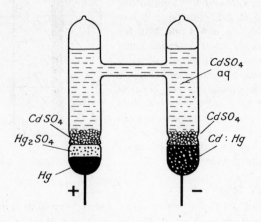

Fig. 698.   A Weston cadmium cell.

23. Primary and Secondary Cells.

The cells which we have so far described are called primary cells. When they are run-down, their active materials must be renewed; the cells cannot be recharged by passing a current through them from another source. A secondary cell is one which can be recharged in this way.

SECONDARY CELLS

24. The Lead Accumulator.

The commonest secondary cell is the lead-acid accumulator. Its active materials are spongy lead, Pb (for the negative plate), lead dioxide, PbO_2 (for the positive plate), and sulphuric acid. The active materials of the plates are supported in grids of hard lead-antimony alloy (Fig. 699 (*a*)). These are assembled in interchanging groups, closely spaced to give a low internal resistance, and often held apart by strips of wood or celluloid (Fig. 699 (*b*)).

When the cell is discharging—giving a current—hydrogen ions drift to the positive plate, and SO_4^{--} ions to the negative. As they give up their charges they attack the plates, and reduce the active materials of each to lead sulphate.

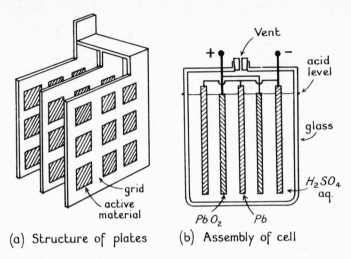

(a) Structure of plates   (b) Assembly of cell

FIG. 699.   Lead-acid accumulator.

At the negative plate the reaction is

$$Pb + SO_4^{--} - 2 \text{ electrons} \rightarrow PbSO_4. \qquad \cdots \quad (6)$$

The chemical action at the positive plate is generally given as

(i) $PbO_2 + 2H^+ + 2 \text{ electrons} \rightarrow PbO + H_2O$;

(ii) $PbO + H_2SO_4 \rightarrow PbSO_4 + H_2O$;

whence, altogether

$$PbO_2 + H_2SO_4 + 2H^+ + 2 \text{ electrons} \rightarrow PbSO_4 + 2H_2O.$$
$$\cdots \quad (7)$$

However, H_2SO_4 molecules do not exist in the solution—they are dissociated into $2H^+$ and SO_4^{--} ions. We may therefore write equation (7) as

$$PbO_2 + SO_4^{--} + 4H^+ + 2 \text{ electrons} \rightarrow PbSO_4 + H_2O.$$
$$\cdots \quad (8)$$

The lead sulphate produced in these reactions is a soft form, which is chemically more active than the hard, insoluble lead sulphate familiar in the general chemistry of lead. In the discharging reactions water is formed and sulphuric acid consumed: the concentration of the acid, and therefore its specific gravity, fall.

25. Charging the Accumulator.

When the cell is to be charged it is connected, in opposition, to a supply of greater e.m.f., via a rheostat and ammeter (Fig. 700). The supply forces a current I through the cell in the opposite direction to

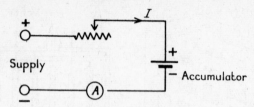

Fig. 700.   Charging an accumulator.

the discharging current, so that hydrogen ions are carried to the negative plate, and SO_4^{--} ions to the positive. The chemical reactions are as follows.

At the negative plate:

$$PbSO_4 + 2H^+ + 2 \text{ electrons} \rightarrow Pb + H_2SO_4. \qquad \text{. .} \quad (9)$$

At the positive plate:

(i) $PbSO_4 + SO_4^{--} - 2 \text{ electrons} \rightarrow PbO_2 + 2SO_3$;

(ii) $2SO_3 + 2H_2O \rightarrow 2H_2SO_4$;

altogether:

$$PbSO_4 + 2H_2O + SO_4^{--} - 2 \text{ electrons} \rightarrow PbO_2 + 2H_2SO_4.$$
$$\text{. . .} \quad (10)$$

The active materials are converted back to lead and lead dioxide, water is consumed, and sulphuric acid is formed. The acid therefore becomes more concentrated during charge, and its specific gravity rises.

26. Properties and Care of the Lead Accumulator.

The e.m.f. of a freshly charged lead accumulator is about 2·2 volts, and the specific gravity of the acid about 1·25. When the cell is being discharged its e.m.f. falls rapidly to about 2 volts, and then becomes steady (Fig. 701); but towards the end of the discharge the e.m.f. begins to fall again. When the terminal voltage load has dropped below about 1·9 volts, or the specific gravity of the acid below about 1·15, the cell should be recharged. If the cell is discharged too far, or left in a discharged condition, hard lead sulphate forms on its plates, and it becomes useless.

The internal resistance of a lead accumulator, like that of any other cell, depends on the area and spacing of its plates. It is much lower than that of any primary cell, however, being usually of the order of

1/10 to 1/100 ohm. The amount of electricity which an accumulator can store is called its *capacity*. It is a vague quantity, but a particular accumulator may give, for example, 4 amperes for 20 hours before needing a recharge. The capacity of this accumulator would be 80 ampere-hours. (One ampere-hour = 3600 coulombs.) If the accumulator were discharged faster—at 8 amperes, say—then it would probably need recharging after rather less than 10 hours; and if it were discharged more slowly—say at 2 amperes—it might hold out for more than 40 hours. The capacity of an accumulator therefore

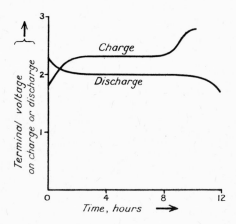

FIG. 701.   Voltage-time curves of lead accumulator.

depends on its rate of discharge; it is usually specified at the "10-hour" or "20-hour" rate. Discharging an accumulator faster than at about the 10-hour rate causes the active material to fall out of the plates.

Accumulators are usually charged at about the "8-hour" rate—say 5 amperes for the cell discussed above. The charging is continued until gas is bubbling freely off the plates. When the plates are gassing, the chemical reactions (9) and (10) have been completed, and the current through the cell is simply decomposing the water in it. Before the charge is started the vent-plugs in the cell-case must be removed to let the gases out; the gases are hydrogen and oxygen and naked lights near are dangerous. The water lost at the end of each charge must be made up by pouring in distilled water until the acid rises to the level marked on the case. If the specific gravity of the acid is then less than 1·25, the charging must be continued. Near the end of the charging, the back-e.m.f. of the cell rises sharply to about 2·6 volts (Fig. 701). It never gives a forward e.m.f. as great as this: as soon as it is put on discharge, its e.m.f. falls to about 2·2 volts.

27. Efficiency of Accumulator.

The number of ampere-hours put into an accumulator on charge is greater than the number which can be got out of it without discharging it too far. The ratio

$$\frac{\text{ampere-hours on discharge}}{\text{ampere-hours on charge}}$$

is called the ampere-hour efficiency of the cell; its value is commonly about 90 per cent. However, to judge an accumulator by its ampere-hour efficiency is to flatter it; not only does it take in more ampere-hours on charge than it gives out on discharge, but it takes them in at a higher voltage. The electrical energy put into an accumulator on charge is the integral of current, e.m.f., and time:

$$W = \int I E \, dt.$$

For simplicity we may say

energy put in = quantity of electricity put in
$$\times \text{ average e.m.f. on charge.}$$

If the quantity of electricity is measured in ampere-hours, the energy is in watt-hours instead of joules. Similarly, on discharge,

energy given out = quantity of electricity given out
$$\times \text{ average e.m.f. on discharge}$$

The energy efficiency of the cell is

$$\frac{\text{energy given out on discharge}}{\text{energy taken in on charge}}$$

$$= \frac{\text{amp.-hours} \times \text{average e.m.f. on discharge}}{\text{amp.-hours} \times \text{average e.m.f. on charge}}$$

$$= \text{amp.-hour efficiency} \times \frac{\text{average e.m.f. on discharge}}{\text{average e.m.f. on charge}}$$

$$\simeq \text{amp.-hour efficiency} \times \frac{2 \cdot 0}{2 \cdot 2}.$$

The energy efficiency is more often called the watt-hour efficiency of the cell; it is about 80 per cent.

28. The Nickel-iron Accumulator.

The nickel-iron (NIFE) accumulator has active materials of nickel hydroxide (positive), iron (negative) and caustic potash solution. Its e.m.f. varies from 1·3 volts to 1·0 on discharge; it has a higher internal resistance than a lead accumulator of similar size; and it is less efficient. Its advantages are that it is more rugged, both mechanically and electrically. Very rapid charging and discharging do not harm it, nor do overdischarging and overcharging. Vibration does not make the active materials fall out of the plates, as it does with a lead cell. Nickel-iron accumulators are therefore used in electric trucks and at sea.

EXAMPLES

1. State Faraday's laws of electrolysis and describe how you would verify them by experiment.

A copper refining cell consists of two parallel copper plate electrodes, 6 cm. apart and 1 metre square, immersed in a copper sulphate solution of resistivity 1·20 ohm/cm. Calculate the potential difference which must be established between the plates to provide a constant current to deposit 480 gm. of copper on the cathode in one hour (e.c.e. of copper = 0·000329 gm./coulomb^{-1}). (*L.*)

First part (see text).

Second part. From $w = zIt$,

$$I = \frac{w}{zt} = \frac{480}{0\cdot000329 \times 3600} \text{ amp.} \quad \ldots \ldots \text{(i)}$$

The resistance of the cell, R, $= \dfrac{\varrho l}{a}$

$$= \frac{1\cdot20 \times 6}{100 \times 100} \text{ ohms.}$$

Hence, from (i), the p.d. $V = IR = \dfrac{480 \times 1\cdot20 \times 6}{0\cdot000329 \times 3600 \times 100 \times 100}$

$$= 0\cdot3 \text{ volt (approx.).}$$

2. State Faraday's laws of electrolysis and show that the ionic dissociation theory offers an explanation of them. Acidulated water is electrolyzed between platinum electrodes. Sketch a graph showing the relation between the strength of the current and the reading of a voltmeter connected to the electrodes. Comment on the nature of the graph.

Give a circuit diagram showing how you would charge a series battery of 12 lead accumulators, each of e.m.f. 2 volts and internal resistance 1/24 ohm, from 240-volt d.c. mains, if the charging current is not to exceed 3 amp. What percentage of the energy taken from the mains would be wasted? (*L.*)

First part (see text). When the water is electrolyzed, no current flows until the p.d. is greater than about 1·7 volts, when the back-e.m.f. of the liberated product is overcome. After this, a straight-line graph is obtained between V and I.

Second part. A series resistance R is required, given by

$$I = 3 = \frac{240 - 12 \times 2}{R + \dfrac{12}{24}}.$$

$$\therefore \ 3R + 1\cdot5 = 216.$$

$$\therefore \ R = \frac{214\cdot5}{3} = 71\cdot5 \text{ ohms.}$$

Energy taken from mains $= EIt = 240 \times 3t = 720t$, where t is the time.

Energy wasted $= (I^2R + I^2r)t = (3^2 \times 71\cdot5 + 3^2 \times 0\cdot5)t$

$$= 648t.$$

$$\therefore \ \text{percentage wasted} = \frac{648t}{720t} \times 100\% = 90\%.$$

3. State Faraday's laws of electrolysis. How would you verify the laws experimentally? Discuss briefly the phenomenon of polarization in electrolysis and how it is overcome in the Daniell cell.

Calculate a value for the e.m.f. of a Daniell cell from energy considerations, using the following data: 1 gm. of zinc dissolved in copper sulphate solution liberates 796 calories (e.c.e. of zinc = 0·000340 gm./coulomb). (*L.*)

First part (see text).

Second part. The e.m.f. *E* of a cell can be defined as the energy per coulomb delivered by the cell (p. 828).

When 1 gm. of zinc is dissolved, no. of coulombs flowing, $Q = \dfrac{1}{0·00034}$.

Energy liberated, $W = 796$ cals. $= 796 \times 4·18$ joules.

$$\therefore \text{ energy liberated per coulomb} = \frac{W}{Q}$$
$$= 796 \times 4·18 \times 0·00034 \text{ joules/coulomb}$$
$$= 1·13 \text{ volts.}$$

EXERCISES XXXVIII

1. State Faraday's laws of electrolysis.

How would you determine the reduction of a tangent galvanometer with the aid of a copper voltameter if the e.c.e. is known?

Given that the e.c.e. of hydrogen is 0·00001038 gm. per coulomb, find the value, in e.m.u. per gm., of the ratio of charge to mass of a hydrogen ion. (*L.*)

2. Describe the electrolytic processes which occur in a Daniell cell when its terminals are joined through a small resistance.

A steady current of 5·0 amp. is passed through a silver voltameter in series with a coil of wire of 10 ohms resistance immersed in 200 gm. of water. What will be the rise of temperature of the latter when 0·10 gm. of silver has been deposited? (Assume that the e.c.e. of silver = 0·001118 gm./coulomb, $J = 4·2 \times 10^7$ ergs/cal.; thermal capacity of the coil and vessel = 10 cal./degree C.) (*L.*)

3. State Faraday's laws of electrolysis. Explain why it is necessary to have a potential greater than about 1·5 volts in order to maintain a large steady current through acidulated water.

In the electrolysis of water 83·7 c.c. of hydrogen were collected at a pressure of 68 cm. of mercury at 25°C. when a current of 0·5 amp. had been passed for 20 minutes. What is the electrochemical equivalent of copper in copper sulphate ($CuSO_4$)? (Atomic weight of copper = 63·57, atomic weight of hydrogen = 1·008, density of hydrogen at S.T.P. = 0·08987 gm./litre.) (*L.*)

4. Describe *one* type of primary cell with which you are acquainted. Explain the functions of its various parts and indicate the origin of the electrical energy.

The readings of a high resistance voltmeter connected to the terminals of a Leclanché cell are (*a*) on an otherwise open circuit, 1·40 volts, (*b*) when a 2-ohm coil is connected across the terminals in parallel with the voltmeter, 1·10 volts, (*c*) on removing the coil after it has been connected for a few minutes, 1·30 volts, (*d*) after another half-hour, 1·40 volts. Explain these readings and calculate the internal resistance of the cell. (*N.*)

5. Describe and explain the action of a Daniell cell and the lead accumulator. Describe some form of standard cell, and explain why it is preferred to the Daniell cell as a standard. (*L.*)

6. Explain the general nature of the chemical changes that take place in a lead accumulator during charging and discharging.

A battery of accumulators, of e.m.f. 50 volts and internal resistance 2 ohms, is charged on a 100-volt direct-current mains. What series resistance will be required to give a charging current of 2 amp.? If the price of electrical energy is 1d. per kilowatt-hour, what will it cost to charge the battery for 8 hours, and what percentage of the energy supplied will be wasted in the form of heat? (C.)

7. State the laws of electrolysis and give a concise account of an elementary theory of electrolysis which is consistent with the laws.

If an electric current passes through a copper voltameter and a water voltameter in series, calculate the volume of hydrogen which will be liberated in the latter, at 25°C. and 78 cm. of mercury pressure, whilst 0·05 gm. of copper is deposited in the former. (Take e.c.e. of hydrogen as 0·0000104 gm. coulomb^{-1}, e.c.e. of copper as 0·00033 gm. coulomb^{-1}, density of hydrogen as 0·0009 gm. cm.$^{-3}$ at S.T.P.) (L.)

8. State Faraday's laws of electrolysis and describe experiments to verify them.

A difference of potential of 60 volts is maintained between two electrodes 12 cm. apart in a solution of common salt. How long will it take a chlorine ion to travel 3 cm. in the solution? (The mobility of chlorine ions may be taken as 0·00053 cm./sec. per volt/cm.) (L.)

9. Explain what happens when an e.m.f. is applied to platinum electrodes immersed in dilute sulphuric acid. What is the relation between the e.m.f. and the current in such a cell?

If the electrochemical equivalent of hydrogen is 1·04 × 10^{-5} gm. coulomb, and if 1 gm. of hydrogen on burning to form water liberates 35,000 calories, calculate the back-e.m.f. produced in a water voltameter when it is connected to a 2-volt accumulator. (C.)

10. State the laws of electrolysis. In an experiment to find the electrochemical equivalent of copper using a voltameter containing copper sulphate and a tangent galvanometer with n turns, a steady deflection of 60° was maintained for 45 min. and the deposit obtained was 0·522 gm. If H_0 at the galvanometer was 0·19 oersted and the mean radius of the turns in the galvanometer coil was 9·0 cm., calculate the value of n. The electrochemical equivalent of silver may be taken as 0·001118 gm. per coulomb and the atomic weights of silver and copper as 108 and 63·6 respectively.

Give your opinion on the accuracy of the experiment, in view of the deflection, 60°, in the tangent galvanometer. (L.)

11. Define *electrical conductivity*. Describe briefly, with the aid of a labelled diagram, a bridge method for determining the conductivity of an aqueous solution of copper sulphate.

An accumulator has eight positive plates interleaved with nine negative plates, the distance between adjacent plates being 0·40 cm. Each plate is 15 cm. long and 12 cm. wide. The internal resistance of the cell is 0·0015 ohm. Assuming the resistance of the plates to be negligible, obtain a value for the conductivity of the electrolyte. (L.)

CHAPTER XXXIX

ELECTROMAGNETISM

1. Oersted's Discovery.

The magnetic effect of the electric current was discovered by Oersted in 1820. Like many others, Oersted suspected a relationship between electricity and magnetism, and was deliberately looking for it. In the

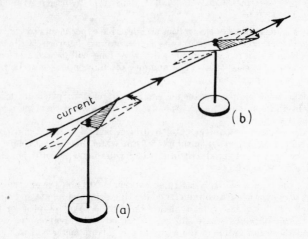

FIG. 702. Deflection of compass-needle by electric current.

course of his experiments, he happened to lead a wire carrying a current over, but parallel to, a compass-needle, as shown in Fig. 702 (a); the needle was deflected. Oersted then found that if the wire was led under the needle, it was deflected in the opposite sense (Fig. 702 (b)). From these observations he concluded that "the electric conflict performs gyrations". What he meant by this we can see by plotting the lines of force of a long vertical wire, as shown in Fig. 703. To get a clear result a strong current is needed, and we must work close to the wire, so that the effect of the earth's field is negligible. It is then seen that the lines of force are circles, concentric with the wire.

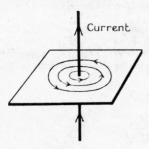

FIG. 703. Magnetic field of long straight current.

2. Directions of Current and Field; Corkscrew Rule.

The relationship between the direction of the lines of force and of the current is expressed in Maxwell's corkscrew rule: if we imagine ourselves driving a corkscrew in the direction of the current, then the direction of rotation of the corkscrew is the direction of the lines of force. Fig. 704 illustrates this rule, the small, heavy circle representing the wire, and the large light one a line of force. At (a) the current is flowing into the paper; its direction is indicated by a cross, which stands for the tail of a retreating arrow. At (b) the current is flowing out of the paper; the dot in the centre of the wire stands for the point of an approaching arrow.

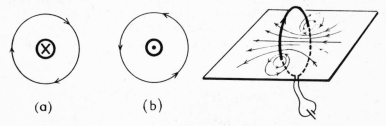

(a)   (b)

FIG. 704. Illustrating corkscrew rule.   FIG. 705. Magnetic field of narrow coil.

If we plot the magnetic field of a circular coil carrying a current, we get the result shown in Fig. 705. Near the circumference of the coil, the lines of force are closed loops, which are not circular, but whose directions are still given by the corkscrew rule, as in Fig. 704. Near the centre of the coil, the lines are almost straight and parallel. Their direction here is again given by the corkscrew rule, but the current and the lines of force are interchanged: if we turn the screw in the direction of the current, then it travels in the direction of the lines.

3. The Solenoid.

The same is true of the magnetic field of a long cylindrical coil, shown in Fig. 706. Such a coil is called a solenoid; it has a field similar to that of a bar-magnet, whose poles are indicated in the figure. If an iron or steel core were put into the coil, it would become magnetized, with the polarity shown.

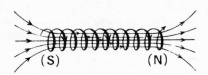

(S)   (N)

FIG. 706.   Magnetic field of solenoid.

If the terminals of a battery are joined by a wire which is simply doubled back on itself, as in Fig. 707, there is no magnetic field at all: each element of the outward run, such as AB, in effect cancels the field of the corresponding element of the inward run, CD. But as soon as

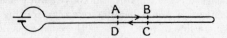

FIG. 707. A doubled-back current has no magnetic field.

the wire is opened out into a loop, its magnetic field appears (Fig. 708). Within the loop, the field is strong, because all the elements of the loop give magnetic fields in the same sense, as we can see by applying the corkscrew rule to each side of the square ABCD. Outside the loop, for example at the point P, corresponding elements of the loop give

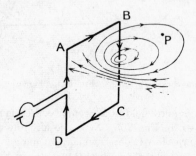

FIG. 708. An open loop of current has magnetic field.

opposing fields (for example, DA opposes BC); but these elements are at different distances from P (DA is farther away than BC). Thus there is a resultant field at P, but it is weak compared with the field inside the loop.

4. Magnetic Needle at Centre of Circular Coil.

When an electric current flows round a circular coil, it sets up a magnetic field which, near the centre of the coil, is almost uniform, and is at right angles to the plane of the coil (Fig. 705, p. 911). Let us suppose that we set up such a coil, with its plane vertical, and pointing north and south, that is, in the magnetic meridian (Fig. 709 (a)). The field due to the current, at the centre of the coil, is now at right angles to the earth's field. If we now suspend a compass-needle at the centre of the coil, the field of the coil will tend to deflect it east–west. The horizontal component of the earth's field, H_0, will tend to deflect it north–south, and so the needle will take up a position at some angle θ

to the meridian (Fig. 709 (*b*)). The angle θ is given by the condition for equilibrium of the needle: that the couples exerted on it by the two fields must be equal and opposite. If the needle is short compared with the radius of the coil, then the field of the coil in its neighbourhood will

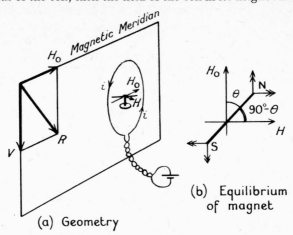

(b) Equilibrium of magnet

(a) Geometry

Fig. 709.   Flat coil in magnetic meridian.

be nearly uniform; let us denote its strength by H. The angle between the needle and the field H is $(90° - \theta)$, and the couple on it due to this field is therefore

$$MH \sin (90° - \theta) = MH \cos \theta,$$

where M is the magnetic moment of the needle. For equilibrium, therefore,

$$MH \cos \theta = MH_0 \sin \theta;$$

whence $H = H_0 \tan \theta.$ . . . . (1)

Equation (1) shows that, if we know the earth's horizontal component H_0, we can measure the field at the centre of the coil, H, by observing the deflection of the needle. We do not need to know the magnetic moment of the needle, and we can measure H_0 by a method which we have described in Chapter XXXIII.

5. Magnetic Field at the Centre of a Circular Coil.

By the method indicated above, we can find how the dimensions of a coil affect its magnetic field, when it carries a given current. We require a large vertical wooden board, which carries concentric circles of pegs, and at whose centre a deflection magnetometer can be placed (Fig. 710). We take about thirty feet of insulated copper wire, and connect them across an accumulator. Then we wrap the whole of the

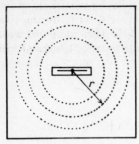

wire—apart from the ends going to the accumulator—round one of the circles of pegs. We measure the radius r of the coil, and the deflection θ of the needle. We do this with each circle of pegs in turn, always wrapping the whole of the wire round the circle; thus we make our measurements with coils of different radii, but all containing the same total length of wire.

FIG. 710. Board for studying field of flat coil.

Equation (1) shows that the field at the centre of the coil, H, is proportional to tan θ, and we find from the experiment that

$$\tan \theta \propto \frac{1}{r^2}.$$

Therefore

$$H \propto \frac{1}{r^2}. \qquad \ldots \ldots \ldots \quad (2)$$

To find how the length of wire in the coil affects its field, we keep the radius constant, and wind on different lengths. (We must fold up the surplus wire to make its magnetic field negligible; if we cut it away, the current would change.) We then find that the field at the centre is proportional to the length of wire in the coil, l:

$$H \propto l. \qquad \ldots \ldots \ldots \quad (3)$$

Relations (2) and (3) together give

$$H \propto \frac{l}{r^2}. \qquad \ldots \ldots \ldots \quad (4)$$

6. Electromagnetic Unit of Current. The Ampere.

The strength of a current, i, is taken as proportional to the magnetic field intensity, H, it creates. Thus $H \propto i$. Hence if i is the current in the circular coil, the field intensity H at the centre is given, with equation (4), by

$$H \propto \frac{il}{r^2},$$

$$\therefore H = k \frac{il}{r^2}, \qquad \ldots \ldots \ldots \quad (5)$$

where k is a constant.

The electromagnetic unit (e.m.u.), or absolute unit, of current is a unit based on the magnetic field created, and is defined as follows:

The electromagnetic unit of current is that current which, when flowing in one centimetre arc of a circle of radius one centimetre, sets up at the centre a field-strength of one oersted. Thus in (5) we have $H = 1$ when $i = 1$, $l = 1$, and $r = 1$. Substituting,

$$\therefore \; 1 = k \times \frac{1 \times 1}{1^2}, \quad \text{or} \quad k = 1.$$

It can hence be stated that

$$H = \frac{il}{r^2} \text{ oersted,} \qquad \ldots \ldots \quad (6)$$

when i is in e.m.u., and l, r are in centimetres.

The e.m.u. of current is rather large; in practice, therefore, a smaller unit, the ampere, is used. By definition,

$$1 \text{ amp.} = \frac{1}{10} \text{ e.m.u. of current.}$$

Thus $\qquad\qquad I \text{ amp.} = \dfrac{I}{10} \text{ e.m.u.}$

The relationship between the e.m.u. of current and the ampere is identical with that between centimetres and millimetres. The electromagnetic unit is also known as the "absolute unit", or "abampere".

6A. Other Electromagnetic or Absolute Units.

(1) The e.m.u. of *quantity* of electricity is the quantity passing a given point in a wire in 1 second when the current flowing is 1 e.m.u. Thus:

$$1 \text{ coulomb} = \frac{1}{10} \text{ e.m.u. of quantity.}$$

(2) The e.m.u. of *p.d.* is the p.d. between two points when 1 erg is expended in taking 1 e.m.u. of charge between the points. Thus:

$$1 \text{ volt} = \frac{1 \text{ joule}}{1 \text{ coulomb}} = \frac{10^7 \text{ ergs}}{\frac{1}{10} \text{ e.m.u.}} = 10^8 \text{ ergs/e.m.u.}$$

$$\therefore \; 1 \text{ volt} = 10^8 \text{ e.m.u. of p.d.}$$

(3) The e.m.u. of *resistance* is the resistance of a wire when the p.d. is 1 e.m.u., and the current flowing is 1 e.m.u. Thus:

$$1 \text{ ohm} = \frac{1 \text{ volt}}{1 \text{ amp.}} = \frac{10^8 \text{ e.m.u.}}{\frac{1}{10} \text{ e.m.u.}}$$

$$\therefore \; 1 \text{ ohm} = 10^9 \text{ e.m.u. of resistance.}$$

7. Circular Coil; Tangent Galvanometer.

If a narrow circular coil of wire has n turns, of radius r, the length of wire in it is $2\pi rn$. A current i through the coil therefore sets up a magnetic field at its centre given by equation (6):

$$H = \frac{il}{r^2}$$

$$= \frac{2\pi rni}{r^2}$$

$$= \frac{2\pi ni}{r}. \qquad \ldots \ldots \quad (7)$$

A coil like this was used in an early form of current-measuring instrument, the tangent galvanometer. The coil was set in the magnetic meridian, and a small magnet was suspended at its centre. The unknown current i was passed through the coil, and the deflection θ of the magnet measured. The current was then given by equation

$$H = H_0 \tan \theta,$$

where H_0 is the horizontal component of the earth's magnetic field. See p. 913. Then by equation (7):

$$\frac{2\pi ni}{r} = H_0 \tan \theta,$$

whence
$$i = \frac{rH_0}{2\pi n} \tan \theta. \qquad \ldots \ldots \quad (8)$$

If the current is in amperes, I, the field at the centre of the coil, H, is, since this is $I/10$ e.m.u.,

$$H = \frac{2\pi nI}{10r} = H_0 \tan \theta,$$

$$\therefore \ I = \frac{10rH_0}{2\pi n} \tan \theta, \qquad \ldots \ldots \quad (9)$$

$$\therefore \ I = K \tan \theta, \qquad \ldots \ldots \quad (10)$$

where $K \ (= 10rH_0/2\pi n)$ is known as the *reduction factor* of the galvanometer. K is not a constant as it involves H_0, which varies from place to place and from day to day.

The tangent galvanometer is never used as a measuring instrument nowadays. It should be noted, however, from (8) that it provides a means of measuring a current i absolutely; that is, without reference to any other instrument, assuming the earth's horizontal component is known.

8. Instrument Details.

The magnet of a tangent galvanometer is made short, so that it is always in the region of nearly uniform field near the centre of the coil. It is fitted with a long aluminium pointer, P'P'' in Fig. 711 (a), which moves over the divided circle C. The case carrying the circle and magnet A rests on a support S, and is set so that the 90° marks on the circle lie in the plane of the coil. The pointers are then over the zeros when the coil is in the magnetic meridian (Fig. 711 (b)). The coil can be set in the meridian only if its plane is vertical; its base therefore carries three levelling screws, L, and a spirit-level should be used.

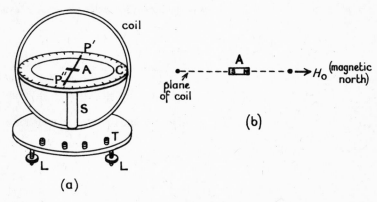

FIG. 711.   Tangent galvanometer.

If we have to measure a current with the tangent galvanometer, we first level it and set the coil and divided circle as just described. We then pass the current through the coil, and read both pointers, P'P''. They may read different angles, θ' and θ'', because the pivot may not be at the centre of the divided circle. The deflection is the average of θ' and θ''; let us denote it by θ_1.

If the conditions of the experiment permit us to interrupt the current for a moment, we next reverse the connexions to the coil. The needle then deflects in the opposite sense, and the pointers read θ''' and θ''''. The average of these readings, θ_2, may not be equal to the previous average, θ_1; if it is not, the difference is due to the coil not being exactly in the magnetic meridian. If the difference between θ_1 and θ_2 is large, we must reset the coil; if not, we may take their average, θ, to be the deflection corresponding to the current.

Most tangent galvanometers are provided with several coils having different numbers of turns, N. These are connected to terminals, T in Fig. 711 (a). For accurate work the coil used should be chosen so as to make the deflection as near to 45° as possible (see p. 918). If the deflection is less than about 30° it cannot be read accurately; if it is greater than about 60° its tangent varies so rapidly with the angle that it, the tangent, cannot be determined accurately.

An accurate measurement is one in which the *percentage* error is small. If the error in reading θ is $\delta\theta$, the percentage error in the current is given by

$$\frac{\tan(\theta + \delta\theta) - \tan\theta}{\tan\theta} \times 100\%.$$

On converting tan to sin/cos and simplifying, the tangent expression becomes

$$\frac{\sin\delta\theta}{\sin\theta \cdot \cos\theta} = \frac{2\sin\delta\theta}{\sin 2\theta} = \frac{2\delta\theta}{\sin 2\theta},$$

when $\delta\theta$ is small and measured in radians. Thus the percentage error is least when $2\theta = 90°$, or $\theta = 45°$.

9. Resistance of Tangent Galvanometer.

The resistance G of a tangent galvanometer can be deduced by connecting an accumulator and a box of known resistances, R, in series with it. Several values, θ, of the deflection, corresponding to different values of R, are observed.

If E is the accumulator e.m.f., then, neglecting its internal resistance, the current flowing is

$$I = \frac{E}{R + G} = K\tan\theta,$$

$$\therefore R + G = \frac{E}{K} \cdot \frac{I}{\tan\theta} = \frac{E}{K}\cot\theta. \quad . \quad . \quad . \quad . \quad (11)$$

From this relation it follows that a straight-line graph is obtained when cot θ is plotted against R. Also, when cot $\theta = 0$, $R + G = 0$ or $R = -G$. Thus the galvanometer resistance G is the negative intercept on the R-axis when the straight-line graph is produced to cut it.

10. Measurement of H_0.

The horizontal component, H_0, of the earth's field can be measured by placing a *copper voltameter* in series with the galvanometer, a rheostat, and a battery. The deflection θ is kept constant at a suitable value, between 40° and 50°, and a current is passed for twenty minutes.

If w is the weight of copper deposited on the cathode, z is the electrochemical equivalent, and t is the time, then, from p. 880,

$$w = zIt.$$

But
$$I = \frac{10rH_0}{2\pi n}\tan\theta,$$

$$\therefore H_0 = \frac{2\pi nI}{10r}\cot\theta = \frac{2\pi nw}{10rzt}\cot\theta. \quad . \quad . \quad . \quad (12)$$

From this formula H_0 can be calculated.

11. Moving-magnet Galvanometers.

A moving-magnet galvanometer is one in which a pivoted or suspended magnet is deflected by the magnetic field of a fixed coil. A
tangent galvanometer is one such instrument, but the name is generally
kept for more sensitive types. Greater sensitivity is obtained by
making the coil only just large enough to allow the magnet to swing,
as in Fig. 712 (a). The field in which the magnet moves is then far from
uniform, and the relationship between current and deflection is complicated. However, the instrument is a sensitive detector of small
currents, and is not damaged by heavy overloads. These properties
make it very useful in bridge circuits, which we have described in a
previous chapter.

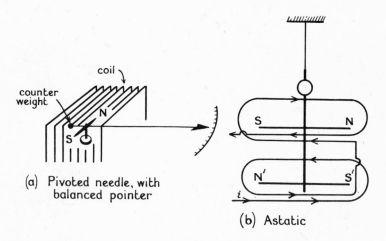

FIG. 712.   Moving-magnet galvanometers.

Fig. 712 (b) shows the principle of a very sensitive form of moving-
magnet galvanometer. It has two magnetic needles, NS, N'S', whose
moments are as nearly equal as they can be made. These magnets are
arranged in opposition. When the system is deflected, the couples on
each magnet, due to the earth's field, are in opposition. The resultant
restoring couple, for a given deflection, is therefore weak. But the coils
are wound round the magnets in opposite senses, so that the couples due
to the current add. The current needed to give a noticeable deflection
is then very small. A galvanometer of this kind is called an *astatic
galvanometer*, and its needles an astatic pair.

Moving-magnet galvanometers have the drawback that they must
be set, with the plane of their coils at least roughly in the magnetic
meridian. They are also disturbed by external magnetic fields.

12. Ampère's or Laplace's Law.

A general expression for the magnetic intensity δH at a point P due to a small element δl of a conductor carrying a current i was given by Ampère and Laplace. This stated:

$$\delta H \propto \frac{i \cdot \delta l \sin \alpha}{r^2}, \qquad \ldots \ldots \quad (13)$$

where r is the distance from the point P to the element, and α is the angle between the element and the line joining it to P (Fig. 713). The formula in (13) cannot be proved directly, as we cannot experiment with an infinitesimally small conductor. We believe in its truth because the deductions for large practical conductors turn out to be true.

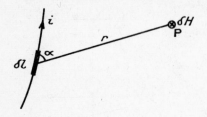   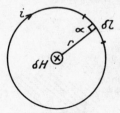

FIG. 713. Laplace's formula.   FIG. 714. Field of circular coil.

The formula for the intensity H at the centre of a narrow circular coil can be immediately deduced from Ampère's law. Here the radius r is constant for all the elements δl, and the angle α is constant and equal to 90° (Fig. 714). If the coil has n turns, the length of wire in it is $2\pi rn$ cm., and the field at its centre is therefore given, if i is in e.m.u., by

$$H = \int dH = \int_0^{2\pi rn} \frac{i dl \sin 90°}{r^2}$$

$$= \frac{i}{r^2} \int_0^{2\pi rn} dl = \frac{i}{r^2} 2\pi rn$$

$$= \frac{2\pi ni}{r}. \qquad \ldots \ldots \ldots \quad (14)$$

If the current is I amperes, then

$$H = \frac{2\pi nI}{10r}. \qquad \ldots \ldots \ldots \quad (15)$$

13. Field due to Long Straight Wire.

We now deduce the intensity at a point outside a long straight wire.

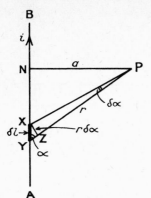

FIG. 715. Field of a long, straight wire.

In Fig. 715, AB represents part of a long straight wire. P is taken as a point so near it that, from P, the wire looks infinitely long—it subtends very nearly 180°. An element XY of this wire, of length δl, makes an angle α with the radius vector, r, from P. It therefore contributes to the magnetic field at P an amount

$$\delta H = \frac{i\delta l \sin \alpha}{r^2}, \quad \ldots \quad \text{(i)}$$

when the wire carries a current of i e.m.u. If a is the perpendicular distance, PN, from P to the wire, then

$$PN = PX \sin \alpha$$

or
$$a = r \sin \alpha,$$

whence
$$r = \frac{a}{\sin \alpha}. \qquad \ldots \ldots \quad \text{(ii)}$$

Also, if we draw XZ perpendicular to PY, we have

$$XZ = XY \sin \alpha$$
$$= \delta l \sin \alpha.$$

And, if δl subtends an angle $\delta\alpha$ at P, then

$$XZ = r\delta\alpha,$$

whence
$$r\delta\alpha = \delta l \sin \alpha.$$

Therefore, from equation (i),

$$\delta H = \frac{i\delta l \sin \alpha}{r^2} = \frac{ir\delta\alpha}{r^2}$$

$$= \frac{i\delta\alpha}{r};$$

whence by equation (ii)

$$\delta H = \frac{i \sin \alpha\delta\alpha}{a}.$$

When the point Y is at the bottom end A of the wire, $\alpha = 0$; and when

Y is at the top B of the wire, $a = \pi$. Therefore the total magnetic field at P is

$$H = \int_{0}^{\pi} \frac{i \sin a \, da}{a}$$

$$= \frac{i}{a} \int_{0}^{\pi} \sin a \, da$$

$$= \frac{i}{a} \Big[-\cos a \Big]_{0}^{\pi}$$

$$= \frac{2i}{a}. \qquad \ldots \ldots \ldots \quad (16)$$

If the current is I amperes, then

$$H = \frac{2I}{10a}. \qquad \ldots \ldots \ldots \quad (17)$$

Equations (16) and (17) show that the magnetic field of a long straight wire, at a point near to it, is inversely proportional to the distance of the point from the wire. This result was discovered experimentally by Biot and Savart, and led Laplace to the general formula in (13) which we have used to derive it.

14. Biot and Savart's Experiment.

In their experiment Biot and Savart measured the intensity outside a long straight wire by means of a vibration magnetometer. With a vertical wire carrying a constant downward current I, the magnetic needle was placed at different distances r due west of the wire and the number of oscillations per minute, n, were observed. The current was switched off, and the number per minute, n_0, in the earth's field H_0 alone were counted.

Due west of the wire, the total field is $(H + H_0)$, where H is that due to the current alone. Thus $H \propto (n^2 - n_0^2)$, as explained on p. 743. When $(n^2 - n_0^2)$ is plotted against $1/r$, a straight line passing through the origin is obtained, thus verifying that $H \propto 1/r$ for a long, straight, current-carrying conductor.

15. Field along Axis of a Narrow Circular Coil.

We will now find the magnetic field at a point anywhere on the axis of a narrow circular coil (P in Fig. 716). We consider an element δl of the coil, at right angles to the plane of the paper. This sets up a field δH at P, in the plane of the paper, and at right angles to the radius vector r. If β is the angle between r and the axis of the coil, then the field δH has components $\delta H \sin \beta$ along the axis, and $\delta H \cos \beta$ at right angles to the axis. If we now consider the element $\delta l'$ diametrically opposite to δl, we see that it sets up a field $\delta H'$ equal in magnitude to δH.

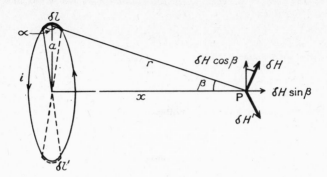

FIG. 716.   Field on axis of flat coil.

This also has a component, $\delta H'\cos\beta$, at right angles to the axis; but this component acts in the opposite direction to $\delta H\cos\beta$ and therefore cancels it. By considering elements such as δl and $\delta l'$ all round the circumference of the coil, we see that the field at P can have no component at right angles to the axis. Its value along the axis is

$$H = \int dH \sin\beta.$$

From Fig. 716, we see that the length of the radius vector r is the same for all points on the circumference of the coil, and that the angle a is also constant, being $90°$. Thus, if the coil has a single turn, and carries a current i e.m.u.,

$$\delta H = \frac{i\,\delta l \sin a}{r^2} = \frac{i}{r^2}\,\delta l.$$

And, if the coil has a radius a, then

$$H = \int dH \sin\beta = \int_0^{2\pi a} \frac{i}{r^2}\,dl \sin\beta$$
$$= \frac{2\pi i a \cdot \sin\beta}{r^2}.\qquad\qquad \dots\dots\dots\text{(i)}$$

When the coil has more than one turn, the distance r varies slightly from one turn to the next. But if the width of the coil is small compared with all its other dimensions, we may neglect it, and write ,

$$H = \frac{2\pi n i a \sin\beta}{r^2},\qquad\qquad \dots\dots\dots\text{(ii)}$$

where n is the number of turns.

Equation (i) can be put into a variety of forms, by using the facts that

$$\sin\beta = \frac{a}{r},$$

and

$$r^2 = x^2 + a^2,$$

where x is the distance from P to the centre of the coil. Thus

$$H = \frac{2\pi i a^2}{r^3} = \frac{2Ai}{(x^2 + a^2)^{3/2}},\qquad\qquad \dots\dots\text{(18)}$$

where A is the area of the coil. When the distance x is large compared with a, equation (18) reduces to

$$H = \frac{2Ai}{x^3}. \qquad \ldots \ldots \ldots \ldots \text{(19)}$$

If the current is I amperes, then

$$H = \frac{2AI}{10x^3}.$$

16. Field on Axis of a Long Solenoid.

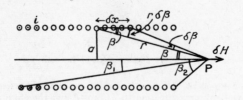

Fig. 717.   Field on axis of solenoid.

We may regard a solenoid as a long succession of narrow coils; if it has n turns per centimetre, then in an element δx of it there are $n\,\delta x$ coils (Fig. 717). At a point P on the axis of the solenoid, the field due to these is, by equation (ii),

$$\delta H = \frac{2\pi i a \sin \beta}{r^2}\, n\,\delta x,$$

in the notation which we have used for the flat coil. If the element δx subtends an angle $\delta\beta$ at P, then, from the figure,

$$r\,\delta\beta = \delta x \sin \beta;$$

whence

$$\delta x = \frac{r\,\delta\beta}{\sin \beta}.$$

Also,

$$a = r \sin \beta.$$

Thus

$$\delta H = \frac{2\pi i r \sin^2 \beta}{r^2}\, n\, \frac{r\,\delta\beta}{\sin \beta}.$$

$$= 2\pi i n \sin \beta\,\delta\beta.$$

If the radii of the coil, at its ends, subtend the angles β_1 and β_2 at P, then the field at P is

$$H = \int_{\beta_1}^{\beta_2} 2\pi n i \sin \beta d\beta$$

$$= 2\pi n i \left[-\cos \beta \right]_{\beta_1}^{\beta_2},$$

$$= 2\pi n i (\cos \beta_1 - \cos \beta_2). \qquad \ldots \ldots \text{(20)}$$

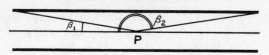

FIG. 718. A very long solenoid.

If the point P is inside a very long solenoid—so long that we may regard it as infinite—then $\beta_1 = 0$ and $\beta_2 = \pi$, as shown in Fig. 718. Then, by equation (20):

$$H = 2\pi n i \left[-\cos \beta \right]_0^\pi,$$

whence $$H = 4\pi n i \qquad \ldots \ldots \quad (21)$$

or $$H = \frac{4\pi n I}{10}, \qquad \ldots \ldots \quad (22)$$

where I is the current in amperes. The quantity nI is often called the ampere-turns per centimetre.

17. Very Long Solenoid or Toroid.

Equation (21) shows that the field along the axis of an infinite solenoid is constant: it depends only on the number of turns per centimetre, and the current. By methods beyond the scope of this book, it can also be shown that the field is the same at points not on the axis. An infinite solenoid therefore gives us a means of producing a uniform magnetic field.

In practice, solenoids cannot be made infinitely long. But if the length of a solenoid is about ten times its diameter, the field near its middle is fairly uniform, and of the strength given by equation (21).

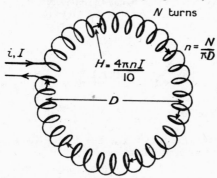

FIG. 719. A toroid.

A form of coil which gives a very nearly uniform field is shown in Fig. 719. It is a solenoid wound on a circular support instead of a straight one, and is called a toroid. If its average diameter D is several times its core diameter d, then the turns of wire are almost equally spaced around its inside and outside circumferences; their number per centimetre is therefore

$$n = \frac{N}{\pi D}, \qquad \cdots \cdots \quad (23)$$

where N is the total number of turns.

The magnetic field within a toroid is very nearly uniform, because the coil has no ends. The coil is equivalent to an infinitely long solenoid, and the field-strength at all points within it is given by

$$H = 4\pi ni = \frac{4\pi nI}{10}. \qquad \cdots \cdots \quad (24)$$

EXAMPLES

1. Describe the deflection magnetometer and explain how you would use it to find how the magnetic field-strength due to a current flowing in a long straight wire varies with distance from the wire.

Two long straight vertical wires separated by a distance of 12 cm. in the magnetic east–west plane carry a current of 7 amp. in opposite directions which are such that neutral points are produced at a perpendicular distance of 8 cm. from the plane of the wires. Find the horizontal component of the earth's magnetic field. (*L.*)

First part. In brief, place the wire parallel to and just above the magnetometer needle, and observe the deflection θ for different distances r. Plot $\tan\theta$ ($\propto H$) against $1/r$, when a straight line passing through the origin is obtained.

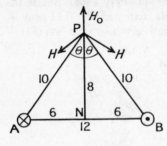

FIG. 720. Example.

Second part. Suppose A is a section of one wire carrying a downward current, and B that of the other wire (Fig. 720). If P is the neutral point, the intensity H due to A is perpendicular to the line AP and acts in the direction shown. Thus if θ = angle APN, where PN is perpendicular to AB,

component of H along PN = $H \sin\theta$.

But $H = \dfrac{2I}{10r} = \dfrac{2 \times 7}{10 \times 10}$, since AP = 10 cm.

$\therefore$ component $= \dfrac{2 \times 7}{10 \times 10} \times \dfrac{6}{10} = 0.084$ oersted.

Similarly, the field intensity due to B at P = $H = 2I/10r$, and component along PN = $H \sin\theta = 0.084$ oersted from above.

$$\therefore \ H_0 = 0.084 + 0.084 = 0.168 \text{ oersted.}$$

2. How does the magnetic field at the centre of a plane circular coil due to a current flowing in it depend on (*a*) the radius of the coil, (*b*) the number of turns in the coil, (*c*) the strength of the current? How would you test *one* of these connexions by experiment?

One winding of a tangent galvanometer has 5 turns with a total resistance of 1 ohm. A second separate winding of the same radius consists of 25 turns of the same wire. The instrument is set up in the usual way and joined directly to a cell; the deflection is 20° when the 5-turn winding is used and 40° when the 25 winding is used. What is the internal resistance of the cell? (*C.*)

First part. The intensity is inversely proportional to the radius, directly proportional to the number of turns and current.

Second part. Let r = internal resistance in ohms, E = e.m.f. of cell.

Then
$$I = \frac{E}{1 + r} = k \tan 20° = \frac{10rH_0}{2\pi n} \tan 20°, \quad \cdots \cdots \text{(i)}$$

and
$$I = \frac{E}{5 + r} = k \tan 40° = \frac{10rH_0}{2\pi n_1} \tan 40°, \quad \cdots \cdots \text{(ii)}$$

since the 25 turns (n_1) has 5 times the resistance of 5 turns (n).

Dividing (i) by (ii),

$$\therefore \frac{5 + r}{1 + r} = \frac{n_1}{n} \frac{\tan 20°}{\tan 40°} = \frac{25 \tan 20°}{5 \tan 40°} = \frac{5 \tan 20°}{\tan 40°}$$

$$\therefore (5 + r) \tan 40° = 5(1 + r) \tan 20°$$

$$\therefore r = \frac{5(\tan 40° - \tan 20°)}{5 \tan 20° - \tan 40°}.$$

$$= 2 \cdot 4 \text{ ohm.}$$

EXERCISES XXXIX

1. Give an expression for the intensity of the magnetic field, and state its direction, at any point distant r from an element of a conductor of length dl carrying a current i. Use the expression to find the intensity at the centre of a circular coil of n turns of radius a.

Describe the structure and mode of use of a current-measuring instrument employing such a coil. (*L.*)

2. Explain, without deducing a formula, how the period of oscillation of a magnet in a magnetic field depends on the field-strength and on the magnetic moment. Upon what other quantity does it depend?

The coil of a tangent galvanometer is placed at right angles to the earth's horizontal magnetic field, H_0. The magnetic needle of the galvanometer lies, as usual, at the centre of the coil. When a current of 1 ampere is passed through the coil so that its magnetic field is in the direction of H_0 the needle is observed to oscillate twice as frequently as when the current was absent. Find the reduction factor of the galvanometer. (*L.*)

3. Define the absolute electromagnetic unit of current and also the practical unit.

Describe how you would determine the value of the horizontal component of the earth's magnetic intensity with the aid of a tangent galvanometer and a copper voltameter.

A tangent galvanometer is set with the plane of the coil parallel to the magnetic meridian. A short bar-magnet is placed so as to lie along the axis of the coil perpendicular to its plane and 30 cm. from its centre, and a current of such magnitude and direction is sent through the coil as to result in zero deflection of the needle. On removing the bar-magnet and turning the plane of the coil through 50°, the needle points E. and W. Calculate the magnetic moment of the magnet, assuming that the horizontal component of the earth's magnetic field is 0·18 oersted. (*N.*)

4. How would you show, without using a galvanometer or ammeter, that the amount of a particular substance deposited during electrolysis is directly proportional to the quantity of electricity which passes?

A current from a battery passes through a copper voltameter in series with a tangent galvanometer of 5 turns of diameter 25 cm. If the deflection of the tangent galvanometer is maintained at 60°, how long will it take for 0·10 gm. of copper to be deposited? Draw a labelled diagram which gives as much information as possible. (Electrochemical equivalent of copper = $3·3 \times 10^{-4}$ gm./coulomb^{-1}.) (*L.*)

5. What kind of magnetic field is produced by a straight wire carrying a current? How would you investigate the variation of the strength of the field with the distance from the wire? Sketch the distribution of the lines of force in a plane perpendicular to two parallel wires carrying current, (*a*) when the direction of the current is the same in both, (*b*) when it is opposite. (*C.*)

6. A vibration magnetometer is set up at the centre of a galvanometer coil which is in the magnetic meridian and is of radius 16 cm. and contains 8 turns. When a current of 1·0 ampere is sent through the coil the magnet deflects through 55°. If the vibration magnetometer makes 20 vibrations in 80 secs. when in the earth's field alone, how many vibrations per sec. will occur when the galvanometer coil is turned so that its axis is in the meridian and a steady current of 0·5 amp. is sent in turn in each direction through the coil? (*L.*)

7. How would you find the resistance of a tangent galvanometer, given a cell of constant e.m.f. and negligible resistance and a known variable resistance?

An accumulator, a tangent galvanometer, and a copper voltameter are connected in series. It is found that in 1 hour a layer of copper 0·010 mm. thick is deposited uniformly over an area of 100 sq. cm. of the cathode, the deflection of the galvanometer remaining steady at 30°. What will be the deflection if a current of 1 ampere is passed through the galvanometer? (The e.c.e. of copper is 0·00033 gm. per coulomb; the specific gravity of copper is 7·8.) (*N.*)

8. How is the unit of current defined on the electromagnetic system of units? Describe, and give the theory of, some method of determining the strength of a current in these units.

A flat circular coil of 2 turns of wire of radius 10 cm. carries a current of 0·8 amp., and is placed with its plane vertical and its axis in the magnetic meridian. A small magnetic needle at its centre makes 10 vibrations per min. when the current passes in one direction and 17·32 per min. when the current is reversed in the coil; the needle continuing to point in the same direction. Calculate the value of the earth's horizontal field. (*O. & C.*)

9. Describe the magnetic field due to current flowing down a long vertical wire. Describe and explain how you would use a deflection magnetometer to find how the intensity of the field varies with distance from the wire. How would you plot your observations and what results would you expect?

Two long vertical wires, A and B, 15 cm. apart, carry downward currents of strength i_1 and i_2 respectively. A is to the magnetic N. of B. A horizontal magnet 6 cm. long, pivoted at its centre, is placed with its pivot 10 cm. from A and 5 cm. from B. If the magnet is not deflected from the magnetic meridian, what is the ratio i_1/i_2?

Draw a map of the field due to the currents in A and B, pointing out any special feature. (*L.*)

10. Give the reasons for the various adjustments and readings which are desirable when setting up and using a tangent galvanometer for the measurement of current. How would you find (*a*) the resistance, (*b*) the sensitivity of a tangent galvanometer when the deflection is 45°? (*L.*)

CHAPTER XL

FORCE ON CURRENT-CARRYING CONDUCTOR

1. Force on Conductor. Fleming's Rule.

When a conductor carrying a current is placed in a magnetic field due to some source other than itself, it experiences a mechanical force. To demonstrate this, a short brass rod R is connected across a pair of brass rails, as shown in Fig. 721. A horseshoe magnet is placed so that

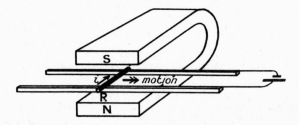

FIG. 721. Force on current in magnetic field.

the rod lies in the field between its poles. When we pass a current through the rod, from an accumulator, the rod rolls along the rails.

The relative directions of the current, the applied field, and the motion are shown in Fig. 722; they are the same as those of the middle finger, the fore-finger, and the thumb of the left hand when held all at right angles to one another. If we place the horseshoe magnet so that its field lies along the rod carrying the current, then the rod experiences no force.

Experiments like this were first made

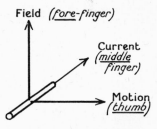

FIG. 722. Left-hand rule.

by Ampère in 1820. As a result of them, he concluded that the force on a conductor is always *at right angles to the plane which contains both the conductor and the direction of the field in which it is placed.* He also showed that, if the conductor makes an angle a with the field, the force on it is proportional to sin a, so that the maximum force is exerted when the conductor is perpendicular to the field.

These results illustrate Newton's third law of motion: action and reaction are equal and opposite. We have seen already that a current-carrying conductor sets up a magnetic field, H_i in Fig. 723; it therefore exerts a force f on a pole m in that field. The pole must exert an equal and opposite force on the conductor. But the pole sets up a magnetic field, H_m, and we may therefore say that the force on the conductor is due to its being situated in the field H_m.

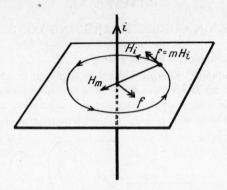

Fig. 723. Action and reaction of pole and current in straight wire.

2. Calculation of Force.

We can use the idea of action and reaction to calculate the force on a current-carrying conductor in a given field. In Fig. 724, δl is an element of a conductor carrying a current i, and m is a north magnetic

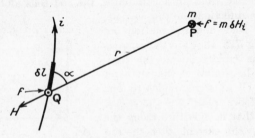

Fig. 724. Calculation of force.

pole. At the point P occupied by the pole, the current sets up a magnetic field δH_i, whose strength is

$$\delta H_i = \frac{i\delta l \sin a}{r^2},$$

in the usual notation (p. 920). The force on the pole acts into the page, and is given by

$$f = m\delta H_i = \frac{mi\delta l \sin a}{r^2}. \qquad \ldots \ldots \quad (1)$$

An equal force acts on the element δl, but out of the page. At the point Q, where the radius vector r meets the element δl, the magnetic pole sets up a field of strength

$$H_m = \frac{m}{r^2}.$$

This field acts along the radius vector r, making the angle a with the conductor. Therefore we may express the force on the conductor, given by equation (1), as

$$f = H_m i \delta l \sin a.$$

The subscript m is necessary here only to distinguish the field of the pole from that of the current; in general, if a current element $i\delta l$ makes an angle a with a magnetic field H, then it experiences a force f, whose direction is given by Fig. 724 and whose magnitude is

$$f = Hi\delta l \sin a \text{ dynes.} \quad \ldots \ldots \quad (2)$$

If I is the current in amperes, then

$$f = \frac{HI\delta l \sin a}{10} \text{ dynes.}$$

Equation (2) is due to Ampère. It contains, as we shall see, the principle of motors and of modern measuring instruments; a simple application of it, in the moving-coil loudspeaker, is described on p. 612.

3. Forces between Currents.

Ampère derived his formula by carrying out experiments on the forces of attraction and repulsion between two current-carrying conductors. Each was acted on by the field of the other, as shown in Fig. 725. Currents flowing in the same direction ("like" currents) attracted each other, Fig. 725 (a), while "unlike" currents (in opposite directions) repelled each other, Fig. 725 (b). This difference from the laws governing poles and charges greatly impressed Ampère.

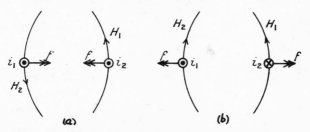

FIG. 725.   Forces between currents.

If two long straight conductors lie parallel and close together at a distance r cm. apart, and carry currents I, I' amp. respectively, then the current I is in a magnetic field of intensity $2I'/10r$ due to the current I' (p. 922). The force per centimetre length f is hence given by

$$f = \frac{IHl}{10} = \frac{IH \times 1}{10} = \frac{I \times 2I' \times 1}{10 \times 10r}.$$

$$\therefore f = \frac{2II'}{100r} \text{ dynes per cm.} \qquad \dots \dots \dots \quad (3)$$

Precise methods of measuring current depend on the forces between currents. In one apparatus a coil C is suspended from the beam of a balance, between two fixed coils A and B (Fig. 726). By flexible leads, the current to be measured is passed through all the coils, in such directions that A repels C but B attracts it. The total force on C is

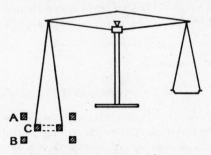

FIG. 726.   Principle of current balance.

measured by the balance; from the force, and the geometry of the coils, the current is then calculated. The instrument is called an *ampere-balance*, and a refined type is used at the National Physical Laboratory for very accurate measurement of current.

4. The Moving-coil Galvanometer.

The ampere-balance is not suitable for everyday measurements of current—its use takes much trouble and time. All except the most accurate of current measurements are made today with the moving-coil galvanometer. In this instrument a coil of fine insulated copper wire, ABDF in Fig. 727 (a), hangs in a strong magnetic field. The field is set up between soft iron pole-pieces, NS, attached to a permanent magnet, R.

The pole-pieces are curved to form parts of a cylinder coaxial with the suspension of the coil. And between them lies a cylindrical core of soft iron, C; it is supported on a brass pin, T in Fig. 727 (b), which is placed so that it does not foul the coil. As this figure shows, the magnetic field H is radial to the core and pole-pieces, over the region in which the coil can swing.

In the more sensitive instruments, the coil is suspended on a phos-phor-bronze wire, WW, which is kept taut by a spring, Z. The current is led into and out of the coil through the suspension, at X and Y, **and** the deflection of the coil is shown by a mirror, M. This is known as a *mirror galvanometer*. More robust but less sensitive forms of the galvanometer have hair-springs and jewelled bearings, instead of the

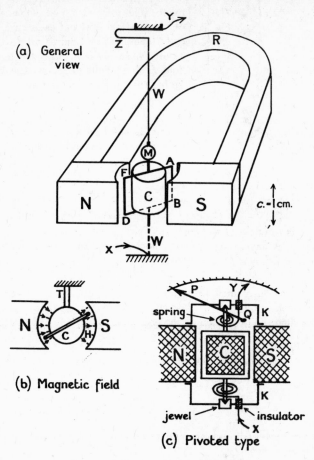

(a) General view

(b) Magnetic field

(c) Pivoted type

Fig. 727.   Moving-coil galvanometers.

phosphor-bronze suspension (Fig. 727 (c)). The coil is wound on a rigid but light former, of bamboo or aluminium, which also carries the pivots. The pivots are insulated from the former if it is aluminium, and the current is led in and out through the springs. The framework, which carries the springs and jewels, KK in the figure, is made from brass or aluminium—if it were steel it would affect the magnetic field. An aluminium pointer, P, shows the deflection of the coil; it is balanced by a counterweight, Q.

5. Theory of Moving-coil Instrument.

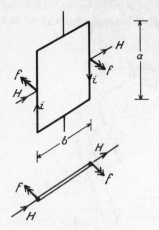

Fig. 728 shows a current i flowing through the coil of a moving-coil instrument. The magnetic field exerts forces f on the vertical limbs of each turn of the coil. These forces tend to rotate the coil about the suspension. Since the magnetic field H is at right angles to the vertical limbs, the forces are given by

$$f = Hil,$$

where l is the height of the coil; f acts at right angles to its plane because the magnetic field is radial. Therefore, if b is the width of the coil, the couple which the forces f exert on each turn is:

$$C = fb = Hilb = HiA,$$

Fig. 728. Couple on coil in radial field.

where A is the area of the coil.

If the coil has n turns, then the total couple which the current exerts on it is

$$C' = nC = HiAn. \qquad \ldots \ldots \quad (4)$$

The coil will turn until the restoring couple due to the twist in the suspension is equal to C'. This couple is proportional to the twist θ, which is also the deflection of the coil; thus

$$C' = k\theta,$$

where k is a constant of the suspension. Hence

$$HiAn = k\theta$$

or
$$i = \frac{k}{HAn} \theta. \qquad \ldots \ldots \ldots \quad (5)$$

If I is the current in amperes, then

$$I = \frac{10k}{HAn} \theta. \qquad \ldots \ldots \ldots \quad (5a)$$

Equation (5) shows that the deflection is proportional to the current. The pointer type of instrument (Fig. 727 (c)) usually has a scale calibrated directly in milliamperes or microamperes. Full-scale reading on such an instrument corresponds to a deflection θ of 90° to 120°; it may represent a current of 50 microamperes to 15 milliamperes, according to the strength of the hair-springs, the geometry of the coil, and the strength of the magnetic field. The less sensitive models are more accurate, because their pivots and springs are more robust, and therefore are less affected by dust, vibration, and hard use. Models known as "first grade" (FG) have an error not greater than one per cent. of full-scale deflection. This error is constant over the scale, so that the inaccuracy may be ten per cent. when the reading is one-tenth of full scale. Readings less than about half full scale must therefore be avoided in accurate work. The best moving-coil instruments have an error of about 0·2 per cent. of full-scale deflection. They are called sub-standard instruments, because their accuracy lies between that of everyday meters and that of elaborate standardizing apparatus such as the potentiometer (p. 851).

When a galvanometer is of the suspended-coil type (Fig. 727 (a)), its sensitivity is generally expressed in terms of the displacement of the spot of light reflected from the mirror on to the scale. At a scale distance of 1 metre a moderately sensitive instrument of this type will give a deflection of 100 cm. per microampere.

All forms of moving-coil galvanometer, have one disadvantage: they are easily damaged by overload. A current much greater than that which the instrument is intended to measure will burn out its hair-springs or suspension.

6. Couple on a Coil in a Uniform Field.

So far we have considered a coil in a radial magnetic field. Now let us consider one in a uniform field. Fig. 729 shows a rectangular coil of one turn, whose plane makes an angle a with a uniform magnetic field H. If it carries a current i e.m.u., the forces f_1 on its vertical limbs are given by

$$f_1 = Hil = Hia,$$

where a is the height of the coil. And the forces f_2 on its horizontal limbs are given by

$$f_2 = Hib \sin a,$$

where b is the width of the coil. The forces f_2 merely compress the coil, and are resisted by its rigidity. The forces f_1 set up a couple, whose moment is, from the lower figure,

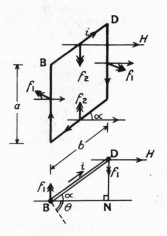

FIG. 729. Couple on coil in uniform field.

$$C = f_1 \times BN$$
$$= f_1 b \cos a.$$

Hence
$$C = Hiab \cos a$$
$$= HiA \cos a, \qquad \ldots \ldots \ldots \quad (6)$$

where A is the area of the coil. If θ is the angle between the field and the normal to the plane of the coil, then $\theta = 90° - \alpha$, and

$$C = HiA \sin \theta. \qquad \qquad \cdots \cdots (7)$$

Equation (7) reminds us of the equation for the couple on a permanent magnet in a magnetic field:

$$C = MH \sin \theta.$$

Here M is the moment of the magnet (equation (4), p. 732) whose axis makes the angle θ with the field H. Thus we see that a coil of area A, carrying a current i, is equivalent to a magnet of moment iA. See also p. 924. Equation (6) shows why a radial field, and not a uniform field, is used in a moving-coil instrument. In a radial field the couple on the coil is given by

$$C = HiA;$$

it is independent of the angle α which the coil makes with the field. In a uniform field the couple varies with α; as the coil turns, the couple on it changes, and the deflection is therefore not proportional to the current.

7. Force on a Moving Electron.

We regard an electric current in a wire as a procession of electrons, in the opposite direction to the conventional current. We must therefore regard the force on a current-carrying conductor as due to forces on the moving electrons in it. If the electrons in the wire drift with a velocity v, and the wire lies at right angles to the field, then the force on each electron is

$$f_e = Hev, \qquad \cdots \cdots \cdots \cdots (8)$$

where e is the electronic charge in e.m.u. The direction of the force, relative to the directions of H and v, is given in Fig. 730.

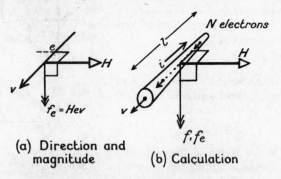

(a) Direction and magnitude

(b) Calculation

Fig. 730. Force on moving electron in magnetic field
(v at right angles to page).

The proof of equation (8) is easily obtained. If there are N free electrons in a wire of length l, their total charge is Ne. If they have a drift velocity v, the time which any one of them takes to travel the distance l is

$$t = \frac{l}{v}.$$

In this time, therefore, the N electrons are swept out of the wire by the current and are replaced by another N electrons. The rate at which charge flows along the wire, which is the current through it, is therefore

$$i = \frac{Ne}{t} = \frac{Nev}{l} \text{ e.m.u.}$$

If the wire is at right angles to a magnetic field H, the force on it is

$$f = Hli = HNev.$$

Therefore the force on a single electron is

$$f_e = \frac{f}{N} = Hev.$$

An electron moving across a magnetic field experiences a force whether it is in a wire or not—for example, it may be one of a beam of electrons in a vacuum tube. Because of this force, a magnetic field can be used to focus or deflect an electron beam, instead of an electrostatic field as on p. 1011. Magnetic deflection and focusing are common in cathode-ray tubes used for television.

8. The Ballistic Galvanometer.

Ballistics is the study of the motion of a body, such as a projectile, which is set off by a blow, and then allowed to move freely. By freely, we mean without friction. A ballistic galvanometer is one used to measure an electrical blow, or impulse: for example, the charge Q which circulates when a condenser is discharged through it. A galvanometer which is intended to be used ballistically has a heavier coil than one which is not; and it has as little damping as possible—an insulating former, no short-circuited turns, no shunt. The mass of its coil makes it swing slowly; in the example above, for instance, the condenser has discharged, and the charge has finished circulating, while the galvanometer coil is just beginning to turn. The galvanometer coil continues to turn, however; and as it does so it twists the suspension. The coil stops turning when its kinetic energy, which it gained from the forces set up by the current, has been converted into potential energy of the suspending fibre. The coil then swings back, as the suspension untwists itself, and it continues to swing back and forth for some time. Eventually it comes to rest, but only because of the damping due to the viscosity of the air, and to the internal friction of the fibre. Theory shows that, if the damping is negligible, *the first deflection of the galvanometer is proportional to the quantity of electricity, Q, that passed through its coil, as it began to move.* This first deflection, θ, is often called the "throw" of the galvanometer; we have, then,

$$Q = k\theta, \qquad \ldots \ldots \ldots \quad (9)$$

where k is a constant of the galvanometer.

Equation (9) is true only if all the energy given to the coil is spent in twisting the suspension. If an appreciable amount of energy is used to overcome damping—i.e. dissipated as heat by eddy currents—then the galvanometer is not ballistic, and θ is not proportional to Q.

To calibrate the ballistic galvanometer, a condenser of known capacitance, e.g. $2\ \mu\mathrm{F}$, is charged by a battery of known e.m.f., e.g. 50 volts, and then discharged through the instrument. See p. 798. Suppose the deflection is 200 divisions. The charge $Q = CV = 100$ micro-coulombs, and thus the galvanometer sensitivity is 2 divisions per micro-coulomb.

9. The Wattmeter.

The wattmeter is an instrument for measuring electrical power. In construction and appearance it resembles a moving-coil voltmeter or ammeter, but it has no permanent magnet. Instead it has two fixed coils, FF in Fig. 731; these set up the magnetic field in which the suspended coil, M, moves. When the instrument is in use, the coils FF are connected in series with the device X whose power consumption is to be measured. The magnetic field H, set up by FF, is then proportional to the current I drawn by X:

$$H \propto I.$$

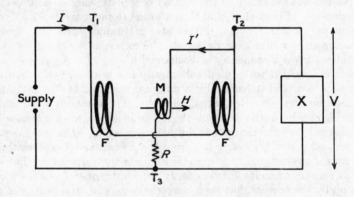

FIG. 731.   Principle of wattmeter.

The moving coil M is connected across the device X. In series with M is a high resistance R, similar to the multiplier of a voltmeter; M is, indeed, often called the volt-coil. The current I' through the volt-coil is small compared with the main current I, and is proportional to the potential difference V across the device X:

$$I' \propto V.$$

The couple acting on the moving coil is proportional to the current through it, and to the magnetic field in which it is placed:

$$C \propto HI'.$$

Consequently $C \propto IV.$

That is to say, the couple on the coil is proportional to the product of the current through the device X, and the voltage across it. The couple is therefore proportional to the power consumed by X, and the power can be measured by the deflection of the coil.

The diagram shows that, because the volt-coil draws current, the current through the fixed coils is a little greater than the current through X. As a rule, the error arising from this is negligible; if not, it can be allowed for as when a voltmeter and ammeter are used separately.

EXAMPLE

Describe the structure and explain the action of a moving-coil galvanometer. Obtain an expression for its steady current sensitivity.

A rectangular coil of 100 turns of mean area 4 cm.² is hung with its plane vertical, in a horizontal, uniform magnetic field of 500 oersteds. The plane of the coil is parallel to the field when there is no twist in the suspension. The coil is deflected through 60° when a steady current of 1 milliampere passes through it. Calculate the torsion couple exerted by the suspension per radian twist. (L.)

First part (see p. 932). The current sensitivity = deflection per unit current = $nAH/10k$ (p. 934).

Second part. With the usual notation,

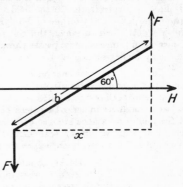

FIG. 732.   Example.

moment of
$$\text{couple} = F \times x = F \times b \cos 60°$$
$$\text{(Fig. 732)}$$

$$= \frac{nIHl}{10} \times b \cos 60°$$

$$= \frac{nAHI}{10} \cos 60° \text{ dyne-cm.}$$

$$= \frac{100 \times 4 \times 500 \times 1}{1000 \times 10 \times 2}$$

$$= 10 \text{ dyne-cm.} = \text{torsion couple.}$$

Also, $60° = \dfrac{\pi}{3}$ radians.

$$\therefore \text{ torsion couple per radian} = 10 \div \frac{\pi}{3} = \frac{30}{\pi} = 10.$$

EXERCISES XL·

1. Describe an experiment to show that a force is exerted on a conductor carrying a current when it is placed in a magnetic field. Give a diagram showing the directions of the current, the field, and the force.

A rectangular coil of 50 turns hangs vertically in a uniform magnetic field of 100 oersteds, so that the plane of the coil is parallel to the field. The mean height of the coil is 5 cm. and its mean width 2 cm. Calculate the strength of the current that must pass through the coil in order to deflect it 30° if the torsional constant of the suspension is 0·01 dyne-cm. per degree.

Give a labelled diagram of a moving-coil galvanometer. (*L.*)

2. Describe a moving-coil type of galvanometer and deduce a relation between its deflection and the steady current passing through it.

A galvanometer, with a scale divided into 150 equal divisions, has a current sensitivity of 10 divisions per milliampere and a voltage sensitivity of 2 divisions per millivolt. How can the instrument be adapted to serve (*a*) as an ammeter reading to 6 amp., (*b*) as a voltmeter in which each division represents 1 volt? (*L.*)

3. State the law of force acting on a conductor carrying an electric current in a magnetic field. Indicate the direction of the force and show how its magnitude depends on the angle between the conductor and the direction of the field.

Sketch the magnetic field due solely to two long parallel conductors carrying respectively currents of 12 and 8 amp. in the same direction. If the wires are 10 cm. apart, find where a third parallel wire also carrying a current must be placed so that the force experienced by it shall be zero. (*L.*)

4. Derive an expression for the force experienced by a straight conductor of length l, placed perpendicular to a uniform magnetic field of strength H and carrying a current i. Explain the direction in which this force acts.

The rectangular coil of a moving-coil galvanometer consists of 200 turns each of area of 4 cm.^{2} and is arranged to swing in a radial magnetic field with two sides of the coil perpendicular to the field. Rotation of the coil is controlled by the springs, which exert a torque of 0·5 dyne-cm. per radian. Calculate the value of the magnetic field in which the coil moves if it is deflected through 5° when a current of 2 micro-amps. passes through it. (The effect of the earth's magnetic field may be neglected.) (*L.*)

5. Describe the construction of a sensitive moving-coil galvanometer. How could the instrument be adapted for use as a millivoltmeter?

A standard cell of e.m.f. 1·018 volts and internal resistance 1000 ohms is joined to two resistances in series of values 149,000 and 2 ohms respectively. The ends of the 2-ohm resistance are also connected to the terminals of a galvanometer of resistance 8 ohms, when a scale deflection of 100 mm. is recorded. What is the sensitivity of the instrument expressed in micro-amperes per scale division? (*L.*)

6. Give a brief description of moving-coil and moving-magnet galvanometers, indicating how the deflecting forces and controls differ in the two types.

Derive a relation between the steady current passing through a moving-coil galvanometer and the deflection produced. How would the period of this instrument on open circuit be affected by increasing (*a*) the number of turns in the suspended coil, (*b*) the thickness of the suspension, and (*c*) the strength of the magnetic field in which the coil is suspended? (*L.*)

7. With the help of a labelled diagram or diagrams describe the construction and explain the action of a pivoted moving-coil galvanometer. Indicate on diagrams how the direction of deflection is related to the direction of current flow and the polarity of the magnet.

If such an instrument has a resistance of 10 ohms and gives a full-scale deflection when a current of 20 milliamps. is passing, how would it be converted into a voltmeter with 3- and 150-volt ranges? What reading would this voltmeter give when connected to a battery of e.m.f. 120 volts and internal resistance 300 ohms? (*L.*)

CHAPTER XLI

ELECTROMAGNETIC INDUCTION
ALTERNATING CURRENT

1. Faraday's Discovery.

After Ampère and others had investigated the magnetic effect of a current Faraday attempted to find its converse: he tried to produce a current by means of a magnetic field. He began work on the problem in 1825 but did not succeed until 1831.

The apparatus with which he worked is represented in Fig. 733; it consists of two coils of insulated wire, A, B, wound on a wooden core. One coil was connected to a galvanometer, and the other to a battery. No

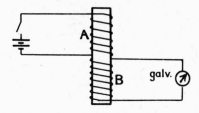

Fig. 733. Faraday's experiment on induction.

current flowed through the galvanometer, as in all Faraday's previous attempts. But when he disconnected the battery Faraday happened to notice that the galvanometer needle gave a kick. And when he connected the battery back again, he noticed a kick in the opposite direction. However often he disconnected and reconnected the battery, he got the same results. The "kicks" could hardly be all accidental—they must indicate momentary currents. Faraday had been looking for a steady current, but the effect he sought turned out to be a transient one—that was why it took him six years to find it.

2. Conditions for Generation of Induced Current.

The results of Faraday's experiments showed that a current flowed in coil B of Fig. 733 only while the magnetic field due to coil A was changing—the field building up as the current in A was switched on, decaying as the current in A was switched off. And the current which flowed in B while the field was decaying was in the opposite direction to the current which flowed while the field was building up. Faraday called the current in B an induced current. He found that it could be made much greater by winding the two coils on an iron core, instead of a wooden one.

941

Once he had realized that an induced current was produced only by a change in the magnetic field inducing it, Faraday was able to find induced currents wherever he had previously sought them. In place of the coil A he used a magnet, and showed that as long as the coil and the magnet were at rest, there was no induced current (Fig. 734 (a)). But when he moved either the coil or the magnet an induced current flowed as long as the motion continued (Fig. 734 (b)). If the current flowed one way when the north pole of the magnet was approaching the end X of the coil, it flowed the other way when the north pole was retreating from X, or the south pole approached X.

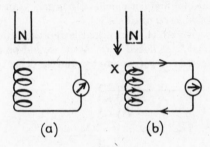

Fig. 734.   Induction of current by moving magnet.

Since a flow of current implies the presence of an e.m.f., Faraday's experiments showed that an e.m.f. could be induced in a coil by moving it relatively to a magnetic field. In discussing induction it is more fundamental to deal with the e.m.f. than the current, because the current depends on both the e.m.f. and the resistance.

3. Direction of E.M.F.; Lenz's Law.

Before considering the magnitude of an induced e.m.f., let us investigate its direction. To do so we must first see which way the galvanometer deflects when a current passes through it in a known direction: we can find this out with a battery and a megohm resistor (Fig. 735 (a)). We then take a coil whose direction of winding we know, and connect this to the galvanometer. In turn we plunge each pole of a magnet into and out of the coil; and we get the results shown in Fig. 735 (b), (c), (d). These results were generalized most elegantly into a rule by Lenz in 1835. He said that *the induced current flows always in such a direction as to oppose the change which is giving rise to it.* If the reader will sketch with a pencil on Fig. 735 the magnetic fields of the induced currents, then he will see what Lenz meant: when the magnet is approaching the coil, the coil repels it; when the magnet is retreating from the coil, the coil attracts it.

Lenz's law is a beautiful example of the conservation of energy: the induced current sets up a force on the magnet, which the mover of the magnet must overcome: the work done in overcoming this force provides the electrical energy of the current. (This energy is dissipated as heat

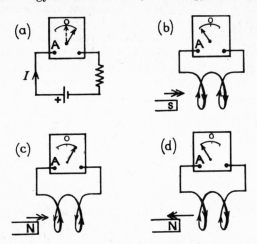

Fig. 735.   Direction of induced currents.

in the coil.) If the induced current flowed in the opposite direction to that which it actually takes, then it would aid—it would speed up—the motion of the magnet. It would enhance its own cause, and grow indefinitely; at the same time, it would continuously increase the kinetic energy of the magnet. Thus both mechanical and electrical energy would be produced, without any agent having to do work. The system would be a perpetual motion machine.

The direction of the induced e.m.f., E, is specified by that of the current, as in Fig. 736. If we wished to reword Lenz's law, substituting e.m.f. for current, we would have to speak of the e.m.f.s *tending* to oppose the change . . . etc., because there can be no opposing force unless the circuit is closed and a current can flow.

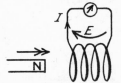

Fig. 736.   Direction of induced e.m.f.

4. Magnitude of E.M.F.

Accurate experiments on induction are difficult to contrive with simple apparatus; but rough-and-ready experiments will show on what factors the magnitude depends. We require coils of the same diameter but different numbers of turns, coils of the same number of turns but different diameters, and two similar magnets, which we can use singly or together. If we use a high-resistance galvanometer, the current will not vary much with the resistance of the coil in which the e.m.f. is induced, and we can take the deflection as a measure of the e.m.f. There is no need to plunge the magnet into and out of the coil: we can

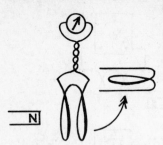

FIG. 737. E.m.f. induced by turning coil.

get just as great a deflection by simply turning the coil through a right angle, so that its plane changes from parallel to perpendicular to the magnet, or vice versa (Fig. 737). We find that the in-duced e.m.f. increases with:

(i) the speed with which we turn the coil;
(ii) the area of the coil;
(iii) the strength of the magnetic field (two magnets give a greater e.m.f. than one);
(iv) the number of turns in the coil.

To generalize these results and to build up useful formulae, we use the idea of *magnetic flux*, or lines of force passing through a coil. Fig. 738 shows a coil, of area A, whose normal makes an angle θ with a uniform magnetic field of strength H. The component of the field at right angles to the plane of the coil is $H \cos \theta$, and we say that the magnetic flux Φ through the coil is

$$\Phi = AH \cos \theta. \qquad \ldots \ldots \ldots (1)$$

(We get the same result if we multiply the field-strength H by the area projected at right angles to the field, $A \cos \theta$.) If either the strength of the field is changed, or the coil is turned so as to change the angle θ, then the flux through the coil changes.

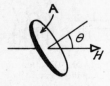

FIG. 738.
Magnetic flux.

Results (i) to (iii) above, therefore, show that the e.m.f. induced in a coil increases with the *rate of change of the magnetic flux* through it. More accurate experiments show that the induced e.m.f. is actually proportional to the rate of change of flux through the coil; this result is sometimes called *Faraday's*, or *Neumann's, law*.

5. Flux Linkages.

To take account of result (iv) above, we introduce the idea of flux linkages. If a coil has more than one turn, then the flux through the whole coil is the sum of the fluxes through the individual turns. If the magnetic field is uniform, the flux through each coil has the same value, Φ; and if the coil has n turns, the total flux through it is $n\Phi$. This quantity is called the number of flux linkages, N:

$$N = n\Phi. \qquad \ldots \ldots \quad (2)$$

In general, therefore, the e.m.f. induced in a coil is proportional to the rate of change of the flux linkages which that coil makes with the magnetic field in which it lies, or

$$\text{induced e.m.f., } E, \propto \frac{dN}{dt}. \qquad \ldots \ldots \quad (3)$$

Taking units into account,

$$E = -\frac{dN}{dt} \text{ e.m.u.}$$

or

$$E = -\frac{1}{10^8}\frac{dN}{dt} \text{ volts};$$

the minus sign in the equations expresses Lenz's law: it means that the induced e.m.f. is in such a direction that, if the circuit is closed, the induced current will oppose the change of flux.

6. Formulae for Flux Linkage.

The flux through a coil—or any other closed loop—in *vacuo* (or air) is defined as *the product of the area A of the coil or loop in square centimetres and the normal field-strength H in oersteds.* Generally, when the medium in the coil has a permeability μ, the flux is μHA (see p. 991); but in air, the flux $= \mu_0 HA$, where μ_0 has the numerical value of 1. The unit of flux is the "maxwell".

If the coil has n turns, and the flux passes through each turn normally, then the number of flux linkages in air is given by

$$N = nAH \text{ maxwells.} \qquad \ldots \ldots \quad (4)$$

7. The Induction Coil.

The induction coil is a device for getting a high voltage from a low one. It was at one time used for X-ray tubes (p. 1017), and is nowadays used in car radios. It consists of a core of iron wires, around which is wrapped a coil of about a hundred turns of thick insulated wire, called the primary (Fig. 739 (a)). Around the primary is wound the secondary coil, which has many thousands of turns of fine insulated wire. The primary is connected to a battery of accumulators, via a make-and-break M, which works in the same way as the contact-breaker of an electric bell: it switches the current on and off many times a second, thus varying the magnetic flux.

When the primary current I_p is switched on, the rise of its magnetic field induces an e.m.f. E_s in the secondary. A similar e.m.f., but in the opposite sense, is induced in the secondary when the primary current is switched off, by the collapse of the magnetic field. The secondary e.m.f.s are determined by the number of turns in the secondary coil, and by the rate of change of the magnetic flux through the iron core. Because of the great number of secondary turns, the secondary e.m.f.s may be high and of the order of thousands of volts (Fig. 739 (*b*)).

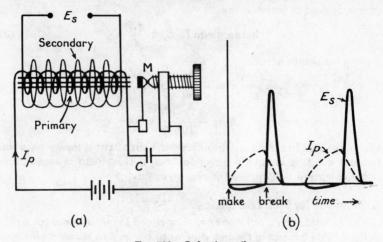

FIG. 739.   Induction coil.

In practice, an induction coil such as we have described—consisting simply of primary, secondary, and contact-breaker—would not give high secondary e.m.f.s. For, at the make of the primary current, the current would rise slowly, because of the self-inductance (see p. 966) of the primary winding. The rate of change of flux linked with the secondary would therefore be small, and the secondary e.m.f. low. And at the break of the primary current a spark would pass between the contacts of the make-and-break. The spark would allow primary current to continue to flow, and the primary current would fall slowly. At the instant of break, before the spark began, the primary current would be falling rapidly and the secondary e.m.f. would be high; but the e.m.f. would remain high for only a very short time: as soon as the spark passed the secondary e.m.f. would fall to a value about as low as at make.

Nothing can be done about the low secondary e.m.f. at make. But the secondary e.m.f. at break can be made high, by preventing sparking at the contact-breaker. To prevent sparking, a condenser, *C* in Fig. 739, is connected across the contacts.

As we shall see on p. 969, the condenser actually *slows down* the fall of the primary current at the instant of break; but in doing so it prevents the induced e.m.f. in the primary from rising high enough to start a spark. And the rate at which the primary current falls, in charging the condenser, is greater than the rate at which it would fall if a spark were passing. Thus, with a condenser, the secondary e.m.f. is less at the instant of break than without one, but it is greater throughout the rest of the fall of the primary current. Consequently the average secondary voltage at break is higher with a condenser than without; in practice it is much higher. To get the greatest possible secondary voltage, the capacitance of the condenser is chosen so that it just suppresses sparking at the contacts. The secondary voltage is then a series of almost unidirectional pulses, as shown in Fig. 739 (b).

The iron core of an induction coil is made from a bundle of wires, to minimize eddy-currents (p. 960). If eddy-currents were to flow they would, by Lenz's law, set up a flux opposing the change of primary current. Thus they would reduce the secondary e.m.f.

8. E.M.F. Induced in a Moving Rod.

Fig. 740 (a) shows an apparatus for demonstrating that an e.m.f. may be induced in a straight rod or wire, when it is moved across a magnetic field. The apparatus consists of a rod AB resting on rails XY, and lying between the poles NS of a permanent magnet. The rails are connected to a galvanometer G.

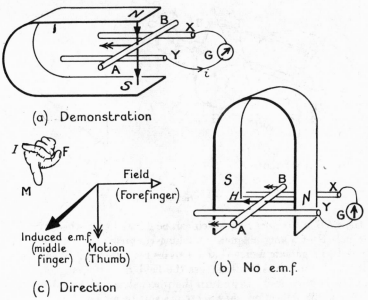

(a) Demonstration

(b) No e.m.f.

(c) Direction

Fig. 740.   E.m.f. induced in moving rod.

If we move the rod to the left, so that it cuts across the field H of the magnet, a current i flows as shown. If we move the rod to the right, the current reverses. We notice that the current flows only while the rod is moving, and we conclude that the motion of the rod AB induces an e.m.f. in it.

By turning the magnet into a vertical position (Fig. 740 (b)) we can show that no e.m.f. is induced in the rod when it moves parallel to the field H. We conclude that an e.m.f. is induced in the rod only when it *cuts across* the field. And, whatever the direction of the field, no e.m.f. is induced when we slide the rod parallel to its own length. The induced e.m.f. is greatest when we move the rod at right angles, both to its own length and to the magnetic field. These results may be summarized in *Fleming's right-hand rule*:

If we extend the thumb and first two fingers of the right hand, so that they are all at right angles to one another, then the directions of field, motion, and induced e.m.f. are related as in Fig. 740 (c).

9. To show E.M.F. ∝ Rate of Change.

The variation of the magnitude of the e.m.f. in a rod with the speed of "cutting" magnetic flux can be demonstrated with the apparatus in Fig. 741 (a).

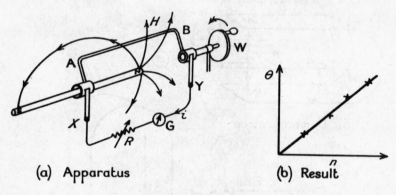

(a) Apparatus   (b) Result

Fig. 741. Induced e.m.f.

Here AB is a copper rod, which can be rotated by a wheel W around one pole N of a long magnet. Brushing contacts at X and Y connect the rod to a galvanometer G and a series resistance R. When we turn the wheel, the rod AB cuts across the field H of the magnet, and an e.m.f. is induced in it. If we turn the wheel steadily, the galvanometer gives a steady deflection, showing that a steady current is flowing round the circuit.

To find how the current and e.m.f. depends on the speed of the rod, we keep the circuit resistance constant, and vary the rate at which we turn the wheel. We time the revolutions with a stop-watch, and find that the deflection θ is proportional to the number of revolutions per second, n (Fig. 741 (b)). It follows that the induced e.m.f. is proportional to the speed of the rod.

10. Calculation of E.M.F. Induced in a Rod.

Let us imagine that a rod, AB in Fig. 742, is pushed along the rails XD, YC with a steady velocity v at right angles to its length. And let us suppose, for simplicity, that there is a uniform magnetic field H at right angles to the plane containing the rod and the direction of its motion. If the ends of the rails are joined by a wire, then the induced e.m.f. E sends a current i round the circuit. Because of the field H, the rod then experiences a force,

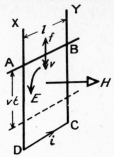

FIG. 742. Calculation of induced e.m.f.

$$f = Hli \text{ dynes}, \quad . \quad . \quad . \quad (5)$$

where l is the length of the rod, and i the current in e.m.u. (equation 2, p. 931). By Lenz's law, this force opposes the motion of the rod. To keep the rod moving, we must have an equal and opposite force f. In a time t seconds we move the rod a distance vt cm., and therefore do fvt ergs of work. In the same time the induced e.m.f. liberates electrical energy, which is dissipated as heat; if E is the e.m.f. in volts, then the energy liberated in t seconds is Eit ergs. This energy comes from the mechanical work we do in moving the rod; thus

$$Eit = fvt. \quad . \quad . \quad . \quad . \quad . \quad (6)$$

Therefore, by equation (5),

$$Eit = Hlivt,$$

whence
$$E = Hlv. \quad . \quad . \quad . \quad . \quad . \quad . \quad (7)$$

This is the e.m.f. in e.m.u. In practical units or volts it is

$$E(\text{volts}) = Hlv \times 10^{-8}. \quad . \quad . \quad . \quad (8)$$

The reader is left to show that, if the field H makes an angle θ with the normal to the plane of the rails, then

$$E(\text{e.m.u.}) = Hlv \cos \theta. \quad . \quad . \quad . \quad (9)$$

11. Induced E.M.F. and Force on Moving Electrons.

We have seen that an electron moving across a magnetic field experiences a mechanical force (p. 936). This explains neatly the e.m.f. induced in a wire: when we move the wire across the field, we move each free electron in it, likewise across the field. As Fig. 743 shows, the force on the electrons, f_e, is at right angles to the plane containing the velocity v of the wire, and the magnetic field H. Thus it tends to drive the electrons along the wire. The direction in which it does so agrees with the direction of the conventional e.m.f., which is the direction of the force on a positive charge.

When a wire AB is swept, as shown in Fig. 744, across a magnetic field H, the force on the electrons in it acts from A to B. Therefore, if the wire is not connected to a closed circuit, electrons will pile up at B: the end B will gain a negative charge, and A will be left with a positive charge. The end A will therefore be at a higher potential than B.

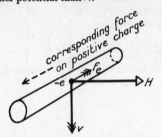

Fig 743. Force on a moving electron.

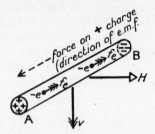

Fig 744. Induced e.m.f. arising from force on moving electrons.

If we now clear our minds of electrons, we see that the conventional e.m.f. acts from B to A. If positive electricity were free to move, it would accumulate at A; in other words, the tendency of the e.m.f., acting from B to A, is to give A a higher potential than B. The *potential difference* between A and B tends to drive positive electricity the other way. Equilibrium is reached when the potential difference V_{AB} is equal to the e.m.f. acting from B to A.

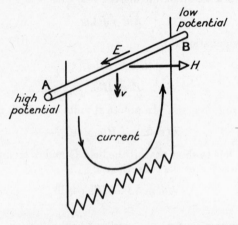

Fig. 745. E.m.f. and potential difference.

When the wire is connected to a closed circuit, current flows from A to B round the external circuit (Fig. 745). Within the source of current—the wire AB—the e.m.f. drives the current (of positive charge) from B to A: from low potential to high. *This is the essential function of an e.m.f.*; an e.m.f. is an agency which can drive an electric current *against* a potential difference. When the e.m.f. arises in a wire moving across a magnetic field, this agency is the force on the electrons moving with the wire.

The e.m.f. induced in a wire can easily be calculated from the force on a moving electron. If the wire moves with a velocity v at right angles to a field H, then so do the electrons in it. Each of them therefore experiences a force

$$f_e = Hev,$$

(equation (8), p. 936), where e is the electronic charge in e.m.u. The work which this force does in carrying the electron along the length l of the wire is $f_e l$. But it is also, by definition, equal to the product of the e.m.f. E, and the charge e. Therefore

$$Ee = f_e l = Hevl \text{ (all in e.m.u.)},$$

whence $$E = Hlv \text{ (e.m.u.)}.$$

APPLICATIONS OF INDUCTION

12. Microphones.

Microphones for the high-quality reproduction of speech and music make use of induced e.m.f. They are less sensitive than the carbon microphone described in the Sound section of this book (p. 610), but

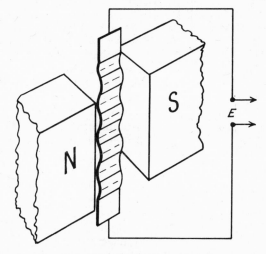

Fig. 746.   Principle of ribbon microphone.

respond to a wider range of frequencies. One type is identical in principle with the moving-coil loudspeaker (p. 612) but is much smaller: about two inches in overall diameter. Sound-waves falling upon the cone make it vibrate, and move the coil across the field of the permanent magnet. The motion of the coil induces an e.m.f. in it, which can be used to reproduce the sound. The e.m.f. is of the order of a millivolt or less.

Another type of microphone consists of an aluminium ribbon, held between the poles of a permanent magnet (Fig. 746). The ribbon is

corrugated to make it flexible, and sound-waves cause it to vibrate in
the field of the magnet, and so induce an e.m.f. E in it. This e.m.f. is
even smaller than that of a moving-coil microphone, but follows more
closely the wave-form of the sound.

13. The Dynamo and Generator.

Faraday's discovery of electromagnetic induction was the beginning
of electrical engineering. Nearly all the electric current used today
is generated by induction, in machines which contain coils moving
continuously in a magnetic field.
Fig. 747 illustrates the principle of
such a machine, which is called a
dynamo, or generator. A coil DEFG,
shown for simplicity as having only
one turn, rotates on a shaft, which
is not shown, between the poles
NS of a horseshoe magnet. The
ends of the coil are connected to
flat brass rings R, which are supported on the shaft by discs of
insulating material, also not shown.
Contact with the rings is made by
small blocks of carbon B, supported
on springs, and shown connected to
a lamp L. As the coil rotates, the
flux linking it changes, and a current
is induced in it which flows, via the
carbon blocks, through the lamp.

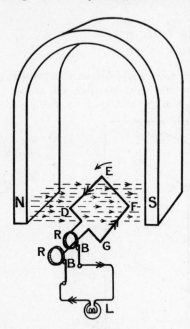

The magnitude (which we study
shortly) and the direction of the
current are not constant. Thus when
the coil is in the position shown,
the limb ED is moving downwards
through the lines of force, and GF

FIG. 747.   A simple dynamo.

is moving upwards. Half a revolution later, ED and GF will have
interchanged their positions, and ED will be moving upwards. Consequently, applying Fleming's right-hand rule, the current round the coil
must reverse as ED changes from downward to upward motion. The
actual direction of the current at the instant shown on the diagram is
indicated by the double arrows, from Fleming's rule. By applying this
rule, it can be seen that the current reverses every time the plane of
the coil passes the vertical position.

We shall see shortly that the magnitude of the e.m.f. and current
varies with time as shown in Fig. 748; this diagram also shows the
corresponding position of DG. This type of current is called an *alternating*

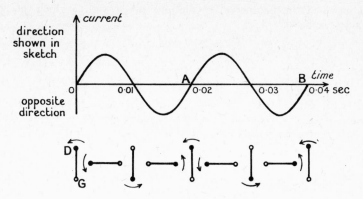

FIG. 748. Current generated by dynamo of Fig. 747, plotted against time and coil position.

current (*A.C.*) A complete alternation, such as from A to B in the figure, is called a "cycle"; and the number of cycles which the current goes through in one second is called its "frequency". The frequency of the current represented in the figure is that of most domestic supplies in Britain—50 cycles per second.

14. E.M.F. in Dynamo.

We can now calculate the e.m.f. in the rotating coil. If the coil has an area A, and its normal makes an angle θ with the magnetic field H, as in Fig. 749, then the flux through the coil is

$$\Phi = AH \cos \theta \text{ (see p. 944)}.$$

The flux linkages with the coil, if it has n turns, are

$$N = n\Phi = nAH \cos \theta.$$

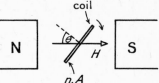

FIG. 749. Coil inclined to magnetic field.

If the coil turns with a steady angular velocity ω or $d\theta/dt$, then the e.m.f. induced in volts in the coil is

$$E = -\frac{dN}{dt} \times 10^{-8}$$

$$= -10^{-8} \times nAH \frac{d}{dt} (\cos \theta)$$

$$= 10^{-8} \times nAH \sin \theta \frac{d\theta}{dt}. \quad . \quad . \quad . \quad . \quad (10)$$

In terms of the number of revolutions per second, f, which the coil makes, we have

$$\frac{d\theta}{dt} = 2\pi f \text{ radians/sec.}$$

and $$\theta = 2\pi ft \text{ radians,}$$

$$\therefore E = 2\pi f n A H \times 10^{-8} \sin 2\pi ft \text{ volts.} \qquad . \quad . \quad (11)$$

Thus the e.m.f. varies sinusoidally with time, like the pressure in a sound-wave, the frequency being f cycles per second.

The maximum (peak) value or amplitude of E occurs when $\sin 2\pi ft$ reaches the value 1. If the maximum value is denoted by E_0, it follows that

$$E_0 = 2\pi f n A H \times 10^{-8} \text{ volts,}$$

and $$E = E_0 \sin 2\pi ft \text{ volts.} \qquad . \quad . \quad . \quad . \quad (12)$$

The e.m.f. E sends an alternating current, of a similar sine equation, through a wire connected across the coil.

15. Alternators.

Generators of alternating current are often called *alternators*. In all but the smallest, the magnetic field of an alternator is provided by an

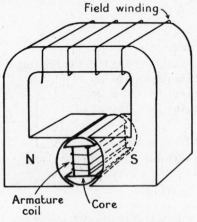

Fig. 750. Field magnet and armature.

electromagnet called a field-magnet or *field*, as shown in Fig. 750; it has a core of cast steel, and is fed with direct current from a separate d.c. generator. The rotating coil, called the armature, is wound on an iron core, which is shaped so that it can turn within the pole-pieces of the field-magnet. With the field-magnet, the armature core forms a system which is almost wholly iron, and can be strongly magnetized by a small current through the field winding. The field in which the armature turns is much stronger than if the coil had no iron core, and the e.m.f. is

proportionately greater. In the small alternators used for bicycle lighting the armature is stationary, and the field is provided by permanent
magnets, which rotate around it. In this way rubbing contacts, for
leading the current into and out of the armature, are avoided.

When no current is being drawn from a generator, the horse-power
required to turn its armature is merely that needed to overcome
friction, since no electrical energy is produced. But when a current is
drawn, the horse-power required increases, to provide the electrical
power. The current, flowing through the armature winding, causes the
magnetic field to set up a couple which opposes the rotation of the
armature, and so demands the extra horse-power. The reader should
check the truth of this statement by marking the direction of the e.m.f.,
current, and force on the limbs of the coil in Fig. 750.

16. The Transformer.

A transformer is a device for stepping up—or down—an alternating
voltage. It has primary and secondary windings, as in an induction

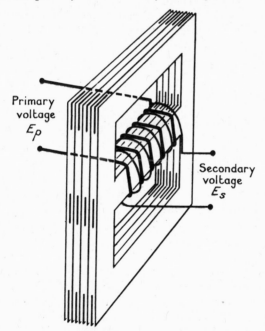

Fig. 751.   Transformer.

coil, but no make-and-break (Fig. 751). It has an iron core, which is
made from E-shaped laminations, interleaved so that the magnetic flux
does not pass through air at all; in this way the greatest flux is obtained

with a given current. When an alternating e.m.f. E_p is impressed on the primary winding, it sends an alternating current through it, which sets up an alternating flux Φ in the core. This induces an alternating e.m.f. in the secondary E_s. If n_p, n_s are the number of turns in the primary and secondary coils, their linkages with the flux Φ are:

$$N_p = n_p\Phi; \quad N_s = n_s\Phi.$$

The magnitude of the e.m.f. induced in the secondary is, from the formula on p. 945:

$$E_s = \frac{dN_s}{dt} \times 10^{-8} = n_s\frac{d\Phi}{dt} \times 10^{-8} \text{ volt.}$$

The changing flux also induces a back-e.m.f. in the primary, whose magnitude is

$$E_p = \frac{dN_p}{dt} = n_p\frac{d\Phi}{dt}.$$

Because the primary winding has inevitably some resistance, the current flowing through it sets up a voltage drop across the resistance. But in practice this is negligible compared with the back-e.m.f. due to the changing flux. Consequently we may say that the voltage applied to the primary, from the source of current, is used simply in overcoming the back-e.m.f. E_p. Therefore it is equal in magnitude to E_p. (This is analogous to saying, in mechanics, that action and reaction are equal and opposite.) Consequently we have

$$\frac{e.m.f. \text{ induced in secondary}}{voltage \text{ applied to primary}} = \frac{E_s}{E_p} = \frac{n_s}{n_p}. \quad \ldots \quad (13)$$

Thus the transformer steps voltage up or down according to its *"turns-ratio"*:

$$\frac{\text{secondary voltage}}{\text{primary voltage}} = \frac{\text{secondary turns}}{\text{primary turns}}.$$

When a load is connected to the secondary winding, a current flows in it. This current flows in such a direction as to reduce the flux in the core. At the instant that the load is connected, therefore, the back-e.m.f. in the primary falls. The primary current then increases. The increase in primary current increases the flux through the core, and continues until the flux is restored to its original value. The back-e.m.f. in the primary is then again equal to the applied voltage, and equilibrium is restored. But now a greater primary current is flowing than before the secondary was loaded. Thus the power drawn from the secondary is drawn, in turn, from the supply to which the primary is connected.

Transformers are used to step up the voltage generated at a power station, from 11,000 to 132,000 volts for high-tension transmission

(p. 824). After transmission they are used to step it down again to a value safer for distribution (240 volts in houses). Inside a house a transformer may be used to step the voltage down from 240 to 4, for ringing bells. Transformers with several secondaries are used in, for example, radio-receivers, where several different voltages are required.

17. D.C. Generators.

Fig. 752 (a) is a diagram of a direct-current generator or dynamo. Its essential difference from an alternator is that the armature winding is connected to a *commutator* instead of slip-rings. The commutator consists of two half-rings of copper C, D, insulated from one another, and turning with the coil. Brushes BB, with carbon tips, press against the

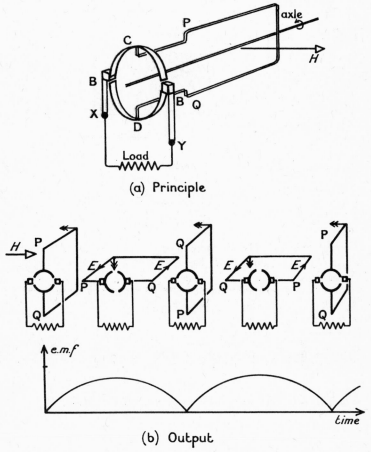

(a) Principle

(b) Output

Fig. 752.   D.C. generator.

commutator and are connected to the external circuit. The commutator
is oriented so that it reverses the connexions from the coil to the circuit
at the instant when the e.m.f. reverses in the coil. Fig. 752 (b) shows
several positions of the coil and commutator, and the e.m.f. observed
at the terminals XY. This e.m.f. pulsates in magnitude, but it acts
always in the same sense round the circuit connected to XY. It is a
pulsating direct e.m.f. The average value in this case can be shown to
be $2/\pi$ of the maximum e.m.f. E_0, given in equation (12), p. 954.

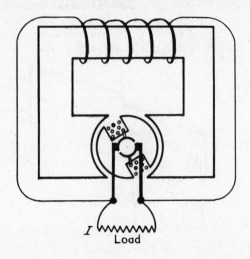

FIG. 753.   D.C. generator with energized field.

In practice, as in an alternator, the armature coil is wound with
insulated wire on a soft iron core, and the field-magnet is energized by
a current (Fig. 753). This current is provided by the dynamo itself.
The steel of the field-magnet has always a small residual magnetism,
so that as soon as the armature is turned an e.m.f. is induced in it. This
then sends a current through the field winding, which increases the
field and the e.m.f.; the e.m.f. rapidly builds up to its working value.

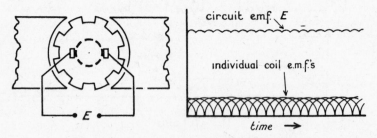

FIG. 754.   D.C. generator with segment commutator.

Most consumers of direct current wish it to be steady, not pulsating as in Fig. 752. A reasonably steady e.m.f. is given by an armature with many coils, inclined to one another, and a commutator with a correspondingly large number of segments. The coils are connected to the commutator in such a way that their e.m.f.s add round the external circuit (Fig. 754).

18. Homopolar Generator.

Another type of generator, which gives a very steady e.m.f., is illustrated in Fig. 755. It consists of a copper disc which rotates between the poles of a magnet; connexions are made to its axle and circumference. If we assume (as is not true) that the magnetic field H is uniform over the radius XY, then we can calculate the induced e.m.f. E. In one revolution the radius XY sweeps out an area $\pi(r_1{}^2 - r_2{}^2)$, where r_1 and r_2 are the radii of the wheel and the axle. If T is the time for one revolution, then the rate at which XY sweeps out area is

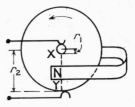

Fig. 755.   E.m.f. induced in a disc.

$$\frac{\pi(r_1{}^2 - r_2{}^2)}{T}.$$

The rate at which it sweeps out flux is therefore

$$\frac{\pi(r_1{}^2 - r_2{}^2)}{T} H = \pi(r_1{}^2 - r_2{}^2)Hf,$$

where f denotes the revolutions of the wheel per second. Thus

$$E = \pi(r_1{}^2 - r_2{}^2)Hf \text{ e.m.u.}$$
$$= \pi(r_1{}^2 - r_2{}^2)Hf \times 10^{-8} \text{ volt.}$$

Generators of this kind are called *homopolar* because the e.m.f. induced in the moving conductor is always in the same sense. They are sometimes used for electroplating, where only a small voltage is required, but they are not useful for most purposes, because they give too small an e.m.f. The e.m.f. of a commutator dynamo can be made large by having many turns in the coil; but the e.m.f. of a homopolar dynamo is limited to that induced in one radius of the disc.

19. Applications of Alternating and Direct Currents.

Direct currents are less easy to generate than alternating currents, and alternating e.m.f.s are more convenient to step up and to step down, and to distribute over a wide area. The national grid system, which supplies electricity to the whole country, is therefore fed with alternating current. Alternating current is just as suitable for heating as is direct current, because the heating effect of a current is independent of its direction. It is also equally suitable for lighting, because filament lamps depend on the heating effect, and gas-discharge lamps —neon, sodium, mercury—run as well on alternating current as on direct. Small motors, of the size used in vacuum-cleaners and common machine-tools, run satisfactorily on alternating current, but large ones, as a general rule, do not. Direct current is therefore used on most electric railway and tramway systems. These systems either have their own generating stations, or convert alternating current from the grid into direct current. One way of converting alternating current into direct is to use a valve rectifier, whose principle we shall describe later. Small rectifiers of this kind are also used in radio-receivers, for which some direct current is essential.

For electro-chemical processes alternating current is useless. The chemical effect of a current reverses with its direction, and if, therefore, we tried to deposit a metal by alternating current, we would merely cause a small amount of the metal to be alternately deposited and dissolved. For electro-plating, and for battery charging, alternating current must be rectified.

20. Eddy-currents.

The core of the armature of a dynamo is built up from thin sheets of soft iron insulated from one another by an even thinner film of oxide, as shown in Fig. 756 (a). These are called laminations, and the armature is said to be laminated. If the armature were solid, then, since iron is a conductor, currents would be induced in it by its motion across the magnetic field (Fig. 756 (b)). These currents would absorb power by opposing the rotation of the armature, and they would dissipate that power as heat, which would damage the insulation of the winding; but when the armature is laminated, these currents cannot flow, because

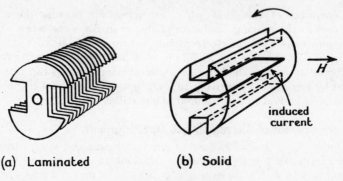

(a) Laminated   (b) Solid

Fig. 756. Armature cores.

the induced e.m.f. acts at right angles to the laminations, and therefore to the insulation between them. The magnetization of the core, however, is not affected, because it acts along the laminations. Thus the eddy-currents are suppressed, while the desired e.m.f.—in the armature coil—is not.

Eddy-currents, by Lenz's law, always tend to oppose the motion of a solid conductor in a magnetic field. The opposition can be shown in many ways. One of the most impressive is to make a chopper with a thick copper blade, and to try to slash it between the poles of a strong electromagnet; then to hold it delicately and allow it to drop between them. The resistance to the motion in the former case can be felt.

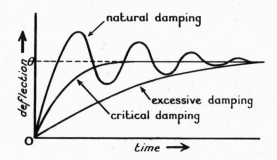

FIG. 757.   Damping of galvanometer.

Sometimes eddy-currents can be made use of—for example, in damping a galvanometer. When a current is passed through the coil of a galvanometer, it applies a couple to the coil which sets it swinging. If the swings are opposed only by the viscosity of the air, they decay very slowly and are said to be naturally damped (Fig. 757). The pointer or light-spot takes a long time to come to its final steady deflection θ. To bring the spot or pointer more rapidly to rest, the damping must be increased. One way of increasing the damping is to wind the coil on a metal former. Then, as the coil swings, the field of the permanent magnet induces eddy-currents in it; and these, by Lenz's law, oppose its motion. They therefore slow down the turning of the coil towards its eventual position, but they also suppress its swings about that position; in the end the coil comes to rest sooner than if it were not damped. Galvanometer coils which are wound on insulating formers can be damped by short-circuiting a few of their turns, or by connecting an external shunt across the whole coil. With a shunt the eddy-currents circulate round the coil and shunt, independently of the current to be measured. The smaller the shunt, the greater the eddy-currents and the damping; if the coil is overdamped, as shown in Fig. 757, it may take almost as long to come to rest as when it is undamped. The damping which is just sufficient to prevent overshoot is called "critical" damping.

21. Electric Motors.

If a simple direct-current dynamo, of the kind described on p. 957, is connected to a battery it will run as a motor (Fig. 758). Current flows round the armature coil, and the magnetic field exerts a couple on this, as in a moving-coil galvanometer. The commutator reverses

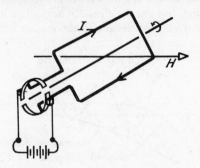

FIG. 758. Principle of D.C. motor.

the current just as the limbs of the coil are changing from upward to downward movement and vice versa. Thus the couple on the armature is always in the same sense, and the shaft turns continuously. (The reader should verify these statements with the help of Fig. 758.)

The armature of a motor is laminated, in the same way and for the same reason, as the armature of a dynamo.

22. Back-e.m.f. in Motor.

When the armature of a motor rotates, an e.m.f. is induced in its windings; by Lenz's law this e.m.f. opposes the current which is making the coil turn. It is therefore called a back-e.m.f. If its magnitude is E, and V is the potential difference applied to the armature by the supply, then the armature current is

$$I_a = \frac{V - E}{R_a}. \qquad \qquad (14)$$

Here R_a is the resistance of the armature, which is generally small—of the order of 1 ohm.

The back-e.m.f. E is proportional to the strength of the magnetic field, and the speed of rotation of the armature. When the motor is first switched on, the back-e.m.f. is zero: it rises as the motor speeds up. In a large motor the starting current would be ruinously great; to limit it, a variable resistance is inserted in series with the armature, which is gradually reduced to zero as the motor gains speed.

When a motor is running, the back-e.m.f. in its armature E is not much less than the supply voltage V. For example, a motor running off the mains ($V = 230$ volts) might develop a back-e.m.f. $E = 220$ volts. If the armature had a resistance of 1 ohm, the armature current would then be 10 amp. (equation (14)). When the motor was switched on, the armature current would be 230 amp. if no starting resistor were used.

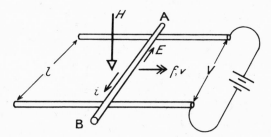

FIG. 759.   Back-e.m.f. and mechanical power.

23. Back-e.m.f. and Power.

The back-e.m.f. in the armature of a motor represents the mechanical power which it develops. To see that this is so, we use an argument similar to that which we used in finding an expression for the e.m.f. induced in a conductor. We consider a rod AB, able to slide along rails, in a plane at right angles to a magnetic field H (Fig. 759). But we now suppose that a current i is maintained in the rod by a battery, which sets up a potential difference V between the rails. The magnetic field then exerts a force f on the rod, given by

$$f = Hli \text{ dynes,}$$

where i is in e.m.u. and l is the length of the rod in cm. The force f makes the rod move; if its velocity is v cm./sec., the mechanical power developed by the force f is

$$P_m = fv \text{ ergs/sec.}$$
or $$P_m = Hliv. \qquad \ldots \ldots \ldots \quad (15)$$

As the rod moves, a back-e.m.f. is induced in it, whose magnitude E is given by the expression for the e.m.f. in a moving rod (p. 949):

$$E = Hlv. \qquad \ldots \ldots \ldots \quad (16)$$

Equations (15) and (16) together give

$$P_m = Ei. \qquad \ldots \ldots \ldots \quad (17)$$

Thus the mechanical power developed is equal to the product of the back-e.m.f. and the current.

Before returning to consider motors, we may complete the analysis of the action represented in Fig. 759. If R is the resistance of the rails and rod, the heat developed in them is i^2R ergs/sec. The power supplied by the battery is iV, and the battery is the only source of power in the whole system. Therefore

$$iV = i^2R + P_m; \qquad \ldots \ldots \ldots \quad (18)$$

the power supplied by the battery goes partly into heat, and partly into useful mechanical power. Also, by equation (17),

$$iV = i^2R + Ei, \qquad \dotfill \quad (19)$$

whence
$$V = iR + E$$

or
$$i = \frac{V - E}{R}.$$

This is equation (14), which we previously obtained simply from Ohm's law.

Let us apply this theory to the example which we were considering. We had:

$$\text{supply voltage, } V, = 230 \text{ volts;}$$
$$\text{back-e.m.f., } E, = 220 \text{ volts;}$$
$$\text{armature resistance, } R_a, = 1 \text{ ohm;}$$
$$\text{armature current, } I_a, = 10 \text{ amp.}$$

The power dissipated as heat in the armature is $I_a{}^2R_a = 100 \times 1 = 100$ watts. The power supplied to the armature is $I_aV = 10 \times 230 = 2300$ watts, and the mechanical power is $I_aE = 10 \times 220 = 2200$ watts. Of the power supplied to the armature, the fraction which appears as mechanical power is 2200/2300 = 96 per cent. This is not, however, the efficiency of the motor as a whole, because current is taken by the winding on the field magnet.

24. The Field Winding.

The field winding of a motor may be connected in series or in parallel with the armature. If it is connected in series, it carries the armature

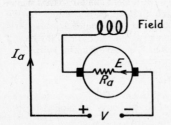

current, which is large (Fig. 760). The field winding therefore has few turns of thick wire, to keep down its resistance, and so the power wasted in it as heat. The few turns are enough to magnetize the iron, because the current is large. If the field coil is connected in parallel with the armature, as in Fig. 761, the motor is said to be "shunt-wound". The field winding has many turns of fine wire to keep down the current which it consumes. In the above example, if the motor is shunt-wound and the field current is 0·5 amp., then the power dissipated as heat in the field is $0·5 \times 230 = 115$ watts. The power consumption of the motor is therefore $2300 + 115 = 2415$ watts, and its efficiency is

FIG. 760. Series-wound motor.

$$\frac{\text{mechanical power developed}}{\text{electrical power consumed}} = \frac{2220}{2415}$$
$$= 92 \text{ per cent.}$$

The working efficiency of the motor will be a little less than this, because some of the mechanical power will be used in overcoming friction in the bearings.

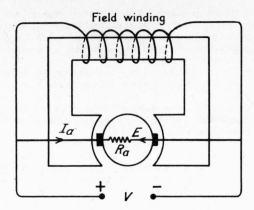

FIG. 761.   Current and voltages in shunt-wound motor.

25. Shunt Field.

Shunt-wound motors are used for driving machine-tools, and in other jobs where a steady speed is required. A shunt motor keeps a nearly steady speed for the following reason. If the load is increased, the speed falls a little; the back-e.m.f. then falls in proportion to the speed, and the current rises, enabling the motor to develop more power to overcome the increased load. In the example p. 963, if the speed falls by 1 part in 220, the back-e.m.f. falls from 220 to 219 volts. The current then rises from $\dfrac{230-220}{1} = 10$ amp. to $\dfrac{230-219}{1} = 11$ amp. And the mechanical power increases from $220 \times 10 = 2200$ watts to $219 \times 11 = 2409$ watts ($\backsimeq 2400$). Thus an increase in load of $\dfrac{2400-2200}{2200} = 9$ per cent. causes a fall in speed of 1 part in 220—less than $\frac{1}{2}$ per cent.

26. Series Field.

Series motors are used where great torque is required in starting—for example, in cranes.

They develop a great starting torque because the armature current flows through the field coil. At the start the armature back-e.m.f. is small, and the current is great—as great as the starting resistance will allow. The field-magnet is therefore very strongly magnetized. The torque on the armature is proportional to the field and to the armature current; since both are great at the start, the torque is very great.'

A series motor does not keep such a steady speed as a shunt motor. Just as in a shunt motor, when the load increases the speed falls; and the fall in speed decreases the back-e.m.f., and allows more current to flow. But, as we will see in a moment, the back-e.m.f., in a series motor, does not fall with the speed as sharply as it does in a shunt motor. To meet a given increase in load, the armature current must increase by a definite amount. And therefore the back-e.m.f. must fall by a definite amount. But it falls less with the speed than it does in a shunt motor. Consequently, to meet a given increase in load, the speed of a series motor must fall more than that of a shunt motor.

We now show that the back-e.m.f. in a series motor falls less with the speed than in a shunt one. The argument is best given in steps:

    (i) when the speed falls, the back-e.m.f. falls;

    (ii) the current through both armature and field winding increases;

    (iii) the field becomes stronger;

    (iv) the increase in the field tends to *increase* the back-e.m.f., i.e. to offset its initial fall;

    (v) thus the very fall of the back-e.m.f., by permitting a greater current and strengthening the field, tends to offset itself;

    (vi) therefore the back-e.m.f. falls slowly with the speed—more slowly than in a shunt motor, where the field is constant;

    (vii) as we have already seen, this means that the speed must fall further, to meet a given increase in load.

27. Self-induction.

The phenomenon which we call self-induction was discovered by the American, Joseph Henry, in 1832. He was led to it by a theoretical argument, starting from the phenomena of induced e.m.f., which he had discovered at about the same time as Faraday.

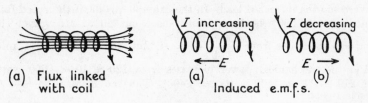

(a) Flux linked with coil   (a)   (b)
Induced e.m.f.s.

Fig. 762. Self-induction.

When a current flows through a coil, it sets up a magnetic field. And that field threads the coil which produces it. Fig. 762 (a). If the current through the coil is changed—by means of a variable resistance, for example—the flux linked with the turn of the coil changes. An e.m.f. is therefore induced in the coil. By Lenz's law the direction of the induced e.m.f. will be such as to oppose the change of current; the e.m.f. will be against the current if it is increasing, with it if it is decreasing (Fig. 762 (b)).

28. Back-E.M.F.

When an e.m.f. is induced in a circuit by a change in the current through that circuit, the process of induction is called self-induction. The e.m.f. induced is called a back-e.m.f. Self-induction opposes the growth of current in a coil, and so makes it gradua'.. This effect can be demonstrated by connecting an iron-cored coil of many turns in series with an ammeter and a few accumulators (Fig. 763 (a)). (The ammeter should be of the "short-period" type and critically damped.) When the current is switched on, the pointer of the ammeter moves slowly over to its final position. If the coil is now replaced by a rheostat of the same *resistance*, the pointer moves much more swiftly to the same reading (Fig. 763 (b)).

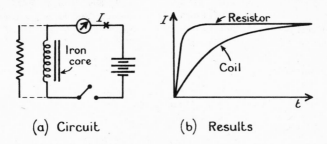

(a) Circuit   (b) Results

FIG. 763.   Self-induction experiment.

Just as self-induction opposes the rise of an electric current when it is switched on, so also it opposes the decay of the current when it is switched off. When the circuit is broken, the current starts to fall very rapidly, and a correspondingly great e.m.f. is induced, which tends to maintain the current. This e.m.f. is often great enough to break down the insulation of the air between the switch contacts, and produce a spark. To do so, the e.m.f. must be about 350 volts or more, because air will not break down—not over any gaps, narrow or wide—when the voltage is less than that value. The e.m.f. at break may be much greater than the e.m.f. of the supply which maintained the current: a spark can easily be obtained, for example, by breaking a circuit consisting of an iron-cored coil and an accumulator.

29. Non-inductive Coils.

In bridge circuits, such as are used for resistance measurements, self-induction is a nuisance. When the galvanometer key of a bridge is closed, the currents in the arms of the bridge are redistributed, unless the bridge happens to be balanced. While the currents are being redistributed they are changing, and self-induction delays the reaching of a new equilibrium. Thus the galvanometer deflection at the instant of closing the key, does not correspond to the steady state which the bridge will eventually reach. It may therefore be misleading. To minimize their self-inductance, the coils of bridges and resistance boxes are wound so as to set up extremely small magnetic fields: as shown in

Fig. 764.
Non-inductive
winding.

Fig. 764, the wire is doubled-back on itself before being coiled up. Every part of the coil is then traversed by the same current travelling in opposite directions, and its magnetic field is negligible. Such a coil is said to be non-inductive.

When describing the use of a bridge, we said that the battery key should be pressed before the galvanometer key. Doing so gives time for the currents in the arms of the bridge to become steady before the galvanometer key is pressed. It therefore minimizes any possible effects of self-induction.

30. Self-inductance.

To discuss the effects of self-induction we must define the property of a coil which gives rise to them. This property is called the self-inductance of the coil, and is defined as follows:

$$self\text{-}inductance = \frac{back\text{-}e.m.f.\ induced\ in\ coil\ by\ a\ changing\ current}{rate\ of\ change\ of\ current\ through\ coil}.$$

Self-inductance is denoted by the symbol L; we may therefore write its definition as

$$L = \frac{E_{back}}{\dfrac{dI}{dt}}.$$

or
$$E_{back} = L\,\frac{dI}{dt}. \qquad \ldots \ldots \quad (20)$$

Equation (20) is the simplest form in which to remember the definition.

The unit of self-inductance is the henry. It is defined by making each term in equation (20) equal to unity; thus *a coil has a self-inductance of 1 henry if the back-e.m.f. in it is 1 volt, when the current through it is changing at the rate of 1 amp. per second.* Equation (20) then becomes:

$$E_{back}\ (\text{volts}) = L\ (\text{henrys}) \times \frac{dI}{dt}\ (\text{amp./sec.}).$$

The iron-cored coils used for smoothing the rectified supply current to a radio-receiver (p. 976) are usually very large and have an inductance of about 30 henrys.

31. Energy Stored; E.M.F. at Break.

The spark which passes when the current in a coil is interrupted liberate energy in the form of heat and light. This energy has been stored in the magnetic field of the coil, just as the energy of a charged condenser is stored in the electrostatic field between its plates (p. 801). When the current in the coil is first switched on, the back-e.m.f. opposes the rise of current; the current flows against the back-e.m.f. and therefore does work against it (p. 827). When the current becomes steady, there is no back-e.m.f. and no more work done against it. The total work done in bringing the current to its final value is stored in the magnetic field of the coil. It is liberated when the current collapses; for then the induced e.m.f. tends to maintain the current, and to do external work of some kind.

To calculate the energy stored in a coil, we suppose that the current through it is rising at a rate dI/dt amp. per second. Then, if L is its self-inductance in henrys, the back-e.m.f. across it is given by

$$E = L \frac{dI}{dt} \text{ volts.}$$

If the value of the current, at the instant concerned, is I amperes, then the rate at which work is being done against the back-e.m.f. is

$$P = EI = LI \frac{dI}{dt} \text{watts.}$$

The total work done in bringing the current from zero to a steady value I_0 is therefore

$$W = \int P dt = \int_{0_f}^{I_0} LI \frac{dI}{dt} dt = \int_0^{I_0} LI dt$$

$$= \tfrac{1}{2} L I_0^2 \text{ joules.}$$

This is the energy stored in the coil.

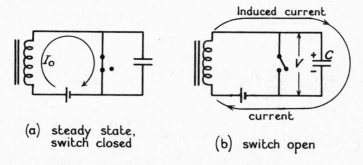

(a) steady state, switch closed   (b) switch open

Fig. 765.   Prevention of sparking by condenser.

To calculate the e.m.f. induced at break is, in general, a complicated business. But we can easily do it for one important practical circuit. To prevent sparking at the contacts of the switch in an inductive circuit, a condenser is often connected across them (Fig. 765 (a)). When the circuit is broken, the collapsing flux through the coil tends to maintain the current; but now the current can continue to flow for a brief time; it can flow by charging the condenser (Fig. 765 (b)). Consequently the current does not decay as rapidly as it would without the condenser, and the back-e.m.f. never rises as high. If the capacitance of the condenser is great enough, the potential difference across it (and therefore across the switch) never rises high enough to cause a spark.

To find the value to which the potential difference does rise, we assume that all the energy originally stored in the magnetic field of the coil is now stored in the electrostatic field of the condenser.

If C is the capacitance of the condenser in farads, and V_0 the final value of potential difference across it in volts, then the energy stored in it is $\frac{1}{2}CV_0{}^2$ joules (p. 807). Equating this to the original value of the energy stored in the coil, we have

$$\tfrac{1}{2}CV_0{}^2 = \tfrac{1}{2}LI_0{}^2.$$

Let us suppose that a current of 1 ampere is to be broken, without sparking, in a circuit of self-inductance 1 henry. To prevent sparking, the potential difference across the condenser must not rise above 350 volts. The least capacitance that must be connected across the switch is therefore given by

$$\tfrac{1}{2}C \times 350^2 = \tfrac{1}{2} \times 1 \times 1^2.$$

Hence
$$C = \frac{1}{350^2} = 8 \times 10^{-6} \text{ farad}$$
$$= 8 \ \mu\text{F}.$$

A paper condenser of capacitance 8 μF, and able to withstand 350 volts, would therefore be required.

32. Mutual Induction.

We have already seen that an e.m.f. may be induced in one circuit by a changing current in another (Fig. 733, p. 941). The phenomenon is often called mutual induction, and the pair of circuits which show it are said to have mutual inductance. The mutual inductance, M, between two circuits is defined by the equation:

$$\left.\begin{array}{l}\text{e.m.f. induced in B, by}\\ \text{changing current in A}\end{array}\right\} = M \times \left\{\begin{array}{l}\text{rate of change of}\\ \text{current in A.}\end{array}\right.$$

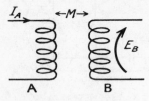

See Fig. 766. In symbols,

$$E_B = M \frac{dI_A}{dt}.$$

Mutual inductance is truly mutual; it is the same from B to A as A to B. Its unit is the same as that of self-inductance, the henry.

Fig. 766. Mutual induction.

ALTERNATING CURRENTS

33. Measurement.

If an alternating current is passed through a moving-coil meter, the pointer does not move. The coil is urged clockwise and anticlockwise at the frequency of the current—50 times per second if it is drawn from the British grid—and does not move at all. In a delicate instrument the pointer may be seen to vibrate, with a small amplitude. Instruments for measuring alternating currents must be so made that the pointer deflects the same way when the current flows through the instrument in either direction: they must be idiostatic (p. 811).

34. The Moving-iron Instrument.

A fairly common type of idiostatic instrument, called the moving-iron type, is shown in Fig. 767. It consists of two iron rods XY, PQ, .

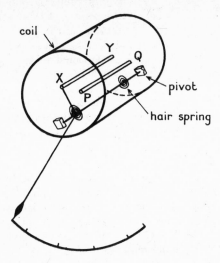

FIG. 767. Moving-iron meter, repulsion type.

surrounded by a coil which carries the current. The coil is fixed to the framework of the meter, and so is one of the rods PQ. The other rod is attached to an axle, which also carries the pointer; its motion is controlled by hair-springs. When a current flows through the coil, it magnetizes the rods, so that their adjacent ends have the same polarity. The polarity of each pair of ends reverses with the current, but whichever direction the current has, the iron rods repel each other. The force on the pivoted rod is therefore always in the same direction, and the pointer is deflected through an angle which is proportional to the average force. To a fair approximation, the pole-strength of the rods at any instant is proportional to the current at that instant; the force between the rods is therefore roughly proportional to the square of the current. The deflection of the pointer is therefore roughly proportional to the average value of the square of the current; we shall return to this point in the next chapter.

35. The Hot-wire Instrument.

A rarer type of idiostatic instrument is the hot-wire type (Fig. 768). In it the current flows through a fine resistance-wire XY, which it heats. The wire warms up to such a temperature that it loses heat—mainly by convection—at a rate equal to the average rate at which heat is

developed in the wire. The rise in temperature of the wire makes it
expand and sag; the sag is taken up by a second fine wire PQ, which is

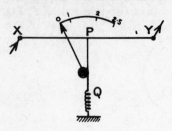

held taut by a spring. The wire PQ
passes round a pulley attached to
the pointer of the instrument, which
rotates as the wire XY sags. The
deflection of the pointer is roughly
proportional to the average rate at
which heat is developed in the wire
XY; it is therefore roughly proportional to the average value of the
square of the alternating current, and
the scale is a square-law one.

Fig. 768. Hot wire meter.

36. Root-mean-square (Effective) Value of A.C.

On p. 954 we saw that an alternating current I varied sinusoidally; that
is, it could be represented by the equation $I = \hat{I} \sin \omega t$, where $\hat{I}$ was the
peak (maximum) value of the current. In commercial practice, alternat-
ing currents are always measured and expressed in terms of their *root-
mean-square* (*r.m.s.*) or "effective" value, which we shall now consider.

Consider two resistors of equal resistance R, one carrying an alternating current and the other a direct current. Suppose both are
dissipating the same power, P, as heat. The root-mean-square (r.m.s.)
value of the alternating current, I_r, is defined as equal to the direct
current, I_d. Thus:

*the root-mean-square value of an alternating current is defined as that
value of steady current which would dissipate heat at the same rate in a
given resistance.*

Since the power dissipated by the direct current is

$$P = I_d{}^2 R,$$

our definition means that, in the a.c. circuit,

$$P = I_r{}^2 R. \qquad \qquad \text{. . . . . (21)}$$

Whatever the wave-form of the alternating current, if I is its value
at any instant, the power which it delivers to the resistance R at that
instant is $I^2 R$. Consequently, the average power P is given by

$$P = \text{average value of } (I^2 R)$$

$$= R \times \text{average value of } (I^2),$$

since R is a constant. Therefore, by equation (21),

$$I_r{}^2 R = R \times \text{average value of } (I^2)$$

or $\qquad \qquad I_r{}^2 = \text{average value of } (I^2). \qquad \text{. . . . (22)}$

The average value of (I^2) is called the mean-square current; the meaning
of the term is illustrated for a non-sinusoidal current in Fig. 769 (*a*).

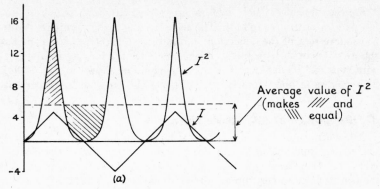

FIG. 769(a). Mean-square values.

$$\therefore I_r = \sqrt{\text{average value of } (I^2)}. \quad \ldots \quad (23)$$

For a sinusoidal current, the average value of I^2 is $I_0^2/2$, where I_0 is the maximum value of the current

$$\therefore I_r = \frac{I_0}{\sqrt{2}}. \quad \ldots \ldots \quad (23a)$$

Equation (23) shows the origin of the term "root-mean-square". We therefore require a meter whose deflection measures not the current through it but the average value of the square of the current. As we have already seen, moving-iron and hot-wire meters have just this property (p. 971).

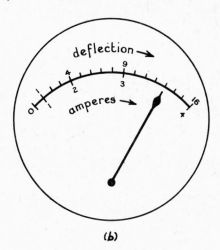

(b)

FIG. 769(b). Scale of A.C. ammeter.

For convenience, such meters are scaled to read amperes, not
(amperes)^2, as in Fig. 769 (b). The scale reading is then proportional to
the square-root of the deflection, and indicates directly the root-mean-
square value of the current I_r. An a.c. meter of the moving-iron or hot-
wire type can be calibrated in direct current, as shown in Fig. 769(b).
This follows at once from the definition of the r.m.s. value of current.

37. Rectification by A.C. Diode Valve.

Alternating current is easier to distribute than direct current, because
alternating voltage can be transformed easily up or down. For electrolysis, battery-charging, and the operation of radio-receivers and
transmitters, however, direct current is essential. It can be obtained
from an alternating current supply by means of a rectifier, which is a
device that will only pass current in one direction. A common type of
rectifier is that called a *diode valve*. It contains a metal filament, F in
Fig. 770 (a), surrounded by a metal anode A. The filament is heated by
a current drawn from a low voltage supply, and emits electrons. A
circuit for varying the anode potential is shown in Fig. 770 (a).

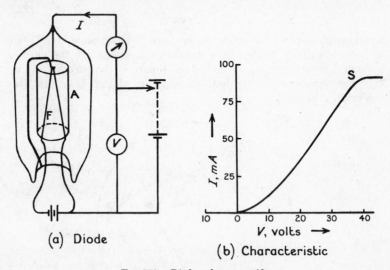

(a) Diode

(b) Characteristic

FIG. 770.   Diode valve as rectifier.

Since electrons are negative charges, such a device passes current when
its anode is made positive with respect to its filament, but not when the
anode is made negative. Fig. 770 (b) shows the curve of anode current
against anode potential for a small diode; it is called the diode's
characteristic curve, or simply its characteristic. The current increases
with the positive anode potential as far as the point S. Beyond this

point the current does not increase, because the anode is collecting all the electrons emitted by the filament; the current is said to be saturated.

At first sight we might expect that any positive anode potential, however small, would draw the full saturation current from the filament to the anode. But it does not, because the charges on the electrons make them repel one another. Thus the cloud of electrons between the anode and filament repels the electrons leaving the filament, and turns some of them back. The electrons round the filament are like the molecules in a cloud of vapour above a liquid; they are continually escaping from it and returning to it. The positive anode draws some away from the cloud, as a wind carries water vapour away from a pool. The wind, or the anode, thins out the cloud, so that more electrons or molecules escape than return. The higher the anode potential, the fewer electrons return to the filament; as the anode potential rises, the current increases, to its saturation limit.

38. Rectifier Circuit.

When a diode is used as a rectifier it is connected in a circuit such as Fig. 771 (a). The low-voltage secondary of the transformer simply

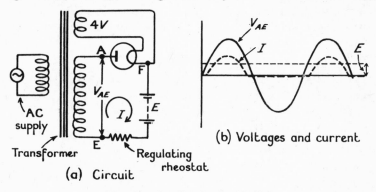

(b) Voltages and current

(a) Circuit

FIG. 771. Rectifier circuit with diode.

provides the heating current from the filament. The current to be rectified is drawn from the high-voltage secondary. One end of this secondary is connected to the load, which could be, as shown, an accumulator on charge; the other end of the load is connected to the anode of the diode, and the other end of the secondary to one of the filament connexions. When the transformer secondary voltage V_{AE} is greater than the e.m.f. E of the accumulator, the anode is positive with respect to the filament; electrons from the hot filament are then drawn to the anode, and a current flows through the load (Fig. 771 (b)). On half-cycles when the anode is negative, the electrons are repelled, and no current flows. Because it only allows current to flow through it in one direction, a thermionic diode is often called a valve.

Some rectifying valves contain a little mercury vapour. When electrons flow through them, they ionize the mercury atoms, as explained on p. 1007. The ions and electrons thus produced make the valve a very good conductor, and reduce the voltage drop across it; they therefore allow more of the voltage from the transformer to appear across the load.

The current from a rectifier flows in pulses, whenever the anode is positive with respect to the filament. Sometimes a smoother current is required, as, for example, in a radio-receiver, where the pulses would cause a humming sound in the loudspeaker. The current can be smoothed by connecting an inductance coil of about 30 henries in series with the load. The inductance prevents rapid fluctuations in current. So also does a condenser of about 16 microfarads connected across the load. Generally the two are used together to give a very smooth output.

39. Metal Rectifier.

Yet other rectifiers are not thermionic at all. One such type consists of an oxidized copper disc, Cu_2O/Cu, pressed against a disc of lead, Pb (Fig. 772 (a)). These conduct well when the lead is made positive, but

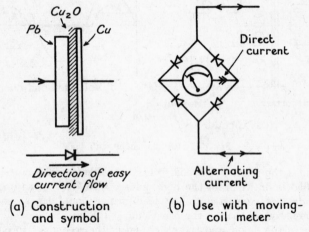

(a) Construction and symbol

(b) Use with moving-coil meter

FIG. 772. Metal rectifier and use.

very badly when it is made negative; they are called metal rectifiers. A metal rectifier can be used to convert a moving-coil milliammeter into an alternating-current ammeter or voltmeter (Fig. 772 (b)). Such a meter is more sensitive than a moving-iron or hot-wire instrument, and has a more open scale near zero: its deflection is roughly proportional to the average value of the current or voltage.

40. A.C. through a Condenser.

In many radio circuits, resistors, condensers, and coils are present. An alternating current can flow through a resistor, but it is not obvious at first that it can flow through a condenser. This can be demonstrated, however, by wiring a condenser, of capacitance one or more micro-farads, in series with a neon lamp, and connecting them to the a.c. mains via a plug. In place of the neon lamp we could use a 110-volt filament lamp of low rating, such as 25 watts. The lamp lights up, showing that a current is flowing through it.

The current flows because the condenser plates are being continually charged, discharged, and charged the other way round by the alternating voltage of the mains (Fig. 773). The current thus flows round the circuit, and can be measured by an a.c. milliammeter inserted in any of the connecting wires.

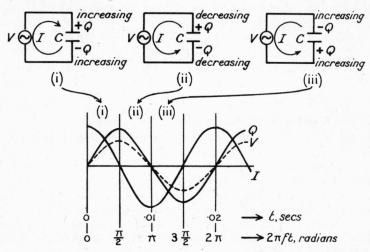

FIG. 773. Flow of A.C. through condenser, frequency 50 cycles/sec.

To find the amplitude of the current, let us denote the amplitude of the voltage by $\hat{V}$, and its frequency by f. Then, as in equation (12), p. 954, the instantaneous voltage at any time t is

$$V = \hat{V} \sin 2\pi f t.$$

If C is the capacitance of the condenser, then the charge Q on its plates is

$$Q = CV,$$

whence

$$Q = C\hat{V} \sin 2\pi f t.$$

The current flowing at any instant, I, is equal to the rate at which charge is accumulating on the condenser plates. Thus

$$I = \frac{dQ}{dt}$$

$$= \frac{d}{dt} \, (C\hat{V} \sin 2\pi ft)$$

$$= 2\pi fC\hat{V} \cos 2\pi ft. \quad \ldots \ldots \quad (24)$$

Equation (24) shows that the amplitude of the current is $2\pi fC\hat{V}$: proportional to the frequency, the capacitance, and the voltage amplitude. These results are easy to explain. The greater the voltage, or the capacitance, the greater the charge on the plates, and therefore the greater the current required to charge or discharge the condenser. And the higher the frequency, the more rapidly is the condenser charged and discharged, and therefore again the greater the current.

A more puzzling feature of equation (24) is the factor giving the time variation of the current, $\cos 2\pi ft$. It shows that the current varies a quarter-cycle out of step with the voltage—or, as is more often said, $\pi/2$ out of phase. Fig. 773 shows this variation, and also helps to explain it. When the voltage is a maximum, so is the charge on the condenser. It is therefore not charging and the current is zero. When the voltage starts to fall, the condenser starts to discharge; the rate of discharging, or current, reaches its maximum when the condenser is completely discharged and the voltage across it is zero.

41. A.C. through an Inductance Coil.

Since a coil is made from conducting wire, we have no difficulty in seeing that an alternating current can flow through it. However, if the coil has appreciable self-inductance, the current is less than would flow through a non-inductive coil of the same resistance. We have already seen how self-inductance opposes changes of current; it must therefore oppose an alternating current, which is continuously changing.

Let us suppose that the resistance of the coil is negligible, a condition which can easily be satisfied in practice. We can simplify the theory by considering first the current, and working back to find the potential difference across the coil. Let us therefore denote the current by

$$I = \hat{I} \sin 2\pi ft, \quad \ldots \ldots \quad (25)$$

where $\hat{I}$ is its amplitude (Fig. 774). If L is the inductance of the coil, the changing current sets up a back-e.m.f. in the coil, of magnitude

$$E = L\frac{dI}{dt}.$$

Thus
$$E = L\frac{d}{dt} \, (\hat{I} \sin 2\pi ft)$$

$$= 2\pi fL\hat{I} \cos 2\pi ft.$$

To maintain the current, the applied supply voltage must be equal to the back-e.m.f. The voltage applied to the coil must therefore be given by

$$V = 2\pi fL\hat{I} \cos 2\pi ft. \qquad \ldots \ldots \quad (26)$$

Equation (26) shows that the amplitude of the voltage across a pure inductance (without resistance) is proportional to the frequency, the magnitude of the self-inductance, and the amplitude of the current. The reader is left to work out the physical explanation of these three facts for himself.

The voltage across a pure inductance is a quarter-cycle, or $\pi/2$ radians, out of phase with the current. Fig. 774 shows this relationship, which follows from comparing equations (25) and (26). It can be explained by considering the relationship between the back-e.m.f., and the changing current, which the reader should do for himself.

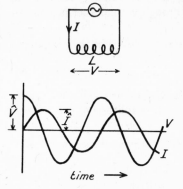

FIG. 774. Passage of a.c. through a coil.

The phase relationship between current and voltage for a pure inductance is, however, different from that for a condenser. For, as Fig. 774 shows, the current through an inductance lags $\pi/2$ behind the voltage; that is to say, it passes its maxima a quarter-cycle later than the voltage. On the other hand, in a condenser the current passes its maxima a quarter-cycle ahead of the voltage (Fig. 773): we say that it leads the voltage by $\pi/2$.

42. Reactance.

The term reactance is used to denote the opposition which an inductance or condenser offers to the passage of an alternating current. We do not use the term resistance for this, because we have already defined resistance as the property of a circuit which enables it to dissipate electrical power as heat; and we have just seen that a condenser or a pure inductance dissipates no electrical power at all.

We define the reactance of an inductance L, or condenser C, by the equation

$$reactance = \frac{amplitude\ of\ voltage\ across\ L\ or\ C}{amplitude\ of\ current\ through\ it}.$$

Denoting reactance by X, we have

$$X = \frac{\hat{V}}{\hat{I}}.$$

Since $\hat{V}$ is measured in volts, and $\hat{I}$ in amperes, the reactance X is expressed in ohms. At one time the unit of reactance was called a virtual ohm, to emphasize the physical distinction between reactance and resistance; but that usage has been given up.

We have already seen (p. 978) that the amplitude of the current through a condenser is given by

$$\hat{I} = 2\pi f C \hat{V}.$$

The reactance of the condenser is therefore

$$X_C = \frac{\hat{V}}{\hat{I}} = \frac{1}{2\pi f C}.$$

X_C is in ohms when f is in cycles per second, and C in farads.

The amplitude of the voltage across a pure inductance is

$$\hat{V} = 2\pi f L \hat{I}.$$

Hence the reactance of the inductance is

$$X_L = \frac{\hat{V}}{\hat{I}} = 2\pi f L.$$

It is in ohms when f is in cycles per second, and L is in henrys.

For convenience we often write

$$\omega = 2\pi f.$$

The quantity ω is called the angular frequency, or pulsatance, of the current and voltage. It is expressed in radians per second. Then an alternating voltage, for example, may be written as

$$V = \hat{V} \sin \omega t.$$

And reactances become

$$X_L = \omega L,$$

$$X_C = \frac{1}{\omega C}.$$

43. Vector Diagram.

In the Mechanics section of this book, it is shown that a quantity which varies sinusoidally with time may be represented as the

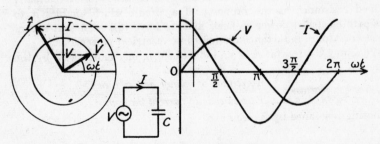

Fig. 775. Vector diagram for condenser.

projection of a rotating vector (p. 38). Alternating currents and voltages may therefore be represented in this way. Fig. 775 shows, on the left, the vectors representing the current through a condenser, and the voltage across it. Since the current leads the voltage by $\pi/2$, the current vector $\hat{I}$ is displaced by 90° ahead of the voltage vector $\hat{V}$.

Fig. 776 shows the vector diagram for a pure inductance. In drawing it, the voltage has been taken as $V = \hat{V} \sin \omega t$, and the current drawn

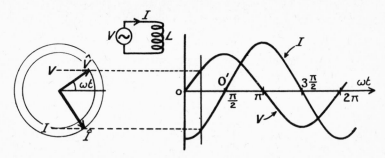

FIG. 776.   Vector diagram for pure inductance.

lagging $\pi/2$ behind it. This enables the diagram to be readily compared with that for a condenser. To show that it is essentially the same as Fig. 774, we have only to shift the origin by $\pi/2$ to the right, from 0 to 0'.

EXAMPLES

1. State the law of electromagnetic induction, and explain why in certain galvanometers the coil is wound on a continuous aluminium former.

The metal propeller of a stationary aircraft is rotating about a horizontal axis which is in the magnetic meridian. If its length from tip to tip is 3 metres, and its speed of rotation 1000 r.p.m., what is the potential difference produced in volts (a) between tip and tip, (b) between tip and axis? (The earth's horizontal field may be taken as 0·2 oersted; 1 volt = 10^8 e.m.u.) (*O. & C.*)

First part (see text). Induced currents in the former bring the deflected coil to rest quickly, thus providing damping.

Second part. (a) The induced e.m.f. between tip and tip is zero, as the e.m.f.s along each radius act in opposite directions.

(b) The propeller has zero velocity at the axis, and a velocity $= r\omega$ at the tip, where r = radius = 1·5 metres = 150 cm. and $\omega = 2\pi f = 2\pi \times 1000/60$.

$$\therefore \text{ average velocity, } v, = \frac{r\omega}{2} = \frac{150 \times 2\pi \times 1000}{2 \times 60}.$$

But   induced e.m.f., $E, = \dfrac{Hlv}{10^8}$ volts

$$= \frac{0\cdot2 \times 150 \times 150 \times 2\pi \times 1000}{2 \times 60 \times 10^8} \text{ volts.}$$

$$= \frac{75\pi}{10^5} = 2\cdot4 \text{ millivolts (approx.).}$$

2. Explain the principles which govern the operation of a direct-current motor. What are the special characteristics of shunt-wound and series-wound direct-current motors?

A shunt-wound motor has an armature resistance of 0·05 ohm and a field-coil resistance of 50 ohms. When it is connected to a 100-volt supply it takes 52 amp. running at normal speed. Calculate (a) the back-e.m.f. generated; (b) the efficiency of the motor if it be assumed that there are no losses other than electrical resistance losses. (O. & C.)

First part (see pp. 962–5).

Second part. (a) Current in field coil, $I, = \dfrac{E}{R} = \dfrac{100}{50} = 2$ amp.

$$\therefore \text{ current in armature} = 52 - 2 = 50 \text{ amp.}$$

$$\therefore \text{ p.d. across armature resistance} = IR = 50 \times 0\text{·}05 = 2\text{·}5 \text{ volts.}$$

$$\therefore \text{ back-e.m.f.} = 100 - 2\text{·}5 = 97\text{·}5 \text{ volts.}$$

(b) Total power supplied $= EI = 100 \times 52 = 5200$ watts.

Total electrical resistance losses $= I^2R = 50^2 \times 0\text{·}05 + 2^2 \times 50$

$$= 325 \text{ watts.}$$

$$\therefore \text{ useful power obtained} = 5200 - 325 = 4875 \text{ watts.}$$

$$\therefore \text{ efficiency} = \frac{4875}{5200} \times 100\% = 94\%.$$

EXERCISES XLI

1. State the laws of electromagnetic induction. Hence derive an expression for the time variation of the electromotive force induced in a single turn of wire rotating about an axis in its plane, the axis being perpendicular to a uniform magnetic field. Explain the action of a simple alternating current generator.

What modification of this generator is required to produce a direct current? Indicate by a sketch how the e.m.f. across the output terminals of a single coil would vary with time in the case of (a) an a.c. and (b) a d.c. generator. How may a more uniform output e.m.f. be obtained in the latter case?

A rectangular coil of wire having 100 turns, of dimensions 30 cm. × 40 cm., is rotated at a constant speed of 600 r.p.m. in a magnetic field of 10^3 gauss, the axis of rotation being in the plane of the coil and perpendicular to the field. Calculate the induced e.m.f. (L.)

2. How would you demonstrate the laws of electromagnetic induction, using a magnet, a solenoid with windings clearly visible, a cell and a suitable galvanometer? Explain carefully how you identify the directions of the induced current in each case.

An engine travels N at a uniform speed of 60 m.p.h. in a straight horizontal path. Calculate the e.m.f. set up at the ends of a conducting axle 150 cm. long if $H = 0\text{·}2$ oersted and the angle of dip is 68°. (You may assume that 8 kilometres = 5 miles.) (L.)

3. What are eddy-currents? Give two examples of the practical use of such currents.

A metal disc of diameter 20 cm. rotates at a constant speed of 600 revolutions per min. about an axis through its centre and perpendicular to its plane in a uniform magnetic field of 50 oersteds established parallel to the axis of rotation. Calculate the e.m.f. in volts between the centre and rim of the disc. Show clearly on a diagram the direction of rotation of the disc and the direction of the magnetic field and of the e.m.f. induced. (*L.*)

4. How would you show that a change in the number of lines of magnetic force, however produced, threading through a circuit produces an induced e.m.f.?

A magnet is suspended by a thin wire so that its axis is horizontal and its centre is above the centre of a circular copper disc, mounted horizontally. Explain what happens to the magnet when the disc is rotated.

What would be the effect of replacing the disc by one of identical dimensions but made of a substance of high resistivity? (*L.*)

5. Describe with the aid of diagrams (*a*) a transformer and (*b*) an induction coil. Explain the action of each.

Draw diagrams to show, in a general way, how the voltage output from each of these appliances varies with the time. (*N.*)

6. Describe and explain the action of a transformer.

A single flat coil, consisting of 100 turns of mean area 200 sq. cm. and resistance 4 ohms, is fitted with a commutator and rotates at 1500 r.p.m. about a diameter at right angles to a uniform magnetic field of 60 oersteds. The brushes bearing on the commutator are connected to a resistance of 16 ohms. Determine (*a*) the mean e.m.f. generated, (*b*) the mean current flowing, (*c*) the mean potential difference across the brushes. (1 volt = 10^8 e.m.u.) (*C.*).

7. State the laws of electromagnetic induction and describe experiments you would perform to illustrate the factors which determine the magnitude of the induced current set up in a closed circuit.

A simple electric motor has an armature of 0·1 ohm resistance. When the motor is running on a 50-volt supply the current is found to be 5 amp. Explain this and show what bearing it has on the method of starting large motors. (*L.*)

8. State the laws relating to the electromotive force induced in a conductor which is moving in a magnetic field.

Describe the mode of action of a simple dynamo.

Find in volts the e.m.f. induced in a straight conductor of length 20 cm., on the armature of a dynamo and 10 cm. from the axis when the conductor is moving in a uniform radial field of 5000 oersteds and the armature is rotating at 1000 r.p.m. (*L.*)

9. State the laws of electromagnetic induction.

Describe the structure and explain the action of an electrical transformer.

Give an account of the energy losses in a transformer and the means by which they are reduced to a minimum. (*L.*)

10. Explain what is meant by *self-induction*. Describe one experiment in each case to illustrate the effect of a coil having self-inductance in (*a*) a direct current circuit, (*b*) an alternating-current circuit.

Describe the essential features of an instrument for measuring alternating current. (*N.*)

11. Explain what is meant by the *R.M.S. value of an alternating current* Describe an ammeter which gives R.M.S. values when used in an a.c. circuit; explain why it gives these values and name *two* electrical characteristics desirable in such an instrument.

Unless a wire resistance is carefully wound it may have both inductance and capacitance. Discuss the effect of each of these (separately) on the reading of an ammeter placed in series with the resistance in a circuit to which an alternating voltage of fixed frequency is applied. (*N.*)

12. Discuss the production of an alternating current by the uniform rotation of a coil in a uniform magnetic field. Distinguish between the peak value and the root mean square value of the current, and find the relation between them.

Describe the construction and mode of action of some form of ammeter for measuring the R.M.S. value of an alternating current. (*O. & C.*)

13. A rectangular coil of wire of resistance R ohms is mounted on an axis which is at right angles to a uniform magnetic field H oersted, the plane of the coil being parallel to the magnetic lines of force. A potential difference E volts is applied between the ends of the coil. Find an expression for the couple on the coil. Explain what must be done in order to convert the system into a simple electric motor which will rotate continuously. What will determine the current in the coil at any time? (*L.*)

14. A rectangular coil of area, A traversed by a current of I units, is placed in a uniform magnetic field of strength H, so that its axis makes an angle θ with the direction of the field. Find an expression for the couple on the coil. Explain with diagrams the construction and mode of action of a direct-current series motor. Why is a starting resistance necessary for a large electric motor? (*O. & C.*)

15. Describe and explain an instrument for measuring alternating current. What do you understand by the R.M.S. value of an alternating current? How is it related to the peak value in the case of a sinusoidal current?

When the coils of an electromagnet are connected to a 240-volt d.c. supply, the current taken is 10 amps. When connected to a 240-volt a.c. supply the current taken is only 1 amp. Explain why there is a smaller current on a.c., and calculate the resistance of the coils. Using the same time axis, draw curves showing how the current through the coils and the applied voltage vary with time when the supply is a.c. (*C.*)

16. State Lenz's law and describe fully a method by which you could verify this law experimentally.

A horizontal metal disc of radius 10·0 cm. is rotated about a central vertical axis at a region where the value of the earth's magnetic flux density is 0·53 gauss (or $5·3 \times 10^{-5}$ volt sec. metre^{-2}) and the angle of dip is 70°. A sensitive galvanometer of resistance 150 ohms is connected between the centre of the disc and a brush pressing on the rim. Assuming the resistance of the disc to be negligible, what will be the current through the galvanometer when the disc is rotated at 1500 rev. min.$^{-1}$? If the system is frictionless, calculate the power required to maintain the motion. (*C.*)

17. Define *electromotive force* and state the *laws of electromagnetic induction*. Using the definition and the laws, derive an expression for the e.m.f. induced in a conductor moving in a magnetic field.

When a wheel with metal spokes 120 cm. long is rotated in a magnetic field of induction of 0·5 gauss normal to the plane of the wheel, an e.m.f. of 10^{-2} volt is induced between the rim and the axle. Find the rate of rotation of the wheel. (*L.*)

CHAPTER XLII

CHARGE AND FLUX
MAGNETIC PROPERTIES OF MATERIALS

1. Charge and Flux.

In the last chapter we saw that an electromotive force is induced in a circuit when the magnetic flux linked with it changes. If the circuit is closed, a current flows, and electric charge is carried round the circuit. As we shall now show, there is a simple relationship between the charge and the change of flux.

2. Flux and Charge Relation.

Let us consider a closed circuit of total resistance R ohms, which has

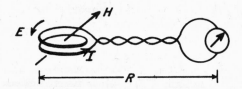

Fig. 777.   Coil with changing flux.

a total flux linkage N with a magnetic field (Fig. 777). If the flux linkages start to change,

$$\text{induced e.m.f., } E, = -\frac{1}{10^8} \cdot \frac{dN}{dt} \text{ volts,}$$

and the current is

$$I = \frac{E}{R} = -\frac{1}{10^8}\frac{1}{R}\frac{dN}{dt} \text{ amps.} \quad \ldots \quad (1)$$

In general, the flux linkages will not change at a steady rate, and the current will not be constant. But, throughout their change, charge is being carried round the circuit. If they take a time t seconds to reach a new constant value, the charge carried round the circuit in that time is

$$Q = \int_0^t I\,dt \text{ coulombs.}$$

Therefore, by equation (1),

$$Q = -\frac{1}{10^8 R} \int_0^t \frac{dN}{dt}\, dt$$

$$= -\frac{1}{10^8 R} \int_{N_0}^{N_t} dN,$$

where N_0 is the number of linkages at $t = 0$, and N_t is the number of linkages at time t. Thus

$$Q = -\frac{N_t - N_0}{10^8 R} = \frac{N_0 - N_t}{10^8 R} \text{ coulombs.}$$

The quantity $N_0 - N_t$ is positive if the linkages N have decreased, and negative if they have increased. But as a rule we are interested only in the magnitude of the charge, and we may write

$$Q = \frac{change\ of\ flux\ linkages}{10^8 R} \text{ coulombs.} \quad \ldots \quad (2)$$

Equation (2) shows that the charge circulated round the circuit is proportional to the change of flux-linkages, and independent of the time.

2. Field Strength.

This result gives a method of measuring a magnetic field. A small coil, called a search coil, is connected to a ballistic galvanometer, and placed at right angles to the field, as in Fig. 777. It is then pulled smartly out of the field, and a charge passes round the circuit and gives a transient deflection of the galvanometer. This charge is proportional to the flux which formerly threaded the coil, and therefore to the strength of the field in which it was placed.

Suppose H is the field-strength in oersteds, A is the area of the coil in sq. cm. and n is the number of turns. Then

$$change\ of\ flux\text{-}linkages = nAH$$

$$\therefore \text{ quantity, } Q, \text{ through galvanometer} = \frac{nAH}{10^8 R} \text{ coulombs,}$$

where R is the total resistance of the galvanometer and search coil. But

$$Q = c\theta \text{ coulombs,}$$

where c is the quantity per unit deflection of the ballistic galvanometer.

$$\therefore \frac{nAH}{10^8 R} = c\theta$$

$$\therefore H = \frac{10^8 R c \theta}{nA}. \qquad \ldots \ldots \quad (3)$$

The constant c is found by discharging a condenser through the galvanometer (see p. 938). If C is the capacitance in farads, V the p.d. in volts of the battery originally charging it, and a the deflection of the galvanometer, then $c = CV/a$ coulombs per unit deflection.

3. The Earth Inductor.

As another example of the use of a search coil and ballistic galvanometer, we describe a method that has been used for measuring the angle of dip of the earth's magnetic field (p. 746). The earth's field is so nearly uniform that the search coil may be large, usually about a foot square; but the field is also so weak that even a large coil must have many turns—of the order of 100. The coil, which is called an earth

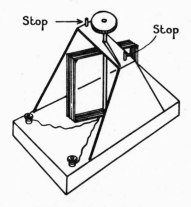

Fig. 778. Earth inductor.

inductor, is pivoted in a wooden frame, and this is fitted with stops so that the coil can be turned rapidly through 180° (Fig. 778). To find the angle of dip, we connect the coil to a ballistic galvanometer, and set it with its plane horizontal, as shown at (i) in Fig. 779. The flux through the coil is then

$$\Phi = VA,$$

where A is the area of the coil, and V is the vertical component of the earth's field. If we were to turn the coil through 90°, the flux would fall to zero; and if we were to turn it through a further 90°, the flux would become VA once more, but it would thread the coil in the opposite direction. Therefore we turn the coil through 180°, and change the flux through it by $2VA$; at the same time we observe the throw, θ, of the galvanometer. The change in flux linkages, if the coil has n turns, is

$$\Delta N = 2n\Phi = 2nVA.$$

If R is the total resistance of galvanometer and search coil, the circulated charge is, by equation (2),

$$Q = \frac{\Delta N}{10^8 R} = \frac{2nVA}{10^8 R}.$$

But $$Q = c\theta,$$

where c is the constant of the galvanometer. Therefore

$$\frac{2nVA}{10^8 R} = c\theta. \qquad \vdots \quad \dots \dots \quad (4)$$

We now set the frame of the earth inductor so that the axis of the coil is vertical, and so that, when the coil is held by one of the stops, its plane lies East–West. See Fig. 779 (ii). The flux threading the coil is now

$$n\Phi' = nH_0 A,$$

where H_0 is the horizontal component of the earth's field. Therefore, when we turn the coil through $180°$, the throw θ' of the galvanometer is given by

$$\frac{2nH_0 A}{10^8 R} = c\theta'. \quad . \quad (4a)$$

Now the angle of dip, δ, is given by

$$\tan \delta = \frac{V}{H_0};$$

therefore, from equations (4) and (4a),

$$\tan \delta = \frac{\theta}{\theta'}.$$

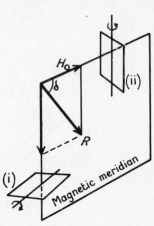

FIG. 779. Measurement of dip.

EXAMPLE

What are the special characteristics of a ballistic galvanometer? Explain, using circuit diagrams, how you would use a ballistic galvanometer to compare (a) the capacitances of two condensers each of the order 1 μF, (b) the magnetic fields between the poles of two electromagnets.

A coil of 100 turns each of area 400 cm.[2] is connected in series with a ballistic galvanometer of sensitivity 100 divisions per micro-coulomb, the total resistance of the circuit being 2000 ohms. Calculate the galvanometer deflection when the coil is turned quickly from its initial position in a horizontal plane through $180°$ about a horizontal axis. How does the speed with which the coil is turned affect the result? ($H_0 = 0.18$ oersted, angle of dip $= 67°$.) (L.)

First part (see text).

Second part. The flux change $= 2nAV$, with the usual notation, where V is the vertical component of the earth's field.

$$\therefore \text{ Quantity, } Q, = \frac{\text{flux change}}{10^8 R} \text{ coulombs}$$

$$= \frac{2nAV}{10^8 R} = \frac{2 \times 100 \times 400 \times 0.18 \tan 67°}{10^8 \times 2000},$$

since $V = H_0 \tan 67°$. This result is independent of the speed.

$$\therefore Q = \frac{2 \times 100 \times 400 \times 0.18 \tan 67° \times 10^6}{10^8 \times 2000} \text{ micro-coulombs}$$

$$= 0.17 \text{ micro-coulomb.}$$

$$\therefore \text{ no. of divisions deflection} = 0.17 \times 100 = 17.$$

MAGNETIC PROPERTIES OF MATERIALS

The magnetic properties of materials require investigation to decide whether they are suitable for permanent magnets, as in the case of loudspeaker magnets, or for temporary magnets, as electromagnets, or for cores of electromagnetic induction machines, as in the case of transformers.

4. Intensity of Magnetization.

The intensity of magnetization, J, of a material is defined as the *magnetic moment per unit volume*. Thus if M is the magnetic moment and V is the volume, then

$$J = \frac{M}{V}. \quad \ldots \ldots \ldots (5)$$

If the material has a uniform cross-sectional area a and a pole-strength m, then, if $2l$ is the magnetic length,

$$M = 2lm, \quad \text{and} \quad V = a \times 2l \text{ (approx.).}$$

$$\therefore J = \frac{M}{V} = \frac{2lm}{2la} = \frac{m}{a}$$

$$= \text{pole-strength per unit area of cross-section.} \quad (6)$$

It should be noted that the latter is not used as a definition of intensity of magnetization, because the idea of magnetic moment is physically sounder than that of pole-strength.

5. Susceptibility.

The *susceptibility*, χ, of a magnetic material is a measure of the ease, or otherwise, with which the material is magnetized by a given magnetic field, and is defined as the ratio J/H, where J is the intensity of magnetization produced by a magnetic field intensity H.

$$\chi = \frac{J}{H}. \quad \ldots \ldots \ldots (7)$$

We shall describe shortly how J is measured (p. 991). Here we shall anticipate the results. As a magnetic material, originally unmagnetized, is subjected to an increasing field, the intensity of magnetization J increases until it reaches a maximum value (Fig. 780 (a)). The material is then "saturated"; that is, its magnetic "domains" are completely aligned with the field H. Fig. 780 (b) also shows how the susceptibility χ varies with H. It increases at first, and passes through a maximum value. As the material approaches saturation the domains cannot yield much further, and the susceptibility falls to a low value.

6. Magnetic Induction.

The flux-density in a material is also called its *magnetic induction*, which is denoted by the symbol B. In electromagnetic induction apparatus, we are interested in the magnetic induction B and not the intensity of magnetization J.

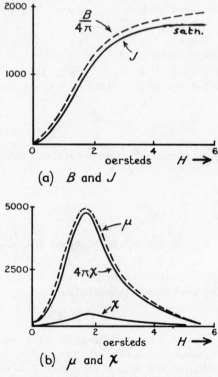

Fig. 780. Variations of B, J, μ, χ with H.
(Differences between broken and full curves exaggerated.)

There is, however, a useful relation between B and J. Suppose a uniform iron bar is placed in a solenoid carrying a current. The flux-density in the iron, B, is then the sum of the flux-density due to the magnetic field and that due to the intensity of magnetization of the iron. The flux-density due to the field $= H$ gauss, where H is the magnetic intensity in oersteds; and on the assumption that 4π lines come from a unit pole, the flux from a pole of strength $m = 4\pi m$ lines.

$$\therefore \text{ flux-density} = \frac{4\pi m}{a} \text{ gauss},$$

where a is the cross-sectional area of the material. But $J = m/a$ (see p. 989).

$$\therefore \text{ flux-density} = 4\pi J$$
$$\therefore \text{ total flux-density}, B, = H + 4\pi J. \qquad \ldots \quad (8)$$

Fig. 780 (a) shows the variation of $B/4\pi$ with H. Since, from (8), $B/4\pi = H/4\pi + J$, it follows that, as H increases and J is constant (saturation), $B/4\pi$ increases.

7. Permeability.

If a material has a magnetic induction (flux-density) B as a result of an applied magnetic field-intensity H, the ratio B/H is called the *permeability*, μ, of the material.

$$\mu = \frac{B}{H}. \qquad \ldots \ldots \ldots (9)$$

The permeability of ordinary iron or steel is of the order of 100 to 10,000. It is not a constant for a given specimen, but varies with the magnetizing field (Fig. 780 (b)).

Since $\qquad\qquad B = H + 4\pi J,$

it follows that $\qquad\qquad \dfrac{B}{H} = 1 + 4\pi \dfrac{J}{H}.$

$$\therefore \ \mu = 1 + 4\pi\chi, \qquad \ldots \ldots \ldots (10)$$

where χ is the susceptibility of the material.

8. Measurement of J and B. Magnetic Cycle.

A deflection magnetometer can be used to investigate the intensity of magnetization, J, and magnetic induction, B, and their variation with the applied magnetic field H.

The specimen is in the form of a rod, and is magnetized by the field of a long solenoid S (Fig. 781). The solenoid S and a coil C known as a "compensating coil" are first set up East–West of the magnetometer, and a current is passed through them. C is then moved until, with no iron in the solenoid, the magnetometer shows no deflection. The coil C has then neutralized, at the magnetometer, the magnetic field of the solenoid, so that when the iron specimen is introduced the deflection of the magnetometer is due solely to the magnetic field of the iron.

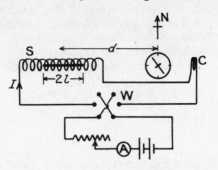

FIG. 781. Measurement of *J-H* and *B-H* curves.

The iron is first demagnetized (p. 999), and then placed in the solenoid. The current I is now increased in steps from zero, and the corresponding deflections θ of the magnetometer are observed. The specimen is taken through a "magnetic cycle" by increasing I until θ is constant, when the specimen has become saturated, then reducing I to zero and *reversing* by W until saturation is reached in the opposite direction, and finally reducing I to zero and increasing it once more in the opposite direction. Fig. 781.

Calculation of J, B, H. The magnetizing field H acting on the specimen is given by

$$H = \frac{4\pi nI}{10} \text{ oersted,}$$

where n is the number of turns per centimetre in the solenoid. Thus $H \propto I$.

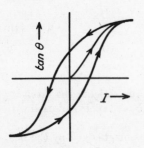

FIG. 782. Magnetization curve by magnetometer method.

The magnetic moment M of the magnetized iron is given by

$$\frac{2Md}{(d^2 - l^2)^2} = H_0 \tan \theta,$$

from which, assuming H_0, M can be found. The volume V of the iron can be found from the formula $V = \pi r^2 \times$ length, where r is the radius of cross-section of the iron, found from a micrometer screw-gauge. Thus knowing M and V, J can be found from the ratio M/V (p. 989). The corresponding magnetic induction, B, can now be calculated from the formula $B = H + 4\pi J$. Fig. 782 shows the variation of $J (\propto \tan \theta)$ with $H (\propto I)$.

9. Hysteresis. Remanence. Coercive Force.

Fig. 783 shows the variation of magnetic induction, B, with the applied field, H, when the specimen is taken through a complete cycle. After the specimen has become saturated, and the field is reduced to zero, the iron is still quite strongly magnetized, setting up a flux-density B_r. This flux-density is called the *remanence*; it is due to the tendency of groups of molecules, or domains, to stay put once they have been aligned.

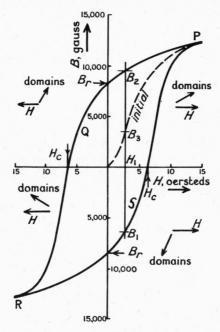

FIG. 783.   A hysteresis loop.

When the field is reversed, the residual magnetism is opposed. Each increase of magnetizing field now causes a decrease of flux-density, as the domains are twisted farther out of alignment. Eventually, the flux-density is reduced to zero, when the opposing field H has the value H_c. This value of H is called the *coercive force* of the iron; it is a measure of the difficulty of breaking up the alignment of the domains.

We now see that, when once the iron has been magnetized, its magnetization curve never passes through the origin again. Instead, it forms the closed loop PQRS, which is called a *hysteresis loop*. Hysteresis, which comes from a Greek work meaning "delayed", can be defined as *the lagging of the magnetic induction, B, behind the magnetizing field, H*, when the specimen is taken through a magnetic cycle.

10. Properties of Magnetic Materials.

Fig. 784 shows the hysteresis loops of iron and steel. Steel is more suitable for permanent magnets, because its high coercivity means that

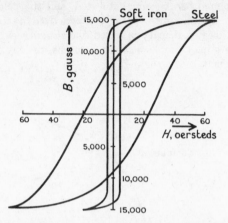

Fig. 784. Hysteresis curves for iron and steel.

it is not easily demagnetized by shaking. The fact that the remanence of iron is a little greater than that of steel is completely outweighed by its much smaller coercivity, which makes it very easy to demagnetize. On the other hand, iron is much more suitable for electromagnets, which have to be switched on and off, as in relays. Iron is also more suitable for the cores of transformers and the armatures of machines. Both of these go through complete magnetizing cycles continuously: transformer cores because they are magnetized by alternating current, armatures because they are turning round and round in a constant field. In each cycle the iron passes through two parts of its hysteresis loop (near Q and S in Fig. 783), where the magnetizing field is having to demagnetize the iron. There the field is doing work against the internal friction of the domains. This work, like all work that is done against friction, is dissipated as heat. The energy dissipated in this way, per cycle, is less for iron than for steel, because iron is easier to demagnetize. It is called the *hysteresis loss*; we will show soon that it is proportional to the area of the B/H loop (p. 997).

In a large transformer the hysteresis loss, together with the heat developed by the current in the resistance of the windings, liberates so much heat that the transformer must be artificially cooled. The cooling is done by circulating oil, which itself is cooled by the atmosphere: it passes through pipes which can be seen outside the transformer, running from top to bottom.

The table on p. 995 gives the properties of some typical magnetic materials; mumetal and ticonal are inventions of the last twenty years,

PROPERTIES OF MAGNETIC MATERIALS

Material	Permeability (max.) μ	Saturation B_m gauss	Remanence B_r gauss	Coercivity H_c oersted	Hysteresis loss W ergs/cm.^{3} per cycle	Critical temp. t.* °C.	Resistivity† ϱ (approx.) 10^{-6} Ω-cm.	Applications
SOFT MATERIALS (iron-like, used for electromagnets with varying currents)								
Iron (99·94%) .	5,500	21,500	13,000	1·0	5,000	770	10	Armatures, relays, large transformer cores, telephone diaphragms
Nickel . .	600	6,100	3,600	3·4	300	360	7	
Cobalt . .	240	18,000	5,000	10	2,000	1,120	10	
Silicon Iron (Stalloy) . (Fe 96, Si 4)	6,700	20,000	12,000	0·5	3,500	690	55	
Mumetal (Ni 74, Fe 20, Cu 5, Mn 1)	80,000	8,500	6,000	0·05	200	—	—	Small transformer cores, magnetic shields
HARD MATERIALS (Steel-like, used for permanent magnets)								
Carbon Steel .	—	10,000	8,000	60	200,000	—	—	Moving-coil instruments, loudspeakers, microphones, telephone ear-piece magnets
Cobalt Steel .	—	—	8,000–10,000	150–240	—	—	—	
Ticonal (Fe 51, Co 24, Ni 14, Al 8, Cu 3)	—	—	12,500	550	—	—	—	

* See page 1000.
† The higher the resistivity of a magnetic material, the less the eddy-currents in it when the flux through it is changed; and therefore the less the energy lost as heat.

the results of deliberate attempts to develop materials with extreme properties.

EXAMPLE

A transformer core is made of silicon iron. It is used with an alternating current of frequency 50 c/s, and is saturated on the peaks of the current. How rapidly will its temperature rise if no heat can escape from it?

Hysteresis loss per cm.^{3} per cycle, from the table,

$$= 3500 \text{ ergs} = 3500 \times 10^{-7} \text{ joule}$$

$$= \frac{3500 \times 10^{-7}}{4 \cdot 18} \text{ calorie.}$$

Hysteresis loss per second $= \dfrac{3500 \times 10^{-7}}{4 \cdot 18} \times 50 \text{ cal.}$

Hysteresis loss per minute $= \dfrac{3500 \times 10^{-7} \times 50 \times 60}{4 \cdot 18} \text{ cal.}$

Mass of 1 cm.^{3} of iron = 7·7 gm.
Specific heat of iron = 0·11.

Therefore temperature rise per minute

$$= \frac{3500 \times 10^{-7} \times 50 \times 60}{4 \cdot 18 \times 7 \cdot 7 \times 0 \cdot 11} \simeq 0 \cdot 3° \text{C. per min.}$$

11. Mechanical Force on Faces of Air Gap.

In a relay and also some other electromagnetic devices, one face of an air gap is free to move, and is attracted by the other. In the telephone earpiece (p. 611 and Fig. 450), the diaphragm bridges the gap between the poles of the magnet, and is attracted. The force acting on it varies with the current through the coils, which varies the total field acting on the iron. If the flux-density in an air gap is uniform, of value B, then it can be shown that the force of attraction between the faces, *per unit area*, is $B^2/8\pi$ dynes/cm.^{2}. The proof of this expression is beyond us, but its form need not surprise us. For B^2 is almost proportional to J^2, where J is the pole-strength per unit area of the faces; and we may expect the force between the faces to be proportional to the pole-strength of each. We may also expect it not to depend on the distance between the faces, because, as long as the faces are close together, the field between them does not vary with their separation.

In the telephone earpiece the force on the diaphragm is

$$f = cB^2,$$

where c is a constant. When the current varies, B varies, and so does f.

Now $$\frac{df}{dB} = 2cB.$$

Thus the change in force with B, and hence with the speech current, is proportional to the average value of B. This in turn depends on the strength of the permanent magnet. The amplitude of vibration of the diaphragm depends on the change in the force f caused by the speech current. It follows that the sensitivity of the earpiece increases with the strength of the permanent magnet used.

We can interpret this mathematical result physically, as follows. The flux-density B is due mainly to the permanent magnet. It magnetizes the soft iron diaphragm, with an intensity proportional to B. The speech current causes a change in the force on the diaphragm, which is proportional to both the speech current and to the intensity of magnetization of the diaphragm. Thus it is proportional to B, and so increases with the strength of the magnet.

12. Hysteresis Loss; Area of Loop.

To calculate the work done in carrying a piece of iron round a hysteresis loop, we adopt the method which we used to calculate the energy stored in the magnetic field of a coil: we consider the back-e.m.f. induced during a change of flux.

Fig. 785 shows a ring of iron, wound with a uniform magnetizing coil of n turns, and mean length l cm. If the current through the coil is I amp., the magnetizing field is

$$H = \frac{4\pi nI}{10l} \text{ oersteds.} \quad \dots \quad \text{(i)}$$

And if B gauss is the flux density in the iron, and A cm.^{2} its cross-sectional area, the flux through it is $\Phi = BA$ maxwells. The flux linkages with the magnetizing coil are therefore

$$N = n\Phi = nBA \text{ maxwell-turns.}$$

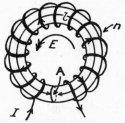

Fig. 785. Work done in magnetization of iron.

Now let us suppose that, in a brief time δt, we increase the current by a small amount, and so increase the flux and flux linkages. During the change a back-e.m.f. will be induced in the coil, of magnitude

$$E = \frac{dN}{dt} 10^{-8} \text{ volt.}$$

Hence, from above,

$$E = nA \frac{dB}{dt} 10^{-8}.$$

To overcome this back-e.m.f., the source of the current I must supply energy to the coil at the rate

$$P = EI \text{ watts.}$$

Thus the total energy supplied to the coil, in increasing the flux through the iron, is

$$\delta W = P \delta t = EI \delta t \text{ joules}$$

$$= InA \frac{dB}{dt} \delta t \times 10^{-8}$$

$$= InA \delta B \times 10^{-8},$$

where δB is the increase in flux-density.

Let us now substitute for the current I in terms of the magnetizing field H. From equation (i) we have

$$I = \frac{10lH}{4\pi n}.$$

Hence
$$\delta W = \frac{10lHnA}{4\pi n}\,\delta B \times 10^{-8}$$

$$= \frac{10^{-7}V}{4\pi}\,H\,\delta B, \qquad \ldots \ldots \ldots \text{(ii)}$$

where V, $= lA$, is the volume of the iron.

Equation (ii) shows that, in taking the flux from any value B_1 to any other B_2, the work done is

$$W = \frac{10^{-7}V}{4\pi}\int_{B_1}^{B_2} H\,dB \text{ joules.} \qquad \ldots \ldots \ldots \text{(iii)}$$

On unit volume of the iron, the work is

$$\frac{10^{-7}}{4\pi}\int_{B_1}^{B_2} H\,dB \text{ joules/cm.}^3$$

The integral in this expression is the area between the B–H curve and the axis of B. Round the complete hysteresis loop, the work done per unit volume is

$$W = \frac{10^{-7}}{4\pi}\oint H\,dB \text{ joules/cm.}^3$$

Here the symbol $\oint$ denotes integration round the closed loop (PQRSP in Fig. 783); the integral is proportional to the area of the loop. In ergs/cm.³ the value of the work done is

$$W = \frac{1}{4\pi}\oint H\,dB \text{ ergs/cm.}^3$$

13. Subsidiary Hysteresis Loops.

When a piece of iron is magnetized, first one way and then the other, it goes round a hysteresis loop even if it is not magnetized to saturation

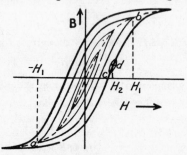

FIG. 786. Subsidiary hysteresis loops

at any point (Fig. 786). The subsidiary loops, *ab* for example, may represent the magnetization of a transformer core by an alternating current in the primary winding: the amplitude H_1 of the magnetizing field is proportional to the amplitude of the current. A transformer core is designed so that it is never saturated under working conditions. For, if it were saturated, the flux through it would not follow the changes in primary current; and the e.m.f. induced in the secondary would be less than it should.

The energy dissipated as heat in going round a subsidiary hysteresis loop is proportional to the area of the loop, just as in going round the main one.

Another kind of subsidiary loop is shown at *cd* in the figure. The iron goes round such a loop when the field is varied above and below the value H_2. This happens in a transformer when the primary carries a fluctuating direct current.

14. Demagnetization.

The only satisfactory way to demagnetize a piece of iron or steel is to carry it round a series of hysteresis loops, shrinking gradually to the origin. If the iron is the core of a toroid, we can do this by connecting the winding to an a.c. supply via a potential divider, as in Fig. 787, and reducing the current to zero. Since the iron goes through fifty loops per second, we do not have to reduce the current very slowly.

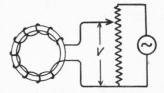

To demagnetize a loose piece of iron or steel, such as a watch, we merely

FIG. 787.   Demagnetization.

put it into, and take it out of, a coil of many turns connected to an a.c. supply. As we draw the watch out, it moves into an ever-weakening field, and is demagnetized.

PARA-, DIA-, AND FERRO-MAGNETISM

15. Paramagnetism. Ferromagnetism.

Many substances become weakly magnetized when they are placed in a strong magnetic field. They lose their magnetism as soon as they are taken out, however. A rod of aluminium, when suspended between the poles of a strong electromagnet, shows poles at its ends which are opposite to those of the electromagnet; it turns until it lies along the field, just as a rod of iron would do, but less forcibly (Fig. 788). The permeability of aluminium is 1·000022 and its susceptibility 0·0000018 (the values for iron are of the order of 1000 and 100 respectively). Other substances which behave in this way are ferric chloride, platinum, and liquid oxygen; they are said to be paramagnetic.

We can explain paramagnetism by considering the electrons in the atom of, say, aluminium. Since the electrons rotate round the nucleus of the atom in closed orbits, they are equivalent to minute currents round those orbits. These currents make the atoms act as weak magnets, which are aligned by an external field. The difference between aluminium and iron, for example, is that aluminium has no domain-structure (p. 993). It can only be weakly magnetized, and as soon as the field is removed, the atoms return to their random orientations; unlike iron, it has no magnetic retentivity. Substances like iron, which have magnetic retentivity are called ferromagnetics. Above a critical temperature known also as the Curie point, ferromagnetics become paramagnetics (see Table on p. 995).

FIG. 788.   Rod of para-
magnetic material in strong
field.

FIG. 789.   Rod of diamagnetic material in strong
field.

16. Diamagnetism.

The explanation of paramagnetism which we have given is too simple, but it is correct as far as it goes. From it, however, we might expect all substances which are not ferromagnetic to be paramagnetic, which they are not. A rod of bismuth, for example, sets itself at right angles to a strong magnetic field; it shows poles similar to the adjacent poles of the magnet which sets up the field (Fig. 789). Bismuth is said to be diamagnetic; its susceptibility is negative, $-0 \cdot 000015$, and its permeability is less than unity: $0 \cdot 99982$. Other diamagnetic substances are water, antimony, and copper.

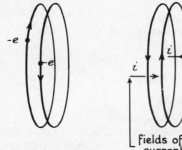

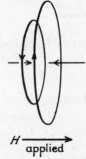

(a) Pair of   (b) Equivalent   (c) Effect of applied
   orbital electrons   currents   magnetic field

FIG. 790.   Explanation of diamagnetism.

Diamagnetic substances have even numbers of electrons per atom. We suppose that they move in pairs around similar orbits, but in opposite senses (Fig. 790 (a)).

Their magnetic fields then cancel, and an external field does not tend to line them up. Why it magnetizes the substance in opposition to itself is harder to see. But if we regard an orbital electron as a circulating current, then it experiences a force when it is placed in a magnetic field (Fig. 790 (*b*)). Either Lenz's law or the left-hand rule will show us that, as in Fig. 790 (*c*), this force tends to dilate an orbit whose field opposes the applied field. Likewise it tends to shrink an orbit whose field assists the applied field. Thus the orbits oppose the applied field.

A rod of diamagnetic material sets itself at right angles to a magnetic field because it is then in stable equilibrium (Fig. 791). If it is turned slightly, poles appear at its ends, and the forces on these poles are always in such directions as to turn the rod back until it is normal to the field.

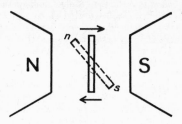

FIG. 791. Equilibrium of diamagnetic rod.

The diamagnetic effect occurs in all substances, but in paramagnetic substances it is normally swamped by the paramagnetic effect. When a paramagnetic substance is heated, however, the thermal agitations of its atoms increase, and hinder their lining up by a magnetic field. Thus the substance's paramagnetism falls as its temperature rises. Diamagnetism is not affected by thermal agitations, and at high temperatures it predominates.

EXERCISES XLII

1. Define the terms *unit magnetic pole, strength of a magnetic field, magnetic induction* (or flux-density), *intensity of magnetization*. State a relation connecting the last three of these quantities.

When a uniformly magnetized steel wire of diameter 2 mm. and length 30 cm. is placed vertically with its lower end on the magnetic east–west line through and 10 cm. from the centre of a deflection magnetometer the needle is deflected from the magnetic meridian by 30°. Calculate the intensity of magnetization of the wire. (Assume horizontal component of earth's field $= 0.18$ oersted.) (*L.*)

2. State Lenz's law relating to induced currents; describe and explain an experiment to illustrate it.

A circular coil whose terminals are short-circuited lies on a horizontal table. Explain how to calculate the charge which flows round the coil when it is turned over on the table. Calculate this charge in micro-coulombs, using the following data: number of turns on the coil $= 500$; mean radius $= 20$ cm.; resistance of coil $= 10$ ohms; angle of dip $= 69°$; $H = 0.18$ oersted. (*N.*)

3. Define *magnetic field-strength* and *intensity of magnetization*. Outline the essential details of a method of finding the relation between them for a long thin rod of iron.

A cylindrical rod of iron 0·6 cm. in diameter and 3·6 cm. long is placed horizontally in the magnetic meridian. If neutral points are obtained at two points 16·9 cm. from the centre of the magnetized rod, calculate the average intensity of magnetization of the iron due to the earth's magnetic field. ($H_0 = 0.2$ oersted.) (*L.*)

4. Define *magnetic field-strength, magnetic induction.*

Describe an experiment to investigate the relation between the magnetic induction, B, and the magnetizing field, H, for iron or steel. Show how B and H are obtained from the observations. Explain what characteristics you would look for in the experimental results if the substance were required for (a) the armature of a dynamo, (b) a permanent magnet. (*L.*)

5. State the laws of electromagnetic induction. A closed circular coil is mounted so that it can be rotated about a diametral axis. By considering the flux changes which occur when the coil is rotated steadily in the earth's magnetic field with the axis of rotation vertical show that an alternating current is produced.

Describe how an earth inductor may be used to determine the angle of dip in the laboratory. (*N.*)

6. Define *magnetic field-strength, intensity of magnetization,* and *susceptibility.*

Draw a diagram to show, in the case of iron, how the intensity of magnetization varies with the magnetizing field, H, (a) when H is small and (b) when H is large.

A uniform rod of iron 12 sq. mm. in cross-section and 4 cm. long is placed horizontally in the magnetic meridian. Draw a sketch of the magnetic field you would expect to find in the neighbourhood of the iron. If the neutral points are at a distance of 15 cm. from the centre of the rod, calculate the susceptibility of the iron. (*L.*)

7. Obtain a relation between *intensity of magnetic field, intensity of magnetization,* and *magnetic induction.*

When a long rod of iron, diameter 0·5 cm., is placed with its axis parallel to a uniform magnetic field of 100 oersteds, a uniform flux of 5,000 maxwells is induced in it. Find (a) the intensity of magnetization, (b) the permeability, (c) the susceptibility of the iron. (*L.*)

8. State the laws relating to (a) the direction, (b) the magnitude of an electromagnetically induced electromotive force, and describe very briefly an experiment illustrating each.

Deduce the relation between the quantity of electricity flowing through a circuit and the flux change producing it.

A flat coil of 150 turns, each of area 300 sq. cm. and of total resistance 50 ohms, is connected to a circuit whose resistance is 40 ohms. Starting with its plane horizontal, the coil is rotated quickly through a half-turn about a diametral axis pointing along the magnetic meridian. If the quantity of electricity which then flows round the circuit is 4 micro-coulombs, find the intensity of the vertical component of the earth's magnetic field. (1 volt = 10^8 e.m.u.) (*N.*)

9. How would you investigate the variation of the intensity of magnetization of a thin iron bar with the magnitude of the applied magnetic field?

Explain the meaning of the term *magnetic hysteresis,* and draw rough diagrams of the hysteresis curves of soft iron and of cobalt steel.

How do these diagrams indicate the suitability of the substances for (a) a permanent magnet, (b) the core of a transformer? (*N.*)

10. Define *susceptibility, permeability,* and state the relation between them.

Describe briefly how you would test if a small rod is diamagnetic, paramagnetic, or ferromagnetic. Draw intensity of magnetization graphs for each type of material and comment on their special features. (*N.*)

11. Explain what is meant by a *ferromagnetic material.* Give a general account of the wide range of magnetic properties exhibited by different ferromagnetic materials and indicate the practical applications of these properties. (*N.*)

12. What is the meaning of *susceptibility, coercivity, hysteresis*? How do the magnitudes of these quantities for a sample of iron determine the magnetic purposes for which it is suitable? Give a very brief account of the procedure you would use to obtain data for a hysteresis curve for iron supplied in the form of a rod. Illustrate your description with a diagram showing the arrangement of the apparatus and the necessary electrical connexions. (*N.*)

13. What is meant by the magnetic field (H) and the magnetic induction (B) inside a bar of iron? How is magnetic induction (μ) defined?

Describe the magnetometer method of finding the relation between induction and magnetization field for soft iron.

Sketch a B–H curve for soft iron and derive from it the form of a μ–H curve using the same scale of H. (*L.*)

14. Describe the structure of a moving coil galvanometer and indicate the main features desirable in a galvanometer for ballistic use.

How would you use a ballistic galvanometer to compare the capacitances of two condensers?

A search coil connected to a ballistic galvanometer has 500 turns of effective diameter 1·00 cm. and resistance 11·0 ohms. On removing the search coil from a certain magnetic field a deflexion of 500 divisions is observed. If the galvanometer has a resistance of 1560 ohms and a sensitivity of 2 divisions mocrocoulomb^{-1} find the induction of the field. (*L.*)

15. Define *intensity of magnetization*.

Describe how you would carry out an experiment to investigate how the intensity of magnetization of a mixture of soft iron filings and sand varies with the concentration by weight of iron filings in the mixture, for uniform magnetizing fields up to 30 oersteds. Show how the results would be calculated from the observations.

If an ammeter reading up to 2·5 amperes and other necessary apparatus were available, how would you provide the uniform magnetizing fields? (*L.*)

CHAPTER XLIII

THE BEGINNINGS OF ATOMIC PHYSICS

CONDUCTION THROUGH GASES

1. Discharges.

Atomic physics can be said to have begun with the study of the conduction of electricity through gases. The passage of electricity through a gas, called a "discharge", was familiar to Faraday, but the steady conduction—as distinct from sparks—takes place when the pressure of the gas is less than about 50 mm. of mercury; in a neon lamp it is about 10 mm. of mercury. Geissler played an important part about 1860 by developing the technique of sealing platinum wires through glass, which enabled electrodes to be mounted in tubes and bulbs of all shapes. At about the same time, Geissler and others improved the vacuum pump, until pressures of about 1/100th mm. of mercury could be reached. At such pressures the walls of a gas discharge tube fluoresce with a green light. In 1869, Hittorf showed that an object in front of the negative electrode, or cathode, of the discharge threw a shadow on the fluorescing walls (Fig. 792). From this he concluded that the

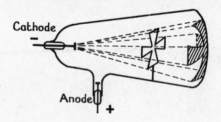

FIG. 792. Cathode rays travel in straight lines.

fluorescence was due to something which proceeded in straight lines from the cathode, wherever the anode, or positive electrode, of the discharge might be. This something he called "cathode rays". In 1879, Crookes deflected cathode rays with a magnet, as in Fig. 793 (a); he thus showed that they were carrying a current. From the direction of the deflection, and the left-hand rule, he found the direction of the current (Fig. 793 (a)). As this was *towards* the cathode, it followed that the cathode rays, which were travelling *from* the cathode, were streams of negatively charged particles (Fig. 793 (b)).

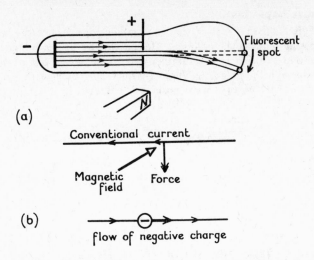

FIG. 793.   Deflection shows cathode rays are negatively charged.

2. Cathode Rays—Electrons.

The particles which make up cathode rays are now called electrons. In 1897, J. J. Thomson deflected them with an electrostatic field, between oppositely charged plates, as in a cathode-ray-oscillograph tube. The motion of an electron in an electric field is similar to that of a projectile in a gravitational field, but it tells us very little about the electron. In particular, measurements of the electron's motion do not give its charge—just as measurements of the path of a shell do not give its mass. However, if these measurements are combined with measurements of the electron's motion in a magnetic field, then the ratio of its charge to its mass, e/m, can be calculated. This is what Thomson did (see p. 1006). So also, in the same year but in a slightly different way, did Kaufmann. Modern measurements give

$$\frac{e}{m} = 1 \cdot 76 \times 10^8 \text{ coulombs per gm.}$$

Thomson showed that e/m had the same value, whatever the gas through which the discharge took place, and whatever the nature of the electrodes. He concluded that electrons were fundamental particles, to be found in the atoms of all substances.

The ratio e/m has a very great magnitude. Consequently, when electrons are accelerated by an electric field, they reach very high speeds (p. 784). Because of these speeds they fly out from the cathode along straight lines, and throw the sharp shadows which Hittorf discovered.

3. Positive Rays—Ions.

In 1896, Goldstein showed that in a gaseous discharge there are also rays passing *towards* the cathode. He did this by boring a hole in the cathode and showing that a luminous streamer passed out of the discharge through the hole (Fig. 794). By deflecting them with a magnet he showed that the rays were positively charged: he therefore called

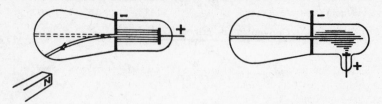

Fig. 794.   Positive rays.   Fig. 795.   Positive rays do not come
                                              from anode.

them positive rays. The positive rays do not come from the anode, because they appear equally strongly when the anode is put in a side-pocket (Fig. 795). It follows that they must originate in the gas itself. We shall see in a moment that they are gaseous ions, analogous to the ions which carry the current in electrolysis: they are gas atoms which have lost an electron.

4. Thomson's Experiments.

The nature of positive rays was first shown by Wien and by J. J. Thomson in 1898. By a method similar to that which he had developed for electrons, Thomson measured the charge to mass ratio, q/M, of positive rays. He found that, unlike e/m for electrons, its value varied from one gas to another, though it was constant for a given gas. For hydrogen, Thomson found

$$\frac{q}{M} \backsimeq 100{,}000 \text{ coulombs per gm.} \qquad \ldots \quad (1)$$

This value of q/M strongly suggests that the positive rays in hydrogen gas are identical with the hydrogen ions in electrolysis. For in electrolysis 96,500 coulombs liberate one gramme-equivalent; and since the equivalent weight of hydrogen is 1·008, the charge-to-mass ratio for hydrogen ions is

$$\frac{q}{M} = \frac{96{,}500}{1 \cdot 008} = 95{,}700 \text{ coulombs per gm.} \qquad \ldots \quad (2)$$

Within the limits of error of Thomson's experiments, this is equal to his value for positive rays.

Thomson next compared the values of q/M for the positive rays of various gases. He found that for nitrogen the value was 1/14 of the value for hydrogen; since the nitrogen atom is 14 times heavier than the hydrogen, the most reasonable conclusion is that positive rays in nitrogen are charged nitrogen atoms. Like hydrogen ions, they have lost an electron. Similarly Thomson showed that q/M for oxygen had 1/16 of its value for hydrogen, and so forth; he left no reasonable doubt that positive rays are streams of charged atoms. They are atoms which have lost one (or more) electrons. In some discharges, negatively charged ions are found; they are atoms which have gained one (or more) electrons.

We can thus identify q in equations (1) and (2) with the electronic charge e, and we can then find how much less massive is the electron than the hydrogen atom, of mass M_H:

$$\frac{m}{M_H} = \frac{\dfrac{e}{M_H}}{\dfrac{e}{m}} = \frac{97,300}{1\cdot76 \times 10^8} = \frac{1}{1840}.$$

Thus the electron is extremely light, even compared with the lightest atom we know (see also p. 1012).

5. Isotopes.

Measurements on positive rays in chlorine show that there are two chlorine atoms, of atomic weights 35 and 37. These cannot be separated chemically, and they must therefore have identical chemical properties. They are called heterobatic isotopes (different weights, same character) or, more often, simply isotopes. The chemical atomic weight of chlorine is 35·5; from this value it follows that the natural gas is a mixture of isotopes, in the proportions 3 of 35 to 1 of 37.

Isotopes have now been found of most chemical elements, including hydrogen and oxygen.

6. The Mechanism of Conduction.

How are the ions and electrons in a gaseous discharge produced? A luminous discharge requires a voltage, V, of at least a hundred volts across the gas at pressures of about 1 mm. mercury. At much higher or lower pressures, it may require thousands of volts. But with a voltage of about ten, although there is no glow, a very weak current, I, can be detected—of the order of 10^{-15} amp. (Fig. 796 (a)). This we attribute to electrons emitted from the cathode by the photo-electric effect (p. 1018); a trace of ultra-violet light in the laboratory would account for the emission. When the voltage is increased the electrons are accelerated by the electric field to a higher speed, and strike the gas atoms more violently on their way to the anode. When the voltage is high enough the electrons strike the atoms with sufficient kinetic energy to knock electrons out of them (Fig. 796 (*b*)). This process is called ionization by collision; the atoms become ions, and move towards the cathode; the extra electrons join the original ones in their flight to the

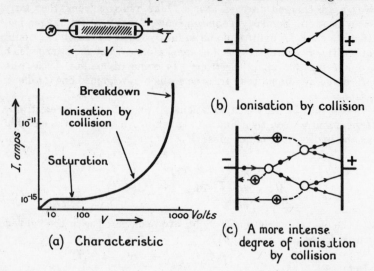

Fig. 796. Discharge through gas at low pressure. [In (*a*) currents and voltages are order of magnitudes only; in (*b*) and (*c*), the numerous non-ionizing collisions are not shown.]

anode. At higher voltages the knocked-out electrons are accelerated enough to produce more ions and electrons on the way (Fig. 796 (*c*)). Eventually a point is reached at which the current grows uncontrollably —the gas is said to break down. In practice, the current is limited by a resistor, in series with the discharge tube; in a commercial neon lamp this resistor, of resistance about 5000 ohms, is hidden in the base.

The current through a gas, like that through an electrolyte, is carried by carriers of both signs—positive and negative. At the anode, the negative electrons enter the wires of the outside circuit, and eventually come round to the cathode. There they meet positive ions, which they now enter, and so re-form neutral gas atoms. Positive ions arriving at the cathode knock off some of the atoms, which diffuse into the body of the discharge, and there, eventually, they are ionized again. Thus a limited amount of gas can carry a current indefinitely.

Once a gas has broken down, current can continue to pass through it even in the dark: that is to say, when there is no ultra-violet light to make the cathode emit electrons. The electrons from the cathode are now simply knocked out of it by the violent bombardment of the positive ions.

Ultra-violet light is not, as a rule, necessary even for starting a gaseous discharge. The somewhat mysterious cosmic rays, which reach the earth from outer space, are able to ionize a gas; they may therefore enable a discharge to start. Once it has started, the emission of electrons by bombardment of the cathode keeps it going.

7. The Gaseous Discharge at Various Pressures.

Fig. 797 (a) represents a glass tube, a foot or two long, connected to a vacuum pump P and a pressure gauge G (pp. 258, 259). It contains an anode A and a cathode K, connected respectively to the positive and negative terminals of the secondary of an induction coil. As the air is pumped out, nothing happens until the pressure has fallen to about 100 mm. Hg (mercury). Then thin streamers of luminous gas appear between the electrodes (Fig. 797 (b)).

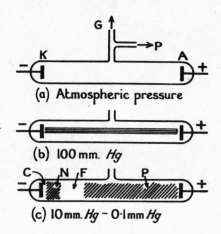

(a) Atmospheric pressure

(b) 100 mm. Hg

(c) 10 mm. Hg - 0·1 mm Hg

FIG. 797.   Stages in development of gaseous discharge.

At about 10 mm. Hg the discharge becomes a steady glow, spread throughout the tube (Fig. 797 (c)). It is broken up by two darker regions, of which the one nearest the cathode, C in the figure, is narrow and hard to see. The dark region C is called the cathode dark space, or sometimes, after its discoverer, the Crookes' dark space. Beyond the cathode dark space is a bright region N called the negative glow, and beyond that the Faraday dark space F—also called after its discoverer. Beyond the Faraday dark space stretches a luminous column P, called the positive column, which fills the rest of the discharge tube. Sometimes the positive column breaks up into alternating bright and dark segments, called striations (Fig. 798).

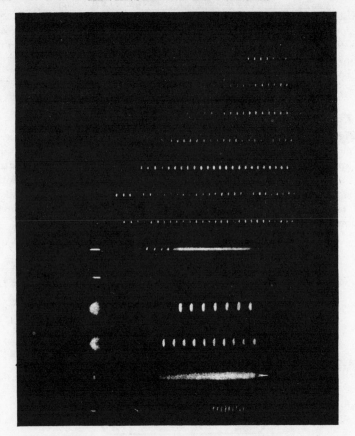

FIG. 798. Photographs of gaseous discharge.

In all the photographs of Fig. 798 the cathode is on the left. The cathode dark space can hardly be seen—it lies just around the cathode —but the negative glow and Faraday dark space are clear. The upper eight photographs show the effect of moving the cathode farther from the anode: the cathode dark space, negative glow, and Faraday dark space remain unchanged, and the positive column grows to fill up the space between the electrodes.

The positive column is the most striking part of the discharge, but the cathode dark space is electrically the most important. In it the electrons from the cathode are being violently accelerated by the electric field, and gaining energy with which to ionize the gas atoms. In the positive column some atoms are being ionized by collisions with electrons; others are being excited, in a way which we cannot describe here, and made to emit their characteristic spectra.

When the pressure of the gas in the discharge tube is reduced still further, the dark spaces swell, and the positive column shrinks. At about 1 mm. Hg the cathode dark space becomes distinct, and at 0·1 mm. Hg it is several centimetres long. Eventually, as the pressure falls, the cathode dark space stretches from the anode to the cathode, and the negative glow and positive column vanish. This happens at about 0·01 mm. Hg in a tube a foot or so long.

When the cathode dark space occupies the whole discharge tube, the walls of the tube fluoresce, in the way we have already described. The electrons flying across the space are the cathode rays studied by Crookes. Where they strike the anode they produce X-rays (p. 1017).

8. Determination of e/m for Cathode Rays or Electrons.

In 1897 J. J. Thomson carried out experiments which showed that cathode rays were particles much lighter than the hydrogen atom. Later they were called *electrons*.

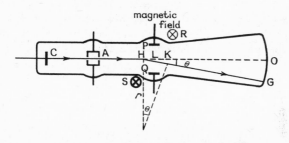

Fig. 799.   Thomson's determination of e/m for electron (*not to scale*).

Thomson's apparatus is shown simplified in Fig. 799. C and A are the cathode and anode respectively, and narrow slits are cut in opposite plates at A so that the cathode rays passing through are limited to a narrow beam. The rays then strike the glass at O, producing a glow there. The rays can be deflected electrostatically by means of connecting a large battery to the horizontal plates P, Q, or magnetically by means of a current passing through Helmholtz coils R, S, on either side of the tube near P and Q, as shown by the small circles in Fig. 799.

The magnetic field is perpendicular to the paper, and if it is uniform a constant force acts on the cathode rays (electrons) normal to its motion. The particles thus begin to move along the arc HK of a circle of radius r. When they leave the field, the particles move in a straight line and strike the glass at G.

With the usual notation, see p. 936,

$$\text{force } F = evH = \frac{mv^2}{r},$$

where e is the charge on an electron and m is its mass.

$$\therefore \quad \frac{e}{m} = \frac{v}{rH}. \qquad \dots \dots \dots \text{(i)}$$

To find the radius r, we note that, from Fig. 799, $\tan \theta = OG/OL$ $= HK/r$.

$$\therefore \quad r = \frac{HK \cdot OL}{OG}.$$

L is about the middle of the solenoid surrounding the plates.

The velocity v was found by applying an electric field between P, Q of such an intensity E as to bring the beam back to O. Then

$$Ee = evH$$

$$\therefore \quad v = \frac{E}{H}.$$

Thomson found that v was considerably less than the velocity of light, 3×10^{10} cm. per sec., so that cathode rays were certainly not waves.

On substituting for v and r in (i), the ratio charge/mass (e/m) for an electron was obtained. Modern determinations show that

$$\frac{e}{m} = 1 \cdot 76 \times 10^8 \text{ coulombs per gm.},$$

or

$$\frac{m}{e} = \frac{1}{1 \cdot 76} \times 10^{-8} \text{ gm. per coulomb.} \qquad \dots \dots \text{(ii)}$$

Now from electrolysis the electrochemical equivalent of hydrogen is $0 \cdot 0000104$ gm. per coulomb, or

$$\frac{M}{e} = 1040 \times 10^{-8} \text{ gm. per coulomb,}$$

assuming the hydrogen ion carries a charge e numerically equal to that on an electron, M being the mass of the hydrogen ion. Hence, from (ii),

$$\frac{m}{M} = \frac{1}{1 \cdot 76 \times 1040} = \frac{1}{1830}.$$

Thus the electron is nearly two thousand times as light as the hydrogen atom.

EXAMPLE

Describe *one* experiment by which the ratio of charge to mass (e/m) for the electron has been determined.

A narrow horizontal beam of electrons passes symmetrically between two vertical metal plates mounted one each side of the beam. The velocity of the electrons is $3 \cdot 00 \times 10^9$ cm. sec.$^{-1}$, the plates are $3 \cdot 00$ cm. long and $1 \cdot 00$ cm. apart.

It is found that when a battery of 568 volts is connected to the plates the electron beam just strikes the end of one of them. Calculate the value of e/m. (N.)

First part (see text).

Second part. Suppose the electron beam enters at A and leaves at B. Fig. 800. If E is the intensity of the field, e is the electron charge. and m is the mass, the force on the electron $= Ee$.

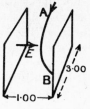

FIG. 800. Example.

But force = mass × acceleration (f).

$$\therefore Ee = mf.$$

$$\therefore f = \frac{Ee}{m}. \quad \cdots \cdots \quad \text{(i)}$$

For motion *perpendicular* to the plates, the initial velocity = 0.

$$\therefore \text{ distance travelled in this direction, } s, = 0{\cdot}5 = \tfrac{1}{2}ft^2, \quad \cdots \quad \text{(ii)}$$

where t is the time. Also, as there is no acceleration *parallel* to the plates,

$$\text{distance, } s, = 3{\cdot}00 = \text{vel.} \times \text{time} = 3{\cdot}00 \times 10^9 \times t$$

$$\therefore t = \frac{3}{3 \times 10^9} = \frac{1}{10^9} \text{ sec.}$$

Hence, from (ii), $\quad f = \dfrac{2s}{t^2} = \dfrac{2 \times 0{\cdot}5}{(1/10^9)^2} = 10^{18} \text{ cm. per sec.}^2$

From (i), $\qquad\qquad\qquad \dfrac{e}{m} = \dfrac{f}{E} = \dfrac{10^{18}}{E},$

and $\qquad\qquad E = \dfrac{568 \text{ volts}}{1{\cdot}00 \text{ cm.}} = \dfrac{568}{300} \text{ e.s.u. per cm.}$

$$\therefore \frac{e}{m} = \frac{10^{18} \times 300}{568} = 5{\cdot}28 \times 10^{17} \text{ e.s.u. per gm.}$$

ATOMIC STRUCTURE

9. Atomic Structure.

The discoveries of the electron and of positive rays led, about 1900, to the idea of atomic structure illustrated in Fig. 801 (*a*). The positive part of the atom, which contained nearly all its mass, was naturally supposed to give it most of its size also; the electrons were supposed to be embedded in the positive body. The diameters of atoms were

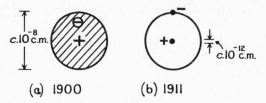

(a) 1900　　　　(b) 1911

FIG. 801. The hydrogen atom.

known, from measurements of the viscosities of gases, etc., to be of the order shown, 10^{-8} cm.

In 1911 Rutherford showed that this idea would not work—he proposed the nuclear or planetary structure which we have already described (Fig. 801 (*b*) and p. 882). Before we can understand how he did so, we must glance at the phenomena of radioactivity.

10. Radioactivity.

In 1896, Becquerel, while studying fluorescence, wrapped a photographic plate in black paper, and placed some uranium-potassium sulphate crystals on top. When he developed the plate, he found that it was fogged where the crystals had been. He found the same result with other salts, and concluded that they emitted radiations of some kind, which were more penetrating than light; he said that the uranium salts were "radioactive". In 1898, Pierre and Marie Curie isolated from uranium ore (pitch-blende) a substance millions of times more radioactive than uranium, which they called radium. Between 1900 and 1910, Rutherford and others investigated the nature of the radiations. By putting radium in a strong magnetic field (Fig. 802) they were able to separate three kinds of radiation:

   (i) relatively slow particles, of small charge-to-mass ratio, called α-particles;

  (ii) fast particles, of great charge-to-mass ratio, called β-particles;

 (iii) uncharged rays called γ-rays.

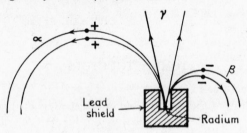

Fig. 802. Separation of a, β, and γ-rays.

The γ-rays were later shown to be not matter but radiation, similar in character to light, but of much shorter wavelength. The β-particles had the same charge-to-mass ratio as cathode rays, and so were identified as electrons. The α-particles had twice the charge-to-mass ratio of the hydrogen atom; they were eventually identified as helium nuclei, which we shall describe later (see p. 1042).

When a radioactive atom emits an α- or β-particle, it changes its chemical nature. The atom into which it changes is generally radioactive also, and so on. Thus the disentangling of radioactive processes was a very difficult problem. We shall describe some of the results and theories which did not exist at the time the work was done, but to which, in fact, it helped to lead.

11. The Nucleus of Atoms.

In 1911, Rutherford placed a thin foil of aluminium between a source of α-particles and a sheet of glass coated with zinc sulphide (Fig. 803). When α-particles strike zinc sulphide they make it emit a flash of light. Thus Rutherford was able to observe the α-particles after they had passed through the foil. He found that they were scattered out of the direct line from the source, and concluded that the scattering was due to collisions with atoms of the aluminium. The scattering must be due to the positive parts of the atoms, because the electrons have so little mass that the α-particles would displace *them*,

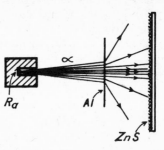

Fig. 803. Scattering of α-particles by aluminium atoms.

rather than they the α-particles. Rutherford observed some very wide angles of scattering—40° or more—and he estimated how closely the α-particles must have approached the atoms. The result was about 10^{-12} cm.

This result showed that the massive positive part of the atom must be far smaller than the atom as a whole. For that, as we have seen, was known to be about 10^{-8} cm. across. Rutherford therefore suggested that the massive positive part of the atom was concentrated in a core, or nucleus, about 10^{-12} cm. in diameter. Around it revolved the electrons, in orbits like planets round the sun: the electrostatic attraction of the nucleus keeping their orbital motion in equilibrium, like gravitational attraction by the sun in the solar system.

12. Atomic Weight and Atomic Number.

The idea of the atomic nucleus was made clearer by some measurements of X-ray wavelengths by Moseley in 1914. These experiments and their interpretation are too complicated to describe here, but Moseley's work showed the meaning of the property of an atom called its atomic number. At that time the atomic number was defined as the number of the element in order of weight, thus:

Element	H	He	Li	Be	B	C	N	O	F
Atomic wt. A	1·008	4·003	6·94	9·02	10·82	12·01	14·01	16·00	19·00
Atomic no. Z	1	2	3	4	5	6	7	8	9

For most elements the atomic number is about equal to half the atomic weight. When the elements are arranged in this way their physical and chemical properties show an orderly progression from one element to the next, with periodic similarities familiar to anyone who has read a little chemistry. There are, however, a few discrepancies. Moseley suggested that the atomic number of an element should be redefined, as the positive charge on its nucleus, in electronic units. (Since atoms normally have no net electric charge, this is also the number of electrons revolving around the nucelus.) As a result of his experiments Moseley arranged the atoms in order of atomic number on his definition. His order agreed with the chemical one except in a few instances. And those instances were the ones where the order based on atomic weight was unsatisfactory. When Moseley's order was followed, the discrepancies disappeared.

13. Nuclear Structure.

Since the hydrogen nucleus was the simplest positive particle known, it was called a *proton*, and at this stage the nuclei of heavier atoms were regarded as mixtures of protons and electrons. As shown in Fig. 804 (*a*), the nucleus of boron was supposed to contain 11 protons

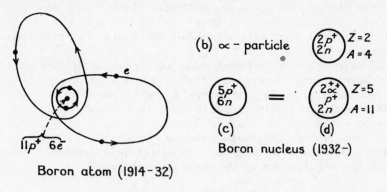

Fig. 804. Atomic and nuclear structures.

(to give the atomic weight of approximately 11) and 6 electrons (to make the atomic number $11 - 6 = 5$). Later work has suggested that the nucleus contains uncharged particles, called neutrons, which have about the same mass as a proton. (Between 1930 and 1932 various workers, in Germany, France, and England, had discovered that beryllium emits such particles, when it is bombarded with α-rays.) We therefore now regard the nucleus as a mixture of neutrons and protons: boron has 5 protons and 6 neutrons (Fig. 804 (*c*)). The α-particle, or helium nucleus (Fig. 804 (*b*)) has an atomic weight, A, of 4, and an atomic number, Z, of 2; it contains 2 protons and 2 neutrons. Because α-particles are emitted in some radioactive changes, we suppose that they exist, as units, in the nucleus (Fig. 804 (d)). See also p. 1042.

X-RAYS

14. X-rays.

In 1895, Röntgen found that some photographic plates, kept carefully wrapped in his laboratory, had become fogged. Instead of merely throwing them aside he set out to find the cause of the fogging. He traced it to a gas-discharge tube, which he was using with a low pressure and high voltage. This tube appeared to emit a radiation that could penetrate paper, wood, glass, rubber, and even aluminium a centimetre and a half thick. Röntgen could not find out whether the radiation was a stream of particles or a train of waves—Newton had the same difficulty with light—and he decided to call it X-rays.

15. Nature and Production of X-rays.

We now regard X-rays as waves, similar to light waves, but of much shorter wavelength: about 10^{-8} cm., or 1 Ångström unit. They are produced when fast electrons, or cathode rays, strike a target, such as the walls or anode of a low-pressure discharge tube. In a modern X-ray tube there is no gas, or as little as high-vacuum technique can achieve: the pressure is about 10^{-5} mm. Hg. The electrons are provided by thermionic emission from a white-hot tungsten filament (p. 974). In Fig. 805, F is the filament and T is the target, or anode. Because there

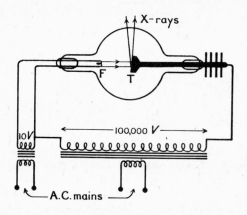

FIG. 805.   An X-ray tube.

is so little gas, the electrons on their way to the anode do not lose any perceptible amount of their energy in ionizing atoms. From the a.c.

mains, transformers provide about 10 volts for heating the filament, and about 100,000 volts for accelerating the electrons. On the half-cycles when the target is positive, the electrons bombard it, and generate X-rays. On the half-cycles when the target is negative, nothing happens at all—there is too little gas in the tube for it to break down. Thus the tube acts, in effect, as its own rectifier (p. 974), providing pulses of direct current between target and filament. The heat generated at the target by the electronic bombardment is so great that the target must be cooled artificially. In the figure, fins for air-cooling are shown, but in large tubes the target is made hollow, and is cooled by circulating water or oil. The target in an X-ray tube is usually tungsten, which has a high melting-point.

16. Effects and Uses of X-rays.

When X-rays strike many minerals, such as zinc sulphide, they make them fluoresce. (It was while studying this fluorescence that Becquerel discovered the radiations from uranium.) If a human—or other—body is placed between an X-ray tube and a fluorescent screen, the shadows of its bones can be seen on the screen, because they absorb X-rays more than flesh does. Unusual objects, such as swallowed safety-pins, if they are dense enough, can also be located. X-ray photographs can likewise be taken, with the plate in place of the screen. In this way cracks and flaws can be detected in metal castings.

When X-rays are passed through a crystal, they are scattered by its atoms and diffracted, as light is by a diffraction grating (p. 714). By recording the diffraction pattern on a photographic plate, and measuring it up, the structure of the crystal can be discovered. This was developed by Sir William Bragg and his son, Sir Lawrence Bragg.

PHOTO-ELECTRICITY

17. Photo-electricity.

In 1888, Hallwachs shone ultra-violet light on to an electrically charged metal plate, standing on an electroscope. He found that the plate gradually lost its charge, if it had been negatively charged at the start, but not if it had been positively charged. Many years later, other experiments showed that ultra-violet light caused metals to emit negatively charged particles, which had the same charge-to-mass ratio as cathode rays: they were electrons. The emission was called photo-electric emission. A few metals, such as caesium, will emit photo-electrons when illuminated with visible light.

Fig. 806 (a) is a diagram of a modern photo-electric cell. The cathode K is a V-shaped plate coated with caesium or some more complicated and very sensitive surface. In front of it is a wire ring, the anode A, which collects the photo-electrons. The heavy curve at (b) in the figure shows how the current through the cell, I, varies with the potential difference across it, V. At first the current rises, but at a potential difference of about 30 volts it saturates. We suppose that the anode is then collecting all the electrons emitted by the cathode. This curve is drawn for a light-flux of 1 lumen upon the cathode (p. 567). If the flux is halved, the saturation current also falls by a half, showing that the number of electrons emitted per second is proportional to the light-flux falling upon the cathode.

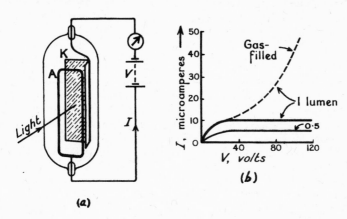

FIG. 806.   A photo-cell (photo-emissive).

Some photo-electric cells contain an inert gas—such as argon—at a pressure of a few millimetres of mercury. The current in such a cell does not saturate, because the electrons ionize the gas atoms by collision. Fig. 806 (b). The greater the potential difference, the greater the kinetic energy of the electrons, and the more intense the ionization of the gas.

Photo-electric cells are used in photometry, in industrial control and counting operations, in television, and in many other ways. Their use in reproducing sound from film is explained in the Sound section of this book (p. 614).

18. Photo-voltaic Cells.

Photo-electric cells of the kind we have just described are called photo-emissive cells, because in them light causes electrons to be emitted. Another type of cell is called photo-voltaic, because it generates an e.m.f., and can therefore provide a current without a battery. One form of such a cell consists of a copper disc, oxidized on one face (Cu_2O/Cu), as shown in Fig. 807 (a). Over the exposed surface of the oxide a film of gold (Au) is deposited, by evaporation in a vacuum;

the film is so thin that light can pass through it. When it does so it generates an e.m.f. in a way which we cannot describe here.

Photo-voltaic cells are sensitive to visible light. Fig. 807 (b) shows how the current from such a cell, through a galvanometer of resistance

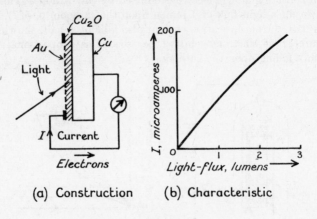

(a) Construction   (b) Characteristic

FIG. 807.   A photo-voltaic cell.

about 100 ohms, varies with the light-flux falling upon it. The current is not quite proportional to the flux. Photo-voltaic cells are obviously convenient for photographic exposure meters, for measuring illumination in factories, and so on, but as measuring instruments they are less accurate than photo-emissive cells.

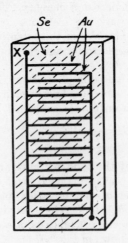

FIG. 808.   A selenium cell.

19. Photo-conductive Cells.

A photo-conductive cell is one whose resistance changes when it is illuminated. A common form consists of a pair of interlocking comb-like electrodes made of gold (Au) deposited on glass (Fig. 808); over these a thin film of selenium (Se) is deposited. In effect, the selenium forms a large number of strips, electrically in parallel; this construction is necessary because selenium has a very high resistivity (about 70,000 ohm-cm. in the dark). The resistance between the terminals, XY, falls from about 10^7 ohms in the dark to about 10^6 ohms in bright light. In conjunction with valve amplifiers, photo-conductive cells were used as fire alarms during the last war. They were the first photo-cells to be discovered—in 1873—but they were the least useful. They are sluggish, taking about a second to respond fully to a change of illumination; and they show hysteresis—one change of illumination affects their response to the next.

EXERCISES XLIII

1. Give a short account of the phenomena observed when an electric discharge passes through a gas at very low pressure (10^{-6} atmosphere). Describe very briefly experiments which reveal the nature of the discharge.

What is the direction of the force acting on a negatively charged particle moving through a magnetic field? Deduce the shape of the path of a charged particle projected at right angles to a uniform magnetic field. (*L.*)

2. Draw a labelled diagram of some form of X-ray tube and of its electrical connexions when in actual use.

Electrons starting from rest and passed through a potential difference of 1000 volts are found to acquire a velocity of 1.88×10^9 cm. per sec. Calculate the ratio of the charge to the mass of the electron in coulombs per gm. (*N.*)

3. You are provided with a glass tube containing an electrode at each end, an exhaust pump, and a source of high potential. Under what conditions (*a*) does the gas within the tube become a relatively good conductor, (*b*) is a beam of electrons (cathode rays) produced within the tube?

What modifications must be made in the tube in order that a strong beam of X-rays may be produced? What would happen in each case if the potential applied was increased?

What experiment would you perform to show the effect of a magnetic field on the conducting particles in (*a*) and (*b*) and on a beam of X-rays? State the result you would expect. (*L.*)

4. Give an account of the production and properties of cathode rays. (*L.*)

5. What are electrons? Briefly describe *one* method by which a beam of electrons may be produced.

Describe and explain experiments to demonstrate: (*a*) the effect of passing a beam of electrons through (i) a magnetic field, (ii) an electric field; (*b*) the effect of focusing the rays on a metal target. (*C.*)

6. Give an account, illustrated by diagrams, of the part played by electrons in *two* of the following: (*a*) the production of X-rays, (*b*) the photo-cell, (*c*) the cathode-ray oscillograph. (*N.*)

7. Give a general account of the conduction of electricity through gases at low pressures, and state briefly the evidence for the belief that cathode rays consist of negatively charged particles. (*O. & C.*)

8. Describe the structure and mode of action of a modern form of X-ray tube.

9. What properties of cathode rays are used in the cathode-ray oscillograph? Draw a labelled diagram to show the construction of this instrument and describe *one* application. (*N.*)

10. Give a short account of the properties of cathode rays. Describe briefly experiments by which *three* of these properties have been demonstrated. In what ways do cathode rays differ from X-rays? (*C.*)

11. What properties of cathode rays are utilized in finding the ratio of their charge to mass? Describe a method of finding this ratio.

The ratio e/m for cathode rays is found to be 1.76×10^7 e.m.u. per gm.; the electrochemical equivalent of hydrogen is 1.05×10^{-5} gm. coulomb. Compare the mass of the electron with the mass of the hydrogen atom (expressing the result as a fraction). (*N.*)

12. Describe a method for measuring the charge per unit mass for the electron, showing how the value is calculated from the observations.

An ion, for which the charge per unit mass is 4.40×10^3 e.m.u. gm.$^{-1}$, has a velocity of 3.52×10^7 cm. sec.$^{-1}$ and moves in a circular orbit in a magnetic field of induction 4×10^3 gauss. What will be the radius of this orbit? (*L.*)

13. Describe the construction of a cathode ray tube. How may it be used to measure e/m and v for a stream of electrons?

An electron is accelerated horizontally through a potential difference of 5 volts in a vacuum. How far will it fall under gravity while subsequently travelling 10 metres horizontally in the vacuum? [1 gm. molecule of a substance is deposited electrolytically by 96,000 coulombs; mass of an electron is 1/1837 of that of a proton.] (*C.*)

14. Describe how a beam of electrons may be produced and detected. Explain, with the aid of diagrams, how such a beam may be deflected by (*a*) an electric and (*b*) a magnetic field.

Hence show how a cathode-ray oscilloscope may be used to demonstrate the waveform of an alternating voltage. What limits the frequency of alternation which may be observed in this way? (*O. & C.*)

15. With the aid of a labelled diagram describe a modern form of X-ray tube and the circuit which is used with it. Give an account of the action which takes place within the tube.

State the properties of X-rays and indicate how their nature has been established. (*N.*)

CHAPTER XLIV

FURTHER ELECTRICITY TOPICS

A.C. CIRCUITS

1. *L* and *R* in series. Consider an inductance L in series with a resistance R, with an alternating voltage V (r.m.s.) of frequency f connected across both components Fig. 809 (i).

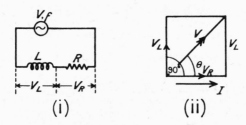

Fig. 809. Inductance and resistance in series.

The sum of the respective voltages V_L and V_R across L and R is equal to V. But the voltage V_L leads by $90°$ on the current I, and the voltage V_R is in phase with I (see pp. 978–9). Thus the two voltages can be drawn to scale as shown in Fig. 809 (ii), and hence, by Pythagoras' theorem, it follows that the vector sum V is given by

$$V^2 = V_L{}^2 + V_R{}^2.$$

But $V_L = IX_L$, $V_R = IR$.

$$\therefore \ V^2 = I^2 X_L{}^2 + I^2 R^2 = I^2 (X_L{}^2 + R^2),$$

$$\therefore \ I = \frac{V}{\sqrt{X_L{}^2 + R^2}}. \qquad \ldots \ldots \text{(i)}$$

Also, from Fig. 809 (ii), the current I lags on the applied voltage V by an angle θ given by

$$\tan \theta = \frac{V_L}{V_R} = \frac{IX_L}{IR} = \frac{X_L}{R}, \qquad \ldots \ldots \text{(ii)}$$

From (i), it follows that the "opposition" Z to the flow of alternating current is given on ohms by

$$Z = \frac{V}{I} = \sqrt{X_L{}^2 + R^2}. \qquad \ldots \ldots \text{(iii)}$$

This "opposition", Z, is known as the *impedance* of the circuit.

1023

2. C and R in series. A similar analysis enables the impedance to be found of a capacitance C and resistance R in series. Fig. 810 (i). In this case the voltage V_C across the condenser lags by 90° on the current I (see p. 978), and the voltage V_R across the resistance is in phase with

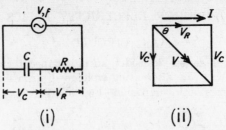

FIG. 810. Capacitance and resistance in series.

the current I. As the vector sum is V, the applied voltage, it follows by Pythagoras' theorem that

$$V^2 = V_C{}^2 + V_R{}^2 = I^2 X_C{}^2 + I^2 R^2 = I^2(X_C{}^2 + R^2),$$

$$\therefore I = \frac{V}{\sqrt{X_C{}^2 + R^2}}. \qquad \ldots \ldots \quad \text{(i)}$$

Also, the current I leads on V by an angle θ given by

$$\tan \theta = \frac{V_C}{V_R} = \frac{I X_C}{IR} = \frac{X_C}{R}. \qquad \ldots \ldots \quad \text{(ii)}$$

It follows from (i) that the impedance Z of the C–R series circuit is

$$Z = \frac{V}{I} = \sqrt{X_C{}^2 + R^2}.$$

It should be noted that although the impedance formula for a C–R series circuit is of the same mathematical form as that for a L–R series circuit, the current in the former case leads on the applied voltage but the current in the latter case lags on the applied voltage.

3. L, C, R in series. The most general series circuit is the case of L, C, R in series (Fig. 811 (i)). The vector diagram has V_L leading by

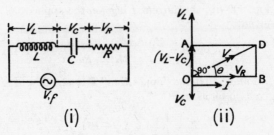

FIG. 811. L, C, R in series.

$90°$ on V_R, V_C lagging by $90°$ on V_R, with the current I in phase with V_R (Fig. 811 (ii)). If V_L is greater than V_C, their resultant is $(V_L - V_C)$ in the direction of V_L, as shown. Thus, from Pythagoras' theorem for triangle ODB, the applied voltage V is given by

$$V^2 = (V_L - V_C)^2 + V_R^2.$$

But $V_L = IX_L$, $V_C = IX_C$, $V_R = IR$.

$$\therefore \quad V^2 = (IX_L - IX_C)^2 + I^2R^2 = I^2[(X_L - X_C)^2 + R^2],$$

$$\therefore \quad I = \frac{V}{\sqrt{(X_L - X_C)^2 + R^2}}. \qquad \qquad \cdots \cdots \quad \text{(i)}$$

Also, I lags on V by an angle θ given by

$$\tan \theta = \frac{DB}{OB} = \frac{V_L - V_C}{V_R} = \frac{IX_L - IX_C}{IR} = \frac{X_L - X_C}{R}. \qquad \text{(ii)}$$

4. Resonance in the L, C, R series circuit. From (i), it follows that the impedance Z of the circuit is given by

$$Z = \sqrt{(X_L - X_C)^2 + R^2}.$$

The impedance varies as the frequency, f, of the applied voltage varies, because X_L and X_C both vary with frequency. Since $X_L = 2\pi fL$, then $X_L \propto f$, and thus the variation of X_L with frequency

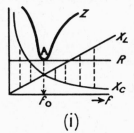
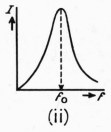

(i)   (ii)

Fig. 812. Resonance curves.

is a straight line passing through the origin (Fig. 812 (i)). Also, since $X_C = 1/2\pi fC$, then $X_C \propto 1/f$, and thus the variation of X_C with frequency is a curve approaching the two axes (Fig. 812 (i)). The resistance R is independent of frequency, and is thus represented by a line parallel to the frequency axis. The difference $(X_L - X_C)$ is represented by the dotted lines shown in Fig. 812 (i), and it can be seen that $(X_L - X_C)$ decreases to zero for a particular frequency f_0, and thereafter increases again. Thus, from $Z = \sqrt{(X_L - X_C)^2 + R^2}$, the impedance diminishes and then increases as the frequency f is varied. The variation of Z with f is shown in Fig. 812 (i), and since the current $I = V/Z$, the current varies as shown in Fig. 812 (ii). Thus the current has a maximum value at the frequency f_0, and this is known as the *resonant frequency* of the circuit.

The magnitude of f_0 is given by $X_L - X_C = 0$, or $X_L = X_C$.

$$\therefore 2\pi f_0 L = \frac{1}{2\pi f_0 C}, \quad \text{or} \quad 4\pi^2 LC f_0 = 1.$$

$$\therefore f_0 = \frac{1}{2\pi\sqrt{LC}}.$$

At frequencies above and below the resonant frequency, the current is less than the maximum current, see Fig. 812 (ii), and the phenomenon is thus basically the same as the forced and resonant vibrations obtained in Sound or Mechanics (p. 668).

The series resonance circuit is used for tuning a radio receiver. In this

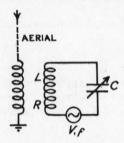

case the incoming waves of frequency f say from a distant transmitting station induces a varying voltage in the aerial, which in turn induces a voltage V of the same frequency in a coil and condenser circuit in the receiver (Fig. 813). When the capacitance C is varied the resonant frequency is changed; and at one setting of C the resonant frequency becomes f, the frequency of the incoming waves. The maximum current is then obtained, and the station is now heard very loudly.

Fig. 813. Tuning a receiver.

5. Parallel A.C. circuits. When components are arranged in parallel, the total or resultant current is the vector sum of the currents in the individual branches. Suppose a condenser of capacitance C is in parallel with a resistance R, for example (Fig. 814 (i)). The current I_R in R is in

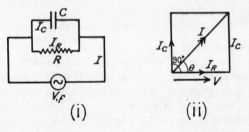

(i)   (ii)

Fig. 814. Capacitance and resistance in parallel.

phase with the applied voltage V, and the current I_C in C leads by 90° on V (Fig. 814 (ii)). The resultant current, I, is thus given, from Pythagoras' theorem, by

$$I^2 = I_C{}^2 + I_R{}^2.$$

$$\therefore\ I^2 = \frac{V^2}{X_C{}^2} + \frac{V^2}{R^2} = V^2\left(\frac{1}{X_C{}^2} + \frac{1}{R^2}\right),$$

$$\therefore\ I = V\left(\frac{1}{X_C{}^2} + \frac{1}{R^2}\right)^{\frac{1}{2}}. \qquad \cdots \cdots \quad \text{(i)}$$

Also, I leads on V by an angle θ given by

$$\tan\theta = \frac{I_C}{I_R} = \frac{V/X_C}{V/R} = \frac{R}{X_C}. \qquad \cdots \cdots \quad \text{(ii)}$$

Suppose now that a coil of inductance L and resistance R is in parallel with a condenser of capacitance C (Fig. 815 (i)). The current

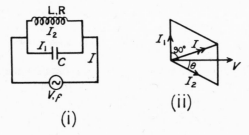

FIG. 815. Parallel circuit.

I_1 in C leads by 90° on the applied voltage V; the current I_2 in the coil lags by an angle θ on V, where $\tan\theta = X_L/R$ (see p. 1023) (Fig. 815 (ii)). The two vectors can be added together by a parallelogram method, or by resolution, to give the resultant current I in the main circuit, and the phase angle between I and V can be obtained by either of these methods. There is no simple formula for the impedance or the phase angle in this case.

6. Power in A.C. circuits. *Resistance R.* The power absorbed generally is $P = IV$. In the case of a resistance, $V = IR$, and $P = I^2R$. The variation of power is shown in Fig. 816 (i), from which it follows

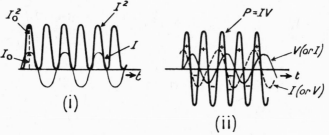

FIG. 816. Power in A.C. circuits.

that the average power absorbed $P = I_0{}^2R/2$, where I_0 is the peak (maximum) value of the current. Since the r.m.s. value of the current is $I_0/\sqrt{2}$, it follows that

$$P = I^2R,$$

where I is the r.m.s. value (see p. 973).

Inductance L. In the case of a pure inductance, the voltage V across it leads by 90° on the current I. Thus if $I = I_0 \sin \omega t$, then $V = V_0 \sin (90° + \omega t) = V_0 \cos \omega t$. Hence, at any instant,

power absorbed $= IV = I_0 V_0 \sin \omega t \cdot \cos \omega t = \frac{1}{2}I_0 V_0 \sin 2\omega t$.

The variation of power, P, with time t is shown in Fig. 816 (ii); it is a sine curve with an average of zero. *Hence no power is absorbed in a pure inductance.* This is explained by the fact that on the first quarter of the current cycle, power is absorbed ($+$) in the magnetic field of the coil (see p. 968). On the next quarter-cycle the power is returned ($-$) to the generator, and so on.

Capacitance. With a pure capacitance, the voltage V across it lags by 90° in the current I (p. 978). Thus if $I = I_0 \sin \omega t$,

$$V = V_0 \sin (\omega t - 90°) = - V_0 \cos \omega t.$$

Hence, numerically,

power at an instant, P, $= IV = I_0 V_0 \sin \omega t \cos \omega t = \dfrac{I_0 V_0}{2} \sin 2\omega t.$

Thus, as in the case of the inductance, *the power absorbed in a cycle is zero* (Fig. 816 (ii)). This is explained by the fact that on the first quarter of the cycle, energy is stored in the electrostatic field of the condenser. On the next quarter the condenser discharges, and the energy is returned to the generator.

7. Formulae for A.C. Power. It can now be seen that, if I is the r.m.s. value of the current in amps. in a circuit containing a resistance R ohms, the power absorbed is I^2R watts. Care should be taken to exclude the inductances and capacitances in the circuit, as no power is absorbed in them.

If the voltage V across a circuit leads by an angle θ on the current I, the voltage can be resolved into a component $V \cos \theta$ in phase with the current, and a voltage $V \sin \theta$ perpendicular to the current. The former component, $V \cos \theta$, represents that part of the voltage across the resistances in the circuit, and hence the power absorbed is

$$P = IV \cos \theta.$$

The component $V \sin \theta$ is that part of the applied voltage across the inductances and capacitances, and as the power absorbed here is zero, it is known as the "wattless component" of the voltage.

TRIODE VALVE—AMPLIFIER, OSCILLATOR, DETECTOR

8. Triode Valve. A few years after the invention of the diode valve Lee de Forest introduced the triode valve. This had three electrodes: a cathode C, the emitter of electrons; an anode A, the collector of electrons; and a *grid* G, a wire with open spaces, placed between the anode and cathode (Fig. 817 (i)). The function of the grid is to control the electron flow to the anode, and for this purpose the grid has a small negative potential relative to the cathode. The grid is nearer the cathode than the anode, and its potential thus affects the electric field round the cathode more, with the result that the grid potential has a more delicate control than the anode potential over the anode current. As we shall see later, this enables the triode to act as an amplifier of alternating voltages as well as a detector.

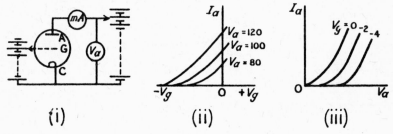

Fɪɢ. 817. Triode valve characteristics.

9. Triode Valve Characteristics. In order to predict the performance of a valve in a circuit, the "characteristics" of the valve must be first determined. The chief characteristics are $I_a - V_g$ (V_a constant), the variation of anode current with grid voltage when the anode voltage is constant; and $I_a - V_a$ (V_g constant), the variation of anode current with anode voltage when grid voltage is constant. The $I_a - V_g$ curves are known as the valve's *mutual characteristics*; the $I_a - V_a$ curves as the *anode characteristics*.

The mutual characteristics obtained are shown in Fig. 817 (ii). When the anode voltage is 80 volts, a negative voltage on the grid such as − 15 volts creates a resultant negative electric intensity at the cathode, and hence no electrons flow past the grid. As the negative voltage is reduced and reaches a certain value the attractive effect of the positive anode voltage overcomes the repulsive effect of the grid voltage, and electrons now reach the anode. As the negative voltage is reduced further, more electrons reach the anode, and the current increases as shown. The general shape of the $I_a - V_g$ curves is an initial curvature, followed by a straight line.

The anode characteristics, $I_a - V_a$ curves, are shown in Fig. 817

(iii), and are explained in a similar way. As the anode voltage, V_a, increases, the anode current increases. Generally, the anode current begins to flow at higher values of V_a when the grid voltage is increased more negatively. If the anode voltage is increased sufficiently, all the electrons emitted by the cathode are collected, and the current has then reached its saturation value (p. 975).

10. Valve constants. There are three main constants or properties of a radio valve. These are:

1. *Anode or A.C. Resistance, R_a,* which is defined by

$$R_a = \frac{\delta V_a}{\delta I_a} \ (V_g \text{ constant}),$$

the changes in V_a and I_a being taken on the *straight* part of the anode characteristics.

2. *Mutual conductance, g_m,* which is defined by

$$g_m = \frac{\delta I_a}{\delta V_g} \ (V_a \text{ constant}),$$

the changes in I_a and V_g being taken on the straight part of the mutual characteristics.

3. *Amplification factor, μ,* which is defined by

$$\mu = \frac{\delta V_a}{\delta V_g},$$

where δV_a produces the same change in anode current (V_g constant) as δV_g (V_a constant).

Thus, generally, R_a is the "resistance" of the valve when the anode circuit variations are considered, g_m is the change in anode current produced by unit grid voltage variation, and μ is a measure of the "step-up" in voltage produced in the anode circuit by a change in the grid voltage.

11. Triode as a Voltage Amplifier. When a valve is used as a voltage amplifier in radio circuits, it is important to realize at the outset that it amplifies *alternating* voltages, and that these voltages are applied in the grid-cathode circuit, as represented by V in Fig. 818 (i). The action of the valve should not only result in an increased alternating voltage V_0 in the anode circuit, known as the "output voltage", but the waveform of V_0 should be exactly the same as V, the applied voltage, so that there is no distortion. In order to obtain no distortion, a steady negative p.d. (grid-bias, G.B.) is also connected in the grid-cathode circuit, as shown in Fig. 818 (i).

The most suitable value of the grid-bias p.d. is OX volts, where X (not shown) corresponds to the middle of the straight part HK of the $I_a - V_g$ characteristic (Fig. 818 (ii)). Then, if the applied alternating voltage V has a peak value less than OX, the actual grid potential values will produce anode current variations corresponding to the straight part of the characteristic. The anode or output current will then have a waveform exactly the same as the applied or input voltage V (Fig. 818 (ii)). As we shall now show, the triode acts as a "voltage amplifier" in this case.

12. Voltage amplification factor. The magnitude of the voltage amplification can be found by replacing the valve circuit in Fig. 818 (i) by an "equivalent A.C. circuit". Since a change of p.d. δV_g in the grid-cathode circuit is equivalent to a change of $\mu \delta V_g$ in the anode circuit, the alternating voltage V is equivalent to an alternating

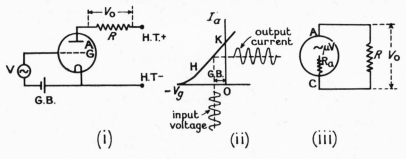

Fig. 818. Triode amplification.

voltage μV in the anode circuit. We therefore consider that, between the anode and cathode, the valve is an alternating voltage generator of e.m.f. μV, with an internal resistance R_a, the A.C. resistance discussed on p. 1031. See Fig. 818 (iii).

To convert the alternating current in the anode circuit to an alternating voltage, a large resistance R is needed, of the order of thousands of ohms. The internal resistance of the H.T. battery and that of the G.B. battery can be neglected by comparison, and since varying voltages are now considered, the magnitudes of the steady H.T. and G.B. voltages can also be ignored. The complete valve equivalent A.C. circuit is therefore as shown in Fig. 818 (iii).

The total resistance of the circuit is $R + R_a$. Thus the alternating current, I, flowing

$$= \frac{\mu V}{R + R_a}.$$

$\therefore$ output alternating voltage, $V_0, = IR = \frac{\mu V R}{R + R_a}.$

$\therefore$ voltage amplification factor $= \dfrac{V_0}{V} = \dfrac{\mu R}{R + R_a}.$ . . (i)

Thus if a triode has an amplification factor μ of 10, an internal resistance R_a of 8000 ohms and a resistance R of 10,000 ohms.

$$\text{voltage amplification factor} = \frac{\mu R}{R + R_a} = \frac{10 \times 10,000}{10,000 + 8000} = 5\cdot 6.$$

Hence if the applied alternating voltage is 0·2 volt (r.m.s.),

$$\text{amplified output voltage} = 5\cdot 6 \times 0\cdot 2 = 1\cdot 1 \text{ volts (r.m.s.)}.$$

13. Basic oscillatory circuit. About 1862 Lord Kelvin showed theoretically that when an electrical disturbance is made in a condenser consisting of a condenser and a coil and then left, *oscillations* of current occur. Thus suppose a current I flows at an instant t in a circuit consisting of a coil of inductance L and negligible resistance, in series with a condenser of capacitance C (Fig. 819). Then, from p. 968, if Q is the charge on the condenser,

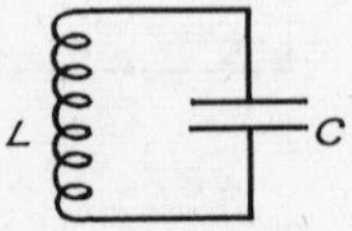

$$\text{p.d. across inductance} = - L \frac{dI}{dt}$$

FIG. 819. Basic oscillatory circuit.

$$= \text{p.d. across condenser} = \frac{Q}{C}$$

$$\therefore - L \frac{dI}{dt} = \frac{Q}{C}$$

$$\text{But } I = \frac{dQ}{dt}. \qquad \therefore - L \frac{d^2Q}{dt^2} = \frac{Q}{C}$$

$$\therefore \frac{d^2Q}{dt^2} = - \frac{I}{LC} \cdot Q \quad \cdots \cdots \quad \text{(i)}$$

This is a "simple harmonic" equation. Thus Q, the charge circulating, varies with time t according to the relation

$$Q = Q_0 \sin \omega t, \quad \cdots \cdots \quad \text{(ii)}$$

where Q is the maximum value of the varying charge and ω is a constant given by $\omega^2 = 1/LC$, or

$$\omega = \frac{1}{\sqrt{LC}}.$$

The *frequency*, f, of the oscillatory charge is given by

$$f = \frac{\omega}{2\pi} = \frac{1}{2\pi\sqrt{LC}}. \quad \cdots \cdots \quad \text{(iii)}$$

A coil-condenser series circuit is thus a basic oscillatory circuit, and the frequency of the oscillations of charge (or current) depends on the magnitudes of the inductance L and capacitance C.

The physical reason for the oscillations is the constant interchange of energy between the condenser and the coil. When the bob of a pendulum is oscillating, its energy at the end of a swing is wholly potential. This gradually changes into kinetic energy until it is wholly kinetic at the middle of the swing, and then becomes potential energy again at the end of the swing. In a similar way, the condenser becomes fully charged at one instant, the energy being electrostatic energy, and as the condenser discharges, the energy is stored in the magnetic field of the coil. When the condenser is fully discharged, the energy is wholly in the magnetic field. After this, the condenser charges up the other way round, storing electrical energy, and when it is fully charged, there is then no energy in the coil's magnetic field.

14. Damped and undamped waves. The oscillations of charge or current in a circuit containing only an inductance and a capacitance

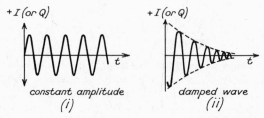

FIG. 820. Undamped (continuous) waves and damped waves.

will theoretically last indefinitely with a constant amplitude (Fig. 820 (i)). In practice, however, some of the energy is dissipated a sheat in the resistance of the coil. Since this energy is no longer available as oscillatory energy, the amplitude of the oscillations gradually diminish, and a *damped* oscillation is thus obtained (Fig. 820 (ii)). This is analogous to the case of a vibrating tuning-fork. If there were no air friction the oscillations of the prongs would proceed indefinitely with constant amplitude, but in practice the amplitude of the oscillations gradually diminishes to zero.

15. Triode as an oscillator. A triode valve can be used to maintain oscillations in a coil (L, R)—condenser (C) electrical circuit. The principle of the method is shown in Fig. 821, which consists of the basic oscillatory circuit connected in the grid-cathode circuit of the valve, a coil L_1, close to the oscillator coil, in the anode circuit, a high-tension (H.T.) battery, and a condenser C_g and a resistance R_g in the grid circuit, for a reason to be explained later.

When the circuit is made,

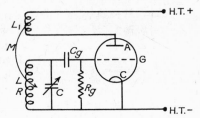

FIG. 821. Triode as oscillator.

oscillations of current occur in the (L, R)—condenser (C) circuit, as
already explained. The oscillatory coil alternating p.d., across C is
amplified by the valve, and oscillatory currents are then obtained in
the anode circuit and hence in the coil L_1. By mutual induction M between the coils, *some energy is fed back to the oscillator circuit*. If the
feed-back is correctly phased and is of the required amount, it will
help to maintain the oscillations of current in the oscillatory current,
which will then become undamped. The magnitude and phase of the
feed-back can be varied by altering the position of the coil L_1 and, if
necessary, reversing its connections in the anode circuit. With audio-
frequency oscillations, a continuous whistle can usually be heard.

16. Efficiency of oscillator. The source of the oscillatory energy is
the H.T. battery in the circuit, and an oscillator is thus said to be a
device for converting d.c. energy into a.c. energy. The *efficiency* of the
circuit is defined as:

$$\frac{\text{output (oscillatory) energy, a.c.}}{\text{input energy, d.c.}} \times 100\%.$$

Once the balance-wheel of a watch is set in motion, energy is imparted
to it regularly only at certain times of its oscillation. In this way the
balance-wheel is supplied with the least amount of energy needed to
maintained undamped oscillations. For the same reason, the triode
oscillator circuit has a condenser C_g and a high-resistance R_g in the
grid-circuit. See Fig. 821. When the circuit is first made the p.d. across
R_g is zero, and hence the grid is at zero potential. The alternating or
oscillatory voltage across the condenser C makes the grid positive in
potential for some part of its cycle, and some electrons are therefore
drawn into the grid circuit, charging the condenser C_g. During the
oscillatory voltage some charge (electrons) leaks away through R_g, and

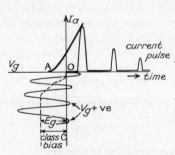

FIG. 822. Variation of grid p.d. and
anode current (*not to scale*).

the grid thus becomes more negative
in potential. Fig. 822 shows roughly
how the grid potential decreases,
and with suitably chosen values of
C_g and R_g it soon settles down to
some steady negative value E_g, which
is the grid-bias while the value is
functioning. In this condition the
oscillatory voltage across the condenser C only produces a pulse of
current in the anode circuit at brief
intervals, as shown in Fig. 822, and
by mutual induction, energy is fed
back simultaneously by the coil L_1 into the oscillatory circuit $(L, R$
and $C)$ to make up for the energy lost as heat in the resistance R.

The valve is here said to be operating under "class C" conditions, that is, the negative grid-bias E_g is at least twice the grid-bias value OA which cuts off the anode current in the $I_a - V_g$ characteristic (Fig. 822). During part of the cycle the grid potential becomes positive, as shown. A fixed negative grid-bias equal to E_g is unsuitable in a valve oscillator circuit. The alternating (oscillatory) voltage across the condenser C, once obtained, would not produce any current in the anode circuit and oscillations would then not continue owing to lack of feed-back of energy.

17. Radio waves and modulation. In 1887 Hertz found by experiment that when an oscillatory voltage of high frequency was connected to two condenser plates far apart, some of the oscillatory energy travelled in space some distance from the plates and was detected. This was the first discovery of the existence of *radio waves*. A transmitting aerial is a form of condenser in which one "plate" is high above the other "plate", the earth. Theory and experiment show that radio waves will not travel out far from a transmitting aerial unless their frequency is very high, and valve oscillator circuits (p. 1033) therefore usually produce alternating voltages of the order of a million (10^6) cycles per second or more, known as *radio-frequencies* (*R.F.*). The Home Service station in Britain, broadcasting on 330 metres wavelength, sends out radio waves of a frequency of 908,000 cycles per second (908 kilocycles per second).

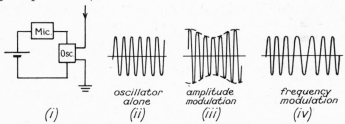

(i)   *(ii)*   *(iii)*   *(iv)*

oscillator alone   amplitude modulation   frequency modulation

FIG. 823. Amplitude and frequency modulation.

At broadcasting stations, the oscillator alone would produce a radio wave of constant amplitude (Fig. 823 (i), (ii)). When *audio-frequency* (*A.F.*) currents, due to speech or music, are fed through a microphone into the oscillatory circuit, the radio waves are affected or "modulated" accordingly. In *amplitude modulation* (*A.M.*), the amplitude of the radio-frequency wave varies exactly as the audio-frequency (Fig. 823) (iii). In *frequency modulation* (*F.M.*) the amplitude of the radio-frequency wave is constant but the audio-frequency is superimposed on the frequency of the radio wave (Fig. 823 (iv)).

18. Diode Valve Detection. The principle of the diode valve was discussed on p. 974. There we showed that a diode valve, which consists of a nickel plate or anode placed in a vacuum opposite a cathode emitting electrons, allowed current to flow through it only when the anode was positive in potential relative to the cathode.

The diode can be used to convert alternating to direct voltage (see p. 975). It can also be used to "detect" the audio-frequency variation

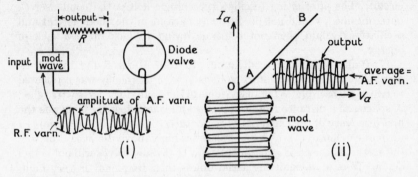

FIG. 824. Diode valve detection.

carried along with the modulated wave sent out by transmitters. If a modulated wave is applied between the anode and cathode of a diode, with a resistor R in the circuit (Fig. 824 (i)), the valve conducts on the positive parts of the cycle. The variation of current I_a in the anode circuit, the output current, is then as shown in Fig. 824 (ii), where OAB is the $I_a - V_a$ curve. The average value of the current, it will be noted, follows the variation of the amplitude of the modulated wave, and hence the voltage across R, called the *output voltage*, has the same audio-frequency variation. In this way the diode is said to act as a "detector" of the audio-frequency. If the modulated wave were applied to the resistance R without using the diode, the average current obtained would be zero.

19. Triode as a detector. We have just shown that the diode can act as a "detector" of the audio-frequency carried with a modulated

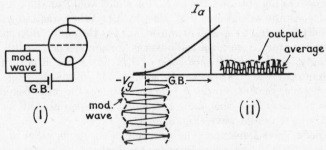

FIG. 825. Triode detection.

wave. The triode can also act as a detector, and in one method, known as *anode-bend detection*, the modulated wave is applied in the grid-cathode circuit, together with a steady grid-bias voltage (G.B.) corresponding to a point on the bend of the $I_a - V_g$ characteristic (Fig. 825 (i), (ii)). The swings of the modulated wave on one half of the cycles now produce an anode-current variation, but very little current flows on the other half-cycles. The output, or anode current, thus varies as shown in Fig. 825 (ii), and hence the *average* current variation follows the variation of the peaks of the current, which is the audio-frequency variation carried along by the modulated wave (see p. 1035). By means of high resistance earphones and a suitable condenser across it the audio-frequency variation can be heard.

MEASUREMENT OF ELECTRONIC CHARGE

20. Theory of Millikan's experiment. In 1909, R. A. Millikan carried out a series of experiments on the determination of the electronic charge. He first measured the terminal velocity of an oil-drop falling through air, and then charged the oil-drop and applied an electric field to oppose gravity. The drop now moved with a different terminal velocity, which was again measured.

Suppose the radius of the oil-drop is a, the densities of oil and air are ϱ and σ respectively, and the viscosity of air is η. When the drop, without a charge, falls steadily under gravity with a terminal velocity v_1,

upthrust + viscous force = weight of drop.

$$\therefore \tfrac{4}{3}\pi a^3 \sigma g + 6\pi \eta a v_1 \text{ (Stokes's law)} = \tfrac{4}{3}\pi a^3 \varrho g,$$

$$\therefore 6\pi \eta a v_1 = \tfrac{4}{3}\pi a^3 (\varrho - \sigma)g, \qquad \ldots \ldots \text{ (i)}$$

$$\therefore a = \left[\frac{9\eta v_1}{2(\varrho - \sigma)g}\right]^{\frac{1}{2}}. \qquad \ldots \ldots \text{ (ii)}$$

Suppose the drop now acquires a negative charge e' and an electric field of intensity E is applied to oppose gravity, so that the drop now has a terminal velocity v_2. Then, since the force due to E on the drop is Ee', we have

$$\tfrac{4}{3}\pi a^3 \sigma g + 6\pi \eta a v_2 = \tfrac{4}{3}\pi a^3 \varrho g - Ee'.$$

$$\therefore Ee' = \tfrac{4}{3}\pi a^3 (\varrho - \sigma)g - 6\pi \eta a v_2$$

Hence, from (i), $Ee' = 6\pi \eta a v_1 - 6\pi \eta a v_2 = 6\pi \eta a (v_1 - v_2).$

Thus, with (ii), $e' = \dfrac{6\pi \eta}{E} \left[\dfrac{9\eta v_1}{2(\varrho - \sigma)g}\right]^{\frac{1}{2}}(v_1 - v_2).$ $\ldots$ (iii)

21. Experiment. In his experiments Millikan used two horizontal plates A, B about 20 cm. in diameter and 1·5 cm. apart, with a small hole H in the centre of the upper plate (Fig. 826). He used a fine spray to "atomize" the oil and create tiny drops above H, and occasionally one would find its way through H, and would be observed in a low-power microscope by reflected light when the chamber was brightly illuminated.

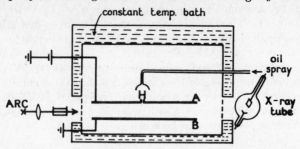

FIG. 826. Principle of Millikan's experiment.

The drop was seen as a pin-point of light, and its downward velocity was measured by timing its fall through a known distance by means of a scale in the eyepiece. The field was applied by connecting a battery of several thousand volts across the plates A, B, and its intensity E was known, since $E = V/d$, where V is the p.d. between the plates and d is their distance apart. Millikan found that the friction between the drops when they were formed by the spray created electric charge, but to give a drop an increased charge an X-ray tube was operated near the chamber to ionize the air.

From equation (iii), it follows that when v_1, v_2, E, ϱ, σ and η are all known, the charge e' on the drop can be calculated. Millikan found, working with hundreds of drops, that the charge e' was always a simple multiple of a basic unit, $4\cdot8 \times 10^{-10}$ e.s.u. He thus concluded that the charge on an electron, e, was $4\cdot8 \times 10^{-10}$ e.s.u., or $1\cdot6 \times 10^{-19}$ coulomb.

22. Other evidence of electronic charge. Avogadro's number, $6\cdot0 \times 10^{23}$, is the number of molecules in a gram-molecule of a gas. In electrolysis, 96,500 coulombs (the faraday) is the quantity of electricity required to deposit a gram-equivalent of an element (see p. 879). When the element is monatomic, the number of ions of one kind which carry the electricity is equal to the number of molecules. Thus the charge on each ion is given by $96{,}500 \div 6\cdot0 \times 10^{23}$, or $1\cdot6 \times 10^{-19}$ coulomb, which was the value found by Millikan directly. This is additional evidence for the existence of the basic or electronic charge.

OTHER POTENTIOMETER MEASUREMENTS

23. Thermoelectric e.m.f. measurement. A high resistance R is required in series with a potentiometer wire to measure an e.m.f. of the order of a millivolt, as in the case of a thermocouple. We shall now show how such a small e.m.f. can be measured accurately.

Suppose the potentiometer wire has a resistance of 5 ohms, the accumulator an e.m.f. of 2 volts, and a p.d. of 1 millivolt is needed across the wire. Then, since $V = IR$,

$$V = \frac{1}{1000} \text{ volt} = \frac{2}{R+5} \times 5 \text{ volts}$$

$$\therefore 10,000 = R + 5, \text{ or } R = 9995 \text{ ohms.}$$

To obtain a series resistance of 9995 ohms, two Post Office boxes, R_1, R_2, are connected in series with the wire (Fig. 827). A total of 9995 ohms is taken out of both boxes, for example 4995 ohms from R_1 and

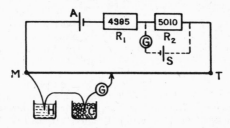

FIG. 827. Measurement of thermo-electric e.m.f.

5000 ohms from R_2, and a standard cell S is placed across R_2 with a sensitive galvanometer G in series. Resistances are then taken from one box, R_1 say, and an equal resistance is added to the other box R_2, until a balance is obtained with S. Suppose this occurs with $R_2 = 5010$ ohms, R_1 being then 4985 ohms, and the e.m.f. of S = 1·0186 volts. Then, by proportion, the p.d. across the potentiometer wire MT of resistance 5 ohms is given by

$$\frac{5}{1010} \times 1 \cdot 0186 \text{ or } 0 \cdot 00102 \text{ volts, which is } 1 \cdot 02 \text{ millivolts.}$$

Thus the p.d. per centimetre of the wire

$$= \frac{1}{100} \times 1 \cdot 02 = 1 \cdot 02 \times 10^{-2} \text{ millivolt.}$$

By this method, it can be seen that the e.m.f. of the accumulator is not eventually required, although it was initially used in finding the order of magnitude of R.

24. Measurements of high voltages and high currents. In electrical engineering, high voltages and high currents need to be measured accurately.

If a voltage X of about a thousand volts, for example, requires to be measured, the voltage is connected across a resistance of 999 ohms and one of 1 ohm in series. A p.d. of about 1 volt is then obtained across the 1 ohm resistor, and an accurate value v of this p.d. is then measured by a potentiometer (see p. 856). It follows that $X = 1000v$ volts, and hence X can be found.

To measure a high current, for example 1000 amp., the current I is passed through a very low resistance such as 0·001 ohm made of manganin, which has an extremely small temperature coefficient. The p.d. V across the resistance is measured by a potentiometer method, and the current I is then given by $I = V/0·001 = 1000V$ numerically.

EXERCISES XLIV

1. A coil of inductance 2 henrys and neligible resistance, and a resistor of 400 ohms, are placed in series across a 100-volt supply of frequency 50 c.p.s. Calculate the current flowing, the p.d. across the coil, the p.d. across the resistor, and the phase angle between the current and voltage supply.

2. A current of 6 milliamp. (r.m.s.), frequency 100 c.p.s., flows in a circuit consisting of a 1 μF. condenser in series with a 2000-ohm resistor. Calculate the p.d. across the condenser, the p.d. across both components, and the power absorbed.

3. A coil of inductance 10 millihenrys and resistance 5 ohms is in series with a 0·0002 μF. condenser, and a voltage of 1 millivolt (r.m.s.) is connected across both components. Calculate (i) the resonant frequency of the circuit, (ii) the current flowing at resonance, (iii) the p.d. across the condenser at resonance, (iv) the power absorbed at resonance.

4. An alternating e.m.f. $E = E_0 \sin pt$ is applied to a circuit consisting of a coil of wire of resistance R and self-inductance L. What a form will the expression for the current in the coil take? What will be (a) the maximum value, (b) the average value, and (c) the root-mean-square value of the current?

Explain the terms *impedance* and *reactance*. (*L. Schol.*)

5. Explain what is meant by the *impedance* and the *reactance* of a circuit consisting of an inductance and a resistance in series. Obtain an expression for the mean rate of dissipation of energy when an e.m.f. $E_0 \sin \omega t$ is applied in this circuit. [You may assume the current $I = I_0 \sin (\omega t - \theta)$.]

A choking coil of self-inductance 1 henry and resistance 100 ohms is connected to 230 volt (r.m.s.) a.c. mains of frequency 50 c.p.s. Compare the energy dissipated in the coil with that which would occur in a non-inductance resistance of 100 ohms similarly connected. (*L. Schol.*)

6. (a) Explain the action of a "choking" coil, (b) an e.m.f. $E_0 \sin pt$ is applied in a circuit containing resistance R, self-inductance L, and a variable capacitance C in series. How does the current in the circuit vary in amplitude and phase as C is varied?

Explain what occurs at "Resonance". (*L. Schol.*)

7. What is a "modulated wave"? Explain fully how a diode valve enables the audio-frequencies in a modulated wave to be detected.

8. Draw labelled sketches illustrating the mutual characteristics and the anode characteristics of a triode valve. Describe, with circuit diagrams, how the two sets of characteristics can be obtained. How are the appearances of the characteristic curves generally explained?

9. Explain fully, with the aid of diagrams, how the triode valve can be used as (i) an amplifier, (ii) a detector.

10. Describe a method for the determination of the electronic charge.

A charged oil drop is held stationary between two parallel horizontal condenser plates when a field of 576 volt cm. $^{-1}$ is applied between them. When the field is removed the drop falls freely with a steady velocity of 0·0120 cm. sec. $^{-1}$. Assuming the viscous force on the drop when falling with velocity v is $6\pi\eta av$, where a is the radius of the drop and η the viscosity of air, calculate: (1) the radius of the drop, (2) the charge on the drop. ($6\eta = 10·9 \times 10^{-4}$ gm. cm. $^{-1}$ sec. $^{-1}$, density of oil $= 0·80$ gm. cm. $^{-3}$.) (*L. Schol.*)

11. Describe and give the theory of the Millikan oil drop experiment for the determination of the electronic charge. What is the importance of the experiment?

In one such experiment a singly charged drop was found to fall under gravity at a terminal velocity of 0·0040 cm. per sec. and to rise at 0·0120 cm. per sec. when a field of 2000 volt per cm. was suitably applied. Calculate the electronic charge given that the radius, a, of the drop was $6·0 \times 10^{-5}$ cm. and that the viscosity, η, of the gas under the conditions of the experiment was 180×10^{-6} gm. per cm. per sec. (*N. Schol.*)

12. (i) A condenser of capacitance 4·00 μF. and a non-reactive coil of resistance 250 ohms are in series with a source of sinusoidal alternating e.m.f. of 200 volts and of frequency $625/2\pi$ cycle sec. $^{-1}$. Find (a) the current in the circuit, (b) the potential difference between the terminals of each component of the circuit.

(ii) In such a circuit, the peak potential differences between the terminals of the coil and the condenser are respectively 400 and 300 volts. These terminals are connected respectively to the X-plates and the Y-plates of a cathode-ray oscillograph. Construct to scale on graph paper the figure on the screen. (*L.*)

13. Explain the meaning of the term *root-mean-square current* as used in reference to alternating currents.

An alternating current passes through a resistance R and an inductance L of negligible resistance arranged in series. Explain why the sum of the a.c. voltages measured separately across R and L is more than that across the combination.

If a 50 c.p.s. 50 volt r.m.s. supply of sine-wave form and a number of identical high resistances (of negligible inductance) are available, describe how you would perform experiments with a cathode-ray oscillograph: (a) to test the linearity of the Y deflection with applied voltage and to find the deflection per volt, (b) to calibrate the time-base frequency control up to 500 c.p.s. in multiples of 50 c.p.s. (*N.*)

14. Describe the essential features of a triode valve and comment on any *one* feature of its construction which you consider of special importance.

Describe *briefly*, with the aid of a diagram, how you would investigate the variation of anode current with anode potential, the grid potential being constant and negative to the filament. Sketch the curve you would expect to obtain.

A triode valve is to be used to amplify a direct current of 10^{-7} amp. flowing in a circuit incorporating a resistance of 10^5 ohm. The valve has a mutual conductance of 2 milliamp. volt $^{-1}$ and an anode slope resistance (impedance) of 10^6 ohm. Draw a diagram of a suitable circuit and calculate the current amplification. (*N.*)

15. A cloud of very small negatively charged water drops was produced in air in a closed vessel containing a pair of horizontal uncharged metal plates, 5·0 mm. apart, and the top of the cloud fell from the upper to the lower plate in 50 sec. The top of a similar cloud fell over this distance in 28 sec. when the plates differed in potential by 1200 volts. Obtain a value for the charge on a single drop, assuming the drops to be of equal size and to have equal charges.

Criticize this experiment as a method for determining the electronic charge. Describe *briefly* how Millikan modified and improved it.

[Take the viscosity of air as $1·8 \times 10^{-4}$ poise; 300 volt $= 1$ e.s.u.] (*L.*)

CHAPTER XLV

ATOMIC STRUCTURE

PRINCIPLES OF RADIOACTIVITY. THE ATOMIC NUCLEUS

1. Alpha, Beta and Gamma Rays. In 1896 BECQUEREL found that a uranium compound affected a photographic plate wrapped in light-proof paper, and he called the phenomenon *radioactivity*. The radiation from the uranium was separated into three components when a magnetic field B was applied perpendicular to the stream of radiation, and they were called α-, β- and γ-rays (Fig. 828). The α- and β-rays were deflected by the field and were thus actually charged particles, but the γ-rays were unaffected, as shown.

2. Alpha-particles. The direction of deflection of the α-rays by a magnetic field showed they were particles carrying a *positive* charge. Lord Rutherford and his collaborators found by deflection experiments that an α-particle had a mass about four times that of a hydrogen atom, and carried a charge $+ 2e$, where e was the

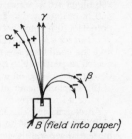

FIG. 828. Effect of magnetic field on α-, β-particles and γ-rays.

numerical value of the charge on an electron. The atomic weight of helium is about four. It was thus fairly certain that an *α-particle was a helium nucleus*, that is, a helium atom which has lost two electrons.

In 1909 Rutherford and Royds showed conclusively that α-particles were helium nuclei. Radon, a gas given off by radium which emits α-particles, was collected above mercury in a thin-walled tube P (Fig. 829). After several days some of the α-particles passed through P into a surrounding vacuum Q, and in about a week, the space in Q was reduced in volume by raising mercury reservoirs. A gas was collected in a capillary tube R at the top of Q. A high voltage from an induction coil was then connected to electrodes at A and B, and the spectrum of the discharge was observed to be exactly the same as the characteristic spectrum of helium

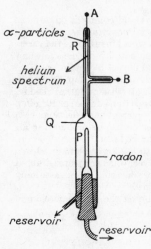

FIG. 829. Rutherford and Royds' experiment on α-particles.

gas. The α-particles had thus become neutral helium atoms in Q, collecting negative charges from the sides of the glass.

α-particles are absorbed by thin metal foil or by a sheet of paper. Their range in air at standard atmospheric pressure is of the order of a few centimetres. They have a weak effect on photographic plates, but they have been counted by the scintillations produced when striking a fluorescent screen, made of zinc sulphide for example. α-particles ionize air considerably when passing through, and their tracks have been made visible by photographing droplets of water which immediately form round the ions (p. 1048).

3. Beta- and Gamma-rays. By deflecting β-particles with perpendicular magnetic and electric fields, their charge-mass ratio could be estimated. This is similar to Thomson's experiment, p. 1011. These experiments showed that *β-particles are electrons moving at high speeds.* Generally, β-particles have a greater penetrating power of materials than α-particles. They also have a greater range in air than α-particles, but their ionization of air is relatively smaller.

The nature of γ-rays was shown by experiments with crystals. Diffraction phenomena are obtained in this case, which suggest that *γ-rays are electromagnetic waves* (compare X-rays, p. 1017). Measurement of their wavelengths, by special techniques with crystals, show they are shorter than the wavelengths of X-rays. γ-rays can penetrate large thicknesses of metals, but they have far less ionizing power in gases that β-particles.

4. Discovery of Nucleus. In 1909 Geiger and Marsden, at Lord Rutherford's suggestion, investigated the scattering of α-particles by thin films of metal of high atomic weight, such as gold foil. They used a radon tube S in a metal block as a source of α-particles, and limited the particles to a narrow pencil (Fig. 830). The thin metal foil A was placed in the centre of an evacuated vessel, and the scattering of the particles after passing through A was observed on a flourescent screen B, placed at the focal plane of a microscope M. Scintillations are seen on B whenever it is struck by α-particles.

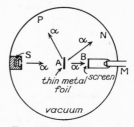

FIG. 830. Discovery of nucleus — Geiger and Marsden.

Geiger and Marsden found that α-particles struck B not only in the direction SA, but also when the microscope M was moved round to N and even to P. Thus though the majority of α-particles were scattered through small angles, some particles were scattered through very large angles. Rutherford found this very exciting news. It meant that some α-particles had come into the repulsive field of a highly concentrated positive charge at the heart or centre of the atom, and on the basis of an inverse-square law repulsion he calculated the number of α-particles scattered in a definite direction. The relationship was verified by Geiger and Marsden in subsequent experiments. An atom thus has a *nucleus*, in which all the positive charge and most of its mass is concentrated.

5. Atomic Mass and Atomic Number. In 1911 Rutherford proposed the basic structure of the atom which is accepted today, and which subsequent experiments by Moseley and others have confirmed. A neutral atom consists of a very tiny nucleus of diameter about 10^{-13} cm. which contains practically the whole mass of the atom. The atom is largely empty. If a drop of water was magnified until it reached the size of the earth, the atoms inside would then be only a few yards in diameter and the atomic nucleus would have a diameter of only about one three-thousandth of an inch.

The nucleus of hydrogen is called a **proton**, and it carries a charge of $+ e$, where e is the numerical value of the charge on an electron. The helium nucleus has a charge of $+ 2e$. The nucleus of copper has a charge of $+ 29e$, and the uranium nucleus carries a charge of $+ 92e$. Generally, the positive charge on a nucleus is $+ Ze$, where Z is the *atomic number* of the element and is defined as the number of protons in the nucleus (see also p. 1015). Under the attractive influence of the positively-charged nucleus, a number of electrons equal to the atomic number move round the nucleus and surround it like a negatively-charged cloud.

6. Discovery of Protons in Nucleus. In 1919 Rutherford found that energetic α-particles could penetrate nitrogen atoms and that protons were ejected after the collision. The apparatus used is shown in Fig. 831. A source of α-particles, A, was placed in a container D from which all the air had been pumped out and replaced by nitrogen. Silver foil, B, sufficiently thick to stop α-particles, was then placed between A and a fluorescent screen C, and scintillations were observed by a microscope M. The particles which had passed through B were shown to have a similar range, and the same charge, as protons.

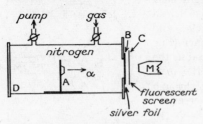

Fig. 831. Discovery of protons in nucleus—Rutherford.

Protons were also obtained with the gas fluorine, and with other elements such as the metals sodium and aluminium. It thus became clear that the nuclei of all elements contain protons. The number of protons must equal the number of electrons surrounding the nucleus, so that each is equal to the atomic number, Z, of the element. A proton is represented by the symbol, $_1H^1$; the top number denotes the *mass number*, the whole number nearest to the atomic weight, and the bottom number the nuclear charge in units of $+ e$. The helium nucleus such as an α-particle is represented by $_2He^4$; its mass number is 4 and its nuclear charge is $+ 2e$, so that the nucleus contains two protons. One of the heaviest nuclei, uranium, can be represented by $_{92}U^{238}$; it has a mass number of 238 and a nuclear charge of $+ 92e$, so that its nucleus contains 92 protons.

7. Discovery of Neutron in Nucleus. In 1930 Bothe and Becker found that a very penetrating radiation was produced when α-particles were incident on beryllium. Since the radiation had no charge it was thought to be γ-radiation of very great energy. In 1932 Curie-Joliot placed a block of paraffin-wax in front of the penetrating radiation, and

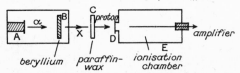

FIG. 832. Discovery of neutron—Chadwick.

showed that protons of considerable range were ejected from the paraffin-wax. The energy of the radiation could be calculated from the range of the ejected proton, and it was then found to be improbably high.

In 1932 Chadwick measured the velocity of protons and of nitrogen nuclei when they were ejected from materials containing hydrogen and nitrogen by the penetrating radiation. He used polonium, A, as a source of α-particles and the unknown radiation X, obtained by impact with beryllium, B, was then incident on a slab C of paraffin-wax (Fig. 832). The velocity of the protons emitted from C could be found from their range in air, which was determined by placing various thicknesses of mica, D, in front of an ionization chamber, E, until no effect was produced here. By previous calibration of the thickness of mica in terms of air thickness, the range in air was found.

Feather measured the velocity of protons ejected from nitrogen gas by means of a cloud chamber. Chadwick then applied the laws of conservation of linear momentum and energy to the respective collisions with the hydrogen and nitrogen atoms, assuming that the unknown radiation was a *particle* carrying no charge and the collisions were elastic. From the equations obtained, he calculated the mass of the particle, and found it to be about the same mass as the proton. Chadwick called the new particle a *neutron*, and it is now considered that all nuclei contain protons and neutrons. The neutron is represented by the symbol $_0n^1$ as it has an atomic mass of 1 and zero charge.

We can now see that a helium nucleus, $_2He^4$, has 2 protons and 2 neutrons, a total mass number of 4 and a total charge of $+2e$. The sodium nucleus, $_{11}Na^{23}$, has 11 protons and 12 neutrons. The uranium nucleus, $_{92}U^{238}$, has 92 protons and 146 neutrons. Generally, a nucleus represented by $_ZX^A$ has Z protons and $(A-Z)$ neutrons.

8. Radioactive Disintegration. Naturally occurring radioactive elements such as uranium, actinium and thorium disintegrate to form new elements, and these in turn are unstable and form other elements. Between 1902 and 1909 Rutherford and Soddy made a study of the elements formed from a particular "parent" element, and the *uranium series* is listed in the table below.

Element	Symbol	Atomic Number	Mass Number	Half-life Period (T)	Particle emitted
Uranium I (U)	UI	92	238	4,500 million years	α
Uranium X_1 (Th)	UX_1	90	234	24 days	β, γ
Uranium X_2 (Pa)	UX_2	91	234	1·2 min.	β, γ
Uranium II (U)	UII	92	234	250,000 years	α
Ionium (Th)	Io	90	230	80,000 years	α, γ
Radium	Ra	88	226	1,600 years	α, γ
Radon	Rn	86	222	3·8 days	α
Radium A (Po)	RaA	84	218	3 min.	α
Radium B (Pb)	RaB	82	214	27 min.	β, γ
Radium C (Bi)	RaC	83	214	20 min.	β, γ
Radium C' (Po)	RaC'	84	214	$1·6 \times 10^{-4}$ sec.	α
Radium C" (Tl)	RaC"	81	210	1·3 min.	β
Radium D (Pb)	RaD	82	210	19 years	β, γ
Radium E (Bi)	RaE	83	210	5 days	β
Radium F (Po)	RaF	84	210	138 days	α, γ
Lead	Pb	82	206	(stable)	

The new element formed after disintegration can be identified by considering the particles emitted from the nucleus of the parent atom. An α-particle, a helium nucleus, has a charge of $+2e$ and a mass number 4. Uranium I, of atomic number 92 and mass number 238, emits an α-particle from its nucleus of charge $+92e$, and hence the new nucleus formed has an atomic number 90 and a mass number 234. This was called uranium X_1, and since the element thorium (Th) has an atomic number 90, uranium X_1 is actually thorium.

A β-particle, an electron, and a γ-ray, an electromagnetic wave, have a negligible effect on the mass of a nucleus when they are emitted. A β-particle has a charge of $-e$. Now uranium X_1 has a nuclear charge of $+90e$ and a mass number 234, and emits β and γ rays. Consequently the mass number is unaltered, but the nuclear charge increases to $+91e$, and hence a new element is formed of atomic number 91. This is uranium X_2 in the series, and is actually the element protactinium. The symbols of the new elements formed are shown in brackets in the column of elements in the Table. The series contains isotopes of uranium (U), lead (Pb), thorium (Th) and bismuth (Bi), that is, elements which have the same atomic numbers but different mass numbers (see p. 1052).

Summarizing, we can say that:

(i) when the nucleus of an element loses an α-particle, the element is displaced two places to the left in the periodic table of the elements, which follows in the order of its atomic number, and lowers its mass number by two units;

(ii) when the nucleus of an element loses a β-particle, the element is displaced one place to the right in the periodic table and its mass number is unaltered.

This law was stated in 1913 by Soddy, Russell and Fajans.

9. Half-life Period. Radioactive transformations which produce new elements appear to obey the statistical law of chance, which states that the number of atoms disintegrating per second, dN/dt, is directly proportional to the number of atoms, N, present at that instant. Hence:

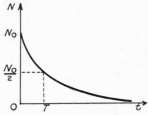

FIG. 833. Radioactive decay with time.

$$\frac{dN}{dt} = -\lambda N,$$

where λ is a constant characteristic of the atom concerned called the *radioactivity decay constant*. Thus, if N_0 is the number of radioactive atoms present at a time $t = 0$, and N is the number at the end of a time t, we have, by integration,

$$\int_{N_0}^{N} \frac{dN}{N} = -\lambda \int_{0}^{t} dt.$$

$$\therefore \left[\log_e N\right]_{N_0}^{N} = -\lambda t.$$

$$\therefore N = N_0 e^{-\lambda t} \qquad . \quad . \quad . \quad . \quad . \quad . \quad \text{(i)}$$

Thus the number N of radioactive atoms left decreases exponentially with the time t, and this is illustrated in Fig. 833.

The *half-life period T* of a radioactive element is defined as the time taken for half the atoms to disintegrate (see Fig. 833), that is, in a time

T the radioactivity of the element diminishes to half its value. Hence, from (i),

$$\frac{N_0}{2} = N_0 e^{-\lambda t}$$

$$\therefore T = \frac{1}{\lambda} \log_e 2 = \frac{0\cdot693}{\lambda}. \qquad \qquad . \quad . \quad \text{(ii)}$$

The half-life period varies considerably in a particular radioactive series. In the uranium series shown in the Table on p. 1046, for example, uranium I has a half-life period of the order of 4,500 million years, radium has one of about 1,600 years, radium F about 138 days, radium B about 27 minutes, and radium C′ about 10^{-4} second.

10. Detectors of Ionizing Particles. Wilson's Cloud Chamber. Many advances in the study of radioactivity and the nucleus came from ingenious methods devised over the years, of detecting sub-atomic particles such as α- and β-particles and protons. One of the first was C. T. R. Wilson's *cloud chamber*, invented in 1911, which was used for photographing ionizing particles or radiation.

In Wilson's method, droplets of water are formed round ions produced by ionizing particles or radiations. The saturated vapour pressure outside a liquid drop is greater than that outside a plane surface of the liquid at the same temperature by $2T\sigma/r(\varrho - \sigma)$, where T is the liquid surface tension, σ and ϱ are the densities of the vapour and the liquid respectively, and r is the radius of the drop. If the radius is very small, the vapour pressure outside the drop is then very large. Suppose r is 10^{-6} cm. For water at 15°C., $T = 75$ dyne cm.$^{-1}$, $\varrho = 1$ gm. cm.$^{-3}$ and $\sigma = 0\cdot0006$ gm. cm.$^{-3}$ approximately, and the saturation vapour pressure p outside a plane surface is 1·3 cm. mercury approximately. The pressure p_0 outside the drop is thus given, in cm. of mercury, by

$$p_0 - 1\cdot3 = \frac{2 \times 75 \times 6 \times 10^{-4}}{10^{-6} \times 1 \times 13\cdot6 \times 980},$$

neglecting σ compared with ϱ in the denominator and converting dyne cm.$^{-2}$ to cm. of mercury, density 13·6 gm. cm.$^{-3}$. On simplifying, $p_0 = 8\cdot0$ cm. mercury, approximately, which is about six times the vapour pressure outside a plane surface of water. Such a small drop of radius 10^{-6} cm., if it could form, would be unstable and evaporate, unless the space round the drop was enclosed and supersaturated to six times the pressure outside a plane surface. An electrically-charged drop effectively reduces the surface tension T, since the stress due to the charge acts outwards on the surface in opposition to the surface tension forces. Thus, generally, a charged drop will not evaporate as readily as an uncharged drop, and a smaller degree of supersaturation round it can result in persistence of the drop.

PLATE III

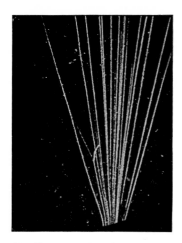

A.—Mass Spectrometer. Positive-
ray parabolas due to mercury,
carbon monoxide, oxygen and
carbon ions. (*Page* 1052.)

(*Sir J. J. Thomson.*)

B.—Transmutation of Nitrogen by
collision with α-particle. An
oxygen nucleus, right-curved
track, and a proton, left straight
track, are produced. (*Page* 1058.)

(*Professor P. M. S. Blackett.*)

SIMILARITY OF

WAVE (C.)

AND

PARTICLE (D.)

(*Page* 1081.)

D.—Electron diffraction rings
produced by a thin gold film.

(*Photo, Science Museum, London.
Courtesy of Professor Sir George Thomson
F.R.S.*)

C.—X-Ray diffraction rings
produced by a crystal.

National Chemical Laboratory, England.)

PLATE IV

A.—Van de Graaff Electrostatic Generator at Aldermaston, England. The dome is the high-voltage terminal. The insulated rings are equipotentials, and provide a uniform potential gradient down the column. Beams of protons or deuterons, produced in the dome, are accelerated down the column to bombard different materials at the bottom, thereby producing nuclear reactions which can be studied.

(Courtesy of U.K. Atomic Energy Authority.)

B.—Nuclear Research Reactor, ZEUS. This view shows the heart of the reactor, containing a highly enriched uranium central core surrounded by a natural uranium blanket for breeding studies.

(Courtesy of U.K. Atomic Energy Authority.)

Basically, Wilson's cloud chamber consists of a chamber Y into which saturated water-vapour is introduced (Fig. 834). When the pressure is suddenly reduced below a hollow glass piston X, the latter drops down and the air in Y undergoes an adiabatic expansion and cools. The dust nuclei are all carried away after a few expansions by drops forming on them, and then the dust-free air in Y is subjected to a controlled adiabatic expansion of about 1·31 to 1·38 times its original volume.

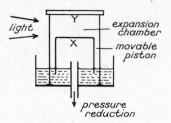

FIG. 834. Principle of cloud chamber—Wilson.

The air is now supersaturated, that is, the vapour pressure is greater than the saturation vapour pressure at the reduced temperature reached but no water-vapour condenses. Simultaneously, the air is exposed to ionizing agents such as α-, β- or γ-rays, and water droplets immediately collect round the ions produced which act as centres of formation. The drops are photographed by light scattered from them, and in this way the tracks of ionizing particles or radiation are made visible. Wilson's cloud chamber has proved of immense value in the study of radioactivity and nuclear structure.

11. Glaser's Bubble Chamber. In the same way as air can be supersaturated with water vapour, a liquid under pressure can be heated to a temperature higher than that at which boiling normally takes place and is then said to be *superheated*. If the pressure is suddenly released, bubbles may not form in the liquid for perhaps 30 seconds or more. During this quiet period, if ionizing particles or radiation are introduced into the liquid, nuclei are obtained for bubble formation. The liquid quickly evaporates into the bubble, which grows rapidly, and the bubble track when photographed shows the path of the ionizing particle.

Glaser invented the bubble chamber in 1951. It is now widely used in nuclear investigations all over the world, and it is superior to the cloud chamber. The density of the liquid ensures shorter tracks then in air, so that a nuclear collision of interest by a particle will be more likely to take place in a given length of liquid than in the same length of air. Photographs of the tracks are much clearer than those taken in the cloud chamber, and they can be taken more rapidly. In 1963 a 60-inch liquid hydrogen bubble chamber was constructed for use at the Rutherford High Energy Laboratory, Didcot, England. High energy protons, accelerated by millions of volts are used to bombard hydrogen nuclei in the chamber. The products of the reaction are bent into a curved track by a very powerful magnetic field, and the appearance and radius of the track then provides information about the nature, momentum or energy of the particles emitted.

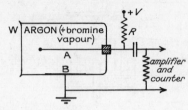

FIG. 835. Principle of Geiger counter.

12. Geiger-Müller Counter. A Geiger-Müller counter is widely used for recording ionizing particles. In one form it consists of an insulated wire A mounted in an earthed thin-walled glass tube B (Fig. 835). The tube contains a little argon gas mixed with bromine vapour. A p.d. V of the order of 400 volts is maintained across A, B. When a single ionizing particle enters B through the thin mica window W, a few electrons and ions are produced in the gas. These rapidly multiply (see p. 1073) and a discharge occurs between A and B. The p.d. produced in the large resistance R is amplified and passed to a counter, which registers the passage of an ionizing particle.

The discharge persists for a short time, as secondary electrons are emitted from the cathode B by the photons (light) produced when positive ions arrive there. This would upset the recording of other ionizing particles following fast on the first one recorded. Bromine vapour quenches the discharge quickly by absorbing the photon energy which would otherwise produce secondary electrons.

13. Scintillations and Photomultiplier. In the early experiments on radioactivity, Rutherford observed the scintillations produced when an α-particle was incident on a material such as zinc sulphide. This is now utilized in the scintillation photomultiplier (Fig. 836). When an ionizing particle or radiation strikes the scintillation material or phosphor R at

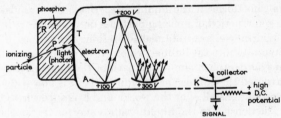

FIG. 836. Principle of photomultiplier.

the top of the tube, light is emitted at a point such as P. This strikes a photosensitive material or cathode T and ejects electrons, which are accelerated towards and focused on an electrode or *dynode* A at a positive potential of 100 volts for example. A is coated with material which emits secondary electrons four or five times as numerous as those incident. The electrons are then focused on another dynode B at a potential of $+200$ volts, and so on along the tube. The result is that a single ionizing particle can produce a million electrons in a photomultiplier tube, and the pulse of current is amplified further and recorded. By choosing a suitable phosphor, scintillation counters can detect electrons and gamma rays, as well as fast neutrons.

14. Emulsions. Special photographic emulsions have been designed for investigating nuclear reactions. The emulsions are much thicker than those used in ordinary photography, and the concentration of silver bromide in gelatine is many times greater than in ordinary photography. α-particles, protons and neutrons can be detected in specially-prepared emulsions by the track of silver granules produced, which has usually a very short range of the order of a millimetre or less. Consequently, after the plate is developed the track is observed under a high power microscope, or a photomicrograph is made. Nuclear emulsions were particularly useful in investigations of cosmic rays at various altitudes.

15. Measurement of Atomic Mass. Thomson's Positive Rays Experiment. We now turn to measurements of the masses of individual atoms. When the density of a gas such as chlorine is measure in the chemical laboratory, the average mass of all the atoms of chlorine is found. In 1911, however, Sir J. J. Thomson measured the masses of individual atoms for the first time. The gas concerned was passed slowly through a bulb B a low pressure, and a high voltage was applied. Cathode rays or electrons then flow from the cathode to the anode (not shown), and positive rays from the anode to

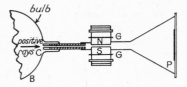

Fig. 837. Principle of Thomson's experiment on positive rays.

the cathode, C, whose axis was pierced by a fine tube (Fig. 837). The positive rays are *ions*, that is, atoms which have lost one or more electrons, and after flowing through C they are subjected to parallel magnetic and electric fields set at right angles to the incident beam, which are applied between the poles N, S of an electromagnet. Pieces of mica, G, G are used to insulate N, S from the magnet core. The ions were deflected by the fields and were incident on a photographic plate P. After development, parabolic traces were found on P.

Theory. Suppose a positive ray or ion has a charge E and mass M, and the electric and magnetic field intensities and E', B respectively

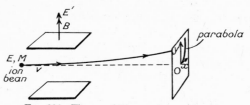

Fig. 838. Theory of Thomson's experiment.

(Fig. 838). To simplify matters, suppose the two fields are uniform over the whole distance up to the plate P and let the ion enter the fields with a velocity v as shown. The time t to reach P is given by l/v, since the forces on the ion due to E' and B are perpendicular to the direction of motion. Hence if y is the deflection in a vertical direction from O,

$$y = \frac{1}{2}ft^2 = \frac{1}{2}\frac{E'E}{M}\left(\frac{l^2}{v^2}\right) \quad \cdots \cdots \quad \text{(i)}$$

and the deflection x in a horizontal direction from O is given by

$$x = \frac{1}{2}ft^2 = \frac{1}{2}\frac{BEv}{M}\left(\frac{l^2}{v^2}\right) = \frac{1}{2}\frac{BEl^2}{Mv}. \quad \cdots \quad \text{(ii)}$$

Eliminating v from (i) and (ii), we obtain

$$x^2 = \frac{E}{M}\left(\frac{B^2l^2}{2E'}\right)y. \quad \cdots \cdots \cdots \quad \text{(iii)}$$

From (iii), it follows that ions with the same charge-mass ratio E/M, although moving with different velocities, all lie on a *parabola* of the form $x^2 = \text{constant} \times y$.

16. Determination of Masses. Isotopes. As the zero of the parabola was ill-defined, Thomson reversed the field to obtain a parabolic trace on the other side of the y-axis, as shown in Fig. 839. Now from (iii),

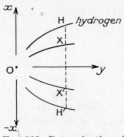

$x^2 \propto E/M$ for a given value of y. Consequently any hydrogen ions present would produce the outermost parabola H, since they have the greatest value of E/M. The masses of ions can thus be measured by comparing the squares of the x-values of the individual parabolas, such as the squares of X'X and H'H, for example. In this way Thomson obtained a *mass spectrometer*, one which gave the masses of individual atoms. (see Plate III, A. p. 1048.)

FIG. 839. Determination of mass of atom.

With chlorine gas, two parabolas were obtained which gave atomic masses of 35 and 37 respectively. Thus the atoms of chlorine have different masses but the same chemical properties, and these atoms are said to be *isotopes* of chlorine. In chlorine, there are three times as many atoms of mass 35 as there are of mass 37, so that the average atomic weight is $(3 \times 35 + 1 \times 37) \div 4$, or 35·5. The element xenon has as many as nine isotopes. One part in 5,000 of hydrogen consists of an isotope of mass 2 called deuterium, or heavy hydrogen. An unstable isotope of hydrogen of mass 3 is called tritium.

17. Dempster's Mass Spectrometer. Thomson's earliest form of mass spectrometer was followed by more sensitive forms. Aston designed a spectrometer in which the masses of atoms could be measured to 1 part in 140. In 1918 Dempster constructed a mass spectrometer whose principle is shown in Fig. 840. A platinum strip G was coated with a

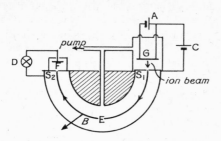

Fig. 840. Principle of Dempster's mass spectrometer.

metallic salt, and this was ionized by passing a current through G by means of a battery A. The positive ions produced were accelerated between G and a narrow slit S_1 by a battery C of about 1,000 volts. The ions then entered a brass semi-circular tube E of radius r; here they were deflected by a powerful uniform magnetic field B everywhere normal to the plane of the paper. The ions followed a circular path, and by varying the p.d. V of the p.d. between G and S_1, the ions would be made to follow a circle of particular radius r. In this special case they passed through a defining slit S_2 at the other end of the tube, and were collected by an insulated plate F connected to an electrometer D.

Theory. If $\bar{e}$, m are the charge and mass of an ion respectively, then, if v is the velocity of the ions on reaching S_1 from G and V is the p.d. between G and S_1,

$$\tfrac{1}{2}mv^2 = \bar{e}V, \quad \ldots \quad \ldots \quad \ldots \quad \text{(i)}$$

assuming the velocity of the ions at G is zero. On entering the uniform magnetic field of intensity B, the radius r of the path of the ions is given by

$$\frac{mv^2}{r} = B\bar{e}v. \quad \ldots \quad \ldots \quad \ldots \quad \text{(ii)}$$

From (i) and (ii), $$v = \frac{2V}{Br},$$

and with (i), $$\frac{m}{\bar{e}} = \frac{2V}{v^2} = \frac{B^2 r^2}{2V}. \quad \ldots \quad \ldots \quad \text{(iii)}$$

With B, r constant, V is varied and ions of the same mass-charge ratio travel the circular path of radius r. The current on D is recorded and peak values are obtained at certain values of V. Using (iii), the mass-charge ratio of the ions are found, and their mass deduced. A resolution of masses of 1% was obtained in 1918.

18. Bainbridge Mass Spectrometer. In 1933 Bainbridge devised a mass spectrometer in which the ions were photographed after being deflected by a magnetic field. The principle of the spectrometer is

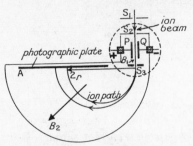

FIG. 841. Principle of Bainbridge's mass spectrometer.

shown in Fig. 841. Positive ions were produced in a discharge tube (not shown) and admitted as a fine beam through slits S_1, S_2. The beam then passed between insulated plates P, Q, connected to a battery, which created an electric field of intensity E. A uniform magnetic field of intensity B_1, perpendicular to E, was also applied over the region of the plates, and all ions with the same velocity v given by $B_1 \bar{e} v = E \bar{e}$ will then pass undeflected through the plates and through a slit S_3. The selected ions are now deflected in a circular path of radius r by a uniform perpendicular magnetic field of intensity B_2, and an image is produced on a photographic plate A, as shown. In this case,

$$\frac{mv^2}{r} = B_2 \bar{e} v.$$

$$\frac{m}{\bar{e}} = \frac{rB_2}{v}.$$

But for the selected ions, $\qquad v = E/B_1$ from above.

$$\therefore \frac{m}{\bar{e}} = \frac{rB_2B_1}{E}$$

$$\therefore \frac{m}{\bar{e}} \propto r,$$

for given magnetic and electric fields.

Since the ions strike the photographic plate at a distance $2r$ from the middle of the slit S_3, it follows that the separation of ions carrying the same charge is directly proportional to their mass. Thus a "linear" mass scale is achieved. A resolution of 1 in 30,000 was obtained with a later type of spectrometer.

Summarizing, (1) Thomson's mass spectrometer produces parabolas with parallel electric and magnetic fields, (2) the Dempster spectrometer deflects ions with the same mass-charge ratio in a circular path of fixed radius by a magnetic field, (3) the Bainbridge spectrometer deflects ions with the same velocity by a perpendicular magnetic field, and the radius of the circular path is directly proportional to the masses of ions carrying the same charge.

19. Einstein's Mass-energy Relation. In 1905 EINSTEIN showed from his Theory of Relativity that mass and energy can be changed from one form to the other. The energy E produced by a change of mass m is given by the relation:

$$E = mc^2,$$

where c is the numerical value of the velocity of light. E is in ergs when m is in grams and c has the numerical value 3×10^{10} (p. 1082). Thus a change of mass of 1 gram could theoretically produce 9×10^{20} ergs of energy, or 9×10^{13} joules. Now 1 kilowatt-hour of energy is $1,000 \times 3,600$ or $3 \cdot 6 \times 10^6$ joules, and hence 9×10^{13} joules is $2 \cdot 5 \times 10^7$ or 25 million kilowatt-hours. Consequently a change in mass of 1 gram could be sufficient to keep the electric lamps in a million houses burning for about a week in winter, on the basis of about seven hours' use per day.

In electronics and in nuclear energy, the unit of energy called an *electron-volt* (eV) is often used. This is defined as the energy gained by a charge equal to that on an electron moving through a p.d. of one volt. Since the electronic charge is $4 \cdot 8 \times 10^{-10}$ e.s.u. and 1 volt is $1/300$ e.s.u. of potential,

$$\therefore 1 \ eV = 4 \cdot 8 \times 10^{-10} \times \frac{1}{300} = 1 \cdot 6 \times 10^{-12} \text{ erg.}$$

The *megelectron-volt* (MeV) is a larger energy unit, and is defined as 1 million eV.

If another unit of energy is needed, then one may use a unit of mass, since mass and energy are interchangeable. The **atomic mass unit** (**a.m.u.**) is defined as one-sixteenth of the mass of the oxygen atom ${}_8O^{16}$.* Now the number of molecules in 1 gram-molecule of oxygen is $6 \cdot 03 \times 10^{23}$, Avogadro's number, and since oxygen is diatomic there are $2 \times 6 \cdot 03 \times 10^{23}$ atoms of oxygen. These all weigh 32 grams.

$$\therefore \text{ mass of 1 atom of oxygen} = \frac{32}{2 \times 6 \cdot 03 \times 10^{23}} \text{ gm.}$$

$$= 16 \text{ a.m.u.}$$

---

* The atomic mass unit was recently adopted as one-twelfth of the mass of the carbon isotope C^{12} in place of the oxygen standard.

$$\therefore \ 1 \ \text{a.m.u.} = \frac{32}{16 \times 2 \times 6 \cdot 03 \times 10^{23}} \ \text{gm.}$$

$$= 1 \cdot 66 \times 10^{-24} \ \text{gm.}$$

We have seen that 1 gram change of mass produces an energy change of 9×10^{20} ergs, and that 1 MeV $= 1 \cdot 6 \times 10^{-6}$ erg.

$$\therefore \ 1 \ \text{a.m.u.} = \frac{1 \cdot 66 \times 10^{-24} \times 9 \times 10^{20}}{1 \cdot 6 \times 10^{-6}} \ \text{MeV.}$$

$$\therefore \ 1 \ \text{a.m.u.} = 931 \ \text{MeV.}$$

This relation is used to change mass units to MeV, and vice-versa, as we shall see shortly.

20. Binding Energy. The protons and neutrons in the nucleus of an atom are called *nucleons*, and they are kept together by an amount of energy called their *binding energy*. This means that work must be done to separate all the nucleons, and hence, from Einstein's mass-energy relation, it follows that the total mass of all the individual nucleons is greater than that of the nucleus, in which they are together. The difference in mass is a measure of the binding energy.

As an example, consider a helium nucleus $_2\text{He}^4$. This has four nucleons, 2 protons and 2 neutrons. The mass of a proton is $1 \cdot 0076$ and the mass of a neutron is $1 \cdot 009$ a.m.u.

$$\therefore \ \text{total mass of 2 protons plus 2 neutrons} = 2 \times 1 \cdot 0076 + 2 \times 1 \cdot 009$$
$$= 4 \cdot 0332 \ \text{a.m.u.}$$

But the helium nucleus has a mass of $4 \cdot 0028$ a.m.u.

$$\therefore \ \text{binding energy} = \text{mass difference of nucleons and nucleus}$$
$$= 4 \cdot 0332 - 4 \cdot 0028 = 0 \cdot 0304 \ \text{a.m.u.}$$
$$= 0 \cdot 0304 \times 931 \ \text{MeV} = 28 \cdot 3 \ \text{MeV.}$$

The *binding energy per nucleon* of a nucleus is binding energy divided by the total number of nucleons. In the case of the helium nucleus, since there are four nucleons (2 protons and 2 neutrons), the binding energy per nucleon is $28 \cdot 3/4$ or about $7 \cdot 1$ MeV. Fig. 842 shows roughly the variation of the binding energy per nucleon among the elements. The great majority have a value of about 8 MeV per nucleon. In spite of considerable binding energy, elements with high mass numbers may have a tendency to disintegrate. This is not surprising because a very heavy nucleus contains many protons (and neutrons) packed into a very tiny volume, and strong forces of repulsion may then exist. An α-particle, perhaps formed by two neutron-proton pairs, may then be expelled from the nucleus. A β-particle is emitted when a neutron changes into a proton in the nucleus.

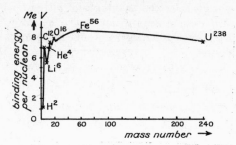

Fig. 842. Variation of binding energy per nucleon with mass number.

21. Stability of Nuclei. It is instructive to consider, from an energy point of view, whether a particular nucleus is likely to disintegrate with the emission of an α-particle. As an illustration, consider radium F or polonium, $_{84}Po^{210}$. If an α-particle could be emitted from the nucleus, the reaction products would be the α-particle or helium nucleus, $_2He^4$, and a lead nucleus, $_{82}Pb^{206}$, a reaction which could be represented by:

$$_{84}Po^{210} \to {}_{82}Pb^{206} + {}_2He^4. \quad . \quad . \quad . \quad . \quad (i)$$

It should be noted that the sum of the mass numbers, 210, and the sum of the nuclear charges, $+ 84e$, of the lead and helium nuclei is equal to the mass number and nuclear charge of the polonium nucleus.

If we require to find whether energy has been released or absorbed in the reaction, we should calculate the total mass of the lead and helium nuclei and compare this with the mass of the polonium nucleus. It is more convenient to use atomic masses rather than nuclear masses, and since the total number of electrons required on each side of (i) to convert the nuclei into atoms is the same, we may use atomic masses in the reaction. These are as follows:

$$\text{lead, } {}_{82}Pb^{206}, = 206 \cdot 034 \text{ a.m.u.}$$

$$\alpha\text{-particle, } {}_2He^4, = 4 \cdot 004 \text{ a.m.u.}$$

$$\therefore \text{ total mass} = 210 \cdot 038 \text{ a.m.u.}$$

Now   polonium $_{84}Po^{210}$, $= 210 \cdot 049$ a.m.u.

Thus the atomic masses of the products of the reaction are together *less* than the original polonium nucleus, that is,

$$_{84}Po^{210} \to {}_{82}Pb^{206} + {}_2He^4 + Q,$$

where Q is the energy released. It therefore follows that polonium can disintegrate with the emission of an α-particle and a release of energy (see *uranium series*, p. 1046), that is, the polonium nucleus is unstable.

Suppose we now consider the possibility of a lead nucleus, $_{82}Pb^{206}$, disintegrating with the emission of an α-particle, $_2He^4$. If this were possible, a mercury nucleus, $_{80}Hg^{202}$, would be formed. The atomic masses are as follows:

$$\text{mercury, } _{80}Hg^{202}, = 202 \cdot 035 \text{ a.m.u.}$$

$$\text{α-particle, } _2He^4, = 4 \cdot 004 \text{ a.m.u.}$$

$$\therefore \text{ total mass} = 206 \cdot 039 \text{ a.m.u.}$$

Now $\qquad$ lead $_{82}Pb^{206}, = 206 \cdot 034$ a.m.u.

Thus, unlike the case previously considered, the atomic masses of the mercury nucleus and α-particle are together *greater* than the lead nucleus, that is,

$$_{82}Pb^{206} + Q \rightarrow {}_{80}Hg^{202} + {}_2He^4,$$

where Q is the energy which must be *given* to the lead nucleus to obtain the reaction products. It follows that the lead nucleus by itself is stable.

Generally, then, a nucleus would tend to be unstable and emit an α-particle if the sum of the atomic masses of the products are together less than that of the nucleus, and it would be stable if the sum of the atomic masses of the possible reaction products are together greater than the atomic mass of the nucleus.

22. Artificial Disintegration. Uranium, thorium and actinium are elements which disintegrate naturally. The artificial disintegration of elements began in 1919, when Rutherford used α-particles to bombard nitrogen and found that protons were produced (p. 1044). Some nuclei of nitrogen had changed into nuclei of oxygen, that is, transmutation had occurred, a reaction which can be represented by:

$$_7N^{14} + {}_2He^4 \rightarrow {}_8O^{17} + {}_1H^1. \text{ (see Plate III, B. p. 1048)}.$$

In 1932 Cockcroft and Walton produced nuclear disintegrations by accelerating protons with a high-voltage machine producing about half a million volts, and then bombarding elements with the high-speed protons. When the light element lithium was used, photographs of the reaction taken in the cloud chamber showed that α-particles were produced. The latter shot out in opposite directions from the point of impact of the protons, and as their range in air was equal, the α-particles had initially equal energy. The nuclear reaction was:

$$_3Li^7 + {}_1H^1 \rightarrow {}_2He^4 + {}_2He^4 + Q, \quad \cdot \quad \cdot \quad \cdot \quad (i)$$

where Q is the energy released in the reaction.

To calculate Q, we should calculate the total mass of the lithium and hydrogen nuclei and subtract the total mass of the two helium nuclei. As already explained, however, the total number of electrons required to convert the nuclei to neutral atoms is the same on both sides of equation (i), and hence atomic masses can be used in the calculation in place of nuclear masses. The atomic masses of lithium and hydrogen are 7·018 and 1·008 a.m.u. respectively, a total of 8·026 a.m.u. The atomic mass of the two α-particles is $2 \times 4\cdot004$ a.m.u. or 8·008 a.m.u. Thus:

$$\text{energy released, } Q, = 8\cdot026 - 8\cdot008 = 0\cdot018 \text{ a.m.u.}$$
$$= 0\cdot018 \times 931 \text{ MeV} = 16\cdot8 \text{ MeV.}$$

Each α-particle has therefore an initial energy of 8·4 MeV, and this theoretical value agreed closely with the energy of the α-particle measured from its range in air.

Cockcroft and Walton were the first scientists to use protons for disrupting atomic nuclei after accelerating them by high voltage. Today, giant high-voltage machines are being built at Atomic Energy centres for accelerating protons to enormously high speeds, and the products of the nuclear explosion with light atoms such as hydrogen will yield valuable information on the structure of the nucleus.

23. Energy released in Fission. In 1934 Fermi began using neutrons to produce nuclear disintegration. These particles are generally more effective than α-particles or protons for this purpose, because they have no charge and are therefore able to penetrate more deeply into the positively-charged nucleus. Usually the atomic nucleus charges only slightly after disintegration, but in 1939 Frisch and Meitner showed that a uranium nucleus had disintegrated into two relatively-heavy nuclei. This is called *nuclear fission*, and as we shall now show, a large amount of energy is released in this case.

Natural uranium consists of about 1 part by weight of uranium atoms $_{92}U^{235}$ and 140 parts by weight of uranium atoms $_{92}U^{238}$. In a nuclear reaction with natural uranium and slow neutrons, it is usually the nucleus $_{92}U^{235}$ which is fissioned. If the resulting nuclei are lanthanum $_{57}La^{148}$ and bromine $_{35}Br^{85}$, together with several neutrons, then:

$$_{92}U^{235} + {_0}n^1 \rightarrow {_{57}}La^{148} + {_{35}}Br^{85} + 3{_0}n^1. \quad \cdots \quad \text{(i)}$$

Now $_{92}U^{235}$ and $_0n^1$ together have a mass of $(235\cdot1 + 1\cdot009)$ or 236·1 a.m.u. The lanthanum, bromine and neutrons produced together have a mass

$$= 148\cdot0 + 84\cdot9 + 3 \times 1\cdot00 = 235\cdot9 \text{ a.m.u.}$$

$\therefore$ energy released = mass difference

$$= 0\cdot2 \text{ a.m.u.} = 0\cdot2 \times 931 \text{ MeV} = 186 \text{ MeV.}$$
$$= 186 \times 1\cdot6 \times 10^{-6} \text{ erg} = 298 \times 10^{-13} \text{ joule (approx.).}$$

This is the energy released per atom of uranium fissioned. In 1 lb. of uranium, 454 gm., there are about

$$\frac{454}{235} \times 6 \times 10^{23} \text{ or } 12 \times 10^{23} \text{ atoms,}$$

since Avogadro's number, the number of atoms in a gram-mol. of any element, is 6.03×10^{23}. Thus if all the atoms in 1 lb. of uranium were fissioned,

total energy released
$$= 12 \times 10^{23} \times 298 \times 10^{-13} \text{ joule}$$
$$= 10^7 \text{ kilowatt-hour (approx.)},$$

which is the amount of energy given out by burning about 3 million tons of coal. The energy released per gram of uranium fissioned $= 8 \times 10^{10}$ joule (approx.).

To make practical use of nuclear fission, the incident neutrons must be moderated in speed so that they are "captured" by the nuclei in a mass of uranium. Carbon rods are used as moderators. The neutrons produced in the nuclear reaction in equation (i), p. 1059, in turn produce fission swiftly in other uranium nuclei, and so on, thus creating a multiplying rapid *chain reaction* throughout the mass of uranium. Details of nuclear reactors can be obtained from the United Kingdom Atomic Energy Authority, London.

24. Energy released in Fusion. In fission, energy is released when a heavy nucleus is split into two lighter nuclei. Energy is also released if light nuclei are *fused* together to form heavier nuclei, and a fusion reaction, as we shall see, is also a possible source of considerable energy. As an illustration, consider the fusion of the nuclei of deuterium, $_1H^2$. Deuterium is an isotope of hydrogen known as "heavy hydrogen", and its nucleus is called a "deuteron". The fusion of two deuterons can result in a helium nucleus, $_2He^3$, as follows:

$$_1H^2 + {}_1H^2 \rightarrow {}_2He^3 + {}_0n^1.$$

Now   mass of two deuterons
$$= 2 \times 2.015 = 4.03 \text{ a.m.u.},$$

and   mass of helium plus neutron
$$= 3.017 + 1.009 = 4.026 \text{ a.m.u.}$$

$\therefore$ mass converted to energy by fusion
$$= 4.03 - 4.026 = 0.004 \text{ a.m.u.}$$
$$= 0.004 \times 931 \text{ MeV} = 3.7 \text{ MeV}$$
$$= 3.7 \times 1.6 \times 10^{-13} \text{ joule} = 6.0 \times 10^{-13} \text{ joule}$$

$\therefore$ energy released per deuteron
$$= 3.0 \times 10^{-13} \text{ joule}.$$

6×10^{23} is the number of atoms in a gram-mol. of deuterium, which is about 2 grams. Thus if all the atoms could undergo fusion,

energy released per gram
$$= 3.0 \times 10^{-13} \times 3 \times 10^{23} \text{ joule}$$
$$= 9 \times 10^{10} \text{ joule (approx.).}$$

Other fusion reactions can release much more energy, for example, the fusion of the nuclei of deuterium, $_1H^2$, and tritium, $_1H^3$, isotopes of hydrogen, releases about 30×10^{10} joules of energy according to the reaction:

$$_1H^2 + _1H^3 \rightarrow _2He^4 + _0n^1.$$

In addition, the temperature required for this fusion reaction is less than that needed for the fusion reaction between two deuterons given above, which is an advantage. Hydrogen contains about 1/5000th by weight of deuterium or heavy hydrogen, needed in fusion reactions, and this can be obtained by electrolysis of sea-water, which is cheap and in plentiful supply.

25. Thermonuclear Reaction. The binding energy curve in Fig. 842 shows that elements with low atomic mass, up to about 56, can produce energy by fusion of their nucleons. For fusion to take place, the nuclei must at least overcome their nuclear repulsion when approaching each other. Consequently, for practical purposes, fusion reactions can best be achieved with the lightest elements such as hydrogen, whose nuclei carry the smallest charges and hence repel each other least.

In attempts to obtain fusion, isotopes of hydrogen such as deuterium, $_1H^2$, and tritium, $_1H^3$, are heated to tens of millions of degrees centigrade. The thermal energy of the nuclei at these high temperatures is sufficient for fusion to occur. One technique of promoting this *thermonuclear reaction* is to pass enormously high currents through the gas, which heat it. A very high percentage of the atoms are then ionized and the name *plasma* is given to the gas. Interstellar space or the *aurora borealis* contains a weak form of plasma, but the interior of stars contains a highly concentrated form of plasma. The gas discharge consists of parallel currents, carried by ions, and the powerful magnetic field round one current due to a neighbouring current (see p. 931) draws the discharge together. This is the so-called "pinch effect". The plasma, however, wriggles and touches the sides of the containing vessel, thereby losing heat. The main difficulty in thermonuclear experiments in the laboratory is to retain the heat in the gas for a sufficiently long time for a fusion reaction to occur, and the stability of plasma is now the subject of considerable research.

It is believed that the energy of the sun is produced by thermonuclear reactions in the heart of the sun, where the temperature is many millions of degrees centigrade. Bethe has proposed a cycle of nuclear reactions in which, basically, protons are converted to helium by fusion, with the liberation of a considerable amount of energy.

ELECTRONS ROUND THE NUCLEUS. ENERGY LEVELS

26. Bohr's Theory of Hydrogen Atom. So far we have discussed the nucleus of the atom, the particles inside the nucleus, and nuclear energy. We now consider the electrons surrounding the nucleus or "extra-nuclear" electrons, which are concerned in such widely different phenomena as spectra, chemical activity, conduction of electricity, photoelectricity and X-rays.

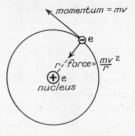

In 1913 Bohr gave a theory which explained satisfactorily, for the first time, the observed wavelengths emitted by the hydrogen atom, the simplest atom. He considered one electron of charge $-e$ and mass m moving in a circular orbit round a central nucleus of charge $+e$ (Fig. 843). The energy of the electron is partly kinetic and partly potential energy. If v is the velocity in the orbit, then

Fig. 843. Bohr's theory of hydrogen atom.

$$\text{kinetic energy} = \tfrac{1}{2}mv^2 \quad . \quad . \quad \text{(i)}$$

If the electron is removed a very long way against the attraction of the nucleus, that is, to infinity, its potential energy is a maximum, but in calculations it is given the value of "zero". In practice, this means that the hydrogen atom loses an electron completely and becomes an ion. Consider now an electron in the atom at a distance r from the nucleus. Since work is required to move the electron from this point to infinity against the attraction of the nucleus, it follows that the potential energy of the electron is *negative*. The *potential* due to the nuclear charge $+e$ at a distance r is given by $+e/r$, and since this is the work done per unit charge, then

$$\text{potential energy of electron} = \frac{e}{r} \times -e = -\frac{e^2}{r}. \quad . \quad \text{(ii)}$$

From (i),　　∴ total energy, E, $= \frac{1}{2}mv^2 - \frac{e^2}{r}. \quad . \quad . \quad \text{(iii)}$

For circular motion,

$$\frac{mv^2}{r} = \text{force towards centre} = \frac{e^2}{r^2} \quad \text{(iv)}$$

$$\therefore \frac{1}{2}mv^2 = \frac{e^2}{2r}$$

$$\therefore \text{total energy, } E, = \frac{e^2}{2r} - \frac{e^2}{r} = -\frac{e^2}{2r}. \quad . \quad \text{(v)}$$

27. Quantum Laws. In mechanics, the angular momentum of a system about an axis is conserved when no external forces act on the system. Thus the angular momentum, or moment of momentum, of the electron about the nucleus, which is $mv \times r$, is constant. Bohr made the brilliant suggestion that the angular momentum of the electron was *quantized*, that is, it obeyed quantum laws.

Planck had proposed a quantum theory of radiation, in which energy is considered not to be emitted continuously but in units of $h\nu$, where ν is the frequency of the radiation and h is a constant known as Planck's constant. Bohr now suggested that the radii r of the circular electron orbits were those for which the angular momentum of the electron was a multiple of $h/2\pi$. Thus if n is a whole number,

$$mvr = \frac{nh}{2\pi} \cdot \quad \cdots \cdots \text{(vi)}$$

From previous,

$$mv^2r = e^2. \quad \cdots \cdots \text{(vii)}$$

Dividing,

$$\therefore v = \frac{2\pi e^2}{nh} \quad \cdots \cdots \text{(viii)}$$

and hence

$$r = \frac{n^2h^2}{4\pi^2me^2}. \quad \cdots \cdots \text{(ix)}$$

In classical physics, charges undergoing acceleration emit radiation and therefore lose energy. On this basis the electron would spiral towards the nucleus and the atom would collapse. Bohr therefore suggested (*a*) that in those orbits where the angular momentum is a multiple of $h/2\pi$ the energy of the electron is constant, and (*b*) that the electron, or atom, can pass from one allowed energy value or *energy level* E_1 to another E_2 of smaller value, but not to a value between, and that the difference of energy is released in the form of radiation of energy $h\nu$, where ν is the frequency of the radiation emitted. Thus

$$E_1 - E_2 = h\nu. \quad \cdots \cdots \text{(x)}$$

Now from (v),

$$E = -\frac{e^2}{2r} = -\frac{2\pi^2me^4}{h^2n^2}$$

$$\therefore E_1 - E_2 = \frac{2\pi^2me^4}{h^2}\left(\frac{1}{n_2{}^2} - \frac{1}{n_1{}^2}\right) = h\nu$$

$$\therefore \nu = \frac{2\pi^2me^4}{h^3}\left(\frac{1}{n_2{}^2} - \frac{1}{n_1{}^2}\right)$$

$$\therefore \frac{1}{\lambda} = \bar{\nu} = \frac{2\pi^2me^4}{ch^3}\left(\frac{1}{n_2{}^2} - \frac{1}{n_1{}^2}\right) \cdot \cdot \text{(xi)}$$

where λ is the wavelength and $\bar{\nu}$, *the wave number*, is the number of wavelengths in one centimetre.

28. Spectral Series of Hydrogen. Before Bohr's theory of the hydrogen atom it had been found that the wave numbers of the hydrogen spectrum could be arranged in the form of a series, named after its discoverer. Among the wave numbers were:

1. *Lyman (ultra-violet) series*—$\bar{\nu} = R\left(\dfrac{1}{1^2} - \dfrac{1}{m^2}\right).$

2. *Balmer (visible) series*—$\bar{\nu} = R\left(\dfrac{1}{2^2} - \dfrac{1}{m^2}\right).$

3. *Paschen (infra-red) series*—$\bar{\nu} = R\left(\dfrac{1}{3^2} - \dfrac{1}{m^2}\right),$

where R is a constant known as *Rydberg's constant* and m is an integer. From Bohr's formula in (xi), it follows that all the spectral series can be obtained simply by putting $n_2 = 1, 2, 3$ respectively and $n_1 = m$ (see Fig. 844). Moreover, (a) the agreement between the experimental and

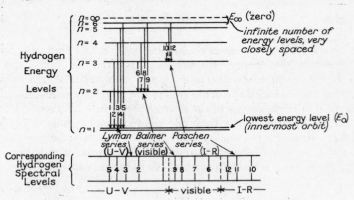

FIG. 844. Energy levels and spectra of hydrogen (*not to scale*).

theoretical values of the wave numbers is excellent, (b) Rydberg's constant determined experimentally is 109,678 cm.$^{-1}$ and from $R = 2\pi^2 me^4/ch^3$ it is 109,700 cm.$^{-1}$, (c) the radius of the first circular orbit calculated from $r = h^2/4\pi^2 me^2$, equation (ix), is $0\cdot528 \times 10^{-8}$ cm. This radius, which corresponds to $n = 1$, is the radius of the stable hydrogen atom, since the energy E is a minimum when $n = 1$, from $E = -2\pi^2 me^4/h^2 n^2$. The value of r is in good agreement with the atomic radius calculated from the kinetic theory of gases.

29. Excitation and Ionization Potentials. Bohr's theory of the hydrogen atom was unable to predict the energy levels in complex atoms, which had many electrons. Quantum or wave mechanics, beyond the scope of this book, is used to explain the spectral frequencies of these atoms. The fundamental ideas of Bohr's theory, however, are still retained, for example, the angular momentum of the electron has quantum values and the energy levels of the atom have only allowed discrete values.

Generally, an atom is most stable when it has a minimum energy E_0, and it is then said to be in its *ground state*. If the atom absorbs energy, for example, when an energetic electron collides with a gas atom as in a discharge tube, or with a metallic atom as in an X-ray tube, and the energy of the atom reaches one of its allowed values E_1, the atom is said to be in an *excited state*. If the atom falls directly from E_1 to E_0, then

$$h\nu_1 = E_1 - E_0,$$

where ν_1 is the frequency of the radiation emitted. Similarly, the frequency ν_2 of the radiation emitted if the atom falls from a higher level E_2 to a lower energy level E_1 is such that $h\nu_2 = E_2 - E_1$.

The energy required to raise an atom from its ground state to an excited state is called the *excitation energy* of the atom. If the energy is eV, where e is the electronic charge, V is known as the *excitation potential* of the atom.

If an atom is in its ground state with energy E_0, and absorbs an amount of energy $e\bar{V}$ which just removes an electron completely from the atom, then $\bar{V}$ is said to be the *ionization potential* of the atom. The potential energy of the atom is here denoted by E_∞, as the ejected electron is so far away from the attractive influence as to be, in effect, at infinity. E_∞ is taken as the "zero" energy of the atom, and its other values are thus negative. The ionization potential is given by $E_\infty - E_0 = e\bar{V}$, or by $-E_0 = e\bar{V}$. Fig. 845 shows roughly the energy levels of an atom, namely, its ground state E_0, its excited states E_1, E_2, . . ., and its

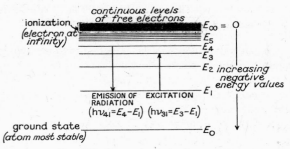

FIG. 845. Energy levels in the atom.

ionization state, E_∞. The energy levels become more closely spaced at the higher excited states. When the atom absorbs energy greater than its ionization energy, the ejected electron is no longer under the attractive influence of the nucleus. The energy of the "free" electron can have one of a continuous range of energies, whereas inside the atom it could only have one of a number of separated allowed values.

30. Optical Spectra. As an illustration of Bohr's theory of energy levels, the ionization potential, E_∞, of helium is $24 \cdot 6 \, eV$ (electron-volt). The ground state thus corresponds to an energy level of E_0 of $-24 \cdot 6 \, eV$. Suppose there is an excitation level, E_n, of helium of $-21 \cdot 4 \, eV$. Then if the helium atom is excited to this level and falls directly to the ground state, the frequency ν_n of the radiation emitted is given by

$$h\nu_n = E_n - E_0$$

$$\therefore \nu_n = \frac{[(-21 \cdot 4) - (-24 \cdot 6)] \times 1 \cdot 6 \times 10^{-12}}{6 \cdot 6 \times 10^{-27}} \text{ cycles per sec.,}$$

since $h = $ Planck's constant $= 6 \cdot 6 \times 10^{-27}$ erg sec. and $1 \, eV = 1 \cdot 6 \times 10^{-12}$ erg. Thus the wavelength, λ_n, is given by

$$\lambda_n = \frac{c}{\nu_n} = \frac{3 \times 10^{10} \times 6 \cdot 6 \times 10^{-27}}{3 \cdot 1 \times 1 \cdot 6 \times 10^{-12}}$$

$$= 3 \cdot 9 \times 10^{-5} \text{ cm.}$$

This is a wavelength in the violet end of the spectrum. Fig. 845 illustrates the emission of radiation as the energy of the atom falls from one level to another.

Emission spectra are classified into *continuous*, *line* and *band* spectra. With few exceptions, incandescent solids and liquids produce a continuous spectrum, one in which all wavelengths are found over a wide range. Line spectra are obtained from *atoms* in gases such as hydrogen in a discharge tube, and the spectrum of a sodium salt vaporized in a Bunsen flame consists of two lines close together. Gases such as carbon dioxide in a discharge tube also produce a band spectrum, each band consisting of a series of lines very close together at the sharp edge or head of the band and farther apart at the other end or tail. Band spectra are essentially due to *molecules*. The different band heads in a band system are due to small allowed discrete energy changes in the vibrational states of the molecule. The fine lines in a given band are due to still smaller allowed discrete energy changes in the rotational states of the molecule.

31. Experiment of Franck and Hertz. An important experiment confirming Bohr's idea of energy levels was first carried out by Franck and Hertz in 1914. They used sodium vapour at a very low pressure of about 1 mm. of mercury in a tube containing a heated tungsten filament F, a grid plate G, and a plate A (Fig. 846 (i)). Electrons were emitted from F, and the distance FG was arranged to be much greater than the mean free path of the electrons in the gas, in which case the electrons would make collisions with the atoms before reaching G. The p.d. V between F and G could be varied by the potentiometer S. The electrons emitted from F were accelerated to kinetic energies depending on the magnitude of V, measured by a voltmeter. A small p.d., less than 1 volt, was applied between A and G so that A was negative in potential relative to G. The plate A was close to G, and electrons reaching G

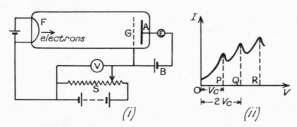

FIG. 846. Franck and Hertz experiment.

and passing through to A were subjected to a retarding field. The number per second reaching A was measured by an electrometer E.

When the accelerating p.d. V between F and G was increased from zero, the current in E rose until the p.d. reached a value P (Fig. 846 (ii)). As V was increased further the current diminished to a minimum, rose again to a new peak at a higher p.d. Q, then diminished again and rose to another peak at a higher p.d. R. The p.d. V_c between successive peaks was found to be constant and equal to 2·10 volts for sodium vapour. Similar results were found for other gases.

32. Critical Potentials. The results of Franck and Hertz can now be explained. The p.d. V between G and F accelerates the electrons from F, so that they gain kinetic energy and collide with the gas atoms. At first, as V is increased from zero, the energy of the electrons is insufficient to raise the atoms to an excited state. As the total energy is constant, the collision is called "elastic". The electrons have sufficient energy to overcome the retarding p.d. between G and A on reaching G and a current is recorded in E. As V is increased further, more electrons reach A. At a p.d. V_c some electrons emitted from F gain sufficient energy to just excite the atoms, which then absorbs their energy. An inelastic collision now takes place. These electrons have insufficient energy to reach A, and the current therefore diminishes. Other electrons emitted from F continue to reach A if they make elastic collisions with the gas atoms.

When the p.d. is increased further, the energy of the electrons increases. At first, those electrons which make inelastic collisions do not have sufficient excess energy to reach A and the current decreases further, but the current rises again as their excess energy increases. At a p.d. of 2 V_c, however, some of the electrons have just sufficient energy to excite the atoms, making two inelastic collisions. One is about half-way between F and G, where the p.d. is about V_c, and the other is near G, where it again acquires energy by moving through a p.d. of V_c. The interval V_c between successive peaks of the curve in Fig. 846 (ii) is thus the excitation potential of the atom.

Other excitation potentials of a gas would give rise to more peaks, and the ionization potential of the gas is eventually reached as the p.d. is increased. Excitation and ionization potentials are called *critical* potentials of the gas. The first excitation potential of sodium is 2·10 volts, and a calculation similar to that on p. 1066 shows that the quantum of energy $h\nu$ in the yellow line of the sodium emission spectrum is equal to 2·10 electron-volts. The experiments of Franck and Hertz showed con-clusively that there are separate or discrete energy levels in the atom.

33. Electron Shells. Chemical Activity. Bohr's theory of the hydrogen atom shows that the energy levels of the electron inside it have separated values. A heavier atom such as sodium has 11 electrons. Years later, it was shown that the electrons in an atom can be accommodated in one of a number of separated groups of energy levels called *shells*; each shell is divided into *subshells*. The occupation of a shell and subshell by an electron is subject to a restriction known as *Pauli's Exclusion Principle*. This important law postulates that no two electrons can co-exist in an atom if they have the same "quantum state", that is, they may not have the same four values of (a) energy, (b) orbital angular momentum, (c) orbital magnetic moment (the magnetic moment due to the electron moving round its orbit and producing a circular current), (d) spin magnetic moment (the magnetic moment due to the spin of an electron about an axis through itself, discovered in 1925).

When Pauli's Exclusion Principle is applied to the electrons in the atom, it is found that the shell nearest the nucleus, the K shell, can accommodate up to a maximum of 2 electrons. The next shell, the L shell, can accommodate up to a maximum of 8 electrons; the M shell up to a maximum of 18 electrons; and the $N, O, \ldots$ shells up to a maxi-mum of 32, 64, .. electrons respectively. The total number of electrons in all the shells is equal to the atomic number Z of the atom, which varies from 1 (hydrogen) to 92 (uranium).

On this basis, hydrogen has 1 electron in the K shell; helium, $Z = 2$, has 2 electrons in the K shell. The maximum number of electrons in the K shell is 2, and hence lithium, $Z = 3$, has 2 electrons in the K shell and 1 electron in the L shell. As the atomic number increases, the electrons fill up the L shell. Fluorine, $Z = 9$, has 2 electrons in the K shell and 7 electrons in the L shell. Neon, $Z = 10$, has 2 electrons in the K shell and 8 electrons in the L shell, the maximum possible. Sodium, $Z = 11$, has 2 electrons in the K, 8 in the L, and 1 in the M shells. Chlorine, $Z = 17$, has 2 electrons in the K, 8 in the L, and 7 in the M shells. The sodium atom has thus 1 "available" electron in its outermost shell, that is, it is an electron donor; on the other hand, the chlorine atom can accommodate 1 more electron in its outermost subshell, that is, it is an electron acceptor. When the very stable compound sodium chloride is formed, the outer electron in the sodium atom passes to the chlorine atom. The outermost shells of each atom are now complete, and this is a very stable electron arrangement (see p. 882).

The chemical activity, or inactivity, of all elements is explained by their electron shell arrangement. Thus fluorine ($K = 2, L = 7$ electrons), chlorine ($K = 2, L = 8, M = 7$ electrons) and bromine ($K = 2, L = 8$, $M = 8, N = 7$ electrons) have each a vacancy for 1 electron in their respective outermost shells to make them complete, and have similar chemical properties. Lithium ($K = 2, L = 1$ electron), sodium ($K = 2$, $L = 8, M = 1$ electron) and potassium ($K = 2, L = 8, M = 8, N = 1$ electron) are all electron donors and have similar chemical activity. In contrast, helium ($K = 2$ electrons), and neon ($K = 2, L = 8$ electrons) have complete shells of electrons and are therefore chemically inactive.

34. X-ray Spectra. In an X-ray tube, very energetic electrons bombard atoms in a metal target such as tungsten, and an electron may be ejected from the innermost shell, the K shell. The atom is then in an excited state and is unstable. If an electron from the L shell now moves into the vacancy in the K shell, the energy of the atom is decreased and simultaneously there is emission of radiation. If E is the change in energy of the atom when the electron moves from the L to the K shell, then $E = h\nu$, where ν is the frequency of the radiation, from Bohr's theory. Thus $\nu = E/h$, and as E is very high for metals, the frequency ν is very high and the wavelength is correspondingly short. It is commonly of the order of 10^{-8} cm., the wavelengths of X-rays.

The X-ray spectra of different metals such as copper, iron and tungsten are similar in appearance. Each indicates energy changes of electrons in the interior of the atom close to the nucleus. By contrast, the optical spectra of metals are related to the energy changes of electrons in the outermost shells of the atoms, which are different for different metals. The optical spectra are therefore different.

35. Crystal Diffraction. The first proof of the wave-nature of X-rays was due to Laue in 1913, many years after X-rays were discovered. He suggested that the regular small spacing of atoms in crystals might provide a natural diffraction grating if the wavelengths of the rays were too short to be used with an optical line grating. Experiments by Friedrich and Knipping showed that X-rays were indeed diffracted by a thin crystal, and produced a pattern of intense spots round a central image on a photographic plate placed to receive

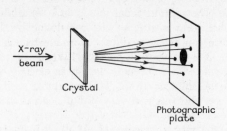

Fig. 847. Laue crystal diffraction.

them (Fig. 847). The rays had thus been scattered by interaction with electrons in the atoms of the crystal, and the pattern obtained gave information on the geometrical spacing of the atoms.

36. Bragg's Law. The study of the atomic structure of crystals by X-ray analysis was initiated in 1914 by Sir William Bragg and his son Sir Lawrence Bragg, with notable achievements. They soon found that a monochromatic beam of X-rays was reflected from a plane in the crystal rich in atoms, a so-called atomic plane, as if the latter acted like a mirror.

This important effect can be explained by Huyghens's wave theory in the same way as the reflection of light by a plane surface. Suppose a monochromatic parallel X-ray beam is incident on a crystal and interacts with atoms such as A, B, C, D in an atomic plane P (Fig. 848 (i)). Each atom scatters the X-rays. Using Huyghens's construction, wavelets can be drawn with the atoms as centres, which all lie on a plane wavefront reflected at an equal angle to the atomic plane P. When

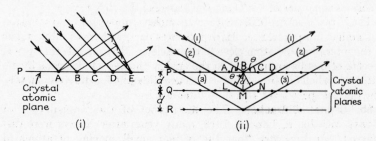

Fig. 848. Reflection (diffraction) at crystal atomic planes.

the X-ray beam penetrates the crystal to other atomic planes such as Q, R parallel to P, reflection occurs in a similar way (Fig. 848 (ii)). Usually, the beam or ray reflected from one plane is weak in intensity. If, however, the reflected beams or rays from all planes are *in phase* with each other, an intense reflected beam is produced by the crystal.

Suppose, then, that the glancing angle on an atomic plane in the crystal is θ, and d is the distance apart of consecutive parallel atomic planes (Fig. 848 (ii)). The path difference between the rays marked (1) and (2) = LM + MN = 2LM = $2d \sin \theta$. Thus an intense X-ray beam is reflected when

$$2d \sin \theta = n\lambda,$$

where λ is the wavelength and n has integral values. This is known as *Bragg's law*. Hence, as the crystal is rotated so that the glancing angle is increased from zero, and the beam reflected at an equal angle is observed each time, an intense beam is suddenly produced for a glancing angle θ_1 such that $2d \sin \theta_1 = \lambda$. When the crystal is rotated further, an intense reflected beam is next obtained for an angle θ_2 when $2d \sin \theta_2 = 2\lambda$. Thus several orders of diffraction images may be observed. Many orders are obtained if λ is small compared with $2d$. Conversely, no images are obtained if λ is greater than $2d$.

The intense diffraction (reflection) images from an X-ray tube are due to X-ray lines *characteristic of the metal used* as the target, or "anti-cathode" as it was originally known. This is because the quantum of energy $h\nu$ in the emitted X-ray depends on the nuclear charge $+Ze$ of the atom, which affects electron energy changes near the nucleus (p. 1069). The frequency, or wavelength λ, thus depends on the atomic number, Z.

37. X-ray Analysis. A special form of spectrometer was designed by Sir William Bragg for his experiments. The crystal was fixed on the table, and an X-ray beam, limited by lead shields A, B, was incident on the crystal at various glancing angles, θ (Fig. 849 (i)). An ionization chamber, Q, was used to measure the intensity of the X-rays

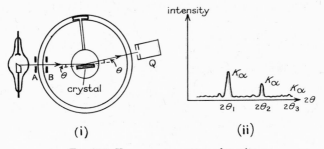

(i)   (ii)

FIG. 849. X-ray spectrometer and results.

reflected by the crystal. Q contained a heavy gas such as methyl iodide, and the intensity of the X-rays was proportional to the ionization current flowing, which was measured by means of an electrometer (not shown) connected to Q. The table and Q were geared so that Q turned through twice the angle of rotation of the crystal, and was always ready to measure the intensity of X-rays satisfying the law $2d \sin \theta = n\lambda$.

Typical results with particular parallel atomic planes in a crystal such as sylvine (KCl) or rocksalt (NaCl) are shown roughly in Fig. 849 (ii). A characteristic X-ray line such as K_α produces peaks of intensity at glancing angles θ_1, θ_2 and θ_3 for the first three orders. Measurement shows that $\sin \theta_1 : \sin \theta_2 : \sin \theta_3 = 1 : 2 : 3$, thus verifying Bragg's law, $2d \sin \theta = n\lambda$.

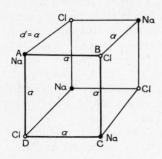

Fig. 850. Unit cell of rocksalt.

38. Crystal Atomic Spacing.

Before the wavelength λ can be calculated, the distance d between consecutive parallel atomic planes is required. As an illustration of the calculation, consider the distance d between those atomic planes of a rocksalt crystal, NaCl, which are parallel to the face ABCD of a unit cell or cube of the crystal (Fig. 850). In this case $d = a$, the side of the cube. We thus require the distance a between consecutive atoms (ions) of sodium and chlorine in the crystal.

The gram-molecular weight of sodium chloride is 58·5 gm., the sum of the atomic weights of sodium and chlorine. This contains about 6×10^{23} molecules, Avogadro's number. The mass of a molecule is thus $58·5 \text{ gm.}/6 \times 10^{23}$. Since the density of rocksalt is about 2·2 gm. cm.$^{-3}$,

$$\text{volume occupied by 1 molecule (2 atoms)} = \frac{58·5}{6 \times 10^{23} \times 2·2} \text{ cm.}^3$$

$$\therefore \text{ volume associated with each atom} = \frac{58·5}{2 \times 6 \times 10^{23} \times 2·2} \text{ cm.}^3$$

$$\therefore \text{ separation of atoms} = \left[\frac{58·5}{2 \times 6 \times 10^{23} \times 2·2} \right]^{1/3} \text{ cm.}$$

$$= 2·8 \times 10^{-8} \text{ cm.}$$

Thus if the first order diffraction image is obtained for a glancing angle θ of 5·4° for a particular X-ray wavelength λ, then

$$\lambda = 2d \sin \theta = 2 \times 2·8 \times 10^{-8} \times \sin 5·4°$$

$$= 0·5 \times 10^{-8} \text{ cm.} = 0·5 \text{ A}°.$$

Knowing λ, the atomic spacing d in other crystals can then be found, thus leading to analysis of crystal structure.

39. Moseley's Law. In 1914 Moseley measured the frequency ν of the characteristic X-rays from many metals, and found that, for a particular type of emitted X-ray such as K_α, the frequency ν varied in a regular way with the atomic number Z of the metal. When a graph of Z v. $\nu^{1/2}$ was plotted, an almost perfect straight line was obtained (Fig. 851). Moseley therefore gave an empirical relation, known as *Moseley's law*, between ν and Z as

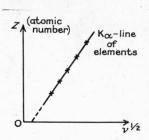

FIG. 851. Moseley's law.

$$\nu = a(Z - b)^2,$$

where a, b are constants.

Since the regularity of the graph was so marked, Moseley predicted the discovery of elements with atomic numbers 43, 61, 72 and 75, which were missing from the graph at that time. These were later discovered. He also found that though the atomic weights of iron, nickel and cobalt increased in this order, their positions from the graph were: iron ($Z = 26$), cobalt ($Z = 27$) and nickel ($Z = 28$). The chemical properties of the three elements agree with the order by atomic number and not by atomic weight. Rutherford's experiments on the scattering of α-particles (p. 1043) showed that the atom contained a central nucleus of charge $+Ze$ where Z is the atomic number, and Moseley's experiments confirm the importance of Z in atomic theory (see also p. 1015).

40. Continuous X-ray Background Radiation. The characteristic X-ray spectrum from a metal is usually superimposed on a background of continuous, or so-called "white", radiation of small intensity. Fig. 852 illustrates the characteristic lines, K_α, K_β, of a metal and the continuous background of radiation for two values of p.d., 40,000 and 32,000 volts, across an X-ray tube. It should be noted that (i) the wavelengths of the characteristic lines are independent of the p.d.—they are characteristic of the metal, (ii) the background of continuous radiation has increasing wavelengths which slowly diminish in intensity, but as the wavelengths diminish they are cut off *abruptly*, as at A and B.

On classical theory, electrons which enter the intense electric field round the nucleus are accelerated, and then lose energy continuously in the form of electromagnetic radiation. The existence of a sharp minimum wavelength at A or B can be explained only by the quantum theory. The energy of an electron before striking the metal atoms of the target is eV, where V is the p.d. across the tube. If a direct collision

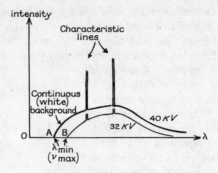

Fig. 852. X-ray characteristic lines and background.

is made with an atom and *all* the energy is absorbed, then, on quantum theory, the X-ray quantum produced has maximum energy.

$$\therefore h\nu_{max} = eV$$

$$\therefore \nu_{max} = \frac{eV}{h} \quad . \quad . \quad . \quad . \quad \text{(i)}$$

$$\therefore \lambda_{min} = \frac{c}{\nu_{max}} = \frac{ch}{eV} \quad . \quad . \quad \text{(ii)}$$

41. Verification of Quantum Theory. These conclusions are borne out by experiment. Thus for a particular metal target, experiment shows that the minimum wavelength is obtained for p.d.s of $40kV$ and $32kV$ at glancing angles of about $3 \cdot 0°$ and $3 \cdot 8°$ respectively. The ratio of the minimum wavelengths is hence, from Bragg's law,

$$\frac{\lambda_1}{\lambda_2} = \frac{\sin 3 \cdot 0°}{\sin 3 \cdot 8°} = 0 \cdot 8 \text{ (approx.).}$$

From (ii), $\lambda_{min} \propto 1/V$.

$$\therefore \frac{\lambda_1}{\lambda_2} = \frac{32}{40} = 0 \cdot 8.$$

With a tungsten target and a p.d. of $30kV$, experiment shows that a minimum wavelength of $0 \cdot 42 \times 10^{-8}$ cm. is obtained, as calculated from values of d and θ. From (ii),

$$\therefore \lambda_{min} = \frac{ch}{eV} = \frac{3 \cdot 0 \times 10^{10} \times 6 \cdot 6 \times 10^{-27}}{1 \cdot 6 \times 10^{-19} \times 30,000 \times 10^7} \text{ cm.}$$

$$= 0 \cdot 41 \times 10^{-8} \text{ cm.,}$$

using $c = 3 \cdot 0 \times 10^{10}$ cm. sec.$^{-1}$, $h = 6 \cdot 6 \times 10^{-27}$ erg sec., $e = 1 \cdot 6 \times 10^{-19}$

coulomb, $V = 30,000$ volts and changing eV from joules to ergs. This is in good agreement with the experimental result.

42. Energy Bands in Solids. In the case of a single atom, the energy levels of its electrons are separate and spaced widely apart. In the case of a solid crystal, however, the atomic nuclei are very close together, and the electrons in one atom are then influenced by the nucleus of a neighbouring atom. The general effect of the overlapping spheres of influence of the nuclei as they come close together is illustrated in Fig. 853. The energy levels broaden into *bands* of allowed values, grouped so closely together that they resemble continuous bands, as at P. Energy bands which electrons can not occupy, called *forbidden bands*, may also appear, as at Q.

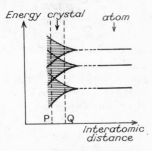

FIG. 853. Energy levels in atom and crystal (*diagrammatic*).

From the viewpoint of bands of energy, a solid *conductor* of electricity could be represented as in Fig. 854 (*a*), which shows the position for an alkali metal such as sodium. The uppermost band A, containing electrons in the outer shells of the atoms, is only half-full of electrons. Electrons in the band can therefore move to other unoccupied levels of higher energy by acquiring an infinitesimal amount of energy from an applied electric field. The band A is actually an overlapping valence and conduction band, the latter being a band with higher energy levels at the top than the valence band. In the metal sodium, then, conduction is due to a partly filled valence band of energies.

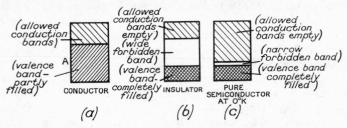

FIG. 854. Bands in conductor, insulator, semiconductor.

In contrast, an *insulator* has a valence band of energy values completely filled by electrons (Fig. 854 (*b*)). This is separated by a wide forbidden band from the uppermost or conduction band, which is completely empty. It is normally impossible to give an electron in the valence band sufficient energy from an applied electric field of moderate value to raise it to the conduction band, so no conduction occurs.

43. Semiconductors. Holes and Electrons. Solids which have electrical properties between those of a conductor and an insulator are known as *semiconductors*, and they are used in transistors. Semiconductors have a band diagram similar to that of an insulator, but the forbidden band has a narrow energy gap (Fig. 854 (c)). At 0°K., a pure or "intrinsic" semiconductor is an insulator. At room temperature, however, the thermal energy of an electron (approximately equal to kT, where k is Boltzmann's constant and T is the absolute temperature) may be high enough for it to reach the conduction band, and it then becomes a conduction or free electron. The higher the temperature, the higher is the number of electrons reaching the conduction band. This explains the characteristic behaviour of the electrical resistance of a semiconductor, which decreases rapidly as the temperature rises.

When an electron leaves the valence band, a vacancy or *hole* is left in the band. Other electrons in the valence band can then move to fill the empty place or hole in the distribution, and the hole movement, which is random, may spread through the crystal structure. At any instant the number of holes present in the pure semiconductor is equal to the number of free or conduction electrons.

When an electric field is applied to the semiconductor, the holes in the valence band drift in one direction and the conduction electrons drift in the opposite direction. Both holes and electrons carry the current, and both produce an electric current in the same direction. Since the holes are occasioned by valence electrons moving in an opposite direction, the hole movement is equivalent to the movement of a *positive* charge equal to that on an electron. Shockley showed by experiment in 1948 that in the semiconductor germanium the mobility of a conduction electron is about twice that of a hole when an electric field is applied. Thus about two-thirds of the current is carried by conduction electrons and one-third by holes. In other semiconductors the electron mobility may be much higher than the hole mobility or less than the hole mobility.

44. Conductors in Metals. The conduction of electricity in metals is due to its free electrons, which are those in the conduction band of energy, as already explained. Free electrons have thermal energy, and wander randomly through the metal from atom to atom. When a battery is connected across the ends of the metal, an electric field is set up. The electrons are now accelerated by the field, so they gain velocity and energy. When they "collide" with a vibrating atom they give up their energy to it and the metal becomes hotter. The electrons are then again accelerated by the field and again give up energy. Although their movement is erratic, on the average the electrons drift in the direction of the field, and this drift constitutes an "electric current".

45. Explanation of Ohm's law. The magnitude of the electric current in the metal is proportional to the mean drift velocity of the electrons, which is superimposed on their thermal speed. Let us suppose that the electron drift velocity after collision with an atom falls practically to zero, and that the field then accelerates the electron to a drift velocity v just before another collision. Then $v = ft$, where f is the acceleration and t is the average time between collisions. The mean drift velocity $\bar{v}$ is half this value, and hence

$$\bar{v} = \tfrac{1}{2}v = \tfrac{1}{2}ft. \qquad . \quad . \quad . \quad . \quad \text{(i)}$$

The force on an electron of charge e in an electric field of intensity E is Ee. The acceleration f of the electron is thus given by

$$f = \frac{Ee}{m}, \qquad . \quad . \quad . \quad . \quad . \quad . \quad \text{(ii)}$$

where m is the mass of an electron. But the intensity $E = V/l$, where V is the p.d. between the ends of the metal and l its length.

$$\therefore f = \frac{Ve}{lm}.$$

Hence, from (i),

$$\bar{v} = \frac{1}{2}ft = \frac{Vet}{2lm}. \qquad . \quad . \quad . \quad . \quad \text{(iii)}$$

Since the magnitude I of the current is proportional to the mean velocity $\bar{v}$, it follows from (iii) that I is directly proportional to V, the applied p.d.

This is the explanation of Ohm's law for a metal. If the number of carriers of the current is increased when the applied electric field is increased, or the mean velocity does not increase proportionately when the electric field is increased, then the current is *not* directly proportional to the potential difference. The number of free electrons in a metal is constant at a given temperature, so that Ohm's law is obeyed. There are many cases, in gases and in the radio valve, for example, where Ohm's law is not obeyed.

46. Conduction in Liquids. In liquid metals the carriers are still free electrons, but the resistance of the liquid is greater than for the solid form.

Dilute solutions of electrolytes contain positive and negative ions, and when an electric field is applied the ions drift in opposite directions towards the electrodes. The ions are present in solution before a battery is connected across the liquid, and as their number is constant, Ohm's law is obeyed if there is no polarization at the electrodes. Ions have relatively large masses and hence move slowly through a liquid. In dilute solutions the conductivity is proportional to the concentration of ions and increases as the temperature rises.

At high concentrations the conductivity diminishes and is no longer proportional to the concentration. Debye and Hückel showed that an ion attracts a cloud of oppositely charged ions round it at high concentrations, and moves with the cloud through the solution at a speed slower than in dilute solutions.

47. Conduction in Gases. The conductivity of electricity in gases can be studied by applying a variable p.d. between electrodes at the ends of a discharge tube containing the gas. There are usually some electrons and positive ions present in a gas due to the action of cosmic

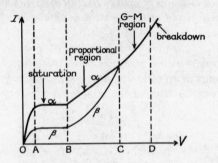

FIG. 855. Conduction in gases.

rays, and a larger number of these particles may be produced by X- or γ-rays, or α- or β-particles, which ionize the air. As the p.d. V is increased, more of the electrons and ions in the discharge tube reach the anode and cathode respectively before they recombine or drift to the walls of the tube, and the current I increases from zero (Fig. 855). The current may be of the order of 10^{-14} to 10^{-10} ampere, depending on the pressure of the gas. At a p.d. corresponding to A all the electrons and ions present in the tube reach the electrodes, and from A to a p.d. represented by B the current is therefore saturated and independent of the p.d. applied.

At a p.d. greater than B, electrons acquire sufficient energy to ionize gas molecules by collision so that more electrons and ions are obtained. Up to a p.d. less than C, the current flowing is directly proportional to the initial number of electron-ion pairs produced in the gas by the ionizing agent. This is hence called a *proportional region* of the characteristic, and an α- or β-particle can thus be distinguished by the difference in their ionizing powers. Beyond C the electric field round the wire is now so intense that very heavy ionization by collision, called an *avalanche* of electron-ion pairs, is produced, and the electrons are swept to the wire along its entire length. The current is the same for an α- or β-particle or γ-ray, so that an ionizing radiation or particle cannot be distinguished in the voltage region CD. This is utilized in the

Geiger-Müller tube (p. 1050). At D the gas breaks down and a glow discharge is obtained.

48. Photo-Electricity. In 1888 Hallwachs discovered that an insulated zinc plate, negatively charged, lost its charge if exposed to ultra-violet light. Hertz had previously noticed that a spark passed more easily across the gap of an induction coil when the negative metal terminal was exposed to sunlight. Later investigators such as Lenard and others showed that electrons were ejected from a zinc plate when exposed to ultra-violet light. Light thus gives energy to the electrons in the surface atoms of the metal, and enables them to break through the surface. This is called the *photoelectric effect*.

In 1902 Lenard found that the velocity of ejection of the electron from an illuminated metal was independent of the intensity of the particular incident monochromatic light. It appeared to vary only with the wavelength or frequency of the incident light, and above a particular wavelength no electrons were emitted. This was a very surprising result. It could not be explained on classical grounds, which predicts that the greater the light energy incident on the metal, the greater should be the energy of the liberated electrons, and that electrons should always be ejected, irrespective of the incident wavelength, if the incident energy is large enough.

49. Theories of light. The Photon. About 1660 Newton had proposed a *corpuscular theory* of light, that is, light consists of particles or corpuscles, and he explained the phenomena of reflection and refraction by applying the laws of mechanics to the particles (p. 697). About the same period Huyghens proposed a *wave theory* of light, that is, light travels by the propagation of a wave or disturbance in the medium (p. 694), and this was applied with particular success to the phenomena of interference and diffraction. Newton's theory was abandoned soon after 1800 when Thomas Young revived interest in Huyghen's wave theory. Among other difficulties, Newton's theory led to the conclusion that the velocity of light in water was greater than in air, which was shown to be untrue experimentally.

In 1902 Planck had shown that the experimental observations in black-body radiation could be explained on the basis that the energy from the body was emitted in separate or discrete packets of energy, known as *quanta* of energy, of amounts $h\nu$, where ν is the frequency of the radiation and h is a constant known as *Planck's constant*. This is the *quantum theory of radiation*. With characteristic genius, Einstein asserted in 1905 that the unexpected experimental result of Lenard—that the energy of the ejected electron was independent of the intensity of the incident light and depended only on the frequency of the light—could be explained by applying a quantum theory of light. He assumed that light of frequency ν contains packets or quanta of energy $h\nu$. On this basis, light consists of *particles*, and these are called *photons*. The number of photons per unit area of cross-section of the beam of light per unit time is proportional to its intensity, but the energy of a photon is proportional to its frequency.

The minimum amount of work or energy to take a free electron out of the surface of a metal against the attractive forces of the positive ions is known as the *work function*, w_0, of the metal. When light of sufficiently high frequency is incident on the metal, an amount w_0 of the incident energy $h\nu$ is used to liberate the electron, leaving an excess energy $h\nu - w_0$, which is given to the ejected electron. The kinetic energy, $\frac{1}{2}mv^2$, of the latter is thus given, on Einstein's theory, by:

$$\tfrac{1}{2}mv^2 = h\nu - w_0. \qquad \ldots \ldots \quad \text{(i)}$$

50. Millikan's experiment. To test the linear relationship between the kinetic energy of the ejected electron and the frequency expressed in (i), Millikan carried out experiments in 1916 using the alkali metals lithium, sodium and potassium. These metals emit electrons when illuminated by ordinary (visible) light, and cylinders of them, A, B, C, were placed round a wheel W (Fig. 856). To avoid tarnishing and oxide films on the metal surface, which lead to considerable error, the metals were housed in a vacuum. Their surfaces were kept clean by a cutting knife K, which could be moved and turned by means of a magnet M outside.

The metal, A say, was kept at a variable positive potential by a battery H, and illuminated by a beam of monochromatic light of wavelength λ_1 from a spectrometer. Any photo-electrons emitted could reach a gauze cylinder G, which was connected to one side of an electrometer

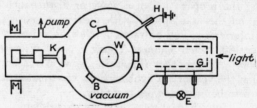

Fig. 856. Millikan's photoelectric experiment.

E whose other terminal was earthed, and a current I would then flow in E. When the potential of A is increased, G has an increasing negative potential relative to A, $-V$ say, and the current I then decreases. At some negative value, $-V_1$, the current becomes zero (Fig. 857 (i)). The potential of G is then the same as the other terminal of E, which is earthed, and the negative potential of G relative to A is thus now given numerically by the p.d. of the battery H. Millikan obtained variations of current, I, with monochromatic light of other wavelengths λ_2, λ_3, using light of constant intensity.

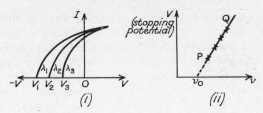

Fig. 857. Results of Millikan's experiment.

51. Deduction from Millikan's results. The negative potential V of G relative to A when no electrons reach G is called the "stopping potential" of G. In this case the kinetic energy of the ejected electron is just equal to the work eV it would do in moving against the opposing p.d. Thus

$$eV = h\nu - w_0. \qquad \ldots \ldots \quad \text{(i)}$$

This is a linear relation between V and ν, and when the stopping potential was plotted against the frequency, a straight line PQ was obtained (Fig. 857 (ii)). Now from (i), the slope of the line is h/e, and knowing e, Millikan calculated h. The result was $6·26 \times 10^{-27}$ erg sec., which was very close to the value of h found from experiments on black-body radiation. This confirmed Einstein's photoelectric theory that light can be considered to consist of particles with energy $h\nu$.

In (i), we can write the work function energy w_0 as $h\nu_0$, where $\nu_0 = w_0/h$. Hence

$$eV = \text{kinetic energy of electron} = h\nu - w_0 = h(\nu - \nu_0).$$

It then follows that no electrons are emitted from a metal when the incident light has a frequency less than ν_0. The magnitude of ν_0 is called the *threshold frequency* of the metal concerned, and is given by the intercept of PQ with the axis of ν (Fig. 857 (ii)).

52. Two aspects of light. The photon theory of light developed by Einstein was in some respects a return to the old particle theory of light. On the one hand there was the "wave theory", suitable for dealing with interference and diffraction phenomena but unable to explain the photo-electric effect and other phenomena concerned with the interaction of light and matter. On the other hand there was the "photon theory", which interpreted the latter effects but was useless in the cases of inter-ference and diffraction. For a time, the two theories appeared mutually contradicting. In 1925, however, it was discovered that electrons, which behave clearly as particles in many respects, can be diffracted like X-rays by a crystal lattice. A classic photograph, taken that year by Sir George Thomson, the son of Sir J. J. Thomson, shows ring diffraction patterns formed by electrons after they were incident on a thin gold film. See Plate III, C, D.

It was then realized that the dual aspect of wave-particle properties exhibited by light are completely general in nature, and that all physical entities can be described either way, the description to choose being purely a matter of convenience. A complete picture can only be mathematical in character, dispensing with a physical description. As Heisenberg states in his book "Principles of Quantum Theory": *Light and matter are both single entities, and the apparent duality arises in the limitation of our language.* In some cases it may be convenient to represent even atoms or nuclei as waves, for instance the α-particle is considered as a wave in the explanation of α-particle disintegration of the nucleus. Conversely, in a treatment of sound through solids, it may be useful on special occasions to consider the sound as due to particles, which are called *phonons*.

53. De Broglie's Formula. In 1925 De Broglie suggested that the wavelength λ of waves "associated" with particles was given by

$$\lambda = \frac{h}{mv}, \qquad \ldots \ldots \quad \text{(i)}$$

where h is Planck's constant and mv is the momentum of the particle. In the same year Davisson and Germer had observed the reflection of a beam of electrons by a crystal, and found there were a number of reflected beams along directions which obeyed a similar formula to that obtained for the reflection of X-rays. The electron reflection was clearly a phenomenon of diffraction caused by the atoms of the crystal, and the results were consistent with a value of λ for the electron beam calculated from De Broglie's formula above.

We can estimate the wavelength of an electron beam. Suppose electrons of charge e and mass m are accelerated through a potential difference V from zero velocity, and acquire a velocity v. Then

$$\tfrac{1}{2}mv^2 = eV, \quad \text{or} \quad v = \sqrt{2eV/m}.$$

$$\therefore \lambda = \frac{h}{mv} = \frac{h}{\sqrt{2emV}}.$$

Substituting $h = 6 \cdot 6 \times 10^{-27}$ erg sec., $e = 1 \cdot 6 \times 10^{-20}$ e.m.u., $m = 9 \cdot 1 \times 10^{-28}$ gm., and changing V in volts to e.m.u. by the factor of 10^8, we obtain

$$\lambda = \frac{1 \cdot 2 \times 10^{-7}}{V^{1/2}} \text{ centimetres}, \qquad \ldots \quad \text{(ii)}$$

where V is in volts. A p.d. of 3,600 volts hence produces a beam of electrons of wavelength 2×10^{-9} cm., which is about 30,000 times smaller than the wavelength of visible light. Electron beams are used in *electron microscopes*, which can thus produce resolving powers far greater than that of an optical microscope.

It is of interest to consider again Bohr's quantum condition for angular momentum in the circular electronic orbits of the hydrogen atom. This states (p. 1063):

$$mvr = \frac{nh}{2\pi}$$

$$\therefore 2\pi r = n\lambda,$$

since $\lambda = h/mv$ from De Broglie's formula. We now see that Bohr's condition is simply a standing (stationary) wave condition, expressing the natural requirement that the length of the orbit should be a whole number of wavelengths. This method of considering stable electron states as a standing wave pattern was extended to any general system by Schroedinger, who established an equation which forms the basis of what is called *quantum mechanics*, or *wave mechanics*. This has been extremely successful in interpreting all electronic properties of atoms and molecules, such as atomic and molecular spectra and the main features of the Periodic Table of elements.

References

The reader is recommended to the following books for further details of Atomic Structure:

Electricity, Magnetism, Atomic Physics—Yarwood (*University Tutorial Press*). *Ions, Electrons, Ionising Radiations*—Crowther (*Edward Arnold*). *Introduction to Atomic Physics*—Tolansky (*Longmans*). *New Age in Physics*—Massey (*Elek*).

EXERCISE XLV

Radioactivity. Atomic Nucleus

1. Describe and explain how the nucleus of the atom was discovered.

2. What are *nucleons, protons, neutrons*? State the number of each of the three particles present in the following atoms: $_2He^4$, $_7N^{14}$, $_{92}U^{235}$.

3. In an early experiment, an α-particle collided with a nitrogen nucleus and a proton was ejected. Write down the nuclear reaction, and explain why this is sometimes called a "transmutation" of a nucleus.

4. Explain the term *binding energy*. Draw a sketch showing the variation of binding energy per nucleon with mass number of the elements.

An α-particle has a mass of 4·004 a.m.u. If a proton has a mass of 1·008 a.m.u. and a neutron has a mass of 1·009 a.m.u., calculate the binding energy of the helium nucleus.

5. In one example of nuclear fission of uranium 235 by a neutron, the reaction is:

$$_{92}U^{235} + _0n^1 \rightarrow _{56}Ba^{141} + _{36}Kr^{92} + 3_0n^1 + Q,$$

where Q is the energy liberated. If the atomic masses of uranium, barium and krypton are respectively 235·12, 140·96, 91·93 a.m.u., and the neutron has a mass of 1·009 a.m.u., calculate Q in MeV, given 1 a.m.u. = 931 MeV.

6. In nuclear fusion, deuterium nuclei $_1H^2$ might fuse together to form a single helium nucleus. If the atomic masses of deuterium and helium are 2·010 and 4·004 a.m.u. respectively, and 1 a.m.u. = 931 MeV, calculate the energy released in MeV.

7. Describe the nature and properties of the charged particles emitted from radioactive substances. Outline experiments to demonstrate *three* of these properties for one type of particle.

Discuss briefly the effect of the emission of such particles on (a) the atomic mass, (b) the atomic number of the element concerned.

What is the source of the energy liberated during the disintegration? (N.)

8. "$_{11}Na^{24}$ is a *radioactive isotope* of sodium which has a *half-life period* of 15 hours and disintegrates with the emission of *β-particles* and *γ-rays*. It emits β-particles that have energies of 4·2 *MeV*."

Explain the meaning of the five terms that are italicized in the statement above. (L.)

9. What is meant by the *half-life period* (*half-life*) of a radioactive material?

Describe how the nature of α-particles has been established experimentally.

The half-life period of the body polonium-210 is about 140 days. During this period the average number of α-emissions per day from a mass of polonium initially equal to 1 microgram is about 12×10^{12}. Assuming that one emission takes place per atom and that the approximate density of polonium is 10 gm. cm.$^{-3}$, estimate the number of atoms in 1 c.c. of polonium. (N.)

10. (a) "Chlorine is an element of *atomic number* 17 and *atomic weight* 35·46 has two naturally occurring *isotopes* of *mass number* 35 and 37."

Comment on this statement and explain the meanings of the terms given in italics. Calculate the relative abundance of the two isotopes.

(b) "The helium nucleus has a mass number 4 but its mass is only 3·9715 times that of the hydrogen nucleus." Comment on the significance of this statement. (L.)

11. Write short notes on: (i) The diode valve, (ii) isotopes, (iii) the thermo-nuclear process. (L.)

12. Describe Wilson's *cloud-chamber*, and explain briefly the principle on which it works. What is a *bubble chamber*?

13. Describe a *Geiger-Müller* tube, and explain its principle of action.

Describe briefly two other methods of detecting ionizing particles.

Electrons round Nucleus (Extra-nuclear Electrons)

14. State the main assumptions of Bohr in his theory of the hydrogen atom.

Write down expressions for (i) the potential energy of the electron in its circular orbit, (ii) its kinetic energy, (iii) its total energy, (iv) its angular momentum. Derive the formula for the radius of the first orbit in terms of e, m, h.

15. Explain briefly how Bohr's theory accounts for the optical spectra of hydrogen. What other experimental evidence shows the existence of discrete energy levels in the atom?

16. Using neon, argon, sodium and chlorine as examples, explain how the chemical properties of the elements depend on the distribution of their electrons in shells round the nucleus.

17. Describe the conduction of electricity through metals, and show qualitatively why Ohm's law is true. Why does temperature rise increase the electrical resistance of a pure metal?

Describe the conduction of electricity through a pure or intrinsic *semiconductor*. Why does temperature rise lower the resistance of a semiconductor?

18. Define *ionization potential*. Describe and explain the variation of current in a gas with applied potential difference, as the p.d. is increased from zero.

19. What is Einstein's *quantum theory of light*? Describe briefly how it is applied to explain the photoelectric effect.

20. Ultra-violet monochromatic light of wavelength 3.3×10^{-5} cm. is incident on a metal. Calculate the energy of the incident photons. If the work function of the metal is $3.5\ eV$, calculate the energy of the liberated photoelectrons. ($1\ eV = 1.6 \times 10^{-12}$ ergs. Planck's constant $= 6.6 \times 10^{-27}$ erg sec.)

21. (*a*) Describe a terrestrial method for determining the velocity of light, explaining clearly how the result is calculated from the observations made.

(*b*) Light of wavelength 4.08×10^{-5} cm. is found to liberate photoelectrons with energy of 1.97×10^{-12} ergs from a certain metal. The largest wavelength limit beyond which no photo-emission occurs for this metal is 6.90×10^{-5} cm. Taking the velocity of light as 3.00×10^{10} cm. sec.$^{-1}$, deduce a value for Planck's constant h. (*L*.)

22. The spacing of a particular set of parallel atomic planes in rocksalt is 2.8×10^{-8} cm. Calculate the wavelength of the first diffraction image obtained by reflection for a glancing angle of $6.2°$. At what glancing angles will the second and third diffraction order images be obtained?

23. The wavelength of an X-ray line is 0.6×10^{-8} cm. Calculate the glancing angle for the first diffraction image obtained by reflection from atomic planes of spacing 2.0×10^{-8} cm.

24. The electrons round the nucleus of an atom are in shells K, L, M. Describe the energy changes when X-radiation is emitted from the atom. Write down an expression for the frequency and wavelength of the X-rays, and explain why the wavelength depends on Z, the atomic number of the atom.

25. Calculate the energy change in an atom when an X-ray of wavelength 1.0×10^{-8} cm. is emitted ($h = 6.6 \times 10^{-27}$ erg sec., $c = 3.0 \times 10^{10}$ cm. sec.$^{-1}$).

26. Draw a sketch showing roughly the variation of intensity of X-rays with wavelength from a metal in a tube operated with a p.d. of 30,000 volts. Calculate the minimum wavelength obtained ($h = 6.6 \times 10^{-27}$ erg sec., $c = 3.0 \times 10^{10}$ cm. sec.$^{-1}$, $e = 1.6 \times 10^{-19}$ coulomb).

27. Explain the origin of (i) characteristic X-rays of a metal, (ii) the X-ray continuous (white) background. What is the minimum wavelength obtained when a p.d. of 60,000 volts is used? ($h = 6.6 \times 10^{-27}$ erg sec., $c = 3.0 \times 10^{10}$ cm. sec.$^{-1}$, $e = 1.6 \times 10^{-19}$ coulomb).

28. What is *Bragg's law*? Write a brief account of the measurement of X-ray wavelengths by reflection at crystals.

29. A point source of light of intensity 10^{-3} watt is placed 5 m. vertically above a horizontal metal plate and photo-emission is observed. The energy required to remove an electron from the metal surface is 8×10^{-19} joule. Accepting the assumption that a photo-electron may collect its energy from a circular area of the plate of radius 10^{-7} cm. (i.e. approximately 10 atomic radii), calculate the time taken for the circular area to receive this energy from the light source. Comment on the result, since in fact photo-emission occurs instantaneously. (*N*.)

APPENDIX I

MICHELSON-MORLEY EXPERIMENT

The Ether

Clerk Maxwell had shown that light was an electromagnetic wave, and later it was thought that light travelled in a medium called the *ether*, which permeated solids and liquids as well as gases. If the ether is at rest relative to the sun, the earth moves through the ether, or the ether moves past the earth, with a velocity equal to its orbital velocity round the sun. This is about 18·6 miles per sec., or about 10^{-4} times the velocity of light in free space, 186,000 miles per sec. If the ether did exist, it could provide a useful frame of reference for Newtonian laws of mechanics.

In 1887 Michelson and Morley devised a sensitive experiment to detect and measure the velocity of the ether drift past the earth. They used Michelson's interferometer, an optical system comprising two similar parallel blocks of glass A, B, with A half-silvered at X, and two plane mirrors M_1, M_2 (Fig. 858 (i)). A

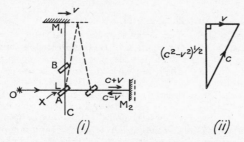

Fɪɢ. 858 Michelson and Morley experiment.

monochromatic beam of light from a source at O divides at X, one part travelling to M_1 and back, the other travelling to M_2 and back. The two beams interfere along the direction C, and an interference pattern of bright and dark bands is seen. If the optical path difference between the two beams is altered by one wavelength, by moving M_1 back for example, the pattern should shift across the field of view and one bright band should move to the position of a neighbouring bright band.

Effect of Ether Drift

Suppose the velocity of the earth relative to the ether is v, and the velocity of light carried by the ether has a velocity c. Then the velocity of light relative to the earth is (i) $(c - v)$ in the direction LM_2, and (ii) $(c + v)$ after reflection at M_2. If the optical path travelled in each direction is d, the total time t taken by the light to arrive back at L is given by

$$t_1 = \frac{d}{c - v} + \frac{d}{c + v} = \frac{2dc}{c^2 - v^2} = \frac{2d}{c}\left(1 - \frac{v^2}{c^2}\right)^{-1}$$

$$= \frac{2d}{c}\left(1 + \frac{v^2}{c^2}\right),$$

1087

if v is much less than c. In the direction LM_1 perpendicular to v, the light travels an optical distance d with a velocity relative to the earth of $\sqrt{c^2 - v^2}$, from the triangle of velocities (Fig. 858 (ii)). The total time t_2 to arrive back at L is now given by

$$t_2 = \frac{2d}{\sqrt{c^2 - v^2}} = \frac{2d}{c}\left(1 - \frac{v^2}{c^2}\right)^{-1/2} = \frac{2d}{c}\left(1 + \frac{v^2}{2c^2}\right).$$

Thus, from above,

$$\text{time difference} = t_1 - t_2 = \frac{dv^2}{c^3}$$

$$\therefore \text{optical path difference} = c(t_1 - t_2) = \frac{dv^2}{c^2}.$$

Now $v/c = 10^{-4}$ (p. 1081), and hence the optical path difference is $10^{-8}\,d$. Using a system of repeated reflections by additional mirrors d was effectively increased to about 10 metres, so that the optical path difference was $10^{-8} \times 1000$ cm. or 10^{-5} cm. This is about 1/6th of the wavelength of sodium light. Michelson and Morley estimated that they could detect a shift of about 1/100th of a wavelength of visible light by means of their interferometer.

Experiment Result. Special Theory of Relativity

Their apparatus was placed on a concrete block floated on mercury, and rotated very slowly through $90°$. The position of the interferometer mirrors was then interchanged, so that the path difference changed from about $+ 10^{-5}$ cm. to $- 10^{-5}$ cm., a change of $2 . 10^{-5}$ cm. or about 1/3rd of the wavelength of sodium light. The corresponding shift in the interference pattern should have been easily detected, but no shift was observed. The experiment was repeated at all seasons of the year, thus varying the direction of the velocity of the earth relative to the ether, but a null result was still observed. Thus *the velocity of light measured by an observer is independent of the velocity of the observer*. The notion of an ether was abandoned by Einstein, and using the fact that the velocity of light is constant for observers in different systems having relative velocities, he arrived at his *Special Theory of Relativity* in 1905. This showed (a) that such observers can reach an understanding of events in other systems if time differences as well as spatial differences are taken into account, (b) that the mass of an object increases as its speed v increases according to the relation

$$m = \frac{m_0}{\sqrt{1 - \dfrac{v^2}{c^2}}},$$

where m_0 is the rest-mass of the object, when $v = 0$, (c) that mass and energy can be converted from one form to the other by the mass-energy relation

$$E = mc^2.$$

Here c is 3×10^{10} numerically and m is in grams when E is in ergs. Einstein's mass-energy relation is used when matter is converted into energy as in nuclear reactors, or when energy in the form of radiation is converted into matter.

APPENDIX II

M.K.S. UNITS

The m.k.s. system of units is one in which the *metre* is used as the unit of length, the *kilogram* as the unit of mass, and the *second* as the unit of time. When these units are adopted in electricity it leads to simplified formulae, as we see shortly, and does away with the complication of different units, electromagnetic, electrostatic, and practical units. The metre-kilogram-second system was adopted by electrical engineers in 1935.

Mechanical Units.

On the m.k.s. system, the *newton* is the unit of force. It is the force which gives a mass of 1 kg. an acceleration of 1 m. per sec.[2] Thus, since force = mass × acceleration,

$$1 \text{ newton} = (100 \text{ gm.}) \times (1000 \text{ cm./sec.}^2) = 10^5 \text{ dynes.}$$

The unit of work or energy on the m.k.s. system is defined as the work done by a force of 1 newton when its point of application moves 1 m. along its line of action.

$$\therefore \text{ work} = 10^5 \text{ dynes} \times 100 \text{ cm.} = 10^7 \text{ ergs} = 1 \text{ joule.}$$

The unit of work or energy on the m.k.s. system is thus the practical unit. The unit of power on the m.k.s. system is hence the joule per second, or the watt.

Electrical Units.

On the m.k.s. system of units, the *ampere* is the unit of current, the *volt* is the unit of p.d., and the *ohm* is the unit of resistance. The ampere is defined by its magnetic effect, as follows:

The ampere is the strength of that constant current which, flowing through two parallel, straight and very long conductors of negligible cross-section, and placed *in vacuo* at a distance of 1 m. from each other, produces between these conductors a force of 2×10^{-7} newton per metre of their length.

The m.k.s. unit of quantity of electricity is thus the *coulomb*; the m.k.s. unit of resistivity is the *ohm-metre*.

Field intensity is expressed in *ampere-turns per metre*; the "ampere-turns" in a coil is the product of the current in amperes and the number of turns, and the "ampere-turns per metre" in a solenoid is the number of ampere-turns per unit length in metres. Magnetic flux is measured in *webers*; magnetic flux-density is thus measured in *webers per sq. metre*. The unit of inductance is the *henry*; the unit of permeability is the *henry per metre*. The unit of pole-strength is the *weber*, and of magnetic moment *weber-metre*. The m.k.s. unit of capacitance is the *farad*; electric field intensity is expressed in *volts per metre*. The unit of permittivity is *farad per metre*.

Formulae.

The following are some of the formulae obtained on the m.k.s. system of units:

1. Force on conductor in perpendicular magnetic field = IBl newtons, where I is in amps., B is in webers per sq. metre, l is in metres.

2. Force between parallel, infinitely long conductors = $2I_2I_1/10^7r$ newtons per metre, where I_2, I_1 are in amperes and r is the distance apart in metres.

3. Induced e.m.f. in coil $= -nd\Phi/dt$ volts, where Φ is the flux in webers and t is in seconds.

4. Induced e.m.f. in straight conductor $= Blv$ volts, where B is the flux-density in webers per sq. metre, l is the length in metres, v is the velocity in metres per second.

5. Field intensity in very long solenoid $= IT/l$ ampere-turns per metre, where I is in amps., T is the number of turns, and l is the length in metres.

6. Field intensity due to circular coil $= IT/2r$ ampere-turns per metre, where I is in amps., T is the number of turns and r is in metres.

7. Field intensity due to infinitely-long straight wire $= I/2\pi r$ ampere-turns per metre, where I is in amperes and r is the distance from the wire in metres.

8. Magnetic induction, $B, = \mu_0 H + J$, where μ_0 is the permeability of a vacuum, H is in ampere-turns per metre, and J is the intensity of magnetization in webers per sq. metre.

9. Force between charges in air $= q_1 q_2/4\pi\varepsilon_0 d^2$ newtons, where ε_0 is the permittivity of air, d is in metres, and q_1, q_2 are in coulombs.

10. Capacitance of parallel-plate condenser with air as a dielectric $= \varepsilon_0 A/d$, where A is in sq. metres and d is in metres.

On the m.k.s. system, $\mu_0 = 4\pi \times 10^{-7}$ numerically.

$$\varepsilon_0 = 1/(36\pi \times 10^9) \text{ numerically.}$$

The following relationships may be used to enable c.g.s. units to be converted to m.k.s. units:

$$4\pi \times 10^{-3} \text{ oersted} = 1 \text{ ampere-turn/metre,}$$

$$10^8 \text{ maxwells} = 1 \text{ weber,}$$

$$10^4 \text{ gauss} = 1 \text{ weber/sq. metre.}$$

ANSWERS TO EXERCISES

EXERCISES I (p. 29)

1. (i) 11 sec., (ii) 605 ft., (iii) 56 ft. per sec. **2.** (i) $5\frac{1}{2}$ sec., (ii) 121 ft., (iii) $15\frac{1}{8}$, $15\frac{1}{8}$ ft. lb. wt. **3.** 19·8 m.p.h., N. 30·5° W. **4.** (i) 500 ft. lb. wt., (ii) 10^9 ergs (iii) 4·9 × 10^9 ergs, (iv) 605 ft. lb. wt. **5.** (i) 5·2 ft. per sec., 57·6 ft. pdls., (ii) 1·2 ft. per sec., 313·6 ft. pdls. **6.** 26·5 m.p.h., S. 41° W.; 7·56 mls. **7.** (i) $2\frac{2}{7}$ ft. per sec., (ii) $4\frac{4}{7}$ ft. per sec.^{2}, (iii) 250·8 ft. pdls. **8.** $5\frac{1}{3}$ ft. per sec., 0·95 lb. °C. **10A.** 13·0 gm. wt. **10B.** 576 ft. **11.** (a) 60, (b) 50, (c) 30 pdls.; (a) $7\frac{1}{2}$ lb. wt., (b) zero. **12.** 172 kg. wt., 20,080 calories ($J = 4\cdot2$ joules/cal.). **13.** 14·4 min., 8 naut. mls., 37° S. of E. **14.** $5\frac{1}{2}$ in. **15.** 83·5%, 0·05. **16.** 10·5° from vertical. **17.** 4871 lb. wt. per sq. ft. **18.** 36·1 m.p.h., 55·4 yds.; 46, 31 yds. from crossing. **19.** 3388 lb. wt.; 39·8 h.p. **20.** (a) 34·3 ft., (b) 128 ft., (c) 82·3 ft.

EXERCISES II (p. 55)

1. (i) 5 radians per sec., (ii) 600 pdls. **2.** (i) 32·8 lb. wt., (ii) 17° 45′. **3.** 69·8°, 43·4 cwt. **4.** 33, 17 lb. wt. **5.** 0·0268 dyne. **6.** 5·99 × 10^{27} gm. **7.** 988 cm. per sec.^{2}. **8.** 104·2 ft. per sec. **9.** 43·2 ft. per sec. **10.** 5° 14′. **11.** 93·3 : 1. **12.** 977 cm. per sec.^{2}. **13.** 5·5 gm. per c.c. **14.** (i) $\frac{1}{20}$ sec., (ii) 0, 2631 ft. per sec.^{2}, (iii) 20·9 ft. per sec., 0. **15.** 99·3 cm. (i) 0, 1·64 ft. per sec.^{2}, (ii) 0·52 ft. per sec., 0, (iii) 0·45 ft. per sec., 0·82 ft. per sec.^{2}. **16.** 0·32 sec. **17.** 1·57 sec. **18.** 999 cm. per sec.^{2}, 446 cm. **19.** (a) 2514 cm. per sec., (b) 78,960 cm. per sec.^{2}. **20.** (a) $\frac{7}{16}l$ nearer floor, (b) $\frac{7}{16}l$ farther from floor. **22.** $v = \dfrac{2\pi}{T}\sqrt{a^2 - x^2}$, acceleration = $-\,4\pi^2 x/T^2$; 210·1, 189·9, 200 gm. wt. **23.** $\frac{1}{2}m\omega^2(a^2 - x^2)$. **25.** 4·9 cm. **26.** 100·7 cm. **27.** $T = 2\pi\sqrt{b/g}$; 2/3 ft. per sec. **28.** 0·45 sec. **29.** 16 cm.; 80 gm.

EXERCISES III (p. 75)

1. (i) 2000, (ii) 8000 gm. cm.^{2}. **2.** (i) 72, (ii) 216 lb. ft.^{2}. **3.** (i) 40,000, (ii) 80,000, (iii) 20,000 gm. cm.^{2}. **4.** 375 ft. pdls. **5.** 11·4 ft./sec.^{2}, 19·1 ft./sec. **6.** (i) 1·98, (ii) 2·31 radians per sec. **7.** 3·85 sec. **8.** 9315 gm. cm.^{2}. **10.** 1 : 14. **11.** 256 cm. per sec. **12.** 101·4 cm., 4·29 × 10^5 gm. cm.^{2}. **13.** 6200 gm. cm.^{2}. **14.** 50 cm.

EXERCISES IV (p. 93)

1. 2·26 in. **2.** 69·3, 138·6 lb. **3.** 50 lb. ft., $16\frac{2}{3}$ lb. **4.** 0·60, 0·52 ft. **5.** $4\frac{1}{8}$, $4\frac{1}{8}$ lb. **6.** 30°. **8.** 171·4 lb. wt. **9.** 34, 16 lb. **11.** 36, $31\frac{3}{4}$ lb. **12.** 9·837 gm., 1·0005. **13.** 0·037 cm., 0·1°.

EXERCISES V (p. 109)

1. Iron:alum., (i) 3:2, (ii) 40:9. **2.** 162 gm. **4.** 5·1 cm. **6.** 2:3. **7.** (a) 75·04 cm., (b) 1003·3 cm. **9.** 1·25. **10.** 40 gm., 240 c.c. **11.** 20·8 gm. **12.** 14·9 cm. **14.** 594·4 gm.; 0·29 gm. **15.** 1·1. **16.** $W\varrho/\sigma$; (a) 0·95, (b) 1·19.

EXERCISES VI (p. 132)

1. 1400, 868 dynes. **2.** (i) 6·63, (ii) 5·52 cm. **3.** 2·7 cm. **4.** (i) 1·00056 × 10⁶ dynes per sq. cm., (ii) 0·14 cm. **7.** $8\pi T(b^2 - a^2)$. **8.** 7·35 cm.; liquid makes acute angle of contact. **10.** 0·8. **11.** 740 dynes. **12.** (a) decrease, (b) increase. **13.** 0·44 cm. **15.** 5·1 cm. **16.** 10,050 ergs; 8:1. **17.** 43·4 dynes per cm. **20.** 19·8 cm. **21.** $\sqrt{r_1{}^2 + r_2{}^2}$. **22.** 30·6 dynes per cm. **23.** 2·91 cm. **24.** 1·16 cm.

EXERCISES VII (p. 150)

1. 6·24 × 10⁷ dynes per sq. cm.; 6 × 10⁻⁵; 1·04 × 10¹² dynes per sq. cm. **2.** 6·84 kg. **3.** 0·076 mm. **5.** 1·1 × 10⁹ dynes. **6.** 7·8 × 10¹¹ dynes per sq. cm. **7.** 22·7 tons. **8.** (a) 0·00022 cm., (b) 546 ergs. **9.** 0·5. **10.** 144·3°C., 3360 kg. **11.** 1·3 × 10⁴. **12.** 0·17 cm. **13.** 4 × 10⁶ dynes, 7·4 × 10⁶ dynes. **14.** 4·95 × 10⁹ dynes per sq. cm. **15.** 28·6 kg. **16.** 12 × 10⁸ dynes per sq. cm., 3·02 kg. **17.** 1·27 × 10⁴ gm. **18.** (a) 2 × 10¹² dynes/sq. cm, (b) 4·7 × 10⁵ ergs. **19.** 16 gm., 39,250 ergs.

EXERCISES VIII (p. 174)

2. 222 watts. **5.** 15·3°. **7.** 0·58. **8.** (a) 0·0004 cm., (b) 0·175 cm. per sec. **9.** 1·64 × 10⁹ ergs; 0·16. **10.** 15 h. 36 m. **11.** 23·2°. **13.** $2\pi\eta a_2{}^3 l\omega/(a_1 - a_2)$. **19.** 49·8 cm. **20.** 5·5 gm. per litre.

EXERCISES XI (p. 216)

1. − 186°C. **2.** 0·99. **3.** 107 cal./gm. **4.** 12·1 gm. **5.** 2·6 ohms. **6.** 1·7 cm. **8.** 50 gm.; 78 cal./gm. **9.** 1·8 × 10⁻⁵ c.g.s. **10.** 10 gm. water. **11.** 59·6 cal./gm. **12.** 20°C. **13.** 2290 joules/gm. **14.** 2740 m. **16.** 0·53. **17.** 779 ft. lb. **19.** 0·23°C. **20.** 93·5 gm. **21.** 0·64 lb. wt.

EXERCISES XII (p. 264)

1. 100°C. **3.** 4·16 × 10⁷ ergs/cal. **4.** Rise = 0·13 atmos. **5.** (a) 7·23 × 10³mm., (b) 247°C., (c) 2·29 × 10⁷ ergs. **6.** 4·2 joules/cal. **7.** 15 ft. **8.** 77·4 cm. **9.** 25, 23 cal. **11.** 1·84 × 10⁵ cm./sec. **14.** 8·3 × 10⁷ ergs/cal. **16.** 4·75 × 10⁴ cm./sec. **17.** (i) 3·35 × 10¹⁰, (ii) 3·11 × 10¹⁰. **18.** 26. **19.** 56·3 ft.

EXERCISES XIII (p. 294)

1. 79°C. **2.** 434°C. **4.** 0·14%. **5.** 0·00038 cm.². **6.** 964 gm. **8.** 62·4 gm. **9.** 4 sec. **10.** 3 × 10⁷ dynes. **12.** 20·5 cm. **13.** 270°C. **14.** 0·436, 0·444 cm.³. **15.** 9·16 × 10⁻⁴ deg.⁻¹C.

EXERCISES XIV (p. 332)

1. 707 mm. **2.** Air: 1·18 × 10⁶ gm.; vapour: 8·96 × 10³ gm. **4.** 78%. **8.** 0·041 gm. **9.** 154 c.c. **10.** 764 mm. **13.** 12·4:1.

EXERCISES XV (p. 373)

1. 84·4 cal. **2.** 0·42 amp. **4.** 0·0004 c.g.s. **5.** 5450° C. **8.** 351 sq. cm. **9.** 284 watts, 4 s. **11.** 0·00096 cal./cm.^{2}; 2·0° C./min. **12.** 20,860 cal. **13.** 5493° C. **14.** 0·25 cal./sec.; 0·2 cm. **15.** $5{\cdot}5 \times 10^{-5}$ c.g.s.

EXERCISES XVI (p. 393)

4. 0·89° C. **5.** 309° C. **6.** 640° C. **7.** (*b*) 0·7. **9.** 412° C. **10.** 77·5 cm.

EXERCISES XVIII (p. 410)

4. 4*a*; 2*na*.

EXERCISES XIX (p. 427)

1. (i) 15 cm., 1·5, (ii) 12 cm., 3. **3.** 6 cm., 0·4. **6.** 4/21 ft. **7.** Object distance = 10 cm., r = 40 cm.; concave. **9.** 2*R*. **10.** 2 radians, or 114°. **11.** Inverted.

EXERCISES XX (p. 448)

1. 35·3°. **2.** 41·8°. **3.** (i) 26·3°, (ii) 56·4°. **4.** (*b*) 3 cm. from bottom. **6.** (i) 41·8°, (ii) 48·8°, (iii) 62·5°. **9.** 1·47. **11.** (*b*) 12 cm. above mirror. **15.** 1·60. **17.** 1·41.

EXERCISES XXI (p. 462)

1. 42°. **2.** (i) 1·52, (ii) 52·20. **5.** Red—50·5°, violet—54·8°. **6.** 55°, 1·69. **8.** 27·9°. **9.** 27·9°. **11.** 28·7°.

EXERCISES XXII (p. 479)

1. Crown (i) 3·07°, (ii) 3·14°, (iii) 3·11°; flint: (i) 2·58°, (ii) 2·66°, (iii) 2·62°. **2.** 0·023, 0·031. **3.** 3·92°, 0·021°. **5.** 63·9°. **6.** 1170 km./sec. **10.** 6·67°, 0·83°. **11.** 0·144°. **12.** (*a*) 49° 12′ (*b*) 50° 38′ (*c*) 1° 26′.

EXERCISES XXIII (p. 516)

1. (i) 40 cm. virtual, (ii) 80 cm. real. **2.** 7·2, 18 cm. from nearest point on sphere. **3.** (*a*) 1·51, (*b*) 7·5 cm. **4.** $v = 6r$, where r is radius. **5.** (i) 12 cm., $m = 1$, (ii) 12 cm., $m = 3$. **6.** $6\frac{2}{3}$ cm., $\frac{3}{8}$. **7.** $13\frac{1}{3}$; 40 cm. **8.** (i) $5\frac{1}{7}$ cm., (ii) $22\frac{1}{2}$ cm. **9.** (i) $9\frac{3}{8}$ cm., (ii) $16\frac{2}{3}$ cm. **10.** (*a*) $11\frac{1}{9}$, (*b*) $5\frac{5}{8}$ cm.; $3\frac{19}{27}$ cm. **11.** $27\frac{1}{4}$ cm. from lens. **13.** 1·44. **14.** 12 in. **15.** 60 cm. from screen. **16.** 40 cm. from convex lens. **17.** 4 in. **18.** $12\frac{6}{7}$; $37\frac{5}{7}$ cm. above water surface. **19.** 1·4. **20.** 20·6 cm. **21.** 1·63. **22.** (*a*) 20·5 cm., (*b*) 12·85 cm., (*c*) 1·63. **23.** 40; 40 cm. **24.** (*a*) 120 cm. from convex lens, (*b*) 92·2 cm., (*c*) 2·2. **25.** (*a*) Beside object O, (*b*) 72·5 cm. from O.

EXERCISES XXIV (p. 538)

1. Concave, $f = 200$ cm.; $22\frac{2}{3}$ cm. 2. Convex, $f = 28\frac{4}{7}$ cm.; $35\frac{5}{17}$ to 25 cm.
3. *Right eye*—far-sighted; near point 50 cm. *Left eye*—short-sighted; near point
$14\frac{2}{7}$ cm. far point $33\frac{1}{3}$ cm. 4. Concave, $f = 20$ cm. Infinity to 20 cm. from eye.
6. Concave, $f = 30$ cm.; 30 cm. 9. 64 cm.; $106\frac{2}{3}$ cm. 11. 0·98, 1·02 cm.; 3·8 cm.
12. 10 cm.

EXERCISES XXV (p. 563)

1. $8:5:2$. 2. (a) Infinity (b) least distance of distinct vision. 3. (a) 4, (b) 4·8.
5. 0·22 in.; 2:1. 6. 2; 22·5 cm. 8. 3·15; 8·75 cm. 9. (a) 22·4, (b) 4·88 cm. diameter.
10. 4 cm. from lens, $m = 5$. 13. $25\frac{1}{4}$ cm. 14. 5, 6. 15. 10, 8. 16. 8·7 cm., 46·7.
17. 67·5 cm., 15·9.

EXERCISES XXVI (p. 586)

1. 0·019 cm. candles, 67·5 c.p. 2. (i) $3\frac{1}{3}$, (ii) 1·6 ft. candles. 3. 125 c.p.
4. 2, 10 ft. candles. 5. 0·5. 6. 1, 0·83 ft. candles; 1·41, 1·2 ft. candles. 7. 2·63 m.
8. 64 lumens/sq. ft. 9. 63·6°. 11. 90·3 per cent.

EXERCISES XVII (p. 599)

3. 12·6. 4. 0·00192°. 6. 2500. 8. $\dfrac{V + v}{V - v}$. 12. 3·875 miles.

EXERCISES XXVIII (p. 624)

6. (i) 90°, circle, (ii) 0°, straight line, (iii) 90°, ellipse. 10. 380, 391 c.p.s.

EXERCISES XXIX (p. 653)

1. (i) 132·8 cm., (ii) 400 cycles/sec. 2. (a) 333, (b) 360·4 metres/sec.; 342
metres/sec. 3. 349 metres/sec. 4. 1106 ft./sec. 5. 53·1°. 10. 4556 ft. 14. 1·83 sec.
15. (a) 70, (b) $74\frac{2}{3}$ ft./sec. 16. $n(V - v)/(V - u)$; (a) 1087, (b) 1080 cycles/sec.
17. 1·08:1. 18. $n = n_0 V \Big/ \left(V \pm \dfrac{v^2 t}{\sqrt{l^2 + v^2 t^2}} \right)$.

EXERCISES XXX (p. 690)

1. (i) $\lambda/2$, (ii) $\lambda/4$, (iii) $\lambda/2$; 566·7 cycles/sec. 3. (a) 512 cycles/sec. (if string
damped lightly in middle) or 768 cycles/sec. (if string plucked in middle), (b) 768
cycles/sec. 4. 424 cycles/sec. 6. 5·8°C. 8. 3 beats per sec. 9. 300 cycles/sec.,
assuming strings exactly similar. 10. 33,696 cm./sec.; 208, 210·6 c.p.s. 12. 400,000
cm./sec. 13. 2·2:1. 17. 74·9 cm. 22. 0·18 cm.

EXERCISES XXXI (p. 700)

7. 11·85 ft.

EXERCISES XXXII (p. 725)

1. 0·00118 cm. **2.** 314·6 cm. **4.** 13·3°.

EXERCISES XXXIII (p. 758)

1. 0·32 oersted. **2.** 0·18 oersted. **4.** 16·4 cm. along equator. **5.** 0·2 oersted.
6. 3·2 sec., $0·6H$. **7.** 10 cm. **8.** 2400 c.g.s. **9.** (a) 0·16 oersted, (b) 2160 c.g.s.
12. 23 c.g.s. **13.** 69°. **15.** 2·6 sec., 0·467 oersted.

EXERCISES XXXIV (p. 793)

1. Potentials: 1·5, 1·1, 0·8, 0·6 e.s.u. Field strengths: 0, 0·32, 0·04, 0·06 e.s.u.
3. 3 cm. from 10 e.s.u.; $11\frac{1}{9}$ e.s.u. **5.** $2e/5$. **6.** 4·78 × 10^{-10} e.s.u. **7.** (a) 3·5, 2 e.s.u.,
(b) 0, 30; − 30, 80; − 80, 0. **8.** 30,000 e.s.u. **9.** 0·05 erg.

EXERCISES XXXV (p. 815)

1. 2 μF: 0·001, 0·0044, 0·01 joule; 4 μF: 0·02, 0·0022, 0·02 joule. **2.** 4 μF.
3. (a) 2400, (b) 480 ergs. **4.** 0·05 cm. **5.** 404 volts/cm. **6.** (i) 5·5 × 10^{-4},
(ii) 0·0025 × 10^{-4} μF. **7.** Increase distance by 0·2 cm. **8.** (a) 1000 V./cm. (b) 27
ergs. **9.** (b) (i) p.d. = E, charge reduced to 1/3rd original charge, (ii) charge
constant, p.d. increased 3 times. **10.** 18,000 volt cm.$^{-1}$. **11.** 60 amp.

EXERCISES XXXVI (p. 837)

1. 18 ohms. **2.** s = 0·53, 17 gm. **3.** 1·1 mm. **5.** $\frac{1}{2}$, 1 , 2 kW. **6.** 36, 39%. **9.** 200
cells, 0·30 gm. **11.** 18·75 kW.

EXERCISES XXXVII (p. 875)

1. (a) 25, (b) 50 V. **2.** (a) 0·3 amp. (b) A: 83 × 10^{-6}, B: 81 × 10^{-3} watt. **3.**
$64n/(n^2 + 16)$; 8 amp., 3/8 ohm. **4.** X = 2000, resis. = 1000 ohms. **5.** 12·5 microamp.
6. 2 microamp. per div. **7.** 3·96 × 10^{-4}, 4 × 10^{-4} amp. **8.** $1\frac{7}{13}$ V. **9.** 0·05 V. 20,500
ohms. (approx.). **10.** 1·008 ohms. **13.** 2·4 ohm. **18.** 96 × 10^{-6} ohm-cm.

EXERCISES XXXVIII (p. 908)

1. 9636 e.m.u./gm. **2.** 5·1°C. **3.** 33 × 10^{-5} gm. coulomb^{-1}. **4.** 0·46 ohm. **6.**
23 ohms, 1·6d., 50%. **7.** 18·6 c.c. **8.** 18·9 min. **9.** 1·5 V. **10.** 8 turns. **11.** 0·093
ohm^{-1} cm.$^{-1}$.

EXERCISES XXXIX (p. 927)

2. 1/3. **3.** 3172 c.g.s. **4.** 3m. 40s. **6.** 0·33 and 0·13 per sec. **7.** 41°. **8.** 0·2 oersted.
9. 91/32.

EXERCISES XL (p. 939)

1. 69 microamp. **2.** (a) Shunt: 0·0125, series: 9995 ohms. **3.** 6 cm. from 12 amp. wire. **4.** 273 oersteds. **5.** 0·0136 microamp./div. **7.** Series 140 and 7490 ohms; 115 V.

EXERCISES XLI (p. 982)

1. 75·4 sin ωt. **2.** 2 millivolts. **3.** 1·6 millivolts. **6.** (a) 1·2 V., (b) 0·06 A., (c) 0·96 V. **8.** 1·05 V. **13.** $nAHE/R$. **14.** HAI sin θ. **15.** 24 ohms. **16.** $2·61 \times 10^{-7}$ amp.; $1·02 \times 10^{-11}$ watt. **17.** 44·2 rev. sec.$^{-1}$.

EXERCISES XLII (p. 1001)

1. 340 c.g.s. **2.** 590 microcoulombs. **3.** 965 c.g.s. **6.** 7220. **7.** (a) 2020, (b) 255, (c) 20. **8.** 0·4 oersted. **14.** 10^4 gauss.

EXERCISES XLIII (p. 1021)

2. $1·8 \times 10^6$. **11.** 1: 1848. **12.** 2·0 cm. **13.** $2·78 \times 10^{-8}$ cm.

EXERCISES XLIV (p. 1040)

1. $0·13A$, $V_L = 84·3V$, $V_R = 53·8V$, angle $= 57·5°$. **2.** $V_C = 9·6V$, $V = 15·3V$, power $= 72$ milliwatts. **3.** (i) 112,600 c.p.s., (ii) 0·2 milliamp, (iii) 1·4V, (iv) 0·2 microwatt. **4.** $I = I_0 \sin(pt - \theta)$, where $I_0 = E_0/\sqrt{R^2 + X_L{}^2}$ and tan $\theta = X_L/R$. (a) Max. value $= I_0$, (b) average $= 2I_0/\pi$, (c) $I_0/\sqrt{2}$. **5.** $P = I_0E_0 \cos \theta/2$; 0·092. **10.** (1) $1·12 \times 10^{-4}$ cm. (2) $2·4 \times 10^{-9}$ e.s.u. **11.** $4·9 \times 10^{-10}$ e.s.u. **12.** (i) (a) 0·424 amp., (b) 106 V across resistance, 170 V across capacitance. **14.** 200. **15.** $3·03 \times 10^{-10}$ e.s.u.

EXERCISES XLV (p. 1083)

5. 197·3 MeV. **6.** 14·9 MeV. **9.** $3·36 \times 10^{22}$. **10.** (b) Isotopes 35 : isotopes 37 = 77 : 23. **20.** $6·0 \times 10^{-12}$, $0·4 \times 10^{-12}$ ergs. **21.** $6·56 \times 10^{-27}$ erg sec. **22.** $0·3 \times 10^{-8}$ cm.; 12·5°, 18·9°. **23.** 8·6°. **25.** $19·8 \times 10^{-9}$ erg. **26.** $0·4 \times 10^{-8}$ cm. **27.** $0·2 \times 10^{-8}$ cm. **29.** 67,750 sec.

INDEX